Basic Technical Mathematics
Third Edition

Other books by the author

Essentials of Basic Mathematics (with Boyd & Plotkin)

Essentials of Algebra (with Boyd & Plotkin)

Introduction to Technical Mathematics, Second Edition

Basic Technical Mathematics with Calculus, Third Edition

Basic Technical Mathematics with Calculus, Third Edition, Metric Version

Technical Calculus with Analytic Geometry

An Introduction to Calculus with Applications

Modules in Technical Mathematics
  Introductory Topics from Arithmetic
  Introduction to Algebra
  Introduction to Trigonometry
  Introduction to Geometry

Plane Trigonometry (with Edmond)

Basic Technical Mathematics
Third Edition

Allyn J. Washington

Dutchess Community College
Poughkeepsie, New York

The Benjamin/Cummings Publishing Company

Menlo Park, California • Reading, Massachusetts
London • Amsterdam • Don Mills, Ontario • Sydney

Sponsoring editor: Adrian Perenon
Production editor: Margaret Moore
Cover designer: Marjorie Spiegelman
Book designer: Peter Martin
Artist: Judith McCarty
Compositor: Typothetae

ISBN 0-8053-9520-2
ABCDE GHIJ-MU-89876543210

The Benjamin / Cummings Publishing Company, Inc.
2727 Sand Hill Road
Menlo Park, California 94025

Preface

Scope of the Book

This book is intended primarily for students in technical and pre-engineering technology programs or where a coverage of basic mathematics is required.

Chapters 1 through 19 provide the necessary background in algebra and trigonometry for analytic geometry and calculus courses, and Chapters 1 through 20 provide the background necessary for calculus courses. There is an integrated treatment of mathematical topics, primarily algebra and trigonometry, which are necessary for a sound mathematical background for the technician. Numerous applications from many fields of technology are included primarily to indicate where and how mathematical techniques are used. However, it is not necessary that the student have a specific knowledge of the technical area from which any given problem is taken.

It is assumed that students using this text will have a background including algebra and geometry. However, the material is presented in sufficient detail for use by those whose background is possibly deficient to some extent in these areas. The material presented here is sufficient for two or three semesters.

One of the primary reasons for the arrangement of topics in this text is to present material in such an order that it is possible for a student to take courses in allied technical areas, such as physics and electricity, concurrently. These allied courses normally require a student to know certain mathematical topics by certain definite times, and yet, with the traditional mathematical order of topics, it is difficult to attain this coverage without loss of continuity. However, this material can be rearranged to fit any appropriate sequence of topics, if this is deemed necessary. Another feature of the material in this text is that certain topics which are traditionally included, primarily for mathematical completeness, have been omitted.

The approach used here is basically an intuitive one. It is not unduly rigorous mathematically, although all appropriate terms and concepts are introduced as needed and given an intuitive or algebraic foundation. The book's aim is to help the student develop a feeling for mathematical methods, not simply to have a collection of formulas when the work in the text has been completed. The text emphasizes that it is essential for the student to have a fluent background in algebra and trigonometry to understand and succeed in any subsequent work in mathematics.

New Features

This third edition of *Basic Technical Mathematics* includes all the basic features of the first two editions. However, most sections have been rewritten to some degree to include additional explanatory material, examples, and exercises. Specifically, among the new features of the third edition are the following: (1) An appendix briefly discussing the use of a scientific calculator has replaced the appendix on the slide rule. Although no specific calculational device is required, it is assumed that most students will use a scientific calculator for most of their calculating work. Also, a number of problems have been designed for solution on a calculator. (2) A new table of trigonometric functions, using degrees and tenths of a degree, has been added. (3) New sections are Section 16–5, devoted to graphical solution of inequalities with two variables (and including an introduction to linear programming), and Section 18–4, devoted to the binomial theorem. (4) Certain sections of the second edition have been separated into two sections to provide more detailed coverage. Thus, Section 1–11 is a separate section covering literal equations and verbal problems, Section 3–5 is devoted completely to right triangle applications, Section 5–3 covers factoring trinomials, and Section 8–1 introduces vectors and develops graphical methods in more detail. (5) Two sections have been moved to provide more timely coverage. Scientific notation is now in Chapter 1 in Section 1–5. Exponential and logarithmic functions are now included in Chapter 12. (6) Logarithms are now presented more as a useful function and less as a calculational device. (7) There are more problems using metric units, and a discussion of the metric system (SI) is included in Appendix B. (8) Important formulas have been set off so that they are easily located and utilized. (9) There are now over 5600 exercises, an increase of about 25%. Each exercises group is numbered with the number of the section which it follows. Exercises are generally grouped such that there is an even-numbered exercise equivalent to each odd-numbered exercise. (10) Many new examples are included, and more detail is included in others. There are now approximately 750 examples, an increase of about 15%.

Other features are: (1) The many examples included in this text are often used advantageously to introduce concepts, as well as to clarify and illustrate points made in the text. (2) There is extensive use of graphical methods. (3) Stated problems are included a few at a time to allow the student to develop techniques of solution. (4) Those topics which experience has shown to be more difficult for the student have been developed in more detail, with many examples. (5) The order of coverage can be changed in several places without loss of continuity. Also, certain sections may be omitted without loss of continuity. Any omissions or changes in order will, of course, depend on the type of course and the completeness required. (6) The chapter on statistics is included in order to introduce the student to statistical and empirical methods. (7) Review exercises are included after each chapter. These may be used either for additional problems or for review assignments. (8) The answers to all the odd-numbered exercises are given at the back of the book. Included are answers to graphical problems and other types which are not always included in textbooks.

Acknowledgments

The author wishes to acknowledge the help and suggestions given him by many of those who have used the first two editions of this text. In particular, I wish to thank Gail Brittain, Stephen Lange, Michael Mayer, John Davenport, Mario Triola of Dutchess Community College, and William K. Viertel, formerly of State University of New York Agricultural and Technical College at Canton. Also, Judith L. Gersting of Indiana University–Purdue University at Indianapolis, Richard C. Wheeler of Wentworth Institute, Edwin P. McCravy of Midlands Technical Education Center, Carl M. Schell of Sinclair Community College, and A. P. Paris of British Columbia Institute of Technology provided many valuable suggestions in their reviews of the text and manuscript. Many others contributed to this third edition through their response to my publisher's survey and to their field representatives. Their efforts are most appreciated, and there is space here only to thank them collectively.

In addition, I wish to thank Carolyn Edmond, formerly of Dutchess Community College, for her help in reading proof and checking answers for this third edition. The assistance, cooperation, and diligent efforts of the Benjamin/Cummings staff during the production of this text are also greatly appreciated. Finally, special mention is due my wife, who helped with her patience during the preparation of this text, and for checking many of the answers of the earlier editions.

A. J. W.

Contents

1

Fundamental Concepts and Operations

1—1 Numbers and Literal Symbols

Mathematics has played a most important role in the development and understanding of the various fields of technology, and in the endless chain of technological and scientific advances of our time. With the mathematics we shall develop in this text, many kinds of applied problems can and will be solved. Of course, we cannot solve the more advanced types of problems which arise, but we can form a foundation for the more advanced mathematics which is used to solve such problems. Therefore, the development of a real understanding of the mathematics presented in this text will be of great value to you in your future work.

A thorough understanding of algebra is essential to the comprehension of any of the fields of elementary mathematics. It is important for the reader to learn and understand the basic concepts and operations presented here, or the development and the applications of later topics will be difficult to comprehend. Unless the algebraic operations are understood well, the result will be a weak foundation for further work in mathematics and in many of the technical areas where mathematics may be applied.

We shall begin our study of mathematics by reviewing some of the basic concepts and operations that deal with numbers and symbols. With

these we shall be able to develop the topics in algebra which are necessary for further progress into other fields of mathematics, such as trigonometry and calculus.

The way we represent numbers today has been evolving for thousands
of years. The first numbers used were those which stand for whole
quantities, and these we call the **positive integers**. The positive integers
are represented by the symbols 1, 2, 3, 4, and so forth.

Of course, it is necessary to have numbers to represent parts of certain
quantities, and for this purpose fractional quantities are introduced. *The
name* **positive rational number** *is given to any number that we can
represent by the division of one positive integer by another. Numbers
that cannot be designated by the division of one integer by another are
termed* **irrational**.

Example A

The numbers 5, 18, and 1978 are positive integers. They are also rational
numbers, since they may be written as $\frac{5}{1}$, $\frac{18}{1}$, and $\frac{1978}{1}$. Normally we do
not write the 1's in the denominators.

The numbers $\frac{1}{2}$, $\frac{5}{8}$, $\frac{11}{3}$, and $\frac{106}{17}$ are positive rational numbers, since both
the numerators and the denominators are integers.

The numbers $\sqrt{2}$, $\sqrt{3}$, and π are irrational. It is not possible to find
any two integers which represent these numbers when one of the integers
is divided by the other. For example, $\frac{22}{7}$ is not an *exact* representation of
π; it is only an approximation.

In addition to the positive numbers, it is necessary to introduce **negative numbers**, not only because we need to have a numerical answer to
problems such as $5 - 8$, but also because the negative sign is used to
designate direction. *Thus,* -1, -2, -3, *and so on are the* **negative
integers**. The number **zero** is an integer, but it is neither positive nor
negative. *This means that the* **integers** *are the numbers* . . . , -3, -2,
-1, 0, 1, 2, 3, . . . , *and so on.*

The integers, the rational numbers, and the irrational numbers, which
include all such numbers which are zero, positive, or negative, constitute
what we call the **real number system**. We shall use real numbers throughout this text, with one important exception. In the chapter on the
j-operator, we shall be using **imaginary numbers**, *which is the name given
to square roots of negative numbers*. The symbol j is used to designate
$\sqrt{-1}$, which is not part of the real number system.

Example B

The number 7 is an integer. It is also a rational number since $7 = \frac{7}{1}$,
and it is a real number since the real numbers include all of the rational
numbers.

The number 3π is irrational, and it is real since the real numbers include all of the irrational numbers.

The numbers $\sqrt{-10}$ and $7j$ are imaginary.

The number $\frac{1}{8}$ is rational and real. The number $\sqrt{5}$ is irrational and
real.

The number $\frac{-3}{7}$ is rational and real. The number $-\sqrt{7}$ is irrational and real.

The number $\sqrt{-7}$ is imaginary.

The number $\frac{\pi}{6}$ is irrational and real. The number $\frac{\sqrt{-3}}{2}$ is imaginary.

A **fraction** *may contain any number or symbol representing a number in its numerator or in its denominator.* Thus, a fraction may be rational, irrational, or imaginary.

Example C

The numbers $\frac{2}{7}$ and $\frac{-3}{2}$ are fractions, and they are also rational.

The numbers $\frac{\sqrt{2}}{9}$ and $\frac{6}{\pi}$ are fractions, but they are not rational numbers. It is not possible to express either as the ratio of one integer to another.

The number $\frac{\sqrt{-3}}{2}$ is a fraction, and it is also imaginary.

The real numbers may be represented as points on a line. We draw a horizontal line and designate some point on it by O, which we call the **origin** (see Fig. 1–1). The number zero, which is an integer, is located at this point. Then equal intervals are marked off from this point toward the right, and the positive integers are placed at these positions. The other rational numbers are located between the positions of the integers. It cannot be proved here, but the rational numbers do not take up all the positions on the line; the remaining points represent irrational numbers.

Now we can give the direction interpretation to negative numbers. By starting at the origin and proceeding to the left, in the **negative direction,** we locate all the negative numbers. As shown in Fig. 1–1, the positive numbers are to the right of the origin and the negative numbers to the left. Representing numbers in this way will be especially useful when we study graphical methods.

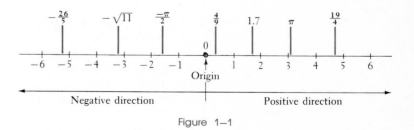

Figure 1–1

Another important mathematical concept we use in dealing with numbers is the **absolute value** of a number. By definition, *the absolute value of a positive number is the number itself, and the absolute value of a negative number is the corresponding positive number (obtained by changing its sign).* We may interpret the absolute value as being the number of units a given number is from the origin, regardless of direction. The absolute value is designated by || placed around the number.

Example D

The absolute value of 6 is 6, and the absolute value of -7 is 7. We designate this by $|6| = 6$ and $|-7| = 7$.

Other examples are $|-\pi| = \pi$, $|\frac{7}{5}| = \frac{7}{5}$, and $|-\sqrt{2}| = \sqrt{2}$.

On the number scale, if a first number is to the right of a second number, then the first number is said to be **greater than** the second. If the first number is to the left of the second, it is **less than** the second number. *"Greater than" is designated by* $>$, *and "less than" is designated by* $<$. These are called **signs of inequality**.

Example E

$$6 > 3, \quad 8 > -1, \quad 5 < 9, \quad 0 > -4, \quad -2 > -4, \quad -1 < 0$$

Every number, except zero, has a **reciprocal**. *The reciprocal of any number is 1 divided by that number.*

Example F

The reciprocal of 7 is $\frac{1}{7}$. The reciprocal of $\frac{2}{3}$ is

$$\frac{1}{\frac{2}{3}} = 1 \cdot \frac{3}{2} = \frac{3}{2}$$

The reciprocal of π is $1/\pi$. The reciprocal of -5 is $-\frac{1}{5}$. Notice that the negative sign is retained in the reciprocal.

In applications, numbers are often used to represent some type of measurement and therefore have certain units of measurement associated with them. Such numbers are referred to as **denominate numbers**. For a discussion of units of measurement, and the symbols which are used, see Appendix B. The following example illustrates the use of units and the symbols which represent them.

Example G

To indicate that an object is ten feet long, we represent the length as 10 ft.

To indicate that the speed of a projectile is 150 meters per second, we represent the speed as 150 m/s. (Note the use of s for second. We use s rather than sec, which is also common.)

To indicate that the volume of a container is 500 cubic centimeters, we represent the volume by 500 cm³. (Also common are cc and cu cm.)

To this point we have been dealing with numbers in their explicit form. However, it is normally more convenient to state definitions and operations on numbers in a generalized form. To do this we represent the numbers by letters, often referred to as **literal numbers**.

For example, we can say, "if a is to the right of b on the number scale, then a is greater than b, or $a > b$." This is more convenient than saying, "if a first number is to the right of a second number, then the first number is greater than the second number." The statement "the reciprocal of a number a is $1/a$" is another example of using letters to stand for numbers in general.

In an algebraic discussion, certain letters are sometimes allowed to take on any value, while other letters represent the same number throughout the discussion. *Those which may vary in a given problem are called* **variables,** *and those which are held fixed are called* **constants.**

Common usage today normally designates the letters near the end of the alphabet as variables, and letters near the beginning of the alphabet as constants. There are exceptions, but these are specifically noted. Letters in the middle of the alphabet are also used, but their meaning in any problem is specified.

Example H

The electric resistance R of a wire may be related to the temperature T by the equation $R = aT + b$. R and T may take on various values, and a and b are fixed for any particular wire. However, a and b may change if a different wire is considered. Here, R and T are the variables and a and b are constants.

Exercises 1—1

In Exercises 1 through 4 designate each of the given numbers as being an integer, rational, irrational, real, or imaginary. (More than one designation may be correct.)

1. $3, -\pi$　　2. $\dfrac{5}{4}, \sqrt{-4}$　　3. $6j, \dfrac{\sqrt{7}}{3}$　　4. $-\dfrac{7}{3}, \dfrac{\pi}{6}$

In Exercises 5 through 8 find the absolute value of each of the given numbers.

5. $3, \dfrac{7}{2}$　　6. $-4, \sqrt{2}$　　7. $-\dfrac{6}{7}, -\sqrt{3}$　　8. $-\dfrac{\pi}{2}, -\dfrac{19}{4}$

In Exercises 9 through 16 insert the correct sign of inequality ($>$ or $<$) between the given pairs of numbers.

9. 6　8　　10. 7　5　　11. π　-1　　12. -4　3

13. -4　-3　　14. $-\sqrt{2}$　-9　　15. $-\dfrac{1}{3}$　$-\dfrac{1}{2}$　　16. 0.2　0.6

In Exercises 17 through 20 find the reciprocals of the given numbers.

17. $3, -2$　　18. $\dfrac{1}{6}, -\dfrac{7}{4}$　　19. $-\dfrac{5}{\pi}, x$　　20. $-\dfrac{8}{3}, \dfrac{y}{b}$

In Exercises 21 through 24 locate the given numbers on a number line as in Fig. 1–1.

21. $2.5, -\dfrac{1}{2}$　　22. $\sqrt{3}, -\dfrac{12}{5}$　　23. $-\dfrac{\sqrt{2}}{2}, 2\pi$　　24. $\dfrac{123}{19}, -\dfrac{\pi}{6}$

In Exercises 25 through 34 answer the given questions.

25. List the following numbers in numerical order, starting with the smallest: $-1, 9, \pi, \sqrt{5}, |-8|, -|-3|, -18$.

26. List the following numbers in numerical order, starting with the smallest: $\frac{1}{5}, -\sqrt{10}, -|-6|, -4, 0.25, |-\pi|$.

27. The value of π expressed to four decimal places is 3.1416. Show by division that $\frac{22}{7}$ has a different value when expressed to four decimal places.

28. If a and b represent positive integers, what kind of number is represented by (a) $a + b$, (b) a/b, (c) $a \cdot b$?

29. Describe the location of a number x on the number line when (a) $x > 0$, (b) $x < -4$.

30. Describe the location of a number x on the number line when (a) $|x| < 1$, (b) $|x| > 2$.

31. The pressure P and volume V of a certain body of gas are related by the equation $P = c/V$ for certain conditions. Identify the symbols as variables or constants.

32. The velocity v and height h of an object are related by the equation $v = \sqrt{2ah}$. Identify the literal symbols as variables or constants.

33. In writing a laboratory report, a student wrote "$-20°C > -30°C$." Is this statement correct?

34. After 2 s, the current in a certain circuit is less than 3 A. Using t to represent time and i to represent current, this statement may be written, "for $t > 2$ s, $i < 3$ A." In this way write the statement, "less than three meters from the light source the illuminance is greater than eight lumens (lm) per square meter." (Let I represent illuminance and s represent distance.)

1–2   Fundamental Laws of Algebra

In performing the basic operations with numbers, we know that certain basic laws are valid. These basic statements are called the fundamental laws of algebra.

For example, we know that if two numbers are to be added, it does not matter in which order they are added. Thus $5 + 3 = 8$, as well as $3 + 5 = 8$. For this case we can say that $5 + 3 = 3 + 5$. This statement, generalized and assumed correct for all possible combinations of numbers to be added, is called the **commutative law** for addition. The law states that *the sum of two numbers is the same, regardless of the order in which they are added*. We make no attempt to prove this in general, but accept its validity.

In the same way we have the **associative law** for addition, which states that *the sum of three or more numbers is the same, regardless of the manner in which they are grouped for addition*. For example,

$$3 + (5 + 6) = (3 + 5) + 6$$

The laws which we have just stated for addition are also true for multiplication. Therefore, *the product of two numbers is the same, regardless of the order in which they are multiplied,* and *the product of three or more numbers is the same, regardless of the manner in which they are grouped for multiplication.* For example, $2 \cdot 5 = 5 \cdot 2$ and $5 \cdot (4 \cdot 2) = (5 \cdot 4) \cdot 2$.

There is one more important law, called the **distributive law**. It states that *the product of one number and the sum of two or more other numbers is equal to the sum of the products of the first number and each of the other numbers of the sum.* For example,

$$4(3 + 5) = 4 \cdot 3 + 4 \cdot 5$$

In practice these laws are used intuitively. However, it is necessary to state them and to accept their validity, so that we may build our later results with them.

Not all operations are associative and commutative. For example, division is not commutative, since the indicated order of division of two numbers does matter. For example, $\frac{6}{5} \neq \frac{5}{6}$ ($\neq$ is read "does not equal").

Using literal symbols, the fundamental laws of algebra are as follows:

Commutative law of addition: $a + b = b + a$
Associative law of addition: $a + (b + c) = (a + b) + c$
Commutative law of multiplication: $ab = ba$
Associative law of multiplication: $a(bc) = (ab)c$
Distributive law: $a(b + c) = ab + ac$

Having identified the fundamental laws of algebra, we shall state the laws which govern the operations of addition, subtraction, multiplication, and division of signed numbers. These laws will be of primary and direct use in all of our work.

1. *To add two real numbers with like signs, add their absolute values and affix their common sign to the result.*

Example A

$$(+2) + (+6) = +(2 + 6) = +8$$
$$(-2) + (-6) = -(2 + 6) = -8$$

2. *To add two real numbers with unlike signs, subtract the smaller absolute value from the larger and affix the sign of the number with the larger absolute value to the result.*

Example B

$$(+2) + (-6) = -(6 - 2) = -4$$
$$(+6) + (-2) = +(6 - 2) = +4$$

3. *To subtract one real number from another, change the sign of the number to be subtracted, and then proceed as in addition.*

Example C

$$(+2) - (+6) = +2 + (-6) = -(6 - 2) = -4$$
$$(-a) - (-a) = -a + a = 0$$

The second part of Example C shows that subtracting a negative number from itself results in zero. *Subtracting the negative number is equivalent to adding a positive number of the same absolute value.* This reasoning is the basis of the rule which states, "the negative of a negative number is a positive number."

4. *The product (or quotient) of two real numbers of like signs is the product (or quotient) of their absolute values. The product (or quotient) of two real numbers of unlike signs is the negative of the product (or quotient) of their absolute values.*

Example D

$$\frac{+3}{+5} = +\left(\frac{3}{5}\right) = +\frac{3}{5}$$

$$(-3)(+5) = -(3 \cdot 5) = -15$$

$$\frac{-3}{-5} = +\left(\frac{3}{5}\right) = +\frac{3}{5}$$

When we have an expression in which there is a combination of the basic operations, we must be careful to perform them in the proper order. Generally it is clear by the grouping of numbers as to the proper order of performing these operations. However, *if the order of operations is not indicated by specific grouping, multiplications and divisions are performed first, and then the additions and subtractions are performed.*

Example E

The expression $20 \div (2 + 3)$ is evaluated by first adding $2 + 3$ and then dividing 20 by 5 to obtain the result 4. Here, the grouping of $2 + 3$ is clearly shown by the parentheses.

The expression $20 \div 2 + 3$ is evaluated by first dividing 20 by 2 and adding this quotient of 10 to 3 in order to obtain the result of 13. Here no specific grouping is shown, and therefore the division is performed before the addition.

Example F

$$(-6) - 2(-4) + \frac{25}{-5} = (-6) - (-8) + (-5) = -6 + 8 - 5 = -3$$

$$\frac{40}{(+7) + (-3)(+5)} = \frac{40}{+7 + (-15)} = \frac{40}{7 - 15} = \frac{40}{-8} = -5$$

$$\frac{(-8)(+3)}{2} - (-5)(+2)(+3) = \frac{-24}{2} - (-10)(+3)$$

$$= (-12) - (-30) = -12 + 30 = 18$$

In the first illustration, we see that the multiplication and division were performed first, and then the addition and subtraction were performed. Also, it can be seen that the addition and subtraction were changed to operations on unsigned (equivalent to positive) numbers. This is generally more convenient, especially when more than one addition or subtraction is involved. In the second illustration, the multiplication in the denominator was performed first, and then the addition was performed. It was necessary to evaluate the denominator before the division could be performed. In the third illustration, the left expression can be evaluated by performing either the multiplication or division first. Also, the order of multiplication in the right expression does not matter. However, these multiplications and divisions must be performed before the subtraction.

1—3 Operations with Zero

Since the basic operations with zero tend to cause some difficulty, we shall demonstrate them separately in this section.

If a represents any real number, the various operations with zero are defined as follows:

$$a \pm 0 = a \text{ (the symbol } \pm \text{ means ``plus or minus'')}$$
$$a \cdot 0 = 0$$
$$\frac{0}{a} = 0 \quad \text{if} \quad a \neq 0$$

Note that there is no answer defined for division by zero. To understand the reason for this, consider the problem of 4/0. If there were an answer to this expression, it would mean that the answer, which we shall call b, should give 4 when multiplied by 0. That is, $0 \cdot b = 4$. However, no such number b exists, since we already know that $0 \cdot b = 0$. Also, the expression 0/0 has no meaning, since $0 \cdot b = 0$ for any value of b which may be chosen. Thus **division by zero is not defined**. All other operations with zero are the same as for any other number.

Example A

$$5 + 0 = 5, \quad 7 - 0 = 7, \quad 0 - 4 = -4,$$

$$\frac{0}{6} = 0, \qquad \frac{0}{-3} = 0, \qquad \frac{5 \cdot 0}{7} = 0,$$

$$\frac{8}{0} \text{ is undefined,} \quad \frac{7 \cdot 0}{0 \cdot 6} \text{ is undefined}$$

There is no need for confusion in the operations with zero. They will not cause any difficulty if we remember that **division by zero is undefined** and that this is the only undefined operation.

In Exercises 1 through 36 evaluate each of the given expressions by performing the indicated operations.

1. $6 + 5$ **2.** $8 + (-4)$ **3.** $(-4) + (-7)$

4. $(-3) + (+9)$ **5.** $16 - 7$ **6.** $(+8) - (+11)$

7. $-9 - (-6)$ **8.** $8 - (-4)$ **9.** $(8)(-3)$

10. $(+9)(-3)$ **11.** $(-7)(-5)$ **12.** $(+5)(-8)$

13. $\dfrac{-9}{+3}$ **14.** $\dfrac{-18}{-6}$ **15.** $\dfrac{-60}{-3}$

16. $\dfrac{+28}{-7}$ **17.** $(-2)(+4)(-5)$ **18.** $(+3)(-4)(+6)$

19. $\dfrac{(+2)(-5)}{10}$ **20.** $\dfrac{-64}{(2)(-4)}$ **21.** $9 - 0$

22. $\dfrac{0}{-6}$ **23.** $\dfrac{+17}{0}$ **24.** $\dfrac{(+3)(0)}{0}$

25. $8 - 3(-4)$ **26.** $20 + 8 \div 4$

27. $3 - 2(6) + \dfrac{8}{2}$ **28.** $0 - (-6)(-8) + (-10)$

29. $\dfrac{(+3)(-6)(-2)}{0 - 4}$ **30.** $\dfrac{7 - (-5)}{(-1)(-2)}$

31. $\dfrac{24}{3 + (-5)} - 4(-9)$ **32.** $\dfrac{-18}{+3} - \dfrac{4 - 6}{-1}$

33. $(-7) - \dfrac{-14}{2} - 3(2)$ **34.** $-7(-3) + \dfrac{+6}{-3} - (-9)$

35. $\dfrac{(+3)(-9) - 2(-3)}{3 - 10}$ **36.** $\dfrac{(+2)(-7) - 4(-2)}{-9 - (-9)}$

In Exercises 37 through 44 determine which of the fundamental laws of algebra is demonstrated.

37. $(6)(7) = (7)(6)$ **38.** $6 + 8 = 8 + 6$

39. $6(3 + 1) = 6(3) + 6(1)$ **40.** $4(5 \cdot 7) = (4 \cdot 5)(7)$

41. $3 + (5 + 9) = (3 + 5) + 9$ **42.** $8(3 - 2) = 8(3) - 8(2)$

43. $(2 \times 3) \times 9 = 2 \times (3 \times 9)$ **44.** $(3 \cdot 6) \cdot 7 = 7 \cdot (3 \cdot 6)$

In Exercises 45 through 48 answer the given questions.

45. What is the sign of the product of an even number of negative numbers?

46. What is the sign of the product of an odd number of negative numbers?

47. Is subtraction commutative? Illustrate.

48. A boat travels at 6 mi/h in still water. A stream flows at 4 mi/h. If the boat travels downstream for 2 h, set up the expression which would be used to evaluate the distance traveled. What fundamental law is illustrated?

1—4 Exponents

We have introduced numbers and the fundamental laws which are used with them in the fundamental operations. Also, we have shown the use of literal numbers to represent numbers. In this section we shall introduce some basic terminology and notation which are important to the basic algebraic operations developed in the following sections.

In multiplication we often encounter a number which is to be multiplied by itself several times. Rather than writing this number over and over repeatedly, we use the notation a^n, where a is the number being considered and n is the number of times it appears in the product. *The number a is called the* **base**, *the number n is called the* **exponent**, *and, in words, the expression is read as the "nth* **power of** a."

Example A

$$4 \cdot 4 \cdot 4 \cdot 4 \cdot 4 = 4^5 \quad \text{(the fifth power of 4)}$$
$$(-2)(-2)(-2)(-2) = (-2)^4 \quad \text{(the fourth power of } -2)$$
$$a \cdot a = a^2 \quad \text{(the second power of } a, \text{ called "} a \text{ squared")}$$
$$\left(\tfrac{1}{5}\right)\left(\tfrac{1}{5}\right)\left(\tfrac{1}{5}\right) = \left(\tfrac{1}{5}\right)^3 \quad \text{(the third power of } \tfrac{1}{5}, \text{ called "} \tfrac{1}{5} \text{ cubed")}$$
$$8 \cdot 8 \cdot 8 \cdot 8 \cdot 8 \cdot 8 \cdot 8 \cdot 8 \cdot 8 = 8^9 \quad \text{(the ninth power of 8)}$$

The basic operations with exponents will now be stated symbolically. We first state them for positive integers as exponents, and then show how zero and negative integers are used as exponents. Therefore, if m and n are positive integers, we have the following important operations for exponents.

$$a^m \cdot a^n = a^{m+n} \tag{1-1}$$

$$\frac{a^m}{a^n} = a^{m-n} \quad (m > n, \, a \neq 0) \qquad \frac{a^m}{a^n} = \frac{1}{a^{n-m}} \quad (m < n, \, a \neq 0) \tag{1-2}$$

$$(a^m)^n = a^{mn} \tag{1-3}$$

$$(ab)^n = a^n b^n, \quad \left(\frac{a}{b}\right)^n = \frac{a^n}{b^n} \quad (b \neq 0) \tag{1-4}$$

In applying Eqs. (1–1) and (1–2), the base a must be the same for the exponents to be added or subtracted. When a problem involves a product of different bases, *only exponents of the same base may be combined.* In the following three examples, Eqs. (1–1) to (1–4) are verified and illustrated.

Example B
Applying Eq. (1–1), we have

$a^3 \cdot a^5 = a^{3+5} = a^8$. We see that this result is correct since we can also write $a^3 \cdot a^5 = (a \cdot a \cdot a)(a \cdot a \cdot a \cdot a \cdot a) = a^8$.

Applying the first form of Eqs. (1–2), we have

$$\frac{a^5}{a^3} = a^{5-3} = a^2, \quad \frac{a^5}{a^3} = \frac{\cancel{a} \cdot \cancel{a} \cdot \cancel{a} \cdot a \cdot a}{\cancel{a} \cdot \cancel{a} \cdot \cancel{a}} = a^2$$

Applying the second form of Eqs. (1–2), we have

$$\frac{a^3}{a^5} = \frac{1}{a^{5-3}} = \frac{1}{a^2}, \quad \frac{a^3}{a^5} = \frac{\cancel{a} \cdot \cancel{a} \cdot \cancel{a}}{\cancel{a} \cdot \cancel{a} \cdot \cancel{a} \cdot a \cdot a} = \frac{1}{a^2}$$

Example C
Applying Eq. (1–3), we have

$$(a^5)^3 = a^{5(3)} = a^{15}, \quad (a^5)^3 = (a^5)(a^5)(a^5) = a^{5+5+5} = a^{15}$$

Applying the first form of Eqs. (1–4), we have

$$(ab)^3 = a^3b^3, \quad (ab)^3 = (ab)(ab)(ab) = a^3b^3$$

Applying the second form of Eqs. (1–4), we have

$$\left(\frac{a}{b}\right)^3 = \frac{a^3}{b^3}, \quad \left(\frac{a}{b}\right)^3 = \left(\frac{a}{b}\right)\left(\frac{a}{b}\right)\left(\frac{a}{b}\right) = \frac{a^3}{b^3}$$

Example D
Other illustrations of the use of Eqs. (1–1) to (1–4) are as follows:

$$\frac{(3 \cdot 2)^4}{(3 \cdot 5)^3} = \frac{3^4 2^4}{3^3 5^3} = \frac{3 \cdot 2^4}{5^3}$$

$$(-x^2)^3 = [(-1)x^2]^3 = (-1)^3(x^2)^3 = -x^6$$
$$ax^2(ax)^3 = ax^2(a^3x^3) = a^4x^5$$

$$\frac{(ry^3)^2}{r(y^2)^4} = \frac{r^2y^6}{ry^8} = \frac{r}{y^2}$$

As we previously pointed out, Eqs. (1–1) to (1–4) were developed for use with positive integers as exponents. We shall now show how their use can be extended to include zero and negative integers as exponents.

In Eqs. (1–2), if $n = m$, we would have $\frac{a^m}{a^m} = a^{m-m} = a^0$. Also, $\frac{a^m}{a^m} = 1$, since any nonzero quantity divided by itself equals 1. Therefore, for Eqs. (1–2) to hold when $m = n$, we have

$$a^0 = 1, \quad (a \neq 0) \tag{1–5}$$

Equation (1–5) gives the definition of zero as an exponent. Since a has not been specified, this equation states that *any nonzero algebraic expression raised to the zero power is* 1. Also, the other laws of exponents are valid for this definition.

Example E

Equation (1–1) states that $a^m \cdot a^n = a^{m+n}$. If $n = 0$, we thus have $a^m \cdot a^0 = a^{m+0} = a^m$. Since $a^0 = 1$, this equation could be written as $a^m(1) = a^m$. This provides further verification for the validity of Eq. (1–5).

Example F

$$5^0 = 1, \qquad (2x)^0 = 1, \qquad (ax + b)^0 = 1$$
$$(a^2xb^4)^0 = 1, \qquad (a^2b^0c)^2 = a^4b^0c^2 = a^4c^2$$
$$2t^0 = 2(1) = 2$$

We note in the last illustration that only t is raised to the zero power. If the quantity $2t$ was raised to the zero power, it would be written as $(2t)^0$.

If we apply the first form of Eqs. (1–2) to the case where $n > m$, the resulting exponent is negative. This leads us to the definition of a negative exponent.

Example G

Applying the first form of Eqs. (1–2) to a^2/a^7, we have

$$\frac{a^2}{a^7} = a^{2-7} = a^{-5}$$

Applying the second form of Eqs. (1–2) to the same fraction leads to

$$\frac{a^2}{a^7} = \frac{1}{a^{7-2}} = \frac{1}{a^5}$$

In order that these results can be consistent, it must be true that

$$a^{-5} = \frac{1}{a^5}$$

Following the reasoning in Example G, if we define

$$a^{-n} = \frac{1}{a^n}, \qquad (a \neq 0) \tag{1–6}$$

then all of the laws of exponents will hold for negative integers.

Example H

$$3^{-1} = \frac{1}{3}, \qquad 4^{-2} = \frac{1}{16}, \qquad \frac{1}{a^{-3}} = a^3, \qquad a^4 = \frac{1}{a^{-4}}$$

Example I

$$(a^0b^2c)^{-2} = \frac{1}{(b^2c)^2} = \frac{1}{b^4c^2}$$

$$\left(\frac{a^3t}{b^2x}\right)^{-2} = \frac{(a^3t)^{-2}}{(b^2x)^{-2}} = \frac{(b^2x)^2}{(a^3t)^2} = \frac{b^4x^2}{a^6t^2}$$

When we discussed the operations with signed numbers in Section 1–2, we noted that multiplications and divisions are performed prior to additions and subtractions, unless grouping specifies another order. Since raising a number to a power is in essence a form of multiplication, this operation is also performed before additions and subtractions. Thus, *unless grouping specifies otherwise, the order of operations is powers, products, and quotients—and then additions and subtractions.*

Example J

$$8 - (-1)^2 - 2(-3)^2 = 8 - (+1) - 2(+9) = 8 - 1 - 18 = -11$$

Note that we squared -1 and -3 as the first operation. The next operation was finding the product in the last term. Finally the subtractions were performed. We did *not* change the sign of -1 before we squared it, for this would have been incorrect.

Exercises 1—4

In Exercises 1 through 44 simplify the given expressions. Express results with positive exponents only.

1. x^3x^4

2. y^2y^7

3. $2b^4b^2$

4. $3k(k^5)$

5. $\dfrac{m^5}{m^3}$

6. $\dfrac{x^6}{x}$

7. $\dfrac{n^5}{n^9}$

8. $\dfrac{s}{s^4}$

9. $(a^2)^4$

10. $(x^8)^3$

11. $(t^5)^4$

12. $(n^3)^7$

13. $(2n)^3$

14. $(ax)^5$

15. $(ax^4)^2$

16. $(3a^2)^3$

17. $\left(\dfrac{2}{b}\right)^3$

18. $\left(\dfrac{x}{y}\right)^7$

19. $\left(\dfrac{x^2}{2}\right)^4$

20. $\left(\dfrac{3}{n^3}\right)^3$

21. 7^0

22. $(8a)^0$

23. $3x^0$

24. $6v^0$

25. 6^{-1}

26. 10^{-3}

27. $\dfrac{1}{s^{-2}}$

28. $\dfrac{1}{t^{-5}}$

29. $(-t^2)^7$

30. $(-y^3)^5$

31. $(2x^2)^6$

32. $(-c^4)^4$

33. $(4xa^{-2})^0$

34. $3(ab^{-1})^0$

35. b^5b^{-3}

36. $2c^4c^{-7}$

37. $(5^0x^2a^{-1})^{-1}$

38. $(3m^{-2}n^4)^{-2}$

39. $\left(\dfrac{4a}{x}\right)^{-3}$

40. $\left(\dfrac{2b^2}{y^5}\right)^{-2}$

41. $(-8gs^3)^2$

42. $ax^2(-a^2x)^2$

43. $\dfrac{15a^2n^5}{3an^6}$

44. $\dfrac{(ab^2)^3}{a^2b^8}$

In Exercises 45 through 48 evaluate the given expressions.

45. $7(-4) - (-5)^2$ 46. $\dfrac{12}{-3} - (-1)^3$

47. $6 + (-2)^5 - (-2)(8)$ 48. $9 - 2(-3)^4 - (-7)$

In Exercises 49 and 50 solve the given problems.

49. In analyzing the deformation of a certain beam, it might be necessary to simplify the expression

$$\frac{wx(-2Lx^2)}{24EI}$$

Perform this simplification.

50. In a certain electric circuit, it might be necessary to simplify the expression

$$\frac{gM}{j\omega C(\omega^2 M^2)} \quad (\omega \text{ is the Greek omega})$$

Perform this simplification.

1—5 Scientific Notation

In technical and scientific work we often encounter numbers which are either very large or very small in magnitude. Illustrations of such numbers are given in the following example.

Example A
Television signals travel at about 30,000,000,000 cm/s. The mass of the earth is about 6,600,000,000,000,000,000,000 tons. A typical protective coating used on aluminum is about 0.0005 in. thick. The wavelength of some x-rays is about 0.000000095 cm.

Writing numbers such as these is inconvenient in ordinary notation, as shown in Example A, particularly when the numbers of zeros needed for the proper location of the decimal point are excessive. Therefore, a convenient notation, known as **scientific notation**, is normally used to represent such numbers.

A *number written in scientific notation is expressed as the product of a number between 1 and 10 and a power of ten.* Symbolically this can be written as

$$P \times 10^k$$

where $1 \le P < 10$, and k can take on any integral value. The following example illustrates how numbers are written in scientific notation.

Example B

$$340{,}000 = 3.4(100{,}000) = 3.4 \times 10^5$$

$$0.017 = \frac{1.7}{100} = \frac{1.7}{10^2} = 1.7 \times 10^{-2}$$

$$0.000503 = \frac{5.03}{10000} = \frac{5.03}{10^4} = 5.03 \times 10^{-4}$$

$$6.82 = 6.82(1) = 6.82 \times 10^0$$

From Example B we can establish a method for changing numbers from ordinary notation to scientific notation. The decimal point is moved so that only one nonzero digit is to its left. The number of places moved is the value of k. It is positive if the decimal point is moved to the left, and it is negative if it is moved to the right. Consider the illustrations in the following example.

Example C

$$\underbrace{340000}_{5 \text{ places}} = 3.4 \times 10^5 \qquad \underbrace{0.017}_{2 \text{ places}} = 1.7 \times 10^{-2}$$

$$\underbrace{0.000503}_{4 \text{ places}} = 5.03 \times 10^{-4} \qquad \underset{0 \text{ places}}{6.82} = 6.82 \times 10^0$$

To change a number from scientific notation to ordinary notation, the procedure above is reversed. The following example illustrates the procedure.

Example D

To change 5.83×10^6 to ordinary notation, we must move the decimal point 6 places to the right. Therefore, additional zeros must be included for the proper location of the decimal point. This means we write $5.83 \times 10^6 = 5{,}830{,}000$.

To change 8.06×10^{-3} to ordinary notation, we must move the decimal point 3 places to the left. Again, additional zeros must be included. Thus, $8.06 \times 10^{-3} = 0.00806$.

An illustration of the importance of scientific notation is demonstrated by the metric system use of prefixes on units to denote certain powers of ten. These are illustrated in Appendix B.

As we see from the previous examples, scientific notation provides an important application of the use of exponents, positive and negative. Also, scientific notation provides a practical way to handle calculations involving numbers of very large or very small magnitudes. This can be seen by the fact that a feature on many calculators is that of scientific notation.

The calculation can be made by first expressing all numbers in scientific notation. Then the actual calculation can be performed on numbers between one and ten, with the laws of exponents used to find the proper power of ten for the result. It is proper to leave the result in scientific notation.

Example E

In determining the result of 95,600,000,000,000/0.0286, we may set up the calculation as

$$\frac{9.56 \times 10^{13}}{2.86 \times 10^{-2}} = \left(\frac{9.56}{2.86}\right) \times 10^{15} = 3.34 \times 10^{15}$$

The power of ten here is sufficiently large that we would normally leave the result in this form. Even on most calculators with the scientific notation feature, it would be necessary to at least express the numerator in scientific notation before performing the calculation.

Example F

In evaluating the product $(7.50 \times 10^9)(6.44 \times 10^{-3})$, we obtain

$$(7.50 \times 10^9)(6.44 \times 10^{-3}) = 48.3 \times 10^6$$

However, since a number in scientific notation is expressed as the product of a number between 1 and 10, and a power of ten, we should rewrite this result as

$$48.3 \times 10^6 = (4.83 \times 10)(10^6)$$
$$= 4.83 \times 10^7$$

Exercises 1—5

In Exercises 1 through 8 change the numbers from scientific notation to ordinary notation.

1. 4.5×10^4 2. 6.8×10^7 3. 2.01×10^{-3} 4. 9.61×10^{-5}

5. 3.23×10^0 6. 8.40×10^0 7. 1.86×10 8. 5.44×10^{-1}

In Exercises 9 through 16 change the given numbers from ordinary notation to scientific notation.

9. 40000   10. 5600000   11. 0.0087   12. 0.702

13. 6.89   14. 1.09   15. 0.063   16. 0.0000908

In Exercises 17 through 24 perform the indicated calculations by first expressing all numbers in scientific notation. (See Example E.)

17. (67000)(3040000000)   18. (56200)(0.00632)

19. (1280)(86500)(43.8)   20. (0.0000659)(0.00486)(3190000000)

21. $\dfrac{87400}{0.00895}$ 22. $\dfrac{0.00728}{670000}$

23. $\dfrac{(0.0732)(6700)}{0.00134}$ 24. $\dfrac{(2430)(97000)}{0.00452}$

In Exercises 25 through 36 change any numbers in ordinary notation to scientific notation or change any numbers in scientific notation to ordinary notation. (See Appendix B for an explanation of symbols used.)

25. The stress on a certain structure is 22,500 lb/in.^{2}.
26. The half-life of uranium 235 is 710,000,000 years.
27. The power of a radio signal received from a lunar probe is 1.6×10^{-12} W.
28. Some computers can perform an addition in 4.5×10^{-9} s.
29. A certain electrical resistor has a resistance of 4.5×10^3 Ω.
30. To attain an energy density of that in some laser beams, an object would have to be heated to about 10^{30} °C.
31. One foot of steel pipe will increase about 0.000011 ft for a 1°C rise in temperature.
32. The wave length of yellow light is about 0.00000059 m.
33. The mass of a proton is 1.67×10^{-24} g.
34. The average distance from the earth to the sun is 9.29×10^7 mi.
35. The diameter of the sun is 864,000 mi.
36. The total acreage of national forests in the United States is approximately 187,000,000 acres.

In Exercises 37 through 40 perform the indicated calculations by first expressing all numbers in scientific notation.

37. There are about 161,000 cm in one mile. What is the area in square centimeters of one square mile?
38. A particular virus is a sphere 0.0000175 cm in diameter. What volume does the virus occupy?
39. The resistance R, in ohms, of a wire of length l and cross-sectional area A is given by $R = \rho l / A$, where ρ (the Greek rho) is known as the resistivity. Find R for a wire for which $\rho = 0.0000000175$ $\Omega \cdot$ m, $l = 0.150$ m and $A = 0.000000435$ m^2.
40. For a certain gas, the product of the volume and pressure is 16.5 Pa·cm^3. If the pressure is 0.00108 Pa, what is the volume?

1—6 Roots and Radicals

A problem that is often encountered is, "what number multiplied by itself n times gives another specified number?" For example, we may ask, "what number squared is 9?" The answer to this question is the **square root** of 9, which is denoted by $\sqrt{9}$.

The general notation for the nth root of a is $\sqrt[n]{a}$. (When $n = 2$, it is common practice not to put the 2 where n appears.) The $\sqrt{}$ sign is called a **radical sign**.

Example A

$$\sqrt{2} \quad \text{(the square root of two)}$$
$$\sqrt[3]{2} \quad \text{(the cube root of two)}$$
$$\sqrt[4]{2} \quad \text{(the fourth root of two)}$$
$$\sqrt[7]{6} \quad \text{(the seventh root of six)}$$
$$\sqrt[3]{8} \quad \text{(the cube root of 8, which also equals 2)}$$

In considering the question "what number squared is 9?" we can easily see that either $+3$ or -3 gives a proper result. This would imply that both of these values equaled $\sqrt{9}$. To avoid this ambiguity, *we define the* **principal *n*th root** *of a to be positive if a is positive, and the principal nth root of a to be negative if a is negative and n is odd.* This means that $\sqrt{9} = 3$ and not -3, and that $-\sqrt{9} = -3$.

Example B

$$\sqrt{4} = 2 \quad (\sqrt{4} \neq -2), \quad \sqrt{169} = 13 \quad (\sqrt{169} \neq -13),$$
$$-\sqrt{64} = -8, \quad -\sqrt{81} = -9, \quad -\sqrt[4]{256} = -4,$$
$$\sqrt[3]{27} = 3, \quad \sqrt[3]{-27} = -3, \quad -\sqrt[3]{27} = -(+3) = -3$$

Another important property of radicals is that *the square root of a product of positive numbers is the product of the square roots.* That is,

$$\sqrt{ab} = \sqrt{a} \cdot \sqrt{b} \qquad (1\text{--}7)$$

This property is useful is simplifying radicals. It is most useful if either *a* or *b* is a perfect square. Consider the following example.

Example C

$$\sqrt{8} = \sqrt{(4)(2)} = \sqrt{4}\sqrt{2} = 2\sqrt{2}$$
$$\sqrt{75} = \sqrt{(25)(3)} = \sqrt{25}\sqrt{3} = 5\sqrt{3}$$
$$\sqrt{80} = \sqrt{(16)(5)} = \sqrt{16}\sqrt{5} = 4\sqrt{5}$$

Earlier we mentioned imaginary numbers. Until Chapter 11 it will be necessary only that we recognize imaginary numbers when they occur. This is done by recalling that the square root of a negative number is an imaginary number. Thus, if we have the square root of a negative number, we can write it as *j* times the square root of the corresponding positive number.

Example D

$$\sqrt{-4} = \sqrt{(4)(-1)} = \sqrt{4}\sqrt{-1} = 2j$$
$$\sqrt{-27} = \sqrt{(27)(-1)} = \sqrt{27}\sqrt{-1} = \sqrt{(9)(3)}\sqrt{-1}$$
$$= \sqrt{9}\sqrt{3}\sqrt{-1} = 3\sqrt{3}j$$

It should be emphasized that although the square root of a negative number gives an imaginary number, the cube root of a negative number gives a negative real number. More generally, *the even root of a negative number is imaginary, and the odd root of a negative number is real.* A more detailed discussion of exponents, radicals, and imaginary numbers is found in Chapters 10 and 11.

Example E

$$\sqrt{-64} = \sqrt{64}j = 8j, \qquad \sqrt[3]{-64} = -4$$

Exercises 1—6

In Exercises 1 through 24 simplify the given expressions.

1. $\sqrt{25}$ 2. $\sqrt{81}$ 3. $-\sqrt{121}$ 4. $-\sqrt{36}$

5. $\sqrt[3]{125}$ 6. $\sqrt[4]{16}$ 7. $\sqrt[3]{-216}$ 8. $\sqrt[5]{-32}$

9. $\sqrt{18}$ 10. $\sqrt{32}$ 11. $\sqrt{12}$ 12. $\sqrt{50}$

13. $\sqrt{-9}$ 14. $\sqrt{-25}$ 15. $\sqrt{-12}$ 16. $\sqrt{-28}$

17. $(\sqrt{5})^2$ 18. $(\sqrt{19})^2$ 19. $(\sqrt[3]{31})^3$ 20. $(\sqrt[4]{53})^4$

21. $2\sqrt{48}$ 22. $4\sqrt{108}$ 23. $\dfrac{7^2\sqrt{81}}{3^2\sqrt{49}}$ 24. $\dfrac{2^5\sqrt[5]{243}}{3\sqrt{144}}$

In Exercises 25 through 28 solve the given problems.

25. A square parcel of land has an area of 400 m². What is the length of a side of the parcel?
26. A cubical water tank holds 512 ft³. What is the length of an edge of the tank?
27. Is it always true that $\sqrt{a^2} = a$?
28. If $0 < x < 1$ (x between 0 and 1), is $x > \sqrt{x}$?

1—7 Addition and Subtraction of Algebraic Expressions

It is the basic characteristic of algebra that letters are used to represent numbers. Since we have used literal symbols to represent numbers, even if in a general sense, we may conclude that all operations valid for numbers are valid for these literal symbols. In this section we shall discuss the terminology and methods for combining literal symbols.

Addition, subtraction, multiplication, division, and taking of roots are known as **algebraic operations.** *Any combination of numbers and literal symbols which results from algebraic operations is known as an* **algebraic expression.**

When an algebraic expression consists of several parts connected by plus signs and minus signs, each part (along with its sign) is known as a **term** *of the expression. If a given expression is made up of the product of a number of quantities, each of these quantities, or any product of them, is called a* **factor** *of the expression.* **It is important to distinguish clearly between terms and factors since some operations that are valid for terms are not valid for factors, and conversely.**

Example A

$3xy + 6x^2 - 7x\sqrt{y}$ is an algebraic expression with three terms. They are $3xy$, $6x^2$, and $-7x\sqrt{y}$.

The first term $3xy$ has individual factors of 3, x, and y. Also, any product of these factors is also a factor of $3xy$. Thus, additional expressions which are factors of $3xy$ are $3x$, $3y$, xy, and $3xy$ itself.

Example B

$7x(y^2 + x) - \dfrac{x + y}{6x}$ is an algebraic expression with terms $7x(y^2 + x)$ and $\dfrac{-(x + y)}{6x}$.

The term $7x(y^2 + x)$ has individual factors of 7, x, and $(y^2 + x)$, as well as products of these factors. The factor $y^2 + x$ has two terms, y^2 and x.

The numerator of the term $-\dfrac{x + y}{6x}$ has two terms, and the denominator has individual factors of 2, 3, and x. The minus sign can be treated as a factor of -1.

An algebraic expression containing only one term is called a **monomial.** *An expression containing two terms is a* **binomial,** *and one containing three terms is a* **trinomial.** *Any expression containing two or more terms is called a* **multinomial.** Thus, any binomial or trinomial expression can also be considered as a multinomial.

In any given term, the numbers and literal symbols multiplying any given factor constitute the **coefficient** *of that factor. The product of all the numbers in explicit form is known as the* **numerical coefficient** *of the term. All terms which differ only in their numerical coefficients are known as* **similar** *or* **like** *terms.*

Example C

$7x^3\sqrt{y}$ is a monomial. It has a numerical coefficient of 7. The coefficient of $\sqrt{y}$ is $7x^3$, and the coefficient of x^3 is $7\sqrt{y}$.

Example D

$4 \cdot 2b + 81b - 6ab$ is a multinomial of three terms. The first term has a numerical coefficient of 8, the second has a numerical coefficient of 81, and the third has a numerical coefficient of -6 (the sign of the term is attached to the numerical coefficient). The first and second terms are similar, since they differ only in their numerical coefficient. The third term is not similar to either of the others, for it has the factor a.

In adding and subtracting algebraic expressions, we combine similar terms. In doing so, we are combining quantities which are alike. All of the similar terms may be combined into a single term, and the final simplified expression will be made up entirely of terms which are not similar.

Example E

$3x + 2x - 5y = 5x - 5y$. Since there are two similar terms in the original expression, they are added together, so the simplified result has two unlike terms.

$6a^2 - 7a + 8ax$ cannot be simplified, since none of the terms are like terms.

Similarly, $6a + 5c + 2a - c = 6a + 2a + 5c - c = 8a + 4c$. (Here we use the commutative and associative laws.)

In writing algebraic expressions, it is often necessary to group certain terms together. For this purpose we use **symbols of grouping.** In this text we shall use **parentheses** ( ), **brackets** [ ], and **braces** { }. The **bar,** which is used with radicals and fractions, also groups terms. The bar attached to the radical sign groups the terms under it, and the bar separating the numerator and denominator of a fraction groups the terms above and under it.

When adding and subtracting algebraic expressions, it is often necessary to remove symbols of grouping. To do so we must *change the sign of every term within the symbols if the grouping is preceded by a minus sign.* If the symbols of grouping are preceded by a plus sign, each term within the symbols retains its original sign. This is a result of the distributive law. Normally, *when several symbols of grouping are to be removed, it is more convenient to remove the innermost symbols first.* This is illustrated in Examples H and I.

Example F

(1) $2a - (3a + 2b) - b = 2a - 3a - 2b - b = -a - 3b$

(2) $-(2x - 3c) + (c - x) = -2x + 3c + c - x = 4c - 3x$

Example G

(1) $3 - 2(m^2 - 2) = 3 - 2m^2 + 4 = 7 - 2m^2$

(2) $4(t - 3 - 2t^2) - (6t + t^2 - 4) = 4t - 12 - 8t^2 - 6t - t^2 + 4$
$$= -9t^2 - 2t - 8$$

Example H

(1) $-[(4 - 5x) - (a - 2x - 7)] = -[4 - 5x - a + 2x + 7]$
$$= -[11 - 3x - a] = -11 + 3x + a$$

(2) $3ax - [ax - (5s - 2ax)] = 3ax - [ax - 5s + 2ax]$
$$= 3ax - ax + 5s - 2ax = 5s$$

Example I

$[a^2b - ab + (ab - 2a^2b)] - \{[(3a^2b + b) - (4ab - 2a^2b)] - b\}$
$$= [a^2b - ab + ab - 2a^2b] - \{[3a^2b + b - 4ab + 2a^2b] - b\}$$
$$= a^2b - ab + ab - 2a^2b - \{3a^2b + b - 4ab + 2a^2b - b\}$$
$$= a^2b - ab + ab - 2a^2b - 3a^2b - b + 4ab - 2a^2b + b$$
$$= -6a^2b + 4ab$$

One of the most common errors made by beginning students is changing the sign of only the first term when removing symbols of grouping preceded by a minus sign. *Remember, if the symbols are preceded by a minus sign, we must change the sign of* all *terms.*

Exercises 1–7

In the following exercises simplify the given algebraic expressions.

1. $5x + 7x - 4x$
2. $6t - 3t - 4t$
3. $2y - y + 4x$
4. $4c + d - 6c$
5. $2a - 2c - e + 3c - a$
6. $x - 2y + 3x - y + z$
7. $a^2b - a^2b^2 - 2a^2b$
8. $xy^2 - 3x^2y^2 + 2xy^2$
9. $v - (4 - 5x + 2v)$
10. $2a - (b - a)$
11. $2 - 3 - (4 - 5a)$
12. $\sqrt{x} + (y - 2\sqrt{x}) - 3\sqrt{x}$
13. $(a - 3) + (5 - 6a)$
14. $(4x - y) - (2x - 4y)$
15. $3(2r + s) - (5s - r)$
16. $3(a - b) - 2(a - 2b)$
17. $-7(6 - 3c) - 2(c + 4)$
18. $-(5t + a^2) - 2(3a^2 - 2st)$
19. $-[(6 - n) - (2n - 3)]$
20. $-[(a - b) - (b - a)]$
21. $2[4 - (t^2 - 5)]$
22. $3[3 - (a - 4)]$
23. $-2[-x - 2a - (a - x)]$
24. $-2[-3(x - 2y) + 4x]$
25. $a\sqrt{xy} - [3 - (a\sqrt{xy} + 4)]$
26. $9v - [6 - (v - 4) + 4v]$
27. $8c - \{5 - [2 - (3 + 4c)]\}$
28. $7y - \{y - [2y - (x - y)]\}$
29. $5p - (q - 2p) - [3q - (p - q)]$
30. $-(4 - x) - [(5x - 7) - (6x + 2)]$
31. $-2\{-(4 - x^2) - [3 + (4 - x^2)]\}$
32. $-\{-[-(x - 2a) - b] - a\}$

33. When discussing gear trains, the expression $-(-R - 1)$ is found. Simplify this expression.

34. In analyzing a certain electric circuit, the expression $I_1 + I_2 - (I_2 - I_3)$ is found. Simplify this expression. (The numbers below the I's are **subscripts**. Different subscripts denote different unknowns.)

35. Under certain conditions, the expression for finding the profit on given sales involves simplifying the expression $5(x + 1) - (400 + 2x)$. Simplify this expression.

36. In developing the theory for an elastic substance, we find the following expression:

$$[(B + \tfrac{4}{3}\alpha) + 2(B - \tfrac{2}{3}\alpha)] - [(B + \tfrac{4}{3}\alpha) - (B - \tfrac{2}{3}\alpha)]$$

Simplify this expression.

1–8 Multiplication of Algebraic Expressions

To find the product of two or more monomials, we use the laws of exponents as given in Section 1–4 and the laws for multiplying signed numbers as stated in Section 1–2. We first multiply the numerical coefficients to determine the numerical coefficient of the product. Then we multiply the literal factors, remembering that the exponents may be combined only if the base is the same. Consider the illustrations in the following example.

Example A

(1) $3ac^3(4sa^2c) = 12a^3c^4s$

(2) $(-2b^2y)(-9aby^5) = 18ab^3y^6$

(3) $2xy(-6cx^2)(3xcy^2) = -36c^2x^4y^3$

We find the product of a monomial and a multinomial by using the distributive law, which states that we *multiply each term of the multinomial by the monomial.* We must be careful to assign the correct sign to each term of the result, using the rules for multiplication of signed numbers. Also, we must properly combine literal factors in each term of the result.

Example B

(1) $2ax(3ax^2 - 4yz) = 2ax(3ax^2) - (2ax)(4yz) = 6a^2x^3 - 8axyz$

(2) $5cy^2(-7cx - ac) = (5cy^2)(-7cx) + (5cy^2)(-ac)$
$$= -35c^2xy^2 - 5ac^2y^2$$

In practice, it is generally not necessary to write out the middle step as it appears in the example above. We can generally write the answer directly. For example, the first part of Example B would usually appear as

$$2ax(3ax^2 - 4yz) = 6a^2x^3 - 8axyz$$

We find the product of two or more multinomials by using the distributive law and the laws of exponents. The result is that we *multiply each term of one multinomial by each term of the other, and add the results.*

Example C

(1) $(x - 2)(x + 3) = x(x) + x(3) + (-2)(x) + (-2)(3)$
$$= x^2 + 3x - 2x - 6 = x^2 + x - 6$$

(2) $(a^2 - 2ab)(xy^2 + x^2) = a^2(xy^2) + a^2(x^2) - 2ab(xy^2) - 2ab(x^2)$
$$= a^2xy^2 + a^2x^2 - 2abxy^2 - 2abx^2$$

(3) $(x - 2y)(x^2 + 2xy + 4y^2) = x^3 + 2x^2y + 4xy^2 - 2x^2y - 4xy^2 - 8y^3$
$$= x^3 - 8y^3$$

Finding the power of an algebraic expression is equivalent to multiplying the expression by itself the number of times indicated by the exponent. In practice, it is often convenient to write the power of an algebraic expression in this form before multiplying. Consider the following example.

Example D

(1) $(x + 5)^2 = (x + 5)(x + 5) = x^2 + 5x + 5x + 25$
$$= x^2 + 10x + 25$$

(2) $(2a - b)^3 = (2a - b)(2a - b)(2a - b)$
$$= (2a - b)(4a^2 - 4ab + b^2)$$
$$= 8a^3 - 8a^2b + 2ab^2 - 4a^2b + 4ab^2 - b^3$$
$$= 8a^3 - 12a^2b + 6ab^2 - b^3$$

Exercises 1—8

In the following exercises perform the indicated multiplications.

1. $(a^2)(ax)$
2. $(2xy)(x^2y^3)$
3. $-ac^2(acx^3)$
4. $-2s^2(-4cs)^2$
5. $(2ax^2)^2(-2ax)$
6. $6pq^3(3pq^2)^2$
7. $a(-d^2x)(-2a)$
8. $-2m^2(-3mn)(m^2n)^2$
9. $a^2(x + y)$
10. $2x(p - q)$
11. $-3s(s^2 - 5t)$
12. $-3b(2b^2 - b)$
13. $5m(m^2n + 3mn)$
14. $a^2bc(2ac - 3a^2b)$
15. $3x(x - y + 2)$
16. $b^2x^2(x^2 - 2x + 1)$
17. $ab^2c^4(ac - bc - ab)$
18. $-4c^2(9gc - 2c + g^2)$
19. $ax(cx^2)(x + y^3)$
20. $-2(-3st^3)(3s - 4t)$
21. $(x - 3)(x + 5)$
22. $(a + 7)(a + 1)$
23. $(x + 5)(2x - 1)$
24. $(4t + s)(2t - 3s)$
25. $(2a - b)(3a - 2b)$
26. $(4x - 3)(3x - 1)$
27. $(x^2 - 2x)(x + 4)$
28. $(2ab^2 - 5t)(-ab^2 - 6t)$
29. $(x + 1)(x^2 - 3x + 2)$
30. $(2x + 3)(x^2 - x + 5)$
31. $(4x - x^3)(2 + x - x^2)$
32. $(5a - 3c)(a^2 + ac - c^2)$
33. $2x(x - 1)(x + 4)$
34. $ax(x + 4)(7 - x^2)$
35. $(2x - 5)^2$
36. $(x - 3)^2$
37. $(x + 3a)^2$
38. $(2m + 1)^2$
39. $(xyz - 2)^2$
40. $(b - 2x^2)^2$
41. $(2 + x)(3 - x)(x - 1)$
42. $(3x - c^2)^3$
43. $3x(x + 2)^2(2x - 1)$
44. $[(x - 2)^2(x + 2)]^2$

45. Under given conditions, when determining the income from a business enterprise, the expression $(40 - x)(200 + 5x)$ is found. Perform the indicated multiplication.

46. In determining a certain chemical volume, the expression $a + b(1 - X) + c(1 - X)^2$ is found. Perform the indicated multiplications.

47. The analysis of the deflection of a certain concrete beam involves the expression $w(l^2 - x^2)^2$. Perform the indicated multiplication.

48. In finding the maximum power in a particular electric circuit, the expression $(R + r)^2 - 2r(R + r)$ is used. Multiply and simplify.

1–9 Division of Algebraic Expressions

To find the quotient of one monomial divided by another, we use the laws of exponents as given in Section 1–4 and the laws for dividing signed numbers as stated in Section 1–2. Again, the exponents may be combined only if the base is the same.

Example A

(1) $\dfrac{16x^3y^5}{4xy^2} = \dfrac{16}{4}(x^{3-1})(y^{5-2}) = 4x^2y^3$

(2) $\dfrac{-6a^2xy^2}{2axy^4} = -\left(\dfrac{6}{2}\right)\dfrac{a^{2-1}x^{1-1}}{y^{4-2}} = -\dfrac{3a}{y^2}$

As noted in the second illustration, we use only positive exponents in the final result, unless there are specific instructions otherwise.

The quotient of a multinomial divided by a monomial is found by dividing each term of the multinomial by the monomial and adding the results. This process is a result of the equivalent operation with arithmetic fractions, which can be shown as

$$\frac{a + b}{c} = \frac{a}{c} + \frac{b}{c}$$

(Be careful: although $\frac{a+b}{c} = \frac{a}{c} + \frac{b}{c}$, we must note that $\frac{c}{a+b}$ is not $\frac{c}{a} + \frac{c}{b}$.)

Example B

(1) $\dfrac{16r^3st^2 - 8r^2t^3}{4rt^2} = \dfrac{16r^3st^2}{4rt^2} - \dfrac{8r^2t^3}{4rt^2} = 4r^2s - 2rt$

(2) $\dfrac{4x^3y - 8x^3y^2 + 6x^2y^4}{2x^2y} = \dfrac{4x^3y}{2x^2y} - \dfrac{8x^3y^2}{2x^2y} + \dfrac{6x^2y^4}{2x^2y}$

$$= 2x - 4xy + 3y^3$$

(3) $\dfrac{a^3bc^4 - 6abc + 9a^2b^3c - 3}{3ab^2c^3} = \dfrac{a^2c}{3b} - \dfrac{2}{bc^2} + \dfrac{3ab}{c^2} - \dfrac{1}{ab^2c^3}$

Usually in practice we would not write the middle step as shown in the first two illustrations of Example B. The divisions are done by inspection, and the expression would appear as shown in the third illustration. However, we must remember that each term in the numerator is divided by the monomial in the denominator.

If each term of an algebraic sum is a number or is of the form ax^n where n is a nonnegative integer, we call the expression a **polynomial** *in* x. The distinction between a multinomial and a polynomial is that a polynomial does not contain terms like $\sqrt{x}$ or $1/x^2$, whereas a multinomial may contain such terms. Also, a polynomial may consist of only one term, whereas a multinomial must have at least two terms. In a polynomial, *the greatest value of n which appears is the* **degree** *of the polynomial.*

Example C

$3 + 2x^2 - x^3$ is a polynomial of degree 3,

$x^4 - 3x^2 - \sqrt{x}$ is not a polynomial,

$4x^5$ is a polynomial of degree 5.

The first two expressions are also multinomials since each contains more than one term. The second illustration is not a polynomial due to the presence of the $\sqrt{x}$ term. The third illustration is a polynomial since the exponent is a positive integer. It is also a monomial.

The problem often arises of dividing one polynomial by another. To solve this problem, we first arrange the dividend (the polynomial to be divided) and the divisor in descending powers of x. Then we divide the first term of the dividend by the first term of the divisor. The result gives the first term of the quotient. Next, we multiply the entire divisor by the first term of the quotient and subtract the product from the dividend. We divide the first term of this difference by the first term of the divisor. This gives the second term of the quotient. We multiply this term by each of the terms of the divisor and subtract this result from the first difference. We repeat this process until the remainder is either zero or a term which is of lower degree than the divisor. This process is similar to that of long division of numbers.

Example D

Divide $4x^3 + 6x^2 + 1$ by $2x - 1$. Since there is no x-term in the dividend, it is advisable to leave space for any x-terms which might arise.

$$
\begin{array}{r}
2x^2 + 4x \qquad + 2 \quad \text{(quotient)} \\
2x - 1 \overline{\smash{\big)}\, 4x^3 + 6x^2 \qquad + 1} \quad \text{(dividend)} \\
\underline{4x^3 - 2x^2} \qquad\qquad\quad \\
8x^2 \qquad + 1 \\
\underline{8x^2 - 4x} \qquad \\
4x + 1 \\
\underline{4x - 2} \\
3 \quad \text{(remainder)}
\end{array}
$$

(divisor)

Exercises 1—9

In Exercises 1 through 36 perform the indicated divisions.

1. $\dfrac{8x^3y^2}{-2xy}$

2. $\dfrac{-18b^7c^3}{bc^2}$

3. $\dfrac{-16r^3t^5}{-4r^5t}$

4. $\dfrac{51mn^5}{17m^2n^2}$

5. $\dfrac{(15x^2)(4bx)(2y)}{30bxy}$

6. $\dfrac{(5st)(8s^2t^3)}{10s^3t^2}$

7. $\dfrac{6(ax)^2}{-ax^2}$

8. $\dfrac{12a^2b}{(3ab^2)^2}$

9. $\dfrac{a^2x + 4xy}{x}$

10. $\dfrac{2m^2n - 6mn}{2m}$

11. $\dfrac{3rst - 6r^2st^2}{3rs}$

12. $\dfrac{-5a^2n - 10an^2}{5an}$

13. $\dfrac{4pq^3 + 8p^2q^2 - 16pq^5}{4pq^2}$

14. $\dfrac{a^2xy^2 + ax^3 - 4ax^2}{ax}$

15. $\dfrac{2\pi fL - \pi fR^2}{\pi fR}$

16. $\dfrac{2(ab)^4 - a^3b^4}{3(ab)^3}$

17. $\dfrac{3ab^2 - 6ab^3 + 9a^3b}{9a^2b^2}$

18. $\dfrac{4x^2y^3 + 8xy - 12x^2y^4}{2x^2y^2}$

19. $\dfrac{x^{n+2} + ax^n}{x^n}$

20. $\dfrac{3a(x + y)b^2 - (x + y)}{a(x + y)}$

21. $\dfrac{x^2 - 3x + 2}{x - 2}$

22. $\dfrac{2x^2 - 5x - 7}{x + 1}$

23. $\dfrac{x - 14x^2 + 8x^3}{2x - 3}$

24. $\dfrac{6x^2 + 6 + 7x}{2x + 1}$

25. $\dfrac{x^3 + 3x^2 - 4x - 12}{x + 2}$

26. $\dfrac{3x^3 + 19x^2 + 16x - 20}{3x - 2}$

27. $\dfrac{2x^4 + 4x^3 + 2}{x^2 - 1}$

28. $\dfrac{2x^3 - 3x^2 + 8x - 2}{x^2 - x + 2}$

29. $\dfrac{x^3 + 8}{x + 2}$

30. $\dfrac{x^3 - 1}{x - 1}$

31. $\dfrac{x^2 - 2xy + y^2}{x - y}$

32. $\dfrac{3a^2 - 5ab + 2b^2}{a - 3b}$

33. In determining the volume of a certain gas, the following expression is used:

$$\frac{RTV^2 - aV + ab}{RT}$$

Perform the indicated division.

34. In hydrodynamics the following expression is found:

$$\frac{2p + v^2d + 2ydg}{2dg}$$

Perform the indicated division.

35. The expression for the total resistance of three resistances in parallel in an electric circuit is

$$\frac{R_1 R_2 R_3}{R_2 R_3 + R_1 R_3 + R_1 R_2}$$

Find the reciprocal of this expression, and then perform the indicated division.

36. The following expression is found when analyzing the motion of a certain object:

$$\frac{s + 6}{s^2 + 8s + 25}$$

Find the reciprocal of this expression, and perform the indicated division.

1–10 Equations

The basic operations for algebraic expressions that we have developed are used in the important process of solving equations. In this section we show how the basic algebraic operations are used in solving equations, and in the following section we will demonstrate some of the important applications of equations.

An **equation** *is an algebraic statement that two algebraic expressions are equal.* It is possible that many values of the letter representing the **unknown** will **satisfy** the equation; that is, many values may produce equality when **substituted** in the equation. It is also possible that only one value for the unknown will satisfy the equation (and this will be true of the equations we solve in this section). Or possibly there may be no values which satisfy the equation, although the statement is still an equation.

Example A
The equation $x^2 - 4 = (x - 2)(x + 2)$ is true for all values of x. For example, if we substitute $x = 3$ we have $9 - 4 = (3 - 2)(3 + 2)$ or $5 = 5$. If we let $x = -1$, we have $-3 = -3$. *An equation that is true for all values of the unknown is termed an* **identity.**

The equation $x^2 - 2 = x$ is true if $x = 2$ or if $x = -1$, but it is not true for any other values of x. If $x = 2$ we obtain $2 = 2$, and if $x = -1$ we obtain $-1 = -1$. However, if we let $x = 4$, we obtain $14 = 4$, which of course is not correct. *An equation valid only for certain values of the unknown is termed a* **conditional equation.** These equations are those which are generally encountered.

Example B

The equation $3x - 5 = x + 1$ is true only for $x = 3$. When $x = 3$ we obtain $4 = 4$; if we let $x = 2$, we obtain $1 = 3$, which is not correct.

The equation $x + 5 = x + 1$ is not true for any value of x. For any value of x we try, we will find that the left side is 4 greater than the right side. However, it is still an equation.

To **solve** an equation we find the values of the unknown which satisfy it. There is one basic rule to follow when solving an equation: **Perform the same operation on both sides of the equation.** We do this to isolate the unknown and thus to find its values.

By performing the same operation on both sides of an equation, the two sides remain equal. Thus, *we may add the same number to both sides, subtract the same number from both sides, multiply both sides by the same number, or divide both sides by the same number (not zero).*

Example C

In solving the following equations, we note that we may isolate x, and thereby solve the equation, by performing the indicated operation.

$x - 3 = 12$	$x + 3 = 12$	$\dfrac{x}{3} = 12$	$3x = 12$
Add 3 to both sides.	Subtract 3 from both sides.	Multiply both sides by 3.	Divide both sides by 3.
$x - 3 + 3 = 12 + 3$	$x + 3 - 3 = 12 - 3$	$3\left(\dfrac{x}{3}\right) = 3(12)$	$\dfrac{3x}{3} = \dfrac{12}{3}$
$x = 15$	$x = 9$	$x = 36$	$x = 4$

Each can be checked by substitution in the original equation. (The term "transposing" is often used to denote the result of adding or subtracting a term from both sides of the equation. In transposing, a term is moved from one side of the equation to the other, and its sign is changed.)

The solution of an equation generally requires a combination of the basic operations. The following examples illustrate the solution of such equations.

Example D

Solve the equation $2t - 7 = 9$.

We are to perform basic operations to both sides of the equation to finally isolate t on one side. The steps to be followed are suggested by the form of the equation, and in this case are as follows.

$$2t - 7 = 9 \quad \text{add 7 to both sides}$$
$$2t = 16 \quad \text{divide both sides by 2}$$
$$t = 8$$

Therefore, we conclude that $t = 8$. Checking in the original equation, we see that we have $2(8) - 7 = 9$, $16 - 7 = 9$, or $9 = 9$. Therefore, the solution checks.

Example E
Solve the equation $3n + 4 = n - 6$.

$$2n + 4 = -6 \qquad n \text{ subtracted from both sides}$$
$$2n = -10 \qquad 4 \text{ subtracted from both sides}$$
$$n = -5 \qquad \text{both sides divided by 2}$$

Checking in the original equation, we have $-11 = -11$.

Example F
Solve the equation $x - 7 = 3x - (6x - 8)$.

$$x - 7 = 3x - 6x + 8 \qquad \text{parentheses removed}$$
$$x - 7 = -3x + 8 \qquad x\text{'s combined on right}$$
$$4x - 7 = 8 \qquad 3x \text{ added to both sides}$$
$$4x = 15 \qquad 7 \text{ added to both sides}$$
$$x = \tfrac{15}{4} \qquad \text{both sides divided by 4}$$

Checking in the original equation, we obtain (after simplifying) $-\tfrac{13}{4} = -\tfrac{13}{4}$.

Exercises 1–10

In Exercises 1 through 24 solve the given equations.

1. $x - 2 = 7$

2. $x - 4 = 1$

3. $x + 5 = 4$

4. $s + 6 = 3$

5. $\dfrac{t}{2} = 5$

6. $\dfrac{x}{4} = 2$

7. $4x = 20$

8. $2x = 12$

9. $3t + 5 = -4$

10. $5x - 2 = 13$

11. $5 - 2y = 3$

12. $8 - 5t = 18$

13. $3x + 7 = x$

14. $6 + 8y = 5 - y$

15. $2(s - 4) = s$

16. $3(n - 2) = -n$

17. $6 - (r - 4) = 2r$

18. $5 - (x + 2) = 5x$

19. $2(x - 3) - 5x = 7$

20. $4(x + 7) - x = 7$

21. $x - 5(x - 2) = 2$

22. $5x - 2(x - 5) = 4x$

23. $7 - 3(1 - 2p) = 4 + 2p$

24. $3 - 6(2 - 3t) = t - 5$

In Exercises 25 through 28 solve the given problems.

25. What conclusion can be made about the equation $2(x - 3) + 1 = 2x - 5$?

26. What conclusion can be made about the equation $1 - (3 - x) = x - 2$?

27. Show that the equation $3(x + 2) = 3x + 4$ is not valid for any values of x.

28. Show that the equation $7 - (2 - x) = x + 2$ is not valid for any values of x.

1–11 Applications of Equations

Equations and their solutions are of great importance in most fields of technology and science. They are used to attain, study, and confirm information of all kinds. One of the most important applications occurs in the use of formulas in mathematics, physics, engineering, and other fields. A formula is an algebraic statement that two expressions stand for the same number. For example, the formula for the area of a circle is $A = \pi r^2$. The symbol A stands for the area, as does the expression πr^2, but πr^2 expresses the area in terms of another quantity, the radius.

Often it is necessary to solve a formula for a particular letter or symbol which appears in it. We do this in the same manner as we solve any equation: we isolate the letter or symbol desired by use of the basic algebraic operations.

Example A
Solve $A = \pi r^2$ for π.

$$\frac{A}{r^2} = \pi \qquad \text{both sides divided by } r^2$$

$$\pi = \frac{A}{r^2} \qquad \text{since each side equals the other, it makes no difference which expression appears on the left}$$

Example B
A formula relating acceleration a, velocity v, initial velocity v_0, and time t, is $v = v_0 + at$. Solve for t.

$$v - v_0 = at \qquad v_0 \text{ subtracted from both sides}$$

$$t = \frac{v - v_0}{a} \qquad \text{both sides divided by } a \text{ and then sides are switched}$$

As we can see from Examples A and B, we can solve for the indicated literal number just as we solved for the unknown in the previous section. That is, we perform the basic algebraic operations on the various literal numbers which appear in the same way we perform them on explicit numbers. Another illustration appears in the following example.

Example C
The effect of temperature is important when accurate instrumentation is required. The volume V of a precision container at temperature T in terms of the volume V_0 at temperature T_0 is given by

$$V = V_0[1 + b(T - T_0)]$$

where b depends on the material of which the container is made. Solve for T.

Since we are to solve for T, we must isolate the term containing T. This can be done by first removing the grouping symbols, and then isolate the term with T.

$$V = V_0[1 + b(T - T_0)] \qquad \text{(original equation)}$$

$$V = V_0[1 + bT - bT_0] \qquad \text{(remove parentheses)}$$

$$V = V_0 + bTV_0 - bT_0V_0 \qquad \text{(remove brackets)}$$

$$V - V_0 + bT_0V_0 = bTV_0 \qquad \text{(subtract } V_0 \text{ and add } bT_0V_0 \text{ to both sides)}$$

$$T = \frac{V - V_0 + bT_0V_0}{bV_0} \qquad \text{(divide both sides by } bV_0 \text{ and switch sides)}$$

In practice it is often necessary to set up equations to be solved by using known formulas and given conditions. The most difficult part in solving such a stated problem is identifying the information which leads to the equation. Often this is due to the fact that some of the information is inferred, but not explicitly stated, in the problem.

Since a careful reading and analysis are important to the solution of stated problems, it is possible only to give a general guideline to follow. Thus, (1) *read the statement of the problem carefully;* (2) *clearly identify the unknown quantities, assign an appropriate letter to represent one of them, and specify the others in terms of this unknown;* (3) *analyze the statement clearly to establish the necessary equation;* and (4) *solve the equation, checking the solution in the original statement of the problem.* Carefully read the following examples.

Example D

Two machine parts together weigh 17 lb. If one weighs 3 lb more than the other, what is the weight of each?

Since the weight of each part is required, we write

let $w = $ the weight of the lighter part

as a way of establishing the unknown for the equation. Any appropriate letter could be used, and we could have let it represent the heavier part.

Also, since "one weighs 3 lb more than the other," we can write

let $w + 3 = $ the weight of the heavier part

Since the two parts together weigh 17 lb, we have the equation

$$w + (w + 3) = 17$$

This can now be solved.

$$2w + 3 = 17$$
$$2w = 14$$
$$w = 7$$

Thus, the lighter part weighs 7 lb and the heavier part weighs 10 lb. This checks with the original statement of the problem.

Example E

A man rowing x mi/h covers 8 mi in one hour when going downstream. By rowing twice as fast while going upstream, he is able to cover only 7 mi in one hour. Find the original rate of speed of his rowing, x, and the rate of flow of the stream.

In this problem we have let x equal the man's original rate of rowing. From the fact that the man was able to cover 8 mi in one hour while going downstream, we conclude that his rate plus the rate of the stream equals 8 mi/h. Thus, $8 - x$ is the rate of the stream. When he is going upstream, the stream retards his progress, which means that the rate at which he actually proceeds upstream is $2x - (8 - x)$. He goes at this rate for one hour, traveling 7 mi. Using the formula $d = rt$ (distance equals rate times time), we have

$$7 = [2x - (8 - x)](1)$$

Solving for x, we obtain

$$7 = 2x - (8 - x)$$
$$7 = 2x - 8 + x$$
$$15 = 3x$$
$$x = 5$$

Therefore, the original rate of rowing was 5 mi/h, and the stream flows at the rate of 3 mi/h. We see that this checks in that the distance covered in one hour going downstream is $(5 + 3)(1) = 8$ mi, and the distance covered in one hour going upstream is $[(2)(5) - 3] = 7$ mi.

Example F

A solution of alcohol and water contains 2 L of alcohol and 6 L of water. How much pure alcohol must be added to this solution so that the resulting solution will be $\frac{2}{5}$ alcohol?

First we let x equal the number of liters of alcohol to be added. The statement of the problem tells us that we want the volume of alcohol compared to the total volume of the final mixture to be $\frac{2}{5}$. The final total volume of alcohol will be $2 + x$, and the final total volume of the mixture of water and alcohol will be $8 + x$. This means that

$$\frac{2 + x}{8 + x} = \frac{2}{5}$$

Multiplying each side by $5(8 + x)$, we have

$$5(2 + x) = 2(8 + x)$$
$$10 + 5x = 16 + 2x$$
$$3x = 6$$
$$x = 2$$

Therefore, 2 L of alcohol are to be added to the solution. Note that this result checks, since there would be 4 L of alcohol of a total volume of 10 L when 2 L of pure alcohol are added to the original solution.

$A_1 = AM + A$

Exercises 1–11

In Exercises 1 through 8 solve for the indicated letter.

1. $ax = b$, for x

2. $cy + d = 0$, for y

3. $4n + 1 = m$, for n

4. $bt - 3 = a$, for t

5. $ax + 6 = 2ax - c$, for x

6. $s - 6n^2 = 3s + 4$, for s

7. $\frac{1}{2}t - (4 - a) = 2a$, for t

8. $7 - (p - \frac{1}{3}x) = 3p$, for x

In Exercises 9 through 24 each of the given formulas arises in the technical or scientific area of study listed. Solve for the indicated letter.

9. $E = IR$, for R (electricity)

10. $PV = RT$, for T (chemistry: gas law)

11. $A = \dfrac{M}{fjd}$, for d (mechanical design)

12. $V = \frac{4}{3}\pi r^3$, for π (geometry)

13. $v = v_0 - gt$, for g (physics: motion)

14. $A_1 = A(M + 1)$, for M (photography)

15. $a = V(k - PV)$, for k (biology: muscle contractions)

16. $s = s_0 + v_0 t - 16t^2$, for v_0 (physics: motion)

17. $l = a + (n - 1)d$, for n (mathematics: progressions)

18. $T_2 w = q(T_2 - T_1)$, for T_1 (chemistry: energy)

19. $L = \pi(r_1 + r_2) + 2d$, for r_1 (physics: pulleys)

20. $h = \dfrac{1}{r_e + r_c(1 - a)}$, for r_e (electricity: transistors)

21. $F = \dfrac{9C}{5} + 32$, for C (science: temperature)

22. $R = \dfrac{2(E - E_p)}{m_0 g}$, for E (modern physics)

23. $R = \dfrac{wL}{H(w + L)}$, for H (architecture: interior lighting)

24. $PV^2 = RT(1 - e)(V + b) - A$, for T (thermodynamics)

In Exercises 25 through 36 solve the given stated problems by first setting up an appropriate equation.

25. Together, two computers cost $7800 per month to rent. If one costs twice as much as the other, what is the monthly cost of each?

26. The combined capacity of two oil tanks is 1375 gallons. If one tank holds 275 gal more than the other tank, what is the capacity of each?

27. The sum of three electric currents is 12 A. If the smallest is 2 A less than the next, which in turn is 2 A less than the largest, what are the values of the three currents?

28. A vial contains 2000 mg which is to be used for two dosages. One patient is to be administered 660 mg more than the other. How much should be administered to each?

29. The length of a spring increases 0.25 ft for each pound it supports. If the spring is 8 ft long when 6 lb are hung from it, what was the original length of the spring?

30. A temperature measured in degrees Fahrenheit is 32 more than $\frac{9}{5}$ the corresponding reading in degrees Celsius. If the Celsius reading of a certain room is 25°C, what is the Fahrenheit reading?

31. An architect designs a rectangular window such that the width of the window is 18 in. less than the height. If the perimeter of the window is 180 in., what are its dimensions?

32. A square tract of land is enclosed with fencing and then divided in half by additional fencing parallel to two of the sides. If 75 m of fencing are used, what is the length of one side of the tract?

33. A car traveling at 30 mi/h leaves a certain point 2 h before a second car. If the second car travels 40 mi/h, when will it overtake the first car?

34. Two supersonic jets, originally 5400 mi apart, start at the same time and travel toward each other. Find the speed of each if one travels 400 mi/h faster than the other and they meet in 1.5 h.

35. A certain type of engine uses a fuel mixture of 15 parts of gasoline to one part of oil. How much gasoline must be mixed with a gasoline-oil mixture, which is 75% gasoline, to make 8 L of the required mixture for the engine?

36. An alloy weighing 20 lb is 30% copper. How many pounds of another alloy which is 80% copper must be added in order for the final alloy to be 50% copper?

1–12 Exercises for Chapter 1

In Exercises 1 through 12 simplify the given expressions.

1. $(-2) + (-5) - (+3)$

2. $(+6) - (+8) - (-4)$

3. $\dfrac{(-5)(+6)(-4)}{(-2)(+3)}$

4. $\dfrac{(-9)(-12)(-4)}{24}$

5. $-5 - 2(-6) + \dfrac{-15}{+3}$

6. $3 - 5(-2) - \dfrac{12}{-4}$

7. $\dfrac{18}{3-5} - (-4)^2$

8. $-(-3)^2 - \dfrac{-8}{(-2)-(-4)}$

9. $\sqrt{16} - \sqrt{64}$

10. $-\sqrt{144} + \sqrt{49}$

11. $(\sqrt{7})^2 - \sqrt[3]{8}$

12. $-\sqrt[4]{16} + (\sqrt{6})^2$

In Exercises 13 through 24 simplify the given expressions. Where appropriate, express results with positive exponents only.

13. $(-2rt^2)^2$

14. $(3x^4y)^3$

15. $\dfrac{18m^3n^4t}{3mn^5t^3}$

16. $\dfrac{15p^4q^2r}{5pq^5r}$

17. $(x^0y^{-1}z^3)^2$

18. $(3a^0b^{-2})^3$

19. $\dfrac{-16s^{-2}(st^2)}{-2st^{-1}}$ 20. $\dfrac{-35x^{-1}y(x^2y)}{5xy^{-1}}$ 21. $\sqrt{45}$

22. $\sqrt{48}$ 23. $\sqrt{-20}$ 24. $\sqrt{-18}$

In Exercises 25 through 52 perform the indicated operations.

25. $a - 3ab - 2a + ab$ 26. $xy - y - 5y - 4xy$

27. $6xy - (xy - 3)$ 28. $-(2x - b) - 3(x - 5b)$

29. $(2x - 1)(x + 5)$ 30. $(x - 4y)(2x + y)$

31. $\dfrac{2h^3k^2 - 6h^4k^5}{2h^2k}$ 32. $\dfrac{4a^2x^3 - 8ax^4}{2ax^2}$

33. $4a - [2b - (3a - 4b)]$

34. $3b - [2b + 3a - (2a - 3b)] + 4a$

35. $2xy - \{3z - [5xy - (7z - 6xy)]\}$

36. $x^2 + 3b + [(b - y) - 3(2b - y + z)]$

37. $(2x + 1)(x^2 - x - 3)$ 38. $(x - 3)(2x^2 - 3x + 1)$

39. $-3y(x - 4y)^2$ 40. $-s(4s - 3t)^2$

41. $3p[(q - p) - 2p(1 - 3q)]$ 42. $3x[2y - r - 4(s - 2r)]$

43. $\dfrac{12p^3q^2 - 4p^4q + 6pq^5}{2p^4q}$ 44. $\dfrac{27s^3t^2 - 18s^4t + 9s^2t}{9s^2t}$

45. $\dfrac{3x^3 - 7x^2 + 11x - 3}{3x - 1}$ 46. $\dfrac{x^3 - 4x^2 + 7x - 12}{x - 3}$

47. $\dfrac{4x^4 + 10x^3 + 18x - 1}{x + 3}$ 48. $\dfrac{8x^3 - 14x + 3}{2x + 3}$

49. $-3\{(r + s - t) - 2[(3r - 2s) - (t - 2s)]\}$

50. $(1 - 2x)(x - 3) - (x + 4)(4 - 3x)$

51. $\dfrac{2y^3 + 9y^2 - 7y + 5}{2y - 1}$ 52. $\dfrac{6x^2 + 5xy - 4y^2}{2x - y}$

In Exercises 53 through 60 solve the given equations.

53. $3s + 8 = 5s$ 54. $6n = 14 - n$

55. $3x + 1 = x - 9$ 56. $4y - 3 = 5y + 7$

57. $6x - 5 = 3(x - 4)$ 58. $-2(4 - y) = 3y$

59. $2s + 4(3 - s) = 6$ 60. $-(4 - v) = 2(2v - 5)$

In Exercises 61 through 68 change any numbers in ordinary notation to scientific notation or change any numbers in scientific notation to ordinary notation. (See Appendix B for an explanation of symbols which are used.)

61. The escape velocity (the velocity required to leave the earth's gravitational field) of a rocket is in excess of 25,000 mi/h.

62. When the first pictures of the surface of Mars were transmitted to Earth, Mars was 213,000,000 mi from Earth.

63. The ratio of the charge to the mass of an electron is 1.76×10^{11} C/kg.

64. Atmospheric pressure is about 1.013×10^5 Pa.
65. An oil film on water is about 0.0000002 in. thick.
66. A typical capacitor has a capacitance of 0.00005 F.
67. The viscosity of air is about 1.8×10^{-5} N·s/m².
68. The electric field intensity in a certain electromagnetic wave is 2.5×10^{-3} V/m.

In Exercises 69 through 84 solve for the indicated letter. Where noted the given formula arises in the technical or scientific area of study listed.

69. $3s + 2 = 5a$, for s

70. $5 - 7t = 6b$, for t

71. $3(4 - x) = 8 + 2n$, for x

72. $6 - 3b = 5(7 - 2v)$, for v

73. $B = \dfrac{\phi}{A}$, for A (ϕ is Greek phi)   (electricity: magnetism)

74. $D = \dfrac{KI^2t}{A}$, for t (medicine: cell damage)

75. $I = P + Prt$, for t (business: interest)

76. $v^2 = v_0^2 + 2gh$, for h (physics: motion)

77. $I(r + nR) = nE$, for R (electricity)

78. $R(R_1 + R_2) = R_1R_2$, for R (electricity)

79. $D_p = \dfrac{ND_0}{N + 2}$, for D_0 (mechanics: gears)

80. $Y_{n+1} = \dfrac{R_D X_n + X_0}{R_D + 1}$, for X_n (chemistry: distillation)

81. $L = L_0[1 + \alpha(t_2 - t_1)]$, for α (the Greek alpha)   (physics: heat)

82. $P_a - P_b = \dfrac{32LV\mu}{g_c D^2}$, for μ (the Greek mu)   (fluid dynamics)

83. $S = \frac{1}{2}n[2a + (n - 1)d]$, for a (mathematics: progressions)

84. $M = Rx - P(x - a)$, for a (mechanics: beams)

In Exercises 85 through 88 perform the indicated operations.

85. When determining the center of mass of a certain object, the expression $[(8x - x^2) - (x^2 - 4x)]$ is used. Simplify this expression.

86. In determining the value of sales in a particular business enterprise, the expression $(700 + 100n)(12 - n)$ is found. Multiply and simplify this expression.

87. Simplify the following expression, which arises in determining the final temperature of a certain mixture of objects originally at different temperatures:

$$500(0.22)(T_f - 20) + 120(T_f - 20) - 22(75 - T_f)$$

88. In studying the dispersion of light, the expression $(k + 2)[(n - jK)^2 - 1]$ is found. Expand this expression.

In Exercises 89 through 94 solve the stated problems by first setting up an appropriate equation.

89. The combustion of carbon usually results in the production of both carbon monoxide and carbon dioxide. If 500 kg of oxygen are available for combustion and it is desired that 9 times as much oxygen be converted to carbon dioxide as is converted to carbon monoxide, how much oxygen would be converted to each of the compounds?

90. The electric current in one transistor is three times that in another transistor. If the sum of the currents is 0.012 A, what is the current in each?

91. The cost of producing a first type of pocket calculator is three times the cost of producing a second type. The total cost of producing two of the first type and three of the second type is $45. What is the cost of producing each type?

92. An air sample contains 4 ppm (parts per million) of two harmful pollutants. The concentration of one is four times the other. What is the concentration of each?

93. Two cars, 735 mi apart, start toward each other. One travels at the rate of 55 mi/h and the other at 43 mi/h. When will they meet?

94. Fifty pounds of a cement-sand mixture is 40% sand. How many pounds of sand must be added for the resulting mixture to be 60% sand?

2

Functions and Graphs

2–1 Functions

In Chapter 1 we established many of the basic algebraic operations. At the end of the chapter we discussed the solution of equations, with applications to formulas. In most of the formulas, one quantity was given in terms of one or more other quantities. It is obvious, then, that the various quantities are related by means of the formula. We see that in the study of natural phenomena, a relationship can be found to exist between certain quantities.

If we were to perform an experiment to determine whether or not a relationship exists between the distance an object drops and the time it falls, observation of the results would indicate (approximately, at least) that $s = 16t^2$, where s is the distance in feet and t is the time in seconds. We would therefore see that distance and time for a falling object are related.

A similar study of the pressure and the volume of a gas at constant temperature would show that as pressure increases, volume decreases according to the formula $PV = k$, where k is a constant. Electrical measurements of current and voltage with respect to a particular resistor would show that $V = kI$, where V is the voltage, I is the current, and k is a constant.

Considerations such as these lead us to the mathematical concept of a **function**, which is one of the most important and basic concepts in mathematics. Thus, *whenever a relationship exists between two variables x and y such that for every value of x there is only one corresponding value of y, we say that y is a function of x.* Here we call the variable x the **independent variable** (since x can be chosen arbitrarily so long as the value chosen produces a real number for y). Also, y is the **dependent variable** (since, once the value of x is chosen, the value of y is determined—that is, y depends on x). We must also realize that x and y are only representative—other literal symbols may be used as independent and dependent variables.

There are many ways to express functions. Formulas, such as those we have discussed, define functions. Other ways to express functions are by means of tables, charts, and graphs.

Example A

In the equation $y = 2x$, we see that y is a function of x, since for each value of x there is only one value of y. For example, if $x = 3$, $y = 6$ and no other value. The dependent variable is y and the independent variable is x.

Example B

The volume of a cube of edge e is given by $V = e^3$. Here V is a function of e, since for each value of e there is one value of V. The dependent variable is V and the independent variable is e.

If the equation relating the volume and edge of a cube was written as $e = \sqrt[3]{V}$, that is, if the edge of a cube was expressed in terms of its volume, we would say that e is a function of V. In this case e would be the dependent variable and V the independent variable.

Example C

The power P developed in a certain resistor by a current I is given by $P = 4I^2$. Here P is a function of I. The dependent variable is P, and the independent variable is I.

Example D

If the formula in Example C is written as $I = \frac{1}{2}\sqrt{P}$, then I is a function of P. The independent variable is P, and the dependent variable is I. Even though P is the independent variable, it is restricted to values which are positive or zero. (This is written as $P \geq 0$.) Otherwise, the values of I would be imaginary. Except when specified, we shall restrict ourselves to real numbers.

Example E

For the equation $y = 2x^2 - 6x$, we say that y is a function of x. The dependent variable is y, and the independent variable is x. Some of the values of y corresponding to chosen values of x are given in the following table.

x	-2	-1	0	$\frac{1}{2}$	1	2	3	π	10
y	20	8	0	$-\frac{5}{2}$	-4	-4	0	$2\pi^2 - 6\pi$	140

For convenience of notation, the phrase "function of x" is written as $f(x)$. This, in turn, is a simplification of the statement that "y is a function of x," so we may now write $y = f(x)$. [Notice that $f(x)$ does *not* mean f times x. The symbols must be written in this form, and not separated, to indicate a function.]

Example F
If $y = 6x^3 - 5x$ we may say that y is a function of x, where this function $f(x)$ is $6x^3 - 5x$. We may also write $f(x) = 6x^3 - 5x$. It is common to write functions in this form, rather than in the form $y = 6x^3 - 5x$. However, y and $f(x)$ represent the same expression.

One of the most important uses of this notation is to designate the value of a function for a particular value of the independent variable. That is, for the expression "the value of the function $f(x)$ when $x = a$" we may write $f(a)$.

Example G
For the function $f(x) = 3x^2 - 5$, the value of $f(x)$ for $x = 2$ may be represented as $f(2)$. Thus, substituting 2 for x, we have

$$f(2) = 3(2^2) - 5 = 7$$

In the same way, the value of $f(x)$ for $x = -1$ is

$$f(-1) = 3(-1)^2 - 5 = -2$$

In certain instances we need to define more than one function of x. Then we use different symbols to denote the functions. For example, $f(x)$ and $g(x)$ may represent different functions of x, such as $f(x) = 5x^2 - 3$ and $g(x) = 6x - 7$. Special functions are represented by particular symbols. For example, in trigonometry we shall come across the "sine of the angle ϕ," where the sine is a function of ϕ. This is designated by $\sin \phi$.

Example H
If $f(x) = \sqrt{3x} + x$ and $g(x) = ax^4 - 5x$, then

$$f(3) = \sqrt{3(3)} + 3 = 3 + 3 = 6$$

and

$$g(3) = a(3^4) - 5(3) = 81a - 15$$

There are occasions when we wish to evaluate a function in terms of a literal number rather than an explicit number. However, whatever number a represents in $f(a)$, we substitute a for x in $f(x)$.

Example I
If $g(t) = 4t^2 - 5t$, to find $g(a^3)$ we substitute a^3 for t in the function. Thus,

$$g(a^3) = 4(a^3)^2 - 5(a^3) = 4a^6 - 5a^3$$

For the same function,

$$g(b + 1) = 4(b + 1)^2 - 5(b + 1)$$
$$= 4(b^2 + 2b + 1) - 5(b + 1)$$
$$= 4b^2 + 8b + 4 - 5b - 5$$
$$= 4b^2 + 3b - 1$$

Example J

The resistance of a particular resistor as a function of temperature is $R = 10 + 0.1T + 0.001T^2$. If a given temperature T is increased by 10°C, what is the value of R for the increased temperature as a function of the temperature T?

We are to determine R for a temperature of $T + 10$. Since $f(T) = 10 + 0.1T + 0.001T^2$, we know that

$$f(T + 10) = 10 + 0.1(T + 10) + 0.001(T + 10)^2$$
$$= 10 + 0.1T + 1 + 0.001T^2 + 0.02T + 0.1$$
$$= 11.1 + 0.12T + 0.001T^2$$

A function may be looked upon as a set of instructions. These instructions tell us how to obtain the value of the dependent variable for a particular value of the independent variable, even if the set of instructions is expressed in literal symbols.

Example K

The function $f(x) = x^2 - 3x$ tell us to "square the value of the independent variable, multiply the value of the independent variable by 3, and subtract the second result from the first." An analogy would be a computer which was so programmed that whan a number was fed into the computer, it would square the number and then subtract 3 times the value of the number. This is represented in diagram form in Fig. 2–1.

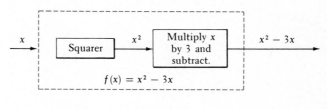

Figure 2–1

The functions $f(t) = t^2 - 3t$ and $f(n) = n^2 - 3n$ are the same as the function $f(x) = x^2 - 3x$, since the operations performed on the independent variable are the same. Although different literal symbols appear, this does not change the function.

As we mentioned earlier, we must be certain that the function is defined for any value of x that may be chosen. *Values of x which lead to division by zero or to imaginary values of y may not be chosen.* Example D and the following example illustrate this point.

Example L

The function $f(u) = \dfrac{u}{u-4}$ is not defined if $u = 4$, since this would require division by zero. Therefore, the values of u are restricted to values other than 4.

The function $g(s) = \sqrt{3-s}$ is not defined for real numbers if s is greater than 3, since such values would result in imaginary values for $g(s)$. Thus, the values of s are restricted to values equal to or less than 3.

Exercises 2—1

In Exercises 1 through 12 determine the appropriate functions.

1. Express the area A of a circle as a function of its radius r.
2. Express the area A of a circle as a function of its diameter d.
3. Express the circumference c of a circle as a function of its radius r.
4. Express the circumference c of a circle as a function of its diameter d.
5. Express the area A of a rectangle of width 5 as a function of its length l.
6. Express the volume V of a right circular cone of height 8 as a function of the radius r of the base.
7. Express the area A of a square as a function of its side s; express the side s of a square as a function of its area A.
8. Express the perimeter p of a square as a function of its side s; express the side s of a square as a function of its perimeter p.
9. A rocket weighs 3000 tons at liftoff. If the first-stage engines burn fuel at the rate of 10 tons per second, find the weight w of the rocket as a function of the time t while the first-stage engines operate.
10. A total of x ft is cut from a 24-ft board. Express the remaining length y as a function of x.
11. Express the simple interest I on \$200 at 4% per year as a function of the number of years t.
12. A taxi fare is 55¢ plus 10¢ for every $\frac{1}{5}$ mile traveled. Express the fare F as a function of the distance s traveled.

In Exercises 13 through 24 evaluate the given functions.

13. Given $f(x) = 2x + 1$, find $f(1)$ and $f(-1)$.
14. Given $f(x) = 5x - 9$, find $f(2)$ and $f(-2)$.
15. Given $f(x) = 5 - 3x$, find $f(-2)$ and $f(4)$.
16. Given $f(x) = 7 - 2x$, find $f(5)$ and $f(-4)$.
17. Given $f(n) = n^2 - 9n$, find $f(3)$ and $f(-5)$.
18. Given $f(v) = 2v^3 - 7v$, find $f(1)$ and $f(\frac{1}{2})$.
19. Given $\phi(x) = \dfrac{6 - x^2}{2x}$, find $\phi(1)$ and $\phi(-2)$.
20. Given $H(q) = \dfrac{8}{q} + 2\sqrt{q}$, find $H(4)$ and $H(16)$.

21. Given $g(t) = at^2 - a^2t$, find $g(-\frac{1}{2})$ and $g(a)$.

22. Given $s(y) = 6\sqrt{y} - 3$, find $s(9)$ and $s(a^2)$.

23. Given $K(s) = 3s^2 - s + 6$, find $K(-s)$ and $K(2s)$.

24. Given $T(t) = 5t + 7$, find $T(-2t)$ and $T(t + 1)$.

In Exercises 25 through 28 state the instructions of the function in words as in Example K.

25. $f(x) = x^2 + 2$ 26. $f(x) = 2x - 6$

27. $g(y) = 6y - y^3$ 28. $\phi(s) = 8 - 5s + s^5$

In Exercises 29 through 32 state any restrictions that might exist on the values of the independent variable.

29. $Y(y) = \dfrac{y + 1}{y - 1}$ 30. $G(z) = \dfrac{1}{(z - 4)(z + 2)}$

31. $F(y) = \sqrt{y - 1}$ 32. $X(x) = \dfrac{6}{\sqrt{1 - x}}$

In Exercises 33 through 40 solve the given problems.

33. The volume of a cylinder of height 6 cm as a function of the radius of the base is given by $V = 6\pi r^2$. What is the volume of the cylinder if the base has a radius of 3 cm?

34. The distance s that a freely falling body travels as a function of the time t is given by $s = 16t^2$, where s is measured in feet and t is measured in seconds. How far does an object fall in 2 s?

35. If the temperature within a certain refrigerator is maintained at 273 K (0°C), its *coefficient of performance* p as a function of the external temperature T (in kelvins) is

$$p = \frac{273}{T - 273}$$

What is its coefficient of performance at 308 K (35°C)?

36. The vertical distance of a point on a suspension cable from its lowest point as a function of the horizontal distance from the lowest point is given by

$$f(x) = \frac{x^4 + 600x^2}{2,000,000}$$

where x is measured in feet. How far above the lowest point is a point on the cable at a horizontal distance of 50 ft from the lowest point?

37. A piece of wire 60 in. long is cut into two pieces, one of which is bent into a circle and the other into a square. Express the total area of the two figures as a function of the perimeter of the square.

38. The net profit P made on selling 20 items, if each costs $15, as a function of the price p is $P = 20(p - 15)$. What is the profit if the price is $28? $12?

39. The voltage of a certain thermocouple as a function of the temperature is given by $E = 2.8T + 0.006T^2$. Find the voltage when the temperature is $T + h$.

40. The electrical resistance of a certain ammeter as a function of the resistance of the coil of the meter is

$$R = \frac{10R_c}{10 + R_c}$$

Find the function which represents the resistance of the meter if the resistance of the coil is doubled.

2–2 Rectangular Coordinates

One of the most valuable ways of representing functions is by graphical representation. By using graphs we are able to obtain a "picture" of the function, and by using this picture we can learn a great deal about the function.

To make a graphical representation, we recall that numbers can be represented by points on a line. For a function we have values of the independent variable and the corresponding values of the dependent variable. Therefore, it is necessary to use two lines to represent the values from these sets of numbers. We do this most conveniently by placing the lines perpendicular to each other.

We place one line horizontally and label it the **x-axis**. The numbers of the set for the independent variable are normally placed on this axis. The other line we place vertically, and label the **y-axis**. Normally the y-axis is used for values of the dependent variable. The point of intersection is called the **origin**. This is the **rectangular coordinate system**.

On the x-axis, positive values are to the right of the origin, and negative values are to the left of the origin. On the y-axis, positive values are above the origin, and negative values are below it. The four parts into which the plane is divided are called **quadrants**, which are numbered as in Fig. 2–2.

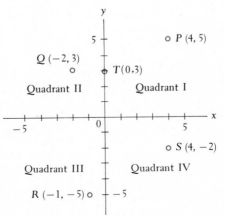

Figure 2–2

A point P in the plane is designated by the pair of numbers (x, y), where x is the value of the independent variable and y is the corresponding value of the dependent variable. *The x-value, called the* **abscissa,** *is the perpendicular distance of P from the y-axis. The y-value, called the* **ordinate,** *is the perpendicular distance of P from the x-axis.* The values x and y together, written as (x, y), are the **coordinates** of the point P.

Example A

The positions of points $P(4, 5)$, $Q(-2, 3)$, $R(-1, -5)$, $S(4, -2)$, and $T(0, 3)$ are shown in Fig. 2–2. Note that this representation allows for *one point for any pair of values* (x, y).

Example B

Three vertices of the rectangle in Fig. 2–3 are $A(-3, -2)$, $B(4, -2)$, and $C(4, 1)$. What is the fourth vertex?

We use the fact that opposite sides of a rectangle are equal and parallel to find the solution. Since both vertices of the base AB of the rectangle have a y-coordinate of -2, the base is parallel to the x-axis. Therefore, the top of the rectangle must also be parallel to the x-axis. Thus, the vertices of the top must both have a y-coordinate of 1, since one of them has a y-coordinate of 1. In the same way the x-coordinates of the left side must both be -3. Therefore, the fourth vertex is $D(-3, 1)$.

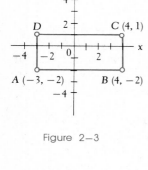

Figure 2–3

Example C

Where are all the points whose ordinates are 2?

All such points are 2 units above the x-axis; thus, the answer can be stated as "on a line 2 units above the x-axis."

Exercises 2—2

In Exercises 1 and 2 determine (at least approximately) the coordinates of the points specified in Fig. 2–4.

1. A, B, C 2. D, E, F

In Exercises 3 and 4 plot (at least approximately) the given points.

3. $A(2, 7)$, $B(-1, -2)$, $C(-4, 2)$ 4. $A(3, \frac{1}{2})$, $B(-6, 0)$, $C(-\frac{5}{2}, -5)$

In Exercises 5 and 6 plot the given points and then join these points, in the order given by straight-line segments. Name the geometric figure formed.

5. $A(-1, 4)$, $B(3, 4)$, $C(1, -2)$ 6. $A(-5, -2)$, $B(4, -2)$, $C(6, 3)$, $D(-3, 3)$

In Exercises 7 and 8 find the indicated coordinates.

7. Three vertices of a rectangle are $(5, 2)$, $(-1, 2)$, and $(-1, 4)$. What are the coordinates of the fourth vertex?

8. Two vertices of an equilateral triangle are $(7, 1)$ and $(2, 1)$. What is the abscissa of the third vertex?

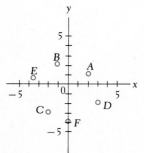

Figure 2–4

In Exercises 9 through 20 answer the given questions.

9. Where are all the points whose abscissas are 1?
10. Where are all the points whose ordinates are -3?
11. Where are all the points whose abscissas equal their ordinates?
12. Where are all the points whose abscissas equal the negative of their ordinates?
13. What is the abscissa of all points on the y-axis?
14. What is the ordinate of all points on the x-axis?
15. Where are all the points for which $x > 0$?
16. Where are all the points for which $y < 0$?
17. Where are all points (x, y) for which $x > 0$ and $y < 0$?
18. Where are all points (x, y) for which $x < 0$ and $y > 1$?
19. In which quadrants is the ratio y/x positive?
20. In which quadrants is the ratio y/x negative?

2–3 The Graph of a Function

Now that we have introduced the concepts of a function and the rectangular coordinate system, we are in a position to determine the graph of a function. In this way we shall obtain a visual representation of a function.

The graph of a function is the set of all points whose coordinates (x, y) satisfy the functional relationship $y = f(x)$. Since $y = f(x)$, we can write the coordinates of the points on the graph as $[x, f(x)]$. Writing the coordinates in this manner tells us exactly how to find them. We assume a certain value for x and then find the value of the function of x. These two numbers are the coordinates of the point.

Since there is no limit to the possible number of points which can be chosen, we normally select a few values of x, obtain the corresponding values of the function, and plot these points. These points are then connected by a *smooth* curve (not short straight lines from one point to the next), and are normally connected from left to right.

Example A

Graph the function $(3x - 5)$.

For purposes of graphing, we let y [or $f(x)$] $= 3x - 5$. We then let x take on various values and determine the corresponding values of y. Note that once we choose a given value of x, we have no choice about the corresponding y-value, as it is determined by evaluating the function. If $x = 0$ we find that $y = -5$. This means that the point $(0, -5)$ is on the graph of the function $3x - 5$. Choosing another value of x, for example, 1, we find that $y = -2$. This means that the point $(1, -2)$ is on the graph of the function $3x - 5$. Continuing to choose a few other values of x, we tabulate the results, as shown in Fig. 2–5. It is best to arrange the table so that the values of x increase; then there is no doubt how they are to be connected, for they are then connected in the order shown. Finally, we connect the points as shown in Fig. 2–5, and see that the graph of the function $3x - 5$ is a straight line.

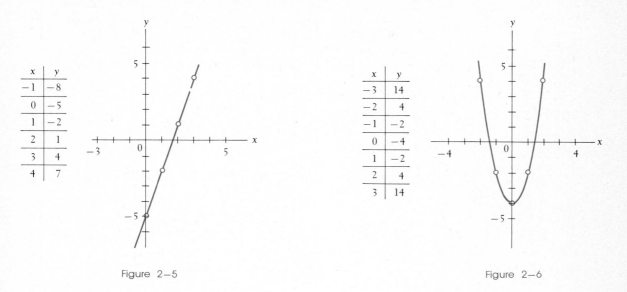

x	y
-1	-8
0	-5
1	-2
2	1
3	4
4	7

Figure 2—5

x	y
-3	14
-2	4
-1	-2
0	-4
1	-2
2	4
3	14

Figure 2—6

Example B
Graph the function $(2x^2 - 4)$.

First we let $y = 2x^2 - 4$ and tabulate the values as shown in Fig. 2–6. In determining the values in the table, we must take particular care to obtain the correct values of y for negative values of x. Mistakes are relatively common when dealing with negative numbers. We must carefully use the laws for signed numbers. For example, for $y = 2x^2 - 4$, if $x = -2$, we have $y = 2(-2)^2 - 4 = 2(4) - 4 = 8 - 4 = 4$. Once the values are obtained, we plot and connect the points with a smooth curve, as shown in Fig. 2–6.

There are some special points which should be noted. Since most common functions are smooth, any irregularities or sudden changes in the graph should be carefully checked. In these cases it usually helps to take values of x between those values where the question arises. Also, if the function is not defined for some value of x (remember, *division by zero is not defined, and only real values of the variables are permissible*), the function does not exist for that value of x. Finally, in applications, we must be careful to plot values that are meaningful; often negative values for quantities such as time are not physically meaningful. The following examples illustrate these points.

Example C
Graph the function $y = x - x^2$.

First we determine the values in the table as shown with Fig. 2–7. Again we must be careful with negative values of x. For $x = -1$, we have $y = (-1) - (-1)^2 = -1 - (+1) = -1 - 1 = -2$. Once all the values have been found and plotted, we note that $y = 0$ for both $x = 0$ and $x = 1$. The question arises—what happens between these values? Trying $x = \frac{1}{2}$, we find that $y = \frac{1}{4}$. Using this point completes the necessary information. Note that in plotting these graphs we do not stop the graph with the last point determined, but indicate that the curve continues.

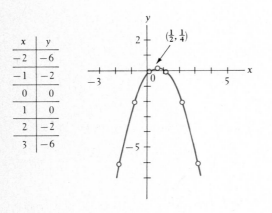

x	y
-2	-6
-1	-2
0	0
1	0
2	-2
3	-6

Figure 2–7

x	y
-4	$3/4$
-3	$2/3$
-2	$1/2$
-1	0
$-1/2$	-1
$-1/3$	-2
$1/3$	4
$1/2$	3
1	2
2	$3/2$
3	$4/3$
4	$5/4$

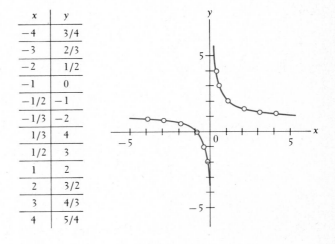

Figure 2–8

Example D
Graph the function $y = 1 + \dfrac{1}{x}$.

In finding the points on this graph as shown in Fig. 2–8, we note that y is not defined for $x = 0$. Thus we must be careful not to have any part of the curve cross the y-axis ($x = 0$). Although we cannot let $x = 0$, we can choose other values of x between -1 and 1 which are close to zero. In doing so, we find that as x gets closer to zero, the points get closer and closer to the y-axis, although they do not reach or touch it. In this case the y-axis is an **asymptote** of the curve.

Example E
Graph the function $y = \sqrt{x + 1}$.

When finding the points for the graph, we may not let x equal any negative value less than -1, for all such values of x lead to imaginary values for y. Also, since we have the positive square root indicated, all values of y are positive. See Fig. 2–9. Note that the graph stops at the point $(-1, 0)$.

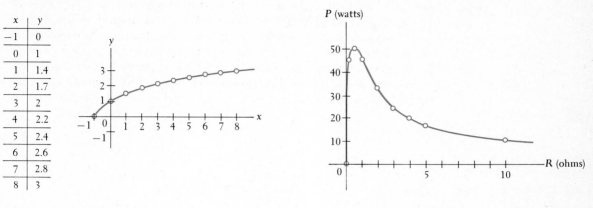

x	y
−1	0
0	1
1	1.4
2	1.7
3	2
4	2.2
5	2.4
6	2.6
7	2.8
8	3

Figure 2–9

Figure 2–10

Example F

The power of a certain voltage source as a function of the load resistance is given by

$$P = \frac{100R}{(0.5 + R)^2}$$

where P is measured in watts and R in ohms. Plot the power as a function of the resistance.

Since a negative value for the resistance has no physical significance, we need to plot P for positive values of R only. The following table of values is obtained.

R (ohms)	0	0.25	0.50	1.0	2.0	3.0	4.0	5.0	10.0
P (watts)	0.0	44.4	50.0	44.4	32.0	24.5	19.8	16.5	9.1

The values 0.25 and 0.50 are used for R when it is found that P is less for $R = 2$ than for $R = 1$. In this way a smoother curve is obtained (see Fig. 2–10).

Empirical data may also be plotted in graphical form, although there may not be a formula connecting the values. When there is no possible formula which relates the sets of numbers, it is customary to connect the points with straight-line segments, merely to make them stand out better. The maximum temperature recorded weekly at a particular location would be an example of this. However, if it is reasonable that a functional relationship may exist, although it is unknown, the points may be connected by a smooth curve. Data from a physics experiment would be an example of this case. Illustrations of such cases are found in the exercises.

Functions of a particular type have graphs which are of a specific form, and many of them have been named. We noted that the graph of the function in Example A is a **straight line**. A **parabola** is illustrated in Example B and in Example C. The graph of the function in Example D is a **hyperbola**. Other types of graphs are found in the exercises and in later chapters. A more detailed analysis of several of these curves is found in Chapter 20. The use of graphs is extensive in mathematics and in nearly all areas of application. For example, in the section which follows we see how graphs can be used to solve equations. Many other uses of graphical methods appear in the later chapters.

Exercises 2–3

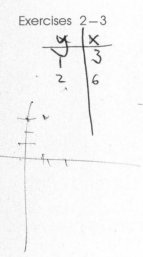

In Exercises 1 through 32 graph the given functions.

1. $y = 3x$
2. $y = -2x$
3. $y = 2x - 4$
4. $y = 3x + 5$
5. $y = 7 - 2x$
6. $y = 5 - 3x$
7. $y = \frac{1}{2}x - 2$
8. $y = 6 - \frac{1}{3}x$
9. $y = x^2$
10. $y = -2x^2$
11. $y = 3 - x^2$
12. $y = x^2 - 3$
13. $y = \frac{1}{2}x^2 + 2$
14. $y = 2x^2 + 1$
15. $y = x^2 + 2x$
16. $y = 2x - x^2$
17. $y = x^2 - 3x + 1$
18. $y = 2 + 3x + x^2$
19. $y = x^3$
20. $y = -2x^3$
21. $y = x^3 - x^2$
22. $y = 3x - x^3$
23. $y = x^4 - 4x^2$
24. $y = x^3 - x^4$
25. $y = \dfrac{1}{x}$
26. $y = \dfrac{1}{x + 2}$
27. $y = \dfrac{1}{x^2}$
28. $y = \dfrac{1}{x^2 + 1}$
29. $y = \sqrt{x}$
30. $y = \sqrt{4 - x}$
31. $y = \sqrt{16 - x^2}$
32. $y = \sqrt{x^2 - 16}$

In Exercises 33 through 40 graph the given functions. In each case plot the first mentioned variable as the ordinate and the second variable as the abscissa.

33. The velocity v (in feet per second) of an object under the influence of gravity, as a function of time t (in seconds), is given by $v = 100 - 32t$. If the object strikes the ground after 4 s, graph v as a function of t.

34. If $1000 is placed in an account earning 6% simple interest, the amount A in the account after t years is given by the function $A = 1000(1 + 0.06t)$. If the money is withdrawn from the account after 6 years, plot A as a function of t.

35. The surface area of a cube is given by $A = 6e^2$, where e is the side of the cube. Plot A as a function of e.

36. The energy in the electric field around an inductor is given by $E = \frac{1}{2}LI^2$, where I is the current in the inductor and L is the inductance. Plot E as a function of I (a) if $L = 1$ unit, (b) if $L = 0.1$ unit, and (c) if the E-axis is marked off in units of L.

37. The illuminance (in lumens per square meter) of a certain source of light as a function of the distance (in meters) from the source is given by $I = 400/r^2$. Plot I as a function of r.

38. The heat capacity (in joules per kilogram) of an organic liquid is related to the temperature (in degrees Celsius) by the equation $c_p = 2320 + 4.73 T$ for the temperature range of $-40°C$ to $120°C$. Graphically show that this equation does not satisfy experimental data above $120°C$. Plot the graph of the equation and the following data points.

c_p	3030	3220	3350
T	140	160	200

39. If a rectangular tract of land has a perimeter of 600 m, its area as a function of its width is $A = 300w - w^2$. Plot A as a function of w.

40. The deflection y of a beam at a horizontal distance x from one end is given by $y = -k(x^4 - 30x^2 + 1000x)$, where k is a constant. Plot the deflection (in terms of k) as a function of x (in feet) if there are 10 ft between the end supports of the beam.

In Exercises 41 through 46 represent the data graphically.

41. The rainfall (in inches) in a certain city was recorded as follows.

Year	1970	1971	1972	1973	1974	1975	1976	1977	1978
Rainfall	35.4	36.7	40.4	40.2	38.2	32.8	33.4	41.2	40.4

42. The hourly temperatures (in degrees Fahrenheit) on a certain day were recorded as follows.

Hour	6 AM	7	8	9	10	11	12	1 PM	2	3	4
Temperature	16	18	20	25	32	36	39	41	39	42	36

43. The density (in kilograms per cubic meter) of water from $0°$ to $10°C$ is given in the following table.

Density	999.85	999.90	999.94	999.96	999.97	999.96
Temperature	0	1	2	3	4	5
Density	999.94	999.90	999.85	999.78	999.69	
Temperature	6	7	8	9	10	

44. The voltage (in volts) and current (in milliamperes) for a certain electrical experiment were measured as follows.

Voltage	10	20	30	40	50	60	70	80
Current	145	188	220	255	285	315	335	370

45. An experiment measuring the load (in kilograms) on a spring and the scale reading of the spring (in centimeters) produced the following results.

Load	0	1	2	3	4	5	6
Reading	7.0	7.6	8.2	8.8	9.4	10.1	12.8

46. The vapor pressure (in kilopascals) of ethane gas as a function of temperature (in degrees Celsius) is given by the following table.

Pressure	260	380	570	790	1060	1430	1840	2390	3270
Temperature	-70	-60	-50	-40	-30	-20	-10	0	15

2—4 Solving Equations Graphically

It is possible to solve equations by the use of graphs. This is particularly useful when algebraic methods cannot be applied conveniently to the equation. Before taking up graphical solutions, however, we shall briefly introduce the related concept of the zero of a function.

*Those values of the independent variable for which the function equals zero are known as the **zeros** of the function. To find the zeros of a given function, we must set the function equal to zero and solve the resulting equation.* Using functional notation, we may write this as $f(x) = 0$.

Example A

Find any zeros of the function $(3x - 9)$.

We write $f(x) = 3x - 9$ and then let $f(x) = 0$, which means that $3x - 9 = 0$. Thus we obtain the solution $x = 3$, which means that 3 is a zero of the function $(3x - 9)$.

Graphically, the zeros of a function may be found where the curve crosses the x-axis. These points are called the **x-intercepts** of the curve. The function is zero at these points since the x-axis represents all points for which y is zero, or $f(x) = 0$.

Example B

Graphically determine any zeros of the function $x^2 - 2x - 1$.

First we set $y = x^2 - 2x - 1$ and then find the points for the graph. After plotting the graph in Fig. 2–11, we see that the curve crosses the x-axis at approximately $x = -0.4$ and $x = 2.4$ (estimating to the nearest tenth). Thus the zeros of this function are approximately -0.4 and 2.4. Checking these values in the function, we have $f(-0.4) = -0.04$ and $f(2.4) = -0.04$, which shows that -0.4 and 2.4 are very close to the exact values.

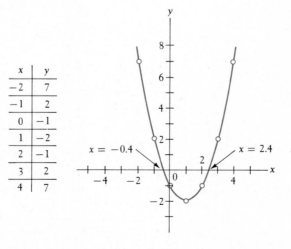

x	y
-2	7
-1	2
0	-1
1	-2
2	-1
3	2
4	7

Figure 2—11

Example C

Graphically determine any zeros of the function $x^2 + 1$.

Graphing the function $y = x^2 + 1$ in Fig. 2–12, we see that it does not cross the *x*-axis anywhere. Therefore, this function does not have any real zeros. We therefore can see that not all functions have real zeros.

We can now see how to solve equations graphically and how this is related to the zeros of a function. To solve an equation, we collect all terms on one side of the equals sign, giving the equation $f(x) = 0$. This equation is solved graphically by first setting $y = f(x)$ and graphing this function. We then find those values of *x* for which $y = 0$. This means that we are finding the zeros of this function. The following examples illustrate the method.

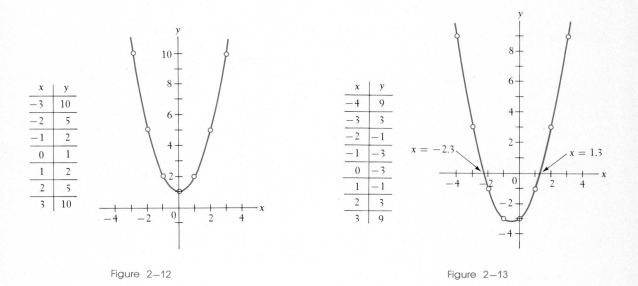

x	y
−3	10
−2	5
−1	2
0	1
1	2
2	5
3	10

Figure 2–12

x	y
−4	9
−3	3
−2	−1
−1	−3
0	−3
1	−1
2	3
3	9

Figure 2–13

Example D

Solve the equation $3x = x(2 - x) + 3$ graphically.

We first collect algebraically all terms on the left side of the equals sign. This leads to the equation $x^2 + x - 3 = 0$. We then let $y = x^2 + x - 3$ and graph this function, as shown in Fig. 2–13. From the graph we see that $y = 0$ (which is equivalent to $x^2 + x - 3 = 0$) for approximately the values $x = -2.3$ and $x = 1.3$. Therefore, the solutions to the original equation are approximately $x = -2.3$ and $x = 1.3$. Checking these values in the original equation, we obtain $-6.9 = -6.89$ for $x = -2.3$ and $3.9 = 3.91$ for $x = 1.3$, which shows that the approximate solutions we obtained were very close to the exact solutions.

Example E

A box, whose volume is 30 in.³, is made with a square base and a height which is 2 in. less than the length of a side of the base. To find the dimensions of the box we must solve the equation $x^2(x - 2) = 30$, where x is the length of a side of the base. (Verify the equation.) What are the dimensions of the box?

We are to solve the equation

$$x^2(x - 2) = 30$$

graphically. First we write the equation as $x^3 - 2x^2 - 30 = 0$. Now we set $y = x^3 - 2x^2 - 30$ and graph this equation as shown in Fig. 2–14. Only positive values of x are used since negative values of x have no meaning to the problem. From the graph we see that $x = 3.9$ is the approximate solution. Therefore, the approximate dimensions are 3.9 in., 3.9 in., and 1.9 in.

x	y
0	-30
1	-31
2	-30
3	-21
4	2
5	45

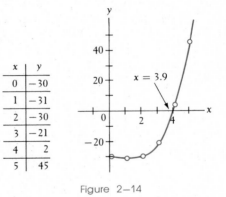

Figure 2–14

Exercises 2–4

In Exercises 1 through 4 find the zeros of the given functions algebraically as in Example A.

1. $5x - 10$ 2. $7x - 4$ 3. $4x + 9$ 4. $2 - 3(x - 5)$

In Exercises 5 through 12 find the zeros of the given functions graphically. Check the solutions in Exercises 5 through 8 algebraically. Check the solutions in Exercises 9 through 12 by substituting in the function.

5. $2x - 7$ 6. $3x - 2$ 7. $5x - (3 - x)$ 8. $3 - 2(2x - 7)$
9. $x^2 + x$ 10. $2x^2 - x$ 11. $x^2 - x + 3$ 12. $x^2 + 3x - 5$

In Exercises 13 through 28 solve the given equations graphically.

13. $7x - 5 = 0$ 14. $8x + 3 = 0$ 15. $6x = 15$
16. $7x = -18$ 17. $x^2 + x - 5 = 0$ 18. $x^2 - 2x - 4 = 0$
19. $3x^2 + 2x = 2$ 20. $2x^2 - x = 7$ 21. $x(x - 4) = 9$
22. $x = 1 + (x + 2)^2$ 23. $x^3 - 4x = 0$ 24. $x^3 - 3x - 3 = 0$
25. $x^4 - 2x = 0$ 26. $2x^5 - 5x = 0$

27. $y = \dfrac{1}{x^2 + 1}$ 28. $x - 2 = \dfrac{1}{x}$

In Exercises 29 through 34 solve the given problems graphically.

29. Under certain conditions the velocity (in feet per second) of an object as a function of the time (in seconds) is given by the equation $v = 60 - 32t$. When is the velocity zero?

30. The perimeter of a field 50 m wide and l meters long is $p = 100 + 2l$. For what value of l is the perimeter 450 m?

31. Under given conditions a company finds that the profit p in producing x articles of a certain type is $p = 90x - x^2 - 1000$. For what values of x is the profit zero?

32. In the study of the velocities of nuclear fission fragments, it is found that under certain conditions the velocity would be zero if the expression $(1 + b)^2 - 3b$ were zero. For what values of b $(b > 0)$, if any, is the velocity zero?

33. In order to find the distance x (in feet) from one end of a certain beam to the point where the deflection is zero, it is necessary to solve the equation $x^3 + x^2 - 5x = 0$. Determine where the deflection is zero.

34. If two electrical resistors, one of which is 1 Ω greater than the other, are placed in parallel, their combined resistance R_T as a function of the smaller resistance R is

$$R_T = \frac{R(R + 1)}{2R + 1}$$

What are the values of the resistors if $R_T = 10$ Ω?

2–5 Exercises for Chapter 2

In Exercises 1 through 4 determine the appropriate functions.

1. Find the volume of a right circular cylinder of height 8 ft as a function of the radius of the base.

2. Find the surface area A of a cube as a function of one of the edges e.

3. Find the temperature in degrees Fahrenheit as a function of degrees Celsius ($32°F = 0°C$ and $212°F = 100°C$).

4. Fencing 1000 m long is to be used to enclose three sides of a rectangular field. Express the area of the field as a function of its length (parallel to the fourth side).

In Exercises 5 through 12 evaluate the given functions.

5. Given $f(x) = 7x - 5$, find $f(3)$ and $f(-6)$.

6. Given $g(x) = 8 - 3x$, find $g(3)$ and $g(-4)$.

7. Given $F(u) = 3u - 2u^2$, find $F(-1)$ and $F(-3)$.

8. Given $h(y) = 2y^2 - y - 2$, find $h(5)$ and $h(-3)$.

9. Given $H(h) = \sqrt{1 - 2h}$, find $H(-4)$ and $H(2h)$.

10. Given $\phi(v) = \dfrac{3v - 2}{v + 1}$, find $\phi(-2)$ and $\phi(v + 1)$.

11. Given $f(x) = 3x^2 - 2x + 4$, find $f(x + h) - f(x)$.

12. Given $F(x) = x^3 + 2x^2 - 3x$, find $F(3 + h) - F(3)$.

In Exercises 13 through 24 graph the given functions.

13. $y = 4x + 2$

14. $y = 5x - 10$

15. $y = 4x - x^2$

16. $y = x^2 - 8x - 5$

17. $y = 3 - x - 2x^2$

18. $y = 6 + 4x + x^2$

19. $y = x^3 - 6x$

20. $y = 3 - x^3$

21. $y = 2 - x^4$

22. $y = x^4 - 4x$

23. $y = \dfrac{x}{x + 1}$

24. $y = \sqrt{25 - x^2}$

In Exercises 25 through 36 find any real zeros of the indicated functions by examining their graphs. Estimate the answer to the nearest tenth where necessary. Use the functions from Exercises 13 through 24 above as indicated.

25. Exercise 13

26. Exercise 14

27. Exercise 15

28. Exercise 16

29. Exercise 17

30. Exercise 18

31. Exercise 19

32. Exercise 20

33. Exercise 21

34. Exercise 22

35. Exercise 23

36. Exercise 24

In Exercises 37 through 44 solve the given equations graphically.

37. $7x - 3 = 0$

38. $2x + 11 = 0$

39. $x^2 + 1 = 6x$

40. $3x - 2 = x^2$

41. $x^3 - x^2 = 2 - x$

42. $5 - x^3 = 2x^2$

43. $\dfrac{1}{x} = 2x$

44. $\sqrt{x} = 2x - 1$

In Exercises 45 through 48 answer the given questions.

45. Where are all the points (x, y) whose abscissas are 1 and for which $y > 0$?

46. Three vertices of a rectangle are $(6, 5)$, $(-4, 5)$, and $(-4, 2)$. What are the coordinates of the fourth vertex?

47. An equation which is found in electronics is

$$h = \frac{\alpha}{1 - \alpha}$$

Find h when $\alpha = 0.95$. That is, since $h = f(\alpha)$, find $f(0.95)$.

48. Under certain conditions, the distance s that an object is above the ground is given by $s = 96t - 16t^2$, where t is the time in seconds. When is the object 100 ft above the ground? Solve graphically.

In Exercises 49 through 58 plot the indicated functions.

49. A computer-leasing firm charges $150 plus $100 for every hour the computer is used during the month. What is the function relating the monthly charge C and the number of hours h that the computer is used? Plot a graph of the function for use up to 50 h.

50. There are 5000 L of oil in a tank which has a capacity of 100,000 L. It is filled at the rate of 7000 L/h. Determine the function relating the number of liters N and the time t while the tank is being filled. Plot N as a function of t.

51. A surveyor measuring the elevation of a point must consider the effect of the curvature of the earth. An approximate relation between the effect H (in feet) of this curvature, and the distance D (in miles) between the surveyor and the point of which he is measuring the elevation, is given by $H = 0.65D^2$. Plot H as a function of D.

52. The distance s (in feet) of an object above the ground as a function of the time t (in seconds) is $s = 100t - 16t^2$. Plot s as a function of t.

53. The resonant frequency f (in hertz) of a certain electric circuit is given by $f = 10,000/\sqrt{L}$, where L is the inductance (in henrys) in the circuit. Plot f as a function of L. (Take values of $L = 0.25, 0.49, 0.64, 1.00, 2.25$, and 4.00.)

54. The pneumatic resistance (in lb-s/ft^5) of a certain type of tubing is given by $R = 0.05/A^2$, where A is the cross-sectional area (in square feet). Plot R as a function of A. (Take values of A in the range of 0.001 to 0.01.)

55. The sales (in millions of dollars) of a certain corporation from 1970 through 1978 are shown in the following table.

Year	1970	1971	1972	1973	1974	1975	1976	1977	1978
Sales	12	14	17	18	20	24	32	35	39

56. The amplitude (in centimeters) of a certain pendulum, measured after each swing, as a function of time (in seconds), is given by the following table. Plot the graph of amplitude as a function of time.

Amplitude	5.0	2.8	1.6	0.9	0.5
Time	0.0	1.2	2.4	3.6	4.8

57. The length (in inches) of a brass rod is measured as a function of the temperature (in degrees Celsius). From the following table, plot the length as a function of temperature (make your scale meaningful).

Length	100.0	100.2	100.4	100.7	101.0	101.2
Temperature	0	100	200	300	400	500

58. The solubility (in kilograms of solute per cubic meter of water) of potassium nitrate as a function of temperature is given in the following table. Plot solubility as a function of temperature (in degrees Celsius).

Solubility	133	209	316	458	639	855	1100	1690
Temperature	0	10	20	30	40	50	60	80

3

The Trigonometric Functions

3—1 Introduction; Angles

The solution to a great many kinds of applied problems involves the use of triangles, especially right triangles. Problems which can be solved by the use of triangles include the determination of distances which cannot readily be determined directly, such as the widths of rivers and distances between various points in the universe. Also, problems involving forces and velocities lend themselves readily to triangle solution. Even certain types of electric circuits are analyzed by the use of triangles.

The basic properties of triangles will allow us to set up some very basic and useful functions involving their sides and angles. These functions are very important to the development of mathematics and to its applications in most fields of technology.

Thus we come to the study of **trigonometry,** the literal meaning of which is "triangle measurement." In this chapter we shall introduce the basic trigonometric functions and some of their elementary applications. Later chapters will consider additional topics in trigonometry. We shall begin our study by considering the concept of an angle.

An **angle** is defined as being *generated* by rotating a *half*-line about its endpoint from an initial position to a terminal position. A half-line is that portion of a line to one side of a fixed point on the line. We call the initial position of the half-line the **initial side,** and the terminal position of the half-line the **terminal side.** The fixed point is the **vertex.** The angle itself is the amount of rotation from the initial side to the terminal side.

If the rotation of the terminal side from the initial side is counterclockwise, the angle is said to be positive. If the rotation is clockwise the angle is negative. In Fig. 3–1, angle 1 is positive and angle 2 is negative.

There are many symbols used to designate angles. Probably the most widely used are certain Greek letters such as θ (theta), ϕ (phi), α (alpha), and β (beta).

Two measurements of angles are widely used. These are the **degree** and the **radian.** *A degree is defined as* $\frac{1}{360}$ *of a complete rotation.* The radian will be discussed in Chapter 7. The degree is divided into 60 equal parts called **minutes,** and each minute is divided into 60 equal parts called **seconds.** The symbols °, ′, and ″ are used to designate degrees, minutes, and seconds, respectively. Decimal parts of angles are also common, particularly with the use of electronic calculators.

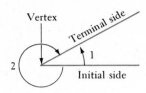

Figure 3–1

Example A

The angles $\theta = 30°$, $\phi = 140°$, $\alpha = 240°$, and $\beta = -120°$ are shown in Fig. 3–2.

In Fig. 3–2 we note that angles α and β have the same initial and terminal sides. Such angles are called **coterminal angles.** An understanding of coterminal angles is important in certain concepts in trigonometry.

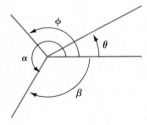

Figure 3–2

Example B

Determine the values of two angles which are coterminal with an angle of 145°32′.

Since there are 360° in a complete rotation, we can find one coterminal angle by considering the angle which is 360° larger than the given angle. This gives us an angle of 505°32′. Another method of finding a coterminal angle is to subtract 145°32′ from 360°, and then consider the resulting angle to be negative. This means that the original angle and the derived angle would make up one complete rotation, when put together. This method leads us to the angle of −214°28′ (see Fig. 3–3). These methods could be employed repeatedly to find other coterminal angles.

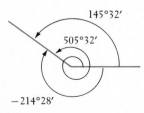

Figure 3–3

It is important to be able to change an angle expressed in degrees and minutes to an angle expressed in degrees and decimal parts of a degree, and conversely. One reason for this is that it has been very common to use degrees and minutes in tables, and most electronic calculators use degrees and decimal parts. The method of making these changes is illustrated in the following examples.

Example C

To change the angle 43°24′ to decimal form, we use the fact that 1′ = ($\frac{1}{60}$)°. Therefore, 24′ = ($\frac{24}{60}$)° = 0.4°. Therefore,

$$43°24′ = 43.4°$$

Also, 17°53′ is changed to decimal form as follows.

$$53′ = \left(\frac{53}{60}\right)^{\circ} = 0.88°$$

Thus, 17°53′ = 17.88° (to the nearest hundredth), or 17°53′ = 17.9° (to the nearest tenth). Here the results have been **rounded off**. (See Appendix B.)

Example D

To change 154.36° to an angle measured to the nearest minute, we use the fact that 1° = 60′. Therefore,

$$0.36° = 0.36(60′) = 21.6′$$

To the nearest minute, we have 154.36° = 154°22′.

If the initial side of the angle is the positive x-axis and the vertex is at the origin, the angle is said to be in **standard position.** The angle is then determined by the position of the terminal side. If the terminal side is in the first quadrant, the angle is called a "first-quadrant angle." Similar terms are used when the terminal side is in the other quadrants. *If the terminal side coincides with one of the axes, the angle is a* **quadrantal angle.** When an angle is in standard position, the terminal side can be determined if we know any point, other than the origin, on the terminal side.

Example E

To draw a third-quadrant angle of 205°, we simply measure 205° from the positive x-axis and draw the terminal side. See angle α in Fig. 3–4.

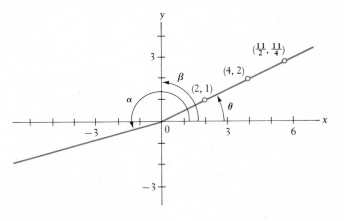

Figure 3–4

Also in Fig. 3-4, θ is in standard position and the terminal side is uniquely determined by knowing that it passes through the point (2, 1). The same terminal side passes through (4, 2) and $(\frac{11}{2}, \frac{11}{4})$, among other points. Knowing that the terminal side passes through any one of these points makes it possible to determine the terminal side.

Angle β in Fig. 3-4 is a quadrantal angle since its terminal side is the positive *y*-axis.

Exercises 3-1

In Exercises 1 through 4 draw the given angles.

1. 60°, 120°, −90°   **2.** 330°, −150°, 450°
3. 50°, −360°, −30°   **4.** 45°, 225°, −250°

In Exercises 5 through 12 determine one positive and one negative coterminal angle for each angle given.

5. 45°   **6.** 73°   **7.** 150°   **8.** 162°
9. 70°30′   **10.** 153°47′   **11.** 278.1°   **12.** 197.6°

In Exercises 13 through 20 change the given angles to equal angles expressed in decimal form. In Exercises 17 through 20 round off results to hundredths.

13. 15°12′   **14.** 246°48′   **15.** 86°3′   **16.** 157°39′
17. 301°16′   **18.** 4°47′   **19.** 96°8′   **20.** 38°28′

In Exercises 21 through 28 change the given angles to equal angles expressed to the nearest minute.

21. 47.5°   **22.** 315.8°   **23.** 19.75°   **24.** 84.55°
25. 5.62°   **26.** 238.21°   **27.** 24.92°   **28.** 142.87°

In Exercises 29 through 32 draw angles in standard position such that the terminal side passes through the given point.

29. (4, 2)   **30.** (−3, 8)   **31.** (−3, −5)   **32.** (6, −1)

3-2 Defining the Trigonometric Functions

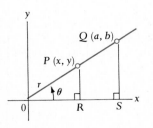

Figure 3-5

Let us place an angle θ in standard position and drop perpendicular lines from points on the terminal side to the *x*-axis as shown in Fig. 3-5. In doing this we set up similar triangles, each with one vertex at the origin. *Using the basic fact from geometry that corresponding sides of similar triangles are proportional, we may set up equal ratios of corresponding sides.*

There are three important distances for a given point on the terminal side of the angle involved in these ratios. *They are the* **abscissa** *(x-value), the* **ordinate** *(y-value), and the* **radius vector** *(the distance from the origin to the point).* The radius vector is denoted as *r*.

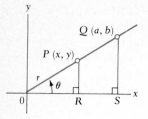

Figure 3–5

Example A

In Fig. 3–5 triangles *OPR* and *OQS* are similar. Therefore, the ratio of the abscissa (*x*-value) to the ordinate (*y*-value) of points *P* and *Q* is the same in each triangle. We can state this as

$$\frac{x}{y} = \frac{a}{b}$$

For any other point on the terminal side of θ that we might choose, the ratio of its abscissa to ordinate would still be the same as those already given.

For any angle θ in standard position, there are six different ratios which may be set up. Because of the property of similar triangles, these ratios are the same, regardless of the point on the terminal side which is chosen. For a different angle, with a different terminal side, the ratios have different values. Thus, the ratios depend on the position of the terminal side, which means that the ratios depend on the angle. In this way we see that *the ratios are functions of the angle. These functions are called the* **trigonometric functions,** *and are defined as follows:*

$$\text{sine } \theta = \frac{\text{ordinate of } P}{\text{radius vector of } P} = \frac{y}{r},$$

$$\text{cosine } \theta = \frac{\text{abscissa of } P}{\text{radius vector of } P} = \frac{x}{r},$$

$$\text{tangent } \theta = \frac{\text{ordinate of } P}{\text{abscissa of } P} = \frac{y}{x},$$

$$\text{cotangent } \theta = \frac{\text{abscissa of } P}{\text{ordinate of } P} = \frac{x}{y},$$

$$\text{secant } \theta = \frac{\text{radius vector of } P}{\text{abscissa of } P} = \frac{r}{x},$$

$$\text{cosecant } \theta = \frac{\text{radius vector of } P}{\text{ordinate of } P} = \frac{r}{y}$$

(3–1)

In this chapter we shall restrict our attention to the trigonometric functions of acute angles. However, it should be emphasized that the definitions in Eqs. (3–1) are general, and may be used for angles of any magnitude. Discussion of the trigonometric functions of angles in general, along with additional important properties, is found in Chapters 7 and 19.

For convenience, the names of the various functions are usually abbreviated to sin θ, cos θ, tan θ, cot θ, sec θ, and csc θ. Note that a given function is not defined if the denominator is zero. The denominator is zero in tan θ and sec θ for $x = 0$, and in cot θ and csc θ for $y = 0$. In all cases we will assume that $r > 0$. If $r = 0$ there would be no terminal side and therefore no angle.

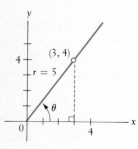

Figure 3–6

Example B

Determine the trigonometric functions of the angle with a terminal side passing through the point (3, 4).

By placing the angle in standard position, as shown in Fig. 3–6, and drawing the terminal side through (3, 4), we find that $r = 5$ (by use of the Pythagorean theorem). Using the values $x = 3$, $y = 4$, and $r = 5$, we find that

$$\sin \theta = \frac{4}{5}, \qquad \cos \theta = \frac{3}{5}$$

$$\tan \theta = \frac{4}{3}, \qquad \cot \theta = \frac{3}{4}$$

$$\sec \theta = \frac{5}{3}, \qquad \csc \theta = \frac{5}{4}$$

If one of the trigonometric functions is known, we can determine the other functions of the angle, using the Pythagorean theorem and the definitions of the functions. The following example illustrates the method.

Example C

If we know that $\sin \theta = \frac{3}{7}$ and that θ is a first quadrant angle, we know that the ratio of the ordinate to the radius vector (of y to r) is 3 to 7. Therefore, the point on the terminal side for which y is 3 can be determined by use of the Pythagorean theorem. The x-value for this point is

$$x = \sqrt{7^2 - 3^2} = \sqrt{49 - 9} = \sqrt{40} = 2\sqrt{10}$$

Therefore, the point $(2\sqrt{10}, 3)$ is on the terminal side as shown in Fig. 3–7.

Therefore, using the values $x = 2\sqrt{10}$, $y = 3$, and $r = 7$ we have the other trigonometric functions of θ. They are

$$\cos \theta = \frac{2\sqrt{10}}{7}, \qquad \tan \theta = \frac{3}{2\sqrt{10}}, \qquad \cot \theta = \frac{2\sqrt{10}}{3},$$

$$\sec \theta = \frac{7}{2\sqrt{10}}, \qquad \csc \theta = \frac{7}{3}$$

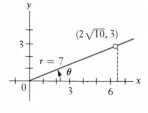

Figure 3−7

Exercises 3−2

In Exercises 1 through 8 determine the trigonometric functions of the angles whose terminal sides pass through the given points.

1. $(4, 3)$ 2. $(5, 12)$ 3. $(15, 8)$ 4. $(7, 24)$
5. $(1, \sqrt{15})$ 6. $(1, 1)$ 7. $(2, 5)$ 8. $(1, \frac{1}{2})$

In Exercises 9 through 16 use the given trigonometric functions to find the indicated trigonometric functions.

9. $\tan \theta = 1$, find $\sin \theta$ and $\sec \theta$ 10. $\sin \theta = \frac{1}{2}$, find $\cos \theta$ and $\csc \theta$
11. $\cos \theta = \frac{2}{3}$, find $\tan \theta$ and $\cot \theta$ 12. $\sec \theta = 3$, find $\tan \theta$ and $\sin \theta$
13. $\sin \theta = 0.7$, find $\cot \theta$ and $\csc \theta$ 14. $\cos \theta = \frac{5}{12}$, find $\sec \theta$ and $\tan \theta$
15. $\cot \theta = 0.25$, find $\cos \theta$ and $\csc \theta$ 16. $\csc \theta = 1.2$, find $\cos \theta$ and $\cot \theta$

In Exercises 17 through 20 each of the listed points is on the terminal side of an angle. Show that each of the indicated functions is the same for each of the points.

17. $(3, 4)$, $(6, 8)$, $(4.5, 6)$, $\sin \theta$ and $\tan \theta$
18. $(5, 12)$, $(15, 36)$, $(7.5, 18)$, $\cos \theta$ and $\cot \theta$
19. $(2, 1)$, $(4, 2)$, $(8, 4)$, $\tan \theta$ and $\sec \theta$
20. $(3, 2)$, $(6, 4)$, $(9, 6)$, $\csc \theta$ and $\cos \theta$

In Exercises 21 and 22 answer the given questions.

21. From the definitions of the trigonometric functions, it can be seen that $\csc \theta$ is the reciprocal of $\sin \theta$. What function is the reciprocal of $\cos \theta$? of $\cot \theta$?
22. Divide the expression for $\sin \theta$ by that for $\cos \theta$. Is the result the expression for any of the other functions?

3–3 Values of the Trigonometric Functions

We have been able to calculate the trigonometric functions if we knew one point on the terminal side of the angle. However, in practice it is more common to know the angle in degrees, for example, and to be required to find the functions of this angle. Therefore, we must be able to determine the trigonometric functions of angles in degrees.

One way to determine the functions of a given angle is to make a scale drawing. That is, we draw the angle in standard position using a protractor, and then measure the lengths of the values of x, y, and r for some point on the terminal side. By using the proper ratios we may determine the functions of this angle.

We may also use certain geometric facts to determine the functions of some particular angles. The following two examples illustrate this procedure.

Example A

From geometry we know that the side opposite a $30°$ angle in a right triangle is one-half the hypotenuse. By using this fact and letting $y = 1$ and $r = 2$ (see Fig. 3–8), we determine that $\sin 30° = \frac{1}{2}$. Also, by use of the Pythagorean theorem we determine that $x = \sqrt{3}$. Therefore, $\cos 30° = \frac{\sqrt{3}}{2}$ and $\tan 30° = \frac{1}{\sqrt{3}}$. In a similar way we may determine the values of the functions of $60°$ to be as follows: $\sin 60° = \frac{\sqrt{3}}{2}$, $\cos 60° = \frac{1}{2}$, and $\tan 60° = \sqrt{3}$.

Example B

Determine $\sin 45°$, $\cos 45°$, and $\tan 45°$.

From geometry we know that in an isosceles right triangle the angles are $45°$, $45°$, and $90°$. We know that the sides are in proportion 1, 1,

$\sqrt{2}$, respectively. Putting the 45° angle in standard position, we find $x = 1$, $y = 1$, and $r = \sqrt{2}$ (see Fig. 3–9). From this we determine

$$\sin 45° = \frac{1}{\sqrt{2}}, \qquad \cos 45° = \frac{1}{\sqrt{2}}, \quad \text{and} \quad \tan 45° = 1$$

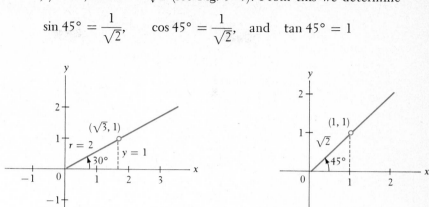

Figure 3—8   Figure 3—9

Summarizing the results for 30°, 45°, and 60°, we have the following table.

	θ	30°	45°	60°	(decimal approximations) 30°	45°	60°
$\sin \theta$		$\dfrac{1}{2}$	$\dfrac{1}{\sqrt{2}}$	$\dfrac{\sqrt{3}}{2}$	0.500	0.707	0.866
$\cos \theta$		$\dfrac{\sqrt{3}}{2}$	$\dfrac{1}{\sqrt{2}}$	$\dfrac{1}{2}$	0.866	0.707	0.500
$\tan \theta$		$\dfrac{1}{\sqrt{3}}$	1	$\sqrt{3}$	0.577	1.000	1.732

The scale-drawing method is only approximate, and the geometric methods work only for certain angles. However, the values of the functions may be determined through more advanced methods (using calculus and what are known as power series).

We now refer to the tables of trigonometric functions presented in Appendix E. Since measuring angles in degrees and minutes or in degrees and decimal parts is common, a table of each type is given. Table 3 gives values of the trigonometric functions to each 10′, and Table 4 gives values to each 0.1°.

To obtain a value of a function from either table, we note that the angles from 0° to 45° are listed in the left-hand column and are read down. The angles from 45° to 90° are listed on the right-hand side and are read up. The functions for angles from 0° to 45° are listed along the top, and those for the angles from 45° to 90° are listed along the bottom.

Example C

Using Table 3, find sin 34°0′ and cos 72°0′.

Sin 34°0′ is found under sin θ (at top) and to the right of 34°00′ (at left). Thus, sin 34°0′ = 0.5592.

Cos 72°0′ is found over cos θ (at bottom) and to the left of 72°00′ (at right). Thus, cos 72°0′ = 0.3090.

Example D

Using Table 3, find tan 42°20′ and sin 64°40′.

Tan 42°20′ is found under tan θ (at top) and to the right of 20′ (which appears under 42°). Tan 42°20′ = 0.9110.

Sin 64°40′ is found over sin θ (at bottom) and to the left of 40′ (which appears *over* 64°). Sin 64°40′ = 0.9038.

Example E

Using Table 4, find cos 8.0° and cot 74.2°.

Cos 8.0° is found under cos θ (at top) and to the right of 8.0 (at left). Thus, cos 8.0° = 0.9903.

Cot 74.2° is found over cot θ (at bottom) and to the left of 0.2 (which appears above 74.0). Thus, cot 74.2° = 0.2830.

Not only are we able to find values of the functions if we know the angle, but also we can find the angle if we know the value of a function. This requires that we reverse the procedures mentioned above. In doing this, we are actually using another important type of mathematical function, an **inverse trigonometric function.** These are discussed in some detail in Chapter 19. For calculator purposes at this point, it is sufficient to recognize the notation which is used. The notation for "the angle whose sine is x" is Sin^{-1} x or Arcsin x. Similar meanings are given to Cos^{-1} x, Arccos x, Tan^{-1} x, and Arctan x.

Example F

Given that sin θ = 0.2616, find θ to the nearest 10′.

We look for 0.2616, or the nearest number to it, in the columns for sin θ in Table 3. Since this number appears exactly under sin θ, we conclude that θ = 15°10′.

Example G

Given that tan θ = 2.375, find θ to the nearest 0.1°.

We look for 2.375, or the nearest number to it, in the columns for tan θ in Table 4. Since the nearest number which appears is 2.379, and this appears over tan θ, we conclude that θ = 67.2° to the nearest tenth of a degree.

There are occasions when it is necessary to use angles expressed to an accuracy greater than 10′ or 0.1°. This greater accuracy can be obtained by use of tables which give five or more digits for the values of the functions, or by scientific electronic calculators. It is also possible to obtain greater accuracy from the tables in Appendix E.

Using Table 3 we can obtain values of the trigonometric functions for angles expressed to the nearest minute. We can also find an angle to the nearest minute for a given value of a function. Since this table shows angles only to the nearest 10′, it is necessary to use **linear interpolation** for angles, expressed to the nearest minute, which are not listed directly.

Linear interpolation assumes that if a particular angle lies between two of those listed in the table, then the functions of that angle are at the same proportional distance between the functions listed. This assumption is not strictly correct, although it is a very good approximation.

Example H

To find sin 23°27′ we must interpolate between sin 23°20′ and 23°30′. Since 27′ is $\frac{7}{10}$ of the way between 20′ and 30′, we shall assume that sin 23°27′ is $\frac{7}{10}$ of the way between sin 23°20′ and sin 23°30′. These values are 0.3961 and 0.3987. The **tabular difference** between them is 26, and $\frac{7}{10}$ of this is 18. Adding 0.0018 to 0.3961, we obtain sin 23°27′ = 0.3979. Another method of indicating the interpolation is shown in Fig. 3–10. From the figure we see that

$$\frac{7}{10} = \frac{x}{26}$$

$$10x = 182$$

$$x = 18.2$$

Since we want to determine the value of the function to four decimal places (the limit of accuracy of the table), we must round off the value of x to the nearest integer. Therefore, x = 18, and

$$\sin 23°27′ = 0.3961 + 0.0018 = 0.3979$$

Example I

To find cos 76°14′, we first determine that we want the value $\frac{4}{10}$ of the way from cos 76°10′ to cos 76°20′. These values are 0.2391 and 0.2363, and their tabular difference is 28. Four-tenths of this is 11 (to the nearest unit). Thus, subtracting this (the value of cos 76°10′ is greater than cos 76°20′—the values of cos θ get *smaller* as θ gets larger) from 0.2391, we get cos 76°14′ = 0.2380. Again we can indicate the interpolation, as in Fig. 3–11. From the figure we see that $\frac{4}{10} = \frac{x}{28}$, or x = 11.

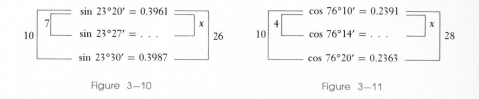

Figure 3—10   Figure 3—11

Example J

Given that $\cos \theta = 0.8811$, find θ to the nearest minute.

We find that this number lies between $\cos 28°10'$ and $\cos 28°20'$. These values are 0.8816 and 0.8802. The tabular difference between $\cos \theta$ and $\cos 28°10'$ is 5, and tabular difference between the two values given in Table 3 is 14. Thus, $\cos \theta$ is assumed to be $\frac{5}{14}$ of the way from the first to the second. To the nearest tenth, this is $\frac{4}{10}$. Hence, $\theta = 28°14'$ (to the nearest '). The solution of this type of problem can also be indicated by means of a figure such as Fig. 3–12, from which we see that $\frac{5}{14} = \frac{x}{10}$, or $x = 4$.

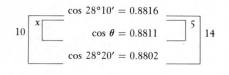

$$\cos 28°10' = 0.8816$$
$$\cos \theta = 0.8811$$
$$\cos 28°20' = 0.8802$$

Figure 3–12

If an electronic calculator is used, it may not be necessary to refer to the tables to obtain values of the trigonometric functions, or to use interpolation to obtain the additional accuracy. However, it should be noted that in this regard the calculator is another source from which these values are available, and does not eliminate the need to understand how these values are used. Also, although we have used interpolation only with Table 3 in the examples of this section, it is a method which can be used with a great many tables, including Table 4 and those for which values may not be available on a calculator. This is illustrated in the exercises which follow.

Exercises 3–3

In Exercises 1 through 4 use a protractor to draw the given angle. Measure off 10 units (centimeters are convenient) along the radius vector. Then measure the corresponding values of x and y. From these values determine the trigonometric functions of the angle.

1. 40°   2. 75°   3. 15°   4. 53°

In Exercises 5 through 12 find the value of each of the trigonometric functions from Table 3 in Appendix E.

5. $\sin 19°0'$ 6. $\cos 43°0'$ 7. $\tan 67°0'$ 8. $\cot 76°0'$

9. $\cos 22°20'$ 10. $\tan 34°50'$ 11. $\sec 56°30'$ 12. $\csc 52°10'$

In Exercises 13 through 20 find the value of each of the trigonometric functions from Table 4 in Appendix E.

13. $\cos 26.0°$ 14. $\cot 33.0°$ 15. $\sin 75.6°$ 16. $\cos 48.1°$

17. $\tan 7.4°$ 18. $\sin 44.6°$ 19. $\cot 49.3°$ 20. $\tan 78.9°$

In Exercises 21 through 28 use Table 3 to find θ to the nearest 10' for each of the given trigonometric functions.

21. $\tan \theta = 0.8441$ **22.** $\sin \theta = 0.3854$ **23.** $\cos \theta = 0.4718$

24. $\sec \theta = 1.264$ **25.** $\csc \theta = 1.409$ **26.** $\tan \theta = 1.523$

27. $\sin \theta = 0.9175$ **28.** $\cos \theta = 0.1260$

In Exercises 29 through 36 use Table 4 to find θ to the nearest 0.1° for each of the given trigonometric functions.

29. $\sin \theta = 0.2385$ **30.** $\cot \theta = 1.819$ **31.** $\tan \theta = 4.870$

32. $\cos \theta = 0.1515$ **33.** $\cos \theta = 0.6800$ **34.** $\sin \theta = 0.9788$

35. $\cot \theta = 0.8433$ **36.** $\tan \theta = 1.926$

In Exercises 37 through 44 find the value of each of the trigonometric functions from Table 3, using interpolation.

37. $\tan 28°56'$ **38.** $\cos 48°44'$ **39.** $\sin 63°15'$ **40.** $\sec 71°47'$

41. $\cot 7°8'$ **42.** $\csc 12°14'$ **43.** $\cos 65°49'$ **44.** $\sin 57°52'$

In Exercises 45 through 52 use Table 3 and interpolation to find θ to the nearest 1' for each of the given trigonometric functions.

45. $\cos \theta = 0.2960$ **46.** $\tan \theta = 0.1086$ **47.** $\sin \theta = 0.5755$

48. $\csc \theta = 1.168$ **49.** $\sec \theta = 1.289$ **50.** $\tan \theta = 0.6539$

51. $\cot \theta = 0.8070$ **52.** $\sin \theta = 0.9789$

In Exercises 53 through 56 additional problems involving interpolation are illustrated. In Exercises 53 and 54 use interpolation with Table 4 to evaluate the given trigonometric functions. In Exercises 55 and 56 use interpolation with the given table of values of the temperature of a cooling object as a function of time to obtain the required values.

53. $\tan 37.17°$ **54.** $\cos 58.72°$

Temperature (degrees Celsius)	150.0	145.6	141.6	137.9	134.6	131.6
Time (minutes)	0.0	1.0	2.0	3.0	4.0	5.0

55. Find T for $t = 1.3$ min.   **56.** Find T for $t = 3.8$ min.

In Exercises 57 through 60 solve the given problems.

57. When a projectile is fired into the air, its horizontal velocity v_x is related to the velocity v with which it is fired by the relation $v_x = v(\cos \theta)$, where θ is the angle between the horizontal and the direction in which it is fired. What is the horizontal velocity of a projectile fired with velocity 200 ft/s at an angle of 36°0' with respect to the horizontal?

58. The coefficient of friction between an object moving down an inclined plane with constant speed and the plane equals the tangent of the angle that the plane makes with the horizontal. If the coefficient of friction between a metal block and a wooden plane is 0.150, at what angle (to the nearest tenth of a degree) is the plane inclined?

59. The voltage at any instant in a coil of wire which is turning in a magnetic field is given by $E = E_{max} (\cos \alpha)$, where E_{max} is the maximum voltage and α is the angle the coil makes with the field. If the maximum voltage produced by a certain coil is 120 V, what voltage is generated when the coil makes an angle of 55°35′ with the field?

60. When a light ray enters glass from the air it bends somewhat toward a line perpendicular to the surface. The *index of refraction* of the glass is defined as

$$n = \frac{\sin i}{\sin r}$$

where i is the angle between the perpendicular and the ray in the air and r is the angle between the perpendicular and the ray in the glass. A typical case for glass is $i = 59.0°$ and $r = 34.5°$. Find the index of refraction for this case. See Fig. 3–13.

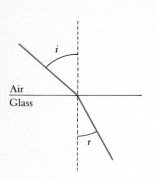

Air
Glass

Figure 3–13

3—4 The Right Triangle

From geometry we know that a triangle, by definition, consists of three sides and has three angles. If one side and any other two of these six parts of the triangle are known, it is possible to determine the other three parts. One of the three known parts must be a side, for if we know only the three angles, we can conclude only that an entire set of similar triangles has those particular angles.

Example A

Assume that one side and two angles are known. Then we may determine the third angle by the fact that the sum of the angles of a triangle is always 180°. Of all the possible similar triangles having these three angles, we have the one with the particular side which is known. Only one triangle with these parts is possible (in the sense that all triangles with the given parts are congruent and have equal corresponding angles and sides).

To **solve a triangle** *means that, when we are given three parts of a triangle (at least one a side), we are to find the other three parts.* In this section we are going to demonstrate the method of solving a right triangle. Since one angle of the triangle will be 90°, it is necessary to know one side and one other part. Also, we know that the sum of the three angles of a triangle is 180°, and this in turn tells us that the sum of the other two angles, both acute, is 90°. *Any two acute angles whose sum is 90° are said to be* **complementary**.

For consistency, when we are labeling the parts of the right triangle we shall use the letters A and B to denote the acute angles, and C to denote the right angle. The letters a, b, and c will denote the sides opposite these angles, respectively. Thus, side c is the hypotenuse of the right triangle.

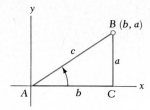

Figure 3—14

We shall find it convenient in solving right triangles to define the trigonometric functions of the acute angles in terms of the sides (see Fig. 3–14). Placing the vertex of angle A at the origin and the vertex of angle C on the positive x-axis, we obtain the following definitions:

$$\sin A = \frac{y}{r} = \frac{a}{c}, \qquad \cos A = \frac{x}{r} = \frac{b}{c}, \qquad \tan A = \frac{y}{x} = \frac{a}{b}$$

$$\cot A = \frac{x}{y} = \frac{b}{a}, \qquad \sec A = \frac{r}{x} = \frac{c}{b}, \qquad \csc A = \frac{r}{y} = \frac{c}{a}$$

(3–2)

If we should place the vertex of angle B at the origin, instead of the vertex of angle A, we would obtain the following definitions for the functions of angle B:

$$\sin B = \frac{b}{c}, \qquad \cos B = \frac{a}{c}, \qquad \tan B = \frac{b}{a}$$

$$\cot B = \frac{a}{b}, \qquad \sec B = \frac{c}{a}, \qquad \csc B = \frac{c}{b}$$

(3–3)

Inspecting these results, we may generalize our definitions of the trigonometric functions of acute angles of a right triangle to be as follows:

$$\sin \alpha = \frac{\text{opposite side}}{\text{hypotenuse}}, \qquad \cos \alpha = \frac{\text{adjacent side}}{\text{hypotenuse}}$$

$$\tan \alpha = \frac{\text{opposite side}}{\text{adjacent side}}, \qquad \cot \alpha = \frac{\text{adjacent side}}{\text{opposite side}}$$

$$\sec \alpha = \frac{\text{hypotenuse}}{\text{adjacent side}}, \qquad \csc \alpha = \frac{\text{hypotenuse}}{\text{opposite side}}$$

(3–4)

Using the definitions in this form, we can solve right triangles without placing the angle in standard position. The angle need only be a part of any right triangle.

We note from the above discussion that $\sin A = \cos B$, $\tan A = \cot B$, and $\sec A = \csc B$. From this we conclude that *cofunctions of acute complementary angles are equal.* The sine function and cosine functions are cofunctions, the tangent function and cotangent function are cofunctions, and the secant function and cosecant function are cofunctions. From this we can see how the tables of trigonometric functions are constructed. Since $\sin A = \cos (90° - A)$, the number representing either of these need appear only once in the tables.

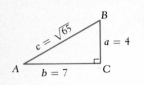

Figure 3–15

Example B

Given $a = 4$, $b = 7$, and $c = \sqrt{65}$ ($C = 90°$), find sin A, cos A, and tan A. (See Fig. 3–15.)

$$\sin A = \frac{\text{side opposite angle } A}{\text{hypotenuse}} = \frac{4}{\sqrt{65}} = 0.496$$

$$\cos A = \frac{\text{side adjacent angle } A}{\text{hypotenuse}} = \frac{7}{\sqrt{65}} = 0.868$$

$$\tan A = \frac{\text{side opposite angle } A}{\text{side adjacent angle } A} = \frac{4}{7} = 0.571$$

Example C

In Fig. 3–15, we have

$$\sin B = \frac{\text{side opposite angle } B}{\text{hypotenuse}} = \frac{7}{\sqrt{65}} = 0.868$$

$$\cos B = \frac{\text{side adjacent angle } B}{\text{hypotenuse}} = \frac{4}{\sqrt{65}} = 0.496$$

$$\tan B = \frac{\text{side opposite angle } B}{\text{side adjacent angle } B} = \frac{7}{4} = 1.75$$

We also note that sin A = cos B and cos A = sin B.

We are now ready to solve right triangles. We do this by expressing the unknown parts in terms of the known parts, as the following examples illustrate. For consistency, unless otherwise noted all results are rounded off to three significant digits, or to the nearest 10′ or 0.1° for angles. (Intermediate results in examples and exercises may contain additional significant digits. Discussions of rounding off and significant digits are given in Appendix B.)

Example D

Given $A = 50°0'$ and $b = 6.70$, solve the right triangle of which these are parts (see Fig. 3–16).

Since $\frac{a}{b} = \tan A$, we have $a = b \tan A$. Thus

$$a = 6.70 \ (\tan 50°0')$$
$$= 6.70 \ (1.192) = 7.99$$

Since $A = 50°0'$, $B = 40°0'$. Since $\frac{b}{c} = \cos A$, we have

$$c = \frac{b}{\cos A} = \frac{6.70}{0.6428} = 10.4$$

We have found that $a = 7.99$, $c = 10.4$, and $B = 40°0'$. It might be noted that we could have computed c by using an equation involving a. However, any error which may have been made in calculating a would also cause c to be in error. Thus, it is generally best to use given values in calculations.

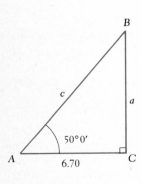

Figure 3–16

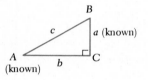

Figure 3—17

Example E

Given $b = 56.8$ and $c = 79.5$, solve the right triangle of which these are parts (see Fig. 3–17). Express angles in tenths.

Since $\cos A = \frac{b}{c}$, we have

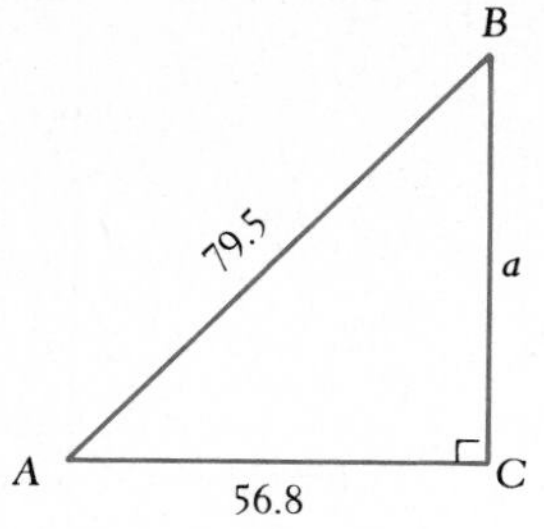

$$\cos A = \frac{56.8}{79.5} = 0.7145$$

This means that

$$A = 44.4°$$

and

$$B = 90.0° - 44.4° = 45.6°$$

We solve for a by use of the Pythagorean theorem since in this way we can express a in terms of the given parts.

$$a^2 + b^2 = c^2 \text{ or } a = \sqrt{c^2 - b^2}$$

Thus,

$$a = \sqrt{79.5^2 - 56.8^2} = \sqrt{6320 - 3226} = \sqrt{3094}$$
$$= 55.6.$$

The above means we have determined that $a = 55.6$, $A = 44.4°$, and $B = 45.6°$.

Example F

Assuming that A and a are known, express the unknown parts of the right triangle in terms of a and A (see Fig. 3–18).

Since $\frac{a}{b} = \tan A$, we have $b = \frac{a}{\tan A}$. Since A is known, $B = 90° - A$.

Since $\frac{a}{c} = \sin A$, we have $c = \frac{a}{\sin A}$.

Figure 3—18

Exercises 3—4

In Exercises 1 through 4 draw appropriate figures and verify through observation that only one triangle may contain the given parts (that is, any others which may be drawn will be congruent—have equal corresponding sides and angles).

1. A 30° angle is included between sides of 3 in. and 6 in.
2. A side of 4 in. is included between angles of 40° and 70°.
3. A right triangle with a hypotenuse of 5 cm and a leg of 3 cm.
4. A right triangle with a 70° angle between the hypotenuse and a leg of 5 cm.

In Exercises 5 through 12 solve the right triangles which have the given parts. Express angles to the nearest 10'. Refer to Fig. 3–19.

5. $A = 32°0'$, $c = 56.8$
6. $B = 12°0'$, $c = 18.0$
7. $a = 56.7$, $b = 44.0$
8. $a = 9.98$, $c = 12.6$
9. $B = 37°40'$, $a = 0.886$
10. $A = 70°10'$, $a = 137$
11. $b = 86.7$, $c = 167$
12. $a = 6.85$, $b = 2.12$

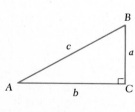

Figure 3—19

In Exercises 13 through 20 solve the right triangles which have the given parts. Express angles to the nearest 0.1°. Refer to Fig. 3–19.

13. $A = 77.8°$, $a = 6700$ 14. $A = 18.4°$, $c = 8.97$

15. $a = 150$, $c = 345$ 16. $a = 93.2$, $c = 124$

17. $B = 32.1°$, $c = 23.8$ 18. $B = 64.3°$, $b = 0.652$

19. $b = 82.1$, $c = 88.6$ 20. $a = 5920$, $b = 4110$

In Exercises 21 through 24 the parts listed refer to those in Fig. 3–19 and are assumed to be known. Express the other parts in terms of these known parts.

21. A, c 22. a, b 23. B, a 24. b, c

3–5 Applications of Right Triangles

Many applied problems can be solved by setting up the solutions in terms of right triangles. These applications are essentially the same as solving right triangles, although it is usually one specific part of the triangle that we wish to determine. The following examples illustrate some of the basic applications of right triangles.

Example A

A tree has a shadow 17.0 ft long. From the point on the ground at the end of the shadow, the **angle of elevation** (the angle between the horizontal and the line of sight, when the object is above the horizontal) of the top of the tree is measured to be 52°0'. How tall is the tree?

By drawing an appropriate figure, as shown in Fig. 3–20, we note the information given and that which is required. Here we have let h be the height of the tree. Thus, we see that

$$\frac{h}{17.0} = \tan 52°0'$$

or

$$h = 17.0(\tan 52°0')$$
$$= 17.0(1.280)$$
$$= 21.8 \text{ ft}$$

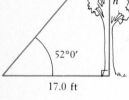

52°0'

17.0 ft

Figure 3–20

Example B

From the roof of a building 46.0 ft high, the **angle of depression** (the angle between the horizontal and the line of sight, when the object is below the horizontal) of an object in the street is 74°0'. What is the distance of the observer from the object?

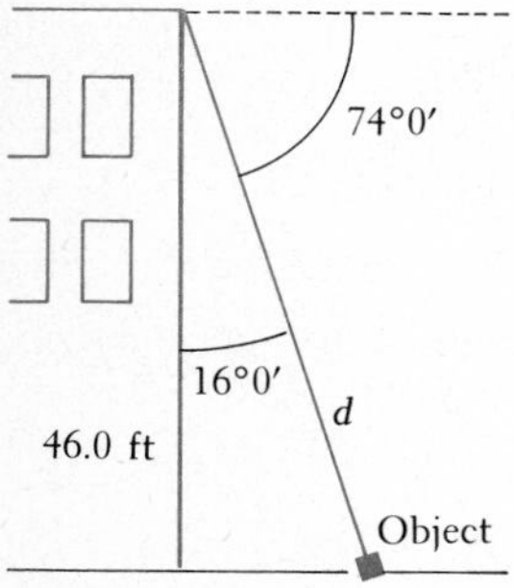

Again we draw an appropriate figure (Fig. 3–21). Here we let d represent the required distance. From the figure we see that

$$\frac{46.0}{d} = \cos 16°0'$$

$$d = \frac{46.0}{\cos 16°0'} = \frac{46.0}{0.9613}$$

$$= 47.9 \text{ ft}$$

74°0'

16°0'

d

46.0 ft

Object

Figure 3–21

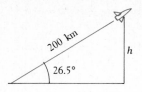

Figure 3—22

Example C

A missile is launched at an angle of 26.5° with respect to the horizontal. If it travels in a straight line over level terrain for 2 min, and its average speed is 6000 km/h, what is its altitude at this time?

In Fig. 3—22 we have let h represent the altitude of the missile after 2 min (altitude is measured on a perpendicular). Also, we determine that the missile has flown 200 km in a direct line from the launching site. This is found from the fact that it travels at 6000 km/h for $\frac{1}{30}$ h (2 min) and from the fact that $(6000 \text{ km/h})(\frac{1}{30}\text{ h}) = 200$ km. Therefore,

$$\frac{h}{200} = \sin 26.5°$$

$$h = 200(\sin 26.5°) = 200(0.4462)$$
$$= 89.2 \text{ km}$$

Example D

A shelf is supported by a straight 65.0-cm support attached to the wall at a point 53.5 cm below the bottom of the shelf. What angle does the support make with the wall? See Fig. 3—23.

In the figure we see that angle θ is to be determined. Therefore, we have

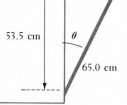

Figure 3—23

$$\cos \theta = \frac{53.5}{65.0} = 0.8231$$

or

$$\theta = 34.6°$$

to the nearest tenth of a degree.

Example E

A television antenna is on the roof of a building. From a point on the ground 36.0 ft from the building, the angles of elevation of the top and the bottom of the antenna are 51°0′ and 42°0′, respectively. How tall is the antenna?

In Fig. 3—24 we let x represent the distance from the top of the building to the ground, and y represent the distance from the top of the antenna to the ground. Therefore,

$$\frac{x}{36.0} = \tan 42°0′$$

$$x = 36.0(\tan 42°0′) = 36.0(0.9004)$$
$$= 32.4 \text{ ft}$$

and

$$\frac{y}{36.0} = \tan 51°0′$$

$$y = 36.0(\tan 51°0′) = 36.0(1.235)$$
$$= 44.5 \text{ ft}$$

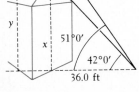

Figure 3—24

The length of the antenna is the difference of these distances, or 12.1 ft.

Exercises 3—5

In the following exercises solve the given problems. Draw an appropriate figure unless the figure is given.

1. The angle of elevation of the sun is 48°0′ at the time a television tower casts a shadow 346 ft long on level ground. Find the height of the tower.

2. A rope is stretched from the top of a vertical pole to a point 10.5 m from the foot of the pole. The rope makes an angle of 28°0′ with the pole. How tall is the pole?

3. The length of a kite string (assumed straight) is 560 ft. The angle of elevation of the kite is 64.0°. How high is the kite?

4. A 20.0-ft ladder leans against the side of a house. The angle between the ground and ladder is 70.0°. How far from the house is the foot of the ladder?

5. From the top of a cliff 110 m high the angle of depression to a boat is 23°20′. How far is the boat from the foot of the cliff?

6. A robot is on the surface of Mars. The angle of depression from a camera in the robot to a rock on the surface of Mars is 13.3°. The camera is 196 cm above the surface. How far is the camera from the rock?

7. On a blueprint, the walls of a rectangular room are 5.65 cm and 3.85 cm long, respectively. What is the angle (to the nearest 0.1°) between the longer wall and a diagonal across the room?

8. A roadway rises 120 ft for every 2200 ft along the road. Find the angle of inclination (to the nearest 10′) of the roadway.

9. A jet cruising at 590 mi/h climbs at an angle of 15°30′. What is its gain in altitude in 2 min?

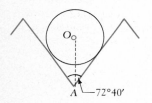

Figure 3—25

10. Ten rivets are equally spaced on the circumference of a circular plate. If the center-to-center distance between two rivets is 6.25 cm, what is the radius of the circle?

11. A loading platform is 3.25 ft above the ground. How long must a ramp be in order that it makes an angle of 20.0° with the ground?

12. In gauging screw threads a wire is placed in the thread. For the cross-section of wire and V-thread shown in Fig. 3—25, determine the distance OA if the diameter of the wire is 0.0550 in. and the angle at A is 72°40′.

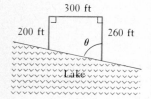

Figure 3—26

13. The level of a pond is 14.5 m above the level of a nearby stream. A straight 75.0-m drainage pipe extends from the pond surface to a point 3.0 m above the stream. What angle (to the nearest 0.1°) does the pipe make with the horizontal?

14. A lakefront property is shown in Fig. 3—26. What is the angle θ (to the nearest 10′) between the shoreline and the property line?

15. An astronaut circling the moon at an altitude of 100 mi notes that the angle of depression of the horizon is 23.8°. What is the radius of the moon?

16. A surveyor wishes to determine the width of a river. She sights a point B on the opposite side of the river from point C. She then measures off 400 ft from C to A such that C is a right angle. She then determines that $\angle A = 56°40′$. How wide is the river?

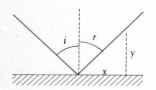

Figure 3—27

17. If a light ray strikes a reflecting surface (Fig. 3—27), the angle of reflection r equals the angle of incidence i. If a light ray has an angle of incidence of 42.0°, what is the distance y from the plane of the surface of a point on the reflected ray, if the horizontal distance x from the point of incidence is 7.42 cm?

18. A man considers building a dormer on his house. What are the dimensions x and y of the dormer in his plans (see Fig. 3–28)?

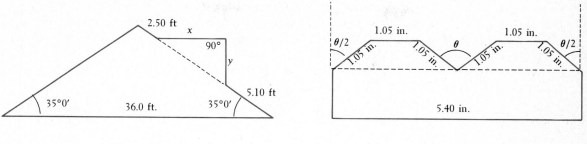

Figure 3—28   Figure 3—29

19. A machine part is indicated in Fig. 3–29. What is the angle θ (to the nearest 10′)?

20. A way of representing the impedance and resistance in an alternating-current circuit is equivalent to letting the impedance be the hypotenuse of a right triangle and the resistance be the side adjacent to the phase angle. If the resistance in a given circuit is 25.4 Ω and the phase angle is 24.5°, what is the impedance?

21. A surveyor sights two points directly ahead. Both are at an elevation 18.5 m lower than the point from which he observes them. How far apart are the points if the angles of depression are 13.5° and 21.3°, respectively?

22. A flagpole is atop a building. From a point on the ground 720 ft from the building, the angles of elevation of the top and bottom of the flagpole are 33°30′ and 31°10′, respectively. How tall is the flagpole?

3—6 Exercises for Chapter 3

In Exercises 1 through 4 find the smallest positive angle and the smallest negative angle (numerically) coterminal with, but not equal to, the given angles.

1. 17°0′   2. 248°20′   3. −217.5°   4. −7.6°

In Exercises 5 through 8 change the given angles to equal angles expressed in decimal form.

5. 31°54′   6. 174°45′   7. 38°6′   8. 321°27′

In Exercises 9 through 12 change the given angles to equal angles expressed to the nearest minute.

9. 17.5°   10. 65.4°   11. 49.7°   12. 126.25°

In Exercises 13 through 16 determine the trigonometric functions of the angles whose terminal side passes through the given points.

13. (24, 7)   14. (5, 4)   15. (4, 4)   16. (1.2, 0.5)

In Exercises 17 through 20 using the given trigonometric functions, find the indicated trigonometric functions.

17. Given $\sin \theta = \frac{5}{13}$, find $\cos \theta$ and $\cot \theta$.
18. Given $\cos \theta = \frac{3}{8}$, find $\sin \theta$ and $\tan \theta$.
19. Given $\tan \theta = 2$, find $\cos \theta$ and $\csc \theta$.
20. Given $\cot \theta = 4$, find $\sin \theta$ and $\sec \theta$.

In Exercises 21 through 32 find the value of each of the given trigonometric functions.

21. $\sin 72°0'$ **22.** $\cos 40°10'$ **23.** $\tan 61°20'$ **24.** $\csc 19°30'$
25. $\tan 37.2°$ **26.** $\sin 49.9°$ **27.** $\cos 12.8°$ **28.** $\tan 20.6°$
29. $\tan 81°15'$ **30.** $\cot 37°17'$ **31.** $\cos 55°53'$ **32.** $\sec 58°54'$

In Exercises 33 through 36 find θ to the nearest 10' for each of the given trigonometric functions.

33. $\sin \theta = 0.5324$ **34.** $\tan \theta = 1.265$
35. $\cos \theta = 0.4669$ **36.** $\sec \theta = 2.107$

In Exercises 37 through 40 find θ to the nearest 0.1° for each of the given trigonometric functions.

37. $\cos \theta = 0.9500$ **38.** $\sin \theta = 0.6305$
39. $\tan \theta = 1.574$ **40.** $\cos \theta = 0.1345$

In Exercises 41 through 44 find θ to the nearest minute for each of the given trigonometric functions.

41. $\cot \theta = 1.132$ **42.** $\cos \theta = 0.7365$
43. $\sin \theta = 0.8666$ **44.** $\csc \theta = 1.533$

In Exercises 45 through 48 solve the right triangles which have the given parts. Express angles to the nearest 10'. Refer to Fig. 3–30.

45. $A = 17°0'$, $b = 6.00$ **46.** $B = 68°10'$, $a = 1080$
47. $a = 81.0$, $b = 64.5$ **48.** $a = 1.06$, $c = 3.82$

In Exercises 49 through 52 solve the right triangles which have the given parts. Express angles to the nearest 0.1°. Refer to Fig. 3–30.

49. $A = 37.5°$, $a = 12.0$ **50.** $B = 15.7°$, $c = 12.6$
51. $b = 6.50$, $c = 7.60$ **52.** $a = 72.1$, $b = 14.3$

In Exercises 53 through 56 solve the right triangles which have the given parts. Express angles to the nearest minute. Refer to Fig. 3–30.

53. $A = 49°43'$, $c = 0.820$ **54.** $B = 4°26'$, $b = 5.60$
55. $a = 10.0$, $c = 15.0$ **56.** $a = 724$, $b = 852$

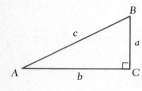

Figure 3–30

In Exercises 57 through 74 solve the given applied problems.

57. An approximate equation found in the diffraction of light through a narrow opening is

$$\sin \theta = \frac{\lambda}{d}$$

where λ (the Greek lambda) is the wavelength of the light and d is the width of the opening. If $\theta = 1°10'$ and $d = 30.0\ \mu m$, what is the wavelength of the light?

58. An equation used for the instantaneous value of electric current in an alternating-current circuit is $i = I_m \cos \theta$. Calculate i for $I_m = 56.0$ mA and $\theta = 10.5°$.

59. In determining the height h of a building which is 220 m distant, a surveyor may use the equation $h = 220 \tan \theta$, where θ is the angle of elevation to the top of the building. What should θ be if $h = 130$ m?

60. A formula used with a certain type of gear is

$$D = \frac{N \sec \theta}{4}$$

where D is the pitch diameter of the gear, N is the number of teeth on the gear, and θ is called the spiral angle. If $D = 6.75$ in. and $N = 20$, find θ (to the nearest 10′).

61. A ship's captain, desiring to travel due south, discovers that, due to an improperly functioning instrument, he has gone 22.6 mi in a direction 4°0′ east of south. How far from his course (to the east) is he?

62. A helicopter pilot notes that she is 150 m above a certain rooftop. If the angle of depression to the rooftop is 18°0′, how far on a direct line from the rooftop is the helicopter?

63. An observer 3500 ft from the launch pad of a rocket measures the angle of elevation to the rocket soon after liftoff to be 54.0°. How high is the rocket, assuming it has moved vertically?

64. A hemispherical bowl is standing level. Its inside radius is 6.50 in. and it is filled with water to a depth of 3.10 in. Through what angle may it be tilted before the water will spill?

65. A railroad embankment has a level top 22.0 ft wide, equal sloping sides of 14.5 ft, and a height of 7.20 ft. What is the width of the base of the embankment?

66. The horizontal distance between the extreme positions of a certain pendulum is 9.50 cm. If the length of the pendulum is 38.0 cm, through what angle does it swing?

67. The span of a roof is 32.0 ft. Its rise is 7.5 ft at the center of the span. What angle, to the nearest 10′, does the roof make with the horizontal?

68. If the impedance in a certain alternating-current circuit is 56.5 Ω and the resistance in the circuit is 17.0 Ω, what is the phase angle to the nearest 0.1°? (See Exercise 20 of Section 3−5.)

69. A bridge is 12.5 m above the surrounding area. If the angle of elevation of the approach to the bridge is 4°40′, how long is the approach?

70. The windshield on an automobile is inclined 42.5° with respect to the horizontal. Assuming that the windshield is flat and rectangular, what is its area if it is 4.80 ft wide and the bottom is 1.50 ft in front of the top?

71. A person in a tall building observes an object drop from a window 20.0 ft away and directly opposite him. If the distance the object drops as a function of time is $s = 16t^2$, how far is the object from the observer (on a direct line) after 2.00 s?

72. The distance from ground level to the underside of a cloud is called the *ceiling*. One observer 1000 m from a searchlight aimed vertically notes that the angle of elevation of the spot of light on a cloud is 76°0′. What is the ceiling?

73. A laser beam is transmitted with a "width" of 0.002°. What is the diameter of a spot of the beam on an object 50,000 km distant? See Fig. 3–31. (Tan 0.001° = 1.745 × 10⁻⁵; see Exercise 29 of Section 7–4.)

74. What angle is subtended at the eye of an observer 5.00 mi from an airplane which is 150 ft long and is perpendicular to the line of sight?

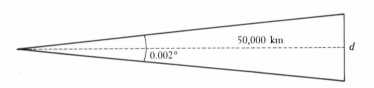

Figure 3–31

4

Systems of Linear Equations;
Determinants

4—1 Linear Equations

In Chapter 1 we introduced the topic of solving equations and showed some of the types of technical problems which could be solved. Many of the equations we encountered at that time were examples of a very important type of equation, the **linear equation**. In general, an equation is termed linear in a given set of variables if each term contains only one variable, to the first power, or is a constant.

Example A

$5x - t + 6 = 0$ is linear in x and t, but $5x^2 - t + 6 = 0$ is not, due to the presence of x^2.

The equation $4x + y = 8$ is linear in x and y, but $4xy + y = 8$ is not, due to the presence of xy.

The equation $x - 6y + z - 4w = 7$ is linear in x, y, z, and w, but $x - \frac{6}{y} + z - 4w = 7$ is not, due to the presence of $\frac{6}{y}$ where y appears in the denominator.

An equation which can be written in the form

$$ax + b = 0 \tag{4–1}$$

is known as a **linear equation in one unknown.** We have already discussed the solution to this type of equation in Section 1–10. In general, *the* **solution,** *or* **root,** *of the equation is* $x = -b/a$. Also, it will be noted that finding the solution is equivalent to finding the zero of the **linear function** $ax + b$.

There also are a great number of applied problems which involve more than one unknown. When forces are analyzed in physics, equations with two unknowns (the forces) often result. In electricity, equations relating several unknown currents arise. Numerous kinds of stated problems from various technical areas involve equations with more than one unknown. The use of equations involving more than one unknown is well established in technical applications.

Example B

A very basic law of direct-current electricity, known as Kirchhoff's first law, may be stated as "The algebraic sum of the currents entering any junction in a circuit is zero." If three wires are joined at a junction, this law leads to the equation

$$i_1 + i_2 + i_3 = 0$$

where i_1, i_2 and i_3 are the currents in each of the wires.

When determining two forces F_1 and F_2 acting on a beam, we might encounter an equation such as

$$2F_1 + 4F_2 = 200$$

An equation which can be written in the form

$$ax + by = c \tag{4-2}$$

is known as a **linear equation in two unknowns.** In Chapter 2, when we were discussing functions we considered many functions of this type. We found that for each value of x there is a corresponding value of y. Each of these pairs of numbers is a **solution** to the equation, although we did not call it that at the time. A solution is any set of numbers, one for each variable, which satisfies the equation. When we represent the solutions in the form of a graph, we see that the graph of any linear equation in two unknowns is a straight line. Also, graphs of linear equations in one unknown, those for which $a = 0$ or $b = 0$, are also straight lines. Thus we see the significance of the name "linear."

Example C

The equation $4x + 8 = 0$ is a linear equation in one unknown, x. We find its solution by subtracting 8 from both sides and then dividing both sides by 4. This results in the root $x = -2$. Solving this equation is equivalent to finding the zero of the function $4x + 8$.

Example D

The equation $2x - y - 6 = 0$ is a linear equation in two unknowns, x and y. To sketch the graph of this equation, we write it in the more convenient form $y = 2x - 6$. The coordinates of each point on the

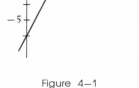

Figure 4–1

graph, which is a straight line, are solutions of this equation. For example, the point $(1, -4)$ is a point on the line. This means that $x = 1$, $y = -4$ is a solution of the equation. In the same way, $x = 0$, $y = -6$ is a solution (see Fig. 4–1).

Two linear equations, each containing the same two unknowns,

$$a_1x + b_1y = c_1$$
$$a_2x + b_2y = c_2$$

(4–3)

are said to form a **system of simultaneous linear equations.** *A solution of the system is any pair of values (x, y) which satisfies both equations.* Methods of finding the solutions to such systems are the principal concern of this chapter.

Example E
The two linear equations

$$2x - y = 5$$
$$3x + 2y = 4$$

form a system of simultaneous linear equations. The solution of this system is $x = 2$, $y = -1$. These values satisfy both equations, since $2(2) - (-1) = 4 + 1 = 5$ and $3(2) + 2(-1) = 6 - 2 = 4$. This is the only pair of values which satisfies *both* equations. Methods for finding such solutions are taken up in the following sections.

Exercises 4–1

In Exercises 1 through 4 determine whether or not the given pairs of values are solutions of the given linear equations in two unknowns.

substitute —

1. $2x + 3y = 9$; $(3, 1)$, $(5, \frac{1}{3})$
2. $5x + 2y = 1$; $(2, -4)$, $(1, -2)$
3. $-3x + 5y = 13$; $(-1, 2)$, $(4, 5)$
4. $x - 4y = 10$; $(2, -2)$, $(2, 2)$

In Exercises 5 through 8, for each given value of x, determine the value of y which gives a solution to the given linear equations in two unknowns.

5. $5x - y = 6$; $x = 1$, $x = -2$
6. $2x + 7y = 8$; $x = -3$, $x = 2$
7. $x - 5y = 12$; $x = 3$, $x = -4$
8. $3x - 2y = 9$; $x = \frac{2}{3}$, $x = -3$

In Exercises 9 through 16 determine whether or not the given pair of values is a solution of the given system of simultaneous linear equations.

9. $x - y = 5$ $x = 4$, $y = -1$
   $2x + y = 7$

10. $2x + y = 8$ $x = -1$, $y = 10$
    $3x - y = -13$

11. $3x - 4y = -10$ $x = -2$, $y = 1$
    $x + 5y = -7$

12. $-3x + y = 1$ $x = \frac{1}{3}$, $y = 2$
    $6x - 3y = -4$

13. $2x - 5y = 0$ $x = \frac{1}{2}$, $y = -\frac{1}{5}$
    $4x + 10y = 4$

14. $3x - 4y = -1$ $x = 1$, $y = -1$
    $6x - y = 5$

15. $3x - 2y = 2.2$ $x = 0.6$, $y = -0.2$
    $5x + y = 2.8$

16. $x - 7y = -3.2$ $x = -1.1$, $y = 0.3$
    $2x + y = 2.5$

In Exercises 17 through 20 answer the given questions.

17. If a board 84 in. long is cut into two pieces such that one piece is 6 in. longer than the other, the lengths x and y of the two pieces are found by solving the system of equations

$$x + y = 84$$
$$x - y = 6$$

Are the resulting lengths 45 in. and 39 in.?

18. If two forces F_1 and F_2 support a 98-lb weight, the forces can be found by solving the system of equations

get rid of decimal
x by 10

$$0.7F_1 - 0.6F_2 = 0, \ 0.7F_1 + 0.8F_2 = 98$$

Are the forces 60 lb and 70 lb?

19. Under certain conditions two electric currents i_1 and i_2 can be found by solving the system of equations

$$3i_1 + 4i_2 = 3, \ 3i_1 - 5i_2 = -6$$

Are the currents $-\frac{1}{3}$ A and 1 A?

20. Using the data that fuel consumption for transportation contributes a percent p_1 of pollution which is 16% less than the percent p_2 of all other sources combined, the equations

$$p_1 + p_2 = 100, \ p_2 - p_1 = 16$$

can be set up. Are the percents $p_1 = 58$ and $p_2 = 42$?

4–2 Solving Systems of Two Linear Equations in Two Unknowns Graphically

We shall now take up the problem of solving for the unknowns when we have a system of two simultaneous linear equations in two unknowns. In this section we shall show how the solution may be found graphically. The sections which follow will discuss other basic methods of solution.

Since a solution of a system of simultaneous linear equations in two unknowns is any pair of values (x, y) which satisfies both equations, graphically, *the solution would be the coordinates of the point of inter-section of the two lines.* This must be the case, for the coordinates of this point constitute the only pair of values to satisfy *both* equations. (In some special cases there may be no solution, in others there may be many solutions. See Examples D and E.)

Therefore, when we solve two simultaneous linear equations in two unknowns graphically, we must plot the graph of each line and determine the point of intersection. This may, of course, lead to approximate results if the lines cross at values between those chosen to determine the graph.

We may use the knowledge that each equation represents a straight line to advantage. By finding two points on the line, we can draw the line. Two points which are easily determined are those where the curve crosses the y-axis and the x-axis. These points are known as the **intercepts** of the line. These points are easily found because in each case one of the coordinates is zero. By setting $x = 0$ and $y = 0$, in turn, and determining the corresponding value of the other unknown, we obtain the coordinates of the intercepts. A third point should be found as a check. This method is sufficient unless the line passes through the origin. Then both intercepts are at the origin and one more point must be determined. Example A illustrates how a line is plotted by finding its intercepts.

Example A

Plot the graph of $2x - 3y = 6$ by finding its intercepts and one check point (see Fig. 4–2).

First let $x = 0$. This gives $-3y = 6$, or $y = -2$. Thus, the point $(0, -2)$ is on the graph. Next we let $y = 0$, and this gives $2x = 6$, or $x = 3$. Thus, the point $(3, 0)$ is on the graph. The point $(0, -2)$ is the y-intercept, and $(3, 0)$ is the x-intercept. These two points are sufficient to plot the line, but we should find another point as a check. Choosing $x = 1$, we find $y = -\frac{4}{3}$. Thus, the point $(1, -\frac{4}{3})$ should be on the line. From Fig. 4–2 we see that it is on the line.

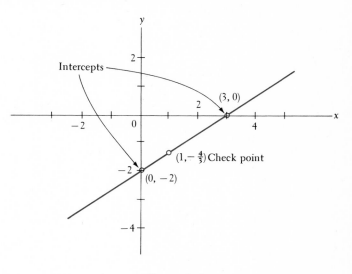

Figure 4–2

Now that we have discussed the meaning of a graphical solution of a system of simultaneous equations and the method of plotting a line, we are in a position to find graphical solutions of systems of linear equations. The following examples illustrate the method.

Example B
Solve the system of equations

$$2x + 5y = 10$$
$$3x - y = 6$$

We find that the intercepts of the first line are the points (5, 0) and (0, 2). A third point is $(-1, \frac{12}{5})$. The intercepts of the second line are (2, 0) and (0, −6). A third point is (1, −3). Plotting these points and drawing the proper straight lines, we see that the lines cross at about (2.3, 1.1). [The actual values are $(\frac{40}{17}, \frac{18}{17})$.] The solution of the system of equations is approximately $x = 2.3$, $y = 1.1$ (see Fig. 4–3).

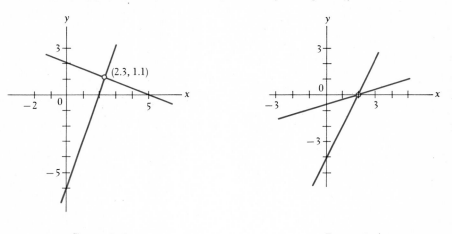

Figure 4–3   Figure 4–4

Example C
Solve the system of equations

$$x - 4y = 2$$
$$-2x + y = -4$$

The intercepts and a third point for the first line are (2, 0), (0, −0.5), and (6, 1). For the second line they are (2, 0), (0, −4), and (1, −2). Since they have one point in common, the point (2, 0), we conclude that the exact solution to the system is $x = 2$, $y = 0$ (see Fig. 4–4).

Example D
Solve the system of equations

$$x - 2y = 6$$
$$3x - 6y = 6$$

The intercepts and a third point for the first line are (6, 0), (0, −3), and (2, −2). For the second line they are (2, 0), (0, −1), and (4, 1). The graphs of these two equations do not intersect (see Fig. 4–5). *Therefore, there are no solutions. Such a system is called* inconsistent.

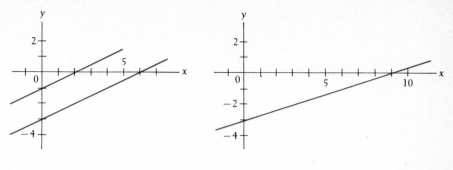

Figure 4–5   Figure 4–6

Example E
Solve the system of equations

$$x - 3y = \quad 9$$
$$-2x + 6y = -18$$

The intercepts and a third point for the first line are $(9, 0)$, $(0, -3)$, and $(3, -2)$. In determining the intercepts for the second line, we find that they are $(9, 0)$ and $(0, -3)$, which are also the intercepts of the first line (see Fig. 4–6). As a check we note that $(3, -2)$ also satisfies the equation of the second line. This means the two lines are really the same line, and *the coordinates of any point on this common line constitute a solution of the system. Such a system is called* **dependent**.

Exercises 4–2

In the following exercises solve each system of equations graphically. Estimate the answer to the nearest tenth of a unit if necessary.

1. $x + y = 4$
   $x - y = 2$

2. $x - 2y = 2$
   $x + y = 8$

3. $2x - y = 6$
   $x + 3y = 3$

4. $-x + 2y = -8$
   $2x - y = -2$

5. $3x + 2y = 6$
   $x - 3y = 3$

6. $4x - 3y = -8$
   $6x + y = 6$

7. $2x - 5y = 10$
   $3x + 4y = -12$

8. $-5x + 3y = 15$
   $2x + 7y = 14$

9. $x - 4y = 8$
   $2x + 5y = 10$

10. $4x - y = 6$
    $2x - y = -4$

11. $y = -x + 3$
    $4x = 6 - 2y$

12. $x - 6 = 6y$
    $y = 3 - 3x$

13. $x - 4y = 6$
    $-x + 2y = 4$

14. $x + y = 3$
    $3x - 2y = 14$

15. $-2x + 2y = 7$
    $4x - 2y = 1$

16. $2x - 3y = -5$
    $3x + 2y = 12$

17. $x - 4y = 2$
    $-2x + 3y = 3$

18. $x - 2y = 4$
    $3x + 2y = 7$

19. $8x - 7y = 3$
    $7y + x = 7$

20. $5x - 2y = 7$
    $3x + 4y = 8$

21. $x - 5y = 10$
    $2x - 10y = 20$

22. $18x - 3y = 7$
    $2y = 1 + 12x$

23. $y = 3x$
    $x - 2y = 6$

24. $4x - y = 3$
    $2x + 3y = 0$

25. $5x = y + 3$
$4x = 2y - 3$

26. $5x + 7y = 5$
$2x - 3y = 4$

27. $3x = 8y + 12$
$-6x + 16y = 6$

28. $y = 6x + 2$
$12x - 2y = -4$

29. The perimeter of a rectangular area is 24 km, and the length is 6 km longer than the width. The dimensions l and w can be found by solving the equations

$$2l + 2w = 24$$
$$l - w = 6$$

(Notice that the first equation represents the perimeter of this rectangle and the second equation represents the relationship of the length to the width.)

30. To assemble a particular piece of machinery, 18 bolts are used. There are two kinds of bolts, and 4 more of one kind are used than the other. The numbers of each kind, a and b, can be found by solving the equations

$$a + b = 18$$
$$a - b = 4$$

31. In electricity, applying Ohm's law to a particular circuit gives the equations needed to find a specified voltage E and current I (in amperes) as

$$E - 4I = 0$$
$$E + 6I = 9$$

32. A computer requires 12 s to do two series of calculations. The first series of calculations requires twice as much time as the second series. The times t_1 and t_2 can be found by solving the equations

$$t_1 + t_2 = 12$$
$$t_1 = 2t_2$$

4–3 Solving Systems of Two Linear Equations in Two Unknowns Algebraically

We have just seen how a system of two linear equations can be solved graphically. This technique is good for obtaining a "picture" of the solution. Finding the solution of systems of equations by graphical methods has one difficulty: the results are usually approximate. If exact solutions are required, we must turn to other methods. In this section we shall present two algebraic methods of solution.

The first method involves elimination by **substitution.** To follow this method, we first solve one of the equations for one of the unknowns. This solution is then substituted into the other equation, resulting in one linear equation in one unknown. This equation can then be solved for the unknown it contains. By substituting this value into one of the original equations, we can find the corresponding value of the other unknown. The following two examples illustrate the method.

Example A

Use the method of elimination by substitution to solve the system of equations

$$x - 3y = 6$$
$$2x + 3y = 3$$

The first step is to solve one of the equations for one of the unknowns. The choice of which equation and which unknown depends on ease of manipulation. In this system, it is somewhat easier to solve the first equation for x. Therefore, performing this operation we have

$$x = 3y + 6$$

We then substitute this expression into the second equation in place of x, giving

$$2(3y + 6) + 3y = 3$$

Solving this equation for y we obtain

$$6y + 12 + 3y = 3$$
$$9y = -9$$
$$y = -1$$

We now put the value $y = -1$ into the first of the original equations. Since we have already solved this equation for x in terms of y, we obtain

$$x = 3(-1) + 6 = 3$$

Therefore, the solution of the system is $x = 3$, $y = -1$. As a check, we substitute these values in the second equation. We obtain $2(3) + 3(-1) = 6 - 3 = 3$, which verifies the solution.

Example B

Use the method of elimination by substitution to solve the system of equations

$$-5x + 2y = -4$$
$$10x + 6y = 3$$

It makes little difference which equation or which unknown is chosen. Therefore, choosing to solve the first equation for y, we obtain

$$2y = 5x - 4$$
$$y = \frac{5x - 4}{2}$$

Substituting this expression into the second equation, we have

$$10x + 6\left(\frac{5x - 4}{2}\right) = 3$$

We now proceed to solve this equation for x.

$$10x + 3(5x - 4) = 3$$
$$10x + 15x - 12 = 3$$
$$25x = 15$$
$$x = \frac{3}{5}$$

Substituting this value into the expression for y, we obtain

$$y = \frac{5(3/5) - 4}{2} = \frac{3 - 4}{2} = -\frac{1}{2}$$

Therefore, the solution of this system is $x = \frac{3}{5}$, $y = -\frac{1}{2}$. Substituting these values in the second equation shows that the solution checks.

The method of elimination by substitution is useful if one equation can easily be solved for one of the unknowns. However, the numerical coefficients often make this method somewhat cumbersome. So we use another method, that of elimination by **addition or subtraction**. To use this method we multiply each equation by a number chosen so that the coefficients for one of the unknowns will be numerically the same in both equations. If these numerically equal coefficients are opposite in sign, we *add* the two equations. If the numerically equal coefficients have the same signs, we subtract one equation from the other. That is, we subtract the left side of one equation from the left side of the other equation, and also do the same to the right sides. After adding or subtracting, we have a simple linear equation in one unknown, which we then solve for the unknown. We substitute this value into one of the original equations to obtain the value of the other unknown.

Example C

Use the method of elimination by addition or subtraction to solve the system of equations

$$x - 3y = 6$$
$$2x + 3y = 3$$

We look at the coefficients to determine the best way to eliminate one of the unknowns. In this case, since the coefficients of the y-terms are numerically the same and are opposite in sign, we may immediately add the two equations to eliminate y. Adding the left sides together and the right sides together, we obtain

$$x + 2x - 3y + 3y = 6 + 3$$
$$3x = 9$$
$$x = 3$$

Substituting this value into the first equation, we obtain

$$3 - 3y = 6$$
$$-3y = 3$$
$$y = -1$$

The solution $x = 3$, $y = -1$ agrees with the results obtained for the same problem illustrated in Example A of this section.

Example D
Use the method of elimination by addition or subtraction to solve the system of equations

$$3x - 2y = 4$$
$$x + 3y = 2$$

Probably the most convenient method is to multiply the second equation by 3. Then subtract the second equation from the first and solve for y. Substitute this value of y into the second equation and solve for x.

$$3x - 2y = 4$$
$$\underline{3x + 9y = 6}$$
$$-11y = -2$$

$$y = \frac{2}{11}$$

$$x + 3\left(\frac{2}{11}\right) = 2$$

$$11x + 6 = 22$$

$$x = \frac{16}{11}$$

We arrive at the solution $x = \frac{16}{11}$, $y = \frac{2}{11}$. Substituting these values into both of the original equations shows that the solution checks.

Example E
The system of Example D can also be solved by multiplying the first equation by 3 and the second by 2, thereby first eliminating y.

$$9x - 6y = 12$$
$$\underline{2x + 6y = 4}$$
$$11x = 16 \qquad \text{Adding the equations}$$

$$x = \frac{16}{11}$$

$$3\left(\frac{16}{11}\right) - 2y = 4 \qquad \text{Substituting into the first of original equations}$$

$$48 - 22y = 44 \qquad \text{Multiplying each term by 11}$$
$$-22y = -4$$

$$y = \frac{2}{11}$$

Therefore, the solution is $x = \frac{16}{11}$, $y = \frac{2}{11}$, as we obtained in Example D.

Example F

Use the method of elimination by addition or subtraction to solve the system of equations

$$4x - 2y = 3$$
$$2x - y = 2$$

When we multiply the second equation by 2 and subtract, we obtain

$$
\begin{array}{rr}
4x - 2y = & 3 \\
4x - 2y = & 4 \\
\hline
0 = & -1
\end{array}
$$

Since we know 0 does not equal -1, we conclude that there is no solution. When we obtain a result of $0 = a$ ($a \neq 0$), the system of equations is inconsistent. If we obtain the result $0 = 0$, the system is dependent.

After solving systems of equations by these methods, it is always a good policy to check the results by substituting the values of the two unknowns into the other original equation to see that the values satisfy the equation. Remember, we are finding the one pair of values which satisfies both equations.

Linear equations in two unknowns are often useful in solving stated problems. In such problems we must read the statement carefully in order to identify the unknowns and the method of setting up the proper equations. Exercises 29, 30, and 32 of Section 4–2 give statements and the resulting equations, which the reader should be able to derive. The following example gives a complete illustration of the method.

Example G

By weight, one alloy is 70% copper and 30% zinc. Another alloy is 40% copper and 60% zinc. How many grams of each of these would be required to make 300 g of an alloy which is 60% copper and 40% zinc?

Let A = required number of grams of first alloy, and B = required number of grams of second alloy. We know that the total weight of the final alloy is 300 g, which leads us to the equation $A + B = 300$. We also know that the final alloy will contain 180 g of copper (60% of 300). The weight of copper from the first alloy is $0.70A$ and that from the second is $0.40B$. This leads to the equation $0.70A + 0.40B = 180$. These two equations can now be solved simultaneously.

$$
\begin{array}{r}
A + B = 300 \\
0.70A + 0.40B = 180
\end{array}
$$

$4A + 4B = 1200$	Multiplying the first equation by 4
$\underline{7A + 4B = 1800}$	Multiplying the second equation by 10
$3A = 600$	Subtracting the first equation from the second
$A = 200$ g	
$B = 100$ g	By substituting into the first equation

Substitution shows that this solution checks with the given information.

Exercises 4-3

In Exercises 1 through 12 solve the given systems of equations by the method of elimination by substitution.

1. $x = y + 3$
$x - 2y = 5$

2. $x = 2y + 1$
$2x - 3y = 4$

3. $y = x - 4$
$x + y = 10$

4. $y = 2x + 10$
$2x + y = -2$

5. $x + y = -5$
$2x - y = 2$

6. $3x + y = 1$
$3x - 2y = 16$

7. $2x + 3y = 7$
$6x - y = 1$

8. $2x + 2y = 1$
$4x - 2y = 17$

9. $3x + 2y = 7$
$-9x + 2y = 11$

10. $3x + 3y = -1$
$-5x - 6y = 1$

11. $4x - 3y = 6$
$2x + 4y = -5$

12. $5x + 4y = -7$
$3x - 5y = -6$

In Exercises 13 through 24 solve the given systems of equations by the method of elimination by addition or subtraction.

13. $x + 2y = 5$
$x - 2y = 1$

14. $x + 3y = 7$
$2x + 3y = 5$

15. $2x - 3y = 4$
$2x + y = -4$

16. $x - 4y = 17$
$3x + 4y = 3$

17. $2x + 3y = 8$
$x - 2y = -3$

18. $3x - y = 3$
$4x - 3y = 14$

19. $x + 2y = 7$
$2x + 4y = 9$

20. $3x - y = 5$
$-9x + 3y = -15$

21. $2x - 3y = 4$
$3x - 2y = -2$

22. $3x + 4y = -5$
$5x - 3y = 2$

23. $3x - 7y = 4$
$2x + 5y = 7$

24. $5x + 2y = -4$
$3x - 5y = 6$

In Exercises 25 through 32 solve the given systems of equations by either method of this section.

25. $2x - y = 5$
$6x + 2y = -5$

26. $3x + 2y = 4$
$6x - 6y = 13$

27. $6x + 3y = -4$
$9x + 5y = -6$

28. $5x - 6y = 1$
$3x - 4y = 7$

29. $3x - 6y = 15$
$4x - 8y = 20$

30. $2x + 6y = -3$
$-6x - 18y = 5$

31. $7x + y = -9$
$3x + 4y = -11$

32. $6x + 6y = -7$
$3x - 12y = 13$

In Exercises 33 and 34 solve the given systems of equations by an appropriate algebraic method.

33. An electrical experiment results in the following equations for currents (in amperes) i_1 and i_2 of a certain circuit:

$$i_1 = 3i_2$$
$$4i_1 - 2i_2 = 5$$

Find i_1 and i_2.

34. In finding moments M_1 and M_2 (in foot-pounds) of certain forces acting on a given beam, the following equations are used:

$$10M_1 + 3M_2 = -140$$
$$4M_1 + 14M_2 = -564$$

Find M_1 and M_2.

In Exercises 35 through 42 set up appropriate systems of two linear equations in two unknowns, and solve the systems algebraically.

$$x + \left(x + 3\right) = 18 m$$

$$x + y = 16$$
$$4x + 3y = 52$$

35. A piece of wire is 18 m long. Where must it be cut for one piece to be 3 m longer than the other piece?

36. The voltage across an electric resistor equals the current times the resistance. The sum of two resistances is 16 Ω. When a current of 4 A passes through the smaller resistance and 3 A through the larger resistance, the sum of the voltages is 52 V. What is the value of each resistance?

37. One electronic data-processing card sorter can sort a cards per minute, and a second card sorter can sort b cards per minute. If the first sorts for 3 min and the second for 2 min, 12,200 cards can be sorted. If the times are reversed, 11,300 cards can be sorted. Find the sorting rates a and b.

38. An airplane travels 1860 mi in 2 h with the wind and then returns in 2.5 h traveling against the wind. Find the speed of the airplane with respect to the air and the velocity of the wind.

$$20\%x + \left(180-x\right)8\% = 180 \times 15$$

39. A chemist has a 20% solution and an 8% solution of sulfuric acid. How many milliliters of each solution should he mix in order to obtain 180 mL of a 15% solution?

40. For proper dosage a drug must be a 10% solution. How many milliliters of a 5% solution and of a 25% solution should be mixed to obtain 1000 mL of the required solution?

41. The cost of booklets at a printing firm consists of a fixed charge and a charge for each booklet. The total cost of 1000 booklets is $550, and the total cost of 2000 booklets is $800. What is the fixed charge and the charge for each booklet?

42. Analyze the following statement from a student's laboratory report. "The sum of the currents was 10 A, and twice the first current was 3 A less twice the second current."

4–4 Solving Systems of Two Linear Equations in Two Unknowns by Determinants

Consider two linear equations in two unknowns,

$$a_1x + b_1y = c_1$$
$$a_2x + b_2y = c_2 \tag{4–3}$$

If we multiply the first of these equations by b_2 and the second by b_1, we obtain

$$a_1b_2x + b_1b_2y = c_1b_2$$
$$a_2b_1x + b_2b_1y = c_2b_1 \tag{4–4}$$

If we now subtract the second equation of (4–4) from the first, we obtain

$$a_1b_2x - a_2b_1x = c_1b_2 - c_2b_1$$

which by use of the distributive law may be written as

$$(a_1b_2 - a_2b_1)x = c_1b_2 - c_2b_1 \tag{4-5}$$

Solving Eq. (4–5) for x, we obtain

$$x = \frac{c_1b_2 - c_2b_1}{a_1b_2 - a_2b_1} \tag{4-6}$$

In the same manner, we may show that

$$y = \frac{a_1c_2 - a_2c_1}{a_1b_2 - a_2b_1} \tag{4-7}$$

If the denominator $a_1b_2 - a_2b_1 = 0$, there is no solution for Eqs. (4–6) and (4–7), since division by zero is not defined.

The expression $a_1b_2 - a_2b_1$, which appears in each of the denominators of Eqs. (4–6) and (4–7), is an example of a special kind of expression called a **determinant of the second order.** The determinant $a_1b_2 - a_2b_1$ is denoted by the symbol

$$\begin{vmatrix} a_1 & b_1 \\ a_2 & b_2 \end{vmatrix}$$

Thus, by definition, a determinant of the second order is given by

$$\begin{vmatrix} a_1 & b_1 \\ a_2 & b_2 \end{vmatrix} = a_1b_2 - a_2b_1 \tag{4-8}$$

The numbers a_1 and b_1 are called the **elements** of the first **row** of the determinant. The numbers a_1 and a_2 are the elements of the first **column** of the determinant. In the same manner, the numbers a_2 and b_2 are the elements of the second row, and the numbers b_1 and b_2 are the elements of the second column. The numbers a_1 and b_2 are the elements of the **principal diagonal,** and the numbers a_2 and b_1 are the elements of the **secondary diagonal.** Thus, one way of stating the definition indicated in Eq. (4–8) is that *the value of a determinant of the second order is found by taking the product of the elements of the principal diagonal and subtracting the product of the elements of the secondary diagonal.*

A diagram which is often helpful for remembering the expansion of a second-order determinant is shown in Fig. 4–7. The following examples illustrate how we carry out the evaluation of determinants.

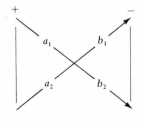

Figure 4—7

Example A

$$\begin{vmatrix} 1 & 4 \\ 3 & 2 \end{vmatrix} = 1(2) - 3(4) = 2 - 12 = -10$$

Example B

$$\begin{vmatrix} -5 & 8 \\ 3 & 7 \end{vmatrix} = (-5)(7) - 3(8) = -35 - 24 = -59$$

Example C

$$\begin{vmatrix} 4 & 6 \\ -3 & 17 \end{vmatrix} = 4(17) - (-3)(6) = 68 + 18 = 86$$

We note that the numerators of Eqs. (4–6) and (4–7) may also be written as determinants. The numerators of Eqs. (4–6) and (4–7) are

$$\begin{vmatrix} c_1 & b_1 \\ c_2 & b_2 \end{vmatrix} \quad \text{and} \quad \begin{vmatrix} a_1 & c_1 \\ a_2 & c_2 \end{vmatrix} \tag{4–9}$$

Therefore, the solutions for x and y of the system of equations (4–3) may be written directly in terms of determinants, without any algebraic operations, as

$$x = \frac{\begin{vmatrix} c_1 & b_1 \\ c_2 & b_2 \end{vmatrix}}{\begin{vmatrix} a_1 & b_1 \\ a_2 & b_2 \end{vmatrix}} \quad \text{and} \quad y = \frac{\begin{vmatrix} a_1 & c_1 \\ a_2 & c_2 \end{vmatrix}}{\begin{vmatrix} a_1 & b_1 \\ a_2 & b_2 \end{vmatrix}} \tag{4–10}$$

For this reason determinants provide a very quick and easy method of solution of systems of equations. Here again the denominator of each of Eqs. (4–10) is the same. *The determinant of the denominator is made up of the coefficients of x and y.* Also, we can see that *the determinant of the numerator of the solution for x may be obtained by replacing the column of a's by the column of c's. The numerator of the solution for y may be obtained from the determinant of the denominator by replacing the column of b's by the column of c's.* This result is often referred to as **Cramer's rule.**

The following examples illustrate the method of solving systems of equations by determinants.

Example D
Solve the following system of equations by determinants:

$$2x + y = 1$$
$$5x - 2y = -11$$

First we set up the determinant for the denominator. This consists of the four coefficients in the system written as shown. Therefore, the determinant of the denominator is

$$\begin{vmatrix} 2 & 1 \\ 5 & -2 \end{vmatrix}$$

For finding x, the determinant in the numerator is obtained from this determinant by replacing the first column by the constants which appear on the right sides of the equations. Thus, the numerator for the solution for x is

$$\begin{vmatrix} 1 & 1 \\ -11 & -2 \end{vmatrix}$$

For finding y, the determinant in the numerator is obtained from the determinant of the denominator by replacing the second column by the constants which appear on the right sides of the equations. Thus, the determinant for the numerator for finding y is

$$\begin{vmatrix} 2 & 1 \\ 5 & -11 \end{vmatrix}$$

Now we set up the solutions for x and y using the determinants above.

$$x = \frac{\begin{vmatrix} 1 & 1 \\ -11 & -2 \end{vmatrix}}{\begin{vmatrix} 2 & 1 \\ 5 & -2 \end{vmatrix}} = \frac{1(-2) - (-11)(1)}{2(-2) - (5)(1)} = \frac{-2 + 11}{-4 - 5} = \frac{9}{-9} = -1$$

$$y = \frac{\begin{vmatrix} 2 & 1 \\ 5 & -11 \end{vmatrix}}{\begin{vmatrix} 2 & 1 \\ 5 & -2 \end{vmatrix}} = \frac{2(-11) - (5)(1)}{-9} = \frac{-22 - 5}{-9} = 3$$

Therefore, the solution to the system of equations is $x = -1$, $y = 3$.

Since the determinant in the denominators is the same, it needs to be evaluated only once. This means that three determinants are to be evaluated in order to solve the system.

Example E
Solve the following system of equations by determinants:

$$\begin{aligned} x - y &= 4 \\ 2x + y &= 11 \end{aligned}$$

$$x = \frac{\begin{vmatrix} 4 & -1 \\ 11 & 1 \end{vmatrix}}{\begin{vmatrix} 1 & -1 \\ 2 & 1 \end{vmatrix}} = \frac{4 - (-11)}{1 - (-2)} = 5 \qquad y = \frac{\begin{vmatrix} 1 & 4 \\ 2 & 11 \end{vmatrix}}{\begin{vmatrix} 1 & -1 \\ 2 & 1 \end{vmatrix}} = \frac{11 - 8}{3} = 1$$

Therefore, the solution is $x = 5$, $y = 1$.

Example F
Solve the following system of equations by determinants:

$$5x + 7y = 4$$
$$3x - 6y = 5$$

$$x = \frac{\begin{vmatrix} 4 & 7 \\ 5 & -6 \end{vmatrix}}{\begin{vmatrix} 5 & 7 \\ 3 & -6 \end{vmatrix}} = \frac{-24 - 35}{-30 - 21} = \frac{59}{51}$$

$$y = \frac{\begin{vmatrix} 5 & 4 \\ 3 & 5 \end{vmatrix}}{\begin{vmatrix} 5 & 7 \\ 3 & -6 \end{vmatrix}} = \frac{25 - 12}{-51} = -\frac{13}{51}$$

Therefore, the solution is $x = \frac{59}{51}$, $y = -\frac{13}{51}$.

Example G
Two investments totaling $18,000 yield an annual income of $700. If the first investment has an interest rate of 5.5% and the second a rate of 3.0%, what is the value of each of the investments?

Let $x =$ the value of the first investment, and $y =$ the value of the second investment. We know that the total of the two investments is $18,000. This leads to the equation $x + y = 18,000$. The first investment yields $0.055x$ dollars annually, and the second yields $0.03y$ dollars annually. This leads to the equation $0.055x + 0.03y = 700$. These two equations are then solved simultaneously.

$$x + y = 18,000$$
$$0.055x + 0.030y = 700$$

$$x = \frac{\begin{vmatrix} 18,000 & 1 \\ 700 & 0.03 \end{vmatrix}}{\begin{vmatrix} 1 & 1 \\ 0.055 & 0.03 \end{vmatrix}} = \frac{540 - 700}{0.03 - 0.055} = \frac{160}{0.025} = 6400$$

The value of y can be found most easily by substituting this value of x into the first equation.

$$y = 18,000 - x = 18,000 - 6400 = 11,600$$

Therefore, the values invested are $6400 and $11,600, respectively.

Some other points should be made here. The equations must be in the form of Eqs. (4–3) before the determinants are set up. This is because the equations for the solutions in terms of determinants are based on that form of writing the system. Also, if either of the unknowns is missing from either equation, its coefficient is taken as zero, and zero is put in the appropriate position in that determinant. Finally, if the determinant of the denominator is zero, and that of the numerator is not zero, the system is inconsistent. If determinants of both numerator and denominator are zero, the system is dependent.

Exercises 4—4

In Exercises 1 through 12 evaluate the given determinants.

1. $\begin{vmatrix} 2 & 4 \\ 3 & 1 \end{vmatrix}$

2. $\begin{vmatrix} -1 & 3 \\ 2 & 6 \end{vmatrix}$

3. $\begin{vmatrix} 3 & -5 \\ 7 & -2 \end{vmatrix}$

4. $\begin{vmatrix} -4 & 7 \\ 1 & -3 \end{vmatrix}$

5. $\begin{vmatrix} 8 & -10 \\ 0 & 4 \end{vmatrix}$

6. $\begin{vmatrix} -4 & -3 \\ 9 & -2 \end{vmatrix}$

7. $\begin{vmatrix} -2 & 11 \\ -7 & -8 \end{vmatrix}$

8. $\begin{vmatrix} -6 & 12 \\ -15 & 3 \end{vmatrix}$

9. $\begin{vmatrix} 7 & -13 \\ 1 & 10 \end{vmatrix}$

10. $\begin{vmatrix} 20 & -5 \\ 28 & 9 \end{vmatrix}$

11. $\begin{vmatrix} 16 & -8 \\ 42 & -15 \end{vmatrix}$

12. $\begin{vmatrix} 43 & -7 \\ -81 & 16 \end{vmatrix}$

In Exercises 13 through 32 solve the given systems of equations by use of determinants. (These systems are the same as those for Exercises 13 through 32 of Section 4–3.)

13. $x + 2y = 5$
    $x - 2y = 1$

14. $x + 3y = 7$
    $2x + 3y = 5$

15. $2x - 3y = 4$
    $2x + y = -4$

16. $x - 4y = 17$
    $3x + 4y = 3$

17. $2x + 3y = 8$
    $x - 2y = -3$

18. $3x - y = 3$
    $4x - 3y = 14$

19. $x + 2y = 7$
    $2x + 4y = 9$

20. $3x - y = 5$
    $-9x + 3y = -15$

21. $2x - 3y = 4$
    $3x - 2y = -2$

22. $3x + 4y = -5$
    $5x - 3y = 2$

23. $3x - 7y = 4$
    $2x + 5y = 7$

24. $5x + 2y = -4$
    $3x - 5y = 6$

25. $2x - y = 5$
    $6x + 2y = -5$

26. $3x + 2y = 4$
    $6x - 6y = 13$

27. $6x + 3y = -4$
    $9x + 5y = -6$

28. $5x - 6y = 1$
    $3x - 4y = 7$

29. $3x - 6y = 15$
    $4x - 8y = 20$

30. $2x + 6y = -3$
    $-6x - 18y = 5$

31. $7x + y = -9$
    $3x + 4y = -11$

32. $6x + 6y = -7$
    $3x - 12y = 13$

In Exercises 33 and 34 solve the given systems of equations by use of determinants.

33. An object traveling at a constant velocity v (in feet per second) is 25 ft from a certain reference point after one second, and 35 ft from it after two seconds. Its initial distance s_0 from the reference point and its velocity can be found by solving the equations

$$s_0 + v = 25$$
$$s_0 + 2v = 35$$

Find s_0 and v.

34. When determining two forces F_1 and F_2 acting on a certain object, the following equations are obtained:

$$0.500F_1 + 0.600F_2 = 10$$
$$0.866F_1 - 0.800F_2 = 20$$

Find F_1 and F_2 (in newtons).

In Exercises 35 through 40 set up appropriate systems of two linear equations in two unknowns and then solve the system by use of determinants.

35. Two meshing gears together have 89 teeth. One of the gears has 4 less than twice the number of teeth of the other gear. How many teeth does each gear have?

36. A rocket is launched so that it averages 3000 mi/h. An hour later, another rocket is launched along the same path at an average speed of 4500 mi/h. Find the times of flight, t_1 and t_2, of the rockets when the second rocket overtakes the first.

37. A total of $8000 is invested, part at 3% and the remainder at 5%. Find the amount invested at each rate if the total annual income is $388.

38. A roof truss is in the shape of an isosceles triangle. The perimeter of the truss is 41 m, and the base is 5 m longer than a rafter (neglecting overhang). Find the length of the base and the length of a rafter.

39. The resistance of a certain wire as a function of temperature can be found from the following equation: $R = \alpha T + \beta$. If the resistance is 0.4 Ω at 20°C and 0.5 Ω at 80°C, find α and β, and then the resistance as a function of temperature.

40. The velocity of sound in steel is 15,900 ft/s faster than the velocity of sound in air. One end of a long steel bar is struck and an observer at the other end measures the time it takes for the sound to reach him. He finds that the sound through the bar takes 0.012 s to reach him and that the sound through the air takes 0.180 s. What are the velocities of sound in air and in steel?

4–5 Solving Systems of Three Linear Equations in Three Unknowns Algebraically

Many problems involve the solution of systems of linear equations which involve three, four, and occasionally even more unknowns. Solving such systems algebraically or by determinants is essentially the same as solving systems of two linear equations in two unknowns. Graphical solutions are not used, since a linear equation in three unknowns represents a plane in space. In this section we shall discuss the algebraic method of solving a system of three linear equations in three unknowns.

A system of three linear equations in three unknowns written in the form

$$
\begin{array}{l}
a_1x + b_1y + c_1z = d_1 \\
a_2x + b_2y + c_2z = d_2 \\
a_3x + b_3y + c_3z = d_3
\end{array}
\qquad (4\text{--}11)
$$

has as its solution the set of values x, y, and z which satisfy all three equations simultaneously. The method of solution involves multiplying *two* of the equations by the proper numbers to eliminate *one* of the unknowns between these equations. We then repeat this process, using a *different pair* of the original equations, being sure that we eliminate the same unknown as we did between the first pair of equations. At this point we have two linear equations in two unknowns which can be solved by any of the methods previously discussed. The unknown originally eliminated may then be found by substitution into one of the original equations. It is wise to check these three values in one of the other original equations.

Example A
Solve the following system of equations:

$$(1) \qquad x + 2y - z = -5$$
$$(2) \qquad 2x - y + 2z = 8$$
$$(3) \qquad 3x + 3y + 4z = 5$$

$$(4) \qquad 2x + 4y - 2z = -10 \qquad \text{(1) multiplied by 2}$$
$$ \qquad \underline{2x - y + 2z = 8} \qquad \text{(2)}$$
$$(5) \qquad 4x + 3y = -2 \qquad \text{Adding (4) and (2)}$$

$$(6) \qquad 4x - 2y + 4z = 16 \qquad \text{(2) multiplied by 2}$$
$$ \qquad \underline{3x + 3y + 4z = 5} \qquad \text{(3)}$$
$$(7) \qquad x - 5y = 11 \qquad \text{Subtracting}$$

$$ \qquad 4x + 3y = -2 \qquad \text{(5)}$$
$$(8) \qquad \underline{4x - 20y = 44} \qquad \text{(7) multiplied by 4}$$
$$(9) \qquad 23y = -46 \qquad \text{Subtracting}$$
$$(10) \qquad y = -2$$

$$(11) \qquad x - 5(-2) = 11 \qquad \text{Substituting (10) in (7)}$$
$$(12) \qquad x = 1$$

$$(13) \qquad 1 + 2(-2) - z = -5 \qquad \text{Substituting (12) and (10) in (1)}$$
$$(14) \qquad z = 2$$

To check, we substitute the solution $x = 1$, $y = -2$, $z = 2$ in (2).

$$2(1) - (-2) + 2(2) \stackrel{?}{=} 8$$
$$8 = 8 \quad \text{(It checks.)}$$

It should be noted that Eqs. (1), (2), and (3) could be solved just as well by eliminating y between (1) and (2), and then again between (1) and (3). We would than have two equations to solve in x and z. Also, z could have been eliminated between Eqs. (1) and (3) to obtain the second equation in x and y.

Example B

Solve the following system of equations:

$$\text{(1)} \qquad 4x + y + 3z = 1$$
$$\text{(2)} \qquad 2x - 2y + 6z = 11$$
$$\text{(3)} \qquad -6x + 3y + 12z = -4$$

(4) $\quad 8x + 2y + 6z = 2 \qquad$ (1) multiplied by 2

$\qquad \dfrac{2x - 2y + 6z = 11}{} \qquad$ (2)

(5) $\quad 10x + 12z = 13 \qquad$ Adding

(6) $\quad 12x + 3y + 9z = 3 \qquad$ (1) multiplied by 3

$\qquad \dfrac{-6x + 3y + 12z = -4}{} \qquad$ (3)

(7) $\quad 18x - 3z = 7 \qquad$ Subtracting

$\qquad 10x + 12z = 13 \qquad$ (5)

(8) $\qquad \dfrac{72x - 12z = 28}{} \qquad$ (7) multiplied by 4

(9) $\qquad 82x = 41 \qquad$ Adding

(10) $\qquad x = \dfrac{1}{2}$

(11) $\qquad 18\left(\dfrac{1}{2}\right) - 3z = 7 \qquad$ Substituting (10) in (7)

(12) $\qquad -3z = -2$

(13) $\qquad z = \dfrac{2}{3}$

(14) $\quad 4\left(\dfrac{1}{2}\right) + y + 3\left(\dfrac{2}{3}\right) = 1 \qquad$ Substituting (13) and (10) in (1)

(15) $\qquad 2 + y + 2 = 1$

(16) $\qquad y = -3$

Therefore, the solution is $x = \frac{1}{2}$, $y = -3$, $z = \frac{2}{3}$. Checking the solution in (2) we have $2(\frac{1}{2}) - 2(-3) + 6(\frac{2}{3}) = 1 + 6 + 4 = 11$.

Example C

Three forces F_1, F_2, and F_3 are acting on a beam. Find the forces (in pounds). The forces are determined by solving the following equations:

$$\text{(1)} \qquad F_1 + F_2 + F_3 = 25$$
$$\text{(2)} \qquad F_1 + 2F_2 + 3F_3 = 59$$
$$\text{(3)} \qquad 2F_1 + 2F_2 - F_3 = 5$$

(4) $\quad 3F_1 + 3F_2 + 3F_3 = 75 \qquad$ (1) multiplied by 3

$\qquad \dfrac{F_1 + 2F_2 + 3F_3 = 59}{} \qquad$ (2)

(5) $\quad 2F_1 + F_2 = 16 \qquad$ Subtracting

$$(6) \quad 3F_1 + 3F_2 \qquad\quad = 30 \qquad \text{(1) added to (3)}$$

$$(7) \quad \frac{2F_1 + \; F_2 \qquad\quad = 16}{F_1 + F_2 \qquad\quad = 10} \qquad \begin{array}{l}\text{(5)}\\ \text{(6) divided by 3}\end{array}$$
$$(8) \quad F_1 \qquad\qquad\quad = 6 \qquad \text{Subtracting}$$

$$(9) \qquad\qquad 6 + F_2 = 10 \qquad \text{(8) substituted in (7)}$$
$$(10) \qquad\qquad\quad F_2 = \; 4$$

$$(11) \qquad 6 + 4 + F_3 = 25 \qquad \text{Substituting (8) and (10) in (1)}$$
$$(12) \qquad\qquad\quad F_3 = 15$$

Therefore, the three forces are 6 lb, 4 lb, and 15 lb, respectively. This solution can be checked by substituting in Eq. (2) or Eq. (3).

Example D

A triangle has a perimeter of 37 in. The longest side is 3 in. longer than the next longest, which in turn is 8 in. longer than the shortest side. Find the length of each side.

Let a = length of the longest side, b = length of the next-longest side, and c = length of the shortest side. Since the perimeter is 37 in., we have $a + b + c = 37$. The statement of the problem also leads to the equations $a = b + 3$ and $b = c + 8$. These equations are then put into standard form and solved simultaneously.

$$(1) \quad a + \; b + c = 37$$
$$(2) \quad a - \; b \qquad\;\; = 3 \qquad \text{Rewriting the second equation}$$
$$(3) \quad \frac{\qquad\;\; b - c = \; 8}{a + 2b \qquad\; = 45} \qquad \begin{array}{l}\text{Rewriting the third equation}\\ \text{Adding (1) and (3)}\end{array}$$
$$(4) \quad a + 2b \qquad\; = 45$$
$$(5) \quad \frac{a - \; b \qquad\;\; = \; 3}{3b \qquad\quad = 42} \qquad \begin{array}{l}\text{(2)}\\ \text{Subtracting}\end{array}$$
$$(6) \qquad\qquad b = 14$$

$$(7) \qquad a - 14 = \; 3 \qquad \text{Substituting (6) in (2)}$$
$$(8) \qquad\qquad a = 17$$

$$(9) \qquad 14 - c = \; 8 \qquad \text{Substituting (6) in (3)}$$
$$(10) \qquad\qquad c = \; 6$$

Therefore, the three sides of the triangle are 17 in., 14 in., and 6 in.

Checking the solution, the sum of the lengths of the three sides is 17 in. + 14 in. + 6 in. = 37 in., and the perimeter was given to be 37 in.

For systems of equations with more than three unknowns, the solution is found in a manner similar to that used with three unknowns. For example, with four unknowns one of the unknowns is eliminated between three different pairs of equations. The result is three equations in the remaining three unknowns. The solution then follows the procedure used with three unknowns.

Exercises 4—5

In Exercises 1 through 16 solve the given systems of equations.

1. $x + y + z = 2$
$x - z = 1$
$x + y = 1$

2. $x + y - z = -3$
$x + z = 2$
$2x - y + 2z = 3$

3. $2x + 3y + z = 2$
$-x + 2y + 3z = -1$
$-3x - 3y + z = 0$

4. $2x + y - z = 4$
$4x - 3y - 2z = -2$
$8x - 2y - 3z = 3$

5. $5x + 6y - 3z = 6$
$4x - 7y - 2z = -3$
$3x + y - 7z = 1$

6. $3r + s - t = 2$
$r - 2s + t = 0$
$4r - s + t = 3$

7. $2x - 2y + 3z = 5$
$2x + y - 2z = -1$
$4x - y - 3z = 0$

8. $2u + 2v + 3w = 0$
$3u + v + 4w = 21$
$-u - 3v + 7w = 15$

9. $3x - 7y + 3z = 6$
$3x + 3y + 6z = 1$
$5x - 5y + 2z = 5$

10. $8x + y + z = 1$
$7x - 2y + 9z = -3$
$4x - 6y + 8z = -5$

11. $x + 2y + 2z = 0$
$2x + 6y - 3z = -1$
$4x - 3y + 6z = -8$

12. $3x + 3y + z = 6$
$2x + 2y - z = 9$
$4x + 2y - 3z = 16$

13. $2x + 3y - 5z = 7$
$4x - 3y - 2z = 1$
$8x - y + 4z = 3$

14. $2x - 4y - 4z = 3$
$3x + 8y + 2z = -11$
$4x + 6y - z = -8$

15. $r - s - 3t - u = 1$
$2r + 4s - 2u = 2$
$3r + 4s - 2t = 0$
$r + 2t - 3u = 3$

16. $3x + 2y - 4z + 2t = 3$
$5x - 3y - 5z + 6t = 8$
$2x - y + 3z - 2t = 1$
$-2x + 3y + 2z - 3t = -2$

In Exercises 17 through 20 solve the given problems.

17. Show that the following system of equations has an unlimited number of solutions, and find one of them.

$$x - 2y - 3z = 2$$
$$x - 4y - 13z = 14$$
$$-3x + 5y + 4z = 0$$

18. Show that the following system of equations has no solution.

$$x - 2y - 3z = 2$$
$$x - 4y - 13z = 14$$
$$-3x + 5y + 4z = 2$$

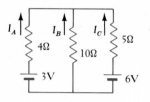

Figure 4—8

19. In applying Kirchhoff's laws (e.g., see Beiser, *Modern Technical Physics*, second ed., p. 445) to the electric circuit shown in Fig. 4—8, the following equations are found. Determine the indicated currents. (In Fig. 4—8, *I* signifies current, in amperes).

$$I_A + I_B + I_C = 0$$
$$4I_A - 10I_B = 3$$
$$- 10I_B + 5I_C = 6$$

20. In a laboratory experiment to measure the acceleration of an object, the distances traveled by the object were recorded for three time intervals. These data led to the following equations:

$$s_0 + 2v_0 + 2a = 20$$
$$s_0 + 4v_0 + 8a = 54$$
$$s_0 + 6v_0 + 18a = 104$$

Here s_0 is the initial displacement (in feet), v_0 is the initial velocity (in feet per second), and a is the acceleration (in feet per second squared). Find s_0, v_0, and a.

In Exercises 21 through 24 set up systems of three linear equations and solve for the indicated quantities.

21. Three machines together produce 64 parts each hour. Three times the production of the first machine equals the production of the other two machines together. Five times the production of the second is 12 parts per hour more than twice the rate of the other two together. Find the production rates of the three machines.

22. Angle A of a triangle equals 20° less than the sum of angles B and C. (The triangle is not a right triangle.) Angle B is one-fifth the sum of angles A and C. Find the angles.

23. By volume, one alloy is 60% copper, 30% zinc, and 10% nickel. A second alloy has percentages 50, 30, and 20, respectively, of the three metals. A third alloy is 30% copper and 70% nickel. How much of each must be mixed so that 100 cm³ of the resulting alloy has percentages of 40, 15, and 45, respectively?

24. The budget of a certain corporation for three positions in a given department is $70,000. Position A pays as much as the other two positions together, and position A pays $5,000 more than twice position C. What do the three positions pay?

4–6 Solving Systems of Three Linear Equations in Three Unknowns by Determinants

Just as systems of two linear equations in two unknowns can be solved by the use of determinants, so can systems of three linear equations in three unknowns. The system as given in Eqs. (4–11) can be solved in general terms by the method of elimination by addition or subtraction. This leads to the following solutions for x, y, and z.

$$x = \frac{d_1 b_2 c_3 + d_3 b_1 c_2 + d_2 b_3 c_1 - d_3 b_2 c_1 - d_1 b_3 c_2 - d_2 b_1 c_3}{a_1 b_2 c_3 + a_3 b_1 c_2 + a_2 b_3 c_1 - a_3 b_2 c_1 - a_1 b_3 c_2 - a_2 b_1 c_3}$$

$$y = \frac{a_1 d_2 c_3 + a_3 d_1 c_2 + a_2 d_3 c_1 - a_3 d_2 c_1 - a_1 d_3 c_2 - a_2 d_1 c_3}{a_1 b_2 c_3 + a_3 b_1 c_2 + a_2 b_3 c_1 - a_3 b_2 c_1 - a_1 b_3 c_2 - a_2 b_1 c_3} \qquad (4\text{–}12)$$

$$z = \frac{a_1 b_2 d_3 + a_3 b_1 d_2 + a_2 b_3 d_1 - a_3 b_2 d_1 - a_1 b_3 d_2 - a_2 b_1 d_3}{a_1 b_2 c_3 + a_3 b_1 c_2 + a_2 b_3 c_1 - a_3 b_2 c_1 - a_1 b_3 c_2 - a_2 b_1 c_3}$$

The expression that appears in each of the denominators of Eqs. (4–12) is an example of a **determinant of the third order**. This determinant is denoted by the symbol

$$\begin{vmatrix} a_1 & b_1 & c_1 \\ a_2 & b_2 & c_2 \\ a_3 & b_3 & c_3 \end{vmatrix}$$

Therefore, a determinant of the third order is defined by the equation

$$\begin{vmatrix} a_1 & b_1 & c_1 \\ a_2 & b_2 & c_2 \\ a_3 & b_3 & c_3 \end{vmatrix} = a_1 b_2 c_3 + a_3 b_1 c_2 + a_2 b_3 c_1 - a_3 b_2 c_1 - a_1 b_3 c_2 - a_2 b_1 c_3 \qquad (4\text{–}13)$$

The elements, rows, columns, and diagonals of a third-order determinant are defined just as are those of a second-order determinant. For example, the principal diagonal is made up of the elements a_1, b_2, and c_3.

Probably the easiest way of remembering the method of determining the value of a third-order determinant is as follows (this method does *not* work for determinants of order higher than three): *Rewrite the first and second columns to the right of the determinant. The products of the elements of the principal diagonal and the two parallel diagonals to the right of it are then added. The products of the elements of the secondary diagonal and the two parallel diagonals to the right of it are subtracted from the first sum. The algebraic sum of these six products gives the value of the determinant (see Fig. 4–9).* Examples A through C illustrate the evaluation of third-order determinants.

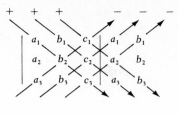

Figure 4—9

Example A

$$\begin{vmatrix} 1 & 5 & 4 \\ -2 & 3 & -1 \\ 2 & -1 & 5 \end{vmatrix} \begin{matrix} 1 & 5 \\ -2 & 3 \\ 2 & -1 \end{matrix} = 15 + (-10) + (+8) - (24) - (1) - (-50) = 38$$

Example B

$$\begin{vmatrix} -1 & 4 & -5 \\ 6 & 1 & 0 \\ 9 & -7 & 3 \end{vmatrix} \begin{matrix} -1 & 4 \\ 6 & 1 \\ 9 & -7 \end{matrix} = (-3) + 0 + 210 - (-45) - 0 - 72 = 180$$

Example C

$$\begin{vmatrix} 3 & -2 & 8 \\ -5 & 5 & -2 \\ 4 & 9 & -6 \end{vmatrix} \begin{matrix} 3 & -2 \\ -5 & 5 \\ 4 & 9 \end{matrix} = (-90) + 16 + (-360) - 160 - (-54) \\ - (-60) = -480$$

Inspection of Eqs. (4–12) reveals that the numerators of these solutions may also be written in terms of determinants. Thus, we may write the general solution to a system of three equations in three unknowns as

$$x = \frac{\begin{vmatrix} d_1 & b_1 & c_1 \\ d_2 & b_2 & c_2 \\ d_3 & b_3 & c_3 \end{vmatrix}}{\begin{vmatrix} a_1 & b_1 & c_1 \\ a_2 & b_2 & c_2 \\ a_3 & b_3 & c_3 \end{vmatrix}} \qquad y = \frac{\begin{vmatrix} a_1 & d_1 & c_1 \\ a_2 & d_2 & c_2 \\ a_3 & d_3 & c_3 \end{vmatrix}}{\begin{vmatrix} a_1 & b_1 & c_1 \\ a_2 & b_2 & c_2 \\ a_3 & b_3 & c_3 \end{vmatrix}} \qquad z = \frac{\begin{vmatrix} a_1 & b_1 & d_1 \\ a_2 & b_2 & d_2 \\ a_3 & b_3 & d_3 \end{vmatrix}}{\begin{vmatrix} a_1 & b_1 & c_1 \\ a_2 & b_2 & c_2 \\ a_3 & b_3 & c_3 \end{vmatrix}} \qquad (4\text{–}14)$$

If the determinant of the denominator is zero and the determinant of the numerator is not zero, the system is **inconsistent**. If the determinant of the denominator is not equal to zero, then there is a unique solution to the system of equations.

An analysis of Eqs. (4–14) shows that the situation is precisely the same as it was when we were using determinants to solve systems of two linear equations. That is, the determinants in the denominators in the expressions for x, y, and z are the same. They consist of elements which are the coefficients of the unknowns. The determinant of the numerator of the solution for x is the same as that of the denominator, except that the column of d's replaces the column of a's. The determinant in the numerator of the solution for y is the same as that of the denominator, except that the column of d's replaces the column of b's. The determinant of the numerator of the solution for z is the same as the determinant of the denominator, except that the column of d's replaces the column of c's. To summarize, we can state that *the determinants in the numerators are the same as those in the denominators, except that the column of d's replaces the column of coefficients of the unknown for which we are solving*. This again is Cramer's rule. Remember that the equations must be written in the standard form shown in Eqs. (4–11) before the determinants are formed.

Example D

Solve the following system of equations by determinants:

$$x + 2y + 2z = 1$$
$$2x - y + z = 3$$
$$4x + y + 2z = 0$$

$$x = \frac{\begin{vmatrix} 1 & 2 & 2 \\ 3 & -1 & 1 \\ 0 & 1 & 2 \end{vmatrix}\begin{matrix} 1 & 2 \\ 3 & -1 \\ 0 & 1 \end{matrix}}{\begin{vmatrix} 1 & 2 & 2 \\ 2 & -1 & 1 \\ 4 & 1 & 2 \end{vmatrix}\begin{matrix} 1 & 2 \\ 2 & -1 \\ 4 & 1 \end{matrix}} = \frac{-2 + 0 + 6 - 0 - 1 - 12}{-2 + 8 + 4 - (-8) - 1 - 8} = \frac{-9}{+9} = -1$$

Since the value of the denominator is already determined, there is no need to write the denominator in determinant form when solving for y and z.

$$y = \frac{\begin{vmatrix} 1 & 1 & 2 \\ 2 & 3 & 1 \\ 4 & 0 & 2 \end{vmatrix}\begin{matrix} 1 & 1 \\ 2 & 3 \\ 4 & 0 \end{matrix}}{9} = \frac{6 + 4 + 0 - 24 - 0 - 4}{9} = \frac{-18}{9} = -2$$

$$z = \frac{\begin{vmatrix} 1 & 2 & 1 \\ 2 & -1 & 3 \\ 4 & 1 & 0 \end{vmatrix}\begin{matrix} 1 & 2 \\ 2 & -1 \\ 4 & 1 \end{matrix}}{9} = \frac{0 + 24 + 2 - (-4) - 3 - 0}{9} = \frac{27}{9} = 3$$

As a check, we substitute these values into the first equation.

$$-1 + 2(-2) + 2(3) \overset{?}{=} 1, \quad 1 = 1. \text{ Thus, it checks.}$$

Example E
Solve the following system by determinants:

$$3x + 2y - 5z = -1$$
$$2x - 3y - z = 11$$
$$5x - 2y + 7z = 9$$

$$x = \dfrac{\begin{vmatrix} -1 & 2 & -5 \\ 11 & -3 & -1 \\ 9 & -2 & 7 \end{vmatrix}\begin{matrix} -1 & 2 \\ 11 & -3 \\ 9 & -2 \end{matrix}}{\begin{vmatrix} 3 & 2 & -5 \\ 2 & -3 & -1 \\ 5 & -2 & 7 \end{vmatrix}\begin{matrix} 3 & 2 \\ 2 & -3 \\ 5 & -2 \end{matrix}} = \dfrac{21 - 18 + 110 - 135 + 2 - 154}{-63 - 10 + 20 - 75 - 6 - 28}$$

$$= \dfrac{-174}{-162} = \dfrac{29}{27}$$

$$y = \dfrac{\begin{vmatrix} 3 & -1 & -5 \\ 2 & 11 & -1 \\ 5 & 9 & 7 \end{vmatrix}\begin{matrix} 3 & -1 \\ 2 & 11 \\ 5 & 9 \end{matrix}}{-162} = \dfrac{231 + 5 - 90 + 275 + 27 + 14}{-162} = \dfrac{462}{-162}$$

$$= -\dfrac{77}{27}$$

$$z = \dfrac{\begin{vmatrix} 3 & 2 & -1 \\ 2 & -3 & 11 \\ 5 & -2 & 9 \end{vmatrix}\begin{matrix} 3 & 2 \\ 2 & -3 \\ 5 & -2 \end{matrix}}{-162} = \dfrac{-81 + 110 + 4 - 15 + 66 - 36}{-162} = \dfrac{48}{-162}$$

$$= -\dfrac{8}{27}$$

Substituting into the second equation, we have

$$2\left(\dfrac{29}{27}\right) - 3\left(-\dfrac{77}{27}\right) - \left(-\dfrac{8}{27}\right) = \dfrac{58 + 231 + 8}{27} = \dfrac{297}{27}$$

$$= 11$$

which shows that the solution checks.

Example F

An 8% solution, a 10% solution, and a 20% solution of nitric acid are to be mixed in order to get 100 mL of a 12% solution. If the volume of acid from the 8% solution equals half the volume of acid from the other two solutions, how much of each is needed?

Let x = volume of 8% solution needed, y = volume of 10% solution needed, and z = volume of 20% solution needed.

We first use the fact that the sum of the volumes of the three solutions is 100 mL. This leads to the equation $x + y + z = 100$. Next we note that there are $0.08x$ mL of pure nitric acid from the first solution, $0.10y$ mL from the second, $0.20z$ mL from the third solution, and $0.12(100)$ mL in the final solution. This leads to the equation $0.08x + 0.10y + 0.20z = 12$. Finally, using the last stated condition, we have $0.08x = \frac{1}{2}(0.10y + 0.20z)$. These equations are then rewritten in standard form, simplified, and solved.

$$\begin{aligned}
x + \quad y + \quad z &= 100 \\
0.08x + 0.10y + 0.20z &= \quad 12 \\
0.08x \qquad\qquad\qquad &= 0.05y + 0.10z
\end{aligned}$$

$$\begin{aligned}
x + \quad y + \quad z &= 100 \\
4x + \quad 5y + \quad 10z &= 600 \\
8x - \quad 5y - \quad 10z &= \quad 0
\end{aligned}$$

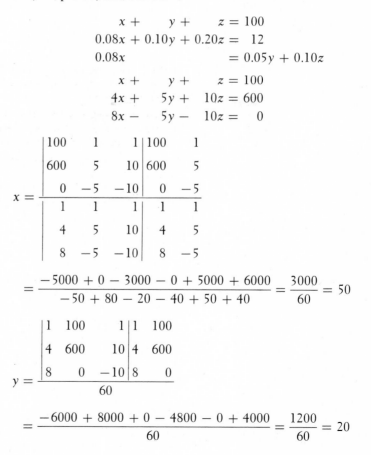

$$x = \frac{\begin{vmatrix} 100 & 1 & 1 \\ 600 & 5 & 10 \\ 0 & -5 & -10 \end{vmatrix} \begin{matrix} 100 & 1 \\ 600 & 5 \\ 0 & -5 \end{matrix}}{\begin{vmatrix} 1 & 1 & 1 \\ 4 & 5 & 10 \\ 8 & -5 & -10 \end{vmatrix} \begin{matrix} 1 & 1 \\ 4 & 5 \\ 8 & -5 \end{matrix}}$$

$$= \frac{-5000 + 0 - 3000 - 0 + 5000 + 6000}{-50 + 80 - 20 - 40 + 50 + 40} = \frac{3000}{60} = 50$$

$$y = \frac{\begin{vmatrix} 1 & 100 & 1 \\ 4 & 600 & 10 \\ 8 & 0 & -10 \end{vmatrix} \begin{matrix} 1 & 100 \\ 4 & 600 \\ 8 & 0 \end{matrix}}{60}$$

$$= \frac{-6000 + 8000 + 0 - 4800 - 0 + 4000}{60} = \frac{1200}{60} = 20$$

$$z = \frac{\begin{vmatrix} 1 & 1 & 100 \\ 4 & 5 & 600 \\ 8 & -5 & 0 \end{vmatrix} \begin{matrix} 1 & 1 \\ 4 & 5 \\ 8 & -5 \end{matrix}}{60}$$

$$= \frac{0 + 4800 - 2000 - 4000 + 3000 - 0}{60} = \frac{1800}{60} = 30$$

Therefore, 50 mL of the 8% solution, 20 mL of the 10% solution, and 30 mL of the 20% solution are required to make the 12% solution. Substitution into the first equation shows that this answer is correct.

Additional techniques which are useful in solving systems of equations are taken up in Chapter 15. Methods of evaluating determinants which are particularly useful for higher order determinants are also discussed.

Exercises 4—6

In Exercises 1 through 12 evaluate the given third-order determinants.

1. $\begin{vmatrix} 5 & 4 & -1 \\ -2 & -6 & 8 \\ 7 & 1 & 1 \end{vmatrix}$

2. $\begin{vmatrix} -7 & 0 & 0 \\ 2 & 4 & 5 \\ 1 & 4 & 2 \end{vmatrix}$

3. $\begin{vmatrix} 8 & 9 & -6 \\ -3 & 7 & 2 \\ 4 & -2 & 5 \end{vmatrix}$

4. $\begin{vmatrix} -2 & 6 & -2 \\ 5 & -1 & 4 \\ 8 & -3 & -2 \end{vmatrix}$

5. $\begin{vmatrix} -3 & -4 & -8 \\ 5 & -1 & 0 \\ 2 & 10 & -1 \end{vmatrix}$

6. $\begin{vmatrix} 10 & 2 & -7 \\ -2 & -3 & 6 \\ 6 & 5 & -2 \end{vmatrix}$

7. $\begin{vmatrix} 4 & -3 & -11 \\ -9 & 2 & -2 \\ 0 & 1 & -5 \end{vmatrix}$

8. $\begin{vmatrix} 9 & -2 & 0 \\ -1 & 3 & -6 \\ -4 & -6 & -2 \end{vmatrix}$

9. $\begin{vmatrix} 5 & 4 & -5 \\ -3 & 2 & -1 \\ 7 & 1 & 3 \end{vmatrix}$

10. $\begin{vmatrix} 20 & 0 & -15 \\ -4 & 30 & 1 \\ 6 & -1 & 40 \end{vmatrix}$

11. $\begin{vmatrix} 0.1 & -0.2 & 0 \\ -0.5 & 1 & 0.4 \\ -2 & 0.8 & 2 \end{vmatrix}$

12. $\begin{vmatrix} 0.2 & -0.5 & -0.4 \\ 1.2 & 0.3 & 0.2 \\ -0.5 & 0.1 & -0.4 \end{vmatrix}$

In Exercises 13 through 28 solve the given systems of equations by use of determinants. (Exercises 15 through 28 are the same as Exercises 1 through 14 of Section 4–5.)

13. $2x + 3y + z = 4$
$3x - z = -3$
$x - 2y + 2z = -5$

14. $4x + y + z = 2$
$2x - y - z = 4$
$3y + z = 2$

15. $x + y + z = 2$
$x - z = 1$
$x + y = 1$

16. $x + y - z = -3$
$x + z = 2$
$2x - y + 2z = 3$

17. $2x + 3y + z = 2$
$-x + 2y + 3z = -1$
$-3x - 3y + z = 0$

18. $2x + y - z = 4$
$4x - 3y - 2z = -2$
$8x - 2y - 3z = 3$

19. $5x + 6y - 3z = 6$
$4x - 7y - 2z = -3$
$3x + y - 7z = 1$

20. $3r + s - t = 2$
$r - 2s + t = 0$
$4r - s + t = 3$

21. $2x - 2y + 3z = 5$
$2x + y - 2z = -1$
$4x - y - 3z = 0$

22. $2u + 2v + 3w = 0$
$3u + v + 4w = 21$
$-u - 3v + 7w = 15$

23. $3x - 7y + 3z = 6$
$3x + 3y + 6z = 1$
$5x - 5y + 2z = 5$

24. $8x + y + z = 1$
$7x - 2y + 9z = -3$
$4x - 6y + 8z = -5$

25. $x + 2y + 2z = 0$
$2x + 6y - 3z = -1$
$4x - 3y + 6z = -8$

26. $3x + 3y + z = 6$
$2x + 2y - z = 9$
$4x + 2y - 3z = 16$

27. $2x + 3y - 5z = 7$
$4x - 3y - 2z = 1$
$8x - y + 4z = 3$

28. $2x - 4y - 4z = 3$
$3x + 8y + 2z = -11$
$4x + 6y - z = -8$

In Exercises 29 through 32 solve the given problems by determinants. In Exercises 31 and 32 set up appropriate equations and then solve them.

29. In analyzing the forces on the bell-crank mechanism shown in Fig. 4–10, the following equations are obtained. Find the indicated forces.

$$A \quad - 0.6F = 80$$
$$B - 0.8F = 0$$
$$6A \quad - 10F = 0$$

30. In applying Kirchhoff's laws (see Exercise 19 of Section 4–5) to the given electric circuit, these equations result.

$$I_A + I_B + I_C = 0$$
$$- 8I_B + 10I_C = 0$$
$$4I_A - 8I_B = 6$$

Determine the indicated currents, in amperes. (See Fig. 4–11).

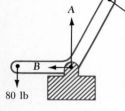

80 lb

Figure 4–10

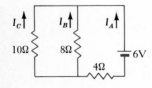

I_C I_B I_A

10Ω 8Ω 6V

4Ω

Figure 4–11

31. Twenty thousand dollars is invested part at 5.5%, part at 4.5%, and part at 4.0% (all of the amount is invested), yielding an annual interest of $1015. The income from the 5.5% investment yields $305 more annually than the other two investments combined. How much money is invested at each percentage?

32. A person traveled a total of 1870 mi from the time he left home until he reached his destination. He averaged 40 mi/h while driving to the airport. The plane averaged 600 mi/h, and he spent twice as long in the plane as in his car. The taxi averaged 30 mi/h between the airport and the destination. Assuming 40 min were used in making connections, what were the times he spent in his car, in the plane, and in the taxi, if the trip took 5.5 h?

4—7 Exercises for Chapter 4

In Exercises 1 through 4 evaluate the given determinants.

1. $\begin{vmatrix} -2 & 5 \\ 3 & 1 \end{vmatrix}$
2. $\begin{vmatrix} 4 & 0 \\ -2 & -6 \end{vmatrix}$
3. $\begin{vmatrix} -8 & -3 \\ -1 & 4 \end{vmatrix}$
4. $\begin{vmatrix} 9 & -1 \\ 7 & -5 \end{vmatrix}$

In Exercises 5 through 12 solve the given systems of equations graphically.

5. $2x - y = 4$
   $3x + 2y = 6$

6. $3x + y = 3$
   $2x - y = 6$

7. $4x - y = 6$
   $3x + 2y = 12$

8. $2x - 5y = 10$
   $3x + y = 6$

9. $7x - 2y = 14$
   $4x + y = 4$

10. $5x + 3y = 15$
    $6x - y = 12$

11. $3x + 4y = 6$
    $2x - 3y = 2$

12. $5x + 2y = 5$
    $2x - 4y = 3$

In Exercises 13 through 24 solve the given systems of equations algebraically.

13. $x + 2y = 5$
    $x + 3y = 7$

14. $2x - y = 7$
    $x + y = 2$

15. $4x + 3y = -4$
    $2x - y = 3$

16. $x + 3y = -2$
    $-2x - 9y = 2$

17. $3x + 4y = 6$
    $9x + 8y = 11$

18. $3x - 6y = 5$
    $7x + 2y = 4$

19. $2x - 5y = 8$
    $5x - 3y = 7$

20. $3x + 4y = 8$
    $2x - 3y = 9$

21. $7x - 2y = -6$
    $4x + 7y = 12$

22. $5x + 3y = 8$
    $6x - 8y = 11$

23. $9x - 11y = 4$
    $6x - 3y = 5$

24. $3x - 4y = 9$
    $7x + 10y = -2$

In Exercises 25 through 36 solve the given systems of equations by use of determinants. (These systems are the same as for Exercises 13 through 24.)

25. $x + 2y = 5$
    $x + 3y = 7$

26. $2x - y = 7$
    $x + y = 2$

27. $4x + 3y = -4$
    $2x - y = 3$

28. $x + 3y = -2$
    $-2x - 9y = 2$

29. $3x + 4y = 6$
    $9x + 8y = 11$

30. $3x - 6y = 5$
    $7x + 2y = 4$

31. $2x - 5y = 8$
$5x - 3y = 7$

32. $3x + 4y = 8$
$2x - 3y = 9$

33. $7x - 2y = -6$
$4x + 7y = 12$

34. $5x + 3y = 8$
$6x - 8y = 11$

35. $9x - 11y = 4$
$6x - 3y = 5$

36. $3x - 4y = 9$
$7x + 10y = -2$

In Exercises 37 through 40 evaluate the given determinants.

37. $\begin{vmatrix} 4 & -1 & 8 \\ -1 & 6 & -2 \\ 2 & 1 & -1 \end{vmatrix}$

38. $\begin{vmatrix} -5 & 0 & -5 \\ 2 & 3 & -1 \\ -3 & 2 & 2 \end{vmatrix}$

39. $\begin{vmatrix} -2 & -4 & 7 \\ 1 & 6 & -3 \\ -7 & 2 & -1 \end{vmatrix}$

40. $\begin{vmatrix} 3 & 2 & -1 \\ 0 & -3 & 4 \\ 3 & -4 & -2 \end{vmatrix}$

In Exercises 41 through 48 solve the given systems of equations algebraically.

41. $2x + y + z = 4$
$x - 2y - z = 3$
$3x + 3y - 2z = 1$

42. $x + 2y + z = 2$
$3x - 6y + 2z = 2$
$2x - z = 8$

43. $3x + 2y + z = 1$
$9x - 4y + 2z = 8$
$12x - 18y = 17$

44. $2x + 2y - z = 2$
$3x + 4y + z = -4$
$5x - 2y - 3z = 5$

45. $2r + s + 2t = 8$
$3r - 2s - 4t = 5$
$-2r + 3s + 4t = -3$

46. $2u + 2v - w = -2$
$4u - 3v + 2w = -2$
$8u - 4v - 3w = 13$

47. $4x + 6y - z = -2$
$3x - 5y + 4z = 8$
$6x + 4y + 2z = 5$

48. $3t + 2u + 6v = 3$
$4t - 3u + 2v = 13$
$5t + u + v = 0$

In Exercises 49 through 56 solve the given systems of equations by use of determinants. (These systems are the same as for Exercises 41 through 48.)

49. $2x + y + z = 4$
$x - 2y - z = 3$
$3x + 3y - 2z = 1$

50. $x + 2y + z = 2$
$3x - 6y + 2z = 2$
$2x - z = 8$

51. $3x + 2y + z = 1$
$9x - 4y + 2z = 8$
$12x - 18y = 17$

52. $2x + 2y - z = 2$
$3x + 4y + z = -4$
$5x - 2y - 3z = 5$

53. $2r + s + 2t = 8$
$3r - 2s - 4t = 5$
$-2r + 3s + 4t = -3$

54. $2u + 2v - w = -2$
$4u - 3v + 2w = -2$
$8u - 4v - 3w = 13$

55. $4x + 6y - z = -2$
$3x - 5y + 4z = 8$
$6x + 4y + 2z = 5$

56. $3t + 2u + 6v = 3$
$4t - 3u + 2v = 13$
$5t + u + v = 0$

In Exercises 57 through 60, let $1/x = u$ and $1/y = v$. Solve for u and v, and then solve for x and y. In this way we will see how to solve systems of equations involving reciprocals.

57. $\dfrac{1}{x} - \dfrac{1}{y} = \dfrac{1}{2}$ 58. $\dfrac{1}{x} + \dfrac{1}{y} = 3$ 59. $\dfrac{2}{x} + \dfrac{3}{y} = 3$ 60. $\dfrac{3}{x} - \dfrac{2}{y} = 4$

$\dfrac{1}{x} + \dfrac{1}{y} = \dfrac{1}{4}$ $\dfrac{2}{x} + \dfrac{1}{y} = 1$ $\dfrac{5}{x} - \dfrac{6}{y} = 3$ $\dfrac{2}{x} + \dfrac{4}{y} = 1$

In Exercises 61 and 62 determine the value of a which makes the system dependent. In Exercises 63 and 64 determine the value of a which makes the system inconsistent.

61. $3x - ay = 6$ 62. $5x + 20y = 15$ 63. $ax - 2y = 5$ 64. $2x - 5y = 7$

$x + 2y = 2$ $2x + ay = 6$ $4x + 6y = 1$ $ax + 10y = 2$

Solve the systems of equations in Exercises 65 through 68 by any appropriate method.

65. In an experiment to determine the values of two electrical resistors, the following equations were determined:

$$2R_1 + 3R_2 = 16$$
$$3R_1 + 2R_2 = 19$$

Determine the resistances R_1 and R_2 (in ohms).

66. The production of nitric acid makes use of air and nitrogen compounds. In order to determine requirements as to size of equipment, a relationship between the air flow rate m (in moles per hour) and exhaust nitrogen rate n is often used. One particular operation produces the following equations:

$$1.58m + 41.5 = 38.0 + 2.00n$$
$$0.424m + 36.4 = 189 + 0.0728n$$

Solve for m and n.

67. In a certain machine there are three important types of parts. Considering the total number of parts used, their cost, and the time used in their manufacture, the number of each type used can be determined by solving the system of equations

$$a + b + c = 37$$
$$2a + 3b + 5c = 131$$
$$3a + 5b + 6c = 180$$

where a, b, and c are the numbers of each part used, respectively. Find a, b, and c.

68. In applying Kirchhoff's laws (see Exercise 19 of Section 4–5) to the given electric circuit, these equations result.

$$I_A + I_B + I_C = 0$$
$$6I_A \qquad - 10I_C = 8$$
$$6I_A - 2I_B \qquad = 5$$

Determine the indicated currents (in amperes). (See Fig. 4–12.)

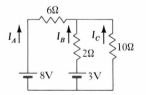

Figure 4—12

In Exercises 69 through 74 set up systems of equations and solve by any appropriate method.

69. A plane traveled 2000 mi, with the wind, in 4 h, and it made the return trip in 5 h. Determine the speed of the plane and that of the wind.

70. The relation between Fahrenheit temperature F and Celsius temperature C can be indicated by $F = aC + b$. If 0°C is equivalent to 32°F and 100°C is equivalent to 212°F, find a and b.

71. If a lever is balanced by placing a single support (fulcrum) under a certain point, then the product of a weight on one side of the fulcrum and its distance from the fulcrum equals the product of a weight on the other side of the fulcrum times its distance from the fulcrum. A certain lever is balanced if a weight of 80 lb is put at one end and a weight of 30 lb at the other end. If the 80-lb weight is moved 1 ft closer to the fulcrum, it requires 20 lb at the other end to maintain the balance. How long is the lever? (Neglect the weight of the lever itself.)

72. The relative density of an object may be defined as its weight in air divided by the difference of its weight in air and its weight when submerged in water. If the sum of the weights in water and in air of an object of relative density equal to 10 is 30 lb, what is its weight in air?

73. An alloy important in the manufacture of electric transformers contains nickel, iron, and molybdenum. The percentage of nickel is 1% less than five times the percentage of iron. The percentage of iron is 1% more than three times the percentage of molybdenum. Find the percentage of each metal in the alloy.

74. A businessman is interested in a building site for a new factory. He determines that at least 30 acres of land are necessary and that over 40 acres would be too expensive. He learns of a 160-acre tract of land which has been subdivided according to terrain such that one portion is 16 acres less than the sum of the other two and that twice the area of the second portion is 8 acres more than the area of the third portion. Would any of the portions be of interest to him?

5

Factoring and Fractions

5—1 Special Products

In Chapter 1 we introduced certain fundamental algebraic operations. These have been sufficient for our purposes to this point. However, material we shall encounter later requires additional algebraic techniques. In this chapter we shall develop certain basic algebraic topics, which in turn will allow us to develop other topics having technical and scientific applications.

In working with algebraic expressions, we encounter certain types of products so frequently that we should become extremely familiar with them. These products are obtained by the methods of multiplication of algebraic expressions developed in Chapter 1 and are stated here in general form.

$$a(x + y) = ax + ay \tag{5-1}$$

$$(x + y)(x - y) = x^2 - y^2 \tag{5-2}$$

$$(x + y)^2 = x^2 + 2xy + y^2 \tag{5-3}$$

$$(x - y)^2 = x^2 - 2xy + y^2 \tag{5-4}$$

$$(x + a)(x + b) = x^2 + (a + b)x + ab \tag{5-5}$$

$$(ax + b)(cx + d) = acx^2 + (bc + ad)x + bd \tag{5-6}$$

These **special products** should be known thoroughly such that the multiplications represented are easily and clearly recognized. When this is the case, they allow us to perform many multiplications quickly and easily, often by inspection. We must realize that they are written in their most concise form. Any of the literal numbers appearing in these products may represent an expression which in turn represents a number.

Example A

Using Eq. (5–1) in the following product, we have

$$6(3r + 2s) = 6(3r) + 6(2s) = 18r + 12s$$

Using Eq. (5–2), we have

$$(3r + 2s)(3r - 2s) = (3r)^2 - (2s)^2 = 9r^2 - 4s^2$$

When we use Eq. (5–1) in the first illustration, we see that $a = 6$. In both illustrations $3r = x$ and $2s = y$.

Example B

Using Eqs. (5–3) and (5–4) in the following products, we have

$$(5a + 2)^2 = (5a)^2 + 2(5a)(2) + 2^2 = 25a^2 + 20a + 4$$
$$(5a - 2)^2 = (5a)^2 - 2(5a)(2) + 2^2 = 25a^2 - 20a + 4$$

In these illustrations, we have let $x = 5a$ and $y = 2$. It should also be emphasized that $(5a + 2)^2$ is not $(5a)^2 + 2^2$, or $25a^2 + 4$. We must be careful to properly follow the correct form of Eqs. (5–3) and (5–4) and include the middle term, $20a$.

Example C

Using Eqs. (5–5) and (5–6) in the following products, we have

$$(x + 5)(x - 3) = x^2 + [(5 + (-3)]x + (5)(-3) = x^2 + 2x - 15$$
$$(4x + 5)(2x - 3) = (4x)(2x) + [5(2) + 4(-3)]x + (5)(-3)$$
$$= 8x^2 - 2x - 15$$

Generally, when we use these special products, we do the middle step as shown in each of the examples above mentally and write down the result directly. This is indicated in the following example.

Example D

$$2(x - 6) = 2x - 12$$
$$(y - 5)(y + 5) = y^2 - 25$$
$$(3x - 2)^2 = 9x^2 - 12x + 4$$
$$(x - 4)(x + 7) = x^2 + 3x - 28$$

At times these special products may appear in combinations. When this happens it may be necessary to indicate an intermediate step.

Example E

In expanding $7(a + 2)(a - 2)$, we use Eqs. (5–2) and (5–1), preferably in that order. Performing this operation, we have

$$7(a + 2)(a - 2) = 7(a^2 - 4) = 7a^2 - 28$$

Example F

In determining the product $(x + y - 2)^2$, we may group the quantity $(x + y)$ in an intermediate step. This leads to

$$(x + y - 2)^2 = [(x + y) - 2]^2 = (x + y)^2 - 2(x + y)(2) + 2^2$$
$$= x^2 + 2xy + y^2 - 4x - 4y + 4$$

In this example we used Eqs. (5–3) and (5–4).

There are four other special products which occur less frequently. However, they are sufficiently important that they should be readily recognized. They are shown in Eqs. (5–7) through (5–10).

$$(x + y)^3 = x^3 + 3x^2y + 3xy^2 + y^3 \qquad (5\text{–}7)$$
$$(x - y)^3 = x^3 - 3x^2y + 3xy^2 - y^3 \qquad (5\text{–}8)$$
$$(x + y)(x^2 - xy + y^2) = x^3 + y^3 \qquad (5\text{–}9)$$
$$(x - y)(x^2 + xy + y^2) = x^3 - y^3 \qquad (5\text{–}10)$$

The following examples illustrate the use of Eqs. (5–7) through (5–10).

Example G

$$(x + 4)^3 = x^3 + 3(x^2)(4) + 3(x)(4^2) + 4^3$$
$$= x^3 + 12x^2 + 48x + 64$$
$$(2x - 5)^3 = (2x)^3 - 3(2x)^2(5) + 3(2x)(5^2) - 5^3$$
$$= 8x^3 - 60x^2 + 150x - 125$$

Example H

$$(x + 3)(x^2 - 3x + 9) = x^3 + 3^3 = x^3 + 27$$
$$(x - 2)(x^2 + 2x + 4) = x^3 - 2^3 = x^3 - 8$$

Exercises 5—1

In Exercises 1 through 28 find the indicated products directly *by inspection*. It should not be necessary to write down intermediate steps.

1. $40(x - y)$
2. $2x(a - 3)$
3. $2x^2(x - 4)$
4. $3a^2(2a + 7)$
5. $(y + 6)(y - 6)$
6. $(s + 2t)(s - 2t)$
7. $(3v - 2)(3v + 2)$
8. $(ab - c)(ab + c)$
9. $(5f + 4)^2$
10. $(i_1 + 3)^2$
11. $(2x + 7)^2$
12. $(5a + 2b)^2$
13. $(x - 2y)^2$
14. $(a - 5p)^2$
15. $(6s - t)^2$
16. $(3p - 4q)^2$
17. $(x + 1)(x + 5)$
18. $(y - 8)(y + 5)$

19. $(3 + c)(6 + c)$ 20. $(t - 1)(t - 7)$ 21. $(3x - 1)(2x + 5)$

22. $(2x - 7)(2x + 1)$ 23. $(4x - 5)(5x + 1)$ 24. $(2y - 1)(3y - 1)$

25. $(5v - 3)(4v + 5)$ 26. $(7s + 6)(2s + 5)$

27. $(3x + 7y)(2x - 9y)$ 28. $(8x - y)(3x + 4y)$

Use the special products of this section to determine the products of Exercises 29 through 48. You may need to write down one or two intermediate steps.

29. $2(x - 2)(x + 2)$ 30. $5(n - 5)(n + 5)$

31. $2a(2a - 1)(2a + 1)$ 32. $4c(2c - 3)(2c + 3)$

33. $6a(x + 2b)^2$ 34. $4y^2(y + 6)^2$

35. $4a(2a - 3)^2$ 36. $6t^2(5t - 3s)^2$

37. $(x + y + 1)^2$ 38. $(x + 2 + 3y)^2$

39. $(3 - x - y)^2$ 40. $2(x - y + 1)^2$

41. $(5 - t)^3$ 42. $(2s + 3)^3$

43. $(2x + 5t)^3$ 44. $(x - 5y)^3$

45. $(x + 2)(x^2 - 2x + 4)$ 46. $(a - 3)(a^2 + 3a + 9)$

47. $(4 - 3x)(16 + 12x + 9x^2)$ 48. $(2x + 3a)(4x^2 - 6ax + 9a^2)$

Use the special products of this section to determine the products in Exercises 49 through 54. Each comes from the technical area indicated.

49. $R(i_1 + i_2)^2$ (electricity)

50. $Fa(L - a)(L + a)$ (mechanics: force on a beam)

51. $16(4 + t)(3 - t)$ (physics: motion)

52. $V^2(V - b)^2$ (thermodynamics)

53. $P(1 + r)^3$ (business: compound interest)

54. $p^2(1 - p)^3$ (mathematics: probability)

5–2 Factoring: Common Factor and Difference of Squares

We often find that we want to determine what expressions can be multiplied together to equal a given algebraic expression. We know from Section 1–7 that when an algebraic expression is the product of two or more quantities, each of these quantities is called a **factor** of the expression. *Therefore, determining these factors, which is essentially reversing the process of finding a product, is called* **factoring**.

In our work on factoring we shall consider only the factoring of polynomials (see Section 1–9) which have integers as coefficients for all terms. Also, all factors will have integral coefficients. *A polynomial or a factor is called* **prime** *if it contains no factors other than $+1$ or -1 and plus or minus itself. We say that an expression is* **factored completely** *if it is expressed as a product of its prime factors.*

Example A

When we factor the expression $12x + 6x^2$ as

$$12x + 6x^2 = 2(6x + 3x^2)$$

we see that it has not been factored completely. The factor $6x + 3x^2$ is not prime, for it may be factored as

$$6x + 3x^2 = 3x(2 + x)$$

Therefore, the expression $12x + 6x^2$ is factored completely as

$$12x + 6x^2 = 6x(2 + x)$$

Here the factors x and $2 + x$ are prime. The numerical coefficient, 6, could be factored into $(2)(3)$, but it is normal practice not to factor numerical coefficients.

To factor expressions easily, we must be familiar with algebraic multiplication, particularly the special products of the preceding section. The solution of factoring problems is heavily dependent on the recognition of special products. The special products also provide methods of checking answers and deciding whether or not a given factor is prime.

Often an algebraic expression contains a monomial that is common to each term of the expression. Therefore, in accordance with Eq. (5–1), *the first step in factoring any expression should be to factor out any* **common monomial factor** that may exist.

Example B

In factoring the expression $6x - 2y$, we note that each term contains the factor 2. Therefore,

$$6x - 2y = 2(3x - y)$$

Here, 2 is the common monomial factor, and $2(3x - y)$ is the required factored form of $6x - 2y$.

Example C

Factor: $4ax^2 + 2ax$.

The numerical factor 2 and the literal factors a and x are common to each term. Therefore, the common monomial factor of $4ax^2 + 2ax$ is $2ax$. This means that

$$4ax^2 + 2ax = 2ax(2x + 1)$$

Note the presence of the 1 in the factored form. Since each of the factors of the second term is also a factor of the common monomial factor, we must include the factor of 1. Otherwise, if the factored form is multiplied out, we would not obtain the proper expression.

Example D
Factor: $6a^5x^2 - 9a^3x^3 + 3a^3x^2$.

After inspecting each term, we determine that each contains a factor of 3, a^3, and x^2. Thus, the common monomial factor is $3a^3x^2$. This means that

$$6a^5x^2 - 9a^3x^3 + 3a^3x^2 = 3a^3x^2(2a^2 - 3x + 1)$$

Another important form for factoring is based on the special product of Eq. (5–2). In Eq. (5–2) we see that the product of the sum and the difference of two numbers results in the difference between the squares of the numbers. Therefore, *factoring the difference between squares gives factors which are the sum and the difference of the numbers.*

Example E
In factoring $x^2 - 16$, we note that x^2 is the square of x and that 16 is the square of 4. Therefore,

$$x^2 - 16 = x^2 - 4^2 = (x + 4)(x - 4)$$

Usually in factoring an expression of this type we do not actually write out the middle step as shown.

Example F
Since $4x^2$ is the square of $2x$ and 9 is the square of 3, we may factor $4x^2 - 9$ as

$$4x^2 - 9 = (2x + 3)(2x - 3)$$

In the same way,

$$16x^4 - 25y^2 = (4x^2 + 5y)(4x^2 - 5y)$$

where we note that $16x^4 = (4x^2)^2$ and $25y^2 = (5y)^2$.

As indicated previously, *if it is possible to factor out a common monomial factor, this factoring should be done first.* We should then inspect the resulting factors to see if further factoring can be done. It is possible, for example, that the resulting factor is a difference of squares. Thus, complete factoring often requires more than one step. Be sure to include all prime factors in writing the result.

Example G
In factoring $20x^2 - 45$, we note that there is a common factor of 5 in each term. Therefore, $20x^2 - 45 = 5(4x^2 - 9)$. However, the factor $4x^2 - 9$ itself is the difference of squares. Therefore, $20x^2 - 45$ is completely factored as

$$20x^2 - 45 = 5(4x^2 - 9) = 5(2x + 3)(2x - 3)$$

In factoring $x^4 - y^4$, we note that we have the difference of squares. Therefore, $x^4 - y^4 = (x^2 + y^2)(x^2 - y^2)$. However, the factor $x^2 - y^2$ is also the difference of squares. This means that

$$x^4 - y^4 = (x^2 + y^2)(x^2 - y^2) = (x^2 + y^2)(x + y)(x - y)$$

The factor $x^2 + y^2$ is prime.

Exercises 5–2

In Exercises 1 through 32 factor the given expressions completely.

1. $6x + 6y$ 2. $3a - 3b$ 3. $5a - 5$

4. $2x^2 + 2$ 5. $3x^2 - 9x$ 6. $4s^2 + 20s$

7. $7b^2y - 28b$ 8. $5a^2 - 20ax$ 9. $2x + 4y - 8z$

10. $10a - 5b + 15c$ 11. $3ab^2 - 6ab + 12ab^3$ 12. $4pq - 14q^2 - 16pq^2$

13. $12pq^2 - 8pq - 28pq^3$ 14. $27a^2b - 24ab - 9a$ 15. $2a^2 - 2b^2 + 4c^2 - 6d^2$

16. $5a + 10ax - 5ay + 20az$ 17. $x^2 - 4$

18. $r^2 - 25$ 19. $100 - y^2$ 20. $49 - z^2$

21. $81s^2 - 25t^2$ 22. $36s^2 - 121t^2$ 23. $144n^2 - 169p^4$

24. $36a^2b^2 - 169c^2$ 25. $2x^2 - 8$ 26. $5a^2 - 125$

27. $3x^2 - 27z^2$ 28. $4x^2 - 100y^2$ 29. $x^4 - 16$

30. $y^4 - 81$ 31. $x^8 - 1$ 32. $2x^4 - 8y^4$

In Exercises 33 through 36 the expressions are to be factored by a method known as **factoring by grouping**. An illustration of this method is

$$2x - 2y + ax - ay = (2x - 2y) + (ax - ay)$$
$$= 2(x - y) + a(x - y) = (2 + a)(x - y)$$

The terms are put into groups, a common factor is factored from each group, and then the factoring is continued.

33. $3x - 3y + bx - by$ 34. $am + an + cn + cm$

35. $a^2 + ax - ab - bx$ 36. $2y - y^2 - 6y^4 + 12y^3$

Factor the expressions given in Exercises 37 through 42. Each comes from the technical area indicated.

37. $iR_1 + iR_2 + ir$ (electricity)   38. $P + Prt$ (business: interest)

39. $mv_1^2 - mv_2^2$ (mechanics: energy)   40. $kD^2 - 4kr^2$ (hydrodynamics)

41. The difference in the expressions for the volume of a cube with edge e and a rectangular solid of edges 2, 2 and e is $e^3 - 4e$. Factor this expression.

42. The difference of the energy radiated by an electric light filament at temperature T_2 and that radiated by a filament at temperature T_1 is given by the formula

$$R = kT_2^4 - kT_1^4$$

Factor the right-hand side of this formula.

5–3 Factoring Trinomials

In the previous section we introduced the concept of factoring, and considered factoring based on special products of Eqs. (5–1) and (5–2). We now note that the special products formed from Eqs. (5–3) through (5–6) all result in trinomial (three term) polynomials. Thus, trinomials of the types formed from these products are important expressions to be factored, and this section is devoted to them.

Factoring expressions based on the special product of Eq. (5–5) will result in factors of the form $x + a$ and $x + b$. The numbers a and b are found by analyzing the constant and the coefficient of x in the expression to be factored.

Example A

In factoring $x^2 + 3x + 2$, the constant term, 2, suggests that the only possibilities for a and b are 2 and 1. The plus sign before the 2 indicates that the sign before the 1 and the 2 in the factors must be the same, either both plus or both minus. Since the coefficient of the middle term is the sum of a and b, the plus sign before the 3 tells us that the sign before the 2 and 1 must be plus. Therefore,

$$x^2 + 3x + 2 = (x + 2)(x + 1)$$

For an expression containing x^2 and 2 to be factored, the middle term must be $3x$. No other combination of a and b gives the proper middle term. Therefore, the expression

$$x^2 + 4x + 2$$

cannot be factored. The a and b would have to be 2 and 1, but the middle term would not be $4x$.

Example B

In order to factor $x^2 + 7x - 8$, we must find two integers whose product is -8 and whose sum is $+7$. The possible factors of -8 are -8 and $+1$, $+8$ and -1, -4 and $+2$, and $+4$ and -2. Inspecting these we see that only $+8$ and -1 have the sum of $+7$. Therefore,

$$x^2 + 7x - 8 = (x + 8)(x - 1)$$

In the same way, we have

$$x^2 - x - 12 = (x - 4)(x + 3)$$

and

$$x^2 - 5xy + 6y^2 = (x - 3y)(x - 2y)$$

In the last illustration we note that we were to find second terms of each factor such that their product was $6y^2$ and sum was $-5xy$. Thus, each term must contain a factor of y.

Example C

In order to factor $x^2 + 10x + 25$, we must find two integers whose sum is $+10$ and whose product is $+25$. Since $5^2 = 25$ we note that this expression may fit the form of Eq. (5–3). This could be the case only if the first and third terms were perfect squares. We see that the sum of $+5$ and $+5$ is $+10$, which means

$$x^2 + 10x + 25 = (x + 5)(x + 5)$$

or

$$x^2 + 10x + 25 = (x + 5)^2$$

Factoring expressions based upon the special product of Eq. (5–6) often requires some trial and error. The coefficient of x^2 gives the possibilities for the coefficients a and c in the factors. The constant gives the possibilities for the numbers b and d in the factors. It is then necessary to try possible combinations to determine which combination provides the middle term of the given expression.

Example D
When factoring the expression $2x^2 + 11x + 5$, the coefficient 2 indicates that the only possibilities for the x-terms in the factors are $2x$ and x. The 5 indicates that only 5 and 1 may be the constants. Therefore, possible combinations are $2x + 1$, and $x + 5$ or $2x + 5$ and $x + 1$. The combination which gives the coefficient of the middle term, 11, is

$$2x^2 + 11x + 5 = (2x + 1)(x + 5)$$

According to this analysis, the expression $2x^2 + 10x + 5$ is not factorable, but the following expression is:

$$2x^2 + 7x + 5 = (2x + 5)(x + 1)$$

Example E
Other examples of factoring based upon the special product of Eq. (5–6) are as follows:

$$4x^2 + 4x - 3 = (2x - 1)(2x + 3)$$
$$3x^2 - 13x + 12 = (3x - 4)(x - 3)$$
$$6s^2 + 19st - 20t^2 = (6s - 5t)(s + 4t)$$

In the first illustration, possible factors with x terms of $4x$ and x can be shown to be incorrect if tried. In the second illustration, other possible factorizations of 12, such as 6×2 and 12×1, can be shown to give improper middle terms. In the third illustration, there are numerous possibilities for the combination of 6 and 20. *We must remember to check carefully that the middle term of the expression is the proper result of the factors we have chosen.*

Example F
In factoring $9x^2 - 6x + 1$, we note that $9x^2$ is the square of $3x$ and 1 is the square of 1. Therefore, we recognize that this expression might fit the perfect square form of Eq. (5–4). This leads us to tentatively factor it as

$$9x^2 - 6x + 1 = (3x - 1)^2$$

However, before we can be certain that this factorization is correct, we must check to see if the middle term of the expansion of $(3x - 1)^2$ is $-6x$. Since $-6x$ properly fits the form of Eq. (5–4), the factorization is correct.

In the same way, we have

$$36x^2 + 84xy + 49y^2 = (6x + 7y)^2$$

As we pointed out in Section 5–2, we must be careful to see that we have factored an expression completely. We look for common monomial factors first, and then check each resulting factor. This check of each factor should be made every time we complete a step in factoring.

Example G

When factoring $2x^2 + 6x - 8$, we first note the common monomial factor of 2. This leads to

$$2x^2 + 6x - 8 = 2(x^2 + 3x - 4)$$

We now notice that $x^2 + 3x - 4$ is also factorable. Therefore,

$$2x^2 + 6x - 8 = 2(x + 4)(x - 1)$$

Now each factor is prime.

Exercises 5–3

In Exercises 1 through 32 factor the given expressions completely.

1. $x^2 + 5x + 4$

2. $x^2 - 5x - 6$

3. $s^2 - s - 42$

4. $a^2 + 14a - 32$

5. $x^2 + 2x + 1$

6. $y^2 + 8y + 16$

7. $x^2 - 4x + 4$

8. $b^2 - 12b + 36$

9. $3x^2 - 5x - 2$

10. $2n^2 - 13n - 7$

11. $3y^2 - 8y - 3$

12. $5x^2 + 9x - 2$

13. $3t^2 - 7tu + 4u^2$

14. $3x^2 + xy - 14y^2$

15. $9x^2 + 7xy - 2y^2$

16. $4r^2 + 11rs - 3s^2$

17. $4m^2 + 20m + 25$

18. $16q^2 + 24q + 9$

19. $4x^2 - 12x + 9$

20. $a^2c^2 - 2ac + 1$

21. $9t^2 - 15t + 4$

22. $6x^2 + x - 12$

23. $8b^2 + 31b - 4$

24. $12n^2 + 8n - 15$

25. $4p^2 - 25pq + 6q^2$

26. $12x^2 + 4xy - 5y^2$

27. $12x^2 + 47xy - 4y^2$

28. $8r^2 - 14rs - 9s^2$

29. $2x^2 - 14x + 12$

30. $6y^2 - 33y - 18$

31. $4x^2 + 14x - 8$

32. $12x^2 + 22x - 4$

In Exercises 33 through 36 factor the given expression by referring directly to the special products in Eqs. (5–7) through (5–10), respectively. These expressions are not trinomials, but their factorization depends on the proper recognition of their forms, as with Eqs. (5–3) and (5–4).

33. $x^3 + 3x^2 + 3x + 1$

34. $x^3 - 6x^2 + 12x - 8$

35. $8x^3 + 1$

36. $x^3 - 27$

Factor the expressions given in Exercises 37 through 40. Each comes from the technical area indicated.

37. $16t^2 - 32t - 128$ (physics: motion)

38. $2p^2 - 108p + 400$ (business)

39. $x^2 - 3Lx + 2L^2$ (mechanics: beams)

40. $V^2 - 2nBV + n^2B^2$ (chemistry)

5—4 Equivalent Fractions

When we deal with algebraic expressions, we must be able to work effectively with fractions. Since algebraic expressions are representations of numbers, the basic operations on fractions from arithmetic will form the basis of our algebraic operations. In this section we shall demonstrate a very important property of fractions, and in the following two sections we shall establish the basic algebraic operations with fractions.

This important property of fractions, often referred to as the **fundamental principle of fractions,** is that *the value of a fraction is unchanged if both numerator and denominator are multiplied or divided by the same number, provided this number is not zero.* Two fractions are said to be **equivalent** if one can be obtained from the other by use of the fundamental theorem.

Example A

If we multiply the numerator and denominator of the fraction $\frac{6}{8}$ by 2, we obtain the equivalent fraction $\frac{12}{16}$. If we divide the numerator and denominator of $\frac{6}{8}$ by 2, we obtain the equivalent fraction $\frac{3}{4}$. Therefore, the fractions $\frac{6}{8}$, $\frac{3}{4}$, and $\frac{12}{16}$ are equivalent.

Example B

We may write

$$\frac{ax}{2} = \frac{3a^2x}{6a}$$

since the right fraction is obtained from the left fraction by multiplying the numerator and the denominator by $3a$. Therefore, the fractions are equivalent.

One of the most important operations to be performed on a fraction is that of reducing it to its **simplest form,** or **lowest terms.** *A fraction is said to be in its simplest form if the numerator and the denominator have no common factors other than +1 or −1.* In reducing a fraction to its simplest form, we use the fundamental theorem by dividing both the numerator and the denominator by all factors which are common to each. (It will be assumed throughout this text that if any of the literal symbols were to be evaluated, numerical values would be restricted so that none of the denominators would be zero. Thereby, we avoid the undefined operation of division by zero.)

Example C

In order to reduce the fraction

$$\frac{16ab^3c^2}{24ab^2c^5}$$

to its lowest terms, we note that both the numerator and the denominator contain the factor $8ab^2c^2$. Therefore, we may write

$$\frac{16ab^3c^2}{24ab^2c^5} = \frac{2b(8ab^2c^2)}{3c^3(8ab^2c^2)} = \frac{2b}{3c^3}$$

In Example C we divided out the common factor. The resulting fraction is in lowest terms since there are no common factors in the numerator and the denominator other than $+1$ or -1.

We must note very carefully that in simplifying fractions, *we divide both the numerator and the denominator by the common factor.* This process is called **cancellation.** However, many students are tempted to try to remove any expression which appears in both the numerator and the denominator. If a *term* is removed in this way, it is an incorrect application of the cancellation process. The following example illustrates this common error in the simplification of fractions.

Example D
When simplifying the expression

$$\frac{x^2(x-2)}{x^2-4}$$

many students would "cancel" the x^2 from the numerator and the denominator. This is *incorrect,* since x^2 is only a term of the denominator.

In order to simplify the fraction above properly, we should factor the denominator. We obtain

$$\frac{x^2(x-2)}{(x-2)(x+2)} = \frac{x^2}{x+2}$$

Here, the common *factor* $x-2$ has been divided out.

The following examples illustrate the proper simplification of fractions.

Example E

$$\frac{4a}{2a^2x} = \frac{2}{ax}$$

We divide out the common factor of $2a$.

$$\frac{4a}{2a^2+x}$$

This cannot be reduced, since there are no common *factors* in the numerator and the denominator.

Example F

$$\frac{x^2-4x+4}{x^2-4} = \frac{(x-2)(x-2)}{(x+2)(x-2)} = \frac{x-2}{x+2}$$

In this simplification, the numerator and the denominator have each been factored first and then the common factor $x-2$ has been divided out. In the final form, neither the x's nor 2's may be cancelled, since they are not common *factors.*

Example G

$$\frac{4x^2 + 14x - 30}{8x - 12} = \frac{2(2x^2 + 7x - 15)}{4(2x - 3)} = \frac{2(2x - 3)(x + 5)}{4(2x - 3)} = \frac{x + 5}{2}$$

Here, the factors common to the numerator and the denominator are 2 and $(2x - 3)$.

In simplifying fractions we must be able to distinguish between factors which differ only in *sign*. Since $-(y - x) = -y + x = x - y$, we have

$$x - y = -(y - x) \tag{5–11}$$

Here we see that **factors $x - y$ and $y - x$ differ only in sign**. The following examples illustrate the simplification of fractions where a change of signs is necessary.

Example H

$$\frac{x^2 - 1}{1 - x} = \frac{(x - 1)(x + 1)}{-(x - 1)} = \frac{x + 1}{-1} = -(x + 1)$$

In the second fraction, we replaced $1 - x$ with the equal expression $-(x - 1)$. In the third fraction the common factor $x - 1$ was divided out. Finally, we expressed the result in the more convenient form by dividing $x + 1$ by -1, which makes the quantity $x + 1$ negative.

Example I

$$\frac{2x^3 - 32x}{20 + 7x - 3x^2} = \frac{2x(x^2 - 16)}{(4 - x)(5 + 3x)} = \frac{2x(x - 4)(x + 4)}{-(x - 4)(3x + 5)}$$

$$= -\frac{2x(x + 4)}{3x + 5}$$

Again, the factor $4 - x$ has been replaced by the equal expression $-(x - 4)$. This allows us to recognize the common factor of $x - 4$. Notice also that the order of the terms of the factor $5 + 3x$ has been changed to $3x + 5$. This is merely an application of the commutative law of addition.

Exercises 5–4

In Exercises 1 through 8 multiply the ⬛⬛⬛⬛⬛⬛⬛ each of the given fractions by the given ⬛⬛⬛⬛

1. $\dfrac{2}{3}$ (by 7)

4. $\dfrac{2x^2y}{3n}$ (by $2xn^2$)

7. $\dfrac{a(x - y)}{x - 2y}$ (by $x + y$)

In Exercises 9 through 16 divide the numerator and the denominator of each of the given fractions by the given factor and obtain an equivalent fraction.

9. $\dfrac{28}{44}$ (by 4)

10. $\dfrac{25}{65}$ (by 5)

11. $\dfrac{4x^2y}{8xy^2}$ (by $2x$)

12. $\dfrac{6a^3b^2}{9a^5b^4}$ (by $3a^2b^2$)

13. $\dfrac{2(x-1)}{(x-1)(x+1)}$ (by $x-1$)

14. $\dfrac{(x+5)(x-3)}{3(x+5)}$ (by $x+5$)

15. $\dfrac{x^2-3x-10}{2x^2+3x-2}$ (by $x+2$)

16. $\dfrac{6x^2+13x-5}{6x^3-2x^2}$ (by $3x-1$)

In Exercises 17 through 40 reduce each fraction to its simplest form.

17. $\dfrac{2a}{8a}$

18. $\dfrac{6x}{15x}$

19. $\dfrac{18x^2y}{24xy}$

20. $\dfrac{2a^2xy}{6axyz^2}$

21. $\dfrac{a+b}{5a^2+5ab}$

22. $\dfrac{t-a}{t^2-a^2}$

23. $\dfrac{6a-4b}{4a-2b}$

24. $\dfrac{5r-20s}{10r-5s}$

25. $\dfrac{4x^2+1}{4x^2-1}$

26. $\dfrac{x^2-y^2}{x^2+y^2}$

27. $\dfrac{x^2-8x+16}{x^2-16}$

28. $\dfrac{4a^2+12ab+9b^2}{4a^2+6ab}$

29. $\dfrac{2x^2+5x-3}{x^2+11x+24}$

30. $\dfrac{4r^2-8rs-5s^2}{6r^2-17rs+5s^2}$

31. $\dfrac{x^4-16}{x+2}$

32. $\dfrac{2x^2-8}{4x+8}$

33. $\dfrac{x^2y^4-x^4y^2}{y^2-2xy+x^2}$

34. $\dfrac{8x^3+8x^2+2x}{4x+2}$

35. $\dfrac{(x-1)(3+x)}{(3-x)(1-x)}$

36. $\dfrac{(2x-1)(x+6)}{(x-3)(1-2x)}$

37. $\dfrac{y-x}{2x-2y}$

38. $\dfrac{x^2-y^2}{y-x}$

39. $\dfrac{(x+5)(x-2)(x+2)(3-x)}{(2-x)(5-x)(3+x)(2+x)}$

40. $\dfrac{(2x-3)(3-x)(x-7)(3x+1)}{(3x+2)(3-2x)(x-3)(7+x)}$

...ises 41 through 44 reduce each fraction to its simplest form. This will ...ce of Eqs. (5–7) through (5–10).

42. $\dfrac{x^3-8}{x^2+2x+4}$

44. $\dfrac{a^3-6a^2+12a-8}{a^2-4a+4}$

...determine which fractions are in simplest form.

$\dfrac{4x^2}{16}$

46. (a) $\dfrac{2x+3}{2x+6}$ (b) $\dfrac{2(x+6)}{2x+6}$

47. (a) $\dfrac{x^2 - x - 2}{x^2 - x}$ (b) $\dfrac{x^2 - x - 2}{x^2 + x}$ 48. (a) $\dfrac{x^3 - x}{1 - x}$ (b) $\dfrac{2x^2 + 4x}{2x^2 + 4}$

5—5 Multiplication and Division of Fractions

From arithmetic we recall that *the product of two fractions is a fraction whose numerator is the product of the numerators and whose denominator is the product of the denominators of the given fractions.* Also, we recall that *we can find the quotient of two fractions by inverting the divisor and proceeding as in multiplication.* Symbolically, multiplication of fractions is indicated by

$$\frac{a}{b} \cdot \frac{c}{d} = \frac{ac}{bd}$$

and division is indicated by

$$\frac{\dfrac{a}{b}}{\dfrac{c}{d}} = \frac{a}{b} \cdot \frac{d}{c} = \frac{ad}{bc}$$

The rule for division may be verified by use of the fundamental principle of fractions. By multiplying the numerator and denominator of the fraction

$$\frac{\dfrac{a}{b}}{\dfrac{c}{d}} \quad \text{by} \quad \frac{d}{c} \qquad \text{we obtain} \qquad \frac{\dfrac{a}{b} \cdot \dfrac{d}{c}}{\dfrac{c}{d} \cdot \dfrac{d}{c}}$$

In the resulting denominator $\dfrac{c}{d} \cdot \dfrac{d}{c}$ becomes 1, and therefore the fraction

is written as $\dfrac{ad}{bc}$.

Example A

$$\frac{3}{5} \cdot \frac{2}{7} = \frac{(3)(2)}{(5)(7)} = \frac{6}{35}$$

$$\frac{3a}{5b} \cdot \frac{15b^2}{a} = \frac{(3a)(15b^2)}{(5b)(a)} = \frac{45ab^2}{5ab} = \frac{9b}{1} = 9b$$

In the second illustration, we have divided out the common factor of $5ab$ to reduce the resulting fraction to its simplest form.

We shall usually want to express the result in its simplest form, which is generally its most useful form. Since all factors in the numerators and all factors in the denominators are to be multiplied, we should *first only indicate the multiplication and then factor the numerator and the denominator.* In this way we can easily identify any factors common to both. If we were to multiply out the numerator and the denominator before factoring, it is very possible that we would be unable to factor the result to simplify it. The following example illustrates this point.

Example B

In performing the multiplication

$$\frac{3(x - y)}{(x - y)^2} \cdot \frac{(x^2 - y^2)}{6x + 9y}$$

if we multiply out the numerators and the denominators before performing any factoring, we would have to simplify the fraction

$$\frac{3x^3 - 3x^2y - 3xy^2 + 3y^3}{6x^3 - 3x^2y - 12xy^2 + 9y^3}$$

It is possible to factor the numerator and the denominator, but finding any common factors this way is very difficult. If we first indicate the multiplications and then factor completely, we have

$$\frac{3(x - y)}{(x - y)^2} \cdot \frac{(x^2 - y^2)}{6x + 9y} = \frac{3(x - y)(x^2 - y^2)}{(x - y)^2(6x + 9y)} = \frac{3(x - y)(x + y)(x - y)}{(x - y)^2(3)(2x + 3y)}$$

$$= \frac{3(x - y)^2(x + y)}{3(x - y)^2(2x + 3y)}$$

$$= \frac{x + y}{2x + 3y}$$

The common factor of $3(x - y)^2$ is readily recognized using this procedure.

Example C

$$\frac{2x - 4}{4x + 12} \cdot \frac{2x^2 + x - 15}{3x - 1} = \frac{2(x - 2)(2x - 5)(x + 3)}{4(x + 3)(3x - 1)}$$

$$= \frac{(x - 2)(2x - 5)}{2(3x - 1)}$$

Here the common factor is $2(x + 3)$. It is permissible to multiply out the final form of the numerator and the denominator, but it is often preferable to leave the numerator and denominator in factored form, as indicated.

The following examples illustrate the division of fractions.

Example D

$$\frac{6x}{7} \div \frac{5}{3} = \frac{6x}{7} \cdot \frac{3}{5} = \frac{18x}{35}$$

$$\frac{\dfrac{3a^2}{5c}}{\dfrac{2c^2}{a}} = \frac{3a^2}{5c} \cdot \frac{a}{2c^2} = \frac{3a^3}{10c^3}$$

Example E

$$\frac{x+y}{3} \div \frac{2x+2y}{6x+15y} = \frac{x+y}{3} \cdot \frac{6x+15y}{2x+2y} = \frac{(x+y)(3)(2x+5y)}{3(2)(x+y)}$$

$$= \frac{2x+5y}{2}$$

Example F

$$\frac{\dfrac{4-x^2}{x^2-3x+2}}{\dfrac{x+2}{x^2-9}} = \frac{4-x^2}{x^2-3x+2} \cdot \frac{x^2-9}{x+2}$$

$$= \frac{(2-x)(2+x)(x-3)(x+3)}{(x-2)(x-1)(x+2)}$$

$$= \frac{-(x-2)(x+2)(x-3)(x+3)}{(x-2)(x-1)(x+2)}$$

$$= -\frac{(x-3)(x+3)}{x-1} \quad \text{or} \quad \frac{(x-3)(x+3)}{1-x}$$

Note the use of Eq. (5–11) in the simplification and in expressing an alternate form of the result. The factor $2 - x$ was replaced by its equivalent $-(x - 2)$, and then $x - 1$ was replaced by $-(1 - x)$.

Exercises 5–5

In Exercises 1 through 28 perform the indicated operations and simplify.

1. $\dfrac{3}{8} \cdot \dfrac{2}{7}$ 2. $\dfrac{11}{5} \cdot \dfrac{13}{33}$ 3. $\dfrac{4x}{3y} \cdot \dfrac{9y^2}{2}$ 4. $\dfrac{18sy^3}{ax^2} \cdot \dfrac{(ax)^2}{3s}$

5. $\dfrac{2}{9} \div \dfrac{4}{7}$ 6. $\dfrac{5}{16} \div \dfrac{25}{13}$ 7. $\dfrac{xy}{az} \div \dfrac{bz}{ay}$ 8. $\dfrac{sr^2}{2t} \div \dfrac{st}{4}$

9. $\dfrac{4x+12}{5} \cdot \dfrac{15t}{3x+9}$ 10. $\dfrac{y^2+2y}{6z} \cdot \dfrac{z^3}{y^2-4}$

11. $\dfrac{u^2-v^2}{u+2v} \cdot \dfrac{3u+6v}{u-v}$ 12. $(x-y)\dfrac{x+2y}{x^2-y^2}$

13. $\dfrac{2a + 8}{15} \div \dfrac{a^2 + 8a + 16}{25}$

14. $\dfrac{a^2 - a}{3a + 9} \div \dfrac{a^2 - 2a + 1}{a^2 - 9}$

15. $\dfrac{x^2 - 9}{x} \div (x + 3)^2$

16. $\dfrac{9x^2 - 16}{x + 1} \div (4 - 3x)$

17. $\dfrac{3ax^2 - 9ax}{10x^2 + 5x} \cdot \dfrac{2x^2 + x}{a^2x - 3a^2}$

18. $\dfrac{2x^2 - 18}{x^3 - 25x} \cdot \dfrac{3x - 15}{2x^2 + 6x}$

19. $\dfrac{x^4 - 1}{8x + 16} \cdot \dfrac{2x^2 - 8x}{x^3 + x}$

20. $\dfrac{2x^2 - 4x - 6}{x^2 - 3x} \cdot \dfrac{x^3 - 4x^2}{4x^2 - 4x - 8}$

21. $\dfrac{ax + x^2}{2b - cx} \div \dfrac{a^2 + 2ax + x^2}{2bx - cx^2}$

22. $\dfrac{x^2 - 11x + 28}{x + 3} \div \dfrac{x - 4}{x + 3}$

23. $\dfrac{35a + 25}{12a + 33} \div \dfrac{28a + 20}{36a + 99}$

24. $\dfrac{2a^3 + a^2}{2b^3 + b^2} \div \dfrac{2ab + a}{2ab + b}$

25. $\dfrac{7x^2}{3a} \div \left(\dfrac{a}{x} \cdot \dfrac{a^2x}{x^2} \right)$

26. $\left(\dfrac{3u}{8v^2} \div \dfrac{9u^2}{2w^2} \right) \cdot \dfrac{2u^4}{15vw}$

27. $\left(\dfrac{4t^2 - 1}{t - 5} \div \dfrac{2t + 1}{2t} \right) \cdot \dfrac{2t^2 - 50}{4t^2 + 4t + 1}$

28. $\dfrac{2x^2 - 5x - 3}{x - 4} \div \left(\dfrac{x - 3}{x^2 - 16} \cdot \dfrac{1}{3 - x} \right)$

In Exercises 29 through 32 perform the indicated operations and simplify. Exercises 29 and 30 require the use of Eqs. (5–7) through (5–10), and Exercises 31 and 32 require the use of factoring by grouping.

29. $\dfrac{x^3 - y^3}{2x^2 - 2y^2} \cdot \dfrac{x^2 + 2xy + y^2}{x^2 + xy + y^2}$

30. $\dfrac{x^3 + 3x^2 + 3x + 1}{6x - 6} \div \dfrac{5x + 5}{x^2 - 1}$

31. $\dfrac{ax + bx + ay + by}{p - q} \cdot \dfrac{3p^2 + 4pq - 7q^2}{a + b}$

32. $\dfrac{x^4 + x^5 - 1 - x}{x - 1} \div \dfrac{x + 1}{x}$

In Exercises 33 and 34 solve the given problems.

33. A rectangular metal plate expands when heated. For small values of Celsius temperature, the length and width of a certain plate, as functions of the temperature, are

$$\dfrac{20{,}000 + 300T + T^2}{1600 - T^2} \quad \text{and} \quad \dfrac{16{,}000 + 360T - T^2}{400 + 2T}$$

respectively. Find the resulting expression for the area of the plate as a function of the temperature.

34. The current in a simple electric circuit is the voltage in the circuit divided by the resistance. Given that the voltage and resistance in a certain circuit are expressed as functions of time

$$V = \dfrac{5t + 10}{2t + 1} \quad \text{and} \quad R = \dfrac{t^2 + 4t + 4}{2t}$$

find the formula for the current as a function of time.

5—6 Addition and Subtraction of Fractions

From arithmetic we recall that *the sum of a set of fractions that all have the same denominator is the sum of the numerators divided by the common denominator.* Since algebraic expressions represent numbers, this fact is also true in algebra. Addition and subtraction of such fractions are illustrated in the following example.

Example A

$$\frac{5}{9} + \frac{2}{9} - \frac{4}{9} = \frac{5 + 2 - 4}{9} = \frac{3}{9} = \frac{1}{3}$$

$$\frac{b}{ax} - \frac{1}{ax} + \frac{2b - 1}{ax} = \frac{b - 1 + (2b - 1)}{ax} = \frac{b - 1 + 2b - 1}{ax}$$

$$= \frac{3b - 2}{ax}$$

If the fractions to be combined do not all have the same denominator, we must first change each to an equivalent fraction so that the resulting fractions do have the same denominator. Normally the denominator which is most convenient and useful is the **lowest common denominator.** This is the product of all of the prime factors which appear in the denominators, with each factor raised to the highest power to which it appears in any one of the denominators. Thus, *the lowest common denominator is the simplest algebraic expression into which all the given denominators will divide evenly.* The following two examples illustrate the method used in finding the lowest common denominator of a set of fractions.

Example B

Find the lowest common denominator of the fractions

$$\frac{3}{4a^2b}, \qquad \frac{5}{6ab^3}, \qquad \text{and} \qquad \frac{1}{4ab^2}$$

Expressing each of the denominators in terms of powers of the prime factors, we have

$$4a^2b = 2^2a^2b, \qquad 6ab^3 = 2 \cdot 3 \cdot ab^3, \qquad \text{and} \qquad 4ab^2 = 2^2ab^2$$

The prime factors to be considered are 2, 3, a, and b. The largest exponent of 2 which appears is 2. This means that 2^2 is a factor of the lowest common denominator. The largest exponent of 3 which appears is 1 (understood in the second denominator). Therefore, 3 is a factor of the lowest common denominator. The largest exponent of a which appears is 2, and the largest exponent of b which appears is 3. Thus, a^2 and b^3 are factors of the lowest common denominator. Therefore, the lowest common denominator of the fractions is $2^2 \cdot 3 \cdot a^2b^3 = 12a^2b^3$. This is the simplest expression into which *each* of the denominators above will divide evenly.

Example C

Find the lowest common denominator of the following fractions:

$$\frac{x-4}{x^2-2x+1}, \qquad \frac{1}{x^2-1}, \qquad \frac{x+3}{x^2-x}$$

Factoring each of the denominators, we find that the fractions are

$$\frac{x-4}{(x-1)^2}, \qquad \frac{1}{(x-1)(x+1)}, \qquad \text{and} \qquad \frac{x+3}{x(x-1)}.$$

The factor $(x-1)$ appears in all of the denominators. It is squared in the denominator of the first fraction and appears to the first power only in the other two fractions. Thus, we must have $(x-1)^2$ as a factor of the common denominator. We do not need a higher power of $x-1$ since, as far as this factor is concerned, each denominator will divide into it evenly. Next, the second denominator contains a factor of $(x+1)$. Therefore, the common denominator must also contain a factor of $(x+1)$, otherwise the second denominator would not divide into it evenly. Finally, the third denominator indicates that a factor of x is also required in the common denominator. The lowest common denominator is, therefore, $x(x+1)(x-1)^2$. All three denominators will divide evenly into this expression, and there is no simpler expression for which this is true.

Once we have found the lowest common denominator for the fractions, we multiply the numerator and denominator of each fraction by the proper quantity to make the resulting denominator in each case the common denominator. After this step, it is necessary only to add the numerators, place this result over the common denominator, and simplify.

Example D

Combine $\dfrac{2}{3r^2} + \dfrac{4}{rs^3} - \dfrac{5}{3s}$.

By looking at the denominators, we see that the factors necessary in the lowest common denominator are 3, r, and s. The 3 appears only to the first power, the largest exponent of r is 2, and the largest exponent of s is 3. Therefore, the lowest common denominator is $3r^2s^3$. We now wish to write each fraction with this quantity as the denominator. Since the denominator of the first fraction already contains factors of 3 and r^2, it is necessary to introduce the factor of s^3. In other words, we must multiply the numerator and denominator of this fraction by s^3. For similar reasons, we must multiply the numerators and the denominators of the second and third fractions by $3r$ and r^2s^2, respectively. This leads to

$$\frac{2}{3r^2} + \frac{4}{rs^3} - \frac{5}{3s} = \frac{2(s^3)}{(3r^2)(s^3)} + \frac{4(3r)}{(rs^3)(3r)} - \frac{5(r^2s^2)}{(3s)(r^2s^2)}$$

$$= \frac{2s^3}{3r^2s^3} + \frac{12r}{3r^2s^3} - \frac{5r^2s^2}{3r^2s^3}$$

$$= \frac{2s^3 + 12r - 5r^2s^2}{3r^2s^3}$$

Example E

$$\frac{a}{x-1} + \frac{a}{x+1} = \frac{a(x+1)}{(x-1)(x+1)} + \frac{a(x-1)}{(x+1)(x-1)}$$

$$= \frac{ax + a + ax - a}{(x+1)(x-1)}$$

$$= \frac{2ax}{(x+1)(x-1)}$$

When we multiply each fraction by the quantity required to obtain the proper denominator, we do not actually have to write the common denominator under each numerator. Placing all the products which appear in the numerators over the common denominator is sufficient. Hence the illustration in this example would appear as

$$\frac{a}{x-1} + \frac{a}{x+1} = \frac{a(x+1) + a(x-1)}{(x-1)(x+1)} = \frac{ax + a + ax - a}{(x-1)(x+1)}$$

$$= \frac{2ax}{(x-1)(x+1)}$$

Example F

$$\frac{x-1}{x^2-25} - \frac{2}{x-5} = \frac{(x-1) - 2(x+5)}{(x-5)(x+5)} = \frac{x-1-2x-10}{(x-5)(x+5)}$$

$$= \frac{-(x+11)}{(x-5)(x+5)}$$

Example G

$$\frac{3x}{x^2-x-12} - \frac{x-1}{x^2-8x+16} - \frac{6-x}{2x-8}$$

$$= \frac{3x}{(x-4)(x+3)} - \frac{x-1}{(x-4)^2} - \frac{6-x}{2(x-4)}$$

$$= \frac{3x(2)(x-4) - (x-1)(2)(x+3) - (6-x)(x-4)(x+3)}{2(x-4)^2(x+3)}$$

$$= \frac{6x^2 - 24x - 2x^2 - 4x + 6 + x^3 - 7x^2 - 6x + 72}{2(x-4)^2(x+3)}$$

$$= \frac{x^3 - 3x^2 - 34x + 78}{2(x-4)^2(x+3)}$$

One note of caution must be sounded here. In doing this kind of problem, many errors may arise in the use of the minus sign. Remember, if a minus sign precedes a given expression, the signs of *all* terms in that expression must be changed before they can be combined with the other terms.

Example H
Simplify the fraction

$$\frac{1 + \dfrac{2}{x - 1}}{\dfrac{x^2 + x}{x^2 + x - 2}}$$

Before performing the indicated division, we first perform the indicated addition in the numerator. The numerator becomes

$$\frac{(x - 1) + 2}{x - 1} \qquad \text{or} \qquad \frac{x + 1}{x - 1}$$

This expression now replaces the numerator of the original fraction. Making this substitution and inverting the divisor, we then proceed with the simplification:

$$\frac{x + 1}{x - 1} \cdot \frac{x^2 + x - 2}{x^2 + x} = \frac{(x + 1)(x + 2)(x - 1)}{(x - 1)(x)(x + 1)} = \frac{x + 2}{x}$$

This is an example of what is known as a **complex fraction**. In a complex fraction the numerator, the denominator, or both numerator and denominator contain fractions.

Exercises 5—6

In Exercises 1 through 36 perform the indicated operations and simplify.

1. $\dfrac{3}{5} + \dfrac{6}{5}$

2. $\dfrac{2}{13} + \dfrac{6}{13}$

3. $\dfrac{1}{x} + \dfrac{7}{x}$

4. $\dfrac{2}{a} + \dfrac{3}{a}$

5. $\dfrac{1}{2} + \dfrac{3}{4}$

6. $\dfrac{5}{9} - \dfrac{1}{3}$

7. $\dfrac{3}{4x} + \dfrac{7a}{4}$

8. $\dfrac{t - 3}{a} - \dfrac{t}{2a}$

9. $\dfrac{a}{x} - \dfrac{b}{x^2}$

10. $\dfrac{2}{s^2} + \dfrac{3}{s}$

11. $\dfrac{6}{5x^3} + \dfrac{a}{25x}$

12. $\dfrac{a}{6y} - \dfrac{2b}{3y^4}$

13. $\dfrac{2}{5a} + \dfrac{1}{a} - \dfrac{a}{10}$

14. $\dfrac{2}{a} - \dfrac{6}{b} - \dfrac{9}{c}$

15. $\dfrac{x + 1}{x} - \dfrac{x - 3}{y} - \dfrac{2 - x}{xy}$

16. $5 + \dfrac{1 - x}{2} - \dfrac{3 + x}{4}$

17. $\dfrac{3}{2x-1} + \dfrac{1}{4x-2}$

18. $\dfrac{5}{6y+3} - \dfrac{a}{8y+4}$

19. $\dfrac{4}{x(x+1)} - \dfrac{3}{2x}$

20. $\dfrac{3}{ax+ay} - \dfrac{1}{a^2}$

21. $\dfrac{s}{2s-6} + \dfrac{1}{4} - \dfrac{3s}{4s-12}$

22. $\dfrac{2}{x+2} - \dfrac{3-x}{x^2+2x} + \dfrac{1}{x}$

23. $\dfrac{3x}{x^2-9} - \dfrac{2}{x+3}$

24. $\dfrac{2}{x^2+4x+4} - \dfrac{3}{x+2}$

25. $\dfrac{3}{x^2-8x+16} - \dfrac{2}{4-x}$

26. $\dfrac{1}{a^2-1} - \dfrac{2}{1-a}$

27. $\dfrac{3}{x^2-11x+30} - \dfrac{2}{x^2-25}$

28. $\dfrac{x-1}{2x^3-4x^2} + \dfrac{5}{x-2}$

29. $\dfrac{x-1}{3x^2-13x+4} - \dfrac{3x+1}{4-x}$

30. $\dfrac{x}{4x^2-12x+5} + \dfrac{2x-1}{4x^2-4x-15}$

31. $\dfrac{t}{t^2-t-6} - \dfrac{2t}{t^2+6t+9} + \dfrac{t}{t^2-9}$

32. $\dfrac{5}{2x^3-3x^2+x} - \dfrac{x}{x^4-x^2} + \dfrac{2-x}{2x^2+x-1}$

33. $\dfrac{1+\dfrac{1}{x}}{1-\dfrac{1}{x}}$

34. $\dfrac{x-\dfrac{1}{x}}{1-\dfrac{1}{x}}$

35. $\dfrac{x-\dfrac{1}{x}-\dfrac{2}{x+1}}{\dfrac{1}{x^2+2x+1}-1}$

36. $\dfrac{\dfrac{2}{a}-\dfrac{1}{4}-\dfrac{3}{4a-4b}}{\dfrac{1}{4a^2-4b^2}-\dfrac{2}{b}}$

The expression $f(x+h) - f(x)$ is frequently used in the study of calculus. In Exercises 37 through 40 determine and then simplify this expression for the given functions.

37. $f(x) = \dfrac{x}{x+1}$

38. $f(x) = \dfrac{3}{2x-1}$

39. $f(x) = \dfrac{1}{x^2}$

40. $f(x) = \dfrac{2}{x^2+4}$

In Exercises 41 through 48 simplify the given expressions.

41. Using the definitions of the trigonometric functions given in Section 3–2, find an expression equivalent to $(\tan \theta)(\cot \theta) + (\sin \theta)^2 - \cos \theta$, in terms of x, y, and r.

42. Using the definitions of the trigonometric functions given in Section 3–2, find an expression equivalent to $\sec \theta - (\cot \theta)^2 + \csc \theta$, in terms of x, y, and r.

43. If $f(x) = 2x - x^2$, find $f(\frac{1}{a})$.

44. If $f(x) = x^2 + x$, find $f(a + \frac{1}{a})$.

45. The analysis of the forces acting on a certain type of concrete slab gives the expression

$$1 - \frac{4c}{\pi l} + \frac{c^3}{3l^3}$$

Combine and simplify.

46. Experimentation to determine the velocity of light may use the expression

$$1 + \frac{v^2}{2c^2} + \frac{3v^4}{4c^4}$$

Combine and simplify.

47. In finding an expression to describe a magnetic field, the following expression is found.

$$\frac{b}{x^2 + y^2} - \frac{2bx^2}{(x^2 + y^2)^2}$$

Perform the indicated subtraction.

48. The expression for the volumetric expansion of liquids in terms of density ρ and temperature T is

$$\frac{\dfrac{1}{\rho_2} - \dfrac{1}{\rho_1}}{\dfrac{(T_2 - T_1)\left(\dfrac{1}{\rho_1} + \dfrac{1}{\rho_2}\right)}{2}}$$

Simplify this expression.

5—7 Equations Involving Fractions

Many important equations in science and technology have fractions in them. Although the solution of these equations will still involve the use of the basic operations stated in Section 1–10, an additional procedure can be used to eliminate the fractions and thereby help lead to the solution. The method is to **multiply each term of the equation by the lowest common denominator.** The resulting equation will not involve fractions and can be solved by methods previously discussed. The following examples illustrate how to solve equations involving fractions.

Example A

Solve for x: $\dfrac{x}{12} - \dfrac{1}{8} = \dfrac{x + 2}{6}$.

We first note that the lowest common denominator of the terms of the equation is 24. Therefore, we multiply each term by 24. This gives

$$\frac{24(x)}{12} - \frac{24(1)}{8} = \frac{24(x+2)}{6}$$

We reduce each term to its lowest terms, and solve the resulting equation.

$$2x - 3 = 4(x+2)$$
$$2x - 3 = 4x + 8$$
$$-2x = 11$$
$$x = -\frac{11}{2}$$

When we check this solution in the original equation, we obtain $-\frac{7}{12}$ on each side of the equals sign. Therefore, the solution is correct.

Example B

Solve for x: $\dfrac{x}{2} - \dfrac{1}{b^2} = \dfrac{x}{2b}$.

We first determine that the lowest common denominator of the terms of the equation is $2b^2$. We then multiply each term by $2b^2$ and continue with the solution.

$$\frac{2b^2(x)}{2} - \frac{2b^2(1)}{b^2} = \frac{2b^2(x)}{2b}$$

$$b^2x - 2 = bx$$

$$b^2x - bx = 2$$

To complete the solution for x, we must factor x from the terms on the left. Therefore, we have

$$x(b^2 - b) = 2$$

$$x = \frac{2}{b^2 - b}$$

Checking shows that each side of the original equation is $1/b^2(b-1)$.

Example C

When developing the equations which describe the motion of the planets, the equation

$$\frac{1}{2}v^2 - \frac{GM}{r} = -\frac{GM}{2a}$$

is found. Solve for M.

We first determine that the lowest common denominator of the terms of the equation is $2ar$. Multiplying each term by $2ar$ and proceeding with the solution, we have

$$\frac{2ar(v^2)}{2} - \frac{2ar(GM)}{r} = -\frac{2ar(GM)}{2a}$$

$$arv^2 - 2aGM = -rGM$$

$$rGM - 2aGM = -arv^2$$

$$M(rG - 2aG) = -arv^2$$

$$M = -\frac{arv^2}{rG - 2aG} \quad \text{or} \quad \frac{arv^2}{2aG - rG}$$

The second form of the result is obtained by using Eq. (5–11). Again, note the use of factoring to arrive at the final result.

Example D

Solve for x: $\dfrac{2}{x + 1} - \dfrac{1}{x} = -\dfrac{2}{x^2 + x}$.

Multiplying each term by the lowest common denominator $x(x + 1)$, and continuing with the solution, we have

$$\frac{2(x)(x + 1)}{x + 1} - \frac{x(x + 1)}{x} = -\frac{2x(x + 1)}{x(x + 1)}$$

$$2x - (x + 1) = -2$$

$$2x - x - 1 = -2$$

$$x = -1$$

Checking this solution *in the original equation,* we see that we have zero in the denominators of the first and third terms of the equation. Since division by zero is undefined (see Section 1–3), $x = -1$ cannot be a solution. *Thus there is no solution to this equation.* This example points out clearly why it is necessary to check solutions in the original equation. It also shows that whenever we multiply each term by a common denominator which *contains the unknown,* it is possible to obtain a value which is not a solution of the original equation. Such a value is termed an **extraneous solution.** Only certain equations will lead to extraneous solutions, but we must be careful to identify them when they occur.

Example E

One pipe can fill a certain oil storage tank in 4 h, while a second pipe can fill it in 6 h. How long will it take to fill the tank if both pipes operate together?

First, we let $x =$ the number of hours required to fill the tank with both pipes operating.

We know that it takes the first pipe 4 h to fill the tank. Therefore, it fills $\frac{1}{4}$ of the tank each hour it operates. This means that it fills $\frac{1}{4}x$ of the tank in x hours. In the same way, the second pipe fills $\frac{1}{6}x$ of the tank in x hours. When x hours have passed, the two pipes will have filled the whole tank (1 represents *one* tank).

$$\frac{x}{4} + \frac{x}{6} = 1$$

Multiplying each term by 12, we have

$$\frac{12x}{4} + \frac{12x}{6} = 12(1)$$

$$3x + 2x = 12$$
$$5x = 12$$
$$x = \frac{12}{5} = 2.4 \text{ h}$$

Therefore, it takes the two pipes 2.4 h to fill the tank when operating together.

Exercises 5—7

In Exercises 1 through 28 solve the given equations and check the results.

1. $\dfrac{x}{2} + 6 = 2x$

2. $\dfrac{x}{5} + 2 = \dfrac{15 + x}{10}$

3. $\dfrac{x}{6} - \dfrac{1}{2} = \dfrac{x}{3}$

4. $\dfrac{3x}{8} - \dfrac{3}{4} = \dfrac{x - 4}{2}$

5. $\dfrac{1}{2} - \dfrac{t - 5}{6} = \dfrac{3}{4}$

6. $\dfrac{2x - 7}{3} + 5 = \dfrac{1}{5}$

7. $\dfrac{3x}{7} - \dfrac{5}{21} = \dfrac{2 - x}{14}$

8. $\dfrac{x - 3}{12} - \dfrac{2}{3} = \dfrac{1 - 3x}{2}$

9. $\dfrac{3}{x} + 2 = \dfrac{5}{3}$

10. $\dfrac{1}{2y} - \dfrac{1}{2} = 4$

11. $3 - \dfrac{x - 2}{x} = \dfrac{1}{3}$

12. $\dfrac{1}{2x} - \dfrac{1}{3} = \dfrac{2}{x}$

13. $\dfrac{2y}{y - 1} = 5$

14. $\dfrac{x}{2x - 3} = 4$

15. $\dfrac{2}{s} = \dfrac{3}{s - 1}$

16. $\dfrac{5}{n + 2} = \dfrac{3}{2n}$

17. $\dfrac{5}{2x + 4} + \dfrac{3}{x + 2} = 2$

18. $\dfrac{3}{4x - 6} + \dfrac{1}{4} = \dfrac{5}{2x - 3}$

19. $\dfrac{4}{4 - x} + 2 - \dfrac{2}{12 - 3x} = \dfrac{1}{3}$

20. $\dfrac{2}{z - 5} - \dfrac{3}{10 - 2z} = 3$

21. $\dfrac{1}{x} + \dfrac{3}{2x} = \dfrac{2}{x + 1}$

22. $\dfrac{3}{t + 3} - \dfrac{1}{t} = \dfrac{5}{2t + 6}$

23. $\dfrac{1}{2x + 3} = \dfrac{5}{2x} - \dfrac{4}{2x^2 + 3x}$

24. $\dfrac{7}{y} = \dfrac{3}{y - 4} + \dfrac{7}{2y^2 - 8y}$

25. $\dfrac{1}{x^2 - x} - \dfrac{1}{x} = \dfrac{1}{x - 1}$

26. $\dfrac{2}{x^2 - 1} - \dfrac{2}{x + 1} = \dfrac{1}{x - 1}$

27. $\dfrac{2}{x^2 - 4} - \dfrac{1}{x - 2} = \dfrac{1}{2x + 4}$

28. $\dfrac{2}{2x^2 + 5x - 3} - \dfrac{1}{4x - 2} + \dfrac{3}{2x + 6} = 0$

In Exercises 29 through 36 solve for the indicated letter.

29. $2 - \dfrac{1}{b} + \dfrac{3}{c} = 0$, for c

30. $\dfrac{2}{3} - \dfrac{h}{x} = \dfrac{1}{2x}$, for x

31. $\dfrac{t - 3}{b} - \dfrac{t}{2b - 1} = \dfrac{1}{2}$, for t

32. $\dfrac{1}{a^2 + 2a} - \dfrac{y}{2a} = \dfrac{2y}{a + 2}$, for y

33. An equation used in nuclear physics is

$$E = V_0 + \dfrac{(m + M)V^2}{2} + \dfrac{p^2}{2I}$$

Solve for M.

34. An equation obtained in analyzing a certain electric circuit is

$$\dfrac{V - 6}{5} + \dfrac{V - 8}{15} + \dfrac{V}{10} = 0$$

Solve for V.

35. Under specified conditions, the combined resistance R of resistances R_1, R_2, and r is given by the equation

$$\dfrac{1}{R} = \dfrac{1}{R_1 + r} + \dfrac{1}{R_2}$$

Solve for R_1.

36. An equation used in hydrodynamics is

$$F = PA + \dfrac{dQ^2}{gA_1} - \dfrac{dQ^2}{gA_2}$$

Solve for A.

In Exercises 37 through 40 set up appropriate equations and solve the given stated problems.

37. One data-processing card sorter can sort a certain number of cards in 6 min, and a second sorter can sort the same number in 9 min. How long would it take the two sorters together to sort this number of cards?

38. One steamshovel can excavate a certain site in 5 days, while it takes a second steamshovel 8 days. How long would it take the two working together?

39. The width of a particular rectangular land area is $\frac{2}{3}$ that of the length. If the perimeter is 192 m, find the dimensions.

40. The current in a certain stream flows at 3 mi/h. A motorboat can travel downstream 23 mi in the same time it can travel 11 mi upstream. What is the boat's rate in still water?

5–8 Exercises for Chapter 5

In Exercises 1 through 12 find the products *by inspection*. No intermediate steps should be necessary.

1. $3a(4x + 5a)$
2. $-7xy(4x^2 - 7y)$
3. $(2a + 7b)(2a - 7b)$
4. $(x - 4z)(x + 4z)$
5. $(2a + 1)^2$
6. $(4x - 3y)^2$
7. $(b - 4)(b + 7)$
8. $(y - 5)(y - 7)$
9. $(2x + 5)(x - 9)$
10. $(4ax - 3)(5ax + 7)$
11. $(2c + d)(8c - d)$
12. $(3s - 2t)(8s + 3t)$

In Exercises 13 through 44 factor the given expressions completely. Exercises 37 through 40 illustrate Eqs. (5–7) through (5–10), and Exercises 41 through 44 illustrate factoring by grouping.

13. $3s + 9t$
14. $7x - 28y$
15. $a^2x^2 + a^2$
16. $3ax - 6ax^4 - 9a$
17. $x^2 - 144$
18. $900 - n^2$
19. $400r^2 - t^4$
20. $25s^4 - 36t^2$
21. $9t^2 - 6t + 1$
22. $4x^2 - 12x + 9$
23. $25t^2 + 10t + 1$
24. $4x^2 + 36xy + 81y^2$
25. $x^2 + x - 56$
26. $x^2 - 4x - 45$
27. $t^2 - 5t - 36$
28. $n^2 - 11n + 10$
29. $2x^2 - x - 36$
30. $5x^2 + 2x - 3$
31. $4x^2 - 4x - 35$
32. $9x^2 + 7x - 16$
33. $10b^2 + 23b - 5$
34. $12x^2 - 7xy - 12y^2$
35. $4x^2 - 64$
36. $4a^2x^2 + 26a^2x + 36a^2$
37. $x^3 + 9x^2 + 27x + 27$
38. $x^3 - 3x^2 + 3x - 1$
39. $8x^3 + 27$
40. $x^3 - 125$
41. $ab^2 - 3b^2 + a - 3$
42. $axy - ay + ax - a$
43. $nx + 5n - x^2 + 25$
44. $ty - 4t + y^2 - 16$

In Exercises 45 through 64 perform the indicated operations and express results in simplest form.

45. $\dfrac{48ax^3y^6}{9a^3xy^6}$
46. $\dfrac{-39r^2s^4t^8}{52rs^5t}$

47. $\dfrac{6x^2 - 7x - 3}{4x^2 - 8x + 3}$
48. $\dfrac{x^2 - 3x - 4}{x^2 - x - 12}$

49. $\dfrac{4x + 4y}{35x^2} \cdot \dfrac{28x}{x^2 - y^2}$
50. $\dfrac{6x - 3}{x^2} \cdot \dfrac{4x^2 - 12x}{12x - 6}$

51. $\dfrac{18 - 6x}{x^2 - 6x + 9} \div \dfrac{x^2 - 2x - 15}{x^2 - 9}$
52. $\dfrac{6x^2 - xy - y^2}{2x^2 + xy - y^2} \div \dfrac{4x^2 - 16y^2}{x^2 + 3xy + 2y^2}$

53. $\dfrac{\dfrac{3x}{7x^2 + 13x - 2}}{\dfrac{6x^2}{x^2 + 4x + 4}}$
54. $\dfrac{\dfrac{3x - 3y}{2x^2 + 3xy - 2y^2}}{\dfrac{3x^2 - 3y^2}{x^2 + 4xy + 4y^2}}$

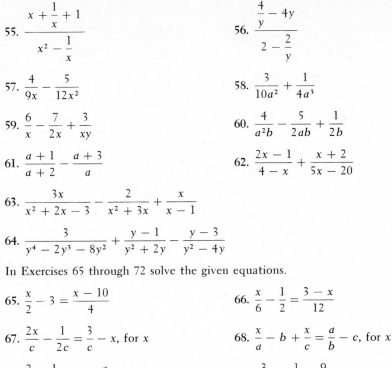

55. $\dfrac{x + \dfrac{1}{x} + 1}{x^2 - \dfrac{1}{x}}$

56. $\dfrac{\dfrac{4}{y} - 4y}{2 - \dfrac{2}{y}}$

57. $\dfrac{4}{9x} - \dfrac{5}{12x^2}$

58. $\dfrac{3}{10a^2} + \dfrac{1}{4a^3}$

59. $\dfrac{6}{x} - \dfrac{7}{2x} + \dfrac{3}{xy}$

60. $\dfrac{4}{a^2 b} - \dfrac{5}{2ab} + \dfrac{1}{2b}$

61. $\dfrac{a + 1}{a + 2} - \dfrac{a + 3}{a}$

62. $\dfrac{2x - 1}{4 - x} + \dfrac{x + 2}{5x - 20}$

63. $\dfrac{3x}{x^2 + 2x - 3} - \dfrac{2}{x^2 + 3x} + \dfrac{x}{x - 1}$

64. $\dfrac{3}{y^4 - 2y^3 - 8y^2} + \dfrac{y - 1}{y^2 + 2y} - \dfrac{y - 3}{y^2 - 4y}$

In Exercises 65 through 72 solve the given equations.

65. $\dfrac{x}{2} - 3 = \dfrac{x - 10}{4}$

66. $\dfrac{x}{6} - \dfrac{1}{2} = \dfrac{3 - x}{12}$

67. $\dfrac{2x}{c} - \dfrac{1}{2c} = \dfrac{3}{c} - x$, for x

68. $\dfrac{x}{a} - b + \dfrac{x}{c} = \dfrac{a}{b} - c$, for x

69. $\dfrac{2}{t} - \dfrac{1}{at} = 2 + \dfrac{a}{t}$, for t

70. $\dfrac{3}{a^2 y} - \dfrac{1}{ay} = \dfrac{9}{a}$, for y

71. $\dfrac{2x}{x^2 - 3x} - \dfrac{3}{x} = \dfrac{1}{2x - 6}$

72. $\dfrac{3}{x^2 + 3x} - \dfrac{1}{x} = \dfrac{1}{x + 3}$

In Exercises 73 through 88 perform the indicated operations.

73. Show that

$$xy = \frac{1}{4}[(x + y)^2 - (x - y)^2]$$

74. Show that

$$x^2 + y^2 = \frac{1}{2}[(x + y)^2 + (x - y)^2]$$

75. To find the side of a rectangle of a given area, it is necessary to factor the expression $x^2 - 3x - 70$. Factor this expression.

76. Under certain conditions, in order to find the total profit of an article selling for p dollars, one must factor the expression $2p^2 - 126p + 360$. Factor this expression.

77. If the edge of one cube is $x + 4$ and the edge of another cube is x, the difference in their volumes is $(x + 4)^3 - x^3$. Expand $(x + 4)^3$, simplify the resulting expression, and then factor.

78. An expression which occurs in the study of nuclear physics is

$$pa^2 + (1 - p)b^2 - [pa + (1 - p)b]^2$$

Expand the third term and then factor by grouping.

79. In finding the velocity of an object subject to specified conditions, it is necessary to simplify the expression

$$\frac{(t + 1)^2 - 2t(t + 1)}{(t + 1)^4}$$

Simplify this expression.

80. An expression found in solving a problem related to alternating-current power is

$$\frac{\dfrac{s + 10}{10}}{\left(\dfrac{s + 20}{20}\right)\left(\dfrac{s + 60}{60}\right)}$$

Simplify this expression.

81. An expression found in determining the tension in a certain cable is

$$1 + \frac{w^2x^2}{6T^2} - \frac{w^4x^4}{40T^4}$$

Combine and simplify.

82. An expression found in the analysis of the dynamics of missile firing is

$$\frac{1}{s} - \frac{1}{s + 4} + \frac{8}{(s + 4)^2}$$

Perform the indicated operations.

83. An expression found in the study of electronic amplifiers is

$$\frac{\left(\dfrac{\mu}{\mu + 1}\right)R}{\dfrac{r}{\mu + 1} + R}$$

Simplify this expression. (μ is the Greek letter mu.)

84. An expression which arises when finding the path between two points requiring the least time is

$$\frac{\dfrac{u^2}{2g} - x}{\dfrac{1}{2gc^2} - \dfrac{u^2}{2g} + x}$$

Simplify this expression.

85. The focal length f of a lens, in terms of its image distance q and object distance p, is given by

$$\frac{1}{f} = \frac{1}{p} + \frac{1}{q}$$

Solve for q.

86. The combined capacitance C of three capacitors connected in series is

$$\frac{1}{C} = \frac{1}{C_1} + \frac{1}{C_2} + \frac{1}{C_3}$$

Solve for C_1.

87. An equation used in studying the deflection of a beam is

$$\theta = \frac{wL^3}{24EI} - \frac{ML}{6EI}$$

Solve for M.

88. An equation determined during the study of the characteristics of a certain chemical solution is

$$X = \frac{H}{RT_1} - \frac{H}{RT}$$

Solve for T.

In Exercises 89 through 92 set up appropriate equations and solve the given stated problems.

89. If one riveter can do a certain job in 12 d, and a second riveter can do it in 16 d, how long will it take them to do it together?

90. Two crews are working on an oil pipeline. Crew A can lay pipe at the rate of 2000 m/d, and crew B can lay pipe at the rate of 2500 m/d. How long will it take the two crews together to lay 10,000 m of pipe?

91. One quality control inspector can properly inspect 50 parts per day, and a second inspector can inspect 30 parts per day. They are put on a project together to inspect 200 parts. After 1.5 d the second inspector becomes ill and leaves the project. How long does the project take?

92. A person travels from city A to city B on a train which averages 40 mi/h. He spends 4 h in city B and then returns to city A on a jet which averages 600 mi/h. If the total trip takes 20 h, how far is it from city A to city B?

6

Quadratic Equations

6-1 Quadratic Equations; Solution by Factoring

The solution of simple equations was first introduced in Chapter 1. Then, in Chapter 4, we extended the solution of equations to systems of linear equations. With the development of the algebraic operations in Chapter 5, we are now in a position to solve another important type of equation, the **quadratic equation**.

Given that a, b, and c are constants, the equation

$$ax^2 + bx + c = 0 \tag{6-1}$$

is called the **general quadratic equation in x.** From Eq. (6–1) we can see that the left side of the equation is a polynomial function of degree 2. *This function, $ax^2 + bx + c$, is known as the* **quadratic function.**

Quadratic equations and quadratic functions are found in applied problems of many technical fields of study. For example, in describing projectile motion, the equation $s_0 + v_0t - 16t^2 = 0$ is found; in analyzing electric power, the function $EI - RI^2$ is found; and in determining the forces on beams, the function $ax^2 + bLx + cL^2$ is used.

Since it is the x^2 term that distinguishes the quadratic equation from other types of equations, the equation is not quadratic if $a = 0$. However, b or c or both may be zero, and the equation is quadratic. We should recognize a quadratic equation even when it does not initially appear in the form of Eq. (6–1). The following examples illustrate the recognition of quadratic equations.

Example A

The following are quadratic equations.

$x^2 - 4x - 5 = 0$	($a = 1$, $b = -4$, and $c = -5$)
$3x^2 - 6 = 0$	($a = 3$, $b = 0$, and $c = -6$)
$2x^2 + 7x = 0$	($a = 2$, $b = 7$, and $c = 0$)
$(a - 3)x^2 - ax + 7 = 0$	(The constants in Eq. (6–1) may include literal expressions. In this case, $a - 3$ takes the place of a, $-a$ takes the place of b, and $c = 7$.)
$4x^2 - 2x = x^2$	(After all the terms have been collected on the left side, the equation becomes $3x^2 - 2x = 0$.)
$(x + 1)^2 = 4$	(Expanding the left side, and collecting all terms on the left, we have $x^2 + 2x - 3 = 0$.)

Example B

The following are not quadratic equations.

$bx - 6 = 0$	(There is no x^2-term.)
$x^3 - x^2 - 5 = 0$	(There should be no term of degree higher than 2. Thus there can be no x^3-term in a quadratic equation.)
$x^2 + x - 7 = x^2$	(When terms are collected, there will be no x^2-term.)

From our previous work, we recall that the solution of an equation consists of all numbers which, when substituted in the equation, produce equality. Normally there are two such numbers for a quadratic equation, although occasionally there is only one number. In any case, there cannot be more than two roots of a quadratic equation. Also, due to the presence of the x^2-term, the roots may be imaginary numbers.

Example C

The quadratic equation

$$3x^2 - 7x + 2 = 0$$

has the roots $x = \frac{1}{3}$ and $x = 2$. This can be seen by substituting these values into the equation.

$$3\left(\frac{1}{3}\right)^2 - 7\left(\frac{1}{3}\right) + 2 = 3\left(\frac{1}{9}\right) - \frac{7}{3} + 2 = \frac{1}{3} - \frac{7}{3} + 2 = \frac{0}{3} = 0$$

$$3(2)^2 - 7(2) + 2 = 3(4) - 14 + 2 = 12 - 14 + 2 = 0$$

The quadratic equation

$$4x^2 - 4x + 1 = 0$$

has the *double root* (both roots the same) of $x = \frac{1}{2}$. This can be seen to be a solution by substitution:

$$4\left(\frac{1}{2}\right)^2 - 4\left(\frac{1}{2}\right) + 1 = 4\left(\frac{1}{4}\right) - 2 + 1 = 1 - 2 + 1 = 0$$

The quadratic equation

$$x^2 + 9 = 0$$

has roots of $x = 3j$ and $x = -3j$. Remembering that $j = \sqrt{-1}$, which means that $j^2 = -1$, we have

$$(3j)^2 + 9 = 9j^2 + 9 = 9(-1) + 9 = -9 + 9 = 0$$
$$(-3j)^2 + 9 = (-3)^2 j^2 + 9 = 9j^2 + 9 = 9(-1) + 9 = 0$$

In this section we shall deal only with those quadratic equations whose quadratic expression is factorable. Therefore, all roots will be rational. *To solve a quadratic equation by factoring, we collect all terms on the left so that the equation will be in the general form of Eq. (6–1). Then we factor the left side and set each factor, individually, equal to zero.* Here we are using the fact that a product is zero if any of its factors is zero. The solutions of the resulting linear equations constitute the solution of the quadratic equation.

Example D

$$x^2 - x - 12 = 0$$
$$(x - 4)(x + 3) = 0$$
$$x - 4 = 0 \quad \text{or} \quad x = 4$$
$$x + 3 = 0 \quad \text{or} \quad x = -3$$

The roots are $x = 4$ and $x = -3$. We can check them in the original equation by substitution. For the root $x = 4$, we have

$$(4)^2 - (4) - 12 \overset{?}{=} 0$$
$$0 = 0$$

For the root $x = -3$, we have

$$(-3)^2 - (-3) - 12 \overset{?}{=} 0$$
$$0 = 0$$

Both roots satisfy the original equation.

Example E

$$2x^2 + 7x - 4 = 0$$
$$(2x - 1)(x + 4) = 0$$

$$2x - 1 = 0 \quad \text{or} \quad x = \frac{1}{2}$$
$$x + 4 = 0 \quad \text{or} \quad x = -4$$

Therefore, the roots are $x = \frac{1}{2}$ and $x = -4$. These roots can be checked by the same procedure used in Example D.

Example F

$$x^2 + 4 = 4x$$
$$x^2 - 4x + 4 = 0$$
$$(x - 2)(x - 2) = 0$$
$$x - 2 = 0 \quad \text{or} \quad x = 2$$

Since both factors are the same, there is a double root of $x = 2$.

It is essential for the expression on the left to be equal to zero, because if a product equals a nonzero number, there is no assurance that either of the factors equals this number. Again, the first step must be to write the equation in the form of Eq. (6–1).

Example G

A car travels to and from a city 180 mi distant in 8.5 h. If the average speed on the return trip is 5 mi/h less than on the trip to the city, what was the average speed of the car when it was going toward the city?

Let $x = $ average speed of car going to the city, and $t = $ time to travel to the city. By our choice of unknowns we may state that $xt = $ 180 (speed times time equals distance). Also, we know that the speed on the return trip was $x - 5$ and that the required time for the return trip was $8.5 - t$. Since the distance traveled returning was also 180 mi, we may state that $(x - 5)(8.5 - t) = 180$. Because we wish to find x, we can eliminate t between the equations by substitution.

$$(x - 5)\left(8.5 - \frac{180}{x}\right) = 180$$

$(x - 5)(17x - 360) = 360x$	Each side multiplied by $2x$.
$17x^2 - 360x - 85x + 1800 = 360x$	Remove parentheses.
$17x^2 - 805x + 1800 = 0$	Collect all terms to one side.
$(17x - 40)(x - 45) = 0$	Factor the quadratic expression.

$$17x - 40 = 0 \quad \text{or} \quad x = \frac{40}{17}$$
$$x - 45 = 0 \quad \text{or} \quad x = 45$$

The factors lead to two possible solutions, but only one of them has meaning for this problem. The solution $x = \frac{40}{17}$ cannot be the solution, since the return rate of 5 mi/h less would then be negative. Therefore, the solution is $x = 45$ mi/h. By substitution it is found that this solution satisfies the given conditions.

Exercises 6–1

In Exercises 1 through 8 determine whether or not the given equations are quadratic by performing algebraic operations which could put each in the form of Eq. (6–1). If the resulting form is quadratic, identify a, b, and c, with $a > 0$.

1. $x^2 + 5 = 8x$
2. $5x^2 = 9 - x$
3. $x(x - 2) = 4$
4. $(3x - 2)^2 = 2$
5. $x^2 = (x + 2)^2$
6. $x(2x + 5) = 7 + 2x^2$
7. $x(x^2 + x - 1) = x^3$
8. $(x - 7)^2 = (2x + 3)^2$

In Exercises 9 through 40 solve the given quadratic equations by factoring.

9. $x^2 - 4 = 0$
10. $x^2 - 400 = 0$
11. $x^2 - 8x - 9 = 0$
12. $s^2 + s - 6 = 0$
13. $x^2 - 7x + 12 = 0$
14. $x^2 - 11x + 30 = 0$
15. $x^2 = -2x$
16. $x^2 = 7x$
17. $4y^2 - 9 = 0$
18. $5p^2 - 80 = 0$
19. $3x^2 - 13x + 4 = 0$
20. $7x^2 + 3x - 4 = 0$
21. $x^2 + 8x + 16 = 0$
22. $4x^2 - 20x + 25 = 0$
23. $6x^2 = 13x - 6$
24. $6z^2 = 6 + 5z$
25. $4x^2 - 3 = -4x$
26. $10t^2 = 9 - 43t$
27. $x^2 - x - 1 = 1$
28. $2x^2 - 7x + 6 = 3$
29. $x^2 - 4b^2 = 0$
30. $a^2x^2 - 1 = 0$
31. $40x - 16x^2 = 0$
32. $18t^2 - 48t + 32 = 0$
33. $(x + 2)^3 = x^3 + 8$
34. $x(x^2 - 4) = x^2(x - 1)$
35. $(x + a)^2 - b^2 = 0$
36. $x^2(a^2 + 2ab + b^2) - x(a + b) = 0$

37. A projectile is fired vertically into the air. The distance (in feet) above the ground, as a function of the time (in seconds), is given by $s = 160t - 16t^2$. How long will it take the projectile to hit the ground?

38. In a certain electric circuit there is a resistance R of 2 Ω and a voltage E of 60 V. The relationship between current i (in amperes), E, and R is $i^2R + iE = 8000$. What current $i(i > 0)$ flows in the circuit?

39. Under certain conditions, the motion of an object suspended by a helical spring requires the solution of the equation $D^2 + 8D + 15 = 0$. Solve for D.

40. In determining the side x of a rectangle under specified conditions, the equation $2x^2 + 5x - 52 = 0$ is found. What is the side x (in centimeters) of the rectangle?

In Exercises 41 through 44 set up the appropriate quadratic equations and solve.

41. In electricity the equivalent resistance of two resistances connected in parallel is given by

$$\frac{1}{R} = \frac{1}{R_1} + \frac{1}{R_2}$$

Two resistances connected in series have an equivalent resistance given by $R = R_1 + R_2$. If two resistances connected in parallel have an equivalent resistance of 3 Ω and the same two resistances have an equivalent resistance of 16 Ω when connected in series, what are the resistances? (This equation is not quadratic. However, after the proper substitution is made, a fractional equation will exist. After fractions have been cleared, a quadratic equation will exist.)

42. The formula that relates the object distance p, image distance q, and focal length f of a lens is

$$\frac{1}{p} + \frac{1}{q} = \frac{1}{f}$$

Determine the positive value of p if $q = p + 3$ cm and $f = p - 1$ cm. (See Exercise 41.)

43. A certain rectangular machine part has a length which is 4 mm longer than its width. If the area of the part is 96 mm², what are its dimensions?

44. A jet, by increasing its speed by 200 mi/h, could decrease the time needed to cover 4000 mi by one hour. What is its speed?

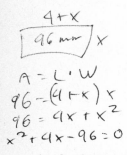

$$4 + x$$
$$\boxed{96\ mm}\ x$$
$$A = L \cdot W$$
$$96 = (4 + x)\ x$$
$$96 = 4x + x^2$$
$$x^2 + 4x - 96 = 0$$

6–2 Completing the Square

Many quadratic equations cannot be solved by factoring. This is true of most quadratic equations which arise in applied situations. In this section, therefore, we develop a method which can be used to solve any quadratic equation. The method is called **completing the square**. In the following section we shall use completing the square to develop a formula which also may be used to solve any quadratic equation.

In the first example which follows we show the solution of a type of quadratic equation which arises while using the method of completing the square. In the examples which follow it, the method itself is used and described.

Example A

In solving $x^2 = 16$, we note that either $+4$ or -4 satisfies the equation. These roots may be obtained by finding the square root of 16. Both the principal root and its negative give us roots, since each value satisfies the equation. Therefore, the roots of $x^2 = 16$ are $+4$ and -4.

We may solve $(x - 3)^2 = 16$ in a similar way by finding the square root of both sides of the equation, using the square root, and its negative, of 16, Thus,

$$x - 3 = 4 \quad \text{or} \quad x - 3 = -4$$

Solving these equations, we obtain the roots 7 and -1.

We may solve $(x - 3)^2 = 17$ in the same way. Thus,

$$x - 3 = \sqrt{17} \quad \text{or} \quad x - 3 = -\sqrt{17}$$

The roots are therefore $3 + \sqrt{17}$ and $3 - \sqrt{17}$. Decimal values of these roots are 7.123 and -1.123.

Example B
We wish to find the roots of the quadratic equation

$$x^2 - 6x - 8 = 0$$

First we note that this equation is not factorable. However, we do recognize that $x^2 - 6x$ is part of one of the special products. If 9 were added to this expression, we would have $x^2 - 6x + 9$, which is $(x - 3)^2$. We can solve this expression for x by taking a square root, which would leave us with $x - 3$. This expression can then be solved for x by any proper method of solving a linear equation. Thus, by creating an expression which is a perfect square and then taking the square root, we may solve the problem as an ordinary linear equation.

We may write the original equation as

$$x^2 - 6x = 8$$

and then add 9 to both sides of the equation. The result is

$$x^2 - 6x + 9 = 17$$

The left side of this equation may be rewritten, giving

$$(x - 3)^2 = 17$$

Taking square roots of both sides of the equation (which is the same as that solved in the third illustration of Example A), we arrive at

$$x - 3 = \pm \sqrt{17}$$

The $\pm$ sign is necessary, since by the definition of a square root, $(-\sqrt{17})^2 = 17$ and $(+\sqrt{17})^2 = 17$. Now, adding 3 to both sides, we obtain

$$x = 3 \pm \sqrt{17}$$

which means that $x = 3 + \sqrt{17}$ and $x = 3 - \sqrt{17}$ are the two roots of the equation.

How do we determine the number which must be added to complete the square? The answer to this question is based on the special products in Eqs. (5–3) and (5–4). We rewrite these in the form

$$(x + a)^2 = x^2 + 2ax + a^2 \tag{6–2}$$

and

$$(x - a)^2 = x^2 - 2ax + a^2 \tag{6–3}$$

The coefficient of x in each case is numerically $2a$, and the number added to complete the square is a^2. Thus *if we take half the coefficient of the x-term and square this result, we have the number which completes the square.* In our example, the numerical coefficient of the x-term was 6, and 9 was added to complete the square. We must be certain that the coefficient of the x^2 term is 1 before we start to complete the square. The following example outlines the steps necessary to complete the square.

Example C

Solve the following quadratic equation by the method of completing the square:

$$2x^2 + 16x - 9 = 0$$

First we divide each term by 2 so that the coefficient of the x^2 term becomes 1.

$$x^2 + 8x - \frac{9}{2} = 0$$

Now we put the constant term on the right-hand side by adding $\frac{9}{2}$ to both sides of the equation.

$$x^2 + 8x = \frac{9}{2}$$

Next we divide the coefficient of the x-term, 8, by 2, which gives us 4. We square 4 and obtain 16, which is the number to be added to both sides of the equation.

$$x^2 + 8x + 16 = \frac{9}{2} + 16 = \frac{41}{2}$$

We write the left side as the square of $(x + 4)$.

$$(x + 4)^2 = \frac{41}{2}$$

Taking the square root of both sides of the equation, we obtain

$$x + 4 = \pm\sqrt{\frac{41}{2}}$$

Solving for x, we have

$$x = -4 \pm \sqrt{\frac{41}{2}}$$

Since $\sqrt{\frac{41}{2}} = \sqrt{\frac{82}{4}} = \frac{1}{2}\sqrt{82}$, we may write the solution without a radical in the denominator as

$$x = \frac{-8 \pm \sqrt{82}}{2}$$

Therefore, the roots are $\frac{1}{2}(-8 + \sqrt{82})$ and $\frac{1}{2}(-8 - \sqrt{82})$. If we approximate $\sqrt{82}$ with 9.055, the approximate values of the roots are 0.528 and -8.528.

Example D

Solve $4x^2 - 12x + 5 = 0$ by completing the square.

$$4x^2 - 12x + 5 = 0$$

$$x^2 - 3x + \frac{5}{4} = 0$$

$$x^2 - 3x \quad\quad = -\frac{5}{4}$$

$$x^2 - 3x + \frac{9}{4} = -\frac{5}{4} + \frac{9}{4}$$

$$\left(x - \frac{3}{2}\right)^2 = \frac{4}{4} = 1$$

$$x - \frac{3}{2} = \pm 1$$

$$x = \frac{3}{2} \pm 1$$

$$x = \frac{5}{2}, \ x = \frac{1}{2}$$

This equation could have been solved by factoring. However, at this point, we want to illustrate the method of completing the square.

Exercises 6–2

In Exercises 1 through 8 solve the given quadratic equations by finding the appropriate square roots as in Example A.

1. $x^2 = 25$ 2. $x^2 = 100$ 3. $x^2 = 7$

4. $x^2 = 15$ 5. $(x - 2)^2 = 25$ 6. $(x + 2)^2 = 100$

7. $(x + 3)^2 = 7$ 8. $(x - 4)^2 = 15$

In Exercises 9 through 24 solve the given quadratic equations by completing the square. Exercises 9 through 12 and 15 through 18 may be checked by factoring.

9. $x^2 + 2x - 8 = 0$ 10. $x^2 - x - 6 = 0$ 11. $x^2 + 3x + 2 = 0$

12. $t^2 + 5t - 6 = 0$ 13. $x^2 - 4x + 2 = 0$ 14. $x^2 + 10x - 4 = 0$

15. $v^2 + 2v - 15 = 0$ 16. $x^2 - 8x + 12 = 0$ 17. $2s^2 + 5s - 3 = 0$

18. $4x^2 + x - 3 = 0$ 19. $3y^2 - 3y - 2 = 0$ 20. $3x^2 + 4x - 3 = 0$

21. $2y^2 - y - 2 = 0$ 22. $9v^2 - 6v - 2 = 0$ 23. $x^2 + 2bx + c = 0$

24. $px^2 + qx + r = 0$

6–3 The Quadratic Formula

We shall now use the method of completing the square to derive a general formula which may be used for the solution of any quadratic equation.

Consider Eq. (6–1), the general quadratic equation

$$ax^2 + bx + c = 0$$

with $a > 0$. When we divide through by a, we obtain

$$x^2 + \frac{b}{a}x + \frac{c}{a} = 0$$

Subtracting c/a from each side, we have

$$x^2 + \frac{b}{a}x = -\frac{c}{a}$$

Half of b/a is $b/2a$, which squared is $b^2/4a^2$. Adding $b^2/4a^2$ to each side gives us

$$x^2 + \frac{b}{a}x + \frac{b^2}{4a^2} = -\frac{c}{a} + \frac{b^2}{4a^2}$$

Writing the left side as a perfect square, and combining fractions on the right side, we have

$$\left(x + \frac{b}{2a}\right)^2 = \frac{b^2 - 4ac}{4a^2}$$

Taking the square root of each side results in

$$x + \frac{b}{2a} = \frac{\pm \sqrt{b^2 - 4ac}}{2a}$$

When we subtract $b/2a$ from each side and simplify the resulting expression, we obtain the **quadratic formula**:

$$x = \frac{-b \pm \sqrt{b^2 - 4ac}}{2a} \tag{6–4}$$

To solve a quadratic equation by using the quadratic formula we need only to write the equation in standard form (see Eq. 6–1), identify a, b, and c, and substitute these numbers directly into the formula. We shall use the quadratic formula to solve the quadratic equations in the following examples.

Example A

$$x^2 - 5x + 6 = 0$$

In this equation $a = 1$, $b = -5$, and $c = 6$. Thus, we have

$$x = \frac{-(-5) \pm \sqrt{25 - 4(1)(6)}}{2} = \frac{5 \pm 1}{2} = 3, 2$$

The roots are $x = 3$ and $x = 2$. (This particular equation could have been solved by the method of factoring.)

Example B

$$2x^2 - 7x + 5 = 0$$

In this equation $a = 2$, $b = -7$, and $c = 5$. Hence,

$$x = \frac{7 \pm \sqrt{49 - 4(2)(5)}}{4} = \frac{7 \pm 3}{4} = \frac{5}{2}, 1$$

Thus, the roots are $x = \frac{5}{2}$ and $x = 1$.

Example C

$$9x^2 + 24x + 16 = 0$$

In this example, $a = 9$, $b = 24$, and $c = 16$. Thus,

$$x = \frac{-24 \pm \sqrt{576 - 4(9)(16)}}{18} = \frac{-24 \pm 0}{18} = -\frac{4}{3}$$

Here both roots are $-\frac{4}{3}$, and the answer should be written as $x = -\frac{4}{3}$ and $x = -\frac{4}{3}$.

Example D

$$3x^2 - 5x + 4 = 0$$

In this example, $a = 3$, $b = -5$, and $c = 4$. Therefore,

$$x = \frac{5 \pm \sqrt{25 - 4(3)(4)}}{6} = \frac{5 \pm \sqrt{-23}}{6}$$

Here we note that the roots contain imaginary numbers. This happens if $b^2 < 4ac$.

Example E

$$2x^2 = 4x + 3$$

First we must put the equation in the proper form. This is

$$2x^2 - 4x - 3 = 0.$$

Now we identify $a = 2$, $b = -4$, $c = -3$, which leads to the solution

$$x = \frac{-(-4) \pm \sqrt{(-4)^2 - 4(2)(-3)}}{2(2)} = \frac{4 \pm \sqrt{16 + 24}}{4}$$

$$= \frac{4 \pm \sqrt{40}}{4} = \frac{4 \pm 2\sqrt{10}}{4} = \frac{2(2 \pm \sqrt{10})}{4}$$

$$= \frac{2 \pm \sqrt{10}}{2}$$

Here we used the method of simplifying radicals as introduced in Section 1–6.

Example F

$$dx^2 - (3 + d)x + 4 = 0$$

In this example, $a = d$, $b = -(3 + d)$, and $c = 4$. We can use the quadratic formula to solve quadratic equations which have literal coefficients. Thus,

$$x = \frac{3 + d \pm \sqrt{[-(3 + d)]^2 - 4(d)(4)}}{2d} = \frac{3 + d \pm \sqrt{9 - 10d + d^2}}{2d}$$

Example G

A square field has a diagonal which is 10 m longer than one of the sides. What is the length of a side?

Let $x =$ the length of a side of the field, and $y =$ the length of the diagonal. Using the Pythagorean theorem, we know that $y^2 = x^2 + x^2$. From the given information we know that $y = x + 10$. Thus, we have

$$(x + 10)^2 = x^2 + x^2$$

We can now simplify and solve this equation as follows.

$$x^2 + 20x + 100 = 2x^2$$
$$x^2 - 20x - 100 = 0$$
$$x = \frac{20 \pm \sqrt{400 + 400}}{2} = 10 \pm 10\sqrt{2}$$

The negative solution has no meaning in this problem. This means that the solution is $10 + 10\sqrt{2} = 24.1$ m.

The quadratic formula provides a quick general method for solving quadratic equations. Proper recognition and substitution of the coefficients a, b, and c is all that is required to complete the solution, regardless of the nature of the roots.

Exercises 6—3

In Exercises 1 through 32 solve the given quadratic equations using the quadratic formula. Exercises 1 through 14 are the same as Exercises 9 through 22 of Section 6–2.

1. $x^2 + 2x - 8 = 0$

2. $x^2 - x - 6 = 0$

3. $x^2 + 3x + 2 = 0$

4. $t^2 + 5t - 6 = 0$

5. $x^2 - 4x + 2 = 0$

6. $x^2 + 10x - 4 = 0$

7. $v^2 + 2v - 15 = 0$

8. $x^2 - 8x + 12 = 0$

9. $2s^2 + 5s - 3 = 0$

10. $4x^2 + x - 3 = 0$

11. $3y^2 - 3y - 2 = 0$

12. $3x^2 + 4x - 3 = 0$

13. $2y^2 - y - 2 = 0$

14. $9v^2 - 6v - 2 = 0$

15. $2x^2 - 7x + 4 = 0$

16. $3x^2 - 5x - 4 = 0$

17. $2t^2 + 10t = -15$

18. $2d^2 + 7 = 4d$

19. $3s^2 = s + 9$ 20. $6r^2 - 6r - 1 = 0$

21. $4x^2 - 9 = 0$ 22. $x^2 - 6x = 0$

23. $15 + 4z - 32z^2 = 0$ 24. $4x^2 - 12x = 7$

25. $x^2 + 2cx - 1 = 0$ 26. $x^2 - 7x + (6 + a) = 0$

27. $b^2x^2 - (b + 1)x + (1 - a) = 0$ 28. $c^2x^2 - x - 1 = x^2$

29. Under certain conditions, the partial pressure P of a certain gas (in pascals) is found by solving the equation $P^2 - 3P + 1 = 0$. Solve for P such that $P < 1$ Pa.

30. A projectile is fired vertically into the air. The distance (in feet) above the ground as a function of time (in seconds) is given by the formula $s = 300 - 100t - 16t^2$. When will the projectile hit the ground?

31. The total surface area of a right circular cylinder is found by the formula $A = 2\pi r^2 + 2\pi rh$. If the height of the cylinder is 4 in., how much is the radius if the area is 9π in.^{2}?

32. In calculating the current in an electric circuit with an inductance L (in henrys), a resistance R (in ohms) and capacitance C (in farads), it is necessary to solve the equation $Lx^2 + Rx + \frac{1}{C} = 0$. Find x in terms of L, R, and C.

In Exercises 33 through 36 set up appropriate equations and solve the given stated problems.

33. A metal cube expands when heated. If the volume changes by 6.00 mm^3 and each edge is 0.20 mm longer after being heated, what was the original length of an edge of the cube?

34. After a laboratory experiment, a student reported that two particular resistances had a combined resistance of 4 Ω when connected in parallel, and a combined resistance of 7 Ω when connected in series. What values would she obtain for the resistances? (See Exercise 41 of Section 6–1.)

35. To cover a given floor with square tiles of a certain size, it is found that 648 tiles are needed. If the tiles were 1 in. larger in both dimensions, only 512 tiles would be required. What is the length of a side of one of the smaller tiles?

36. A jet pilot flies 2400 mi at a given speed. If the speed were increased by 300 mi/h, the trip would take one hour less. What would be the speed of the jet?

6—4 Exercises for Chapter 6

In Exercises 1 through 12 solve the given quadratic equations by factoring.

1. $x^2 + 3x - 4 = 0$ 2. $x^2 + 3x - 10 = 0$

3. $x^2 - 10x + 16 = 0$ 4. $x^2 - 6x - 27 = 0$

5. $3x^2 + 11x = 4$ 6. $6y^2 = 11y - 3$

7. $6t^2 = 13t - 5$ 8. $3x^2 + 5x + 2 = 0$

9. $6s^2 = 25s$ 10. $6n^2 - 23n - 35 = 0$

11. $4x^2 - 8x = 21$ 12. $6x^2 = 8 - 47x$

In Exercises 13 through 24 solve the given quadratic equations by using the quadratic formula.

13. $x^2 - x - 110 = 0$

14. $x^2 + 3x - 18 = 0$

15. $x^2 + 2x - 5 = 0$

16. $x^2 - 7x - 1 = 0$

17. $2x^2 - x - 36 = 0$

18. $3x^2 + x - 14 = 0$

19. $4x^2 - 3x - 2 = 0$

20. $5x^2 + 7x - 2 = 0$

21. $2x^2 + 2x + 5 = 0$

22. $3x^2 - 4x - 1 = 0$

23. $6x^2 = 9 - 4x$

24. $8x^2 = 5x + 2$

In Exercises 25 through 36 solve the given quadratic equations by any appropriate method.

25. $x^2 + 4x - 4 = 0$

26. $x^2 + 3x + 1 = 0$

27. $3x^2 + 8x + 2 = 0$

28. $3p^2 = 28 - 5p$

29. $4v^2 = v + 5$

30. $6x^2 - x + 2 = 0$

31. $2x^2 + 3x + 7 = 0$

32. $4y^2 - 5y = 8$

33. $a^2x^2 + 2ax + 2 = 0$

34. $16r^2 - 8r + 1 = 0$

35. $ax^2 = a^2 - 3x$

36. $2bx = x^2 - 3b$

In Exercises 37 through 40 solve the given quadratic equations by completing the square.

37. $x^2 - x - 30 = 0$

38. $x^2 - 2x - 5 = 0$

39. $2x^2 - x - 4 = 0$

40. $4x^2 - 8x - 3 = 0$

In Exercises 41 through 44 solve the equations involving fractions. After multiplying through by the lowest common denominator, quadratic equations should result.

41. $\dfrac{x - 4}{x - 1} = \dfrac{2}{x}$

42. $\dfrac{x - 1}{3} = \dfrac{5}{x} + 1$

43. $\dfrac{x^2 - 3x}{x - 3} = \dfrac{x^2}{x + 2}$

44. $\dfrac{x - 2}{x - 5} = \dfrac{15}{x^2 - 5x}$

In Exercises 45 through 52 solve the given quadratic equations by any appropriate method.

45. To determine the electric current in a certain alternating-current circuit, it is necessary to solve the equation $m^2 + 10m + 2000 = 0$. Solve for m.

46. Under specified conditions, the deflection of a beam requires the solution of the equation $40x - x^2 - 400 = 0$, where x is the distance (in feet) from one end of the beam. Solve for x.

47. Under specified conditions, the power developed in an element of an electric circuit is $P = EI - RI^2$, where P is the power, E is the specified voltage, and R is a specified resistance. Assuming that P, E, and R are constants, solve for I.

48. For laminar flow of fluids, the coefficient K_e, used to calculate energy loss due to sudden enlargements, is given by

$$K_e = 1.00 - 2.67\frac{S_a}{S_b} + \left(\frac{S_a}{S_b}\right)^2$$

where S_a/S_b is the ratio of cross-sectional areas. If $K_e = -0.500$, what is the value of S_a/S_b?

49. A company determines that the cost C (in dollars) of manufacturing x units of a certain product is given by $C = 0.1x^2 + 0.8x + 7$. How many units can be made for $25?

50. In determining the width w of a parcel of land, the equation $w^2 + 60w = 5000$ is used. What is the width (in meters) of the parcel?

51. In the theory to study the motion of biological cells and viruses, the equation $n = 2.5p - 12.6p^2$ is used. Solve for p in terms of n.

52. A general formula for the distance s traveled by an object, given an initial velocity v and acceleration a in time t, is $s = vt + \frac{1}{2}at^2$. Solve for t.

In Exercises 53 through 58 set up appropriate equations and solve the given stated problems.

53. The sum of two electric voltages is 20 V, and their product is 96 V^2. What are the voltages?

54. The length of one field is 400 m more than the side of a square field. The width is 100 m more than the side of the square field. If the rectangular field has twice the area of the square field, what are the dimensions of each field?

55. The manufacturer of a disk-shaped machine part of radius 1.00 in. discovered that he could prevent taking a loss in its production if the amount of material used in each was reduced by 20%. If the thickness remains the same, by how much must the radius be reduced in order to prevent a loss?

56. A roof truss is in the shape of a right triangle with the hypotenuse along the base. If one rafter (neglect overhang) is 4 ft longer than the other, and the base is 36 ft, what are the lengths of the rafters?

57. An electric utility company is placing utility poles along a road. It is determined that five less poles per kilometer would be necessary if the distance between poles were increased by 10 m. How many poles are being placed each kilometer?

58. A rectangular duct in a building's ventilating system is made of sheet metal 7 ft wide and has a cross-sectional area of 3 ft^2. What are the cross-sectional dimensions of the duct?

7

Trigonometric Functions
of Any Angle

7–1 Signs of the Trigonometric Functions

When we were dealing with trigonometric functions in Chapter 3, we restricted ourselves primarily to the functions of acute angles measured in degrees. Since we did define the functions in general, we can use these same definitions for finding the functions of any possible angle. We shall not only find the trigonometric functions of angles measured in degrees, but we shall introduce radian measure as well. From there we shall show how the trigonometric functions can be defined for numbers. In this section we shall determine the signs of the trigonometric functions in each of the four quadrants.

We recall the definitions of the trigonometric functions which were given in Section 3–2: Here the point (x, y) is a point on the terminal side of angle θ, and r is the radius vector.

$$\sin \theta = \frac{y}{r}, \qquad \cos \theta = \frac{x}{r}, \qquad \tan \theta = \frac{y}{x}$$

$$\cot \theta = \frac{x}{y}, \qquad \sec \theta = \frac{r}{x}, \qquad \csc \theta = \frac{r}{y}$$

(7–1)

We see that the functions are defined so long as we know the abscissa, ordinate, and radius vector of the terminal side of θ. Remembering that r is always considered positive, we can see that the various functions will vary in sign, depending on the signs of x and y.

If the terminal side of the angle is in the first or second quadrant, the value of sin θ will be positive, but if the terminal side is in the third or fourth quadrant, sin θ is negative. This is because y is positive if the point defining the terminal side is above the x-axis, and y is negative if this point is below the x-axis.

Example A

The value of sin 20° is positive, since the terminal side of 20° is in the first quadrant. The value of sin 160° is positive, since the terminal side of 160° is in the second quadrant. The values of sin 200° and sin 340° are negative, since the terminal sides of these angles are in the third and fourth quadrants, respectively.

The sign of tan θ depends upon the ratio of y to x. In the first quadrant both x and y are positive, and therefore the ratio y/x is positive. In the third quadrant both x and y are negative, and therefore the ratio y/x is positive. In the second and fourth quadrants either x or y is positive and the other is negative, and so the ratio of y/x is negative.

Example B

The values of tan 20° and tan 200° are positive, since the terminal sides of these angles are in the first and third quadrants, respectively. The values of tan 160° and tan 340° are negative, since the terminal sides of these angles are in the second and fourth quadrants, respectively.

The sign of cos θ depends upon the sign of x. Since x is positive in the first and fourth quadrants, cos θ is positive in these quadrants. In the same way, cos θ is negative in the second and third quadrants.

Example C

The values of cos 20° and cos 340° are positive, since these angles are first and fourth quadrant angles, respectively. The values of cos 160° and cos 200° are negative, since these angles are second- and third-quadrant angles, respectively.

Since csc θ is defined in terms of r and y, as is sin θ, the sign of csc θ is the same as that of sin θ. For the same reason, cot θ has the same sign as tan θ, and sec θ has the same sign as cos θ. A method for remembering the signs of the functions in the four quadrants is as follows:

All functions of first-quadrant angles are positive. Sin θ and csc θ are positive for second-quadrant angles. Tan θ and cot θ are positive for third-quadrant angles. Cos θ and sec θ are positive for fourth-quadrant angles. All others are negative.

This discussion does not include the quadrantal angles, those angles with terminal sides on one of the axes. They will be discussed in the following section.

Example D

sin 50°, sin 150°, sin (−200°), cos 8°, cos 300°, cos (−40°), tan 220°, tan (−100°), cot 260°, cot (−310°), sec 280°, sec (−37°), csc 140°, and csc (−190°) are all positive.

Example E

sin 190°, sin 325°, cos 100°, cos (−95°), tan 172°, tan 295°, cot 105°, cot (−6°), sec 135°, sec (−135°), csc 240°, and csc 355° are all negative.

Example F

Determine the trigonometric functions of θ if the terminal side ·of θ passes through $(-1, \sqrt{3})$.

We know that $x = -1$, $y = +\sqrt{3}$, and from the Pythagorean theorem we find that $r = 2$. Therefore, the trigonometric functions of θ are:

$$\sin \theta = +\frac{\sqrt{3}}{2}, \qquad \cos \theta = -\frac{1}{2}, \qquad \tan \theta = -\sqrt{3}$$

$$\cot \theta = -\frac{1}{\sqrt{3}}, \qquad \sec \theta = -2, \qquad \csc \theta = +\frac{2}{\sqrt{3}}$$

We note that the point $(-1, \sqrt{3})$ is on the terminal side of a second-quadrant angle, and that the signs of the functions of θ are those of a second-quadrant angle.

Exercises 7−1

In Exercises 1 through 8 determine the algebraic sign of the given trigonometric functions.

1. sin 60°,   cos 120°,   tan 320°
2. tan 185°,   sec 115°,   sin (−36°)
3. cos 300°,   csc 97°,   cot (−35°)
4. sin 100°, sec (−15°),   cos 188°
5. cot 186°,   sec 280°,   sin 470°
6. tan (−91°),   csc 87°,   cot 103°
7. cos 700°,   tan (−560°),   csc 530°
8. sin 256°,   tan 321°,   cos (−370°)

In Exercises 9 through 16 find the trigonometric functions of θ, where the terminal side of θ passes through the given point.

9. (2, 1)   10. (−1, 1)   11. (−2, −3)   12. (4, −3)
13. (−5, 12)   14. (−3, −4)   15. (5, −2)   16. (3, 5)

In Exercises 17 through 24 determine the quadrant in which the terminal side of θ lies, subject to the given conditions.

17. sin θ positive, cos θ negative
18. tan θ positive, cos θ negative
19. sec θ negative, cot θ negative
20. cos θ positive, csc θ negative
21. csc θ negative, tan θ negative
22. sec θ positive, csc θ positive
23. sin θ negative, tan θ positive
24. cot θ negative, sin θ negative

7–2 Trigonometric Functions of Any Angle

The trigonometric functions of acute angles were discussed in Section 3–3, and in the last section we determined the signs of the trigonometric functions in each of the four quadrants. In this section we shall show how we can find the trigonometric functions of an angle of any magnitude. This information will be very important in Chapter 8 when we discuss oblique triangles and in Chapter 9 when we graph the trigonometric functions.

Any angle in standard position is coterminal with some positive angle less than 360°. Since the terminal sides of coterminal angles are the same, the trigonometric functions of coterminal angles are the same. Therefore, we need consider only the problem of finding the values of the trigonometric functions of positive angles less than 360°.

Example A
The following pairs of angles are coterminal.

$$390° \text{ and } 30°, \qquad -60° \text{ and } 300° \qquad 900° \text{ and } 180°, \qquad -150° \text{ and } 210°$$

From this we conclude that the trigonometric functions of both angles in these pairs are equal. That is, for example, sin 390° = sin 30° and tan (−150°) = tan 210°.

Considering the definitions of the functions, we see that the values of the functions depend only on the values of x, y, and r. The values of the functions of second-quadrant angles are numerically equal to the functions of corresponding first-quadrant angles. For example, considering the angles shown in Fig. 7–1, for angle θ_2 with terminal side passing through $(-3, 4)$, tan $\theta_2 = -\frac{4}{3}$, and for angle θ_1 with terminal side passing through $(3, 4)$, tan $\theta_1 = \frac{4}{3}$. In Fig. 7–1, we see that the triangles containing angles θ_1 and α are congruent, which means that θ_1 and α are equal. We know that the trigonometric functions of θ_1 and θ_2 are numerically equal. This means that

$$|F(\theta_2)| = |F(\theta_1)| = |F(\alpha)| \tag{7–2}$$

where F represents any of the trigonometric functions.

The angle labeled α is called the **reference angle**. *The reference angle of a given angle is the acute angle formed by the terminal side of the angle and the x-axis.*

Using Eq. (7–2) and the fact that $\alpha = 180° - \theta_2$, we may conclude that the value of any trigonometric function of any second-quadrant angle is found from

$$F(\theta_2) = \pm F(180° - \theta_2) = \pm F(\alpha) \tag{7–3}$$

The sign to be used depends on whether the *function* is positive or negative in the second quadrant.

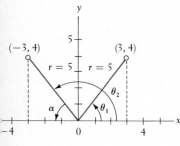

Figure 7–1

Example B

In Fig. 7–1, the trigonometric functions of θ_2 are as follows:

$$\sin \theta_2 = +\sin (180° - \theta_2) = +\sin \alpha = +\sin \theta_1 = \frac{4}{5}$$

$$\cos \theta_2 = -\cos \theta_1 = -\frac{3}{5}$$

$$\tan \theta_2 = -\frac{4}{3}, \qquad \cot \theta_2 = -\frac{3}{4}$$

$$\sec \theta_2 = -\frac{5}{3}, \qquad \csc \theta_2 = +\frac{5}{4}$$

In the same way we may derive the formulas for finding the trigonometric functions of any third- or fourth-quadrant angle. Considering the angles shown in Fig. 7–2, we see that the reference angle α is found by subtracting 180° from θ_3 and that functions of α and θ_1 are numerically equal. Considering the angles shown in Fig. 7–3, we see that the reference angle α is found by subtracting θ_4 from 360°. Therefore, we have

$$\text{and} \quad \begin{aligned} F(\theta_3) &= \pm F(\theta_3 - 180°) \\ F(\theta_4) &= \pm F(360° - \theta_4) \end{aligned} \qquad \begin{aligned} &(7\text{–}4) \\ &(7\text{–}5) \end{aligned}$$

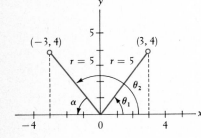

Figure 7–1

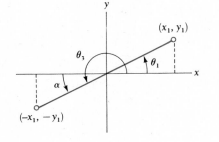

Figure 7–2

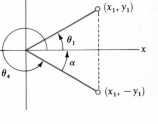

Figure 7–3

Example C

In Fig. 7–2, if $\theta_3 = 210°$, the trigonometric functions of θ_3 are found by using Eq. (7–4) as follows.

$$\sin 210° = -\sin (210° - 180°) = -\sin 30° = -\frac{1}{2} = -0.5000$$

$$\cos 210° = -\cos 30° = -0.8660$$
$$\tan 210° = +0.5774 \qquad \cot 210° = +1.732$$
$$\sec 210° = -1.155 \qquad \csc 210° = -2.000$$

Example D

In Fig. 7–3, if $\theta_4 = 315°$, the trigonometric functions of θ_4 are found by using Eq. (7–5) as follows.

$$\sin 315° = -\sin (360° - 315°) = -\sin 45° = -0.7071$$
$$\cos 315° = +\cos 45° = +0.7071$$
$$\tan 315° = -1.000 \qquad \cot 315° = -1.000$$
$$\sec 315° = +1.414 \qquad \csc 315° = -1.414$$

Example E

Other illustrations of the use of Eqs. (7–3), (7–4), and (7–5) are as follows.

$$\sin 160° = +\sin (180° - 160°) = \sin 20° = 0.3420$$
$$\tan 110° = -\tan (180° - 110°) = -\tan 70° = -2.747$$
$$\cos 225° = -\cos (225° - 180°) = -\cos 45° = -0.7071$$
$$\cot 260° = +\cot (260° - 180°) = \cot 80° = 0.1763$$
$$\sec 304° = +\sec (360° - 304°) = \sec 56° = 1.788$$
$$\sin 357° = -\sin (360° - 357°) = -\sin 3° = -0.0523$$

The following examples illustrate how Eqs. (7–3) through (7–5) are used to determine θ when a function of θ is given.

Example F

Given that $\sin \theta = 0.2250$, find θ for $0° < \theta < 360°$.

Here we are asked to find any angles between $0°$ and $360°$ for which $\sin \theta = 0.2250$. Since $\sin \theta$ is positive for first- and second-quadrant angles, there will be two such angles.

From the tables we find $\theta = 13°0'$. We also know that $\theta = 180°0' - 13°0' = 167°0'$. These are the two required answers.

Example G

Given that $\tan \theta = 2.050$ and $\cos \theta < 0$, find θ when $0° < \theta < 360°$.

Since $\tan \theta$ is positive and $\cos \theta$ is negative, θ must be in the third quadrant. We note from the tables that $2.050 = \tan 64°0'$. Therefore, $\theta = 180°0' + 64°0' = 244°0'$. Since the required angle is to be between $0°$ and $360°$, this is the only possible answer.

If angles are expressed to the nearest $10'$ or $0.1°$, we find the nearest value in the appropriate table as we did in Chapter 3. Also, in expressing angles to the nearest $1'$, interpolation is used if the value is obtained from Table 3. It is also possible to find these values on a scientific calculator.

Example H

To find $\sin 251.4°$, we first determine that the angle is a third-quadrant angle. Thus,

$$\sin 251.4° = -\sin (251.4° - 180.0°) = -\sin 71.4°$$
$$= -0.9478$$

To find tan 103°37′, we first determine that the angle is a second-quadrant angle. Thus,

$$\tan 103°37′ = -\tan (180°0′ - 103°37′) = -\tan 76°23′$$
$$= -4.129$$

The value is obtained by use of interpolation in Table 3.

Given that cos θ = 0.1354 for 0° < θ < 360°, θ = 82°10′ to the nearest 10′ from Table 3. Also, since the cosine is positive in the fourth quadrant, θ may also equal 360°0′ − 82°10′ = 277°50′. Thus, the two answers are 82°10′ and 277°50′. If we expressed θ to the nearest 0.1° from Table 4, we would obtain 82.2° and 277.8° for θ.

With the use of Eqs. (7–3) through (7–5) we may find the value of any function, as long as the terminal side of the angle lies *in* one of the quadrants. This problem reduces to finding the function of an acute angle. We are left with the case of the terminal side being along one of the axes, a **quadrantal angle.** Using the definitions of the functions, and remembering that $r > 0$, we arrive at the values in the following table.

θ	$\sin \theta$	$\cos \theta$	$\tan \theta$	$\cot \theta$	$\sec \theta$	$\csc \theta$
0°	0.000	1.000	0.000	Undef.	1.000	Undef.
90°	1.000	0.000	Undef.	0.000	Undef.	1.000
180°	0.000	−1.000	0.000	Undef.	−1.000	Undef.
270°	−1.000	0.000	Undef.	0.000	Undef.	−1.000
360°	Same as the functions of 0° (same terminal side)					

The values in the table may be verified by referring to the figures in Fig. 7–4.

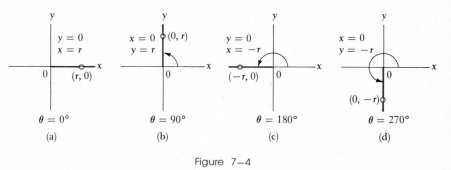

Figure 7–4

Example 1

Since sin θ = y/r, from Fig. 7–4 (a) we see that sin 0° = 0/r = 0.

Since tan θ = y/x, from Fig. 7–4 (b) we see that tan 90° = $r/0$, which is undefined due to the division by zero.

Since cos θ = x/r, from Fig. 7–4 (c) we see that cos 180° = $-r/r$ = −1.

Since cot θ = x/y, from Fig. 7–4 (d) we see that cot 270° = $0/-r$ = 0.

Exercises 7−2

In Exercises 1 through 8 express the given trigonometric functions in terms of the same function of a positive acute angle.

1. sin 160°, cos 220°

2. tan 91°, sec 345°

3. tan 105°, csc 302°

4. cos 190°, cot 290°

5. sin (−123°), cot 174°

6. sin 98°, sec (−315°)

7. cos 400°, tan (−400°)

8. tan 920°, csc (−550°)

In Exercises 9 through 28 determine the values of the given trigonometric functions by use of tables.

9. sin 195°0′

10. tan 311°0′

11. cos 106°0′

12. sin 254°0′

13. cot 136°0′

14. cos 297°0′

15. sec (−115°0′)

16. csc (−193°0′)

17. tan 193°10′

18. sin 311°50′

19. cos 206°40′

20. sec 328°20′

21. sin 103.3°

22. tan 219.1°

23. cot 330.5°

24. cos 198.8°

25. sin 322°52′

26. cot 254°17′

27. tan 118°33′

28. cos (−67°5′)

In Exercises 29 through 36 find θ to the nearest 10′ for $0 < \theta < 360°$.

29. tan θ = 0.5317

30. cos θ = 0.6428

31. sin θ = −0.3638

32. cot θ = −1.319

33. sin θ = 0.8708

34. csc θ = 2.311

35. cos θ = −0.1207

36. tan θ = −2.368

In Exercises 37 through 44 find θ to the nearest 0.1° for $0 < \theta < 360°$.

37. sin θ = −0.8480

38. cot θ = −0.2126

39. cos θ = 0.4003

40. tan θ = −1.830

41. cot θ = 0.5265

42. sin θ = 0.6374

43. tan θ = 0.2833

44. cos θ = −0.9287

In Exercises 45 through 48 find θ to the nearest minute for $0 < \theta < 360°$.

45. sin θ = −0.9527

46. cos θ = 0.8727

47. cot θ = −0.7144

48. tan θ = −2.664

In Exercises 49 through 52 determine the function which satisfies the given conditions.

49. Find tan θ when sin θ = −0.5736 and cos θ > 0.

50. Find sin θ when cos θ = 0.4226 and tan θ < 0.

51. Find cos θ when tan θ = −0.8098 and csc θ > 0.

52. Find cot θ when sec θ = 1.122 and sin θ < 0.

In Exercises 53 through 56 insert the proper sign, > or < or =, between the given expressions.

53. sin 90°   2 sin 45°

54. cos 360°   2 cos 180°

55. tan 180°   tan 0°

56. sin 270°   3 sin 90°

In Exercises 57 through 60 evaluate the given expressions.

57. Under specified conditions, a force F (in pounds) is determined by solving the following equation for F:

$$\frac{F}{\sin 115.0°} = \frac{46.0}{\sin 35.0°}$$

Find the magnitude of the force.

58. A certain ac voltage can be found from the equation $V = 100 \cos 565.0°$. Find the voltage V.

59. A formula for finding the area of a triangle, knowing sides a and b, and angle C is $A = \frac{1}{2}ab \sin C$. Find the area of a triangle for which $a = 37.2$, $b = 57.2$, and $C = 157.0°$.

60. In calculating the area of a triangular tract of land, a surveyor used the formula in Exercise 59. He used the values $a = 273$ m, $b = 156$ m, and $C = 112.5°$. Find the required area.

In Exercises 61 through 64 the trigonometric functions of negative angles are considered. In Exercises 62, 63, and 64 use the equations derived in Exercise 61.

61. From Fig. 7–5 we see that $\sin \theta = y/r$ and $\sin (-\theta) = -y/r$. From this we conclude that $\sin (-\theta) = -\sin \theta$. In the same way, verify the remaining Eqs. (7–6):

$$\sin (-\theta) = -\sin \theta, \qquad \cos (-\theta) = \cos \theta$$
$$\tan (-\theta) = -\tan \theta, \qquad \cot (-\theta) = -\cot \theta \qquad (7\text{–}6)$$
$$\sec (-\theta) = \sec \theta, \qquad \csc (-\theta) = -\csc \theta$$

62. Find (a) $\sin (-60°)$ and (b) $\cos (-176°)$.
63. Find (a) $\tan (-100°)$ and (b) $\cot (-215°)$.
64. Find (a) $\sec (-310°)$ and (b) $\csc (-35°)$.

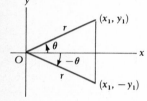

Figure 7–5

7–3 Radians

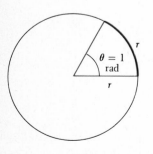

Figure 7–6

For many problems in which trigonometric functions are used, particularly those involving the solution of triangles, the degree measurement of angles is quite sufficient. However, in numerous other types of applications and in more theoretical discussions, another way of expressing the measure of angle is more meaningful and convenient. This unit measurement is the **radian**. *A radian is the measure of an angle with its vertex at the center of a circle and with an intercepted arc on the circle equal in length to the radius of the circle.* See Fig. 7–6.

Since the circumference of any circle in terms of its radius is given by $c = 2\pi r$, the ratio of the circumference to the radius is 2π. This means that the radius may be laid off 2π (about 6.28) times along the circumference, regardless of the length of the radius. Therefore, we see that

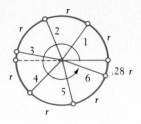

Figure 7–7

radian measure is independent of the radius of the circle. In Fig. 7–7 the numbers on each of the radii indicate the number of radians in the angle measured in standard position. The circular arrow shows an angle of 6 radians.

Since the radius may be laid off 2π times along the circumference, it follows that there are 2π radians in one complete rotation. Also, there are 360° in one complete rotation. Therefore, 360° is *equivalent* to 2π radians. It then follows that the relation between degrees and radians is 2π rad = 360°, or

$$\pi \text{ rad} = 180° \tag{7–7}$$

From this relation we find that

$$1° = \frac{\pi}{180} \text{ rad} = 0.01745 \text{ rad} \tag{7–8}$$

and that

$$1 \text{ rad} = \frac{180°}{\pi} = 57.3° \tag{7–9}$$

We see from Eqs. (7–7) through (7–9) that (1) *to convert an angle measured in degrees to the same angle measured in radians, we multiply the number of degrees by $\pi/180$, and (2) to convert an angle measured in radians to the same angle measured in degrees, we multiply the number of radians by $180/\pi$.*

Example A

$$18.0° = \left(\frac{\pi}{180}\right)(18.0) = \frac{\pi}{10.0} = \frac{3.14}{10.0} = 0.314 \text{ rad}$$

$$120° = \left(\frac{\pi}{180}\right)(120) = \frac{6.28}{3.00} = 2.09 \text{ rad}$$

$$0.400 \text{ rad} = \left(\frac{180°}{\pi}\right)(0.400) = \frac{72.0°}{3.14} = 22.9°$$

$$2.00 \text{ rad} = \left(\frac{180°}{\pi}\right)(2.00) = \frac{360°}{3.14} = 114.6°$$

Due to the nature of the definition of the radian, it is very common to express radians in terms of π. Expressing angles in terms of π is illustrated in the following example.

Example B

$$30° = \left(\frac{\pi}{180}\right)(30) = \frac{\pi}{6}\,\text{rad}$$

$$45° = \left(\frac{\pi}{180}\right)(45) = \frac{\pi}{4}\,\text{rad}$$

$$\frac{\pi}{2}\,\text{rad} = \left(\frac{180°}{\pi}\right)\left(\frac{\pi}{2}\right) = 90°$$

$$\frac{3\pi}{4}\,\text{rad} = \left(\frac{180°}{\pi}\right)\left(\frac{3\pi}{4}\right) = 135°$$

We wish now to make a very important point. Since π is a special way of writing the number (slightly greater than 3) that is the ratio of the circumference of a circle to its diameter, it is the ratio of one distance to another. Thus radians really have no units and *radian measure amounts to measuring angles in terms of numbers*. It is this property of radians that makes them useful in many situations. Therefore, when radians are being used, it is customary that no units are indicated for the angle. *When no units are indicated, the radian is understood to be the unit of angle measurement.*

Example C

$$60.0° = \left(\frac{\pi}{180}\right)(60.0) = \frac{\pi}{3.00} = 1.05$$

$$2.50 = \left(\frac{180°}{\pi}\right)(2.50) = \frac{450°}{3.14} = 143°$$

Since no units are indicated for 1.05 or 2.50 in this example, they are known to be radian measure.

We can also use Table 3 directly to find the function of an acute angle given in radians. The following examples illustrate this use of the table.

Example D

In determining the value of sin 0.4538, we locate 0.4538 in the column labeled radians, and opposite it we note 0.4384 in the sine column. Therefore, sin 0.4538 = 0.4384.

In the same manner we find, using the nearest radian value shown in Table 3, that

$$\tan 0.9977 = 1.550, \quad \cos 0.6813 = 0.7771, \quad \text{and} \quad \sec 1.1368 = 2.381$$

If we wish to find the value of a function of an angle greater than $\frac{\pi}{2}$, we must first determine which quadrant the angle is in, and then find the reference angle. In this determination we should note the radian measure equivalents of 90°, 180°, 270°, and 360°. For 90° we have

$\frac{\pi}{2} = 1.571$; for 180° we have $\pi = 3.142$; for 270° we have $\frac{3}{2}\pi = 4.712$; and for 360° we have $2\pi = 6.283$.

Example E

(a) Find sin 3.402.

Since 3.402 is greater than 3.142, but less than 4.712, we know that this angle is in the third quadrant and that it has a reference angle of $3.402 - 3.142 = 0.260$. Thus,

$$\sin 3.402 = -\sin 0.260 = -0.2560$$

using the nearest value shown in the table.

(b) Find cos 5.210.

Since 5.210 is between 4.712 and 6.283, we know that this angle is in the fourth quadrant and that its reference angle is $6.283 - 5.210 = 1.073$. Thus,

$$\cos 5.210 = \cos 1.073 = 0.4772$$

using the nearest value shown in the table.

Often when one first encounters radian measure, expressions such as sin 1 and sin $\theta = 1$ are confused. The first is equivalent to sin 57.3°, since 57.3° = 1 (radian). The second means that θ is the angle for which the sine is 1. Since sin 90° = 1, we can say that $\theta = 90°$ or that $\theta = \pi/2$. The following examples give additional illustrations of evaluating expressions involving radians.

Example F

$$\sin \frac{\pi}{3} = \frac{\sqrt{3}}{2} \quad \text{since} \quad \frac{\pi}{3} = 60°$$

$$\sin 0.605 = 0.5688 \quad \text{(We note that } 0.605 = 34°40'.)$$

$$\tan \theta = 1.709 \text{ means that } \theta = 59°40' \text{ (smallest positive } \theta)$$

Since 59°40' = 1.04, we can state that tan 1.04 = 1.709. This can also be determined directly from the radian column of Table 3.

Example G

Express θ in radians, such that cos $\theta = 0.8829$ and $0 < \theta < 2\pi$.

We are to find θ in radians for the given value of the cos θ. Also, since θ is restricted to values between 0 and 2π, we must find a first-quadrant angle and a fourth-quadrant angle (cos θ is positive in the first and the fourth quadrants). From the table we see that

$$\cos 0.4887 = 0.8829$$

Therefore, for the fourth-quadrant angle,

$$\cos (2\pi - 0.4887) = \cos (6.283 - 0.4887) = \cos (5.794)$$

This means

$$\theta = 0.4887 \quad \text{or} \quad \theta = 5.794$$

Exercises 7—3

In Exercises 1 through 8 express the given angle measurements in terms of π.

1. 15°, 150°   2. 12°, 225°   3. 75°, 330°   4. 36°, 315°

5. 210°, 270°   6. 240°, 300°   7. 160°, 260°   8. 66°, 350°

In Exercises 9 through 16 the given numbers express angle measure. Express the measure of each angle in terms of degrees.

9. $\dfrac{2\pi}{5}, \dfrac{3\pi}{2}$ 10. $\dfrac{3\pi}{10}, \dfrac{5\pi}{6}$ 11. $\dfrac{\pi}{18}, \dfrac{7\pi}{4}$ 12. $\dfrac{7\pi}{15}, \dfrac{4\pi}{3}$

13. $\dfrac{17\pi}{18}, \dfrac{5\pi}{3}$ 14. $\dfrac{11\pi}{36}, \dfrac{5\pi}{4}$ 15. $\dfrac{\pi}{12}, \dfrac{3\pi}{20}$ 16. $\dfrac{7\pi}{30}, \dfrac{4\pi}{15}$

In Exercises 17 through 24 express the given angles in radian measure. (Use 3.14 as an *approximation* for π.)

17. 23°0′   18. 54°0′   19. 252.0°   20. 104.0°

21. 333°30′   22. 168°40′   23. 178.5°   24. 86.1°

In Exercises 25 through 32 the given numbers express angle measure. Express the measure of each angle in terms of degrees to the nearest 0.1°.

25. 0.750   26. 0.240   27. 3.00   28. 1.70

29. 2.45   30. 34.4   31. 16.4   32. 100

In Exercises 33 through 40 evaluate the given trigonometric functions by first changing the radian measure to degree measure to the nearest 0.1°. When using Table 4, choose the nearest value shown.

33. $\sin \dfrac{\pi}{4}$ 34. $\cos \dfrac{\pi}{6}$ 35. $\tan \dfrac{5\pi}{12}$ 36. $\sin \dfrac{7\pi}{18}$

37. $\cot \dfrac{5\pi}{6}$ 38. $\tan \dfrac{4\pi}{3}$ 39. $\cos 4.59$ 40. $\cot 3.27$

In Exercises 41 through 48 evaluate the given trigonometric functions directly, without first changing the radian measure to degree measure. When using Table 3, choose the nearest value shown.

41. $\tan 0.7359$ 42. $\sec 0.9308$ 43. $\cot 4.24$ 44. $\tan 3.47$

45. $\cos 2.07$ 46. $\cot 2.34$ 47. $\sin 4.86$ 48. $\csc 6.19$

In Exercises 49 through 56 find θ for $0 < \theta < 2\pi$. In Table 3 use the nearest value shown.

49. $\sin \theta = 0.3090$ 50. $\cos \theta = -0.9135$ 51. $\tan \theta = -0.2126$

52. $\sin \theta = -0.0436$ 53. $\cos \theta = 0.6742$ 54. $\tan \theta = 1.860$

55. $\sec \theta = -1.307$ 56. $\csc \theta = 3.940$

In Exercises 57 through 60 evaluate the given expressions.

57. In optics, when determining the positions of maximum light intensity under specified conditions, the equation $\tan \alpha = \alpha$ is found. Show that a solution to this equation is $\alpha = 1.43\pi$.

58. The instantaneous voltage in a 120-V, 60-Hz power line is given approximately by the equation $V = 170 \sin 377t$, where t is the time (in seconds) after the generator started. Calculate the instantaneous voltage (a) after 0.001 s and (b) after 0.010 s.

59. The velocity v of an object undergoing simple harmonic motion at the end of a spring is given by

$$v = A\sqrt{\frac{k}{m}} \cos \sqrt{\frac{k}{m}}\, t$$

Here m is the mass of the object (in grams), k is a constant depending on the spring, A is the maximum distance the object moves, and t is the time (in seconds). Find the velocity (in centimeters per second) after 0.100 s of a 36.0-g object at the end of a spring for which $k = 400$ g/s^2, if $A = 5.00$ cm.

60. At a point x ft from the base of a building, the angle of elevation of the top of the building is θ. An excellent approximation to the error e in measuring the height of the building due to a small error $(\theta_1 - \theta)$ in measuring θ is given by $e = x(\theta_1 - \theta) \sec^2\theta$. Here it is necessary for $(\theta_1 - \theta)$ to be measured in radians. Calculate the error e (in feet), if $x = 180$ ft, $\theta_1 = 30.5°$, and $\theta = 30.0°$.

7–4 Applications of the Use of Radian Measure

Radian measure has numerous applications in mathematics and technology, some of which were indicated in the last four exercises of the previous section. In this section we shall illustrate the usefulness of radian measure in certain specific geometric and physical applications.

From geometry we know that the length of an arc on a circle is proportional to the central angle, and that the length of the arc of a complete circle is the circumference. Letting s stand for the length of arc, we may state that $s = 2\pi r$ for a complete circle. Since 2π is the central angle (in radians) of the complete circle, we have

$$s = \theta r \tag{7–10}$$

for any circular arc with central angle θ. If we know the central angle in radians and the radius of a circle, we can find the length of a circular arc directly by using Eq. (7–10). (See Fig. 7–8.)

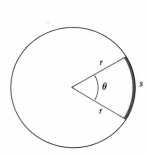

Figure 7–8

Example A

If $\theta = \pi/6$ and $r = 3.00$ in.,

$$s = \left(\frac{\pi}{6}\right)(3.00) = \frac{\pi}{2.00} = 1.57 \text{ in.}$$

If the arc length is 7.20 cm for a central angle of 150° on a certain circle, we may find the radius of the circle by

$$7.20 = (150)\left(\frac{\pi}{180}\right)r = \frac{5.00\pi}{6.00}r \quad \text{or} \quad r = \frac{(6.00)(7.20)}{(5.00)(3.14)} = 2.75 \text{ cm}$$

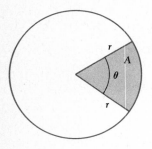

Figure 7–9

Another geometric application of radians is in finding the area of a sector of a circle. (See Fig. 7–9.) We recall from geometry that areas of sectors of circles are proportional to their central angles. The area of a circle is given by $A = \pi r^2$. This can be written as $A = \frac{1}{2}(2\pi)r^2$. We now note that the angle for a complete circle is 2π, and therefore the area of any sector of a circle in terms of the radius and the central angle is

$$A = \frac{1}{2}\theta r^2 \tag{7–11}$$

Example B

The area of a sector of a circle with central angle 18.0° and a radius of 5.00 in. is

$$A = \frac{1}{2}(18.0)\left(\frac{\pi}{180}\right)(5.00)^2 = \frac{1}{2}\left(\frac{\pi}{10.0}\right)(25.0) = 3.93 \text{ in.}^2$$

Given that the area of a sector is 75.5 ft² and the radius is 12.2 ft, we can find the central angle by

$$75.5 = \frac{1}{2}\theta(12.2)^2, \quad \theta = \frac{2(75.5)}{(12.2)^2} = \frac{151}{149} = 1.01$$

This means that the central angle is 1.01 rad, or 57.9°.

The next illustration deals with velocity. We know that average velocity is defined by the equation $v = s/t$, where v is the average velocity, s is the distance traveled, and t is the elapsed time. If an object is moving around a circular path with constant speed, the actual distance traveled is the length of arc traversed. Therefore, if we divide both sides of Eq. (7–10) by t, we obtain

$$\frac{s}{t} = \frac{\theta}{t}r$$

or

$$v = \omega r \tag{7–12}$$

Equation (7–12) expresses the relationship between the **linear velocity** v and the **angular velocity** ω of an object moving around a circle of radius r. The most convenient units for ω are radians per unit of time. In this way the formula can be used directly. However, in practice, ω is often given in revolutions per minute, or in some similar unit. In cases like these, it is necessary to convert the units of ω to radians per unit of time before substituting in Eq. (7–12).

Example C
An object is moving about a circle of radius 6.00 m with an angular velocity of 4.00 rad/s. The linear velocity is

$$v = (6.00)(4.00) = 24.0 \text{ m/s}$$

(Remember that radians are numbers and are not included in the final set of units.) This means that the object is moving along the circumference of the circle at 24.0 m/s.

Example D
A flywheel rotates with an angular velocity of 20.0 r/min. If its radius is 18.0 in., find the linear velocity of a point on the rim.
Since there are 2π radians in each revolution,

$$20.0 \text{ r/min} = 40.0\pi \text{ rad/min}$$

Therefore,

$$v = (40.0)(3.14)(18.0) = 2260 \text{ in./min}$$

This means that the linear velocity is 2260 in./min, which is equivalent to 188 ft/min or 3.13 ft/s.

Example E
A pulley belt 10.0 ft long takes 2.00 s to make one complete revolution. The radius of the pulley is 6.00 in. What is the angular velocity (in revolutions per minute) of a point on the rim of the pulley?
Since the linear velocity of a point on the rim of the pulley is the same as the velocity of the belt, $v = 10.0/2.00 = 5.00$ ft/s. The radius of the pulley is $r = 6.00$ in. $= 0.500$ ft, and we can find ω by substituting into Eq. (7–12). This gives us

$$5.00 = \omega(0.500)$$

or

$$\omega = 10.0 \text{ rad/s}$$
$$= 600 \text{ rad/min}$$
$$= 95.5 \text{ r/min}$$

As it is shown in Appendix B, the change of units can be handled algebraically as

$$10.0 \frac{\text{rad}}{\text{s}} \times 60 \frac{\text{s}}{\text{min}} = 600 \frac{\text{rad}}{\text{min}}, \quad \frac{600 \text{ rad/min}}{2\pi \text{ rad/r}} = 600 \frac{\text{rad}}{\text{min}} \times \frac{1}{2\pi} \frac{\text{r}}{\text{rad}}$$

Exercises 7—4

In Exercises 1 through 28 solve the given problems.

1. In a circle of radius 10.0 in., find the length of arc intercepted on the circumference by a central angle of 60°0′.

2. In a circle of diameter 4.50 ft, find the length of arc intercepted on the circumference by a central angle of 42°0′.

3. Find the area of the circular sector indicated in Exercise 1.

4. Find the area of a sector of a circle, given that the central angle is 120.0° and the diameter is 56.0 cm.

5. Find the radian measure of an angle at the center of a circle of radius 5.00 in. which intercepts an arc length of 60.0 in.

6. Find the central angle of a circle which intercepts an arc length of 780 mm when the radius of the circle is 520 mm.

7. Two concentric (same center) circles have radii of 5.00 and 6.00 in. Find the portion of the area of the sector of the larger circle which is outside the smaller circle when the central angle is 30.0°.

8. In a circle of radius 6.00 m, the length of arc of a sector is 10.0 m. What is the area of the sector?

9. A pendulum 3.00 ft long oscillates through an angle of 5.0°. Find the distance through which the end of the pendulum swings in going from one extreme position to the other.

10. The radius of the earth is about 3960 mi. What is the length, in miles, of an arc of the earth's equator for a central angle of 1.0°?

11. In turning, an airplane traveling at 540 km/h moves through a circular arc for 2.00 min. What is the radius of the circle, given that the central angle is 8°0′?

12. An ammeter needle is deflected 52°0′ by a current of 0.200 A. The needle is 3.00 in. long and a circular scale is used. How long is the scale for a maximum current of 1.00 A?

13. A flywheel rotates at 300 r/min. If the radius is 6.00 cm, through what total distance does a point on the rim travel in 30.0 s?

14. For the flywheel in Exercise 13, how far does a point halfway out along a radius, move in one second?

15. Two streets meet at an angle of 82.0°. What is the length of the piece of curved curbing at the intersection if it is constructed along the arc of a circle 15.0 ft in radius? See Fig. 7—10.

16. In traveling one-third of the way along a traffic circle a car travels 0.125 km. What is the radius of the traffic circle?

17. An automobile is traveling at 60.0 mi/h (88.0 ft/s). The tires are 28.0 in. in diameter. What is the angular velocity of the tires in rad/s?

18. Find the velocity, due to the rotation of the earth, of a point on the surface of the earth at the equator (see Exercise 10).

19. An astronaut in a spacecraft circles the moon once each 1.95 h. If his altitude is constant at 70.0 mi, what is his velocity? The radius of the moon is 1080 mi.

20. What is the linear velocity of the point in Exercise 13?

82.0°

Figure 7—10

21. The armature of a dynamo is 1.38 ft in diameter and is rotating at 1200 r/min. What is the linear velocity of a point on the rim of the armature?

22. A pulley belt 38.5 cm long takes 2.50 s to make one complete revolution. The diameter of the pulley is 11.0 cm. What is the angular velocity, in r/min, of the pulley?

23. The moon is about 240,000 mi from the earth. It takes the moon about 28 days to make one revolution. What is its angular velocity about the earth, in rad/s?

24. A phonograph record 6.90 in. in diameter rotates 45.0 times per minute. What is the linear velocity of a point on the rim in ft/s?

25. A 1500-kW wind turbine (windmill) rotates at 40.0 r/min. What is the linear velocity of a point on the end of a blade, if the blade is 100 ft long (from the center of rotation)?

26. The propeller of an airplane is 2.44 m in diameter and rotates at 2200 r/min. What is the linear velocity of a point on the tip of the propeller?

27. A circular sector whose central angle is 210° is cut from a circular piece of sheet metal of diameter 12.0 cm. A cone is then formed by bringing the two radii of the sector together. What is the lateral surface area of the cone?

28. A conical tent is made from a circular piece of canvas 15.0 ft in diameter, with a sector of central angle 120° removed. What is the surface area of the tent?

In Exercises 29 through 32 another use of radians is illustrated.

29. It can be shown through advanced mathematics that an excellent approximate method of evaluating $\sin \theta$ or $\tan \theta$ is given by

$$\sin \theta = \tan \theta = \theta \tag{7-13}$$

for small values of θ (the equivalent of a few degrees or less), if θ is expressed in radians. (Note the values for θ, $\sin \theta$, and $\tan \theta$ in Table 3 for small values of θ.) Equation (7–13) is particularly useful for very small values of θ—even some scientific calculators cannot adequately handle angles of $1''$ or $0.001°$ or less. Using Eq. (7 – 13), evaluate $\sin 1''$.

30. Using Eq. (7–13), evaluate $\tan 0.001°$.

31. An astronomer observes that a star 12.5 light years away moves through an angle of $0.2''$ in one year. Assuming it moved in a straight line perpendicular to the initial line of observation, how many miles did the star move? (One light year = 5.88×10^{12} mi.)

32. In calculating a back line of a lot a surveyor discovers an error of $0.05°$ in an angle measurement. If the lot is 136.0 m deep, by how much is the back line calculation in error? See Fig. 7–11.

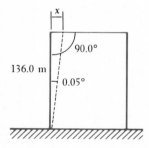

Figure 7—11

7—5 Exercises for Chapter 7

In Exercises 1 through 4 find the trigonometric functions of θ given that the terminal side of θ passes through the given point.

1. $(6, 8)$ 2. $(-12, 5)$ 3. $(7, -2)$ 4. $(-2, -3)$

In Exercises 5 through 8 express the given trigonometric functions in terms of the same function of a positive acute angle.

5. cos 132°,   tan 194°   **6.** sin 243°,   cot 318°

7. sin 289°,   sec (−15°)   **8.** cos 103°,   csc (−100°)

In Exercises 9 through 12 express the given angle measurements in terms of π.

9. 40°,   153°   **10.** 22.5°,   324°   **11.** 48°,   202.5°   **12.** 27°,   162°

In Exercises 13 through 20 the given numbers represent angle measure. Express the measure of each angle in terms of degrees.

13. $\dfrac{7\pi}{5}$, $\dfrac{13\pi}{18}$ **14.** $\dfrac{3\pi}{8}$, $\dfrac{7\pi}{20}$ **15.** $\dfrac{\pi}{15}$, $\dfrac{11\pi}{6}$ **16.** $\dfrac{17\pi}{10}$, $\dfrac{5\pi}{4}$

17. 0.560   **18.** 1.35   **19.** 3.60   **20.** 14.5

In Exercises 21 through 28 express the given angles in radians. (Do not answer in terms of π.)

21. 100°   **22.** 305°   **23.** 20°30′   **24.** 148°30′

25. 262°25′   **26.** 18°47′   **27.** 136.2°   **28.** 385.4°

In Exercises 29 through 48 determine the values of the given trigonometric functions.

29. cos 245°0′   **30.** sin 141°0′   **31.** cot 295.0°   **32.** tan 184.0°

33. csc 247°30′   **34.** sec 96°20′   **35.** sin 205.2°   **36.** cos 326.7°

37. tan 301.4°   **38.** cot 103.9°   **39.** tan 256°42′   **40.** cos 162°32′

41. $\sin \dfrac{9\pi}{5}$ **42.** $\sec \dfrac{5\pi}{8}$ **43.** $\cos \dfrac{7\pi}{6}$ **44.** $\tan \dfrac{23\pi}{12}$

45. sin 0.590   **46.** tan 0.800   **47.** csc 2.15   **48.** cot 5.19

In Exercises 49 through 52 find θ to the nearest 0.1° for 0° < θ < 360°.

49. tan θ = 0.1817   **50.** sin θ = −0.9323

51. cos θ = −0.4730   **52.** cot θ = 1.196

In Exercises 53 through 56 find θ to the nearest 10′ for 0° < θ < 360°.

53. sin θ = 0.2924   **54.** cot θ = −2.560

55. cos θ = 0.3297   **56.** tan θ = −0.7730

In Exercises 57 through 60 find θ to the nearest minute for 0° < θ < 360°.

57. cos θ = −0.7222   **58.** tan θ = −1.683

59. cot θ = 0.4291   **60.** sin θ = 0.2626

In Exercises 61 through 64 find θ for 0 < θ < 2π.

61. cos θ = 0.8387   **62.** sin θ = 0.1045

63. sin θ = −0.8650   **64.** tan θ = 2.840

In Exercises 65 through 80 solve the given problems.

65. The voltage in a certain alternating-current circuit is given by the equation $v = V \cos 25t$, where V is the maximum possible voltage and t is the time in seconds. Find v for $t = 0.1$ s and $V = 150$ V.

66. The displacement (distance from equilibrium position) of a particle moving with simple harmonic motion is given by $d = A \sin 5t$, where A is the maximum displacement and t is the time. Find d, given that $A = 16.0$ cm and $t = 0.460$ s.

67. A pendulum 5.00 ft long swings through an angle of 4.50°. Through what distance does the bob swing in going from one extreme position to the other?

68. Two pulleys have radii of 10.0 in. and 6.00 in., and their centers are 40.0 in. apart. If the pulley belt is uncrossed, what must be the length of the belt?

69. A piece of circular filter paper 15.0 cm in diameter is folded such that its effective filtering area is the same as that of a sector with central angle of 220°. What is the filtering area?

70. A funnel is made from a circular piece of sheet metal 10.0 in. in radius, from which two pieces were removed. The first piece removed was a circle of radius 1.00 in. at the center, and the second piece removed was a sector of central angle 200°. What is the surface area of the funnel?

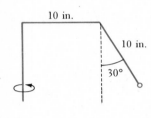

10 in.

10 in.

30°

Figure 7—12

71. If the apparatus shown in Fig. 7—12 is rotating at 2.00 r/s, what is the linear velocity of the ball?

72. A lathe is to cut material at the rate of 350 ft/min. Calculate the radius of a cylindrical piece that is turned at the rate of 120 r/min.

73. A thermometer needle passes through 55.0° for a temperature change of 40°C. If the needle is 5.00 cm long and the scale is circular, how long must the scale be for a maximum temperature change of 150°C?

74. Under certain conditions an electron will travel in a circular path when in a magnetic field. If an electron is moving with a linear velocity of 20,000 m/s in a circular path of radius 0.500 m, how far does it travel in 0.100 s?

75. A cam is constructed so that part of it is a circular arc with a central angle of 72.0° and a radius of 5.30 mm. What is the length of arc along this part of the cam?

76. A horizontal water pipe has a radius of 6.00 ft. If the depth of water in the pipe is 3.00 ft, what percentage of the volume of the pipe is filled?

77. An electric fan blade 15.0 cm in radius rotates at 900 r/min. What is the linear velocity of a point at the end of the blade?

78. A circular saw blade 8.20 in. in diameter rotates at 1500 r/min. What is the linear velocity of a point at the end of one of the teeth?

79. A laser beam is transmitted with a "width" of 0.0008°, and makes a circular spot of radius 2.50 km on a distant object. How far is the object from the source of the laser beam? (See Exercise 29 of Section 7—4.)

80. The plant Venus subtends an angle of 15″ to an observer on Earth. If the distance between Venus and Earth is 1.04×10^8 mi, what is the diameter of Venus? (See Exercise 29 of Section 7—4.)

8

Vectors and Oblique Triangles

8—1 Introduction to Vectors

A great many quantities with which we deal may be described by specifying their magnitudes. Generally, one can describe lengths of objects, areas, time intervals, monetary amounts, temperatures, and numerous other quantities by specifying a number: the magnitude of the quantity. Such quantities are know as **scalar** quantities.

Many other quantities are fully described only when both their magnitude and direction are specified. Such quantities are known as **vectors.** Examples of vectors are velocity, force, and momentum. Vectors are of utmost importance in many fields of science and technology. The following example illustrates a vector quantity and the distinction between scalars and vectors.

Example A

A jet flies over a certain point traveling at 600 mi/h. From this statement alone we know only the *speed* of the jet. Speed is a scalar quantity, and it designates only the *magnitude* of the rate.

If we were to add the phrase "in a direction 10° south of west" to the sentence above about the jet, we would be specifying the direction of travel as well as the speed. We then know the *velocity* of the jet; that is, we know the *direction* of travel as well as the *magnitude* of the rate at which the jet is traveling. Velocity is a vector quantity.

Let us analyze an example of the action of two vectors: Consider a boat moving in a stream. For purposes of this example, we shall assume that the boat is driven by a motor which can move it at 4 mi/h in still water. We shall assume the current is moving downstream at 3 mi/h. We immediately see that the motion of the boat depends on the direction in which it is headed. If the boat heads downstream, it can travel at 7 mi/h, for the current is going 3 mi/h and the boat moves at 4 mi/h with respect to the water. If the boat heads upstream, however, it progresses at the rate of only 1 mi/h, since the action of the boat and that of the stream are counter to each other. If the boat heads across the stream, the point which it reaches on the other side will not be directly opposite the point from which it started. We can see that this is so because we know that as the boat heads across the stream, the stream is moving the boat downstream *at the same time*.

This last case should be investigated further. Let us assume that the stream is $\frac{1}{2}$ mi wide where the boat is crossing. It will then take the boat $\frac{1}{8}$ h to cross. In $\frac{1}{8}$ h the stream will carry the boat $\frac{3}{8}$ mi downstream. Therefore, when the boat reaches the other side it will be $\frac{3}{8}$ mi downstream. From the Pythagorean theorem, we find that the boat traveled $\frac{5}{8}$ mi from its starting point to its finishing point.

$$d^2 = \left(\frac{4}{8}\right)^2 + \left(\frac{3}{8}\right)^2 = \frac{16 + 9}{64} = \frac{25}{64}; \qquad d = \frac{5}{8} \text{ mi}$$

Since this $\frac{5}{8}$ mi was traveled in $\frac{1}{8}$ h, the magnitude of the velocity of the boat was actually

$$v = \frac{d}{t} = \frac{5/8}{1/8} = \frac{5}{8} \cdot \frac{8}{1} = 5 \text{ mi/h}$$

Also, we see that the direction of this velocity can be represented along a line making an angle θ with the line directed across the stream (see Fig. 8—1).

We have just seen two velocity vectors being *added*. Note that these vectors are not added the way numbers are added. We have to take into account their direction as well as their magnitude. Reasoning along these lines, let us now define the sum of two vectors.

We will represent a vector quantity by a letter printed in boldface type. The same letter in italic (lightface) type represents the magnitude only. Thus, **A** is a vector of magnitude A. In handwriting, one usually places an arrow over the letter to represent a vector, such as $\vec{A}$.

Let **A** and **B** represent vectors directed from O to P and P to Q, respectively (see Fig. 8—2). *The vector sum* **A + B** *is the vector* **R**, *from the* **initial point** O *to the* **terminal point** Q. *Here, vector* **R** *is called the* **resultant**. *In general, a resultant is a single vector which can replace any number of other vectors and still produce the same physical effect.*

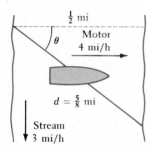

Figure 8—1

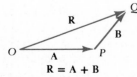

R = A + B

Figure 8—2

There are two common methods of adding vectors by means of a diagram. The first is illustrated in Fig. 8–3. To add **B** to **A**, we shift **B** parallel to itself until its tail touches the head of **A**. In doing so we must be careful to keep the magnitude and direction of **B** unchanged. The vector sum **A** + **B** is the vector **R**, which is drawn from the tail of **A** to the head of **B**.

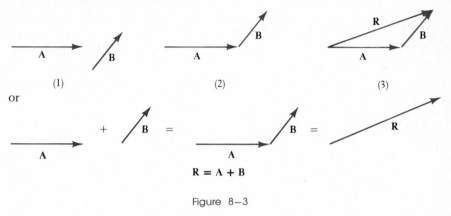

Figure 8–3

Three or more vectors may also be added in the same general manner. We place the initial point of the second vector at the terminal point of the first vector, the initial point of the third vector at the terminal point of the second vector, and so forth. The resultant is the vector from the initial point of the first vector to the terminal point of the last vector. The order in which they are placed together does not matter, as shown in the following example.

Example B
The addition of vectors **A**, **B**, and **C** is shown in Fig. 8–4.

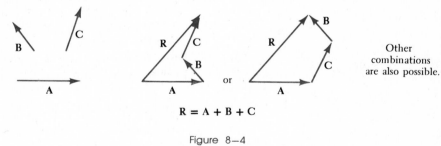

Figure 8–4

Another method which is convenient when two vectors are being added is to let the two vectors being added be the sides of a parallelogram. The resultant is then the diagonal of the parallelogram. The initial point of the resultant is the common initial point of the vectors being added. In using this method the vectors are first placed tail to tail. See the following example.

Example C
Using the parallelogram method, add vectors **A** and **B** of Fig. 8—3. See Fig. 8—5.

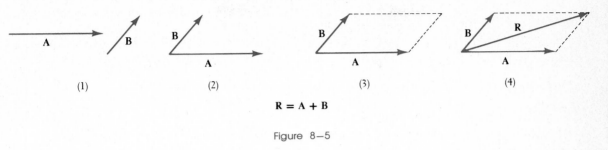

(1)   (2)   (3)   (4)

R = A + B

Figure 8—5

If vector **A** has the same direction as vector **B**, and **A** also has a magnitude *n* times that of **B**, we may state that **A** = *n***B**. Thus, 2**A** represents a vector twice as long as **A**, but in the same direction.

Example D
For the vectors **A** and **B** in Fig. 8—3, find 3**A** + 2**B**. See Fig. 8—6.

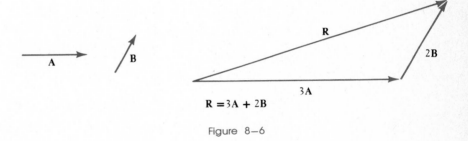

R = 3A + 2B

Figure 8—6

Vector **B** may be subtracted from vector **A** by reversing the direction of **B** and proceeding as in vector addition. Thus, **A** − **B** = **A** + (−**B**), where the minus sign indicates that vector −**B** has the opposite direction of vector **B**. Vector subtraction is shown in the following example.

Example E
For vectors **A** and **B**, find 2**A** − **B**. See Fig. 8—7.

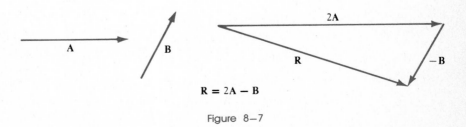

R = 2A − B

Figure 8—7

In addition to being able to add and subtract vectors, we often need to consider a given vector as the sum of two other vectors. *Two vectors which when added together give the original vector are called the components of the original vector.* In the example of the boat, the velocities of 4 mi/h cross-stream and 3 mi/h downstream are components of the 5 mi/h vector directed at the angle θ.

In practice, there are certain components of a vector which are of particular importance. If a vector is so placed that its initial point is at the origin of a rectangular coordinate system, and its direction is indicated by an angle in standard position, we may find its x- and y-components. These components are vectors directed along the coordinate axes which, when added together, result in the given vector. *Finding these component vectors is called resolving the vector into its components.*

Example F

Resolve a vector 10.0 units long and directed at an angle of 120°0′ into its x- and y-components (see Fig. 8–8).

Placing the initial point of the vector at the origin, and putting the angle in standard position, we see that the vector directed along the x-axis, $\mathbf{V}_x$, is related to the vector $\mathbf{V}$, of magnitude V by

$$V_x = V \cos 120°0′ = -V \cos 60°0′$$

(The minus sign indicates that the x-component is directed in the negative direction, that is, to the left.) Since the vector directed along the y-axis, $\mathbf{V}_y$, could also be placed along the dashed line, it is related to the vector $\mathbf{V}$ by

$$V_y = V \sin 120°0′ = V \sin 60°0′$$

Thus, the vectors $\mathbf{V}_x$ and $\mathbf{V}_y$ have the magnitudes

$$V_x = -10.0(0.5000) = -5.00, \qquad V_y = 10.0(0.8660) = 8.66$$

Therefore, we have resolved the given vector into two components, one directed along the negative x-axis of magnitude 5.00, and the other directed along the positive y-axis of magnitude 8.66.

Example G

Resolve vector $\mathbf{A}$ of magnitude 375 and direction $\theta \doteq 205.3°$ into its x- and y-components. See Fig. 8–9.

By placing $\mathbf{A}$ such that θ is in standard position, we see that

$$A_x = A \cos 205.3° = 375(-0.9041) = -339$$

and

$$A_y = A \sin 205.3° = 375(-0.4274) = -160$$

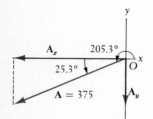

Figure 8–8

Figure 8–9

Here, values for the trigonometric functions were found directly by use of a calculator.

We can also calculate these as follows:

$$A_x = A \cos 205.3° = 375(-\cos 25.3°) = 375(-0.9041) = -339$$

and

$$A_y = A \sin 205.3° = 375(-\sin 25.3°) = 375(-0.4274) = -160$$

Thus, **A** has two components, one directed along the negative *x*-axis of magnitude 339, and the other directed along the negative *y*-axis of magnitude 160.

Exercises 8−1

In Exercises 1 through 4 add the given vectors by drawing the appropriate resultant. Use the parallelogram method in Exercises 3 and 4.

1.   2.   3.   4.

In Exercises 5 through 24 find the indicated vector sums and differences with the given vectors by means of diagrams.

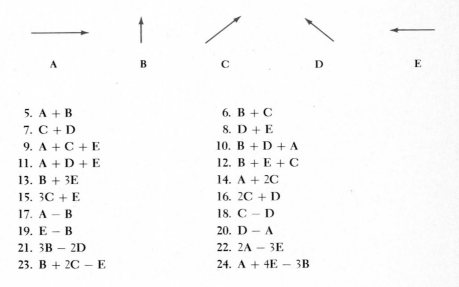

A   B   C   D   E

5. A + B   6. B + C
7. C + D   8. D + E
9. A + C + E   10. B + D + A
11. A + D + E   12. B + E + C
13. B + 3E   14. A + 2C
15. 3C + E   16. 2C + D
17. A − B   18. C − D
19. E − B   20. D − A
21. 3B − 2D   22. 2A − 3E
23. B + 2C − E   24. A + 4E − 3B

In Exercises 25 through 32 find the *x*- and *y*-components of the given vectors by use of the trigonometric functions.

25. Magnitude 8.60, $\theta = 68°0'$ **26.** Magnitude 9750, $\theta = 243°0'$
27. Magnitude 76.8, $\theta = 145.0°$ **28.** Magnitude 0.0998, $\theta = 296.0°$
29. Magnitude 9.04, $\theta = 283°30'$ **30.** Magnitude 16,000, $\theta = 156.5°$
31. Magnitude 2.65, $\theta = 197.3°$ **32.** Magnitude 67.8, $\theta = 22.5°$

8—2 Vector Addition by Components

Adding vectors by diagrams gives only approximate results. By use of the trigonometric functions and the Pythagorean theorem, it is possible to obtain accurate numerical results for the sum of vectors. In the following example we shall illustrate how this is done in the case when the two given vectors are at right angles.

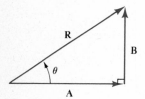

Figure 8—10

Example A

Add vectors **A** and **B**, with $A = 14.5$ and $B = 9.10$. The vectors are at right angles as shown in Fig. 8–10.

We can find the magnitude R of the resultant vector **R** by use of the Pythagorean theorem. This leads to

$$R = \sqrt{A^2 + B^2} = \sqrt{(14.5)^2 + (9.10)^2}$$
$$= \sqrt{210 + 82.8} = \sqrt{293} = 17.1$$

We shall now determine the direction of **R** by specifying its direction as the angle θ, that is, the angle **R** makes with **A**. Therefore,

$$\tan \theta = \frac{B}{A} = \frac{9.10}{14.5} = 0.6276$$

To the nearest 10', $\theta = 32°10'$, or to the nearest 0.1°, $\theta = 32.1°$. Thus, **R** is a vector with magnitude $R = 17.1$ and in a direction $32°10'$ from vector **A**.

If vectors are to be added and they are not at right angles, we first place each with tail at the origin. Next, we resolve each vector into its *x*- and *y*-components. We then add all of the *x*-components and add the *y*-components to determine the *x*- and *y*-components of the resultant. Then by use of the Pythagorean theorem and the tangent, as in Example A, we find the magnitude and direction of the resultant. *Remember, a vector is not completely specified unless both its magnitude and its direction are given.*

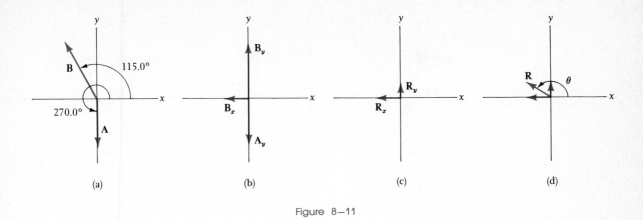

(a)   (b)   (c)   (d)

Figure 8–11

Example B

Find the resultant of two vectors **A** and **B** such that $A = 1200$, $\theta_A = 270.0°$, $B = 1750$, and $\theta_B = 115.0°$.

We first place the vectors on a coordinate system with the tail of each at the origin as shown in Fig. 8–11(a). We then resolve each into its x- and y-components, as shown in Fig. 8–11(b) and as calculated below. (Note that **A** is vertical and has no horizontal component.) Next, the components are combined as in Fig. 8–11(c) and as calculated. Finally, the magnitude and direction of the resultant, as shown in Fig. 8–11(d), are calculated.

$$A_x = A \cos 270.0° = 1200(0) = 0$$
$$A_y = A \sin 270.0° = 1200(-1.000) = -1200$$
$$B_x = B \cos 115.0° = 1750 \cos 115.0° = -1750 \cos 65.0°$$
$$= -1750(0.4226) = -740$$
$$B_y = B \sin 115.0° = 1750 \sin 115.0° = 1750 \sin 65.0°$$
$$= 1750(0.9063) = 1590$$
$$R_x = A_x + B_x = 0 - 740 = -740$$
$$R_y = A_y + B_y = -1200 + 1590 = 390$$
$$R = \sqrt{R_x^2 + R_y^2} = \sqrt{(-740)^2 + (390)^2} = \sqrt{547600 + 152100}$$
$$= \sqrt{699700} = 836$$

$$\tan \theta = \frac{R_y}{R_x} = \frac{390}{-740} = -0.5270, \quad \theta = 152.2°$$

Thus, the resultant has a magnitude of 836 and is directed at an angle of 152.2°. In determining θ, the reference angle was 27.8°, and we know that θ is a second quadrant angle since R_x is negative and R_y is positive.

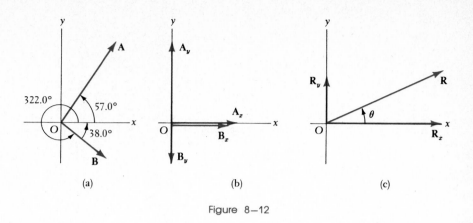

Figure 8–12

Example C
Find the resultant **R** of the two vectors given in Fig. 8–12(a), **A** of magnitude 8.00 and direction 57.0° and **B** of magnitude 5.00 and direction 322.0°.

$$A_x = (8.00)(\cos 57.0°) = (8.00)(0.5446) = 4.36$$
$$A_y = (8.00)(\sin 57.0°) = (8.00)(0.8387) = 6.71$$
$$B_x = (5.00)(\cos 38.0°) = (5.00)(0.7880) = 3.94$$
$$B_y = -(5.00)(\sin 38.0°) = -(5.00)(0.6157) = -3.08$$
$$R_x = A_x + B_x = 4.36 + 3.94 = 8.30$$
$$R_y = A_y + B_y = 6.71 - 3.08 = 3.63$$
$$R = \sqrt{(8.30)^2 + (3.63)^2} = \sqrt{68.9 + 13.2} = \sqrt{82.1} = 9.06$$

$$\tan \theta = \frac{R_y}{R_x} = \frac{3.63}{8.30} = 0.4373, \qquad \theta = 23.6°$$

The resultant vector is 9.06 units long and is directed at an angle of 23.6°, as shown in Fig. 8–12(c).

Some general formulas can be derived from the previous examples. For a given vector **A**, directed at an angle θ, and of magnitude A, with components A_x and A_y, we have the following relations:

$$A_x = A \cos \theta, \qquad A_y = A \sin \theta \tag{8–1}$$

$$A = \sqrt{A_x^2 + A_y^2} \tag{8–2}$$

$$\tan \theta = \frac{A_y}{A_x} \tag{8–3}$$

Example D
Find the resultant of the three given vectors with $A = 422$, $B = 405$, and $C = 210$, as shown in Fig. 8–13.

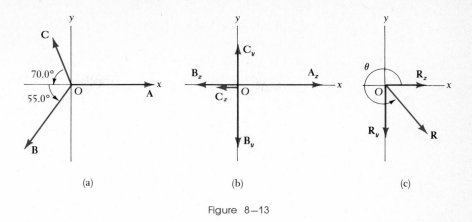

Figure 8–13

We can find the x- and y-components of the vectors by using Eq. (8–1). The following table is helpful for determining the necessary values.

Vector	x-component	y-component
A	$= +422$	$= 0$
B	$-405 \cos 55.0° = -232$	$-405 \sin 55.0° = -332$
C	$-210 \cos 70.0° = -72$	$+210 \sin 70.0° = +197$
R	$+118$	-135

From this table it is possible to compute R and θ:

$$R = \sqrt{(118)^2 + (-135)^2} = 179, \qquad \tan \theta = \frac{-135}{118} = -1.144$$

$$\theta = 311.2°$$

Exercises 8–2

In Exercises 1 through 4, vectors **A** and **B** are at right angles. Find the magnitude and direction of the resultant.

1. $A = 14.7$ 2. $A = 592$ 3. $A = 3.08$ 4. $A = 1730$
   $B = 19.2$ $B = 195$ $B = 7.14$ $B = 3290$

In Exercises 5 through 12 with the given sets of components, find R and θ.

5. $R_x = 5.18,\ R_y = 8.56$ 6. $R_x = 89.6,\ R_y = -52.0$
7. $R_x = -0.982,\ R_y = 2.56$ 8. $R_x = -729,\ R_y = -209$
9. $R_x = -646,\ R_y = 2030$ 10. $R_x = -31.2,\ R_y = -41.2$
11. $R_x = 0.694,\ R_y = -1.24$ 12. $R_x = 7.62,\ R_y = -6.35$

In Exercises 13 through 24 add the given vectors by using the trigonometric functions and the Pythagorean theorem.

13. $A = 18.0,\ \theta_A = 0°0'$ 14. $A = 150,\ \theta_A = 90°0'$
    $B = 12.0,\ \theta_B = 27°0'$ $B = 128,\ \theta_B = 43°0'$

15. $A = 56.0,\ \theta_A = 76.0°$ 16. $A = 6.89,\ \theta_A = 123.0°$
    $B = 24.0,\ \theta_B = 200.0°$ $B = 29.0,\ \theta_B = 260.0°$

17. $A = 9.82$, $\theta_A = 34°0'$
   $B = 17.4$, $\theta_B = 752°30'$

18. $A = 1.65$, $\theta_A = 36°30'$
   $B = 0.980$, $\theta_B = 253°0'$

19. $A = 12.6$, $\theta_A = 98.4°$
   $B = 15.1$, $\theta_B = 332.2°$

20. $A = 121$, $\theta_A = 292.0°$
   $B = 112$, $\theta_B = 198.7°$

21. $A = 21.9$, $\theta_A = 236.2°$
   $B = 96.7$, $\theta_B = 11.5°$
   $C = 62.9$, $\theta_C = 143.4°$

22. $A = 6300$, $\theta_A = 189.0°$
   $B = 1760$, $\theta_B = 320.0°$
   $C = 3240$, $\theta_C = 75.0°$

23. The vectors shown in Fig. 8–14

24. The vectors shown in Fig. 8–15

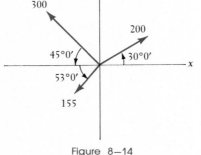

Figure 8–14

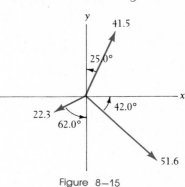

Figure 8–15

8–3 Application of Vectors

As we mentioned at the beginning of the chapter, vectors are important in science and technology. In this section a number of these applications are illustrated in the examples and exercises.

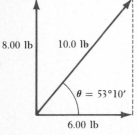

Figure 8–16

Example A

An object on a horizontal table is acted on by two horizontal forces. The two forces have magnitudes of 6.00 and 8.00 lb, and the angle between their lines of action is 90°0′. What is the resultant of these forces?

By means of an appropriate diagram (Fig. 8–16) we may better visualize the actual situation. We note that a good choice of axes (unless specified, it is often convenient to choose the x- and y-axes to fit the problem) is to have the x-axis in the direction of the 6.00-lb force and the y-axis in the direction of the 8.00-lb force. (This is possible since the angle between them is 90°.) With this choice we note that the two given forces will be the x- and y-components of the resultant. Therefore, we arrive at the following results:

$$F_x = 6.00 \text{ lb}, \qquad F_y = 8.00 \text{ lb}, \qquad F = \sqrt{36.0 + 64.0} = 10.0 \text{ lb}$$

$$\tan \theta = \frac{F_y}{F_x} = \frac{8.00}{6.00} = 1.333, \qquad \theta = 53°10'$$

We would state that the resultant has a magnitude of 10.0 lb and acts at an angle of 53°10′ from the 6.00-lb force.

Example B

A ship sails 32.0 mi due east and then turns 40.0°N of E. After sailing an additional 16.0 mi, where is it with reference to the starting point?

The distance an object moves and the direction in which it moves give the **displacement** of an object. Therefore, in this problem we are to determine the resultant displacement of the ship from the two given displacements. The problem is diagrammed in Fig. 8–17, where the first displacement has been labeled vector **A** and the second as vector **B**.

Since east corresponds to the positive *x*-direction, we see that the *x*-component of the resultant is $A + B_x$, and the *y*-component of the resultant is B_y. Therefore, we have the following results:

$$R_x = A + B_x = 32.0 + 16.0 \cos 40.0°$$
$$= 32.0 + 16.0(0.7660) = 32.0 + 12.3$$
$$= 44.3 \text{ mi}$$
$$R_y = 16.0 \sin 40.0° = 16.0(0.6428) = 10.3 \text{ mi}$$
$$R = \sqrt{(44.3)^2 + (10.3)^2} = \sqrt{2069} = 45.5 \text{ mi}$$

$$\tan \theta = \frac{10.3}{44.3} = 0.2325$$

$$\theta = 13.1°$$

Therefore, the ship is 45.5 mi from the starting point, in a direction 13.1° N of E.

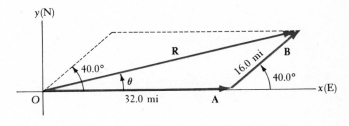

Figure 8–17

Example C

An airplane headed due east is in a wind which is blowing from the southeast. What is the resultant velocity of the plane with respect to the surface of the earth, if the plane's velocity with respect to the air is 600 km/h, and that of the wind is 100 km/h (see Fig. 8–18)?

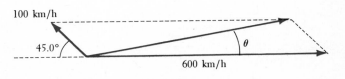

Figure 8–18

Let v_{px} be the velocity of the plane in the x-direction (east), v_{py} the velocity of the plane in the y-direction, v_{wx} the x-component of the velocity of the wind, v_{wy} the y-component of the velocity of the wind, and v_{pa} the velocity of the plane with respect to the air. Therefore,

$$v_{px} = v_{pa} - v_{wx} = 600 - 100 \ (\cos 45.0°) = 600 - 70.7 = 529 \text{ km/h}$$

$$v_{py} = v_{wy} = 100 \ (\sin 45.0°) = 70.7 \text{ km/h}$$

$$v = \sqrt{(529)^2 + (70.7)^2} = \sqrt{280,000 + 5000} = 534 \text{ km/h}$$

$$\tan \theta = \frac{v_{py}}{v_{px}} = \frac{70.7}{529} = 0.1336, \qquad \theta = 7.6°$$

We have determined that the plane is traveling 534 km/h and is flying in a direction 7.6° north of east. From this we observe that a plane does not necessarily head in the direction of its desired destination.

Example D

A block is resting on an inclined plane which makes an angle of 30.0° with the horizontal. If the block weighs 100 lb, what is the force of friction between the block and the plane?

The weight of the block is the force exerted on the block due to gravity. Therefore, the weight is directed vertically downward. The frictional force tends to oppose the motion of the block and is directed upward along the plane. The frictional force must be sufficient to counterbalance that component of the weight of the block which is directed down the plane for the block to be at rest. The plane itself "holds up" that component of the weight which is perpendicular to the plane. A convenient set of coordinates (Fig. 8–19) would be one with the x-axis directed up the plane and the y-axis perpendicular to the plane. The magnitude of the frictional force $\mathbf{F}_f$ is given by

$$F_f = 100 \sin 30.0° = 100(0.5000) = 50.0 \text{ lb}$$

(Since the component of the weight down the plane is 100 sin 30.0° and is equal to the frictional force, this relation is true.)

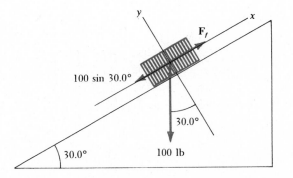

All forces are assumed to act
at the center of the block.

Figure 8–19

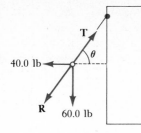

40.0 lb

R   60.0 lb

Figure 8–20

Example E

A 60.0-lb object hangs from a hook on a wall. If a horizontal force of 40.0 lb pulls the object away from the wall so that the object is in equilibrium (no resultant force in any direction), what is the tension T in the rope attached to the wall?

For the object to be in equilibrium, the tension in the rope must be equal and opposite to the resultant of the 40.0-lb force and the 60.0-lb force which is the weight of the object (see Fig. 8–20). Thus, the magnitude of the x-component of the tension is 40.0 lb and the magnitude of the y-component is 60.0 lb.

$$T = \sqrt{(40.0)^2 + (60.0)^2} = \sqrt{5200} = 72.1 \text{ lb}$$

$$\tan \theta = \frac{60.0}{40.0} = 1.500, \qquad \theta = 56.3°$$

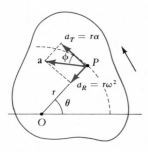

Figure 8–21

Example F

If an object rotates about a point O, the tangential component of the acceleration $\mathbf{a}_T$ and the centripetal component of the acceleration $\mathbf{a}_R$ of a point P are given by the expressions shown in Fig. 8–21. The radius of the circle through which P is moving is r, the angular velocity at any instant is ω, and α is the rate at which the angular velocity ω is changing. Given that $r = 2.35$ m, $\omega = 5.60$ rad/s and $\alpha = 3.75$ rad/s², calculate the magnitude of the resultant acceleration and the angle it makes with the tangential component.

$$(\mathbf{a}_R \perp \mathbf{a}_T), \qquad a_R = r\omega^2 = (2.35)(5.60)^2 = 73.7 \text{ m/s}^2$$
$$a_T = r\alpha = (2.35)(3.75) = 8.81 \text{ m/s}^2$$
$$a = \sqrt{a_R^2 + a_T^2} = \sqrt{(73.7)^2 + (8.81)^2} = 74.2 \text{ m/s}^2$$

The angle ϕ between $\mathbf{a}$ and $\mathbf{a}_T$ is found from the relation $\cos \phi = a_T/a$. Hence,

$$\cos \phi = \frac{8.81}{73.7} = 0.1195 \quad \text{or} \quad \phi = 83.1°$$

Exercises 8–3

In Exercises 1 through 24 solve the given problems.

1. Two forces, one of 45.0 lb and the other of 68.0 lb, act on the same object and at right angles to each other. Find the resultant of these forces.

2. Two forces, one of 150 lb and the other of 220 lb, pull on an object. The angle between these forces is 90°0′. What is the resultant of these forces?

3. Two forces, one of 350 N and the other of 520 N, pull on an object. The angle between these forces is 25.0°. What is the resultant of these forces?

4. The angle between two forces acting on an object is 63°0′. If the two forces are 86.0 N and 103 N, respectively, what is their resultant?

5. A jet travels 450 mi due west from a city. It then turns and travels 240 mi south. What is its displacement from the city?

6. A ship sails 78.3 km due north after leaving its pier. It then turns and sails 51.2 km east. What is the displacement of the ship from its pier?

7. Town B is 52.0 mi southeast of town A. Town C is 45.0 mi due west of town B. What is the displacement of town C from town A?

8. A surveyor locates a tree 36.5 m northeast of her. She knows that it is 20.0 m north of a utility pole. What is the surveyor's displacement from the utility pole?

9. What are the horizontal and vertical components of the velocity of a stone thrown into the air with a velocity of 120 ft/s at an angle of 48°0′ with respect to the horizontal?

10. A rocket is traveling at an angle of 74.0° with respect to the horizontal at a speed of 3500 km/h. What are the horizontal and vertical components of the velocity?

11. A child weighing 60.0 lb sits in a swing and is pulled sideways by a horizontal force of 20.0 lb. What is the tension in each of the supporting ropes? What is the angle between the horizontal and the ropes?

12. A rope 10.0 ft long is fastened to supports which are 8.00 ft apart and at the same level. A 100-lb weight is then hung from its center. How much is the tension in the supporting rope?

13. A stone is thrown horizontally from a plane traveling at 200 m/s. If the stone is thrown at 50.0 m/s in a direction perpendicular to the direction of the plane, what is the velocity of the stone just after it is released?

14. A plane is headed due north at a velocity of 500 km/h with respect to the air. If the wind is from the southwest at 80.0 km/h, what is the resultant speed of the plane, and in what direction is it traveling?

15. A 70.0-lb force is applied to a 40.0-lb box by a rigid metal rod at an angle of 45°0′ above the horizontal (see Fig. 8–22). Will the box be lifted from the ground?

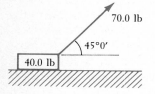

Figure 8–22

16. Assume that the plane in Fig. 8–19 is frictionless. If the acceleration due to gravity is 9.80 m/s², what is the component of the acceleration of the object down the plane? (This is the acceleration the object will have, since it is restricted to moving down the plane.)

17. In Fig. 8–19, if the plane is inclined at 20.0° what is the force exerted on the 100-lb object by the plane itself?

18. In Fig. 8–19, if a horizontal 10.0-lb force is exerted to the right on the 100-lb object, what would the force of friction have to be so that the object did not move down the plane?

19. An object is dropped from a plane moving at 120 m/s. If the vertical velocity, as a function of time, is given by $v_y = 9.80t$, what is the velocity of the object after 4.50 s? In what direction is it moving?

20. The magnitude of the horizontal and vertical components of displacement of a certain projectile are given by $d_H = 120t$ and $d_V = 160t - 16t^2$, where t is the time in seconds. Find the displacement (in feet) of the object after 3.00 s.

21. In Fig. 8–21, given that $a = 56.4$ ft/s², $a_R = 37.9$ ft/s², and $r = 6.00$ ft, find α, the rate of change of angular velocity.

22. A boat travels across a river, reaching the opposite bank at a point directly opposite that from which it left. If the boat travels 6.00 km/h in still water, and the current of river flows at 3.00 km/h, what was the velocity of the boat in the water?

23. In Fig. 8–23, a long straight conductor perpendicular to the plane of the paper carries an electric current i. A bar magnet having poles of strength

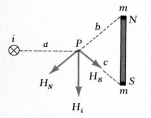

Figure 8–23

m lies in the plane of the paper. The vectors $\mathbf{H}_i$, $\mathbf{H}_N$, and $\mathbf{H}_S$ represent the components of the magnetic intensity $\mathbf{H}$ due, respectively, to the current and to the N and S poles of the magnet. The magnitude of the components of $\mathbf{H}$ are given by

$$H_i = \frac{1}{2\pi}\frac{i}{a}, \qquad H_N = \frac{1}{4\pi}\frac{m}{b^2}, \qquad \text{and} \qquad H_S = \frac{1}{4\pi}\frac{m}{c^2}$$

Given that $a = 0.300$ m, $b = 0.400$ m, $c = 0.300$ m, the length of the magnet is 0.500 m, $i = 4.00$ A, and $m = 2.00$ A·m, calculate the resultant magnetic intensity $\mathbf{H}$. The component $\mathbf{H}_i$ is parallel to the magnet.

24. Solve the problem of Exercise 23 if $\mathbf{H}_i$ is directed away from the magnet, making an angle of $10°0'$ with the direction of the magnet.

8–4 Oblique Triangles, the Law of Sines

To this point we have limited our study of triangle solution to right triangles. However, many triangles which require solution do not contain a right angle. Such a triangle is termed an **oblique triangle.** Let us now discuss the solutions of oblique triangles.

In Section 3–4 we stated that we need three parts, at least one of them a side, in order to solve any triangle. With this in mind we may determine that there are four possible combinations of parts from which we may solve a triangle. These combinations are:

Case 1. Two angles and one side
Case 2. Two sides and the angle opposite one of them
Case 3. Two sides and the included angle
Case 4. Three sides

There are several ways in which oblique triangles may be solved, but we shall restrict our attention to the two most useful methods, the **Law of Sines** and the **Law of Cosines.** In this section we shall discuss the Law of Sines, and show that it may be used to solve Case 1 and Case 2.

Let ABC be an oblique triangle with sides a, b, and c opposite angles A, B, and C, respectively. By drawing a perpendicular h from B to side b, or its extension, we see from Fig. 8–24(a) that

$$h = c \sin A \qquad \text{or} \qquad h = a \sin C \qquad\qquad (8\text{–}4)$$

and from Fig. 8–24(b)

$$h = c \sin A \qquad \text{or} \qquad h = a \sin (180° - C) = a \sin C \qquad (8\text{–}5)$$

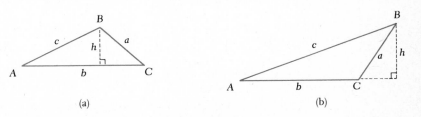

| (a) | (b) |

Figure 8–24

We note that the results are precisely the same in Eqs. (8–4) and (8–5). Setting the results for h equal to each other, we have

$$c \sin A = a \sin C \qquad \text{or} \qquad \frac{a}{\sin A} = \frac{c}{\sin C} \qquad (8\text{–}6)$$

By dropping a perpendicular from A to a we also derive the result

$$c \sin B = b \sin C \qquad \text{or} \qquad \frac{b}{\sin B} = \frac{c}{\sin C} \qquad (8\text{–}7)$$

Combining Eqs. (8–6) and (8–7) we have the **Law of Sines:**

$$\frac{a}{\sin A} = \frac{b}{\sin B} = \frac{c}{\sin C} \qquad (8\text{–}8)$$

The Law of Sines is a statement of proportionality between the sides of a triangle and the sines of the angles opposite them.

Now we may see how the Law of Sines is applied to the solution of a triangle in which two angles and one side are known (Case 1). If two angles are known, the third may be found from the fact that the sum of the angles in a triangle is 180°. At this point we must be able to determine the ratio between the given side and the sine of the angle opposite it. Then, by use of the Law of Sines, we may find the other sides.

Example A
Given that $c = 6.00$, $A = 60°0'$, and $B = 40°0'$, find a, b, and C.
   First we can see that

$$C = 180°0' - (60°0' + 40°0') = 80°0'$$

Thus,

$$\frac{a}{\sin 60°0'} = \frac{6.00}{\sin 80°0'} \qquad \text{or} \qquad a = \frac{(6.00)(0.8660)}{0.9848} = 5.28$$

$$\frac{b}{\sin 40°0'} = \frac{6.00}{\sin 80°0'} \qquad \text{or} \qquad b = \frac{(6.00)(0.6428)}{0.9848} = 3.92$$

Thus, $a = 5.28$, $b = 3.92$, and $C = 80°0'$.

Example B
Solve the triangle with the following given parts: $a = 63.7$, $A = 56°0'$, and $B = 97°0'$.
   We may immediately determine that $C = 27°0'$. Thus,

$$\frac{b}{\sin 97°0'} = \frac{63.7}{\sin 56°0'} \qquad \text{or} \qquad b = \frac{63.7(0.9925)}{0.8290} = 76.3$$

and

$$\frac{c}{\sin 27°0'} = \frac{63.7}{\sin 56°0'} \qquad \text{or} \qquad c = \frac{63.7(0.4540)}{0.8290} = 34.9$$

Thus, $b = 76.3$, $c = 34.9$, and $C = 27°0'$.

Example C

Solve the triangle with the following given parts: $b = 5.06$, $A = 42.0°$, and $C = 28.5°$.

We determine that $B = 109.5°$. Thus,

$$\frac{a}{\sin 42.0°} = \frac{5.06}{\sin 109.5°} \qquad \text{or} \qquad a = \frac{5.06(0.6691)}{0.9426} = 3.59$$

and

$$\frac{c}{\sin 28.5°} = \frac{5.06}{\sin 109.5°} \qquad \text{or} \qquad c = \frac{5.06(0.4772)}{0.9426} = 2.56$$

Thus, $a = 3.59$, $c = 2.56$, and $B = 109.5°$.

If the given information is appropriate, the Law of Sines may be used to solve applied problems. The following example illustrates the use of the Law of Sines in such a problem.

Example D

A plane traveling at 650 mi/h with respect to the air is headed 30°0′ east of north. The wind is blowing from the south, which causes the actual course to be 27°0′ east of north. Find the velocity of the wind and the velocity of the plane with respect to the ground.

From the given information the angles are determined, as shown in Fig. 8–25. Then applying the Law of Sines, we have the relations

$$\frac{v_w}{\sin 3°0'} = \frac{v_{pg}}{\sin 150°0'} = \frac{650}{\sin 27°0'}$$

where v_w is the magnitude of the velocity of the wind and v_{pg} is the magnitude of the velocity of the plane with respect to the ground. Thus,

$$v_w = \frac{650(0.0523)}{0.4540} = 74.9 \text{ mi/h}$$

and

$$v_{pg} = \frac{650(0.5000)}{0.4540} = 716 \text{ mi/h}$$

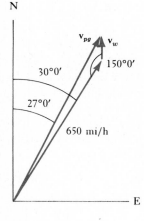

Figure 8–25

If we have information equivalent to Case 2 (two sides and the angle opposite one of them), we may find that there are *two* triangles which satisfy the given information. The following example illustrates this point.

Example E

Solve the triangle with the following given parts: $a = 60.0$, $b = 40.0$, and $B = 30.0°$.

By making a good scale drawing (Fig. 8–26), we note that the angle opposite a may be either at position A or A'. Both positions of this angle satisfy the given parts. Therefore, there are two triangles which result.

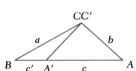

Figure 8–26

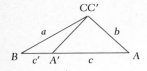

Figure 8—26

Using the Law of Sines, we solve the case in which A, opposite side a, is an acute angle.

$$\frac{60.0}{\sin A} = \frac{40.0}{\sin 30.0°} \quad \text{or} \quad \sin A = \frac{60.0(0.5000)}{40.0} = 0.7500$$

Therefore, $A = 48.6°$ and $C = 101.4°$. Using the Law of Sines again to find c, we have

$$\frac{c}{\sin 101.4°} = \frac{40.0}{\sin 30.0°} \quad \text{or} \quad c = \frac{40.0(0.9803)}{0.5000} = 78.4$$

The other solution is the case in which A', opposite side a, is an obtuse angle. Here we have

$$\frac{60.0}{\sin A'} = \frac{40.0}{\sin 30°0'}$$

which leads to $\sin A' = 0.7500$. Thus, $A' = 131.4°$. For this case we have C' (the angle opposite c when $A' = 131.4°$) as $18.6°$.

Using the Law of Sines to find c', we have

$$\frac{c'}{\sin 18.6°} = \frac{40.0}{\sin 30.0°} \quad \text{or} \quad c' = \frac{40.0(0.3190)}{0.5000} = 25.5$$

This means that the second solution is $A' = 131.4°$, $C' = 18.6°$, and $c' = 25.5$.

Example F

In Example E, if $b > 60.0$, only one solution would result. In this case, side b would intercept side c at A. It also intercepts the extension of side c, but this would require that angle B not be included in the triangle (see Fig. 8–27). Thus only one solution may result if $b > a$.

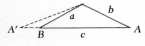

Figure 8—27

In Example E, there would be no solution if side b were not at least 30.0. For if this were the case, side b would not be sufficiently long to even touch side c. It can be seen that b must at least equal $a \sin B$. If it is just equal to $a \sin B$, there is one solution, a right triangle (Fig. 8–28).

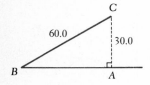

Figure 8—28

Summarizing the results for Case 2 as illustrated in Examples E and F, we make the following conclusions. Given sides a and b, and angle A (assuming here that a and A ($A < 90°$) are the given corresponding parts), we have:

(1) *no solution if $a < b \sin A$,*
(2) *a right triangle solution if $a = b \sin A$,*
(3) *two solutions if $b \sin A < a < b$,*
(4) *one solution if $a > b$.*

For the reason that two solutions may result from it, Case 2 is often referred to as the **ambiguous case**.

If we attempt to use the Law of Sines for the solution of Case 3 or Case 4, we find that we do not have sufficient information to complete one of the ratios. These cases can, however, be solved by the Law of Cosines, which we shall consider in the next section.

Example G
Given the 3 sides, $a = 5$, $b = 6$, $c = 7$, we would set up the ratios

$$\frac{5}{\sin A} = \frac{6}{\sin B} = \frac{7}{\sin C}$$

However, since there is no way to determine a complete ratio from these equations, we cannot find the solution of the triangle in this manner.

Exercises 8–4

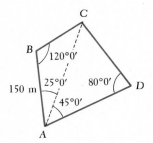

Figure 8–29

In Exercises 1 through 20 solve the triangles with the given parts.

1. $a = 45.7$, $A = 65°0'$, $B = 49°0'$
2. $b = 3.07$, $A = 26°0'$, $C = 120°0'$
3. $c = 4380$, $A = 37.0°$, $B = 34.0°$
4. $a = 93.2$, $B = 17.9°$, $C = 82.6°$
5. $a = 4.60$, $b = 3.10$, $A = 18.0°$
6. $b = 3.62$, $c = 2.94$, $B = 69.3°$
7. $b = 77.5$, $c = 36.4$, $B = 20.7°$
8. $a = 150$, $c = 250$, $C = 76.4°$
9. $b = 0.0742$, $B = 51°0'$, $C = 3°30'$
10. $c = 729$, $B = 121°0'$, $C = 44°10'$
11. $a = 63.8$, $B = 58.4°$, $C = 22.2°$
12. $a = 13.0$, $A = 55.2°$, $B = 67.5°$
13. $b = 438$, $B = 47.4°$, $C = 64.5°$
14. $b = 283$, $B = 13.7°$, $C = 76.3°$
15. $a = 5.24$, $b = 4.44$, $B = 48.1°$
16. $a = 89.4$, $c = 37.3$, $C = 15.6°$
17. $b = 2880$, $c = 3650$, $B = 31.4°$
18. $a = 0.841$, $b = 0.965$, $A = 57.1°$
19. $a = 45.0$, $b = 126$, $A = 64°0'$
20. $a = 10.0$, $c = 5.00$, $C = 30°0'$

In Exercises 21 through 28 use the Law of Sines to solve the given problems.

21. Find the lengths of the two steel supports of the sign shown in Fig. 8–29.
22. Find the unknown sides of the four-sided piece of land shown in Fig. 8–30.
23. The angles of elevation of an airplane, measured from points A and B, 7540 ft apart on the same side of the airplane (the airplane and points A and B are in the same vertical plane), are 32.0° and 44.0°. How far is point A from the airplane?

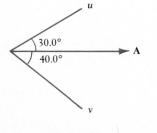

Figure 8–30

24. Resolve vector **A** ($A = 160$) into two components in the directions u and v, as shown in Fig. 8–31.
25. A ship leaves a port and travels due west. At a certain point it turns 30.0° N of W and travels an additional 42.0 mi to a point 63.0 mi from the port. How far from the port is the point where the ship turned?
26. City B is 40°0′ south of east of city A. A pilot wishes to know what direction he should head the plane in flying from A to B if the wind is from the west at 40.0 km/h and his velocity with respect to the air is 300 km/h. What should his heading be?
27. A communications satellite is directly above the extension of a line between receiving towers A and B. It is determined from radio signals that the angle of elevation of the satellite from tower A is 89.2°, and the angle of elevation from tower B is 86.5°. If A and B are 1290 km apart, how far is the satellite from A? (Neglect the curvature of the earth.)
28. A person measures a triangular piece of land and reports the following information: "One side is 58.4 ft long and another side is 21.1 ft long. The angle opposite the shorter side is 24°0′." Could this information be correct?

Figure 8–31

8—5 The Law of Cosines

As we noted at the end of the preceding section, the Law of Sines cannot be used if the only information given is that of Case 3 or Case 4. Therefore, it is necessary to develop a method of finding at least one more part of the triangle. Here we can use the Law of Cosines. After obtaining another part by the Law of Cosines, we can then use the Law of Sines to complete the solution. We do this because the Law of Sines generally provides a simpler method of solution than the Law of Cosines.

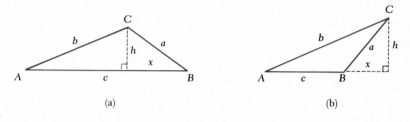

(a)   (b)

Figure 8—32

Consider any oblique triangle, for example either of the ones in Fig. 8–32. For each we obtain $h = b \sin A$. By using the Pythagorean theorem we obtain $a^2 = h^2 + x^2$ for each. Thus,

$$a^2 = b^2 \sin^2 A + x^2 \qquad (8\text{–}9)$$

In Fig. 8–32(a), we have $c - x = b \cos A$, or $x = c - b \cos A$. In Fig. 8–32(b), we have $c + x = b \cos A$, or $x = b \cos A - c$. Substituting these relations into Eq. (8–9), we obtain

$$a^2 = b^2 \sin^2 A + (c - b \cos A)^2$$

and $(8\text{–}10)$

$$a^2 = b^2 \sin^2 A + (b \cos A - c)^2$$

respectively. When expanded, these give

$$a^2 = b^2\sin^2 A + b^2\cos^2 A + c^2 - 2bc \cos A$$

and

$$a^2 = b^2 (\sin^2 A + \cos^2 A) + c^2 - 2bc \cos A \qquad (8\text{–}11)$$

Recalling the definitions of the trigonometric functions, we know that $\sin \theta = y/r$ and $\cos \theta = x/r$. Thus, $\sin^2\theta + \cos^2\theta = (y^2 + x^2)/r^2$. However, $x^2 + y^2 = r^2$, which means that

$$\sin^2 \theta + \cos^2 \theta = 1 \qquad (8\text{–}12)$$

This equation holds for any angle θ, since we made no assumptions as to the properties of θ. By substituting Eq. (8–12) into Eq. (8–11), we arrive at the **Law of Cosines:**

$$a^2 = b^2 + c^2 - 2bc \cos A \qquad (8\text{–}13)$$

Using the method above, we may also show that

$$b^2 = a^2 + c^2 - 2ac \cos B$$

and

$$c^2 = a^2 + b^2 - 2ab \cos C$$

Therefore, if we know two sides and the included angle (Case 3) we may directly solve for the side opposite the given angle. Then, by using the Law of Sines, we may complete the solution. If we are given all three sides (Case 4), we may solve for the angle opposite one of these sides by use of the Law of Cosines. Again we use the Law of Sines to complete the solution.

Example A

Solve the triangle with $a = 45.0$, $b = 67.0$, and $C = 35°0'$. Using the Law of Cosines, we have

$$c^2 = (45.0)^2 + (67.0)^2 - 2(45.0)(67.0)(0.8192)$$
$$= 2025 + 4489 - 4940 = 1574$$
$$c = 39.7$$

From the Law of Sines, we now have

$$\frac{45.0}{\sin A} = \frac{67.0}{\sin B} = \frac{39.7}{0.5736}$$

which leads to

$$\sin A = 0.6502 \quad \text{or} \quad A = 40°30'$$

We could solve for B from the above relation, or by use of the fact that the sum of all three angles is 180°. Thus,

$$B = 104°30'$$

Example B

If, in Example A, $C = 145°0'$, we have

$$c^2 = (45.0)^2 + (67.0)^2 - 2(45.0)(67.0)(-0.8192)$$
$$= 2025 + 4489 + 4940 = 11450$$
$$c = 107$$

From the Law of Sines we then find $A = 14°0'$ and $B = 21°0'$.

Example C

Solve the triangle for which $a = 49.3$, $b = 21.6$, and $c = 42.6$.

$$\cos A = \frac{b^2 + c^2 - a^2}{2bc} = \frac{(21.6)^2 + (42.6)^2 - (49.3)^2}{2(21.6)(42.6)}$$

$$= \frac{467 + 1815 - 2430}{1840} = -0.0804$$

Since the value of cos A is negative, we know that A is between $90°$ and $180°$. Thus,

$$A = 180.0° - 85.4° = 94.6°$$

We then find that $B = 25.9°$ and $C = 59.5°$, from the Law of Sines.

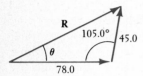

R
105.0°
45.0
θ
78.0

Figure 8–33

Example D
Find the resultant of two vectors having magnitudes of 78.0 and 45.0, and directed toward the east and $15.0°$ east of north, respectively (see Fig. 8–33).

The magnitude of the resultant is given by

$$R = \sqrt{(78.0)^2 + (45.0)^2 - 2(78.0)(45.0)(\cos 105.0°)}$$
$$= \sqrt{6084 + 2025 + 1817} = 99.6$$

Also, $\theta = 25.9°$ is found from the Law of Sines.

Example E
A vertical radio antenna is to be built on a hill which makes an angle of $6.0°$ with the horizontal. If guy wires are to be attached at a point that is 150 ft up on the antenna and at points 100 ft from the base of the antenna, what will be the lengths of guy wires which are positioned directly up and directly down the hill?

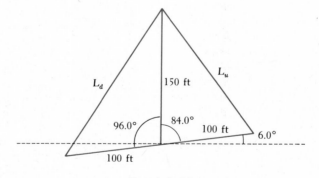

L_d 150 ft L_u
96.0°   84.0°   100 ft   6.0°
100 ft

Figure 8–34

Making an appropriate figure such as Fig. 8–34, we are able to establish the equations necessary for the solution:

$$L_u^2 = (100)^2 + (150)^2 - 2(100)(150)\cos 84.0°$$
$$L_d^2 = (100)^2 + (150)^2 - 2(100)(150)\cos 96.0°$$
$$L_u^2 = 10{,}000 + 22{,}500 - 30{,}000(0.1045)$$
$$= 32{,}500 - 3135 = 29{,}365$$
$$L_u = 171 \text{ ft};$$
$$L_d^2 = 32{,}500 + 3135 = 35{,}635$$
$$L_d = 189 \text{ ft}$$

Exercises 8—5

In Exercises 1 through 20 solve the triangles with the given parts.

1. $a = 6.00$, $b = 7.56$, $C = 54.0°$

2. $b = 87.3$, $c = 34.0$, $A = 130.0°$

3. $a = 4530$, $b = 924$, $C = 98.0°$

4. $a = 0.0845$, $c = 0.116$, $B = 85.0°$

5. $a = 39.5$, $b = 45.2$, $c = 67.1$

6. $a = 23.3$, $b = 27.2$, $c = 29.1$

7. $a = 385$, $b = 467$, $c = 800$

8. $a = 0.243$, $b = 0.263$, $c = 0.153$

9. $a = 320$, $b = 847$, $C = 158.0°$

10. $b = 18.3$, $c = 27.1$, $A = 58.7°$

11. $a = 21.4$, $c = 4.28$, $B = 86.3°$

12. $a = 11.3$, $b = 5.10$, $C = 77.6°$

13. $a = 103$, $c = 159$, $C = 104.6°$

14. $a = 49.3$, $b = 54.5$, $B = 114.0°$

15. $a = 0.493$, $b = 0.595$, $c = 0.639$

16. $a = 69.7$, $b = 49.3$, $c = 56.2$

17. $a = 723$, $b = 598$, $c = 158$

18. $a = 1.78$, $b = 6.04$, $c = 4.80$

19. $a = 15.6$, $A = 15.1°$, $B = 150.5°$

20. $a = 17.5$, $b = 24.5$, $c = 37.0$

In Exercises 21 through 28 use the Law of Cosines to solve the given problems.

21. To measure the distance AC, a man walks 500 ft from A to B, then turns 30°0′ to face C, and walks 680 ft to C. What is the distance AC?

22. An airplane traveling at 700 km/h leaves the airport at noon going due east. At 2 PM the pilot turns 10.0° north of east. How far is the plane from the airport at 3 PM?

23. Two forces, one of 56.0 lb and the other of 67.0 lb, are applied to the same object. The resultant force is 82.0 lb. What is the angle between the two forces?

24. A triangular metal frame has sides of 8.00 ft, 12.0 ft, and 16.0 ft. What is the largest angle between parts of the frame?

25. A boat, which can travel 6.00 km/h in still water, heads downstream at an angle of 20°0′ with the bank. If the stream is flowing at the rate of 3.00 km/h, how fast is the boat traveling and in what direction?

26. An airplane's velocity with respect to the air is 520 mi/h, and it is headed 24.0° north of west. The wind is from due southwest and has a velocity of 55.0 mi/h. What is the true direction of the plane and what is its velocity with respect to the ground?

27. One end of a 13.1-m pole is 15.7 m from an observer's eyes and the other end is 19.3 m from his eyes. Through what angle does the observer see the pole?

28. A triangular piece of land is bounded by 134 ft of stone wall, 205 ft of road frontage, and 147 ft of fencing. What angle does the fence make with the road?

8—6 Exercises for Chapter 8

In Exercises 1 through 4 find the x- and y-components of the given vectors by use of the trigonometric functions.

1. $A = 65.0$, $\theta_A = 28.0°$

2. $A = 8.05$, $\theta_A = 149.0°$

3. $A = 0.920$, $\theta_A = 215°0′$

4. $A = 657$, $\theta_A = 343°0′$

In Exercises 5 through 8 vectors **A** and **B** are at right angles. Find the magnitude and direction of the resultant.

5. $A = 327$ 6. $A = 684$ 7. $A = 4960$ 8. $A = 26.5$
    $B = 505$ $B = 295$ $B = 3290$ $B = 89.8$

In Exercises 9 through 16 add the given vectors by use of the trigonometric functions and the Pythagorean theorem.

9. $A = 780, \theta_A = 28°0'$ 10. $A = 0.0120, \theta_A = 10°30'$
    $B = 346, \theta_B = 320°0'$ $B = 0.0078, \theta_B = 260°0'$

11. $A = 22.5, \theta_A = 130°10'$ 12. $A = 18,700, \theta_A = 110°40'$
    $B = 7.60, \theta_B = 200°0'$ $B = 4830, \theta_B = 350°20'$

13. $A = 51.3, \theta_A = 12.2°$ 14. $A = 70.3, \theta_A = 122.5°$
    $B = 42.6, \theta_B = 291.7°$ $B = 30.2, \theta_B = 214.8°$

15. $A = 75.0, \theta_A = 15.0°$ 16. $A = 8100, \theta_A = 141.0°$
    $B = 26.5, \theta_B = 192.0°$ $B = 1540, \theta_B = 165.0°$
    $C = 54.8, \theta_C = 344.0°$ $C = 3470, \theta_C = 296.0°$

In Exercises 17 through 32 solve the triangles with the given parts.

17. $A = 48°0', B = 68°0', a = 14.5$ 18. $A = 132°0', b = 7.50, C = 32°0'$
19. $a = 22.8, B = 33.5°, C = 125.3°$ 20. $A = 71.0°, B = 48.5°, c = 8.42$
21. $b = 76.0, c = 40.5, B = 110°0'$ 22. $A = 77°0', a = 12.0, c = 5.00$
23. $b = 14.5, c = 13.0, C = 56.6°$ 24. $B = 40.0°, b = 7.00, c = 18.0$
25. $a = 186, B = 130.0°, c = 106$ 26. $b = 750, c = 1100, A = 56.0°$
27. $a = 7.86, b = 2.45, C = 22.0°$ 28. $a = 0.208, c = 0.697, B = 105.0°$
29. $a = 17.0, b = 12.0, c = 25.0$ 30. $a = 900, b = 995, c = 1100$
31. $a = 5.30, b = 8.75, c = 12.5$ 32. $a = 47.4, b = 40.0, c = 45.5$

In Exercises 33 through 50 solve the given problems.

33. A jet climbs at an angle $35.0°$ while traveling 600 km/h. How long will it take to climb to an altitude of 10,000 m?

34. A bullet is fired into the air at 2000 mi/h at an angle of $25°0'$ with the horizontal. What is the vertical component of the velocity?

35. A balloon is rising at the rate of 15.0 ft/s and at the same time is being blown horizontally by the wind at the rate of 22.5 ft/s. Find the resultant velocity.

36. A motorboat which travels at 8.00 km/h in still water heads directly across a stream which flows at 3.00 km/h. What is the resultant velocity of the boat?

37. A velocity vector is the resultant of two other vectors. If the given velocity is 450 mi/h and makes angles of $34°0'$ and $76°0'$ with the two components, find the magnitudes of the components.

38. A person on a hill in the middle of a plain relates that the angles of depression of two objects on the plain below (on directly opposite sides of the hill) are $30.0°$ and $40.0°$. She knows that the objects are 15,800 m apart. How far is she from the closest object?

39. In order to find the distance between points A and B on opposite sides of a river, a distance AC is measured off as 1000 ft, where point C is on the

same side of the river as *A*. Angle *BAC* is measured to be 102°0′ and angle *ACB* is 33°0′. What is the distance between *A* and *B*?

40. A 22.0-ft ladder leans against a wall, making an angle of 29°0′ with the wall. If the foot of the ladder is 10.7 ft from the foot of the wall, find the angle of inclination of the wall to the ground.

41. Two points on opposite sides of an obstruction are respectively 117 m and 88 m from a third point. The lines joining the first two points and the third point intersect at an angle of 115.0° at the third point. How far apart are the original two points?

42. A crate is being held aloft by two ropes which are tied at the same point on the crate. They are 14.5 m and 10.5 m long, respectively, and the angle between them is 104.0°. If the ropes are supported at the same level, how far apart are they?

43. Two cars are at the intersection of two straight roads. One travels 5.20 mi on one road, and the other car travels 3.75 mi on the other road. The drivers contact each other on CB radio and find they are at points known to be 4.50 mi apart. What angle do the roads make at the intersection?

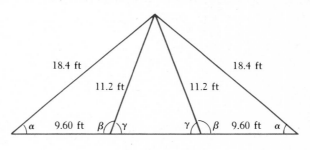

Figure 8—35

44. Determine the angles of the structure indicated in Fig. 8—35.

45. Atlanta is 290 mi and 51.0° south of east from Nashville. The pilot of an airplane due north of Atlanta radios Nashville and finds her plane is on a line 10.5° south of east from Nashville. How far is the plane from Nashville?

46. The edges of a saw tooth are 2.10 mm and 3.25 mm. The base of the tooth is 2.25 mm. At what angle do the edges of the tooth meet?

47. Determine the weight *w* being supported by the ropes shown in Fig. 8—36. The tension in the right support rope is 87.5 lb.

48. Boston is 650 km and 21.0° south of west from Halifax, Nova Scotia. Radio signals locate a ship 10.5° east of south from Halifax and 5.6° north of east from Boston. How far is the ship from each city?

49. Find the resultant of the forces indicated in Fig. 8—37.

50. A jet plane is traveling horizontally at 1200 ft/s. A missile is fired horizontally from it 30°0′ from the direction in which the plane is traveling. If the missile leaves the plane at 2000 ft/s, what is its velocity 10.0 s later if the vertical component is given by $v_V = -32t$ (in feet per second)?

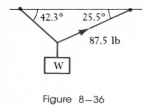

Figure 8—36

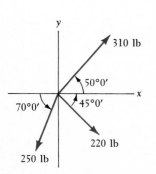

Figure 8—37

9

Graphs of the Trigonometric Functions

9–1 Graphs of $y = a \sin x$ and $y = a \cos x$

One of the clearest ways to demonstrate the variation of the trigonometric functions is by means of their graphs. The graphs are useful for analyzing properties of the trigonometric functions, and in themselves are valuable in many applications. Several of these applications are indicated in the exercises, particularly in the last two sections of this chapter.

The graphs are constructed on the rectangular coordinate system. In plotting the trigonometric functions, it is normal to express the angle in radians. In this way x and the function of x are expressed as *numbers*, and these numbers may have any desired unit of measurement. Therefore, in order to determine the graphs, it is necessary to be able to readily use angles expressed in radians. If necessary, Section 7–3 should be reviewed for this purpose.

In this section the graphs of the sine and cosine functions are demonstrated. We begin by constructing a table of values of x and y, for the function $y = \sin x$:

x	0	$\frac{\pi}{6}$	$\frac{\pi}{3}$	$\frac{\pi}{2}$	$\frac{2\pi}{3}$	$\frac{5\pi}{6}$	π	$\frac{7\pi}{6}$	$\frac{4\pi}{3}$	$\frac{3\pi}{2}$	$\frac{5\pi}{3}$	$\frac{11\pi}{6}$	2π
y	0	0.5	0.87	1	0.87	0.5	0	-0.5	-0.87	-1	-0.87	-0.5	0

Plotting these values, we obtain the graph shown in Fig. 9–1.

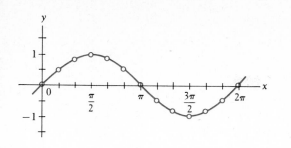

Figure 9–1

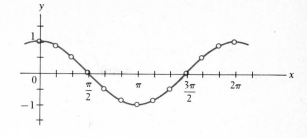

Figure 9–2

The graph of $y = \cos x$ may be constructed in the same manner. The table below gives the proper values for the graph of $y = \cos x$. The graph is shown in Fig. 9–2.

x	0	$\dfrac{\pi}{6}$	$\dfrac{\pi}{3}$	$\dfrac{\pi}{2}$	$\dfrac{2\pi}{3}$	$\dfrac{5\pi}{6}$	π	$\dfrac{7\pi}{6}$	$\dfrac{4\pi}{3}$	$\dfrac{3\pi}{2}$	$\dfrac{5\pi}{3}$	$\dfrac{11\pi}{6}$	2π
y	1	0.87	0.5	0	−0.5	−0.87	−1	−0.87	−0.5	0	0.5	0.87	1

The graphs are continued beyond the values shown in the table to indicate that they continue on indefinitely in each direction. From the values and the graphs, *it can be seen that the two graphs are of exactly the same shape, with the cosine curve displaced $\pi/2$ units to the left of the sine curve.* The shape of these curves should be recognized readily, with special note as to the points at which they cross the axes. This information will be especially valuable in "sketching" similar curves, since the basic shape always remains the same. We shall find it unnecessary to plot numerous points every time we wish to sketch such a curve.

To obtain the graph of $y = a \sin x$, we note that all of the y-values obtained for the graph of $y = \sin x$ are to be multiplied by the number a. In this case the greatest value of the sine function is $|a|$ instead of 1. *The number $|a|$ is called the* **amplitude** *of the curve and represents the greatest y-value of the curve.* This is also true for $y = a \cos x$.

Example A

Plot the curve of $y = 2 \sin x$.

The table of values to be used is as follows; Fig. 9–3 shows the graph.

x	0	$\dfrac{\pi}{6}$	$\dfrac{\pi}{3}$	$\dfrac{\pi}{2}$	$\dfrac{2\pi}{3}$	$\dfrac{5\pi}{6}$	π	$\dfrac{7\pi}{6}$	$\dfrac{4\pi}{3}$	$\dfrac{3\pi}{2}$	$\dfrac{5\pi}{3}$	$\dfrac{11\pi}{6}$
y	0	1	1.73	2	1.73	1	0	−1	−1.73	−2	−1.73	−1

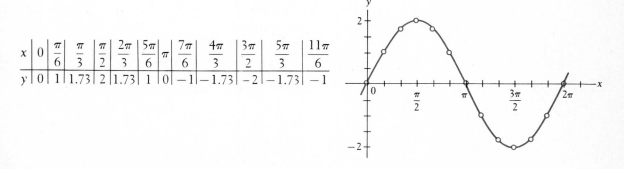

Figure 9–3

Example B

Plot the curve of $y = -3 \cos x$.

The table of values to be used is as follows; Fig. 9–4 shows the graph.

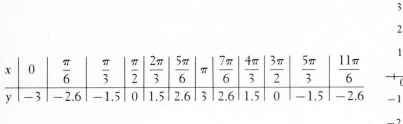

x	0	$\dfrac{\pi}{6}$	$\dfrac{\pi}{3}$	$\dfrac{\pi}{2}$	$\dfrac{2\pi}{3}$	$\dfrac{5\pi}{6}$	π	$\dfrac{7\pi}{6}$	$\dfrac{4\pi}{3}$	$\dfrac{3\pi}{2}$	$\dfrac{5\pi}{3}$	$\dfrac{11\pi}{6}$
y	-3	-2.6	-1.5	0	1.5	2.6	3	2.6	1.5	0	-1.5	-2.6

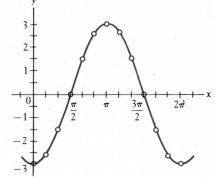

Figure 9–4

Note from Example B that *the effect of the minus sign before the number a is to invert the curve.* The effect of the number *a* can also be seen readily from these examples.

By knowing the general shape of the sine curve, where it crosses the axes, and the amplitude, we can rapidly *sketch* curves of form $y = a \sin x$ and $y = a \cos x$. There is generally no need to plot any more points than those corresponding to the values of the amplitude and those where the curve crosses the axes.

Example C

Sketch the graph of $y = 4 \cos x$.

First we set up a table of values for the points where the curve crosses the *x*-axis and for the highest and lowest points on the curve.

x	0	$\dfrac{\pi}{2}$	π	$\dfrac{3\pi}{2}$	2π
y	4	0	-4	0	4

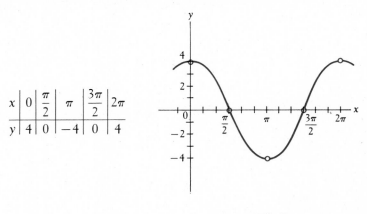

Figure 9–5

Now we plot the above points and join them, knowing the basic shape of the curve. See Fig. 9–5.

Example D

Sketch the curve of $y = -2 \sin x$.

We list here the important values associated with this curve.

x	0	$\dfrac{\pi}{2}$	π	$\dfrac{3\pi}{2}$	2π
y	0	-2	0	2	0

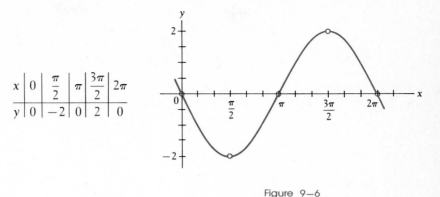

Figure 9—6

Since we know the general shape of the sine curve, we can now sketch the graph as shown in Fig. 9—6. Note the inversion of the curve due to the minus sign.

Exercises 9—1

In Exercises 1 through 4 complete the following table for the given functions, and then plot the resulting graph.

x	$-\pi$	$-\dfrac{3\pi}{4}$	$-\dfrac{\pi}{2}$	$-\dfrac{\pi}{4}$	0	$\dfrac{\pi}{4}$	$\dfrac{\pi}{2}$	$\dfrac{3\pi}{4}$	π	$\dfrac{5\pi}{4}$	$\dfrac{3\pi}{2}$	$\dfrac{7\pi}{4}$	2π	$\dfrac{9\pi}{4}$	$\dfrac{5\pi}{2}$	$\dfrac{11\pi}{4}$	3π
y																	

1. $y = \sin x$ **2.** $y = \cos x$ **3.** $y = 3 \cos x$ **4.** $y = -4 \sin x$

In Exercises 5 through 20 sketch the curves of the indicated functions.

5. $y = 3 \sin x$ **6.** $y = 5 \sin x$ **7.** $y = \frac{5}{2} \sin x$
8. $y = 0.5 \sin x$ **9.** $y = 2 \cos x$ **10.** $y = 3 \cos x$
11. $y = 0.8 \cos x$ **12.** $y = \frac{3}{2} \cos x$ **13.** $y = -\sin x$
14. $y = -3 \sin x$ **15.** $y = -1.5 \sin x$ **16.** $y = -0.2 \sin x$
17. $y = -\cos x$ **18.** $y = -8 \cos x$ **19.** $y = -2.5 \cos x$
20. $y = -0.4 \cos x$

Although units of π are often convenient, we must remember that π is really only a number. Numbers which are not multiples of π may be used as well. In Exercises 21 through 24 plot the indicated graphs by finding the values of y corresponding to the values of 0, 1, 2, 3, 4, 5, 6, and 7 for x. (Remember, the numbers 0, 1, 2, and so forth represent radian measure.) Values from Table 3 may be used.

21. $y = \sin x$ **22.** $y = 3 \sin x$ **23.** $y = \cos x$ **24.** $y = 2 \cos x$

9–2 Graphs of $y = a \sin bx$ and $y = a \cos bx$

In graphing the curve of $y = \sin x$ we note that the values of y start repeating every 2π units of x. This is because $\sin x = \sin (x + 2\pi) = \sin (x + 4\pi)$, and so forth. For any trigonometric function F, we say that it has a **period** P, if $F(x) = F(x + P)$. For functions which are periodic, such as the sine and cosine, *the period refers to the x-distance between any point and the next corresponding point for which the values of y start repeating.*

Let us now plot the curve $y = \sin 2x$. This means that we choose a value for x, multiply this value by two, and find the sine of the result. This leads to the following table of values for this function.

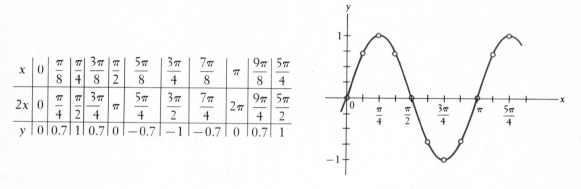

x	0	$\dfrac{\pi}{8}$	$\dfrac{\pi}{4}$	$\dfrac{3\pi}{8}$	$\dfrac{\pi}{2}$	$\dfrac{5\pi}{8}$	$\dfrac{3\pi}{4}$	$\dfrac{7\pi}{8}$	π	$\dfrac{9\pi}{8}$	$\dfrac{5\pi}{4}$
$2x$	0	$\dfrac{\pi}{4}$	$\dfrac{\pi}{2}$	$\dfrac{3\pi}{4}$	π	$\dfrac{5\pi}{4}$	$\dfrac{3\pi}{2}$	$\dfrac{7\pi}{4}$	2π	$\dfrac{9\pi}{4}$	$\dfrac{5\pi}{2}$
y	0	0.7	1	0.7	0	-0.7	-1	-0.7	0	0.7	1

Figure 9–7

Plotting these values, we have the curve shown in Fig. 9–7.

From the table and Fig. 9–7, we note that the function $y = \sin 2x$ starts repeating after π units of x. The effect of the 2 before the x has been to make the period of this curve half the period of the curve of $\sin x$. This leads us to the following conclusion: If the period of the trigonometric function $F(x)$ is P, then the period of $F(bx)$ is P/b. Since each of the functions $\sin x$ and $\cos x$ has a period of 2π, *each of the functions $\sin bx$ and $\cos bx$ has a period of $2\pi/b$.*

Example A

The period of $\sin 3x$ is $2\pi/3$, which means that the curve of the function $y = \sin 3x$ will repeat every $2\pi/3$ (approximately 2.09) units of x.

The period of $\cos 4x$ is $2\pi/4 = \pi/2$, and that of $\sin \frac{1}{2}x$ is $2\pi/\frac{1}{2} = 4\pi$.

Example B

The period of $\sin \pi x$ is $2\pi/\pi = 2$. That is, the curve of the function $\sin \pi x$ will repeat every 2 units. It is then noted that the periods of $\sin 3x$ and $\sin \pi x$ are nearly equal. This is to be expected since π is only slightly greater than 3.

The period of $\cos 3\pi x$ is $2\pi/3\pi = 2/3$.

Combining the result for the period with the results of Section 9–1, we conclude that *each of the functions $y = a \sin bx$ and $y = a \cos bx$ has an amplitude of $|a|$ and a period of $2\pi/b$*. These properties are very useful in sketching these functions, as it is shown in the following examples.

Example C

Sketch the graph of $y = 3 \sin 4x$ for $0 \le x \le \pi$.

We immediately conclude that the amplitude is 3 and the period is $2\pi/4 = \pi/2$. Therefore, we know that $y = 0$ when $x = 0$ and $y = 0$ when $x = \pi/2$. Also we recall that the sine function is zero halfway between these values, which means that $y = 0$ when $x = \pi/4$. The function reaches its amplitude values halfway between the zeros. Therefore, $y = 3$ for $x = \pi/8$ and $y = -3$ for $x = 3\pi/8$. A table for these important values of the function $y = 3 \sin 4x$ is as follows.

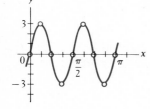

x	0	$\dfrac{\pi}{8}$	$\dfrac{\pi}{4}$	$\dfrac{3\pi}{8}$	$\dfrac{\pi}{2}$	$\dfrac{5\pi}{8}$	$\dfrac{3\pi}{4}$	$\dfrac{7\pi}{8}$	π
y	0	3	0	-3	0	3	0	-3	0

Using this table and the knowledge of the form of the sine curve, we sketch the function (Fig. 9–8).

Figure 9–8

Example D

Sketch the graph of $y = -2 \cos 3x$ for $0 \le x \le 2\pi$.

We note that the amplitude is 2 and that the period is $2\pi/3$. Since the cosine curve is at its amplitude value for $x = 0$, we have $y = -2$ for $x = 0$ (the negative value is due to the minus sign before the function) and $y = -2$ for $x = 2\pi/3$. The cosine function also reaches its amplitude value halfway between these values, or $y = 2$ for $x = \pi/3$. The cosine function is zero halfway between the x-values listed for the amplitude; that is, $y = 0$ for $x = \pi/6$ and for $x = \pi/2$. A table of the important values follows.

x	0	$\dfrac{\pi}{6}$	$\dfrac{\pi}{3}$	$\dfrac{\pi}{2}$	$\dfrac{2\pi}{3}$	$\dfrac{5\pi}{6}$	π	$\dfrac{7\pi}{6}$	$\dfrac{4\pi}{3}$	$\dfrac{3\pi}{2}$	$\dfrac{5\pi}{3}$	$\dfrac{11\pi}{6}$	2π
y	-2	0	2	0	-2	0	2	0	-2	0	2	0	-2

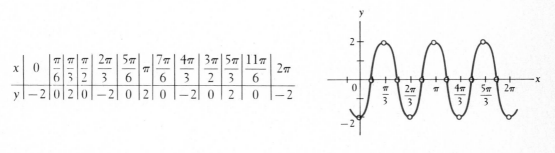

Figure 9–9

Using this table and the knowledge of the form of the cosine curve, we sketch the function as shown in Fig. 9–9.

Example E

Sketch the function $y = \cos \pi x$ for $0 \le x \le \pi$.

For this function the amplitude is 1; the period is $2\pi/\pi = 2$. Since the value of the period is not in terms of π, it is more convenient to use regular decimal units for x when sketching than to use units in terms of π as in the previous graphs. Therefore, we have the following table.

x	0	0.5	1	1.5	2	2.5	3
y	1	0	-1	0	1	0	-1

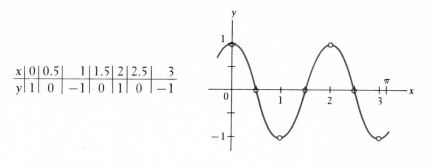

Figure 9—10

The graph of this function is shown in Fig. 9–10.

Exercises 9–2

In Exercises 1 through 20 find the period of each of the given functions.

1. $y = 2 \sin 6x$ 2. $y = 4 \sin 2x$ 3. $y = 3 \cos 8x$

4. $y = \cos 10x$ 5. $y = -2 \sin 12x$ 6. $y = -\sin 5x$

7. $y = -\cos 16x$ 8. $y = -4 \cos 2x$ 9. $y = 5 \sin 2\pi x$

10. $y = 2 \sin 3\pi x$ 11. $y = 3 \cos 4\pi x$ 12. $y = 4 \cos 10\pi x$

13. $y = 3 \sin \frac{1}{3}x$ 14. $y = -2 \sin \frac{2}{3}x$ 15. $y = -\frac{1}{2} \cos \frac{2}{3}x$

16. $y = \frac{1}{3} \cos \frac{1}{4}x$ 17. $y = 0.4 \sin \frac{2\pi x}{3}$ 18. $y = 1.5 \cos \frac{\pi x}{10}$

19. $y = 3.3 \cos \pi^2 x$ 20. $y = 2.5 \sin \frac{2x}{\pi}$

In Exercises 21 through 40 sketch the graphs of the given functions. For this, use the functions given for Exercises 1 through 20.

In Exercises 41 through 44 sketch the indicated graphs.

41. The electric current in a certain 60 Hz alternating-current circuit is given by $i = 10 \sin 120\pi t$, where i is the current (in amperes) and t is the time (in seconds). Sketch the graph of i vs. t for $0 \le t \le 0.1$ s.

42. A generator produces a voltage given by $V = 200 \cos 50\pi t$, where t is the time (in seconds). Sketch the graph of V vs. t for $0 \le t \le 0.1$ s.

43. The vertical displacement x of a certain object oscillating at the end of a spring is given by $x = 6 \cos 4\pi t$, where x is measured in inches and t in seconds. Sketch the graph of x vs. t for $0 \le t \le 1$ s.

44. The velocity of a piston in an engine is given by $v = 1200 \sin 1200\pi t$, where v is the velocity (in centimeters per second) and t is the time (in seconds). Sketch the graph of v vs. t for $0 \le t \le 0.01$ s.

9–3 Graphs of $y = a \sin (bx + c)$ and $y = a \cos (bx + c)$

There is one more important quantity to be discussed in relation to graphing the sine and cosine functions. This quantity is the **phase angle** of the function. In the function $y = a \sin (bx + c)$, c represents this phase angle. Its meaning is illustrated in the following example.

Example A

Sketch the graph of $y = \sin (2x + \frac{\pi}{4})$.

Note that $c = \frac{\pi}{4}$. This means that in order to obtain the values for the table we must assume a value of x, multiply it by two, add $\frac{\pi}{4}$ to this value, and then find the sine of this result. In this manner we arrive at the following table.

x	$-\dfrac{\pi}{8}$	0	$\dfrac{\pi}{8}$	$\dfrac{\pi}{4}$	$\dfrac{3\pi}{8}$	$\dfrac{\pi}{2}$	$\dfrac{5\pi}{8}$	$\dfrac{3\pi}{4}$	$\dfrac{7\pi}{8}$	π
y	0	0.7	1	0.7	0	-0.7	-1	-0.7	0	0.7

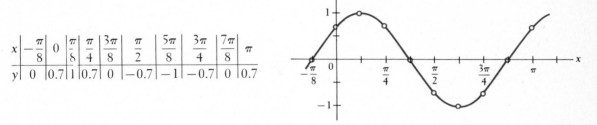

Figure 9–11

We use the value of $x = -\frac{\pi}{8}$ in the table, for we note that it corresponds to finding $\sin 0$. Now using the values listed in the table, we plot the graph of $y = \sin (2x + \frac{\pi}{4})$. See Fig. 9–11.

We can see from the table and from the graph that the curve of

$$y = \sin\left(2x + \frac{\pi}{4}\right)$$

is precisely the same as that of $y = \sin 2x$, except that it is shifted $\frac{\pi}{8}$ units to the left. The effect of c in the equation of $y = a \sin (bx + c)$ is to shift the curve of $y = a \sin bx$ to the left if $c > 0$, and to shift the curve to the right if $c < 0$. The amount of this shift is given by c/b. Due to its importance in sketching curves, *the quantity c/b is called the* **displacement.**

Therefore, the results above combined with the results of Section 9–2 may be used to sketch curves of the functions $y = a \sin (bx + c)$ and $y = a \cos (bx + c)$. These are the important quantities to determine:

    (1) **the amplitude** (equal to $|a|$)

    (2) **the period** $\left(\text{equal to } \dfrac{2\pi}{b}\right)$

    (3) **the displacement** $\left(\text{equal to } \dfrac{c}{b}\right)$

By use of these quantities, the curves of these sine and cosine functions can be readily sketched.

Example B

Sketch the graph of $y = 2 \sin (3x - \pi)$ for $0 \le x \le \pi$.

First we note that $a = 2$, $b = 3$, and $c = -\pi$. Therefore, the amplitude is 2, the period is $\frac{2\pi}{3}$, and the displacement is $\frac{\pi}{3}$ to the right.

With this information we can tell that the curve "starts" at $x = \frac{\pi}{3}$ and "starts repeating" $\frac{2\pi}{3}$ units to the right of this point. (Be sure to grasp this point well. The period tells how many units there are along the x-axis *between* such corresponding points.) The value of y is zero when $x = \frac{\pi}{3}$ and when $x = \pi$. It is also zero halfway between these values of x, or when $x = \frac{2\pi}{3}$. The curve reaches the amplitude value of 2 midway between $x = \frac{\pi}{3}$ and $x = \frac{2\pi}{3}$, or when $x = \frac{\pi}{2}$. Extending the curve to the left to $x = 0$, we note that, since the period is $\frac{2\pi}{3}$, the curve passes through $(0, 0)$. Therefore, we have the following table of important values.

x	0	$\dfrac{\pi}{6}$	$\dfrac{\pi}{3}$	$\dfrac{\pi}{2}$	$\dfrac{2\pi}{3}$	$\dfrac{5\pi}{6}$	π
y	0	-2	0	2	0	-2	0

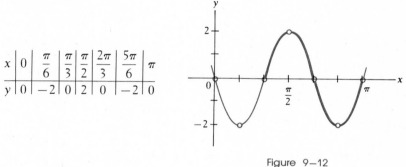

Figure 9–12

From these values we sketch the graph shown in Fig. 9–12.

Example C

Sketch the graph of the function $y = -\cos (2x + \frac{\pi}{6})$.

First we determine that the amplitude is 1, the period is $\frac{2\pi}{2} = \pi$, and that the displacement is $(\frac{\pi}{6}) \div 2 = \frac{\pi}{12}$ to the left ($c > 0$). From these values we construct the following table, remembering that the curve starts repeating π units to the right of $-\frac{\pi}{12}$.

x	$-\dfrac{\pi}{12}$	$\dfrac{\pi}{6}$	$\dfrac{5\pi}{12}$	$\dfrac{2\pi}{3}$	$\dfrac{11\pi}{12}$
y	-1	0	1	0	-1

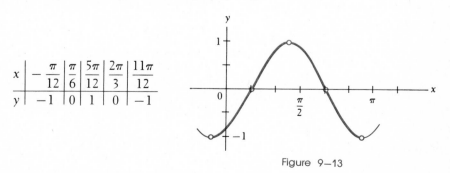

Figure 9–13

From this table we sketch the graph as shown in Fig. 9–13.

Example D

Sketch the graph of the function $y = 2 \cos (\frac{x}{2} - \frac{\pi}{6})$.

From the values $a = 2$, $b = \frac{1}{2}$, and $c = -\frac{\pi}{6}$, we determine that the amplitude is 2, the period is $2\pi \div \frac{1}{2} = 4\pi$, and the displacement is $\frac{\pi}{6} \div \frac{1}{2} = \frac{\pi}{3}$ to the right. From these values we construct this table of values.

x	$\dfrac{\pi}{3}$	$\dfrac{4\pi}{3}$	$\dfrac{7\pi}{3}$	$\dfrac{10\pi}{3}$	$\dfrac{13\pi}{3}$
y	2	0	-2	0	2

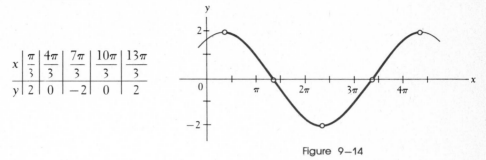

Figure 9–14

The graph is shown in Fig. 9–14. We note that when the coefficient of x is less than 1, the period is greater than 2π.

Example E

Sketch the graph of the function $y = 0.7 \sin (\pi x + \frac{\pi}{4})$.

From the values $a = 0.7$, $b = \pi$, and $c = \frac{\pi}{4}$, we can determine that the amplitude is 0.7, the period is $\frac{2\pi}{\pi} = 2$, and the displacement is $(\frac{\pi}{4}) \div \pi = \frac{1}{4}$ to the left. From these values we construct the following table of values.

x	$-\dfrac{1}{4}$	$\dfrac{1}{4}$	$\dfrac{3}{4}$	$\dfrac{5}{4}$	$\dfrac{7}{4}$
y	0	0.7	0	-0.7	0

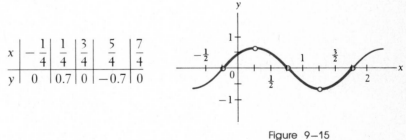

Figure 9–15

Since π is not used in the values of x, it is more convenient to use decimal number units for the graph (Fig. 9–15).

Each of the heavy portions of the graphs in Fig. 9–12, 9–13, 9–14, and 9–15 is called a **cycle** of the curve. *A cycle is the shortest section of the graph which includes one period.*

Exercises 9–3

In Exercises 1 through 24 determine the amplitude, period, and displacement for each of the functions. Then sketch the graphs of the functions.

1. $y = \sin \left(x - \dfrac{\pi}{6}\right)$

2. $y = 3 \sin \left(x + \dfrac{\pi}{4}\right)$

3. $y = \cos\left(x + \dfrac{\pi}{6}\right)$

4. $y = 2\,\cos\left(x - \dfrac{\pi}{8}\right)$

5. $y = 2\,\sin\left(2x + \dfrac{\pi}{2}\right)$

6. $y = -\sin\left(3x - \dfrac{\pi}{2}\right)$

7. $y = -\cos\,(2x - \pi)$

8. $y = 4\,\cos\left(3x + \dfrac{\pi}{3}\right)$

9. $y = \dfrac{1}{2}\,\sin\left(\dfrac{1}{2}x - \dfrac{\pi}{4}\right)$

10. $y = 2\,\sin\left(\dfrac{1}{4}x + \dfrac{\pi}{2}\right)$

11. $y = 3\,\cos\left(\dfrac{1}{3}x + \dfrac{\pi}{3}\right)$

12. $y = \dfrac{1}{3}\,\cos\left(\dfrac{1}{2}x - \dfrac{\pi}{8}\right)$

13. $y = \sin\left(\pi x + \dfrac{\pi}{8}\right)$

14. $y = -2\,\sin\,(2\pi x - \pi)$

15. $y = \dfrac{3}{4}\,\cos\left(4\pi x - \dfrac{\pi}{5}\right)$

16. $y = 6\,\cos\left(3\pi x + \dfrac{\pi}{2}\right)$

17. $y = -0.6\,\sin\,(2\pi x - 1)$

18. $y = 1.8\,\sin\left(\pi x + \dfrac{1}{3}\right)$

19. $y = 4\,\cos\,(3\pi x + 2)$

20. $y = 3\,\cos\,(6\pi x - 1)$

21. $y = \sin\,(\pi^2 x - \pi)$

22. $y = -\dfrac{1}{2}\sin\left(2x - \dfrac{1}{\pi}\right)$

23. $y = -\dfrac{3}{2}\cos\left(\pi x + \dfrac{\pi^2}{6}\right)$

24. $y = \pi\,\cos\left(\dfrac{1}{\pi}x + \dfrac{1}{3}\right)$

In Exercises 25 through 28 sketch the indicated curves.

25. A wave traveling in a string may be represented by the equation

$$y = A\,\sin\left(\dfrac{t}{T} - \dfrac{x}{\lambda}\right)$$

Here A is the amplitude, t is the time the wave has traveled, x is the distance from the origin, T is the time required for the wave to travel one *wavelength* λ (the Greek lambda). Sketch three cycles of the wave for which $A = 2.00$ cm, $T = 0.100$ s, $\lambda = 20.0$ cm, and $x = 5.00$ cm.

26. The cross-section of a particular water wave is

$$y = 0.5\,\sin\left(\dfrac{\pi}{2}x + \dfrac{\pi}{4}\right)$$

where x and y are measured in feet. Sketch two cycles of y vs. x.

27. A particular electromagnetic wave is described by the equation

$$y = a\,\cos\left(8\pi \times 10^{14}t + \dfrac{\pi}{6}\right)$$

Sketch two cycles of the graph of y (in centimeters) vs. t (in seconds).

28. The voltage in a certain alternating-current circuit is given by

$$y = 120 \cos\left(120\pi t + \frac{\pi}{6}\right)$$

where t represents the time (in seconds). Sketch three cycles of the curve.

9—4 Graphs of $y = \tan x$, $y = \cot x$, $y = \sec x$, $y = \csc x$

In this section we shall briefly consider the graphs of the other trigonometric functions. We shall establish the basic form of each curve, and from these we shall be able to sketch other curves for these functions.

Considering the values and signs of the trigonometric functions as established in Chapter 7, we set up the following table for the function $y = \tan x$. The graph is shown in Fig. 9—16.

x	0	$\dfrac{\pi}{6}$	$\dfrac{\pi}{3}$	$\dfrac{\pi}{2}$	$\dfrac{2\pi}{3}$	$\dfrac{5\pi}{6}$	π	$\dfrac{7\pi}{6}$	$\dfrac{4\pi}{3}$	$\dfrac{3\pi}{2}$	$\dfrac{5\pi}{3}$	$\dfrac{11\pi}{6}$	2π
y	0	0.6	1.7	*	−1.7	−0.6	0	0.6	1.7	*	−1.7	−0.6	0

*Undefined.

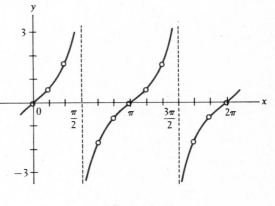

Figure 9—16

Since the curve is not defined for $x = \frac{\pi}{2}$, $x = \frac{3\pi}{2}$, and so forth, we look at the table and note that the value of $\tan x$ becomes very large when x approaches the value $\frac{\pi}{2}$. We must keep in mind, however, that there is no point on the curve corresponding to $x = \frac{\pi}{2}$. We note that the period of the tangent curve is π. This differs from the period of the sine and cosine functions.

By following the same procedure, we can set up tables for the graphs of the other functions. We present in Figures 9–17 through 9–20 the graphs of $y = \tan x$, $y = \cot x$, $y = \sec x$, and $y = \csc x$ (the graph of $y = \tan x$ is shown again to illustrate it more completely). The dashed lines in these figures are **asymptotes** (see Sections 2–3 and 20–6).

To sketch functions such as $y = a \sec x$, we first sketch $y = \sec x$, and then multiply each y-value by a. Here a is not an amplitude, since these functions are not limited in the values they take on, as are the sine and cosine functions.

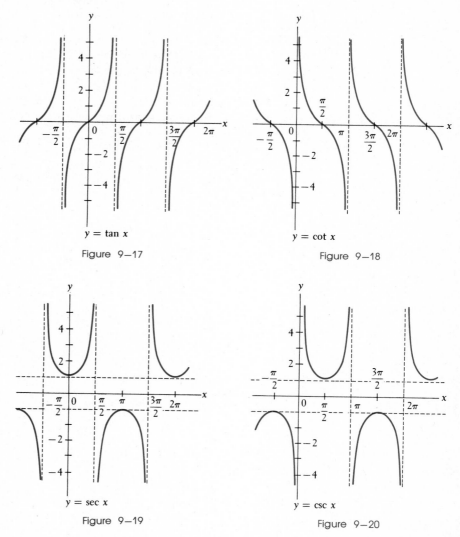

$y = \tan x$

Figure 9–17

$y = \cot x$

Figure 9–18

$y = \sec x$

Figure 9–19

$y = \csc x$

Figure 9–20

Example A

Sketch the graph of $y = 2 \sec x$.

First we sketch in $y = \sec x$, shown as the light curve in Fig. 9–21. Now we multiply the y-values of the secant function by 2 (approximately, of course). In this way we obtain the desired curve, shown as the heavy curve in Fig. 9–21.

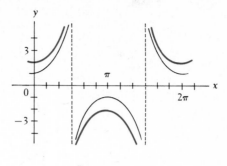

Figure 9–21

Example B
Sketch the graph of $y = -\frac{1}{2} \cot x$.

   We sketch in $y = \cot x$, shown as the light curve in Fig. 9–22. Now we multiply each y-value by $-\frac{1}{2}$. The effect of the negative sign is to invert the curve. The resulting curve is shown as the heavy curve in Fig. 9–22.

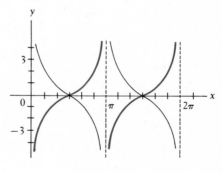

Figure 9–22

   By knowing the graphs of the sine, cosine, and tangent functions, it is possible to graph the other three functions. Remembering the definitions of the trigonometric functions (Eqs. 7–1), we see that $\sin x$ and $\csc x$ are reciprocals, $\cos x$ and $\sec x$ are reciprocals, and $\tan x$ and $\cot x$ are reciprocals. That is,

$$\csc x = \frac{1}{\sin x}, \qquad \sec x = \frac{1}{\cos x}, \qquad \cot x = \frac{1}{\tan x} \qquad (9\text{–}1)$$

   Thus, to sketch $y = \cot x$, $y = \sec x$, or $y = \csc x$, we sketch the corresponding reciprocal function, and from this graph determine the necessary values.

Example C
Sketch the graph of $y = \csc x$.

We first sketch in the graph of $y = \sin x$ (light curve). Where $\sin x$ is 1, $\csc x$ will also be 1, since $1/1 = 1$. Where $\sin x$ is 0, $\csc x$ is undefined, since $1/0$ is undefined. Where $\sin x$ is 0.5, $\csc x$ is 2, since $1/0.5 = 2$. Thus, as $\sin x$ becomes larger, $\csc x$ becomes smaller, and as $\sin x$ becomes smaller, $\csc x$ becomes larger. The two functions always have the same sign. We sketch the graph of $y = \csc x$ from this information, as shown by the heavy curve in Fig. 9–23.

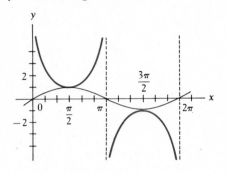

Figure 9–23

Exercises 9—4

In Exercises 1 through 4 fill in the following table for each function and then plot the curve from these points.

x	$-\dfrac{\pi}{2}$	$-\dfrac{\pi}{3}$	$-\dfrac{\pi}{4}$	$-\dfrac{\pi}{6}$	0	$\dfrac{\pi}{6}$	$\dfrac{\pi}{4}$	$\dfrac{\pi}{3}$	$\dfrac{\pi}{2}$	$\dfrac{2\pi}{3}$	$\dfrac{3\pi}{4}$	$\dfrac{5\pi}{6}$	π
y													

1. $y = \tan x$ 2. $y = \cot x$ 3. $y = \sec x$ 4. $y = \csc x$

In Exercises 5 through 12 sketch the curves of the given functions by use of the basic curve forms (Figs. 9–17, 9–18, 9–19, 9–20). See Examples A and B.

5. $y = 2 \tan x$ 6. $y = 3 \cot x$ 7. $y = \frac{1}{2}\sec x$

8. $y = \frac{3}{2}\csc x$ 9. $y = -2 \cot x$ 10. $y = -\tan x$

11. $y = -3 \csc x$ 12. $y = -\frac{1}{2} \sec x$

In Exercises 13 through 20 plot the graphs by first making an appropriate table for $0 \le x \le \pi$.

13. $y = \tan 2x$ 14. $y = 2 \cot 3x$ 15. $y = \frac{1}{2}\sec 3x$

16. $y = \csc 2x$ 17. $y = 2 \cot\left(2x + \dfrac{\pi}{6}\right)$ 18. $y = \tan\left(3x - \dfrac{\pi}{2}\right)$

19. $y = \csc\left(3x - \dfrac{\pi}{3}\right)$ 20. $y = 3 \sec\left(2x + \dfrac{\pi}{4}\right)$

In Exercises 21 through 24 sketch the given curves by first sketching the appropriate reciprocal function. See Example C.

21. $y = \sec x$ 22. $y = \cot x$ 23. $y = \csc 2x$ 24. $y = \sec \pi x$

In Exercises 25 through 28 construct the appropriate graphs.

25. For an object sliding down an inclined plane at constant speed, the coefficient of friction μ (the Greek mu) between the object and the plane is given by $\mu = \tan \theta$, where θ is the angle between the plane and the horizontal. Sketch a graph of the coefficient of friction vs. the angle of inclination of the plane for $0 \leq \theta \leq 60°$.

26. The tension T at any point in a cable supporting a distributed load is given by $T = T_0 \sec \theta$, where T_0 is the tension where the cable is horizontal, and θ is the angle between the cable and the horizontal at any point. Sketch a graph of T vs. θ for a cable for which $T_0 = 200$ lb.

27. From a point x meters from the base of a building 200 m high, the angle of elevation θ of the top of the building can be found from the equation $x = 200 \cot \theta$. Plot x as a function of θ.

28. An expression relating the initial velocity v_0 of a projectile, the time t of its flight, and the angle θ above the horizontal at which it is fired is $v_0 = gt \csc \theta$, where g is the acceleration due to gravity. Plot v_0 (in feet per second) for $g = 32.0$ ft/s² and $t = 10.0$ s.

9—5 Applications of the Trigonometric Graphs

There are a great many applications of the trigonometric functions and their graphs, a few of which have been indicated in the exercises of the previous sections. In this section we shall introduce an important physical concept and indicate some of the technical applications.

In Section 7—4, we discussed the velocity of an object moving in a circular path. The movement of the **projection** on a diameter of a particle revolving about a circle with constant velocity is known as **simple harmonic motion**. For example, this could be the motion of the shadow of an object which is moving around a circle. Another example would be the vertical (or horizontal) position of the end of a spoke of a wheel in motion.

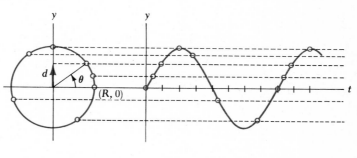

Figure 9—24

Example A

When we consider Fig. 9—24, let us assume that motion starts with the end of the radius at $(R, 0)$ and that it is moving with constant angular velocity ω. This means that the length of the projection of the radius along the y-axis is given by $d = R \sin \theta$. The length of this projection is shown for a few different positions of the end of the radius. Since $\theta/t = \omega$, or $\theta = \omega t$, we have

$$d = R \sin \omega t \qquad\qquad (9\text{--}2)$$

as the equation for the length of the projection, with time as the independent variable. Normally, the position as a function of time is the important relationship.

For the case where $R = 10.0$ in. and $\omega = 4.00$ rad/s, we have

$$d = 10.0 \sin 4.00t$$

By sketching the graph of this function, we can readily determine the length of the projection d for a given time t. The graph is shown in Fig. 9–25.

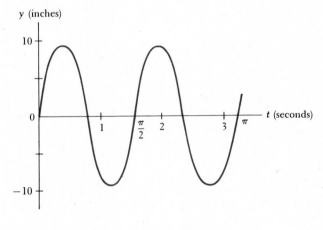

Figure 9–25

Example B

If the end of the radius is at $(\frac{R}{\sqrt{2}}, \frac{R}{\sqrt{2}})$, where $\theta = \frac{\pi}{4}$, when $t = 0$, we can express the projection d as a function of the time as

$$d = R \sin\!\left(\omega t + \frac{\pi}{4}\right)$$

If the end of the radius is at $(0, R)$, where $\theta = \frac{\pi}{2}$, when $t = 0$, we can express the projection d as a function of the time as

$$d = R \sin\!\left(\omega t + \frac{\pi}{2}\right) \quad \text{or} \quad d = R \cos \omega t$$

This can be seen from Fig. 9–24. If the motion started at the first maximum of the indicated curve, the resulting curve would be that of the cosine function.

Other examples of simple harmonic motion are (1) the movement of a pendulum bob through its arc (a very close approximation to simple harmonic motion), (2) the motion of an object on the end of a spring, (3) the motion of an object "bobbing" in the water, and (4) the movement of the end of a vibrating rod (which we hear as sound). Other phenomena which give rise to equations just like those for simple harmonic motion are found in the fields of optics, sound, and electricity. Such phenomena have the same mathematical form because they result from vibratory motion or motion in a circle.

Example C

A very important use of the trigonometric curves arises in the study of alternating current, which is caused by the motion of a wire passing through a magnetic field. If this wire is moving in a circular path, with angular velocity ω, the current i in the wire at time t is given by an equation of the form

$$i = I_m \sin (\omega t + \alpha) \tag{9-3}$$

where I_m is the maximum current attainable and α is the phase angle. The current may be represented by a sine wave, as in the following example.

Example D

In Example C, given that $I_m = 6.00$ A, $\omega = 120\pi$ rad/s (60 Hz), and $\alpha = \pi/6$, we have the equation

$$i = 6.00 \sin \left(120\pi t + \frac{\pi}{6} \right)$$

From this equation we see that the amplitude is 6.00, the period is $\frac{1}{60}$ s, and the displacement is $\frac{1}{720}$ s to the left. From these values we draw the graph as shown in Fig. 9–26. Since the current takes on both positive and negative values, we conclude that it moves in opposite directions.

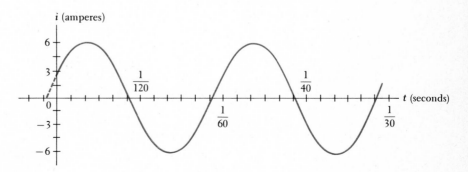

Figure 9–26

Exercises 9—5

In Exercises 1 and 2 draw two cycles of the curve of the projection of Example A as a function of time for the given values.

1. $R = 4.00$ in., $\omega = 1.00$ rad/s   2. $R = 8.00$ cm, $\omega = 0.500$ Hz

In Exercises 3 and 4, for the projection described in Example A, assume that the end of the radius starts at $(0, R)$. Draw two cycles of the projection as a function of time for the given values. (See Example B.)

3. $R = 2.00$ ft, $\omega = 1.00$ Hz   4. $R = 2.50$ in., $\omega = 0.300$ rad/s

In Exercises 5 and 6, for the projection described in Example A, assume that the end of the radius starts at the indicated point. Draw two cycles of the projection as a function of time for the given values. (See Example B.)

5. $R = 6.00$ cm, $\omega = 2.00$ Hz, starting point $(\frac{\sqrt{3}R}{2}), \frac{R}{2})$
6. $R = 3.20$ ft., $\omega = 0.200$ rad/s, starting point $(\frac{R}{2}, \frac{\sqrt{3}R}{2})$

In Exercises 7 and 8, for the alternating-current discussed in Example C, draw two cycles of the current as a function of time for the given values.

7. $I_m = 2.00$ A, $\omega = 60.0$ Hz, $\alpha = 0$
8. $I_m = 0.600$ A, $\omega = 100$ rad/s, $\alpha = \pi/4$

In Exercises 9 and 10, for an alternating-current circuit in which the voltage is given by

$$e = E \cos (\omega t + \alpha)$$

draw two cycles of the voltage as a function of time for the given values.

9. $E = 170$ V, $\omega = 50.0$ rad/s, $\alpha = 0$
10. $E = 110$ V, $\omega = 60.0$ Hz, $\alpha = -\pi/3$

In Exercises 11 through 16 draw the required curves.

11. Angular displacement θ of a pendulum bob is given in terms of its initial $(t = 0)$ displacement θ_0 by the equation $\theta = \theta_0 \cos \omega t$. If $\omega = 2.00$ rad/s and $\theta_0 = \pi/30$ rad, draw two cycles for the resulting equation.

12. Displacement of the end of a vibrating rod is given by $y = 1.50 \cos 200\pi t$. Sketch two cycles of y (in centimeters) vs. t (in seconds).

13. An object of weight w and cross-sectional area A is depressed a distance x_0 from its equilibrium position when in a liquid of density d and then released; its displacement as a function of time is given by

$$x = x_0 \cos \sqrt{\frac{dgA}{w}} t$$

where g ($= 32.0$ ft/s²) is the acceleration due to gravity. If a 4.00-lb object with a cross-sectional area of 2.00 ft² is depressed 3.00 ft in water (let $d = 62.4$ lb/ft³), find the equation which expresses the displacement as a function of time. Draw two cycles of the curve.

14. A wave is traveling in a string. The displacement, as a function of time, from its equilibrium position, is given by $y = A \cos (2\pi/T)t$. T is the period (measured in seconds) of the motion. If $A = 0.200$ in. and $T = 0.100$ s, draw two cycles of the displacement as a function of time.

15. The displacement, as a function of time, from the position of equilibrium, of an object on the end of a spring is given by $x = A \cos (\omega t + \alpha)$. Draw two cycles of the curve for displacement as a function of time for $A = 2.00$ in., $\omega = 0.500$ Hz, and $\alpha = \pi/6$.

16. The angular displacement θ of a pendulum bob (see Exercise 11) is given by $\theta = \theta_0 \sin (\omega t + \frac{\pi}{6})$. If $\theta_0 = 0.100$ rad and $\omega = \frac{\pi}{2}$ rad/s, sketch two cycles of the graph of θ vs. t.

9—6 Composite Trigonometric Curves

Many applications of trigonometric functions involve the combination of two or more functions. In this section we shall discuss two important methods in which trigonometric curves can be combined.

If we wish to find the curve of a function which itself is the sum of two other functions, we may find the resulting graph by first sketching the two individual functions, and then adding the y-values graphically. This method is called **addition of ordinates,** and is illustrated in the following examples.

Example A
Sketch the graph of $y = 2 \cos x + \sin 2x$.

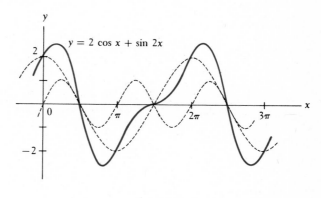

Figure 9—27

On the same set of coordinate axes we sketch the curves $y = 2 \cos x$ and $y = \sin 2x$. These are shown as dashed curves in Fig. 9—27. For various values of x, we determine the distance above or below the x-axis of each curve and add these distances, noting that those above the axis are positive and those below the axis are negative. We thereby graphically *add* the y-values of these two curves for these values of x to obtain the points on the resulting curve shown as a heavy curve in Fig. 9—27. We add the y-values for a sufficient number of x-values to obtain the proper representation. Some points are easily found. Where one curve crosses the x-axis, its y-value is zero, and therefore the resulting curve has its point on the other curve for this value of x. In this example, $\sin 2x$ is zero at $x = 0$, $\frac{\pi}{2}$, π, and so forth. We see that points on the resulting curve lie on the curve of $2 \cos x$. We should also add the values where each curve is at its amplitude values. In this case, $\sin 2x$ equals 1 at $\frac{\pi}{4}$, and the two y-values should be added together here to get a point on the resulting curve. At $x = \frac{5\pi}{4}$, we must take care in adding the values, since $\sin 2x$ is positive and $2 \cos x$ is negative. Reasonable care and accuracy are necessary to obtain a proper resulting curve.

Example B

Sketch the graph of $y = \dfrac{x}{2} - \cos x$.

The method of addition of ordinates is applicable regardless of the kinds of functions being added. Here we note that $y = \frac{x}{2}$ is a straight line, and that it is to be combined with a trigonometric curve.

We could graph the functions $y = \frac{x}{2}$ and $y = \cos x$ and then subtract the ordinates of $y = \cos x$ from the ordinates of $y = \frac{x}{2}$. But it is easier, and far less confusing, to add values, so we shall sketch $y = \frac{x}{2}$ and $y = -\cos x$ and add the ordinates to obtain points on the resulting curve. These graphs are shown as dashed curves in Fig. 9–28. The important points on the resulting curve are obtained by using the values of x corresponding to the zeros and amplitude values of $y = -\cos x$.

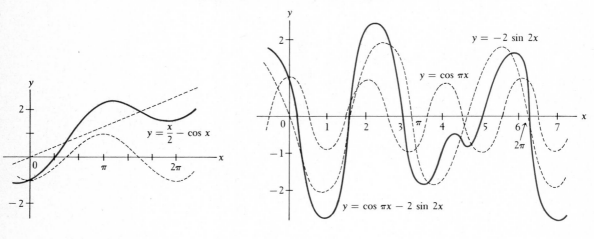

Figure 9–28   Figure 9–29

Example C

Sketch the graph of $y = \cos \pi x - 2 \sin 2x$.

The curves of $y = \cos \pi x$ and $y = -2 \sin 2x$ are shown as dashed curves in Fig. 9–29. Points for the resulting curve are found primarily at the x-values where each of the curves has its zero or amplitude values. Again, special care should be taken where one of the curves is negative and the other is positive.

Another important application of trigonometric curves is made when they are added at *right angles*. This can be accomplished in practice by applying different voltages to an oscilloscope. Let us consider the following examples.

Example D

Plot the graph for which the values of x and y are given by the equations $y = \sin 2\pi t$ and $x = 2 \cos \pi t$. (Equations given in this form, x and y in terms of a third variable, are called **parametric equations.**)

Since both x and y are given in terms of t, by assuming values for t we may find corresponding values of x and y, and use these values to plot the resulting points (see Fig. 9–30).

t	0	$\frac{1}{4}$	$\frac{1}{2}$	$\frac{3}{4}$	1	$\frac{5}{4}$	$\frac{3}{2}$	$\frac{7}{4}$	2	$\frac{9}{4}$
x	2	1.4	0	−1.4	−2	−1.4	0	1.4	2	1.4
y	0	1	0	−1	0	1	0	−1	0	1
Point number	1	2	3	4	5	6	7	8	9	10

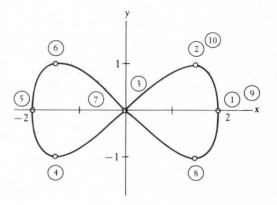

Figure 9–30

Since x and y are trigonometric functions of a third variable t, and since the x- and y-axes are at right angles, values of x and y obtained in this manner result in a combination of two trigonometric curves at right angles. Figures obtained in this manner are called **Lissajous figures.**

Example E

If we place a circle on the x-axis and another on the y-axis, we may represent the coordinates (x, y) for the curve of Example D by the lengths of the projections (see Example A of Section 9–5) of a point moving around each circle. A careful study of Fig. 9–31 will clarify this. We note that the radius of the circle giving the x-values is 2, whereas the radius of the other is 1. This is due to the manner in which x and y are defined. Also due to the definitions, the point revolves around the y-circle twice as fast as the corresponding point revolves around the x-circle.

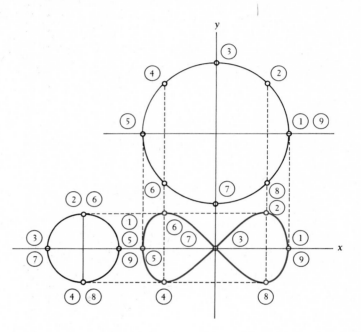

Figure 9–31

Example F

Plot the Lissajous figure for which the x- and y-values are given by the equation $x = 2 \sin 3t$ and $y = 3 \sin (t + \frac{\pi}{3})$.

Since values of t which are multiples of π give convenient values of x and y, the table is constructed with these values of t. Figure 9–32 shows the graph.

t	x	y	Point number
0	0	2.6	1
$\frac{\pi}{6}$	2	3	2
$\frac{\pi}{3}$	0	2.6	3
$\frac{\pi}{2}$	-2	1.5	4
$\frac{2\pi}{3}$	0	0	5
$\frac{5\pi}{6}$	2	-1.5	6
π	0	-2.6	7
$\frac{7\pi}{6}$	-2	-3	8
$\frac{4\pi}{3}$	0	-2.6	9
$\frac{3\pi}{2}$	2	-1.5	10
$\frac{5\pi}{3}$	0	0	11
$\frac{11\pi}{6}$	-2	1.5	12
2π	0	2.6	13

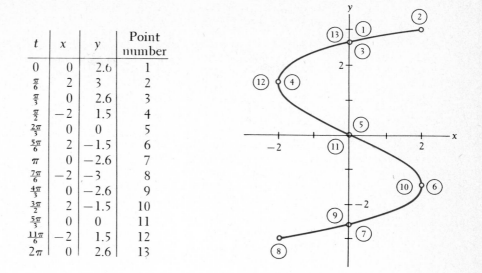

Figure 9–32

Exercises 9–6

In Exercises 1 through 20 use the method of addition of ordinates to sketch the given curves.

1. $y = x + \sin x$

2. $y = x + 2 \cos x$

3. $y = \frac{1}{3}x - \cos x$

4. $y = \frac{1}{4}x - \sin x$

5. $y = \frac{1}{10}x^2 + \sin 2x$

6. $y = \frac{1}{3}x^2 + \cos 3x$

7. $y = \dfrac{1}{x^2 + 1} - \sin \pi x$

8. $y = \frac{1}{5}x^3 - \cos \pi x$

9. $y = \sin x + \cos x$

10. $y = \sin x + \sin 2x$

11. $y = \sin x - \sin 2x$

12. $y = \cos 3x - \sin x$

13. $y = 2 \cos 2x + 3 \sin x$

14. $y = \frac{1}{2}\sin 4x + \cos 2x$

15. $y = 2 \sin x - \cos x$

16. $y = \sin \dfrac{x}{2} - \sin x$

17. $y = 2 \cos 4x - \cos\left(x - \dfrac{\pi}{4}\right)$

18. $y = \sin \pi x - \cos 2x$

19. $y = 2 \sin\left(2x - \dfrac{\pi}{6}\right) + \cos\left(2x + \dfrac{\pi}{3}\right)$

20. $y = 3 \cos 2\pi x + \sin \dfrac{\pi}{2}x$

In Exercises 21 through 28 plot the Lissajous figures.

21. $y = \sin t, \; x = \sin t$

22. $y = 2 \cos t, \; x = \cos t$

23. $y = \sin \pi t, \; x = \cos \pi t$

24. $y = \sin 2t, \; x = \cos\left(t + \dfrac{\pi}{4}\right)$

25. $y = 2 \sin \pi t,\ x = \cos \pi \left(t + \dfrac{1}{6}\right)$ **26.** $y = \sin^2 \pi t,\ x = \cos 2\pi t$

27. $y = \cos 2t,\ x = 2 \cos 3t$ **28.** $y = 3 \sin 3\pi t,\ x = 2 \sin \pi t$

In Exercises 29 through 34 sketch the appropriate figures.

29. The current in a certain electric circuit is given by the formula $i = 4 \sin 60\pi t + 2 \cos 120\pi t$. Sketch the curve representing the current (in amperes) as a function of time (in seconds).

30. In optics, two waves are said to interfere destructively if, when they pass through the same medium, the amplitude of the resulting wave is zero. Sketch the curve of $y = \sin x + \cos (x + \frac{\pi}{2})$, and determine whether or not it would represent destructive interference of two waves.

31. An object oscillating on a spring, under specific conditions, has a displacement given by $y = 0.4 \sin 4t + 0.3 \cos 4t$. Plot y (in feet) versus t (in seconds).

32. The resultant voltage in a certain electric circuit is given by the formula $e = 50 \sin 50\pi t + 80 \sin 60\pi t$. Sketch the curve representing voltage as a function of time.

33. Two signals are being sent to an oscilloscope, and are seen on the oscilloscope as being at right angles. The equations governing the displacement of these signals are $x = 2 \cos 120\pi t$ and $y = 3 \cos 120\pi t$, respectively. Sketch the figure which would appear on the oscilloscope.

34. In the study of optics, light is said to be elliptically polarized if certain optic vibrations are out of phase. These may be represented by Lissajous figures. Determine the Lissajous figure for two waves of light given by $w_1 = \sin \omega t,\ w_2 = \sin (\omega t + \frac{\pi}{4})$.

9–7 Exercises for Chapter 9

In Exercises 1 through 24 sketch the curves of the given trigonometric functions.

1. $y = \frac{2}{3} \sin x$ **2.** $y = -4 \sin x$ **3.** $y = -2 \cos x$

4. $y = 2.3 \cos x$ **5.** $y = 2 \sin 3x$ **6.** $y = 3 \sin \frac{1}{2}x$

7. $y = 2 \cos 2x$ **8.** $y = 4 \cos 6x$ **9.** $y = \sin \pi x$

10. $y = 3 \sin 4\pi x$ **11.** $y = 5 \cos 2\pi x$ **12.** $y = -\cos 3\pi x$

13. $y = 2 \sin\left(3x - \dfrac{\pi}{2}\right)$ **14.** $y = 3 \sin\left(\dfrac{x}{2} + \dfrac{\pi}{2}\right)$

15. $y = -2 \cos (4x + \pi)$ **16.** $y = 0.8 \cos\left(\dfrac{x}{6} - \dfrac{\pi}{2}\right)$

17. $y = -\sin\left(\pi x + \dfrac{\pi}{6}\right)$ **18.** $y = 2 \sin (3\pi x - \pi)$

19. $y = 8 \cos\left(4\pi x - \dfrac{\pi}{2}\right)$ **20.** $y = 3 \cos (2\pi x + \pi)$

21. $y = 3 \tan x$

22. $y = \frac{1}{4} \sec x$

23. $y = -\frac{1}{3} \csc x$

24. $y = -5 \cot x$

In Exercises 25 through 32 sketch the given curves by the method of addition of ordinates.

25. $y = \frac{1}{2} \sin 2x - x$

26. $y = \frac{1}{2}x - \cos \frac{1}{3}x$

27. $y = \sin 2x + 3 \cos x$

28. $y = \sin 3x + 2 \cos 2x$

29. $y = 2 \sin x - \cos 2x$

30. $y = \sin 3x - 2 \cos x$

31. $y = \cos\left(x + \frac{\pi}{4}\right) - 2 \sin 2x$

32. $y = 2 \cos \pi x + \cos (2\pi x - \pi)$

In Exercises 33 through 36 plot the Lissajous figures.

33. $y = 2 \sin \pi t, \; x = -\cos 2\pi t$

34. $y = \sin t, \; x = \sin\left(t + \frac{\pi}{6}\right)$

35. $y = \cos \pi t, \; x = \cos\left(2\pi t + \frac{\pi}{4}\right)$

36. $y = \cos\left(2t + \frac{\pi}{3}\right), \; x = \cos\left(t - \frac{\pi}{6}\right)$

In Exercises 37 through 48 sketch the appropriate figures.

37. A simple pendulum is started by giving it a velocity from its equilibrium position. The angle θ between the vertical and the pendulum is given by $\theta = a \sin (\sqrt{\frac{g}{l}}t)$, where a is the amplitude (in radians), g ($= 32.0$ ft/s^2) is the acceleration due to gravity, l is the length of the pendulum (in feet), and t is the length of time of the motion. Sketch two cycles of θ as a function of t for the pendulum whose length is 2.00 ft and $a = 0.100$ rad.

38. The electric current in a certain circuit is given by $i = i_0 \sin (t/\sqrt{LC})$, where i_0 is the initial current in the circuit, L is an inductance, and C is a capacitance. Sketch two cycles of i as a function of t (in seconds) for the case where $i_0 = 0.500$ A, $L = 1.00$ H, and $C = 100$ μF.

39. A certain object is oscillating at the end of a spring. The displacement as a function of time is given by the relation $y = 0.200 \cos (8t + \frac{\pi}{3})$, where y is measured in meters and t in seconds. Plot the graph of y vs. t.

40. A circular disk suspended by a thin wire attached to the center at one of its flat faces is twisted through an angle θ. Torsion in the wire tends to turn the disk back in the opposite direction (thus the name "torsion pendulum" is given to this device). The angular displacement as a function of time is given by $\theta = \theta_0 \cos (\omega t + \alpha)$, where θ_0 is the maximum angular displacement, ω is a constant which depends on the properties of the disk and wire, and α is the phase angle. Plot the graph of θ vs. t if $\theta_0 = 0.100$ rad, $\omega = 2.50$ rad/s and $\alpha = \pi/4$.

41. The charge q on a certain capacitor as a function of time is given by $q = 0.001(1 - \cos 100t)$. Sketch two cycles of q as a function of t. Charge is measured in coulombs, and time is measured in seconds.

42. If the upper end of a spring is not fixed and is being moved with a sinusoidal motion, the motion of the bob at the end of the spring is affected. Plot the curve if the motion of the upper end of a spring is being moved by an external force and the bob moves according to the equation $y = 4 \sin 2t - 2 \cos 2t$.

43. Under certain conditions, the path of a certain moving particle is given by $x = 2 \cos 3\pi t$ and $y = \sin 3\pi t$. Plot the path of the object.

44. Two signals are applied to an oscilloscope. The equations governing the displacement of these signals are $x = 2 \cos 40\pi t$ and $y = \sin 120\pi t$. Sketch the figure which appears on the oscilloscope.

45. The height of a certain rocket ascending vertically is given by the formula $h = 800 \tan \theta$, where θ is the angle of elevation from an observer 800 m from the launch pad. Plot h (in meters) vs. θ.

46. An equation relating a force F and its x-component F_x is $F = F_x \sec \theta$, where θ is the angle between F and F_x. Plot F vs. θ for $F_x = 500$ lb.

47. The area of a rectangle as a function of a diagonal is $A = d^2 \sin \theta \cos \theta$, where θ is the angle between the diagonal and one of the sides. Plot A vs. θ for $d = 10.0$ m.

48. The instantaneous power in an electric circuit is defined as the product of the instantaneous voltage e and the instantaneous current i. If we have $e = 100 \cos 200t$ and $i = 2 \cos (200t + \frac{\pi}{4})$, plot the graph of the voltage and the graph of the current (in amperes), on the same coordinate system, vs. the time (in seconds). Then sketch the power (in watts) vs. time by multiplying appropriate values of e and i.

10

Exponents and Radicals

10–1 Integral Exponents

In Chapter 1 we introduced exponents and radicals. To this point only a basic understanding of the meaning and elementary operations with them has been necessary. However, in our future work a more detailed understanding of exponents and radicals, and operations on them, will be required. Therefore, in this chapter we shall develop the necessary operations.

The laws of exponents were given in Section 1–4. We now write them again for reference.

$$a^m \cdot a^n = a^{m+n} \tag{10-1}$$

$$\frac{a^m}{a^n} = a^{m-n} \quad \text{or} \quad \frac{a^m}{a^n} = \frac{1}{a^{n-m}}, \qquad a \neq 0 \tag{10-2}$$

$$(a^m)^n = a^{mn} \tag{10-3}$$

$$(ab)^n = a^n b^n, \qquad \left(\frac{a}{b}\right)^n = \frac{a^n}{b^n}, \qquad b \neq 0 \tag{10-4}$$

$$a^0 = 1, \qquad a \neq 0 \tag{10-5}$$

$$a^{-n} = \frac{1}{a^n}, \qquad a \neq 0 \tag{10-6}$$

Although Eqs. (10–1) through (10–4) were originally defined for positive integers as exponents, we showed in Section 1–4 that with the definitions given in Eqs. (10–5) and (10–6) they are valid for all integral exponents. Later in this chapter we shall show how fractions may be used as exponents. Since the equations above are very important to the development of the topics in this chapter, they should again be reviewed — and learned thoroughly.

In this chapter we review the use of exponents in using Eqs. (10–1) through (10–6). Then we show how they are used and handled in somewhat more involved expressions.

Example A
Applying Eq. (10–1), we have

$$a^5 \cdot a^{-3} = a^{5+(-3)} = a^{5-3} = a^2$$

Applying Eq. (10–1) and then Eq. (10–6), we have

$$a^3 \cdot a^{-5} = a^{3-5} = a^{-2} = \frac{1}{a^2}$$

We note that a final result is usually expressed with positive exponents, unless specified otherwise.

Example B
Applying Eqs. (10–2) and (10–5), we have

$$\frac{a^2 b^3 c^0}{ab^7} = \frac{a^{2-1}(1)}{b^{7-3}} = \frac{a}{b^4}$$

Applying Eqs. (10–4) and (10–3), we have

$$(x^{-2}y)^3 = (x^{-2})^3(y^3) = x^{-6}y^3 = \frac{y^3}{x^6}$$

Here, the simplification was completed by the use of Eq. (10–6).

There are many occasions in using Eqs. (10–1) through (10–6) when more than one sequence of steps may be used in the simplification process. Consider the illustration in the following example.

Example C

$$\left(\frac{4}{a^2}\right)^{-3} = \frac{1}{\left(\frac{4}{a^2}\right)^3} = \frac{1}{\frac{4^3}{a^6}} = \frac{a^6}{4^3}$$

or

$$\left(\frac{4}{a^2}\right)^{-3} = \frac{4^{-3}}{a^{-6}} = \frac{a^6}{4^3}$$

In the first method we used Eq. (10–6) first, then Eq. (10–4), and finally, we inverted the divisor. In the second method we first used Eq. (10–4) and then Eq. (10–6).

In simplifying expressions, care must be taken to apply the laws of exponents properly. Certain relatively common problems are pointed out in the following two examples.

Example D

The expression $(-5x)^0$ equals 1, whereas the expression $-5x^0$ equals -5. For $(-5x)^0$ the parentheses indicate that the expression $-5x$ is raised to the zero power, whereas for $-5x^0$ only x is raised to the zero power and we have

$$-5x^0 = -5(1) = -5$$

Also, $(-5)^0 = 1$, whereas $-5^0 = -1$. Again note the use of parentheses. For $(-5)^0$ it is -5 which is raised to the zero power, whereas for -5^0 only 5 is raised to the zero power.

Example E

Simplify $(2a + b^{-1})^{-2}$.

In simplifying an expression we should give the result with positive exponents. For this expression we may use various orders of operations. One is as follows:

$$(2a + b^{-1})^{-2} = \frac{1}{(2a + b^{-1})^2} = \frac{1}{\left(2a + \dfrac{1}{b}\right)^2} = \frac{1}{\left(\dfrac{2ab + 1}{b}\right)^2}$$

$$= \frac{1}{\dfrac{(2ab + 1)^2}{b^2}} = \frac{b^2}{(2ab + 1)^2}$$

We may leave the result in this form, or multiply out the denominator and obtain

$$(2a + b^{-1})^{-2} = \frac{b^2}{(2ab + 1)^2} = \frac{b^2}{4a^2b^2 + 4ab + 1}$$

However, a common type of error is sometimes made with this type of expression. An incorrect step which is made is to express

$$(2a + b^{-1})^{-2} \quad \text{as} \quad (2a)^{-2} + (b^{-1})^{-2} \quad \text{or} \quad \frac{1}{4a^2} + b^2$$

Remember: As noted in Section 5–1, when raising a binomial (or any multinomial) to a power, we cannot simply raise each term to the power to obtain the result.

From the above examples, we see that *when a factor is moved from the denominator to the numerator of a fraction, or conversely, the sign of the exponent is changed.* We should heed carefully the word "factor"; this rule does not apply to moving terms in the numerator or denominator.

Example F

$$\frac{1}{x^{-1}}\left(\frac{x^{-1}-y^{-1}}{x^2-y^2}\right)=\frac{x}{1}\left(\frac{\dfrac{1}{x}-\dfrac{1}{y}}{x^2-y^2}\right)=x\left(\frac{\dfrac{y-x}{xy}}{x^2-y^2}\right)$$

$$=\frac{\dfrac{x(y-x)}{xy}}{(x-y)(x+y)}=\frac{x(y-x)}{xy}\cdot\frac{1}{(x-y)(x+y)}$$

$$=\frac{x(y-x)}{xy(x-y)(x+y)}=\frac{-(x-y)}{y(x-y)(x+y)}$$

$$=-\frac{1}{y(x+y)}$$

Note that in this example the x^{-1} and y^{-1} in the numerator could not be moved directly to the denominator with positive exponents because they are only terms of the original numerator.

Example G

$$3(x+4)^2(x-3)^{-2}-2(x-3)^{-3}(x+4)^3$$

$$=\frac{3(x+4)^2}{(x-3)^2}-\frac{2(x+4)^3}{(x-3)^3}=\frac{3(x-3)(x+4)^2-2(x+4)^3}{(x-3)^3}$$

$$=\frac{(x+4)^2[3(x-3)-2(x+4)]}{(x-3)^3}=\frac{(x+4)^2(x-17)}{(x-3)^3}$$

Expressions such as the one in this example are commonly found in problems in calculus.

Exercises 10—1

In Exercises 1 through 40 express each of the given expressions in the simplest form which contains only positive exponents.

1. $x^7 \cdot x^{-4}$ 2. $y^9 \cdot y^{-2}$ 3. $a^2 \cdot a^{-6}$ 4. $s \cdot s^{-5}$

5. $(2ax^{-1})^2$ 6. $(3xy^{-2})^3$ 7. $(5an^{-2})^{-1}$ 8. $(6s^2t^{-1})^{-2}$

9. $(-4)^0$ 10. -4^0 11. $-7x^0$ 12. $(-7x)^0$

13. $\left(\dfrac{2}{n^3}\right)^{-1}$ 14. $\left(\dfrac{3}{x^3}\right)^{-2}$ 15. $\left(\dfrac{a}{b^{-2}}\right)^{-3}$ 16. $\left(\dfrac{2n^{-2}}{m^{-1}}\right)^{-2}$

17. $(a+b)^{-1}$ 18. $a^{-1}+b^{-1}$ 19. $3x^{-2}+2y^{-2}$ 20. $(3x+2y)^{-2}$

21. $\left(\dfrac{3a^2}{4b}\right)^{-3}\left(\dfrac{4}{a}\right)^{-5}$ 22. $\left(\dfrac{2n}{p^2}\right)^{-2}\left(\dfrac{p}{4}\right)^{-1}$

23. $\left(\dfrac{v^{-1}}{2t}\right)^{-2}\left(\dfrac{t^2}{v^{-2}}\right)^{-3}$ 24. $\left(\dfrac{a^{-2}}{b^2}\right)^{-3}\left(\dfrac{a^{-3}}{b^5}\right)^2$

25. $(x^2y^{-1})^2-x^{-4}$ 26. $(st^{-2})^{-1}-s^{-2}$

27. $4a^{-2} + (3a^2)^{-2}$

28. $3(a^{-1}z^2)^{-3} + c^{-2}z^{-1}$

29. $(a^{-1} + b^{-1})^{-1}$

30. $(2a - b^{-2})^{-1}$

31. $(n^{-2} - 2n^{-1})^2$

32. $(2^{-3} - 4^{-1})^2$

33. $\dfrac{x - y^{-1}}{x^{-1} - y}$

34. $\dfrac{x^{-2} - y^{-2}}{x^{-1} - y^{-1}}$

35. $\dfrac{ax^{-2} + a^{-2}x}{a^{-1} + x^{-1}}$

36. $\dfrac{2x^{-2} - 2y^{-2}}{(xy)^{-3}}$

37. $2t^{-2} + t^{-1}(t + 1)$

38. $3x^{-1} + x^{-3}(y + 2)$

39. $(x - 1)^{-1} + (x + 1)^{-1}$

40. $4(2x - 1)(x + 2)^{-1} - (2x - 1)^2(x + 2)^{-2}$

In Exercises 41 through 44 perform the indicated operations.

41. When discussing electronic amplifiers, the expression $(1/r + 1/R)^{-1}$ is found. Simplify this expression.

42. Physical units associated with numbers are often expressed in terms of negative exponents (see Appendix B). If the units of a certain quantity are $(m \cdot s^{-1})^2$, express these units without the use of negative exponents.

43. An expression which is used for the focal length of a certain lens is $[(\mu - 1)(r_1^{-1} - r_2^{-1})]^{-1}$. Rewrite this expression without the use of negative exponents.

44. An expression encountered in the mathematics of finance is

$$\frac{p(1 + i)^{-1}[(1 + i)^{-n} - 1]}{(1 + i)^{-1} - 1}$$

where n is an integer. Simplify this expression.

10–2 Fractional Exponents

In Section 10–1 we reviewed the use of integral exponents, including exponents which are negative integers and zero. We now show how rational numbers may be used as exponents. With the appropriate definitions all of the laws of exponents are valid for all rational numbers as exponents.

Equation (10–3) states that $(a^m)^n = a^{mn}$. If we were to let $m = \frac{1}{2}$ and $n = 2$, we would have $(a^{1/2})^2 = a^1$. However, we already have a way of writing a quantity which when squared equals a. This is written as $\sqrt{a}$. To be consistent with previous definitions and to allow the laws of exponents to hold, we define

$$a^{1/n} = \sqrt[n]{a} \tag{10-7}$$

In order that Eqs. (10–3) and (10–7) may hold at the same time, we define

$$\overline{a^{m/n} = \sqrt[n]{a^m}} \qquad (10\text{--}8)$$

It can be shown that these definitions are valid for all the laws of exponents.

Example A

We shall verify here that Eq. (10–1) holds for the above definitions:

$$a^{1/4}a^{1/4}a^{1/4}a^{1/4} = a^{(1/4)+(1/4)+(1/4)+(1/4)} = a^1$$

Now $a^{1/4} = \sqrt[4]{a}$, by definition. Also, by definition $\sqrt[4]{a}\ \sqrt[4]{a}\ \sqrt[4]{a}\ \sqrt[4]{a} = a$. Equation (10–1) is thereby verified for $n = 4$. Equation (10–3) is verified by the following:

$$a^{1/4}a^{1/4}a^{1/4}a^{1/4} = a^{4(1/4)} = a = \sqrt[4]{a^4}$$

We may interpret Eq. (10–8) as "the mth power of the nth root of a," as well as the way in which it is written, which is "the nth root of the mth power of a." This is illustrated in the following example.

Example B

$$(\sqrt[3]{a})^2 = \sqrt[3]{a^2} = a^{2/3}$$
$$8^{2/3} = (\sqrt[3]{8})^2 = (2)^2 = 4 \qquad \text{or} \qquad 8^{2/3} = \sqrt[3]{8^2} = \sqrt[3]{64} = 4$$

Although both interpretations of Eq. (10–8) are possible as indicated in Example B, in evaluating numerical expressions involving fractional exponents, it is almost always best to find the root first, as indicated by the denominator of the fractional exponent. This will allow us to find the root of the smaller number, which is normally easier to find.

Example C

To evaluate $(64)^{5/2}$, we should proceed as follows:

$$(64)^{5/2} = [(64)^{1/2}]^5 = 8^5 = 32{,}768$$

If we raised 64 to the fifth power first we would have

$$(64)^{5/2} = (64^5)^{1/2} = (1{,}073{,}741{,}824)^{1/2}$$

We would now have to evaluate the indicated square root. This demonstrates why it is preferable to find the indicated root first.

Example D

$$(16)^{3/4} = (16^{1/4})^3 = 2^3 = 8$$

$$4^{-1/2} = \frac{1}{4^{1/2}} = \frac{1}{2}, \qquad 9^{3/2} = (9^{1/2})^3 = 3^3 = 27$$

We note in the illustration of $4^{-1/2}$ that Eq. (10–6) must also hold for negative rational exponents. The only change in the exponent which is made in writing it as $1/4^{1/2}$ is that the sign of the exponent is changed.

The question may arise as to why we use fractional exponents, since we have already defined expressions which are equivalent to their meanings. The answer is that fractional exponents are often easier to handle in more complex expressions involving roots, and therefore any expression involving radicals can be solved by use of fractional exponents. Also, they can be used to find roots of numbers on a calculator.

Example E

$$(8a^2b^4)^{1/3} = [(8^{1/3})(a^2)^{1/3}(b^4)^{1/3}] = 2a^{2/3}b^{4/3}$$

$$a^{3/4}a^{4/5} = a^{3/4+4/5} = a^{31/20}$$

$$(25a^{-2}c^4)^{3/2} = [(25a^{-2}c^4)^{1/2}]^3 = \left(\frac{(25)^{1/2}(c^4)^{1/2}}{(a^2)^{1/2}}\right)^3 = \left(\frac{5c^2}{a}\right)^3$$

$$= \frac{125c^6}{a^3}$$

Example F

$$\left(\frac{4^{-3/2}x^{2/3}y^{-7/4}}{2^{3/2}x^{-1/3}y^{3/4}}\right)^{2/3} = \left(\frac{x^{2/3+1/3}}{2^{3/2}4^{3/2}y^{3/4+7/4}}\right)^{2/3}$$

$$= \frac{x^{(1)(2/3)}}{2^{(3/2)(2/3)}4^{(3/2)(2/3)}y^{(10/4)(2/3)}} = \frac{x^{2/3}}{8y^{5/3}}$$

Example G

$$(4x^4)^{-1/2} - 3x^{-3} = \frac{1}{(4x^4)^{1/2}} - \frac{3}{x^3}$$

$$= \frac{1}{2x^2} - \frac{3}{x^3}$$

$$= \frac{x-6}{2x^3}$$

Example H

$$(2x+1)^{1/2} + (x+3)(2x+1)^{-1/2}$$

$$= (2x+1)^{1/2} + \frac{x+3}{(2x+1)^{1/2}}$$

$$= \frac{(2x+1)^{1/2}(2x+1)^{1/2} + (x+3)}{(2x+1)^{1/2}}$$

$$= \frac{(2x+1) + (x+3)}{(2x+1)^{1/2}} = \frac{3x+4}{(2x+1)^{1/2}}$$

Exercises 10−2

In Exercises 1 through 28 evaluate the given expressions.

1. $(25)^{1/2}$ 2. $(49)^{1/2}$ 3. $(27)^{1/3}$

4. $(81)^{1/4}$ 5. $8^{4/3}$ 6. $(125)^{2/3}$

7. $(100)^{25/2}$ 8. $(16)^{5/4}$ 9. $8^{-1/3}$

10. $16^{-1/4}$ 11. $(64)^{-2/3}$ 12. $(32)^{-4/5}$

13. $5^{1/2}5^{3/2}$ 14. $8^{1/3}4^{1/2}$ 15. $(4^4)^{3/2}$

16. $(3^6)^{2/3}$ 17. $\dfrac{121^{-1/2}}{100^{1/2}}$ 18. $\dfrac{1000^{1/3}}{400^{-1/2}}$

19. $\dfrac{7^{-1/2}}{6^{-1}7^{1/2}}$ 20. $\dfrac{15^{2/3}}{5^2 15^{-1/3}}$ 21. $\dfrac{(-27)^{1/3}}{6}$

22. $\dfrac{(-8)^{2/3}}{-2}$ 23. $\dfrac{-8}{(-27)^{-1/3}}$ 24. $\dfrac{-4}{(-64)^{-2/3}}$

25. $(125)^{-2/3} - (100)^{-3/2}$ 26. $36^{-1/2} + 27^{-2/3}$

27. $\dfrac{25^{-1/2}}{5} + \dfrac{20^{-1/2}}{20^{1/2}}$ 28. $\dfrac{4^{-1}}{(36)^{-1/2}} - \dfrac{5^{-1/2}}{5^{1/2}}$

In Exercises 29 through 52 use the laws of exponents to simplify the given expressions. Express all answers with positive exponents.

29. $a^{2/3}a^{1/2}$ 30. $x^{5/6}x^{-1/3}$ 31. $\dfrac{y^{-1/2}}{y^{2/5}}$

32. $\dfrac{2r^{4/5}}{r^{-1}}$ 33. $\dfrac{s^{1/4}s^{2/3}}{s^{-1}}$ 34. $\dfrac{x^{3/10}}{x^{-1/5}x^2}$

35. $\dfrac{y^{-1}}{y^{1/3}y^{-1/4}}$ 36. $\dfrac{a^{-2/5}a^2}{a^{-3/10}}$ 37. $(8a^3b^6)^{1/3}$

38. $(8b^{-4}c^2)^{2/3}$ 39. $(16a^4b^3)^{-3/4}$ 40. $(32x^5y^4)^{-2/5}$

41. $\left(\dfrac{9t^{-2}}{16}\right)^{3/2}$ 42. $\left(\dfrac{a^{5/7}}{a^{2/3}}\right)^{7/4}$ 43. $\left(\dfrac{4a^{5/6}b^{-1/5}}{a^{2/3}b^2}\right)^{-1/2}$

44. $\left(\dfrac{a^0b^8c^{-1/8}}{ab^{63/64}}\right)^{32/3}$ 45. $\dfrac{6x^{-1/2}y^{2/3}}{18x^{-1}} \cdot \dfrac{2y^{1/4}}{x^{1/3}}$ 46. $\dfrac{3^{-1}a^{1/2}}{4^{-1/2}b} \div \dfrac{9^{1/2}a^{-1/3}}{2b^{-1/4}}$

47. $(x^{-1} + 2x^{-2})^{-1/2}$ 48. $(a^{-2} - a^{-4})^{-1/4}$ 49. $(a^3)^{-4/3} + a^{-2}$

50. $(4x^6)^{-1/2} - 2x^{-1}$ 51. $[(a^{1/2} - a^{-1/2})^2 + 4]^{1/2}$

52. $(3x - 1)^{-2/3}(1 - x) - (3x - 1)^{1/3}$

In Exercises 53 through 56 perform the indicated operations.

53. In determining the number of electrons involved in a certain calculation with semiconductors, the expression $9.60 \times 10^{18}T^{3/2}$ is used. Evaluate this expression for $T = 289K$.

54. In studying the properties of biological fluids, the expression $0.036M^{3/4}$ is used. Evaluate this expression for $M = 1.6 \times 10^5$.

55. An approximate expression for the efficiency of an engine is given by $E = 100(1 - R^{-2/5})$, where R is the compression ratio. What is the efficiency (in percent) of an engine for which $R = 243/32$?

56. An estimate of gas diffusivity may be made by the equation

$$D_m = 0.01 \frac{T^{1/2}}{(v_a{}^{1/3} + v_b{}^{1/3})^2}\left(\frac{1}{m_a} + \frac{1}{m_b}\right)^{1/2}$$

where T is the temperature in degrees Fahrenheit and the other symbols are constants which depend on the gases under consideration. Calculate the diffusivity of a gas in air at 484°F if $v_a = 27$, $v_b = 125$, $m_a = 25$, and $m_b = 144$. (The units of diffusivity are in lb·mol/ft·h.)

10–3 Simplest Radical Form

Radicals were first introduced in Section 1–6, and we used them again in developing the concept of a fractional exponent. As we mentioned in the preceding section, it is possible to use fractional exponents for any operation required with radicals. For operations involving multiplication and division, this method has certain advantages. But for adding and subtracting radicals, there is normally little advantage in changing form.

We shall now define the operations with radicals so that these definitions are consistent with the laws of exponents. This will enable us from now on to use either fractional exponents or radicals, whichever is more convenient.

$$\sqrt[n]{a^n} = (\sqrt[n]{a})^n = a \tag{10-9}$$

$$\sqrt[n]{a}\,\sqrt[n]{b} = \sqrt[n]{ab} \tag{10-10}$$

$$\sqrt[m]{\sqrt[n]{a}} = \sqrt[mn]{a} \tag{10-11}$$

$$\frac{\sqrt[n]{a}}{\sqrt[n]{b}} = \sqrt[n]{\frac{a}{b}}, \quad b \neq 0 \tag{10-12}$$

The number under the radical is called the **radicand,** and the number indicating the root being taken is called the **order** of the radical. To avoid difficulties with imaginary numbers (which are considered in the next chapter), we shall assume that all letters represent positive numbers.

Example A

$$\sqrt[3]{2}\,\sqrt[3]{3} = \sqrt[3]{6}, \qquad \sqrt[3]{\sqrt{5}} = \sqrt[6]{5}, \qquad \frac{\sqrt{7}}{\sqrt{3}} = \sqrt{\frac{7}{3}}$$

There are certain operations which should be performed on radicals to put them in their simplest form. The following examples will illustrate these operations.

Example B

To simplify $\sqrt{75}$, we recall that $75 = (25)(3)$ and that $\sqrt{25} = 5$. Using Eq. (10–10), we write $\sqrt{75} = \sqrt{25}\,\sqrt{3} = 5\sqrt{3}$. This illustrates one step which should always be carried out in simplifying radicals. *Always remove all perfect nth-power factors from the radicand of a radical of order n.*

Example C

$$\sqrt[3]{40} = \sqrt[3]{8}\,\sqrt[3]{5} = 2\sqrt[3]{5}$$
$$\sqrt{a^3 b^2} = \sqrt{a^2}\,\sqrt{a}\,\sqrt{b^2} = ab\sqrt{a}$$
$$\sqrt{72} = \sqrt{(36)(2)} = \sqrt{36}\,\sqrt{2} = 6\sqrt{2}$$
$$\sqrt[5]{64x^8 y^{12}} = \sqrt[5]{(32)(2)(x^5)(x^3)(y^{10})(y^2)} = \sqrt[5]{(32)(x^5)(y^{10})}\,\sqrt[5]{2x^3 y^2}$$
$$= 2xy^2\,\sqrt[5]{2x^3 y^2}$$

When working with fractions, an expression is not considered to be in simplest form if the denominator contains a radical. This includes the case in which the denominator of a fraction is included under the radical sign. We therefore rewrite it in an equivalent form, in which the denominator contains no radical expression. This procedure is called **rationalizing the denominator.** The resulting form is more convenient for purposes of calculation, although today this is of much less importance than it was before the common use of calculators. However, the rationalized form is often a more useful form.

Example D

To simplify $\sqrt{\frac{2}{5}}$ we write it in an equivalent form in which the denominator is not included under the radical sign. In order to do this we create a perfect square in the denominator by multiplying the numerator and the denominator under the radical by 5. This gives us $\sqrt{\frac{10}{25}}$ which may be written as $\frac{1}{5}\sqrt{10}$ or $\frac{\sqrt{10}}{5}$. These steps are written as follows:

$$\sqrt{\frac{2}{5}} = \sqrt{\frac{2 \cdot 5}{5 \cdot 5}} = \sqrt{\frac{10}{25}} = \frac{\sqrt{10}}{\sqrt{25}} = \frac{\sqrt{10}}{5}$$

Example E

$$\sqrt{\frac{5}{7}} = \sqrt{\frac{5 \cdot 7}{7 \cdot 7}} = \frac{\sqrt{35}}{\sqrt{49}} = \frac{\sqrt{35}}{7}, \qquad \frac{3}{\sqrt{8}} = \frac{3\sqrt{2}}{\sqrt{8 \cdot 2}} = \frac{3\sqrt{2}}{\sqrt{16}} = \frac{3\sqrt{2}}{4}$$

$$\sqrt[3]{\frac{2}{3}} = \sqrt[3]{\frac{2 \cdot 9}{3 \cdot 9}} = \sqrt[3]{\frac{18}{27}} = \frac{\sqrt[3]{18}}{\sqrt[3]{27}} = \frac{\sqrt[3]{18}}{3}$$

In the second illustration a perfect square was made by multiplying by $\sqrt{2}$. We should try to choose the smallest possible number which can be used. In the third illustration we wanted a perfect cube in the denominator, since a cube root is being found.

The following examples illustrate another procedure which can be used to simplify certain radicals. The procedure is to *reduce the order of the radical*, when possible.

Example F

$$\sqrt[6]{8} = \sqrt[6]{2^3} = 2^{3/6} = 2^{1/2} = \sqrt{2}$$

In this example we started with a sixth root and' ended with a square root. Thus the order of the radical was reduced. Fractional exponents are often helpful when we perform this operation.

Example G

$$\sqrt[8]{16} = \sqrt[8]{2^4} = 2^{4/8} = 2^{1/2} = \sqrt{2}$$

$$\frac{\sqrt[4]{9}}{\sqrt{3}} = \frac{\sqrt[4]{3^2}}{\sqrt{3}} \equiv \frac{3^{2/4}}{3^{1/2}} = 1$$

$$\frac{\sqrt[6]{8}}{\sqrt{7}} = \frac{\sqrt[6]{2^3}}{\sqrt{7}} = \frac{2^{1/2}}{7^{1/2}} = \sqrt{\frac{2}{7}} = \frac{\sqrt{14}}{7}$$

$$\sqrt[9]{27x^6y^{12}} = \sqrt[9]{3^3x^6y^9y^3} = 3^{3/9}x^{6/9}y^{9/9}y^{3/9} = 3^{1/3}x^{2/3}y\,y^{1/3}$$
$$= y\sqrt[3]{3x^2y}$$

A radical is said to be *simplified* if the above steps are completed. That is,

(1) *all perfect nth-power factors are removed from a radical of order n,*
(2) *all denominators are rationalized, and*
(3) *if possible, the order of the radical is reduced.*

Example H

Simplify the radical $\sqrt{\dfrac{3a}{4b} - 2 + \dfrac{4b}{3a}}$, for $3a \geq 4b$.

$$\sqrt{\frac{3a}{4b} - 2 + \frac{4b}{3a}} = \sqrt{\frac{(3a)(3a) - 2(3a)(4b) + (4b)(4b)}{(3a)(4b)}}$$

$$= \sqrt{\frac{(3a - 4b)^2}{4(3ab)}} = \frac{3a - 4b}{2}\sqrt{\frac{1}{3ab}}$$

$$= \frac{3a - 4b}{6ab}\sqrt{3ab}$$

Exercises 10-3

In Exercises 1 through 56 write each expression in simplest radical form.

1. $\sqrt{24}$

2. $\sqrt{150}$

3. $\sqrt{45}$

4. $\sqrt{98}$

5. $\sqrt{x^2y^5}$

6. $\sqrt{s^3t^6}$

7. $\sqrt{pq^2r^7}$

8. $\sqrt{x^2y^4z^3}$

9. $\sqrt{5x^2}$

10. $\sqrt{12ab^2}$

11. $\sqrt{18a^3bc^4}$

12. $\sqrt{54m^5n^3}$

13. $\sqrt[3]{16}$

14. $\sqrt[4]{48}$

15. $\sqrt[5]{96}$

16. $\sqrt[3]{-16}$

17. $\sqrt[3]{8a^2}$

18. $\sqrt[3]{5a^4b^2}$

19. $\sqrt[4]{64r^3s^4t^5}$

20. $\sqrt[5]{16x^5y^3z^{11}}$

21. $\sqrt[6]{8}\sqrt[6]{4}$

22. $\sqrt[7]{4}\sqrt[7]{64}$

23. $\sqrt[3]{ab^4}\sqrt[3]{a^2b}$

24. $\sqrt[6]{3m^4n^5}\sqrt[6]{9m^2n^8}$

25. $\sqrt{\dfrac{3}{2}}$

26. $\sqrt{\dfrac{6}{5}}$

27. $\sqrt{\dfrac{a}{b}}$

28. $\sqrt{\dfrac{a}{b^3}}$

29. $\sqrt[3]{\dfrac{3}{4}}$

30. $\sqrt[4]{\dfrac{2}{5}}$

31. $\sqrt[5]{\dfrac{1}{9}}$

32. $\sqrt[6]{\dfrac{5}{4}}$

33. $\sqrt[4]{400}$

34. $\sqrt[8]{81}$

35. $\sqrt[6]{64}$

36. $\sqrt[9]{27}$

37. $\sqrt{4 \times 10^4}$

38. $\sqrt{4 \times 10^5}$

39. $\sqrt{4 \times 10^6}$

40. $\sqrt{16 \times 10^5}$

41. $\sqrt[4]{4a^2}$

42. $\sqrt[6]{b^2c^4}$

43. $\sqrt[4]{\dfrac{1}{4}}$

44. $\dfrac{\sqrt[4]{80}}{\sqrt[4]{5}}$

45. $\sqrt[4]{\sqrt[3]{16}}$

46. $\sqrt[5]{\sqrt[4]{9}}$

47. $\sqrt{\sqrt{\sqrt{2}}}$

48. $\sqrt{b^4\sqrt{a}}$

49. $\sqrt{\dfrac{1}{2} - \dfrac{1}{3}}$

50. $\sqrt{\dfrac{5}{4} - \dfrac{1}{8}}$

51. $\sqrt{\dfrac{1}{a^2} + \dfrac{1}{b}}$

52. $\sqrt{\dfrac{x}{y} + \dfrac{y}{x}}$

53. $\sqrt{a^2 + 2ab + b^2}$

54. $\sqrt{a^2 + b^2}$

55. $\sqrt{x^2 + \dfrac{1}{4}}$

56. $\sqrt{\dfrac{1}{2} + 2r + 2r^2}$

In Exercises 57 through 60 perform the required operation.

57. The period (in seconds) for one cycle of a simple pendulum is given by $T = 2\pi\sqrt{L/g}$, where L is the length of the pendulum (in feet) and g is the acceleration due to gravity ($g = 32$ ft/s²). If L is 3 ft, what is the period of the pendulum?

58. Under certain circumstances, the frequency in an electric circuit containing an inductance L and capacitance C is given by $f = 1/2\pi\sqrt{LC}$. If $L = 0.1$ H and $C = 250 \times 10^{-6}$ F, find f.

59. The distance between ion layers in a crystalline solid such as table salt is given by the expression $\sqrt[3]{M/2N\rho}$, where M is the molecular weight, N is called Avogadro's number, and ρ is the density. Express this in simplest form.

60. When dealing with the voltage of an electronic device, the expression $V(x/d)^{4/3}$ arises. Write this expression in rationalized radical form.

10—4 Addition and Subtraction of Radicals

When we first introduced the concept of adding algebraic expressions, we found that it was possible to combine similar terms, that is, those which differed only in numerical coefficients. The same is true of adding radicals. We must have similar radicals in order to perform the addition, rather than simply to be able to indicate addition. By similar radicals we mean radicals which differ only in their numerical coefficients, and which must therefore be of the same order and have the same radicand.

In order to add radicals, we first express each radical in its simplest form, and then add those which are similar. For those which are not similar, we can only indicate the addition.

Example A

$$2\sqrt{7} - 5\sqrt{7} + \sqrt{7} = -2\sqrt{7}$$
$$\sqrt[5]{6} + 4\sqrt[5]{6} - 2\sqrt[5]{6} = 3\sqrt[5]{6}$$
$$\sqrt{5} + 2\sqrt{3} - 5\sqrt{5} = 2\sqrt{3} - 4\sqrt{5}$$

We note that in the last illustration we are able only to indicate the final subtraction.

Example B

$$\sqrt{2} + \sqrt{8} = \sqrt{2} + 2\sqrt{2} = 3\sqrt{2}$$
$$\sqrt[3]{24} + \sqrt[3]{81} = 2\sqrt[3]{3} + 3\sqrt[3]{3} = 5\sqrt[3]{3}$$

Notice that $\sqrt{8}$, $\sqrt[3]{24}$, and $\sqrt[3]{81}$ were simplified before performing the addition.

We note in the illustrations of Example B that the radicals do not initially appear to be similar. However, after each is simplified we are able to recognize the similar radicals.

Example C

$$6\sqrt{7} - \sqrt{28} + 3\sqrt{63} = 6\sqrt{7} - 2\sqrt{7} + 3(3\sqrt{7})$$
$$= 6\sqrt{7} - 2\sqrt{7} + 9\sqrt{7} = 13\sqrt{7}$$
$$3\sqrt{125} - \sqrt{20} + \sqrt{27} = 3(5\sqrt{5}) - 2\sqrt{5} + 3\sqrt{3}$$
$$= 13\sqrt{5} + 3\sqrt{3}$$

Example D

$$\sqrt{24} + \sqrt{\frac{3}{2}} = 2\sqrt{6} + \frac{\sqrt{6}}{2} = \frac{4\sqrt{6} + \sqrt{6}}{2} = \frac{5}{2}\sqrt{6}$$

One radical was simplified by removing the perfect square factor and the other by rationalizing the denominator.

Example E

$$\sqrt{\frac{2}{3a}} - 2\sqrt{\frac{3}{2a}} = \frac{1}{3a}\sqrt{6a} - \frac{2}{2a}\sqrt{6a} = \frac{1}{3a}\sqrt{6a} - \frac{1}{a}\sqrt{6a}$$

$$= \frac{\sqrt{6a} - 3\sqrt{6a}}{3a} = \frac{-2\sqrt{6a}}{3a} = -\frac{2}{3a}\sqrt{6a}$$

Example F

$$\sqrt{\frac{4}{a} - 4 + a} + \sqrt{\frac{1}{a} - \sqrt{16a^3}} = \sqrt{\frac{4 - 4a + a^2}{a}} + \sqrt{\frac{1}{a} - 4a\sqrt{a}}$$

$$= \sqrt{\frac{(2-a)^2 \cdot a}{a \cdot a}} + \sqrt{\frac{1 \cdot a}{a \cdot a}} - 4a\sqrt{a}$$

$$= \frac{2-a}{a}\sqrt{a} + \frac{1}{a}\sqrt{a} - 4a\sqrt{a}$$

$$= \sqrt{a}\left(\frac{2-a}{a} + \frac{1}{a} - 4a\right) = \sqrt{a}\left(\frac{2 - a + 1 - 4a^2}{a}\right)$$

$$= \frac{(3 - a - 4a^2)\sqrt{a}}{a}$$

This simplification is valid for $a < 2$, since we let $\sqrt{(2-a)^2} = 2 - a$.

Exercises 10—4

In Exercises 1 through 36 perform the indicated operations and express the answers in simplest form.

1. $2\sqrt{3} + 5\sqrt{3}$
2. $8\sqrt{11} - 3\sqrt{11}$
3. $2\sqrt{7} + \sqrt{5} - 3\sqrt{7}$
4. $8\sqrt{6} - 2\sqrt{3} - 5\sqrt{6}$
5. $\sqrt{5} + \sqrt{20}$
6. $\sqrt{7} + \sqrt{63}$
7. $2\sqrt{3} - 3\sqrt{12}$
8. $4\sqrt{2} - \sqrt{50}$
9. $\sqrt{8} - \sqrt{32}$
10. $\sqrt{27} + 2\sqrt{18}$
11. $2\sqrt{28} + 3\sqrt{175}$
12. $5\sqrt{300} - 7\sqrt{48}$
13. $2\sqrt{20} - \sqrt{125} - \sqrt{45}$
14. $2\sqrt{44} - \sqrt{99} + \sqrt{176}$
15. $3\sqrt{75} + 2\sqrt{48} - 2\sqrt{18}$
16. $2\sqrt{28} - \sqrt{108} - 2\sqrt{175}$
17. $\sqrt{60} + \sqrt{\frac{5}{3}}$
18. $\sqrt{84} - \sqrt{\frac{3}{7}}$
19. $\sqrt{\frac{1}{2}} + \sqrt{\frac{25}{2}} - \sqrt{18}$
20. $\sqrt{6} - \sqrt{\frac{2}{3}} - \sqrt{18}$
21. $\sqrt[3]{81} + \sqrt[3]{3000}$
22. $\sqrt[3]{-16} + \sqrt[3]{54}$
23. $\sqrt[4]{32} - \sqrt[8]{4}$
24. $\sqrt[6]{\sqrt{2}} - \sqrt[12]{2^{13}}$
25. $\sqrt{a^3 b} - \sqrt{4ab^5}$
26. $\sqrt{2x^2 y} + \sqrt{8y^3}$
27. $\sqrt{6}\sqrt{5}\sqrt{3} - \sqrt{40a^2}$
28. $\sqrt{60n} + 2\sqrt{15b^2 n} - b\sqrt{135n}$
29. $\sqrt[3]{24a^2 b^4} - \sqrt[3]{3a^5 b}$
30. $\sqrt[5]{32a^6 b^4} + 3a\sqrt[5]{243ab^9}$
31. $\sqrt{\frac{a}{c^5}} - \sqrt{\frac{c}{a^3}}$
32. $\sqrt{\frac{2x}{3y}} + \sqrt{\frac{27y}{8x}}$

33. $\sqrt[3]{\dfrac{a}{b}} - \sqrt[3]{\dfrac{8b^2}{a^2}}$

34. $\sqrt[4]{\dfrac{c}{b}} - \sqrt[4]{bc}$

35. $\sqrt{\dfrac{a-b}{a+b}} - \sqrt{\dfrac{a+b}{a-b}}$

36. $\sqrt{\dfrac{16}{x} + 8 + x} - \sqrt{1 - \dfrac{1}{x}}$

In Exercises 37 and 38 solve the given problems.

37. Find the sum of the two roots of the quadratic equation $ax^2 + bx + c = 0$.

38. In the study of the kinetic theory of gases, the expression

$$a\sqrt{\dfrac{h^3 m^5}{\pi}} + b\sqrt{\dfrac{h^3 m^3}{\pi}}$$

is found. Perform the indicated addition.

10—5 Multiplication of Radicals

When multiplying expressions containing radicals, we use Eq. (10–10) along with the normal procedures of algebraic multiplication. Note that the orders of the radicals being multiplied in Eq. (10–10) are the same. The following examples illustrate the method.

Example A

$$\sqrt{5}\,\sqrt{2} = \sqrt{10},$$
$$\sqrt{33}\,\sqrt{3} = \sqrt{99} = \sqrt{9(11)} = \sqrt{9}\,\sqrt{11} = 3\sqrt{11}$$

We note that we must be careful to express the resulting radical in simplest form.

Example B

$$\sqrt[3]{6}\,\sqrt[3]{4} = \sqrt[3]{24} = \sqrt[3]{8}\,\sqrt[3]{3} = 2\sqrt[3]{3}$$
$$\sqrt[5]{8a^3b^4}\,\sqrt[5]{8a^2b^3} = \sqrt[5]{64a^5b^7} = \sqrt[5]{32a^5b^5}\,\sqrt[5]{2b^2} = 2ab\sqrt[5]{2b^2}$$

Example C

$$\sqrt{2}(3\sqrt{5} - 4\sqrt{2}) = 3\sqrt{2}\sqrt{5} - 4\sqrt{2}\sqrt{2} = 3\sqrt{10} - 4\sqrt{4}$$
$$= 3\sqrt{10} - 4(2) = 3\sqrt{10} - 8$$

When raising a single term radical expression to a power we use the basic meaning of the power. When raising a binomial to a power, we proceed as with any binomial and use Eq. (10–10).

Example D

$$(2\sqrt{7})^2 = 2^2(\sqrt{7})^2 = 4(7) = 28$$
$$(\sqrt{a} - \sqrt{b})^2 = (\sqrt{a})^2 - 2\sqrt{a}\sqrt{b} + (\sqrt{b})^2 = a + b - 2\sqrt{ab}$$

Example E

$$(5\sqrt{7} - 2\sqrt{3})(4\sqrt{7} + 3\sqrt{3})$$
$$= 20\sqrt{7}\,\sqrt{7} + 15\sqrt{7}\,\sqrt{3} - 8\sqrt{3}\,\sqrt{7} - 6\sqrt{3}\,\sqrt{3}$$
$$= 20(7) + 15\sqrt{21} - 8\sqrt{21} - 6(3)$$
$$= 140 + 7\sqrt{21} - 18$$
$$= 122 + 7\sqrt{21}$$

Example F

$$(\sqrt{6} - \sqrt{2} - \sqrt{3})(\sqrt{6} + \sqrt{2})$$
$$= (\sqrt{6} - \sqrt{2})(\sqrt{6} + \sqrt{2}) - \sqrt{3}(\sqrt{6} + \sqrt{2})$$
$$= (6 - 2) - \sqrt{18} - \sqrt{6} = 4 - 3\sqrt{2} - \sqrt{6}$$

Example G

$$\left(3\sqrt{\frac{a}{b}} - \sqrt{ab}\right)\left(2\sqrt{\frac{a}{b}} - \sqrt{ab}\right) = 6\frac{a}{b} - 5\sqrt{\frac{a^2b}{b}} + ab$$

$$= \frac{6a}{b} - 5a + ab = \frac{6a - 5ab + ab^2}{b}$$

$$= \frac{a(6 - 5b + b^2)}{b}$$

Again, we note that *to multiply radicals and combine them under one radical sign, it is necessary that the order of the radicals be the same.* If necessary we can make the order of each radical the same by appropriate operations on each radical separately. Fractional exponents are frequently useful for this purpose.

Example H

$$\sqrt[3]{2}\,\sqrt{5} = 2^{1/3}5^{1/2} = 2^{2/6}5^{3/6} = (2^25^3)^{1/6} = \sqrt[6]{500}$$
$$\sqrt[3]{4a^2b}\,\sqrt[4]{8a^3b^2} = (2^2a^2b)^{1/3}(2^3a^3b^2)^{1/4} = (2^2a^2b)^{4/12}(2^3a^3b^2)^{3/12}$$

$$= (2^8a^8b^4)^{1/12}(2^9a^9b^6)^{1/12} = (2^{17}a^{17}b^{10})^{1/12}$$

$$= 2a(2^5a^5b^{10})^{1/12}$$

$$= 2a\sqrt[12]{32a^5b^{10}}$$

Exercises 10−5

In Exercises 1 through 48 perform the indicated multiplications, expressing answers in simplest form.

1. $\sqrt{3}\,\sqrt{10}$ 2. $\sqrt{2}\,\sqrt{51}$ 3. $\sqrt{6}\,\sqrt{2}$ 4. $\sqrt{7}\,\sqrt{14}$

5. $\sqrt[3]{4}\,\sqrt[3]{2}$ 6. $\sqrt[3]{3}\,\sqrt[3]{27}$ 7. $\sqrt[5]{4}\,\sqrt[5]{16}$ 8. $\sqrt[3]{25}\,\sqrt[3]{50}$

9. $(5\sqrt{2})^2$ 10. $(3\sqrt{3})^2$ 11. $(2\sqrt[3]{2})^3$ 12. $(3\sqrt[3]{5})^3$

13. $\sqrt{\frac{2}{3}}\,\sqrt{5}$ 14. $\sqrt[3]{8}\,\sqrt{\frac{5}{2}}$ 15. $\sqrt{\frac{5}{6}}\,\sqrt{\frac{2}{11}}$ 16. $\sqrt{\frac{6}{7}}\,\sqrt{\frac{2}{3}}$

17. $\sqrt{3}(\sqrt{2} - \sqrt{5})$ 18. $\sqrt{5}(\sqrt{7} + \sqrt{2})$

19. $2\sqrt{2}(\sqrt{8} - 3\sqrt{6})$

20. $3\sqrt{5}(\sqrt{15} - 2\sqrt{5})$

21. $(2 - \sqrt{5})(2 + \sqrt{5})$

22. $(6 - \sqrt{3})(6 + \sqrt{3})$

23. $(6 - \sqrt{3})^2$

24. $(2 - \sqrt{5})^2$

25. $(3\sqrt{5} - 2\sqrt{3})(6\sqrt{5} + 7\sqrt{3})$

26. $(3\sqrt{7} - \sqrt{8})(\sqrt{7} + \sqrt{2})$

27. $(3\sqrt{11} - \sqrt{6})(2\sqrt{11} + 5\sqrt{6})$

28. $(2\sqrt{10} + 3\sqrt{15})(\sqrt{10} - 7\sqrt{15})$

29. $\sqrt{a}(\sqrt{ab} + \sqrt{c})$

30. $\sqrt{3x}(\sqrt{3x} - \sqrt{xy})$

31. $\sqrt{5n}(\sqrt{15n} + \sqrt{20m})$

32. $\sqrt{2x}(\sqrt{8xy} - 3\sqrt{y})$

33. $(\sqrt{2a} - \sqrt{b})(\sqrt{2a} + 3\sqrt{b})$

34. $(2\sqrt{mn} - 3\sqrt{n})(3\sqrt{mn} + 2\sqrt{n})$

35. $(\sqrt{2} + \sqrt{3} + \sqrt{5})(\sqrt{3} - \sqrt{5})$

36. $(2\sqrt{7} - \sqrt{5})(\sqrt{14} - 2\sqrt{5} + \sqrt{7})$

37. $\sqrt{2}\sqrt[3]{3}$

38. $\sqrt[5]{16}\sqrt[3]{8}$

39. $\sqrt[4]{ab}\sqrt[3]{bc}$

40. $\sqrt{2x}\sqrt[5]{16x}$

41. $(\sqrt[5]{\sqrt{6}} - \sqrt{5})(\sqrt[5]{\sqrt{6}} + \sqrt{5})$

42. $\sqrt[3]{5} - \sqrt{17}\sqrt[3]{5} + \sqrt{17}$

43. $(\sqrt{2x^2} - \sqrt[3]{y})(\sqrt{4x} + \sqrt[3]{y^2})$

44. $(\sqrt{a} - \sqrt[3]{b})(2\sqrt{a} - \sqrt[3]{b})$

45. $\left(\sqrt{\dfrac{2}{a}} + \sqrt{\dfrac{a}{2}}\right)\left(\sqrt{\dfrac{2}{a}} - 2\sqrt{\dfrac{a}{2}}\right)$

46. $\left(\sqrt{\dfrac{x}{y}} - \sqrt{xy}\right)\left(\sqrt{\dfrac{y}{x}} + \sqrt{xy} - 1\right)$

47. $(2x - \sqrt{x - 2y})^2$

48. $(3 + \sqrt{6 - 2a})(2 - \sqrt{6 - 2a})$

In Exercises 49 and 50 perform the indicated operations.

49. Determine the product of the two roots of the quadratic equation $ax^2 + bx + c = 0$.

50. Relationships involving mass transfer of liquid involve the expression

$$\sqrt{\frac{dG}{u}}\sqrt[3]{\frac{MD}{u}}$$

Express this in simplest radical form.

10-6 Division of Radicals

We have already dealt with some cases of division of radicals in the previous sections. When we have the indicated division of one radical by another, the result is considered to be in simplest form when the denominators contain no radicals. Therefore, the rationalization of denominators, as we did in Section 10–3, is the principal step to be carried out. This means that the process of division is one in which we change the fraction to an equivalent form in which the denominator is free of radicals. In doing so, multiplication of the numerator and the denominator by the appropriate quantity is a primary step.

Example A

$$\frac{\sqrt{3}}{\sqrt{5}} = \frac{\sqrt{3}\sqrt{5}}{\sqrt{5}\sqrt{5}} = \frac{\sqrt{15}}{5}, \quad \frac{\sqrt{a}}{\sqrt[3]{b}} = \frac{\sqrt{a}}{\sqrt[3]{b}} \cdot \frac{\sqrt[3]{b^2}}{\sqrt[3]{b^2}} = \frac{\sqrt{a}\sqrt[3]{b^2}}{b} = \frac{a^{3/6}b^{4/6}}{b} = \frac{\sqrt[6]{a^3 b^4}}{b}$$

Notice that the denominator was rationalized and that the factors of the numerator were written in terms of fractional exponents so they could be combined under one radical.

If the denominator is the sum (or difference) of two terms, at least one of which is a radical, the fraction can be rationalized by multiplying both the numerator and the denominator by the difference (or sum) of the same two terms, if the radicals are square roots.

Example B

The fraction $1/(\sqrt{3} - \sqrt{2})$ can be rationalized by multiplying the numerator and the denominator by $\sqrt{3} + \sqrt{2}$. In this way the radicals will be removed from the denominator.

$$\frac{1}{\sqrt{3} - \sqrt{2}} \cdot \frac{\sqrt{3} + \sqrt{2}}{\sqrt{3} + \sqrt{2}} = \frac{\sqrt{3} + \sqrt{2}}{(\sqrt{3})^2 - (\sqrt{2})^2} = \frac{\sqrt{3} + \sqrt{2}}{3 - 2} = \sqrt{3} + \sqrt{2}$$

The reason this technique works is that an expression of the form $a^2 - b^2$ is created in the denominator, where a or b (or both) is a radical. We see that the result is a denominator free of radicals.

Example C

$$\frac{\sqrt{2}}{2\sqrt{5} + \sqrt{3}} = \frac{\sqrt{2}}{2\sqrt{5} + \sqrt{3}} \cdot \frac{2\sqrt{5} - \sqrt{3}}{2\sqrt{5} - \sqrt{3}} = \frac{2\sqrt{2}\sqrt{5} - \sqrt{2}\sqrt{3}}{(2\sqrt{5})^2 - (\sqrt{3})^2}$$

$$= \frac{2\sqrt{10} - \sqrt{6}}{2^2(\sqrt{5})^2 - (\sqrt{3})^2} = \frac{2\sqrt{10} - \sqrt{6}}{20 - 3} = \frac{2\sqrt{10} - \sqrt{6}}{17}$$

Example D

$$\frac{\sqrt{x - y}}{1 - \sqrt{x - y}} = \frac{\sqrt{x - y}(1 + \sqrt{x - y})}{(1 - \sqrt{x - y})(1 + \sqrt{x - y})}$$

$$= \frac{\sqrt{x - y} + x - y}{1 - x + y} \qquad (x > y)$$

Example E

$$\frac{1 + \dfrac{\sqrt{3}}{2}}{1 - \dfrac{\sqrt{3}}{2}} = \frac{\dfrac{2 + \sqrt{3}}{2}}{\dfrac{2 - \sqrt{3}}{2}} = \frac{2 + \sqrt{3}}{2} \cdot \frac{2}{2 - \sqrt{3}} = \frac{2 + \sqrt{3}}{2 - \sqrt{3}}$$

$$= \frac{(2 + \sqrt{3})(2 + \sqrt{3})}{(2 - \sqrt{3})(2 + \sqrt{3})} = \frac{4 + 4\sqrt{3} + 3}{4 - 3} = 7 + 4\sqrt{3}$$

Exercises 10—6

In Exercises 1 through 32 perform the indicated operations and express the answers in simplest form.

1. $\dfrac{\sqrt{21}}{\sqrt{3}}$

2. $\dfrac{\sqrt{105}}{\sqrt{5}}$

3. $\sqrt{7} \div \sqrt{2}$

4. $3\sqrt{2} \div 2\sqrt{3}$

5. $\dfrac{\sqrt[3]{x^2}}{\sqrt[3]{24}}$

6. $\dfrac{\sqrt{6}}{\sqrt[3]{2}}$

7. $\dfrac{\sqrt{a}}{\sqrt[3]{4}}$
8. $\dfrac{\sqrt[4]{32}}{\sqrt[5]{b^3}}$
9. $\dfrac{\sqrt{2a}-b}{\sqrt{a}}$

10. $\dfrac{\sqrt{8x}+\sqrt{2}}{\sqrt{2}}$
11. $\dfrac{\sqrt{3a}-\sqrt{b}}{\sqrt{3}}$
12. $\dfrac{\sqrt{7x}-\sqrt{14}}{\sqrt{7}}$

13. $\dfrac{1}{\sqrt{7}+\sqrt{3}}$
14. $\dfrac{4}{\sqrt{6}+\sqrt{2}}$
15. $\dfrac{\sqrt{7}}{\sqrt{5}-\sqrt{2}}$

16. $\dfrac{\sqrt{8}}{2\sqrt{3}-\sqrt{5}}$
17. $\dfrac{3}{2\sqrt{5}-6}$
18. $\dfrac{\sqrt{7}}{4-2\sqrt{7}}$

19. $\dfrac{2\sqrt{3}}{3\sqrt{3}-1}$
20. $\dfrac{6\sqrt{5}}{5-2\sqrt{5}}$
21. $\dfrac{\sqrt{2}-1}{\sqrt{7}-3\sqrt{2}}$

22. $\dfrac{3-\sqrt{5}}{2\sqrt{2}+\sqrt{5}}$
23. $\dfrac{2-\sqrt{3}}{5-2\sqrt{3}}$
24. $\dfrac{2\sqrt{15}-3}{\sqrt{15}+4}$

25. $\dfrac{2\sqrt{3}-5\sqrt{5}}{\sqrt{3}+2\sqrt{5}}$
26. $\dfrac{2\sqrt{6}+\sqrt{11}}{\sqrt{6}-3\sqrt{11}}$
27. $\dfrac{\sqrt{7}-\sqrt{14}}{2\sqrt{7}-3\sqrt{14}}$

28. $\dfrac{\sqrt{15}-3\sqrt{5}}{2\sqrt{15}-\sqrt{5}}$
29. $\dfrac{8}{3\sqrt{a}-2\sqrt{b}}$
30. $\dfrac{6}{1+2\sqrt{x}}$

31. $\dfrac{\sqrt{x+y}}{\sqrt{x-y}-\sqrt{x}}$
32. $\dfrac{\sqrt{1+a}}{a-\sqrt{1-a}}$

In Exercises 33 and 34 perform the indicated operations.

33. In the theory of semiconductors, the expression $km^{3/2}(E-E_1)^{1/2}$ is found. Write this expression in simplified radical form.

34. In the theory of waves in wires, the following expression is found:

$$\frac{\sqrt{d_1}-\sqrt{d_2}}{\sqrt{d_1}+\sqrt{d_2}}$$

Evaluate this expression if $d_1 = 10$ and $d_2 = 3$.

10–7 Exercises for Chapter 10

In Exercises 1 through 28 express each of the given expressions in the simplest form which contains only positive exponents.

1. $2a^{-2}b^0$
2. $(2c)^{-1}z^{-2}$
3. $\dfrac{2c^{-1}}{d^{-3}}$
4. $\dfrac{-5x^0}{3y^{-1}}$

5. $3(25)^{3/2}$
6. $32^{2/5}$
7. $400^{-3/2}$
8. $1000^{-2/3}$

9. $\left(\dfrac{3}{t^2}\right)^{-2}$
10. $\left(\dfrac{2x^3}{3}\right)^{-3}$
11. $\dfrac{-8^{2/3}}{49^{-1/2}}$
12. $\dfrac{81^{-3/4}}{7^{-1}}$

13. $(2a^{1/3}b^{5/6})^6$
14. $(ax^{-1/2}y^{1/4})^8$

15. $(-32m^{15}n^{10})^{3/5}$
16. $(27x^{-6}y^9)^{2/3}$

17. $2x^{-2}-y^{-1}$
18. $a^{-1}+b^{-2}$

19. $\dfrac{2x^{-1}}{x^{-1} + y^{-1}}$

20. $\dfrac{3a}{(2a)^{-1} - a}$

21. $(a - 3b^{-1})^{-1}$

22. $(2s^{-2} + t)^{-2}$

23. $(x^3 - y^{-3})^{1/3}$

24. $(x^2 + 2xy + y^2)^{-1/2}$

25. $(8a^3)^{2/3}(4a^{-2} + 1)^{1/2}$

26. $\left[\dfrac{(9a)^0(4x^2)^{1/3}(3b^{1/2})}{(2b^0)^2}\right]^{-6}$

27. $2x(x - 1)^{-2} - 2(x^2 + 1)(x - 1)^{-3}$

28. $4(1 - x^2)^{1/2} - (1 - x^2)^{-1/2}$

In Exercises 29 through 68 perform the indicated operations and express the answer in simplest radical form.

29. $\sqrt{68}$

30. $\sqrt{96}$

31. $\sqrt{ab^5c^2}$

32. $\sqrt{x^3y^4z^6}$

33. $\sqrt{9a^3b^4}$

34. $\sqrt{8x^5y^2}$

35. $\sqrt{84st^3u^2}$

36. $\sqrt{52x^2y^5}$

37. $\dfrac{5}{\sqrt{2s}}$

38. $\dfrac{3a}{\sqrt{5x}}$

39. $\sqrt{\dfrac{11}{27}}$

40. $\sqrt{\dfrac{7}{8}}$

41. $\sqrt[4]{8m^6n^9}$

42. $\sqrt[3]{9a^7b^{-3}}$

43. $\sqrt[4]{\sqrt[3]{64}}$

44. $\sqrt{a^{-3}\sqrt[5]{b^{12}}}$

45. $\sqrt{200} + \sqrt{32}$

46. $2\sqrt{68} - \sqrt{153}$

47. $\sqrt{63} - 2\sqrt{112} - \sqrt{28}$

48. $2\sqrt{20} - \sqrt{80} - 2\sqrt{125}$

49. $a\sqrt{2x^3} + \sqrt{8a^2x^3}$

50. $2\sqrt{m^2n^3} - \sqrt{n^5}$

51. $\sqrt[3]{8a^4} + b\sqrt[3]{a}$

52. $\sqrt[4]{2xy^5} - \sqrt[4]{32xy}$

53. $\sqrt{5}(2\sqrt{5} - \sqrt{11})$

54. $2\sqrt{8}(5\sqrt{2} - \sqrt{6})$

55. $2\sqrt{2}(\sqrt{6} - \sqrt{10})$

56. $3\sqrt{5}(\sqrt{15} + 2\sqrt{35})$

57. $(2 - 3\sqrt{17})(3 + \sqrt{17})$

58. $(5\sqrt{6} - 4)(3\sqrt{6} + 5)$

59. $(2\sqrt{7} - 3\sqrt{3})(3\sqrt{7} + \sqrt{3})$

60. $(3\sqrt{2} - \sqrt{13})(5\sqrt{2} + 3\sqrt{13})$

61. $\dfrac{\sqrt{2}}{\sqrt{3} - 4\sqrt{2}}$

62. $\dfrac{4}{3 - 2\sqrt{7}}$

63. $\dfrac{\sqrt{7} - \sqrt{5}}{\sqrt{5} + 3\sqrt{7}}$

64. $\dfrac{4 - 2\sqrt{6}}{3 + 2\sqrt{6}}$

65. $\sqrt{a^{-1} + b^2}$

66. $\sqrt{a^{-2} + \dfrac{1}{b^2}}$

67. $\left(\dfrac{2 - \sqrt{15}}{2}\right)^2 - \left(\dfrac{2 - \sqrt{15}}{2}\right)$

68. $\sqrt{2 + \dfrac{b}{a} + \dfrac{a}{b}} + \sqrt{a^4b^2 + 2a^3b^2 + a^2b^2}$

In Exercises 69 through 76 perform the indicated operations.

69. In the study of electricity, the expression $e^{-i(\omega t - \alpha t)}$ is found. Rewrite this expression so that it contains no minus signs in the exponent.

70. An expression found when convection of heat is discussed is $k^{-1}x + h^{-1}$. Write this expression without the use of negative exponents.

71. In the study of fluid flow in pipes, the expression $0.220N^{-1/6}$ is found. Evaluate this expression for $N = 64 \times 10^6$.

72. In the study of biological effects of sound, the expression $(2n/\omega r)^{-1/2}$ is found. Express this in simplest radical form.

73. The root-mean-square velocity of a gas molecule is given by $v = \sqrt{3RT/M}$, where R is the gas constant, T is the thermodynamic temperature, and M is the molecular weight. Express the velocity (in meters per second) of an oxygen molecule in simplest radical form if $T = 300$ K, $R = 8.31$ J/mol $\cdot$ K, and $M = 0.032$ kg/mol. Then calculate the value of the expression.

74. A surveyor measuring distances with a steel tape must be careful to correct for the tension which is applied to the tape and for the sag in the tape. If she applies what is known as "normal tension," these two effects will cancel each other. An expression involving the normal tension T_n which is found for a certain tape is

$$\frac{0.2W\sqrt{2.7 \times 10^5}}{\sqrt{T_n - 20}}$$

Express this in simplest radical form.

75. The frequency of a certain electric circuit is given by

$$\frac{1}{2\pi\sqrt{\dfrac{LC_1C_2}{C_1 + C_2}}}$$

Express this in simplest radical form.

76. In determining the deflection of a certain type of beam, the expression

$$l\sqrt{\frac{a}{2l + a}}$$

is used. Express this in simplest radical form.

11

The *j*-Operator

11—1 Complex Numbers

In Chapter 1, when we were introducing the topic of numbers, imaginary numbers were mentioned. Again, when we considered quadratic equations and their solutions in Chapter 6, we briefly came across this type of number. However, until now we have purposely avoided any extended discussion of imaginary numbers. In this chapter we shall discuss the properties of these numbers and show some of the ways in which they may be applied.

When we defined radicals we were able to define square roots of positive numbers easily, since any positive or negative number squared equals a positive number. For this reason we can see that it is impossible to square any real number and have the product equal a negative number. We must define a new number system if we wish to include square roots of negative numbers. With the proper definitions, we shall find that these numbers can be used to great advantage in certain applications.

If the radicand in a square root is negative, we can express the indicated root as the product of $\sqrt{-1}$ and the square root of a positive number. *The symbol $\sqrt{-1}$ is defined as the* **imaginary unit,** *and is denoted by the symbol j.* (The symbol i is also often used for this purpose, but in electrical work i usually represents current. Therefore, we shall use j for the imaginary unit to avoid confusion.) In keeping with the definition of j, we have

$$j^2 = -1 \qquad\qquad (11\text{--}1)$$

Example A

$$\sqrt{-9} = \sqrt{(9)(-1)} = \sqrt{9}\sqrt{-1} = 3j$$
$$\sqrt{-16} = \sqrt{16}\sqrt{-1} = 4j$$

Example B

$$(\sqrt{-4})^2 = (\sqrt{4}j)^2 = 4j^2 = -4$$

We note that the simplification of this expression does not follow Eq. (10–10), which states that $\sqrt{ab} = \sqrt{a}\sqrt{b}$ for square roots. This is the reason it was noted as being valid only if a and b are positive. In fact, Eq. (10–10) does not necessarily hold in general for negative values for a or b. If $(\sqrt{-4})^2$ did follow Eq. (10–10) we would have

$$(\sqrt{-4})^2 = \sqrt{(-4)(-4)} = \sqrt{16} = 4$$

We note that we obtain 4, and do not obtain the correct result of -4.

Example C

To further illustrate the method of handling square roots of negative numbers, consider the difference between $\sqrt{-3}\sqrt{-12}$ and $\sqrt{(-3)(-12)}$. For these expressions we have

$$\sqrt{-3}\sqrt{-12} = (\sqrt{3}j)(\sqrt{12}j) = \sqrt{3}\sqrt{12}j^2 = \sqrt{36}j^2$$
$$= 6(-1) = -6$$

and

$$\sqrt{(-3)(-12)} = \sqrt{36} = 6$$

For $\sqrt{-3}\sqrt{-12}$ we have the product of square roots of negative numbers, whereas for $\sqrt{(-3)(-12)}$ we have the product of negative numbers under the radical. We must be careful to note the difference.

From Examples B and C we see that *when we are dealing with the square roots of negative numbers,* **each should be expressed in terms of j before proceeding.** To do this, for any positive real number a we write

$$\sqrt{-a} = \sqrt{a}j, \qquad (a > 0) \qquad\qquad (11\text{--}2)$$

Example D

$$\sqrt{-6} = \sqrt{(6)(-1)} = \sqrt{6}\sqrt{-1} = \sqrt{6}j$$
$$\sqrt{-18} = \sqrt{(18)(-1)} = \sqrt{(9)(2)}\sqrt{-1} = 3\sqrt{2}j$$

In working with imaginary numbers, we often need to be able to raise these numbers to some power. Therefore, using the definitions of exponents and of *j*, we have the following results:

$$j = j, \qquad\qquad j^4 = j^2j^2 = (-1)(-1) = 1$$
$$j^2 = -1, \qquad\qquad j^5 = j^4j = j$$
$$j^3 = j^2j = -j, \qquad j^6 = j^4j^2 = (1)(-1) = -1$$

The powers of *j* go through the cycle of j, -1, $-j$, 1, j, -1, $-j$, 1, and so forth. Noting this and the fact that *j* raised to a power which is a multiple of 4 equals one allows us to raise *j* to any integral power almost on sight.

Example E

$$j^{10} = j^8j^2 = (1)(-1) = -1$$
$$j^{45} = j^{44}j = (1)(j) = j$$
$$j^{531} = j^{528}j^3 = (1)(-j) = -j$$

Using real numbers and the imaginary unit *j*, we define a new kind of number. *A* **complex number** *is any number which can be written in the form a + bj, where a and b are real numbers. If a = 0, we have a number of the form bj, which is a* **pure imaginary number.** *If b = 0, then a + bj is a real number. The form a + bj is known as the* **rectangular form** *of a complex number, where a is known as the* **real part** *and bj is known as the* **imaginary part.** We can see that complex numbers include all the real numbers and all of the pure imaginary numbers.

A comment here about the words "imaginary" and "complex" is in order. The choice of the names of these numbers is historical in nature, and unfortunately it leads to some misconceptions about the numbers. The use of "imaginary" does not infer that the numbers do not exist. Imaginary numbers do in fact exist, as they are defined above. In the same way, the use of "complex" does not infer that the numbers are complicated and therefore difficult to understand. With the appropriate definitions and operations, we can work with complex numbers, just as with any type of number.

For complex numbers written in terms of *j* to follow all the operations defined in algebra, we define equality of two complex numbers in a special way. Complex numbers are not positive or negative in the ordinary sense of these terms, but the real and imaginary parts of complex numbers *are* positive or negative. *We define two complex numbers to be equal if the real parts are equal and the imaginary parts are equal.* That is, two complex numbers, $a + bj$ and $x + yj$, are equal if $a = x$ and $b = y$.

Example F

$$a + bj = 3 + 4j \text{ if } a = 3 \text{ and } b = 4$$
$$x + yj = 5 - 3j \text{ if } x = 5 \text{ and } y = -3$$

Example G

What values of x and y satisfy the equation $4 - 6j - x = j + jy$?

One way to solve this is to rearrange the terms so that all the known terms are on the right and all the terms containing the unknowns x and y are on the left. This leads to $-x - jy = -4 + 7j$. From the definition of equality of complex numbers, $-x = -4$ and $-y = 7$, or $x = 4$ and $y = -7$.

Example H

What values of x and y satisfy the equation

$$x + 3(xj + y) = 5 - j - jy$$

Rearranging the terms so that the known terms are on the right and the terms containing x and y are on the left, we have

$$x + 3y + 3jx + jy = 5 - j$$

Next, factoring j from the two terms on the left will put the expression on the left into proper form. This leads to

$$(x + 3y) + j(3x + y) = 5 - j$$

Using the definition of equality, we have

$$x + 3y = 5 \quad \text{and} \quad 3x + y = -1$$

We now solve this system of equations. The solution is $x = -1$ and $y = 2$. Actually, the solution can be obtained at any point by writing each side of the equation in the form $a + bj$ and then equating first the real parts and then the imaginary parts.

The **conjugate** *of the complex number* $a + bj$ *is the complex number* $a - bj$. We see that the sign of the imaginary part of a complex number is changed to obtain its conjugate.

Example I

$3 - 2j$ is the conjugate of $3 + 2j$. We may also say that $3 + 2j$ is the conjugate of $3 - 2j$. Thus each is the conjugate of the other.

Exercises 11–1

In Exercises 1 through 8 express each number in terms of j.

1. $\sqrt{-81}$ 2. $\sqrt{-121}$ 3. $-\sqrt{-4}$ 4. $-\sqrt{-0.01}$

5. $\sqrt{-8}$ 6. $\sqrt{-48}$ 7. $\sqrt{-\frac{7}{4}}$ 8. $\sqrt{-\frac{5}{3}}$

In Exercises 9 through 12 simplify each of the given expressions.

9. $(\sqrt{-7})^2$; $\sqrt{(-7)^2}$ 10. $\sqrt{(-15)^2}$; $(\sqrt{-15})^2$

11. $\sqrt{(-2)(-8)}$; $\sqrt{-2}\sqrt{-8}$ 12. $\sqrt{-9}\sqrt{-16}$; $\sqrt{(-9)(-16)}$

In Exercises 13 through 20 simplify the given expressions.

13. j^7 **14.** j^{49} **15.** $-j^{22}$ **16.** j^{408}

17. $j^2 - j^6$ **18.** $2j^5 - j^7$ **19.** $j^{15} - j^{13}$ **20.** $3j^{48} + j^{200}$

In Exercises 21 through 28 perform the indicated operations and simplify each complex number to its rectangular form $a + bj$.

21. $2 + \sqrt{-9}$ **22.** $-6 + \sqrt{-64}$ **23.** $2j^2 + 3j$ **24.** $j^3 - 6$

25. $\sqrt{18} - \sqrt{-8}$ **26.** $\sqrt{-27} + \sqrt{12}$

27. $(\sqrt{-2})^2 + j^4$ **28.** $(2\sqrt{2})^2 - (\sqrt{-1})^2$

In Exercises 29 through 32 find the conjugate of each complex number.

29. $6 - 7j$ **30.** $-3 + 2j$ **31.** $2j$ **32.** 6

In Exercises 33 through 40 find the values of x and y which satisfy the given equations.

33. $7x - 2yj = 14 + 4j$ **34.** $2x + 3jy = -6 + 12j$

35. $6j - 7 = 3 - x - yj$ **36.** $9 - j = xj + 1 - y$

37. $x - y = 1 - xj - yj - j$ **38.** $2x - 2j = 4 - 2xj - yj$

39. $x + 2 + 7j = yj - 2xj$ **40.** $2x + 6xj + 3 = yj - y + 7j$

In Exercises 41 and 42 answer the given questions.

41. What condition must be satisfied if a complex number and its conjugate are to be equal?

42. What type of number is a complex number if it is equal to the negative of its conjugate?

11–2 Basic Operations with Complex Numbers

The basic operations of addition, subtraction, multiplication, and division are defined in the same way for complex numbers in rectangular form as they are for real numbers. These operations are performed without regard for the fact that j has a special meaning. However, we must **be careful to express all complex numbers in terms of j before performing these operations.** Once this is done, we may proceed as with real numbers. We have the following definitions for these operations on complex numbers.

Addition (and subtraction):

$$(a + bj) + (c + dj) = (a + c) + (b + d)j \qquad (11\text{--}3)$$

Multiplication:

$$(a + bj)(c + dj) = (ac - bd) + (ad + bc)j \qquad (11\text{--}4)$$

Division:

$$\frac{a + bj}{c + dj} = \frac{(a + bj)(c - dj)}{(c + dj)(c - dj)} = \frac{(ac + bd) + (bc - ad)j}{c^2 + d^2} \qquad (11\text{--}5)$$

Recalling Examples B and C of Section 11–1, we see the reason for expressing all complex numbers in terms of j before proceeding with any indicated operations.

We note from Eq. (11–3) that the addition or subtraction of complex numbers is accomplished by combining the real parts and combining the imaginary parts. Consider the following examples.

Example A

$$(3 - 2j) + (-5 + 7j) = (3 - 5) + (-2 + 7)j = -2 + 5j$$

Example B

$$(7 + 9j) - (6 - 4j) = 7 + 9j - 6 + 4j = 1 + 13j$$

Example C

$$(3\sqrt{-4} - 4) - (6 - 2\sqrt{-25}) - \sqrt{-81}$$
$$= [3(2j) - 4] - [6 - 2(5j)] - 9j$$
$$= [6j - 4] - [6 - 10j] - 9j$$
$$= 6j - 4 - 6 + 10j - 9j$$
$$= -10 + 7j$$

Here we note that our first step was to express the numbers in terms of j.

When complex numbers are multiplied, Eq. (11–4) indicates that we proceed as in any algebraic multiplication, properly expressing numbers in terms of j and evaluating powers of j. This is illustrated in Examples C and D.

Example D

$$(6 - \sqrt{-4})(\sqrt{-9}) = (6 - 2j)(3j) = 18j - 6j^2$$
$$= 18j - 6(-1) = 6 + 18j$$

Example E

$$(-9 - 6j)(2 + j) = -18 - 9j - 12j - 6j^2$$
$$= -18 - 21j - 6(-1) = -12 - 21j$$

We note that our procedure in dividing two complex numbers is the same procedure that we used for rationalizing the denominator of a fraction with a radical in the denominator. We use this procedure so that we can express any answer in the form of a complex number. We need merely to multiply numerator and denominator by the conjugate of the denominator in order to perform this operation.

Example F

$$\frac{7 - 2j}{3 + 4j} = \frac{7 - 2j}{3 + 4j} \cdot \frac{3 - 4j}{3 - 4j} = \frac{21 - 28j - 6j + 8j^2}{9 - 16j^2}$$

$$= \frac{21 - 34j + 8(-1)}{9 - 16(-1)} = \frac{13 - 34j}{25}$$

This could be written in the form $a + bj$ as $\frac{13}{25} - \frac{34}{25}j$, but is generally left as a single fraction.

Example G

$$\frac{6 + j}{2j} = \frac{6 + j}{2j} \cdot \frac{-2j}{-2j} = \frac{-12j - 2j^2}{4} = \frac{2 - 12j}{4} = \frac{1 - 6j}{2}$$

Example H

$$\frac{j^3 + 2j}{1 - j^5} = \frac{-j + 2j}{1 - j} = \frac{j}{1 - j} \cdot \frac{1 + j}{1 + j} = \frac{-1 + j}{2}$$

Exercises 11—2

In Exercises 1 through 48 perform the indicated operations, expressing all answers in the form $a + bj$.

1. $(3 - 7j) + (2 - j)$ 2. $(-4 - j) + (-7 - 4j)$
3. $(7j - 6) - (3 + j)$ 4. $(2 - 3j) - (2 + 3j)$
5. $(4 + \sqrt{-16}) + (3 - \sqrt{-81})$ 6. $(-1 + 3\sqrt{-4}) + (8 - 4\sqrt{-49})$
7. $(5 - \sqrt{-9}) - (\sqrt{-4} + 5)$ 8. $(\sqrt{-25} - 1) - \sqrt{-9}$
9. $j - (j - 7) - 8$ 10. $(7 - j) - (4 - 4j) + (6 - j)$
11. $(2\sqrt{-25} - 3) - (5 - 3\sqrt{-36}) - (\sqrt{-49})$
12. $(6 - 2\sqrt{-64}) - \sqrt{-100} - (\sqrt{-81} - 5)$
13. $(7 - j)(7j)$ 14. $(-2j)(j - 5)$
15. $\sqrt{-16}(2\sqrt{-1} - 5)$ 16. $(\sqrt{-4} - 1)(\sqrt{-9})$
17. $(4 - j)(5 + 2j)$ 18. $(3 - 5j)(6 + 7j)$
19. $(2\sqrt{-9} - 3)(3\sqrt{-4} + 2)$ 20. $(5\sqrt{-64} - 5)(7 + \sqrt{-16})$
21. $\sqrt{-18}\sqrt{-4}\sqrt{-9}$ 22. $\sqrt{-6}\sqrt{-12}\sqrt{3}$
23. $(\sqrt{-5})^5$ 24. $(\sqrt{-36})^4$
25. $\sqrt{-108} - \sqrt{-27}$ 26. $2\sqrt{-54} + \sqrt{-24}$
27. $3\sqrt{-28} - 2\sqrt{12}$ 28. $5\sqrt{24} - 3\sqrt{-45}$
29. $7j^3 - 7\sqrt{-9}$ 30. $6j - 5j^2\sqrt{-63}$
31. $j\sqrt{-7} - j^6\sqrt{112} + 3j$ 32. $j^2\sqrt{-7} - \sqrt{-28} + 8$
33. $(3 - 7j)^2$ 34. $(4j + 5)^2$ 35. $(1 - j)^3$ 36. $(1 + j)(1 - j)^2$

37. $\dfrac{6j}{2 - 5j}$ 38. $\dfrac{4}{3 + 7j}$ 39. $\dfrac{2}{6 - \sqrt{-1}}$ 40. $\dfrac{\sqrt{-4}}{2 + \sqrt{-9}}$

41. $\dfrac{1-j}{1+j}$ **42.** $\dfrac{9-8j}{j-1}$ **43.** $\dfrac{\sqrt{-2}-5}{\sqrt{-2}+3}$ **44.** $\dfrac{2+3\sqrt{-3}}{5-\sqrt{-3}}$

45. $\dfrac{\sqrt{-16}-\sqrt{2}}{\sqrt{2}+j}$ **46.** $\dfrac{1-\sqrt{-4}}{2+9j}$ **47.** $\dfrac{j^2-j}{2j-j^8}$ **48.** $\dfrac{j^5-j^3}{3+j}$

In Exercises 49 through 52 demonstrate the indicated properties.

49. Show that the sum of a complex number and its conjugate is a real number.

50. Show that the product of a complex number and its conjugate is a real number.

51. Show that the difference between a complex number and its conjugate is an imaginary number.

52. Show that the reciprocal of the imaginary unit is the negative of the imaginary unit.

11—3 Graphical Representation of Complex Numbers

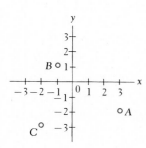

Figure 11—1

We showed in Section 1–1 how we could represent real numbers as points on a line. Because complex numbers include all real numbers as well as imaginary numbers, it is necessary to represent them graphically in a different way. Since there are two numbers associated with each complex number (the real part and the imaginary part), we find that we can represent complex numbers by representing the real parts by the x-values of the rectangular coordinate system, and the imaginary parts by the y-values. In this way *each complex number is represented as a point in the plane,* the point being designated as $a + bj$. When the rectangular coordinate system is used in this manner it is called the **complex plane.**

Example A

In Fig. 11–1, the point A represents the complex number $3 - 2j$; point B represents $-1 + j$; point C represents $-2 - 3j$. We note that these are equivalent to the points $(3, -2)$, $(-1, 1)$, and $(-2, -3)$. However, we must keep in mind that the meaning is different. Complex numbers were not included when we first learned to graph functions.

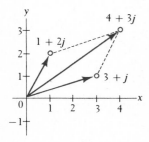

Figure 11—2

Let us represent two complex numbers and their sum in the complex plane. Consider, for example, the two complex numbers $1 + 2j$ and $3 + j$. By algebraic addition the sum is $4 + 3j$. When we draw lines from the origin to these points (see Fig. 11–2), we note that if we think of the complex numbers as being vectors, their sum is the vector sum. Because complex numbers can be used to represent vectors, these numbers are particularly important. Any complex number can be thought of as representing a vector from the origin to its point in the complex plane. To add two complex numbers graphically, we find the point corresponding to one of them and draw a line from the origin to this point. We

repeat this process for the second point. Next we complete a parallelogram with the lines drawn as adjacent sides. The resulting fourth vertex
is the point representing the sum of the two complex numbers. Note
that this is equivalent to adding vectors by graphical means.

Example B
Add the complex numbers $5 - 2j$ and $-2 - j$ graphically.
    The solution is indicated in Fig. 11–3. We can see that the fourth
vertex of the parallelogram is very near $3 - 3j$, which is, of course, the
algebraic sum.

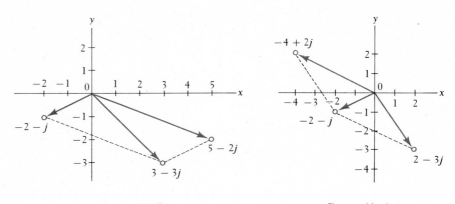

Figure 11–3   Figure 11–4

Example C
Subtract $4 - 2j$ from $2 - 3j$ graphically.
    Subtracting $4 - 2j$ is equivalent to adding $-4 + 2j$. Thus, we com-
plete the solution by adding $-4 + 2j$ and $2 - 3j$ (see Fig. 11–4). The
result is $-2 - j$.

Example D
Show graphically that the sum of a complex number and its conjugate is
a real number.
    If we choose the complex number $a + bj$, we know that its conjugate
is $a - bj$. The y-coordinate for the conjugate is as far below the x-axis
as the y-coordinate of $a + bj$ is above it. Therefore, the sum of the
imaginary parts must be zero and the sum of the two numbers must
therefore lie on the x-axis, as shown in Fig. 11–5. Since any point on the
x-axis is real, we have shown that the sum of $a + bj$ and $a - bj$ is real.

Figure 11–5

Exercises 11–3

In Exercises 1 through 4 locate the given complex numbers in the complex
plane.

1. $2 + 6j$ 2. $-5 + j$ 3. $-4 - 3j$ 4. $3 - 4j$

In Exercises 5 through 20 perform the indicated operations graphically; check
them algebraically.

5. $(5 - j) + (3 + 2j)$ 6. $(3 - 2j) + (-1 - j)$

7. $(2 - 4j) + (-2 + j)$ 8. $(-1 - 2j) + (6 - j)$
9. $(3 - 2j) - (4 - 6j)$ 10. $(2 - j) - j$
11. $(1 + 4j) - (3 + j)$ 12. $(-j - 2) - (-1 - 3j)$
13. $(4 - j) + (3 + 2j)$ 14. $(5 + 2j) - (-4 - 2j)$
15. $(3 - 6j) - (-1 + 5j)$ 16. $(-6 - 3j) + (2 - 7j)$
17. $(2j + 1) - 3j - (j + 1)$ 18. $(6 - j) - 9 - (2j - 3)$
19. $(j - 6) - j + (j - 7)$ 20. $j - (1 - j) + (3 + 2j)$

In Exercises 21 through 24 on the same coordinate system plot the given number, its negative, and its conjugate.

21. $3 + 2j$ 22. $-2 + 4j$ 23. $-3 - 5j$ 24. $5 - j$

11–4 Polar Form of a Complex Number

We have just seen the relationship between complex numbers and vectors. Since one can be used to represent the other, we shall use this fact to write complex numbers in another way. The new form has certain advantages when basic operations are performed on complex numbers.

By drawing a vector from the origin to the point in the complex plane which represents the number $x + yj$, we see the relation between vectors and complex numbers. Further observation indicates an angle in standard position has been formed. Also, the point $x + yj$ is r units from the origin. In fact, we can find any point in the complex plane by knowing this angle θ and the value of r. We have already developed the relations between x, y, r, and θ, in Eqs. (8–1) to (8–3). Let us rewrite these equations in a slightly different form. By referring to Eqs. (8–1) through (8–3) and to Fig. 11–6, we see that

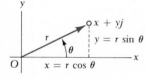

Figure 11–6

$$x = r \cos \theta, \qquad y = r \sin \theta \qquad\qquad (11\text{–}6)$$

$$r^2 = x^2 + y^2, \qquad \tan \theta = \frac{y}{x} \qquad\qquad (11\text{–}7)$$

Substituting Eqs. (11–6) into the rectangular form $x + yj$ of a complex number, we have

$$x + yj = r \cos \theta + j(r \sin \theta)$$

or

$$x + yj = r(\cos \theta + j \sin \theta) \qquad\qquad (11\text{–}8)$$

The right side of Eq. (11–8) is called the **polar form** *of a complex number. Sometimes it is referred to as the* **trigonometric form**. Other notations which are used to represent the polar form are $r \angle \theta$ and r cis θ. *The length r is called the* **absolute value** *or the* **modulus**, *and the angle θ is called the* **argument** *of the complex number*. Therefore, Eq. (11–8), along with Eqs. (11–7), define the polar form of a complex number.

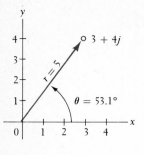

Figure 11–7

Example A

Represent the complex number $3 + 4j$ graphically, and give its polar form.

From the rectangular form $3 + 4j$ we see that $x = 3$ and $y = 4$. Using Eqs. (11–7), we have

$$r = \sqrt{3^2 + 4^2} = 5, \qquad \tan \theta = \frac{4}{3} = 1.333, \qquad \theta = 53.1°$$

Thus, the polar form is

$$5(\cos 53.1° + j \sin 53.1°)$$

The graphical representation is shown in Fig. 11–7.

A note on significant digits is in order here. In writing a complex number as $3 + 4j$ in Example A, no approximate values are intended. However, in expressing the polar form as $5(\cos 53.1° + j \sin 53.1°)$ we rounded off the angle to the nearest $0.1°$, as it is not possible to express the result exactly in degrees. Thus, in dealing with nonexact numbers we shall express trigonometric functions to four significant digits and angles to the nearest $0.1°$, for this is the accuracy in Table 4 in Appendix E. Other results, when approximate, will be expressed to three significant digits. Of course, in applied situations most numbers used are derived through measurement and are therefore approximate.

Example B

Represent the complex number $2.08 - 3.12j$ graphically, and give its polar form.

From Eqs. (11–7), we have

$$r = \sqrt{(2.08)^2 + (3.12)^2} = \sqrt{14.06} = 3.75$$

$$\tan \theta = \frac{-3.12}{2.08} = -1.500$$

Since we know that θ is a fourth-quadrant angle, we have $\theta = 303.7°$. Therefore, the polar form is

$$3.75(\cos 303.7° + j \sin 303.7°)$$

See Fig. 11–8.

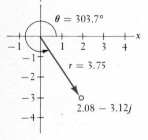

Figure 11–8

Example C

Express the complex number $3.00(\cos 120.0° + j \sin 120.0°)$ in rectangular form.

From the given polar form, we know that $r = 3.00$ and $\theta = 120.0°$. Using Eqs. (11–6), we have

$$x = 3.00 \cos 120.0° = 3.00(-0.5000) = -1.50$$
$$y = 3.00 \sin 120.0° = 3.00(-0.8660) = 2.60$$

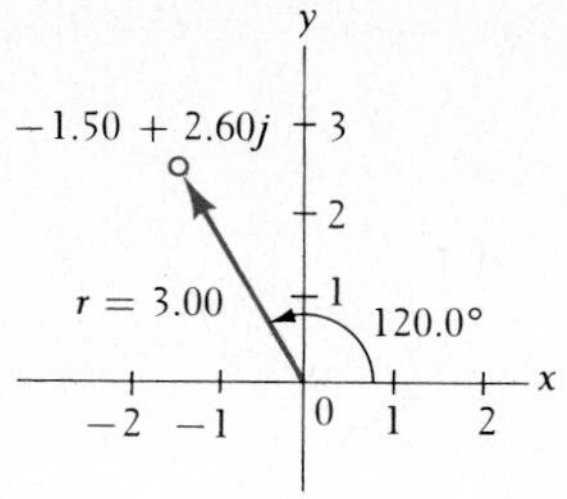

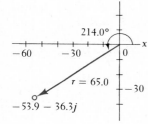

Figure 11—9

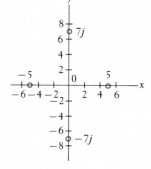

Figure 11—10

Therefore, the rectangular form is

$$-1.50 + 2.60j$$

See Fig. 11—9.

Example D

Express the complex number $65.0(\cos 214.0° + j \sin 214.0°)$ in rectangular form.

From the polar form, we have $r = 65.0$ and $\theta = 214.0°$. This means that

$$x = 65.0 \cos 214.0° = 65.0(-0.8290) = -53.9$$
$$y = 65.0 \sin 214.0° = 65.0(-0.5592) = -36.3$$

Therefore, the rectangular form is

$$-53.9 - 36.3j$$

See Fig. 11—10.

Example E

Represent the numbers 5, -5, $7j$, and $-7j$ in polar form.

Since any positive real number lies on the positive x-axis in the complex plane, real numbers are expressed in polar form by

$$a = a(\cos 0° + j \sin 0°)$$

Negative real numbers, being on the negative x-axis, are written as

$$a = |a|(\cos 180° + j \sin 180°)$$

Thus, $5 = 5(\cos 0° + j \sin 0°)$ and $-5 = 5(\cos 180° + j \sin 180°)$.

Positive pure imaginary numbers lie on the positive y-axis and are expressed in polar form by

$$bj = b(\cos 90° + j \sin 90°)$$

Similarly, negative pure imaginary numbers, being on the negative y-axis, are written as

$$-bj = |b|(\cos 270° + j \sin 270°)$$

Thus, $7j = 7(\cos 90° + j \sin 90°)$ and $-7j = 7(\cos 270° + j \sin 270°)$. The graphical representations of the *complex numbers* 5, -5, $7j$, and $-7j$ are shown in Fig. 11—11.

Figure 11—11

Exercises 11—4

In Exercises 1 through 16 represent each of the complex numbers graphically, and give the polar form of each number.

1. $8 + 6j$ 2. $-8 - 15j$ 3. $3 - 4j$

4. $-5 + 12j$ 5. $-2.00 + 3.00j$ 6. $7.00 - 5.00j$

7. $-5.50 - 2.40j$ 8. $4.60 - 4.60j$ 9. $1 + \sqrt{3}j$

10. $\sqrt{2} - \sqrt{2}j$ 11. $3.50 - 7.20j$ 12. $6.20 + 9.50j$

13. -3 14. 6 15. $9j$ 16. $-2j$

In Exercises 17 through 32 represent each of the complex numbers graphically, and give the rectangular form of each number.

17. $5.00(\cos 54.0° + j \sin 54.0°)$ 18. $3.00(\cos 232.0° + j \sin 232.0°)$

19. $1.60(\cos 150.0° + j \sin 150.0°)$ 20. $2.50(\cos 315.0° + j \sin 315.0°)$

21. $10.0(\cos 345.5° + j \sin 345.5°)$ 22. $220(\cos 155.2° + j \sin 155.2°)$

23. $6(\cos 180° + j \sin 180°)$ 24. $12(\cos 270° + j \sin 270°)$

25. $8(\cos 360° + j \sin 360°)$ 26. $15(\cos 0° + j \sin 0°)$

27. $4.75(\cos 172.8° + j \sin 172.8°)$ 28. $1.50(\cos 62.3° + j \sin 62.3°)$

29. $\cos 240.0° + j \sin 240.0°$ 30. $\cos 99.0° + j \sin 99.0°$

31. $28.0[\cos(-250.0°) + j \sin (-250.0°)]$ 32. $172[\cos(-105.0°) + j \sin(-105.0°)]$

In Exercises 33 and 34 solve the given problems.

33. Considering the relationship between complex numbers and vectors, what is the magnitude and direction of a displacement vector which is represented by $0.120 + 0.160j$ mm?

34. What is the magnitude and direction of a force which is represented by $3.72 - 5.12j$ lb? (See Exercise 33.)

11–5 Exponential Form of a Complex Number

Another important form of a complex number is known as the **exponential form,** which is written $re^{j\theta}$. In this expression r and θ have the same meaning as given in the last section and e represents a special irrational number equal to about 2.718. (In the calculus involved with exponential functions, the meaning of e is clarified.) We now define

$$re^{j\theta} = r(\cos \theta + j \sin \theta) \qquad (11\text{--}9)$$

When θ is expressed in radians, the expression $j\theta$ is an actual exponent, and it can be shown to obey all the laws of exponents. For this reason and because it is more meaningful in applications, *we shall always express θ in radians when using the exponential form.* The following examples show how complex numbers can be changed to and from exponential form.

Example A

Express the number $3 + 4j$ in exponential form.

From Example A of Section 11–4, we know that this complex number may be written in polar form as $5(\cos 53.1° + j \sin 53.1°)$. Therefore, we know that $r = 5$. We now express $53.1°$ in terms of radians as

$$\frac{53.1\pi}{180} = 0.927 \text{ rad}$$

Thus, the exponential form is $5e^{0.927j}$. This means that

$$3 + 4j = 5(\cos 53.1° + j \sin 53.1°) = 5e^{0.927j}$$

Example B

Express the number $8.50(\cos 136.3° + j \sin 136.3°)$ in exponential form.

Since this complex number is in polar form we note that $r = 8.50$ and that we must express $136.3°$ in radians. Therefore, changing $136.3°$ to radians, we have

$$\frac{136.3\pi}{180} = 2.38 \text{ rad}$$

Therefore, the required exponential form is $8.50e^{2.38j}$. This means that

$$8.50(\cos 136.3° + j \sin 136.3°) = 8.50e^{2.38j}$$

Example C

Express the number $3.07 - 7.43j$ in exponential form.

From the rectangular form of the number, we have $x = 3.07$ and $y = -7.43$. Therefore,

$$r = \sqrt{(3.07)^2 + (-7.43)^2} = \sqrt{64.63} = 8.04$$

$$\tan \theta = \frac{-7.43}{3.07} = -2.420, \qquad \theta = 292.5°$$

Changing $292.5°$ to radians, we have $292.5° = 5.10$ rad. Therefore, the exponential form is $8.04e^{5.10j}$. This means that

$$3.07 - 7.43j = 8.04e^{5.10j}$$

Example D

Express the complex number $2.00e^{4.80j}$ in polar and rectangular forms.

We first express 4.80 rad as $275.0°$. From the exponential form we know that $r = 2.00$. Thus, the polar form is $2.00 (\cos 275.0° + j \sin 275.0°)$. Next we find that $\cos 275.0° = 0.0872$ and $\sin 275.0° = -0.9962$. The rectangular form is $2.00 (0.0872 - 0.9962j) = 0.174 - 1.99j$. This means that

$$2.00e^{4.80j} = 2.00(\cos 275.0° + j \sin 275.0°) = 0.174 - 1.99j$$

Example E

Express the complex number $3.40e^{2.46j}$ in polar and rectangular forms.

We first express 2.46 rad as $141.0°$. From the exponential form we know that $r = 3.40$. Thus, the polar form is $3.40(\cos 141.0° + j \sin 141.0°)$. Next we find that $\cos 141.0° = -0.7771$ and $\sin 141.0° = 0.6293$. The rectangular form is $3.40(-0.7771 + 0.6293j) = -2.64 + 2.14j$. This means that

$$3.40e^{2.46j} = 3.40(\cos 141.0° + j \sin 141.0°) = -2.64 + 2.14j$$

An important application of the use of complex numbers is in alternating current. When an alternating current flows through a given circuit, usually the current and voltage have different phases. That is, they do not reach their peak values at the same time. Therefore, one way of accounting for the magnitude as well as the phase of an electric current or voltage is to write it as a complex number. Here the modulus is the actual value of the current or voltage, and the argument is a measure of the phase.

Example F

A current of $2.00 - 4.00j$ amperes flows through a given circuit. Write this current in exponential form and determine the value of current in the circuit.

From the rectangular form, we have $x = 2.00$ and $y = -4.00$. Therefore, $r = \sqrt{(2.00)^2 + (-4.00)^2} = \sqrt{20.00} = 4.47$. Also, $\tan \theta = -\frac{4.00}{2.00} = -2.000$. Since $\tan 63.4° = 2.000$, $\theta = -63.4°$ (it is normal to express the phase in terms of negative angles). Changing $63.4°$ to radians, we have $63.4° = 1.11$ rad. Therefore, the exponential form of the current is $4.47e^{-1.11j}$. The modulus is 4.47, meaning the current is 4.47 A.

At this point we shall summarize the three important forms of a complex number.

Rectangular:	$x + yj$
Polar:	$r(\cos \theta + j \sin \theta)$
Exponential:	$re^{j\theta}$

It follows that

$$x + yj = r(\cos \theta + j \sin \theta) = re^{j\theta} \tag{11-10}$$

where

$$r^2 = x^2 + y^2, \qquad \tan \theta = \frac{y}{x} \tag{11-7}$$

Exercises 11—5

In Exercises 1 through 16 express the given complex numbers in exponential form.

1. $3.00(\cos 60.0° + j \sin 60.0°)$ 2. $5.00(\cos 135.0° + j \sin 135.0°)$

3. $4.50(\cos 282.0° + j \sin 282.0°)$ 4. $2.10(\cos 228.0° + j \sin 228.0°)$

5. $375(\cos 95.0° + j \sin 95.0°)$ 6. $16.0(\cos 7.0° + j \sin 7.0°)$

7. $0.515(\cos 198.3° + j \sin 198.3°)$ 8. $4650(\cos 326.5° + j \sin 326.5°)$

9. $3 - 4j$ 10. $-1 - 5j$

11. $-3 + 2j$ 12. $6 + j$

13. $5.90 + 2.40j$ 14. $47.3 - 10.9j$

15. $-634 - 528j$ 16. $-8570 + 5470j$

In Exercises 17 through 24 express the given complex numbers in polar and rectangular forms.

17. $3.00e^{0.500j}$ 18. $2.00e^{1.00j}$ 19. $4.64e^{1.85j}$ 20. $2.50e^{3.84j}$

21. $3.20e^{5.41j}$ 22. $0.800e^{3.00j}$ 23. $0.172e^{2.39j}$ 24. $820e^{3.49j}$

In Exercises 25 and 26 perform the indicated operations.

25. The electric current in a certain alternating-current circuit is given by $0.500 + 0.220j$ amperes. Write this current in exponential form and determine the magnitude of the current in the circuit.

26. The voltage in a certain alternating-current circuit is $125e^{1.31j}$. Determine the magnitude of the voltage in the circuit and the in-phase component (the real part) of the voltage.

11—6 Products, Quotients, Powers, and Roots of Complex Numbers

We have previously performed products and quotients using the rectangular forms of the given numbers. However, these operations can also be performed with complex numbers in polar and exponential forms. We find that these operations are convenient, and also useful for purposes of finding powers and roots of complex numbers.

We may find the product of two complex numbers by using the exponential form and the laws of exponents. Multiplying $r_1 e^{j\theta_1}$ by $r_2 e^{j\theta_2}$, we have

$$r_1 e^{j\theta_1} \cdot r_2 e^{j\theta_2} = r_1 r_2 e^{j\theta_1 + j\theta_2} = r_1 r_2 e^{j(\theta_1 + \theta_2)} \tag{11–11}$$

We use Eq. (11–11) to express the product of two complex numbers in polar form:

$$r_1 e^{j\theta_1} \cdot r_2 e^{j\theta_2} = r_1(\cos\theta_1 + j\sin\theta_1) \cdot r_2(\cos\theta_2 + j\sin\theta_2)$$

and

$$r_1 r_2 e^{j(\theta_1 + \theta_2)} = r_1 r_2[\cos(\theta_1 + \theta_2) + j\sin(\theta_1 + \theta_2)]$$

Therefore, the polar expressions are equal:

$$r_1(\cos\theta_1 + j\sin\theta_1)r_2(\cos\theta_2 + j\sin\theta_2) = r_1 r_2[\cos(\theta_1 + \theta_2) + j\sin(\theta_1 + \theta_2)] \tag{11–12}$$

Example A

Multiply the complex numbers $2 + 3j$ and $1 - j$ by using the polar form of each.

$$r_1 = \sqrt{4 + 9} = 3.61, \qquad \tan\theta_1 = 1.500, \qquad \theta_1 = 56.3°$$
$$r_2 = \sqrt{1 + 1} = 1.41, \qquad \tan\theta_2 = -1.000, \quad \theta_2 = 315.0°$$
$$(3.61)(\cos 56.3° + j\sin 56.3°)(1.41)(\cos 315.0° + j\sin 315.0°)$$
$$= (3.61)(1.41)[\cos(56.3° + 315.0°) + j\sin(56.3° + 315.0°)]$$
$$= 5.09(\cos 371.3° + j\sin 371.3°)$$
$$= 5.09(\cos 11.3° + j\sin 11.3°)$$

Example B

When we use the exponential form to multiply the two complex numbers in Example A, we have:

$$r_1 = 3.61, \qquad \theta_1 = 56.3° = 0.983 \text{ rad}$$
$$r_2 = 1.41, \qquad \theta_2 = 315° = 5.50 \text{ rad}$$
$$3.61\,e^{0.983j}1.41\,e^{5.50j} = 5.09e^{6.48j} = 5.09e^{0.20j}$$

If we wish to *divide* one complex number in exponential form by another, we arrive at the following result:

$$r_1 e^{j\theta_1} \div r_2 e^{j\theta_2} = \frac{r_1}{r_2} e^{j(\theta_1 - \theta_2)} \qquad (11\text{--}13)$$

Therefore, the result of dividing one number in polar form by another is given by:

$$\frac{r_1(\cos\theta_1 + j\sin\theta_1)}{r_2(\cos\theta_2 + j\sin\theta_2)} = \frac{r_1}{r_2}[\cos(\theta_1 - \theta_2) + j\sin(\theta_1 - \theta_2)] \qquad (11\text{--}14)$$

Example C

Divide the first complex number of Example A by the second. Using polar form, we have the following:

$$\frac{3.61(\cos 56.3° + j\sin 56.3°)}{1.41(\cos 315.0° + j\sin 315.0°)} = \frac{3.61}{1.41}[\cos(56.3° - 315.0°)$$
$$+ j\sin(56.3° - 315.0°)]$$
$$= 2.56[\cos(-258.7°) + j\sin(-258.7°)]$$
$$= 2.56(\cos 101.3° + j\sin 101.3°)$$

Example D

Repeating Example C, using exponential forms, we obtain

$$\frac{3.61e^{0.983j}}{1.41e^{5.50j}} = 2.56e^{-4.52j} = 2.56e^{1.76j}$$

To raise a complex number to a power, we simply multiply one complex number by itself the required number of times. For example, in Eq. (11–11), if the two numbers being multiplied are equal, we have (letting $r_1 = r_2 = r$ and $\theta_1 = \theta_2 = \theta$)

$$(re^{j\theta})^2 = r^2 e^{j2\theta} \qquad (11\text{--}15)$$

Multiplying the expression in Eq. (11–15) by $re^{j\theta}$ gives $r^3 e^{j3\theta}$. This leads to the general expression for raising a complex number to the *n*th power,

$$(re^{j\theta})^n = r^n e^{jn\theta} \qquad (11\text{--}16)$$

Extending this to polar form, we have

$$[r(\cos \theta + j \sin \theta)]^n = r^n(\cos n\theta + j \sin n\theta) \qquad (11-17)$$

Equation (11-17) is known as **DeMoivre's theorem**. It is valid for all real values of n, and may also be used for finding the roots of complex numbers if n is a fractional exponent.

Example E
Using DeMoivre's theorem, find $(2 + 3j)^3$.
From Example A of this section, we know $r = 3.61$ and $\theta = 56.3°$. Thus, we have
$$[3.61 (\cos 56.3° + j \sin 56.3°)]^3$$
$$= (3.61)^3[\cos 3 \times 56.3° + j \sin 3 \times 56.3°]$$
$$= 47.0(\cos 168.9° + j \sin 168.9°)$$

From Example B we know that $\theta = 0.983$ rad. Thus, in exponential form,
$$(3.61 e^{0.983j})^3 = (3.61)^3 e^{3 \times 0.983j} = 47.0 e^{2.95j}$$

Therefore,
$$(2 + 3j)^3 = 47.0(\cos 168.9° + j \sin 168.9°) = 47.0 e^{2.95j}$$

Example F
Find $\sqrt[3]{-1}$.
Since we know that -1 is a real number, we can find its cube root by means of the definition. That is, $(-1)^3 = -1$. We shall check this by DeMoivre's theorem. Writing -1 in polar form, we have

$$-1 = 1(\cos 180° + j \sin 180°)$$

Applying DeMoivre's theorem, with $n = \frac{1}{3}$, we obtain

$$(-1)^{1/3} = 1^{1/3}(\cos \frac{1}{3}180° + j \sin \frac{1}{3}180°) = \cos 60° + j \sin 60°$$

$$= 0.500 + 0.866j$$

We note that we did not obtain -1 as an answer. If we check the answer which was obtained, in the form $\frac{1}{2}(1 + \sqrt{3}j)$, by actually cubing it, we obtain -1! Thus it is a correct answer.

We should note that it is possible to take $\frac{1}{3}$ of any angle up to $1080°$ and still have an angle less than $360°$. Since $180°$ and $540°$ have the same terminal side, let us try writing -1 as $1(\cos 540° + j \sin 540°)$. Using DeMoivre's theorem, we have

$$(-1)^{1/3} = 1^{1/3}(\cos \frac{1}{3}540° + j \sin \frac{1}{3}540°)$$

$$= \cos 180° + j \sin 180° = -1$$

We have found the answer we originally anticipated.

Angles of 180° and 900° also have the same terminal side, so we try

$$(-1)^{1/3} = 1^{1/3}(\cos \frac{1}{3}900° + j \sin \frac{1}{3}900°) = \cos 300° + j \sin 300°$$

$$= 0.500 - 0.866j$$

Checking this, we find that it is also a correct root. We may try 1260°, but $\frac{1}{3}(1260°) = 420°$, which has the same functional values as 60°, and would give us the answer $0.500 + 0.866j$ again.

We have found, therefore, three cube roots of -1. They are -1, $0.500 + 0.866j$, and $0.500 - 0.866j$. When this is generalized, it can be proved that there are n nth roots of any complex number. The method for finding the n roots is to use θ to find one root, and then add 360° to θ, $n - 1$ times, in order to find the other roots.

Example G
Find the square roots of j.

We must first properly write j in polar form so that we may use DeMoivre's theorem to find the roots. In polar form, j is

$$j = 1(\cos 90° + j \sin 90°)$$

To find the square roots, we apply DeMoivre's theorem with $n = \frac{1}{2}$.

$$j^{1/2} = 1^{1/2}\left(\cos \frac{90°}{2} + j \sin \frac{90°}{2}\right) = \cos 45° + j \sin 45° = 0.707 + 0.707j$$

To find the other square root using DeMoivre's theorem, we must write j in polar form as

$$j = 1[\cos(90° + 360°) + j \sin(90° + 360°)] = 1(\cos 450° + j \sin 450°).$$

Applying DeMoivre's theorem to j in this form, we have

$$j^{1/2} = 1^{1/2}\left(\cos \frac{450°}{2} + j \sin \frac{450°}{2}\right) = \cos 225° + j \sin 225°$$

$$= -0.707 - 0.707j$$

Thus, the two square roots of j are $0.707 + 0.707j$ and $-0.707 - 0.707j$.

Example H
Find the six 6th roots of 1.

Here we shall use directly the method for finding the roots of a number, as outlined at the end of Example F:

$$1 = 1(\cos 0° + j \sin 0°)$$

First root: $$1^{1/6} = 1^{1/6}\left(\cos \frac{0°}{6} + j \sin \frac{0°}{6}\right) = \cos 0° + j \sin 0° = 1$$

Second root: $$1^{1/6} = 1^{1/6}\left(\cos \frac{0° + 360°}{6} + j \sin \frac{0° + 360°}{6}\right)$$

$$= \cos 60° + j \sin 60° = \frac{1}{2} + j \frac{\sqrt{3}}{2}$$

Third root: $1^{1/6} = 1^{1/6}\left(\cos\dfrac{0° + 720°}{6} + j\sin\dfrac{0° + 720°}{6}\right)$

$= \cos 120° + j\sin 120° = -\dfrac{1}{2} + j\dfrac{\sqrt{3}}{2}$

Fourth root: $1^{1/6} = 1^{1/6}\left(\cos\dfrac{0° + 1080°}{6} + j\sin\dfrac{0° + 1080°}{6}\right)$

$= \cos 180° + j\sin 180° = -1$

Fifth root: $1^{1/6} = 1^{1/6}\left(\cos\dfrac{0° + 1440°}{6} + j\sin\dfrac{0° + 1440°}{6}\right)$

$= \cos 240° + j\sin 240° = -\dfrac{1}{2} - j\dfrac{\sqrt{3}}{2}$

Sixth root: $1^{1/6} = 1^{1/6}\left(\cos\dfrac{0° + 1800°}{6} + j\sin\dfrac{0° + 1800°}{6}\right)$

$= \cos 300° + j\sin 300° = \dfrac{1}{2} - j\dfrac{\sqrt{3}}{2}$

At this point we can see advantages for the various forms of writing complex numbers. Rectangular form lends itself best to addition and subtraction. Polar form is generally used for multiplying, dividing, raising to powers, and finding roots. Exponential form is used for theoretical purposes (e.g., deriving DeMoivre's theorem).

Exercises 11–6

In Exercises 1 through 12 perform the indicated operations. Leave the result in polar form.

1. $[4(\cos 60° + j\sin 60°)][2(\cos 20° + j\sin 20°)]$
2. $[3(\cos 120° + j\sin 120°)][5(\cos 45° + j\sin 45°)]$
3. $[0.5(\cos 140° + j\sin 140°)][6(\cos 110° + j\sin 110°)]$
4. $[0.4(\cos 320° + j\sin 320°)][5.5(\cos 150° + j\sin 150°)]$

5. $\dfrac{8(\cos 100° + j\sin 100°)}{4(\cos 65° + j\sin 65°)}$

6. $\dfrac{9(\cos 230° + j\sin 230°)}{3(\cos 80° + j\sin 80°)}$

7. $\dfrac{12(\cos 320° + j\sin 320°)}{5(\cos 210° + j\sin 210°)}$

8. $\dfrac{2(\cos 90° + j\sin 90°)}{4(\cos 75° + j\sin 75°)}$

9. $[2(\cos 35° + j\sin 35°)]^3$

10. $[3(\cos 120° + j\sin 120°)]^4$

11. $[2(\cos 135° + j\sin 135°)]^8$

12. $(\cos 142° + j\sin 142°)^{10}$

In Exercises 13 through 24 change each number to polar form and then perform the indicated operations. Express the final result in rectangular and polar forms. Check by performing the same operation in rectangular form.

13. $(3 + 4j)(5 - 12j)$ 14. $(-2 + 5j)(-1 - j)$ 15. $(7 - 3j)(8 + j)$

16. $(1 + 5j)(4 + 2j)$ 17. $\dfrac{7}{1 - 3j}$ 18. $\dfrac{8j}{7 + 2j}$

19. $\dfrac{3 + 4j}{5 - 12j}$ 20. $\dfrac{-2 + 5j}{-1 - j}$ 21. $(3 + 4j)^4$

22. $(-1 - j)^8$ 23. $(2 + 3j)^5$ 24. $(1 - 2j)^6$

In Exercises 25 through 32 use DeMoivre's theorem to find the indicated roots. Be sure to find all roots.

25. $\sqrt{4(\cos 60° + j \sin 60°)}$ 26. $\sqrt[3]{27(\cos 120° + j \sin 120°)}$ 27. $\sqrt[3]{3 - 4j}$
28. $\sqrt{-5 + 12j}$ 29. $\sqrt[4]{1}$ 30. $\sqrt[3]{8}$ 31. $\sqrt[3]{-j}$ 32. $\sqrt[4]{j}$

In Exercises 33 and 34 perform the indicated multiplications.

33. In Example F we showed that one cube root of -1 is $0.500 - 0.866j$. The exact form of this root is $\frac{1}{2}(1 - \sqrt{3}j)$. Cube this expression in rectangular form and show that the result is -1.

34. In Example G we showed that one of the square roots of j is equal to $0.707 + 0.707j$. The exact form of this root is $\frac{1}{2}\sqrt{2}(1 + j)$. Square this expression and show that the result is j.

11–7 An Application to Alternating-Current (AC) Circuits

We shall complete our study of the *j*-operator by showing its use in one aspect of alternating-current circuit theory. This application will be made to measuring voltage between any two points in a simple ac circuit, similar to the application mentioned in Section 11–5. We shall consider a circuit containing a resistance, a capacitance, and an inductance.

Briefly, a resistance is any part of a circuit which tends to obstruct the flow of electric current through the circuit. It is denoted by R (units in ohms, with symbol Ω) and in diagrams by $-\!\!\bigvee\!\!\bigvee\!\!-$. In essence, a capacitance is two nonconnected plates in a circuit; no current actually flows across the gap between them. In an ac circuit, an electric charge is continually going to and from each plate and, therefore, the current in the circuit is not effectively stopped. It is denoted by C (units in farads, with symbol F) and in diagrams by $-\!|\!|\!-$ (Fig. 11–12). An inductance, basically, is a coil of wire in which current is induced because the current is continuously changing in the circuit. It is denoted by L (units in henrys, with symbol H) and in diagrams by $-\!\text{oooo}\!-$. All these elements affect the voltage in an alternating-current circuit. We shall state here the relation each has to the voltage and current in the circuit.

$$R \qquad C \qquad L$$

Figure 11–12

In Chapter 9, when we were discussing the graphs of the trigonometric functions, we noted that the current and voltage in an ac circuit could be represented by a sine or cosine curve. Therefore, each reaches peak values periodically. If they reach their respective peak values at the same time, we say they are *in phase*. If the voltage reaches its peak before the current, we say that the voltage *leads* the current. If the voltage reaches its peak after the current, we say that the voltage *lags* the current. In the study of electricity it is shown that the voltage across a resistance is in phase with the current. The voltage across a capacitor lags the current by 90°, and the voltage across an inductance leads the current by 90°.

Each element in an ac circuit tends to offer a type of resistance to the flow of current. The effective resistance of any part of the circuit is called the **reactance**, and it is denoted by X. The voltage across any part of the circuit whose reactance is X is given $V = IX$, where I is the current (in amperes) and V is the voltage (in volts). Therefore, the voltage across a resistor, capacitor, and inductor, is, respectively

$$V_R = IX_R, \qquad V_C = IX_C, \qquad V_L = IX_L \qquad\qquad (11–18)$$

To determine the voltage across a combination of these elements of a circuit, we must account for the reactance as well as the phase of the voltage across the individual elements. Since the voltage across a resistor is in phase with the current, we shall represent X_R along the x-axis as a real number R (the actual value of the resistance). Since the voltage across an inductance *leads* the current by 90°, we shall represent this voltage as a positive, pure imaginary number. In the same way, by representing the voltage across a capacitor as a negative, pure imaginary number, we show that the voltage lags the current by 90°. These representations are meaningful since the positive y-axis (positive, pure imaginary numbers) is +90° from the positive x-axis, and the negative y-axis (negative, pure imaginary numbers) is −90° from the positive x-axis.

The total voltage across a combination of all three elements is given by $V_R + V_L + V_C$, which we shall represent by V_{RLC}. Therefore,

$$V_{RLC} = IR + IX_L j - IX_C j = I[R + j(X_L - X_C)]$$

This expression is also written as

$$V_{RLC} = IZ \qquad\qquad (11–19)$$

where the symbol Z is called the **impedance** of the circuit. It is the total effective resistance to the flow of current by a combination of the elements in the circuit, taking into account the phase of the voltage in each element. From its definition, we see that Z is a complex number,

$$Z = R + j(X_L - X_C) \qquad\qquad (11–20)$$

with a magnitude

$$|Z| = \sqrt{R^2 + (X_L - X_C)^2} \qquad\qquad (11–21)$$

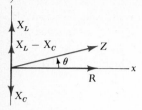

Figure 11–13

Also, as a complex number, it makes an angle θ with the *x*-axis given by

$$\tan \theta = \frac{X_L - X_C}{R} \tag{11-22}$$

All these equations are based on phase relations of voltages with respect to the current. Therefore, the angle θ represents the phase angle between the current and the voltage (see Fig. 11–13).

In the examples and exercises of this section, the commonly used units and symbols for them are used. For a summary of these units and symbols, including prefixes, see Appendix B.

Example A

In the series circuit shown in Fig. 11–14(a), $R = 12.0\ \Omega$ and $X_L = 5.00\ \Omega$. A current of 2.00 A is in the circuit. Find the voltage across each element, the impedance, the voltage across the combination, and the phase angle between the current and voltage.

Since the voltage across any element is the product of the current and reactance, we have the voltage across the resistor (between points *a* and *b*) as $V_R = (2.00)(12.0) = 24.0$ V. The voltage across the inductor (between points *b* and *c*) is $V_L = (2.00)(5.00) = 10.0$ V. To find the voltage across the combination, between points *a* and *c*, we must first find the magnitude of the impedance. The voltage is *not* the arithmetic sum of V_R and V_L; we must account for the phase. By Eq. (11–20), the impedance is $Z = 12.0 + 5.00j$ with magnitude

$$|Z| = \sqrt{R^2 + X_L^2} = \sqrt{(12.0)^2 + (5.00)^2} = \sqrt{169} = 13.0\ \Omega$$

Therefore, the voltage across the combination is

$$V_{RL} = (2.00)(13.0) = 26.0\ V$$

The phase angle between the voltage and current is found by Eq. (11–22). This gives $\tan \theta = \frac{5.00}{12.0} = 0.4167$ which means that $\theta = 22.6°$. The voltage leads the current by 22.6°, as shown in Fig. 11–14(b).

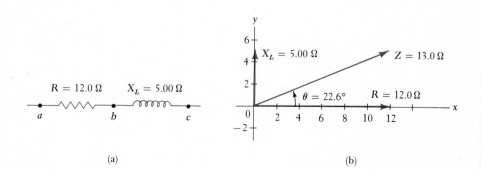

(a)   (b)

Figure 11–14

Example B

For a circuit in which $R = 8.00\ \Omega$, $X_L = 7.00\ \Omega$, and $X_C = 13.0\ \Omega$, find the impedance and the phase angle between the current and the voltage.

By the definition of impedance, Eq. (11–20), we have

$$Z = 8.00 + (7.00 - 13.0)j = 8.00 - 6.00j$$

where the magnitude of the impedance is

$$|Z| = \sqrt{(8.00)^2 + (-6.00)^2} = \sqrt{64.0 + 36.0} = 10.0\ \Omega$$

The phase angle is found by

$$\tan\theta = \frac{-6.00}{8.00} = -0.7500$$

Therefore, $\theta = -36.9°$ (negative angles are used, having a useful purpose in this type of problem). This means that the voltage lags the current by $36.9°$ (see Fig. 11–15).

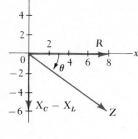

Figure 11–15

Example C

Let $R = 6.00\ \Omega$, $X_L = 8.00\ \Omega$, and $X_C = 4.00\ \Omega$. Find the impedance and the phase angle between the current and voltage.

$$Z = 6.00 + (8.00 - 4.00)j = 6.00 + 4.00j$$

$$|Z| = \sqrt{(6.00)^2 + (4.00)^2} = \sqrt{36.0 + 16.0} = 7.21\ \Omega$$

$$\tan\theta = \frac{4.00}{6.00} = 0.6667, \qquad \theta = 33.7°$$

The voltage leads the current by $33.7°$ (see Fig. 11–16).

Note that the resistance is represented in the same way as a vector along the positive x-axis. Actually resistance is not a vector quantity, but is represented in this manner in order to assign an angle as the phase of the current. The important concept in this analysis is that the phase *difference* between the current and voltage is constant, and therefore any direction may be chosen arbitrarily for one of them. Once this choice is made, other phase angles are measured with respect to this direction. A common choice, as above, is to make the phase angle of the current zero. If an arbitrary angle is chosen, it is necessary to treat the current, voltage, and impedance as complex numbers.

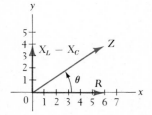

Figure 11–16

Example D

In a particular circuit, the current is $2.00 - 3.00j$ amperes and the impedance is $6.00 + 2.00j$ ohms. The voltage across this part of the circuit is

$$V = (2.00 - 3.00j)(6.00 + 2.00j) = 12.0 - 14.0j - 6.00j^2$$
$$= 12.0 - 14.0j + 6.00$$
$$= 18.0 - 14.0 \text{ volts}$$

The magnitude of the voltage is

$$|V| = \sqrt{(18.0)^2 + (-14.0)^2} = \sqrt{324 + 196} = \sqrt{520} = 22.8\ V$$

Since the voltage across a resistor is in phase with the current, this voltage can be represented as having a phase difference of zero with respect to the current. Therefore, the resistance is indicated as an arrow in the positive *x*-direction, denoting the fact that the current and voltage are in phase. Such a representation is called a **phasor**. The arrow denoted by *R*, as in Fig. 11–16, is actually the phasor representing the voltage across the resistor. Remember, the positive *x*-axis is arbitrarily chosen as the direction of the phase of the current.

To show properly that the voltage across an inductance leads the current by 90°, its reactance (effective resistance) is multiplied by *j*. We know that there is a positive 90° angle between a real number and a positive imaginary number. In the same way, by multiplying the capacitive reactance by −*j*, we show the 90° difference in phase between the voltage and current in a capacitor, with the current leading. Therefore, jX_L represents the phasor for the voltage across an inductor and $-jX_C$ is the phasor for the voltage across the capacitor. The phasor for the voltage across the combination of the resistance, inductance, and capacitance is *Z*, where the phase difference between the voltage and current for the combination is the angle *θ*.

This also points out well the significance of the word "operator" in the term "*j*-operator." Multiplying a phasor by *j* means to perform the operation of rotating it through 90°. We have seen that this is the same result obtained when a real number is multiplied by *j*.

An alternating current is produced by a coil of wire rotating through a magnetic field. If the angular velocity of this wire is *ω*, the capacitive and inductive reactances are given by the relations

$$X_C = \frac{1}{\omega C} \quad \text{and} \quad X_L = \omega L \tag{11–23}$$

Therefore, if *ω*, *C*, and *L* are known, the reactance of the circuit may be determined.

Example E

Given that $R = 12.0 \ \Omega$, $L = 0.300 \ \text{H}$, $C = 250 \ \mu\text{F}$, $\omega = 80.0 \ \text{rad/s}$, determine the impedance and the phase difference between the current and voltage.

$$X_C = \frac{1}{(80.0)(250 \times 10^{-6})} = 50.0 \ \Omega$$

$$X_L = (0.300)(80.0) = 24.0 \ \Omega$$

$$Z = 12.0 + (24.0 - 50.0)j = 12.0 - 26.0j$$

$$|Z| = \sqrt{(12.0)^2 + (-26.0)^2} = 28.6 \ \Omega$$

$$\tan \theta = \frac{-26.0}{12.0} = -2.167, \quad \theta = -65.2°$$

The voltage lags the current (see Fig. 11–17).

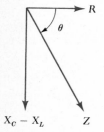

$X_C - X_L \qquad Z$

Figure 11–17

An important concept in the application of this theory is that of **resonance**. For resonance, the impedance of any circuit is a minimum, or the total impedance is R. Thus $X_L - X_C = 0$. Also, it can be seen that the current and voltage are in phase under these conditions. Resonance is required for the tuning of radio and television receivers.

Exercises 11–7

For Exercises 1 through 4 use the circuit shown in Fig. 11–18. A current of 3.00 A flows through the circuit. Determine the indicated quantities.

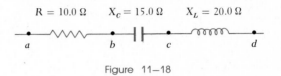

$R = 10.0\ \Omega$ $X_C = 15.0\ \Omega$ $X_L = 20.0\ \Omega$

Figure 11–18

1. Find the voltage across the resistor (between points a and b).
2. Find the voltage across the capacitor (between points b and c).
3. (a) Find the magnitude of the impedance across the resistor and the capacitor (between points a and c).
   (b) Find the phase angle between the current and voltage for this combination.
   (c) Find the voltage across this combination.
4. (a) Find the magnitude of the impedance across the resistor, capacitor, and inductor (between points a and d).
   (b) Find the phase angle between the current and voltage for this combination.
   (c) Find the voltage across this combination.

In Exercises 5 through 8 use the following information to find the required quantities. In a given circuit $R = 6.00\ \Omega$, $X_C = 10.0\ \Omega$, and $X_L = 7.00\ \Omega$. Find (a) the magnitude of the impedance and (b) the phase angle between the current and voltage, under the specified conditions.

5. With the resistor removed (an LC circuit)
6. With the capacitor removed (an RL circuit)
7. With the inductor removed (an RC circuit)
8. With all elements present (an RLC circuit)

In Exercises 9 through 18 find the required quantities.

9. Given that the current in a given circuit is $8.00 - 2.00j$ amperes and the impedance is $2.00 + 5.00j$ ohms, find the magnitude of the voltage.
10. Given that the voltage in a given circuit is $8.00 - 3.00j$ volts and the impedance is $2.00 - 1.00j$ ohms, find the magnitude of the current.
11. Given that $\omega = 1000$ rad/s, $C = 0.500\ \mu F$, and $L = 3.00$ H, find the capacitive and inductive reactances.
12. A coil of wire is rotating through a magnetic field at 60.0 Hz. Determine the capacitive reactance for a capacitor of $2.00\ \mu F$ which is in the circuit.
13. If the capacitor and inductor in Exercise 11 are put in a series circuit with a resistance of $4000\ \Omega$, what is the impedance of this combination? Find the phase angle.

14. Rework Exercise 13, assuming that the capacitor is removed.

15. If $\omega = 100$ rad/s and $L = 0.500$ H, what must be the value of C to produce resonance?

16. What is the frequency ω (in hertz) for resonance in a circuit for which $L = 2.00$ H and $C = 25.0$ μF?

17. The average power supplied to any combination of components in an ac circuit is given by the relation $P = VI \cos \theta$, where P is the power (in watts), V is the effective voltage, I is the effective current, and θ is the phase angle between the current and voltage. Assuming that the effective voltage across the resistor, capacitor, and inductor combination in Exercise 13 is 200 V, determine the power supplied to these elements.

18. Find the power supplied to a resistor of 120 Ω and a capacitor of 0.700 μF if $\omega = 1000$ rad/s and the effective voltage is 110 V.

11-8 Exercises for Chapter 11

In Exercises 1 through 16 perform the indicated operations, expressing all answers in the simplest rectangular form.

1. $(6 - 2j) + (4 + j)$ 2. $(12 + 7j) + (-8 + 6j)$
3. $(18 - 3j) - (12 - 5j)$ 4. $(-4 - 2j) - (-6 - 7j)$
5. $(2 + j)(4 - j)$ 6. $(-5 + 3j)(8 - 4j)$
7. $(2j)(6 - 3j)(4 + 3j)$ 8. $j(3 - 2j) - (j^3)(5 + j)$

9. $\dfrac{3}{7 - 6j}$ 10. $\dfrac{4j}{2 + 9j}$ 11. $\dfrac{6 - 4j}{7 - 2j}$ 12. $\dfrac{3 - 2j}{4 + j}$

13. $\dfrac{5j - (3 - j)}{4 - 2j}$ 14. $\dfrac{2 + (j - 6)}{5 - 2j}$ 15. $\dfrac{j(7 - 3j)}{2 + j}$ 16. $\dfrac{(2 - j)(3 + 2j)}{4 - 3j}$

In Exercises 17 through 20 find the values of x and y for which the equations are valid.

17. $3x - 2j = yj - 2$ 18. $2xj - 2y = (y + 3)j - 3$
19. $2x - j + 4 = 6y + 2xj$ 20. $3yj + xj = 6 + 3x + y$

In Exercises 21 through 24 perform the indicated operations graphically; check them algebraically.

21. $(-1 + 5j) + (4 + 6j)$ 22. $(7 - 2j) + (5 + 4j)$
23. $(9 + 2j) - (5 - 6j)$ 24. $(1 + 4j) - (-3 - 3j)$

In Exercises 25 through 32 give the polar and exponential forms of each of the complex numbers.

25. $1 - j$ 26. $4 + 3j$ 27. $-2 - 7j$ 28. $6 - 2j$
29. $1.07 + 4.55j$ 30. $-327 + 158j$ 31. 10 32. $-4j$

In Exercises 33 through 40 give the rectangular form of each of the complex numbers.

33. $2(\cos 225° + j \sin 225°)$ 34. $4(\cos 60° + j \sin 60°)$
35. $5.00(\cos 123.0° + j \sin 123.0°)$ 36. $2.00(\cos 296.0° + j \sin 296.0°)$
37. $2.00e^{0.25j}$ 38. $e^{3.62j}$ 39. $5.37e^{1.90j}$ 40. $4.47e^{6.04j}$

In Exercises 41 through 48 perform the indicated operations. Leave the result in polar form.

41. $[3(\cos 32° + j \sin 32°)][5(\cos 52° + j \sin 52°)]$

42. $[2.5(\cos 162° + j \sin 162°)][8(\cos 115° + j \sin 115°)]$

43. $\dfrac{24(\cos 165° + j \sin 165°)}{3(\cos 106° + j \sin 106°)}$

44. $\dfrac{18(\cos 403° + j \sin 403°)}{4(\cos 192° + j \sin 192°)}$

45. $[2(\cos 16° + j \sin 16°)]^{10}$

46. $[3(\cos 36° + j \sin 36°)]^6$

47. $[3(\cos 110.5° + j \sin 110.5°)]^3$

48. $[5(\cos 220.3° + j \sin 220.3°)]^4$

In Exercises 49 through 52 change each number to polar form and then perform the indicated operations. Express the final result in rectangular and polar forms. Check by performing the same operation in rectangular form.

49. $(1 - j)^{10}$

50. $(\sqrt{3} + j)^8 (1 + j)^5$

51. $\dfrac{(5 + 5j)^4}{(-1 - j)^6}$

52. $(\sqrt{3} - j)^{-8}$

In Exercises 53 through 56 use DeMoivre's theorem to find the indicated roots. Be sure to find all roots.

53. $\sqrt[3]{-8}$ 54. $\sqrt[3]{1}$ 55. $\sqrt[4]{-j}$ 56. $\sqrt[5]{-32}$

In Exercises 57 through 68 find the required quantities.

57. In a given circuit $R = 7.50\ \Omega$ and $X_C = 10.0\ \Omega$. Find the magnitude of the impedance and the phase angle between the current and voltage.

58. In a given circuit $R = 15.0\ \Omega$, $X_C = 27.0\ \Omega$, and $X_L = 35.0\ \Omega$. Find the magnitude of the impedance and the phase angle between the current and voltage.

59. A coil of wire is going around a circle at 60.0 r/s. If this coil generates a current in a circuit containing a resistance of 10.0 Ω, an inductance of 0.010 H, and a capacitance of 500 μF, what is the magnitude of the impedance of the circuit? What is the angle between the current and voltage?

60. A coil of wire rotates at 120 r/s. If the coil generates a current in a circuit containing a resistance of 12.0 Ω, an inductance of 0.040 H and an impedance of 22.0 Ω, what must be the value of a capacitor (in farads) in the circuit?

61. In a given circuit the current is $5.00 - 2.00j$ amperes and the impedance is $6.00 + 3.00j$ ohms. Find the magnitude of the voltage.

62. In a given circuit $I = 6.00$ A and $V = 3.00 - 2.50j$ volts. Find the magnitude of the impedance.

63. What is the magnitude and direction of a force which is represented by $600 - 550j$ pounds?

64. What is the magnitude and direction of a velocity which is represented by $2500 + 1500j$ kilometers per hour?

65. In the study of shearing effects in the spinal column, the expression $\frac{1}{u + j\omega n}$ is found. Express this in rectangular form.

66. In the theory of light reflection on metals, the expression

$$\frac{\mu(1 - kj) - 1}{\mu(1 - kj) + 1}$$

is encountered. Simplify this expression.

67. Show that $e^{j\pi} = -1$.

68. Show that $(e^{j\pi})^{1/2} = j$.

12

Exponential and Logarithmic Functions

12–1 Definition of a Logarithm

In Chapter 10, we dealt in some detail with exponents. There is a special use of exponents which is important in computational work and for theoretical purposes. Exponents used in this manner are given the name **logarithms.** Today, with the extensive use of computers and electronic calculators, logarithms are used much less for computation than in the past. However, their usefulness in advanced mathematics and in applications in technical fields remains of great importance.

To illustrate the importance of logarithms, many applications may be cited. The basic units used to measure the intensity of sound, and those used to measure the intensity of earthquakes, are defined in terms of logarithms. In chemistry, the distinction between a base and an acid is defined in terms of logarithms. In electrical transmission lines, power gains and losses are measured in terms of logarithmic units. In electronics and in mechanical systems, the use of exponential functions, which are closely related to logarithms, is extensive. Many of these applications are illustrated throughout the chapter.

Chapter 10 dealt with exponents in expressions of the form x^n, where we showed that n could be any rational number. Here we shall deal with expressions of the form b^x, where x is any real number. When we look at these expressions, we note the primary difference is that in the second expression *the exponent is variable*. We have not previously dealt with variable exponents. *Thus let us define the* **exponential function** *to be*

$$y = b^x \tag{12–1}$$

In Eq. (12–1), x *is called the logarithm of the number* y *to the base* b. In our work with logarithms we shall restrict all numbers to the real number system. This leads us to choose the base as a positive number other than 1. We know that 1 raised to any power will result in 1, which would make y a constant regardless of the value of x. Negative numbers for b would result in imaginary values for y if x were any fractional exponent with an even integer for its denominator.

Example A
$y = 2^x$ is an exponential function, where x is the logarithm of y to the base 2. This means that 2 raised to a given power gives us the corresponding value of y.

If $x = 2$, $y = 2^2 = 4$; this means that 2 is the logarithm of 4 to the base 2. If $x = 4$, $y = 2^4 = 16$; this means that 4 is the logarithm of 16 to the base 2. If $x = \frac{1}{2}$, $y = 2^{1/2} = 1.41$; this means that $\frac{1}{2}$ is the logarithm of 1.41 to the base 2.

Using the definition of a logarithm, Eq. (12–1) may be solved for x, and is written in the form

$$x = \log_b y \tag{12–2}$$

This equation is read in accordance with the definition of x in Eq. (12–1): x **equals the logarithm of** y **to the base** b. This means that x is the power to which the base b must be raised in order to equal the number y; that is, x is a logarithm, and a logarithm is an exponent. Note that Eqs. (12–1) and (12–2) state the same relationship, but in a different manner. Equation (12–1) is the **exponential form**, and Eq. (12–2) is the **logarithmic form**.

Example B
The equation $y = 2^x$ would be written as $x = \log_2 y$ if we put it in logarithmic form. When we choose values of y to find the corresponding values of x from this equation, we ask ourselves, "2 raised to what power gives y?" Hence if $y = 4$, we know that 2^2 is 4, and x would be 2. If $y = 8$, $2^3 = 8$, or $x = 3$.

Example C
$3^2 = 9$ in logarithmic form is $2 = \log_3 9$; $4^{-1} = \frac{1}{4}$ in logarithmic form is $-1 = \log_4 \left(\frac{1}{4}\right)$. Remember, the exponent may be negative. The base must be positive.

Example D

$(64)^{1/3} = 4$ in logarithmic form is $\frac{1}{3} = \log_{64} 4$,

$(32)^{3/5} = 8$ in logarithmic form is $\frac{3}{5} = \log_{32} 8$

Example E

$\log_2 32 = 5$ in exponential form is $32 = 2^5$,

$\log_6 \left(\frac{1}{36}\right) = -2$ in exponential form is $\frac{1}{36} = 6^{-2}$

Example F

Find b, given that $-4 = \log_b \left(\frac{1}{81}\right)$.

Writing this in exponential form, we have $\frac{1}{81} = b^{-4}$. Thus $b = 3$, since $3^4 = 81$.

Example G

Find y, given that $\log_4 y = \frac{1}{2}$.

In exponential form we have $y = 4^{1/2}$ or $y = 2$.

We see that exponential form is very useful for determining values written in logarithmic form. For this reason it is important that you learn to transform readily from one form to the other.

Exercises 12—1

In Exercises 1 through 12 express the given equations in logarithmic form.

1. $3^3 = 27$	2. $5^2 = 25$	3. $4^4 = 256$	4. $8^2 = 64$
5. $4^{-2} = \frac{1}{16}$	6. $3^{-2} = \frac{1}{9}$	7. $2^{-6} = \frac{1}{64}$	8. $(12)^0 = 1$
9. $8^{1/3} = 2$	10. $(81)^{3/4} = 27$	11. $\left(\frac{1}{4}\right)^2 = \frac{1}{16}$	12. $\left(\frac{1}{2}\right)^{-2} = 4$

In Exercises 13 through 24 express the given equations in exponential form.

13. $\log_3 81 = 4$	14. $\log_{11} 121 = 2$	15. $\log_9 9 = 1$
16. $\log_{15} 1 = 0$	17. $\log_{25} 5 = \frac{1}{2}$	18. $\log_8 16 = \frac{4}{3}$
19. $\log_{243} 3 = \frac{1}{5}$	20. $\log_{1/32} \left(\frac{1}{8}\right) = \frac{3}{5}$	21. $\log_{10} 0.1 = -1$
22. $\log_7 \left(\frac{1}{49}\right) = -2$	23. $\log_{0.5} 16 = -4$	24. $\log_{1/3} 3 = -1$

In Exercises 25 through 40 determine the value of the unknown.

25. $\log_4 16 = x$	26. $\log_5 125 = x$	27. $\log_{10} 0.01 = x$
28. $\log_{16} \left(\frac{1}{4}\right) = x$	29. $\log_7 y = 3$	30. $\log_8 N = 3$
31. $\log_8 y = -\frac{2}{3}$	32. $\log_7 y = -2$	33. $\log_b 81 = 2$
34. $\log_b 625 = 4$	35. $\log_b 4 = -\frac{1}{3}$	36. $\log_b 4 = \frac{2}{3}$
37. $\log_{10} 10^{0.2} = x$	38. $\log_5 5^{1.3} = x$	39. $\log_3 27^{-1} = x$
40. $\log_b \left(\frac{1}{4}\right) = -\frac{1}{2}$		

In Exercises 41 through 44 perform the indicated operations.

41. If there are initially 1000 bacteria in a culture, and the number of bacteria then doubles each hour, the number of bacteria as a function of time is $N = 1000(2^t)$. By writing this equation in logarithmic form, solve for t.

42. Under specified conditions, the instantaneous voltage E in a given circuit can be expressed as

$$E = E_m e^{-Rt/L}$$

By rewriting this equation in logarithmic form, solve for t.

43. An equation relating the number N of atoms of radium at any time t in terms of the number of atoms at $t = 0$, N_0, is $\log_e(N/N_0) = -kt$, where k is a constant. By expressing this equation in exponential form, solve for N.

44. In the theory dealing with the optical brightness of objects, the equation $D = \log_{10}(I_0/I)$ is found. By writing this equation in exponential form, solve for I.

12–2 Graphs of $y = b^x$ and $y = \log_b x$

When we are working with functions, we must keep in mind that a function is defined by the operation being performed on the independent variable, and not by the letter chosen to represent it. However, for consistency, it is normal practice to let y represent the dependent variable and x represent the independent variable. Therefore, the **logarithmic function** is

$$y = \log_b x \qquad\qquad (12\text{--}3)$$

Equations (12–2) and (12–3) express the same *function*, the logarithmic function. They do not represent different functions, due to the difference in location of the variables, since they represent the same operation on the independent variable. Equation (12–3) simply expresses the function with the usual choice of variables.

Graphical representation of functions is often valuable when we wish to demonstrate their properties. We shall now show the graphs of the exponential function [Eq. (12–1)] and the logarithmic function [Eq. (12–3)].

Example A

Plot the graph of $y = 2^x$.

Assuming values for x and then finding the corresponding values for y, we obtain the following table.

x	-3	-2	-1	0	1	2	3	4
y	$\frac{1}{8}$	$\frac{1}{4}$	$\frac{1}{2}$	1	2	4	8	16

From these values we plot the curve, as shown in Fig. 12–1. We note that the x-axis is an asymptote of the curve.

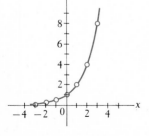

Figure 12–1

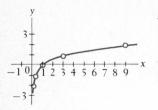

Figure 12–2

Example B

Plot the graph of $y = \log_3 x$.

We can find the points for this graph more easily if we first put the equation in exponential form: $x = 3^y$. By assuming values for y, we can find the corresponding values for x.

x	$\frac{1}{9}$	$\frac{1}{3}$	1	3	9	27
y	-2	-1	0	1	2	3

Using these values, we construct the graph seen in Fig. 12–2.

Any exponential or logarithmic curve, where $b > 1$, will be similar in shape to those of Examples A and B. From these curves we can draw certain conclusions:

(1) *If $0 < x < 1$, $\log_b x < 0$; if $x = 1$, $\log_b 1 = 0$; if $x > 1$, $\log_b x > 0$.*
(2) *If $x > 1$, x increases more rapidly than $\log_b x$.*
(3) *For all values of x, $b^x > 0$.*
(4) *If $x > 1$, b^x increases more rapidly than x.*

Although the bases important to applications are greater than 1, to understand how the curve of the exponential function differs somewhat if $b < 1$, let us consider the following example.

Example C

Plot the graph of $y = (\frac{1}{2})^x$.

The values are found for the following table; the graph is plotted in Fig. 12–3.

x	-3	-2	-1	0	1	2	3	4
y	8	4	2	1	$\frac{1}{2}$	$\frac{1}{4}$	$\frac{1}{8}$	$\frac{1}{16}$

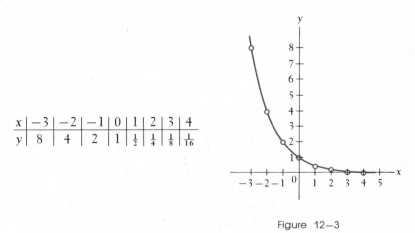

Figure 12–3

We note that as the values of x increase, the values of $(\frac{1}{2})^x$ decrease. This is different from the behavior of $y = b^x$, where $b > 1$.

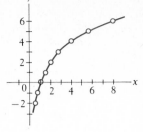

Figure 12–4

Example D

Plot the graph of $y = 2 \log_2 x$.

As in Example B, it is generally more convenient to work with the exponential form. In order to change this equation to exponential form, we first divide each side by 2. Thus, we have

$$\frac{y}{2} = \log_2 x, \qquad x = 2^{y/2}$$

Choosing values of y, we then calculate corresponding values of x and obtain the following table.

x	0.5	0.7	1	1.4	2	2.8	4	5.7	8
y	-2	-1	0	1	2	3	4	5	6

See Fig. 12–4.

Exercises 12–2

In Exercises 1 through 12 plot graphs of the given functions. Values of x from -3 or -2 through 2 or 3 are appropriate.

1. $y = 3^x$
2. $y = 4^x$
3. $y = 6^x$
4. $y = 10^x$
5. $y = (1.5)^x$
6. $y = (2.7)^x$
7. $y = (\frac{1}{3})^x$
8. $y = (\frac{1}{4})^x$
9. $y = 2(2^x)$
10. $y = 1.5(4^x)$
11. $y = 0.5(3^x)$
12. $y = 0.1(10^x)$

In Exercises 13 through 24 plot graphs of the given functions. Values of y from -3 or -2 through 2 or 3 are appropriate for Exercises 13 through 20. Care should be taken in selecting appropriate values used in Exercises 21 through 24.

13. $y = \log_2 x$
14. $y = \log_4 x$
15. $y = \log_6 x$
16. $y = \log_{10} x$
17. $y = \log_{1.5} x$
18. $y = \log_{2.7} x$
19. $y = \log_{32} x$
20. $y = \log_{1/2} x$
21. $y = 2 \log_3 x$
22. $y = 3 \log_2 x$
23. $y = 0.2 \log_4 x$
24. $y = 5 \log_{10} x$

In Exercises 25 through 28 plot the indicated graphs.

25. The electric current in a certain type of circuit is given by $i = I_0 e^{-Rt/L}$, where I_0 is the initial current, R is a resistance, and L is an inductance (see Section 11–7). Plot the graph for i vs. t for a circuit in which $I_0 = 5.0$ A, $R = 10 \ \Omega$, and $L = 5.0$ H. Use $e = 2.7$, and $0 \le t < 4$ s.

26. If $1000 is placed in a bank account in which interest is compounded daily with an effective 8% annual interest, the amount in the account after t years is $A = 1000(1.08)^t$. Plot A as a function of t for $0 \le t \le 5$ years.

27. Under certain conditions the temperature T (in degrees Celsius) of a cooling object as a function of time (in minutes) is $T = 50.0(10^{-0.1t})$. Plot T as a function of t.

28. In Exercise 20 the graph of $y = \log_{1/2} x$ is plotted. By inspecting the graph, and noting the properties of $\log_{1/2} x$, determine some of the differences of logarithms to a base less than 1 from those to a base greater than 1.

12–3 Properties of Logarithms

Since a logarithm is an exponent, it must follow the laws of exponents. Those laws which are of the greatest importance at this time are listed here for reference.

$$b^u \cdot b^v = b^{u+v} \tag{12–4}$$

$$b^u/b^v = b^{u-v} \tag{12–5}$$

$$(b^u)^n = b^{nu} \tag{12–6}$$

We shall now show how these laws for exponents give certain useful properties to logarithms.

If we let $u = \log_b x$ and $v = \log_b y$ and write these equations in exponential form, we have $x = b^u$ and $y = b^v$. Therefore, forming the product of x and y, we obtain

$$xy = b^u b^v = b^{u+v} \qquad \text{or} \qquad xy = b^{u+v}$$

Writing this last equation in logarithmic form yields

$$u + v = \log_b xy$$

or

$$\log_b x + \log_b y = \log_b xy \tag{12–7}$$

Equation (12–7) states the property that *the logarithm of the product of two numbers is equal to the sum of the logarithms of the numbers.*

Using the same definitions of u and v to form the quotient of x and y, we then have

$$\frac{x}{y} = \frac{b^u}{b^v} = b^{u-v} \qquad \text{or} \qquad \frac{x}{y} = b^{u-v}$$

Writing this last equation in logarithmic form, we have

$$u - v = \log_b\left(\frac{x}{y}\right)$$

or

$$\log_b x - \log_b y = \log_b\left(\frac{x}{y}\right) \tag{12–8}$$

Equation (12–8) states the property that *the logarithm of the quotient of two numbers is equal to the logarithm of the numerator minus the logarithm of the denominator.*

If we again let $u = \log_b x$ and write this in exponential form, we have $x = b^u$. To find the nth power of x, we write

$$x^n = (b^u)^n = b^{nu}$$

Expressing this equation in logarithmic form yields

$$nu = \log_b(x^n)$$

or

$$n \log_b x = \log_b(x^n) \qquad (12\text{–}9)$$

This last equation states that *the logarithm of the nth power of a number is equal to n times the logarithm of the number.* The exponent n may be integral or fractional and, therefore, we may use Eq. (12–9) for finding powers and roots of numbers.

Example A

Using Eq. (12–7) we may express $\log_4 15$ as a sum of logarithms as follows:

$$\log_4 15 = \log_4(3 \cdot 5) = \log_4 3 + \log_4 5$$

Using Eq. (12–8) we may express $\log_4(\frac{5}{3})$ as the difference of logarithms as follows:

$$\log_4\left(\frac{5}{3}\right) = \log_4 5 - \log_4 3$$

Using Eq. (12–9) we may express $\log_4 9$ as twice $\log_4 3$ as follows:

$$\log_4 9 = \log_4(3^2) = 2 \log_4 3$$

Example B

Using Eqs. (12–7) through (12–9) we may express a sum or difference of logarithms as the logarithm of a single quantity.

$$\log_4 3 + \log_4 x = \log_4(3 \cdot x) = \log_4 3x$$

$$\log_4 3 - \log_4 x = \log_4\left(\frac{3}{x}\right)$$

$$\log_4 3 + 2 \log_4 x = \log_4 3 + \log_4(x^2) = \log_4 3x^2$$

$$\log_4 3 + 2 \log_4 x - \log_4 y = \log_4\left(\frac{3x^2}{y}\right)$$

We may use Eq. (12–9) to find another important property of logarithms. Since $b = b^1$ in logarithmic form is $\log_b b = 1$, we have

$$\log_b(b^n) = n \log_b b = n(1) = n$$

or

$$\log_b(b^n) = n \qquad (12\text{–}10)$$

Equation (12–10) may be used to evaluate certain logarithms when the exact values may be determined.

Example C

We may evaluate $\log_3 9$ in the following manner: Using Eq. (12–10), we have

$$\log_3 9 = \log_3(3^2) = 2$$

We can establish the exact value since the base of logarithms and the number being raised to the power are the same. Of course, this could have been evaluated directly from the definition of a logarithm.

However, we cannot establish an exact value of $\log_4 9$ in this way. We have

$$\log_4 9 = \log_4(3^2) = 2 \log_4 3$$

We must leave it in this form until we are able to evaluate $\log_4 3$. This can be done, and we shall consider this type of expression later in the chapter.

Example D

Calculate $\log_3(3^{0.4})$.

Using Eq. (12–10) we may calculate this logarithm. This gives us

$$\log_3(3^{0.4}) = 0.4$$

Although we did not calculate $3^{0.4}$ at this point, we were able to calculate $\log_3 3^{0.4}$.

Example E

We may also use Eq. (12–10) in combination with other properties of logarithms. The following illustration shows how it can be used alone or in combination with Eq. (12–8) to evaluate the indicated logarithm.

$$\log_5(\tfrac{1}{25}) = \log_5 1 - \log_5 25 = 0 - \log_5(5^2) = -2$$
$$\log_5(\tfrac{1}{25}) = \log_5(5^{-2}) = -2$$

Either method is appropriate.

In the following examples, the properties of logarithms of Eqs. (12–7) through (12–10) are further illustrated.

Example F

$$\log_2 6 = \log_2(2 \cdot 3) = \log_2 2 + \log_2 3 = 1 + \log_2 3$$
$$\log_3(\tfrac{2}{9}) = \log_3 2 - \log_3 9 = \log_3 2 - \log_3(3^2) = \log_3 2 - 2$$
$$= -2 + \log_3 2$$

Example G

$$\log_{10} \sqrt{7} = \log_{10}(7^{1/2}) = \tfrac{1}{2} \log_{10} 7$$

This demonstrates the property which is especially useful for finding roots of numbers. We see that we need merely to multiply the logarithm of the number by the fractional exponent representing the root to obtain the logarithm of the root.

Similarly,

$$\log_{10} \sqrt[3]{10x} = \log_{10}(10x)^{1/3} = \tfrac{1}{3}\log_{10}(10x)$$
$$= \tfrac{1}{3}(\log_{10}10 + \log_{10}x)$$
$$= \tfrac{1}{3}(1 + \log_{10}x)$$

Example H

Use the basic properties of logarithms to solve for y in terms of x: $\log_b y = 2\log_b x + \log_b a$.

Using Eq. (12–9) and then Eq. (12–7), we have

$$\log_b y = \log_b(x^2) + \log_b a = \log_b(ax^2)$$

Now, since we have the logarithm to the base b of different expressions on each side of the resulting equation, the expressions must be equal. Therefore, $y = ax^2$.

Exercises 12–3

In Exercises 1 through 12 express each as a sum, difference, or multiple of logarithms. See Example A.

1. $\log_5 xy$ **2.** $\log_3 7y$ **3.** $\log_7\left(\frac{5}{a}\right)$ **4.** $\log_3\left(\frac{r}{s}\right)$

5. $\log_2(a^3)$ **6.** $\log_8(n^5)$ **7.** $\log_6 abc$ **8.** $\log_2\left(\frac{xy}{z}\right)$

9. $\log_5 \sqrt[4]{y}$ **10.** $\log_4 \sqrt[7]{x}$ **11.** $\log_2\left(\frac{\sqrt{x}}{a^2}\right)$ **12.** $\log_3\left(\frac{\sqrt{y}}{8}\right)$

In Exercises 13 through 20 express each as the logarithm of a single quantity. See Example B.

13. $\log_b a + \log_b c$ **14.** $\log_2 3 + \log_2 x$

15. $\log_5 9 - \log_5 3$ **16.** $\log_8 6 - \log_8 a$

17. $\log_b x^2 - \log_b \sqrt{x}$ **18.** $\log_4 3^3 + \log_4 9$

19. $2\log_e 2 + 3\log_e n$ **20.** $\tfrac{1}{2}\log_b a - 2\log_b 5$

In Exercises 21 through 28 determine the exact value of each of the given logarithms.

21. $\log_2\left(\frac{1}{32}\right)$ **22.** $\log_3\left(\frac{1}{81}\right)$ **23.** $\log_2(2^{2.5})$ **24.** $\log_5(5^{0.1})$

25. $\log_7 \sqrt{7}$ **26.** $\log_6 \sqrt[3]{6}$ **27.** $\log_3 \sqrt[4]{27}$ **28.** $\log_5 \sqrt[3]{25}$

In Exercises 29 through 40 express each as a sum, difference, or multiple of logarithms. In each case part of the logarithm may be determined exactly.

29. $\log_3 18$ **30.** $\log_5 75$ **31.** $\log_2\left(\frac{1}{6}\right)$ **32.** $\log_{10}(0.05)$

33. $\log_3 \sqrt{6}$ **34.** $\log_2 \sqrt[3]{24}$ **35.** $\log_2(4^2 \cdot 3^3)$ **36.** $\log_7(7^4 \cdot 3^5)$

37. $\log_{10} 3000$ **38.** $\log_{10}(40^2)$ **39.** $\log_{10}\left(\frac{27}{100}\right)$ **40.** $\log_5\left(\frac{4}{125}\right)$

In Exercises 41 through 48 solve for y in terms of x.

41. $\log_b y = \log_b 2 + \log_b x$ **42.** $\log_b y = \log_b 6 + \log_b x$

43. $\log_4 y = \log_4 x - \log_4 5$ **44.** $\log_3 y = \log_3 7 - \log_3 x$

45. $\log_{10} y = 2\log_{10} 7 - 3\log_{10} x$ **46.** $\log_b y = 3\log_b \sqrt{x} + 2\log_b 10$

47. $5\log_2 y - \log_2 x = 3\log_2 4 + \log_2 a$ **48.** $4\log_2 x - 3\log_2 y = \log_2 27$

In Exercises 49 through 52 using $\log_{10} 2 = 0.301$, evaluate each of the given expressions.

49. $\log_{10} 4$ **50.** $\log_{10} 20$ **51.** $\log_{10}(0.5)$ **52.** $\log_{10} 8000$

In Exercises 53 through 56 plot the indicated graphs and perform the indicated operations.

53. Plot the graphs of $y = 2 \log_2 x$ and $y = \log_2 x^2$, and show that they are the same.

54. Plot the graphs of $y = \log_2 4x$ and $y = 2 + \log_2 x$, and show that they are the same.

55. An equation used in thermodynamics is $S = C \log_e T - nR \log_e P$. Express this equation with a single logarithm on the right side.

56. An equation used for a certain electric circuit is $\log_e i - \log_e I = -t/RC$. Solve for i.

12–4 Logarithms to the Base 10

In Section 12–1 we stated that a base of logarithms must be a positive number, not equal to one. In the examples and exercises of the previous sections we used a number of different bases. There are, however, only two bases which are used extensively. They are 10 and e, where e equals approximately 2.718. The number e was first introduced in Section 11–5.

Base 10 logarithms are used primarily for calculations and in certain types of applications. Base e logarithms are used extensively in technical and scientific work. In this section we discuss how to determine the base 10 logarithm of any given number. Base e logarithms are considered in Section 12–7.

In Section 1–5, we showed that any number may be expressed in scientific notation as the product of a number between 1 and 10 and a power of 10. Writing this as $N = P \times 10^k$, and taking logarithms of both sides of this equation, we have

$$\log_b N = \log_b (P \times 10^k) = \log_b P + \log_b 10^k = \log_b P + k \log_b 10$$

If we let $b = 10$, then $k \log_{10} 10 = k$, and this equation becomes

$$\log_{10} N = k + \log_{10} P \tag{12–11}$$

Equation (12–11) shows us that if we have a method for finding logarithms to the base 10 of numbers between 1 and 10, then we can find the logarithm of *any* number to base 10. The value of k can be found by writing the number N in scientific notation, and P is a number between 1 and 10. Logarithms to the base 10 have been tabulated, and tables of these **common logarithms** may be found in Appendix E. Logarithms may be calculated for any base, but for purposes of computation, logarithms to the base 10 are the most convenient. From now on we shall not write the number 10 to indicate the base, and log N will be assumed to be to the base 10. Thus,

$$\log N = k + \log P \qquad (12\text{--}12)$$

In Eq. (12–12), *k is called the* **characteristic,** *and log P is known as the* **mantissa.** Remember, *k* is the power of 10 of the number, when it is written in scientific notation, and the term log *P* is the logarithm of the number between 1 and 10.

Example A
For N = 3600 = 3.6 × 10³, we see that the characteristic *k* = 3, and the mantissa log *P* = log 3.6. Therefore, log 3600 = 3 + log 3.6.
For N = 80.9 = 8.09 × 10¹, we see that *k* = 1 and log *P* = log 8.09. Therefore, log 80.9 = 1 + log 8.09.

Example B
For N = 0.00543 = 5.43 × 10⁻³, we see that *k* = −3 and log *P* = log 5.43. Therefore, log 0.00543 = −3 + log 5.43.
For N = 0.741 = 7.41 × 10⁻¹, we see that *k* = −1 and log *P* = log 7.41. Therefore, log 0.741 = −1 + log 7.41.

To find log *P* we use Table 2 in Appendix E. The following examples illustrate how to use this table.

Example C
Find log 572.
We first write the number in scientific notation as 5.72 × 10². The characteristic is 2, and we must now find log 5.72. We look in the column headed N and find 57 (the first two significant digits). Then, to the right of this, we look under the column headed 2 (the third significant digit) and we find 7574. All numbers between 1 and 10 will have common logarithms between 0 and 1 (log 1 = 0 and log 10 = 1). Therefore, log 5.72 = 0.7574, and the logarithm of 572 = 2 + 0.7574. We then write this in the usual form of 2.7574, and write this result as

log 572 = 2.7574

It should be emphasized that both the mantissa and characteristic of a logarithm must be found before the logarithm of a number is complete. The mantissa is found from Table 2, and the characteristic is found from the location of the decimal point. A rather common error is to assume the logarithm has been found when the mantissa is determined. However, the characteristic is just as much a proper part of the logarithm as the mantissa.

Example D
Find log 0.00485.

Writing this number in scientific notation gives us 4.85×10^{-3}, and we see that $k = -3$. From the tables we find that log $4.85 = 0.6857$. Thus, log $0.00485 = -3 + 0.6857$. We do *not* write this as -3.6857, for this would say that the mantissa was also negative, which it is not. To avoid this possible confusion, we shall write it in the form $7.6857 - 10$. We shall follow this policy whenever the characteristic is negative. That is, we shall write a negative characteristic as the appropriate positive number with 10 subtracted. For example, for a characteristic of -6, we write 4 before the mantissa and -10 after it. Thus,

$$\log 0.00485 = 7.6857 - 10$$

Example E
Other examples of logarithms are as follows:

$$89,000 = 8.9 \times 10^4: k = 4, \log 8.9 = 0.9494; \log 89000 = 4.9494$$
$$0.307 = 3.07 \times 10^{-1}: k = -1, \log 3.07 = 0.4871;$$
$$\log 0.307 = 9.4871 - 10$$
$$0.00629 = 6.29 \times 10^{-3}: k = -3, \log 6.29 = 0.7987;$$
$$\log 0.00629 = 7.7987 - 10$$

Table 2 is a four-place table, which means that we can obtain accuracy to four significant digits. However, only three digits may be read directly, and the fourth place is found by interpolation. We discussed this in Section 3–3, in reference to finding values from trigonometric tables. The method for finding values from logarithmic tables is the same. It is illustrated in the following examples.

Example F
Find log 686300.

In scientific notation, $686300 = 6.863 \times 10^5$. This means that the characteristic is 5. To find the mantissa from the table, we must interpolate, finding the value $\frac{3}{10}$ (since the fourth digit is 3) of the way between log 6.86 and log 6.87. These latter two values are 0.8363 and 0.8370. The tabular difference is 7, and $(\frac{3}{10})(7) = 2$ (to one significant digit). Adding this to the mantissa 0.8363 gives 0.8365. Hence, log $686300 = 5.8365$.

Example G
Find log 0.02178.

In scientific notation, $0.02178 = 2.178 \times 10^{-2}$. Therefore, the characteristic is -2. To find the mantissa, we must interpolate, finding the value $\frac{8}{10}$ of the way between log 2.17 and log 2.18. These two values are 0.3365 and 0.3385. The tabular difference is 20, and $(\frac{8}{10})(20) = 16$. Adding this to 0.3365, we find the mantissa to be 0.3381. Therefore, we have log $0.02178 = 8.3381 - 10$.

We may also use Table 2 to find N if we know log N. In this case we may refer to N as the **antilogarithm** of log N. The following examples illustrate the determination of antilogarithms.

Example H

Given log $N = 1.5263$, find N.

Direct observation of the given logarithm tells us that the characteristic is 1 and that $N = P \times 10^1$. In Table 2 we find 5263 opposite 33 and under 6. Thus, $P = 3.360$. This means that $N = 3.360 \times 10^1$, or in ordinary notation, $N = 33.60$.

Example I

Given log $N = 8.2611 - 10$, find N.

Using the method described in Example D, we determine that the characteristic is $8 - 10 = -2$. We look for 0.2611 in the tables, and find that it is between 2601 (log 1.82) and 2625 (log 1.83). These latter two values have a tabular difference of 24, and the difference between 2611 and 2601 is 10. Thus, the number we want is $\frac{10}{24}$, or 0.4 of the way between 1.82 and 1.83. Hence,

$$N = 1.824 \times 10^{-2} = 0.01824$$

The basic properties of logarithms allow us to find the logarithms of products, quotients, and roots. The following example illustrates the method.

Example J

Find log $\sqrt{0.846}$.

From the properties of logarithms we write log $\sqrt{0.846} = \frac{1}{2}$ log 0.846. From the tables we find that log 8.46 = 0.9274. Therefore, log 0.846 = 9.9274 − 10. To obtain the desired logarithm we must divide this by 2. This will result in a 5 to be subtracted. To assure our answer being in the usual form of a negative characteristic, we shall write log 0.846 as 19.9274 − 20. Thus, log $\sqrt{0.846}$ = 9.9637 − 10, when we divide through by 2. In this type of problem we choose that part of the characteristic which is to be subtracted so that 10 will result after division. This is done by *adding* the proper multiple of 10 to each part of the characteristic.

Exercises 12—4

In Exercises 1 through 16 find the common logarithm of each of the given numbers.

1. 567	**2.** 60.5	**3.** 0.0640
4. 0.000566	**5.** 9.24×10^6	**6.** 3.19×10^{15}
7. 1.17×10^{-4}	**8.** 8.04×10^{-8}	**9.** 1.053
10. 73.27	**11.** 0.2384	**12.** 0.004309
13. 7.331×10^8	**14.** 1.656×10^{-5}	**15.** $\sqrt{0.002006}$
16. $\sqrt[3]{38310000}$		

In Exercises 17 through 32 find the antilogarithm N from the given logarithms.

17. 4.4378	**18.** 0.9294	**19.** 8.6955 − 10	**20.** 3.0212 − 10
21. 3.3010	**22.** 8.8241	**23.** 9.8597 − 10	**24.** 7.4409 − 10
25. 1.9495	**26.** 2.4367	**27.** 6.6090 − 10	**28.** 9.3755 − 10
29. 0.1543	**30.** 10.2750	**31.** 17.7625 − 20	**32.** 35.6641 − 40

In Exercises 33 through 40 find the logarithms of the given numbers.

33. A certain radar signal has a frequency of 1.15×10^9 Hz.
34. The earth travels about 595,000,000 mi in one year.
35. A certain bank charges 7.5% interest on loans that it makes.
36. The coefficient of thermal expansion of steel is about 1.2×10^{-5} per °C.
37. A typical x-ray tube operates with a voltage of 150,000 V.
38. The bending moment of a particular concrete column is 4.60×10^6 lb-in.
39. Electronic calculators which display numbers in scientific notation can calculate results which are as numerically small as 10^{-99}.
40. In an air sample taken in an urban area, $5/10^6$ of the air was carbon monoxide.

12—5 Computations Using Logarithms

Logarithms were developed in the seventeenth century for the purpose of making tedious and complicated calculations which arose in astronomy and navigation. Until recently (the mid 1970s), when calculators came into extensive use, logarithms were used commonly for calculational purposes. The slide rule was also used extensively, but its accuracy was generally limited to three significant digits. (The construction of a slide rule is based on logarithms.) Also, logarithms are used for some computations performed by calculators.

Logarithms can be used to make more complicated calculations by means of additions, subtractions, and basic multiplications and divisions. By means of logarithms and the basic arithmetic operations we can determine the answer to such problems as $\sqrt[5]{7.60}$ or $(89.1)^{0.3}$. In this section we show how logarithms are used to make such calculations to an accuracy up to four significant digits. (Greater accuracy is obtainable with more extensive tables.) Even if logarithms are not required for such calculations, performing them with logarithms provides an opportunity to better understand the meaning and properties of logarithms. The following examples illustrate the use of logarithms in computations.

Example A
By the use of logarithms, calculate the value of $(42.80)(215.0)$.

Equation (12–7) tells us that $\log xy = \log x + \log y$. If we find $\log 42.80$ and $\log 215.0$ and add them, we shall have the logarithm of the product. Using this result, we look up the antilogarithm, which is the desired product.

$$\begin{aligned}
\log 42.80 &= 1.6314 \\
\log 215.0 &= \underline{2.3324} \\
\log(42.80)(215.0) &= 3.9638 \\
\log 9200 &= 3.9638
\end{aligned}$$

Thus, $(42.80)(215.0) = 9200$.

Example B

By the use of logarithms, calculate the value of 8.640 ÷ 45.55.

From Eq. (12–8), we know that $\log (x/y) = \log x - \log y$. Therefore, by subtracting log 45.55 from log 8.640, we shall have the logarithm of the quotient. The antilogarithm gives the desired result.

$$\begin{aligned}
\log 8.640 &= 10.9365 - 10 \\
\log 45.55 &= \underline{\ 1.6585} \\
\log(8.640/45.55) &= \ \ 9.2780 - 10
\end{aligned}$$

We wrote the characteristic of log 8.640 as $10 - 10$, so that when we subtracted, the part of the result containing the mantissa would be positive although the characteristic was negative. The antilogarithm of $9.2780 - 10$ is 0.1897. Interpolation is required to determine the fourth significant digit. Therefore,

$$\frac{8.640}{45.55} = 0.1897$$

Example C

By the use of logarithms, calculate the value of $\sqrt[5]{0.03760}$.

From Eq. (12–9), we know that $\log x^n = n \log x$. Therefore, by writing $\sqrt[5]{0.03760} = (0.03760)^{1/5}$, we know that we can find the logarithm of the result by multiplying log 0.03760 by $\frac{1}{5}$. Now, we determine that $\log 0.03760 = 8.5752 - 10$. Since we wish to multiply this by $\frac{1}{5}$, we shall write this logarithm as

$$\log 0.03760 = 48.5752 - 50$$

by adding and subtracting 40. Multiplying by $\frac{1}{5}$, we have

$$\tfrac{1}{5} \log 0.03760 = \tfrac{1}{5}(48.5752 - 50) = 9.7150 - 10$$

The antilogarithm of $9.7150 - 10$ is 0.5188. Therefore,

$$\sqrt[5]{0.03760} = 0.5188$$

The following examples illustrate calculations which involve the use of a combination of the basic properties of logarithms.

Example D

Calculate the value of

$$N = \frac{6.875 \sqrt{98.66}}{7.880}$$

$$\log N = \log 6.875 + \tfrac{1}{2} \log 98.66 - \log 7.880$$

$$\begin{aligned}
\log 6.875 &= 0.8373 \qquad \log 98.66 = 1.9941 \\
\tfrac{1}{2} \log 98.66 &= \underline{0.9970} \\
&\ \ \ \ 1.8343 \\
\log 7.880 &= \underline{0.8965} \\
\log N &= 0.9378 \qquad N = 8.666
\end{aligned}$$

Example E
Calculate the value of

$$N = \left[\frac{(0.05325)\sqrt{0.8884}}{\sqrt[3]{895.3}} \right]^{0.3}$$

$\log N = 0.3(\log 0.05325 + \frac{1}{2} \log 0.8884 - \frac{1}{3} \log 895.3)$

$$
\begin{array}{ll}
\log 0.05325 = 8.7263 - 10 & \log 0.8884 = 19.9486 - 20 \\
\frac{1}{2} \log 0.8884 = 9.9743 - 10 & \\
\phantom{\frac{1}{3} \log 895.3 =} 18.7006 - 20 & \\
\frac{1}{3} \log 895.3 = 0.9840 & \log 895.3 = 2.9520 \\
\phantom{\frac{1}{3} \log 895.3 =} 17.7166 - 20 & \\
0.3(97.7166 - 100) = 29.3150 - 30 & N = 0.2065
\end{array}
$$

Example F

The velocity of an object moving with constant acceleration can be found from the equation $v = \sqrt{v_0{}^2 + 2as}$, where v_0 is the initial velocity, a is the acceleration, and s is the distance traveled. Determine the velocity of an object if $v_0 = 86.46$ ft/s, $a = 17.92$ ft/s², and $s = 136.7$ ft.

Before we can compute the square root, we must square v_0, determine the product $2as$, and add these results. Another calculation is then necessary to determine the square root:

$$\log v_0{}^2 = 2 \log 86.46 = 2(1.9368) = 3.8736 \qquad v_0{}^2 = 7475$$

$$\log 2as = \log 2 + \log 17.92 + \log 136.7$$

$$
\begin{array}{ll}
\log 2 = 0.3010 & \\
\log 17.92 = 1.2534 & \\
\log 136.7 = 2.1357 & \\
\log 2as = 3.6901 & 2as = 4899 \\
 & v_0{}^2 + 2as = 12374
\end{array}
$$

$$\log v = \tfrac{1}{2} \log 12370 = \tfrac{1}{2}(4.0924) = 2.0462$$
$$v = 111.2 \text{ ft/s}$$

Note that 12374 was rounded off to 12370 for purposes of calculation, since only four significant digits can be used.

In Exercises 1 through 32 use logarithms to perform the indicated calculations.

1. $(5.980)(14.30)$ **2.** $(0.7640)(551.0)$ **3.** $(0.8256)(0.04532)$

4. $(0.0008080)(2623)$ **5.** $\dfrac{790.0}{8.020}$ **6.** $\dfrac{31.60}{0.4540}$

7. $\dfrac{76.98}{43.82}$ **8.** $\dfrac{0.008670}{0.6521}$ **9.** $(6.750)^6$

10. $(0.9040)^5$ **11.** $(89.00)^{0.3}$ **12.** $(0.04030)^{0.6}$

13. $\sqrt[5]{7.600}$ **14.** $\sqrt[3]{95.40}$ **15.** $\sqrt{641.6}$

16. $\sqrt[8]{308.7}$

17. $\dfrac{(4510)(0.6120)}{738.0}$

18. $\dfrac{87.42}{(11.54)(0.9316)}$

19. $\dfrac{\sqrt{0.07530}}{86.02}$

20. $(\sqrt{5.270})(\sqrt[3]{42.19})$

21. $\dfrac{89.42\,\sqrt[3]{0.1142}}{0.04290}$

22. $\left(\dfrac{75.19}{900.5\,\sqrt{15.00}}\right)^{0.1}$

23. $(8.723)^{9.742}$ (Find log log 8.723.)

24. $(4.072)^{-10}$ (Be careful, especially if your method of solution leads to a negative "mantissa.")

25. What is the area of a rectangular field 325.5 m by 246.4 m?

26. In testing a new engine in order to determine its fuel economy, a car traveled 426.4 mi on 11.40 gallons of gasoline. What is the miles per gallon rating of the car's engine?

27. Plutonium is radioactive and disintegrates such that of 1000 mg originally present, $1000(0.5)^{0.0000410t}$ mg will remain after t years. Calculate the amount present after 10,000 years.

28. The molecular mass M of a gas may be calculated from the formula $PV = mRT/M$, where P is the pressure, V is the volume, m is the mass, R is a constant for all gases, and T is the thermodynamic temperature. Determine M (in kilograms) if you are given that $P = 1.081 \times 10^5$ Pa, $V = 2.485 \times 10^{-4}$ m³, $R = 8.314$ J/mol·K, $T = 373.6$ K, and $m = 1.267 \times 10^{-3}$ kg.

29. The velocity of sound in air is given by $v = \sqrt{1.410p/d}$, where p is the pressure and d is the density. Given that $p = 1.013 \times 10^5$ Pa and $d = 1.293$ kg/m³, find v (in meters per second).

30. In undergoing an adiabatic (no *heat* gained or lost) expansion, the relation between the initial and final temperatures and volumes is given by $T_f = T_i(V_i/V_f)^{0.4}$, where the temperatures are expressed in kelvins. Given that $V_i = 1.506$ cm³, $V_f = 0.1290$ cm³ and $T_i = 373.2$ K, find T_f.

31. Given the density of iron as 491.0 lb/ft³, find the radius of a spherical iron ball which weighs 25.65 lb.

32. When a light ray is incident on glass, the percentage of light reflected is given by

$$I_r = 100\left(1 - \frac{4n_a n_g}{(n_a + n_g)^2}\right)$$

where n_a and n_g are the indices of refraction of air and glass, respectively. What percentage of light is reflected if $n_g = 1.532$ and $n_a = 1.000$?

12–6 Logarithms of Trigonometric Functions

When we are working with trigonometric functions, there is often a great deal of calculational work to be done. Logarithms may be used to make these calculations. In such cases, if we wish to use logarithms, we could look up the function of the desired angle and then find the logarithm of this number to perform some operation on it.

Example A
Find log sin 23°20′. (Use Tables 2 and 3 in Appendix E.)

$$\sin 23°20′ = 0.3961, \qquad \log 0.3961 = 9.5978 - 10$$

To facilitate work when using trigonometric functions, we can use tables of logarithms of the trigonometric functions, which allow us to find these logarithms in one step.

Example B
Find log sin 23°20′. (Use Table 5.)
  By direct reading we find log sin 23°20′ = 9.5978 − 10.

Like other similar tables, these tables enable us to find by interpolation values not directly listed. We may also find an angle directly, if we know the logarithm of some function of that angle.

Example C
Find log tan 57°34′.
  We find that log tan 57°30′ = 0.1958 and that log tan 57°40′ = 0.1986. The tabular difference is 28, and 0.4(28) = 11 (to 2 digits). Thus,

$$\log \tan 57°34′ = 0.1969$$

Example D
Given that log cos θ = 9.9049 − 10, find θ.
  From Table 5 we find that

$$\log \cos 36°30′ = 9.9052 - 10$$

and

$$\log \cos 36°40′ = 9.9042 - 10$$

We find that the tabular difference between listed values is 10, and the tabular difference between 9.9049 and 9.9052 is 3. Therefore,

$$\theta = 36°33′$$

(Be careful—the values of the cosine and its logarithm *decrease* as θ increases.)

Example E
Solve the following oblique triangle, using logarithms for your calculations: $a = 34.12$, $A = 31°20′$, $B = 52°43′$.
  We first determine that the solution may be completed by the law of sines. Next we find $C = 95°57′$, and then we can find sides b and c. From the law of sines we have

$$b = \frac{a \sin B}{\sin A} \qquad \text{and} \qquad c = \frac{a \sin C}{\sin A}$$

By using a and sin A in both calculations, we reduce the amount of information required from the tables.

$$\log b = \log 34.12 + \log \sin 52°43' - \log \sin 31°20'$$

$$
\begin{aligned}
\log 34.12 &= 1.5330 \\
\log \sin 52°43' &= \underline{9.9007 - 10} \\
& 11.4337 - 10 \\
\log \sin 31°20' &= \underline{9.7160 - 10} \\
& 1.7177
\end{aligned}
$$

$$b = 52.20$$

$$\log c = \log 34.12 + \log \sin 95°57' - \log \sin 31°20'$$

$$
\begin{aligned}
\log 34.12 &= 1.5330 \\
\log \sin 95°57' &= \underline{9.9976 - 10} \quad (\log \sin 84°3') \\
& 11.5306 - 10 \\
\log \sin 31°20' &= \underline{9.7160 - 10} \\
& 1.8146
\end{aligned}
$$

$$c = 65.26$$

Example F

A ship passes a certain point at noon going north at 12.35 mi/h. A second ship passes the same point at 1 PM going east at 16.42 mi/h. How far apart are the ships at 3 PM?

At 3 PM the first ship is 37.05 mi from the point and the second ship is 32.84 mi from it (Fig. 12–5). Since the angle between their directions is 90°, the distance d between them can be found from the Pythagorean theorem. Also, by finding the angle α from tan $\alpha = 37.05/32.84$, we can then solve for d by using $d = 32.84/\cos \alpha$. This second method has the advantage that once we determine α, we can find log cos α immediately from the table by shifting from the log tan column to the log cos column:

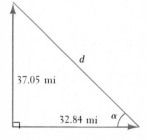

Figure 12–5

$$\log \tan \alpha = \log 37.05 - \log 32.84$$

$$
\begin{aligned}
\log 37.05 &= 1.5688 \\
\log 32.84 &= \underline{1.5164} \\
\log \tan \alpha &= 0.0524 \\
\alpha &= 48°27'
\end{aligned}
$$

$$\log d = \log 32.84 - \log \cos \alpha$$

$$
\begin{aligned}
\log 32.84 &= 11.5164 - 10 \\
\log \cos \alpha &= \underline{9.8217 - 10} \\
\log d &= 1.6947 \\
d &= 49.51 \text{ mi}
\end{aligned}
$$

Exercises 12−6

In Exercises 1 through 12 use Table 5 to find the values of the indicated logarithms.

1. log sin 22°10′   2. log cos 31°40′   3. log tan 52°0′
4. log cot 61°50′   5. log sin 38°14′   6. log cos 12°7′
7. log tan 56°45′   8. log sin 75°42′   9. log cos 322°17′
10. log cot 228′12′   11. log cos 79°6′   12. log tan 85°52′

In Exercises 13 through 20 use Table 5 to find the smallest positive θ.

13. log sin θ = 9.6740 − 10   14. log cot θ = 9.9341 − 10
15. log cos θ = 9.8056 − 10   16. log tan θ = 9.9140 − 10
17. log tan θ = 0.0599   18. log sin θ = 8.9150 − 10
19. log cos θ = 9.9998 − 10   20. log cot θ = 0.4767

In Exercises 21 through 28 solve the given triangles by logarithms.

21. $A = 82°5′, C = 90°0′, c = 86.17$ 22. $B = 54°10′, C = 90°0′, b = 15.70$
23. $A = 65°40′, B = 72°10′, a = 9100$ 24. $A = 63°14′, C = 18°16′, c = 0.5320$
25. $A = 67°10′, B = 44°42′, b = 9.328$ 26. $A = 47°36′, a = 17.45, b = 10.29$
27. $a = 298.5, b = 382.6, C = 90°0′$ 28. $a = 7392, b = 4218, c = 4005$

In Exercises 29 through 36 solve the given problems by logarithms.

29. A 24.2-ft. vertical steel girder is supported by a cable connected at the top of the girder and at the level of the foot of the girder. If the angle between the girder and cable is 37.5°, how long is the cable?

30. A jet cruising at 730.0 km/h is descending at an angle of 9.5°. What is its loss in altitude in 3.000 min?

31. A 56.62-lb block is on an inclined plane which makes an angle of 22°42′ with respect to the horizontal. What are the components of the weight parallel to and perpendicular to the plane?

32. A surveyor finds one side of a rectangular piece of land to be 137.8 ft, and the angle between this side and the diagonal to be 36°17′. What is the area of the piece of land?

33. Two spring balances support an object as shown in Fig. 12−6. What is the weight of the object? We can find T_2 by using the fact that there is no net force acting horizontally. This means that

$$T_1 \sin \alpha = T_2 \sin \beta$$

34. An airplane headed south has a speed with respect to the air of 418.5 mi/h. The speed with respect to the ground is 425.0 mi/h in a direction of 3°16′ east of south. Find the direction and speed of the wind.

35. For a given electrical circuit, $R = 21.35 \, \Omega$ and $X_C = 13.37 \, \Omega$. Find the phase angle between the current and voltage (see Section 11−7).

36. The limiting distance d of resolution of a microscope is given by the formula $d = \lambda/2 \sin \theta$, where λ is the wavelength of the light being used and θ is an angle associated with the object and lens. Calculate d for $\lambda = 0.5893 \, \mu m$ and $\theta = 81°30′$.

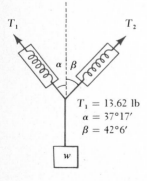

$T_1 = 13.62$ lb
$\alpha = 37°17′$
$\beta = 42°6′$

Figure 12−6

12—7 Logarithms to Bases Other Than 10; Natural Logarithms

As we mentioned earlier, another number which is important as a base of logarithms is the number e. *Logarithms to the base e are called* **natural logarithms.** Since e is an irrational number equal to approximately 2.718, it may appear to be a very unnatural choice as a base of logarithms. However, in the development of the calculus, the reason for its choice, and the fact that it is a very natural number for a base of logarithms, is shown.

Just as the notation $\log x$ refers to logarithms to the base 10, the notation $\ln x$ is used to denote logarithms to the base e. Due to the extensive use of natural logarithms, the notation $\ln x$ is more convenient than $\log_e x$, although they mean the same thing.

Since more than one base is important, there are times when it is useful to be able to change a logarithm in one base to another base. If $u = \log_b x$, then $b^u = x$. Taking logarithms of both sides of this last expression to the base a, we have

$$\log_a b^u = \log_a x$$
$$u \log_a b = \log_a x$$

Solving this last equation for u, we have

$$u = \frac{\log_a x}{\log_a b}$$

However, $u = \log_b x$, which means that

$$\log_b x = \frac{\log_a x}{\log_a b} \tag{12–13}$$

Equation (12–13) allows us to change a logarithm in one base to a logarithm in another base. The following examples illustrate the method of performing this operation.

Example A

Change $\log 20 = 1.3010$ to a logarithm with base e; that is, find $\ln 20$.
  In Eq. (12–13), if we let $b = e$ and $a = 10$, we have

$$\log_e x = \frac{\log_{10} x}{\log_{10} e}$$

or

$$\ln x = \frac{\log x}{\log e}$$

In this example, $x = 20$. Therefore,

$$\ln 20 = \frac{\log 20}{\log e} = \frac{\log 20}{\log 2.718} = \frac{1.3010}{0.4343} = 2.996$$

Here we divided 1.3010 by 0.4343 to obtain the final result. Even though 1.3010 and 0.4343 are logarithms, it is their quotient that we need. We can calculate the quotient of 1.301 and 0.4343 by any appropriate means, which, of course, includes logarithms. Using logarithms, we have

$$\log 1.301 = 10.1143 - 10$$
$$\log 0.4343 = \underline{\ 9.6378 - 10\ }$$
$$0.4765$$

The antilogarithm of 0.4765 is 2.996, which means that $\ln 20 = 2.996$.

Example B

Find $\log_5 560$.

In Eq. (12–13), if we let $b = 5$ and $a = 10$, we have

$$\log_5 x = \frac{\log x}{\log 5}$$

In this example, $x = 560$. Therefore, we have

$$\log_5 560 = \frac{\log 560}{\log 5} = \frac{2.7482}{0.6990} = 3.932$$

Therefore, we have found that $\log_5 560 = 3.932$.

Since natural logarithms are used extensively, it is often convenient to have Eq. (12–13) written specifically for use with logarithms to the base 10 and natural logarithms. Since $\log e = 0.4343$, and $\ln 10 = 2.3026$, we can write

$$\ln x = 2.3026 \log x \qquad (12\text{–}14)$$

and

$$\log x = 0.4343 \ln x \qquad (12\text{–}15)$$

Example C

Using Eq. (12–14), find $\ln 0.811$.

From Eq. (12–14), we have

$$\ln 0.811 = 2.3026 \log 0.811$$

In many applications of natural logarithms, it is preferable to write the logarithms in their explicit form, even when they are negative. Therefore, here we will express $\log 0.811$ as

$$\log 0.811 = 9.9090 - 10 = -0.0910$$

Thus,

$$\ln 0.811 = 2.3026(-0.0910)$$
$$= -0.2095$$

Values of natural logarithms are also available from tables and scientific calculators. In tables of natural logarithms it is not possible to present a table of mantissas, since mantissas of numbers which differ only by a power of ten are not the same. This can be seen by taking natural logarithms of a number written in scientific notation. For $N = P \times 10^k$, we have

$$\ln N = \ln P + \ln 10^k$$
$$= \ln P + k \ln 10$$

or

$$\ln N = k \ln 10 + \ln P \qquad\qquad (12\text{--}16)$$

Thus, a table of natural logarithms can be used directly only for the numbers which are tabulated. Its use can be extended by use of Eq. (12–16). In Appendix E, Table 6 is such a table of natural logarithms. The following example illustrates the use of this table and Eq. (12–16).

Example D

Using Table 6 and Eq. (12–16), determine the value of ln 820.

Since 820 does not appear in the column labeled n in Table 6, we cannot find its value directly from the table. However, we can write $820 = 8.2 \times 10^2$ and use Eq. (12–16). Here we have

$$\ln 820 = 2 \ln 10 + \ln 8.2$$

We determine ln 8.2 from the table, and note that the value of $2 \ln 10$ is also given. Thus,

$$\ln 820 = 4.6052 + 2.1041$$
$$= 6.7093$$

It is possible to use natural logarithms for calculations in the same way that we use common logarithms. By using Table 6 with interpolation, three-place accuracy is obtainable. Other applications of natural logarithms are found in many fields of technology. One such application is shown in the following example, and others are found in the exercises.

Example E

Under certain conditions, the electric current i in a circuit containing a resistance and an inductance (see Section 11–7) is given by $\ln \frac{i}{I} = -\frac{Rt}{L}$, where I is the current at $t = 0$, R is the resistance, t is the time, and L is the inductance. Calculate how long (in seconds) it takes i to reach 0.430 A, if $I = 0.750$ A, $R = 7.50$ Ω, and $L = 1.25$ H.

Solving for t, we have

$$t = -\frac{L \ln(i/I)}{R} = -\frac{L(\ln i - \ln I)}{R}$$

Thus, for the given values, we have

$$t = - \frac{1.25(\ln 0.430 - \ln 0.750)}{7.50} \text{ s}$$

$$\ln 0.430 = \frac{\log 0.430}{\log e} = \frac{-0.3665}{0.4343} = -0.8439$$

$$\ln 0.750 = \frac{\log 0.750}{\log e} = \frac{-0.1249}{0.4343} = -0.2876$$

$$t = - \frac{1.25(-0.8439 + 0.2876)}{7.50} = \frac{1.25(0.5563)}{7.50} = 0.0927 \text{ s}$$

Therefore, the current changes from 0.750 A to 0.430 A in 0.0927 s.

Exercises 12−7

In Exercises 1 through 8 use logarithms to the base 10 to find the natural logarithms of the given numbers.

1. 26.0   2. 631   3. 1.56   4. 45.7
5. 0.501   6. 0.052   7. 0.00732   8. 0.000443

In Exercises 9 through 16 use logarithms to the base 10 to find the indicated logarithms.

9. $\log_7 42$ 10. $\log_2 86$ 11. $\log_5 245$ 12. $\log_3 706$
13. $\log_{12} 122$ 14. $\log_{20} 86$ 15. $\log_{40} 750$ 16. $\log_{100} 3720$

In Exercises 17 through 24 use Eq. (12–14) to find the natural logarithms of the indicated numbers.

17. 51.4   18. 293   19. 1.39   20. 65.6
21. 0.991   22. 0.0020   23. 0.0129   24. 0.0000608

In Exercises 25 through 28 use Eq. (12–15) and Table 6 to find the logarithms to the base 10 of the indicated numbers.

25. 2.7   26. 40   27. 87   28. 0.63

In Exercises 29 through 32 perform the indicated calculations by use of natural logarithms from Table 6.

29. 2.50×4700 30. $\dfrac{380}{0.900}$ 31. $\sqrt{75.0}$ 32. $(2.9)^{10}$

In Exercises 33 through 40 solve the given problems.

33. Solve for y in terms of x: $\ln y - \ln x = 1.0986$
34. Solve for y in terms of x: $\ln y + 2 \ln x = 1 + \ln 5$
35. If interest is compounded continuously (daily compounded interest closely approximates this), a bank account can double in t years according to the equation $i = \frac{\ln 2}{t}$, where i is the interest rate. What interest rate is required for an account to double in 8.5 years?

36. One approximate formula for world population growth is $T = 50.0 \ln 2$, where T is the number of years for the population to double. According to this formula, how long does it take for the population to double?

37. For the electric circuit of Example E, find how long it takes the current to reach 0.1 of the initial value of 0.750 A.

38. Under specific conditions, an equation relating the pressure P and volume V of a gas is $\ln P = C - \gamma \ln V$, where C and γ (the Greek gamma) are constants. Find P (in atmospheres) if $C = 3.000$, $\gamma = 1.50$, and $V = 2.20$ ft³.

39. If 100 mg of radium radioactively decays, an equation relating the amount Q which remains, and the time t is

$$\ln Q - \ln 100 = kt$$

where k is a constant. If $Q = 90.0$ mg, and $k = -0.000410$ per year, find t.

40. For a certain electric circuit, the voltage v is given by $v = e^{-0.1t}$. What is $\ln v$ after 2.00 s?

12—8 Exponential and Logarithmic Equations

In solving equations in which there is an unknown exponent, it is often advantageous to take logarithms of both sides of the equation and then proceed. In solving logarithmic equations, one should keep in mind the basic properties of logarithms, since these can often help transform the equation into a solvable form. There is, however, no general algebraic method for solving such equations, and here we shall solve only some special cases.

Example A
Solve the equation $2^x = 8$.

By writing this in logarithmic form, we have

$$x = \log_2 8 = 3$$

We could also solve this equation by taking logarithms of both sides. This would yield

$$\log 2^x = \log 8$$
$$x \log 2 = \log 8$$

$$= \frac{\log 8}{\log 2} = \frac{0.9031}{0.3010} = 3.00$$

This last method is more generally applicable, since the first method is good only if we can directly evaluate the logarithm which results.

Example B
Solve the equation $3^{x-2} = 5$.

Taking logarithms of both sides, we have

$$\log 3^{x-2} = \log 5 \qquad \text{or} \qquad (x - 2)\log 3 = \log 5$$

Solving this last equation for x, we have

$$x = 2 + \frac{\log 5}{\log 3} = 2 + \frac{0.6990}{0.4771} = 2 + 1.465 = 3.465$$

Thus, the solution to this equation is $x = 3.465$.

Example C
Solve the equation $2(4^{x-1}) = 17^x$.

By taking logarithms of both sides, we have the following:

$$\log 2 + (x - 1) \log 4 = x \log 17$$
$$x \log 4 - x \log 17 = \log 4 - \log 2$$
$$x(\log 4 - \log 17) = \log 4 - \log 2$$
$$x = \frac{\log 4 - \log 2}{\log 4 - \log 17} = \frac{\log (4/2)}{\log 4 - \log 17}$$
$$= \frac{\log 2}{\log 4 - \log 17} = \frac{0.3010}{0.6021 - 1.2304}$$
$$= \frac{0.3010}{-0.6283} = -0.479$$

Some of the important measurements in scientific and technical work are defined in terms of logarithms. We shall consider here some of the important applications which are basic logarithmic formulas. In using them we shall solve some equations in which logarithms are involved. The following example illustrates one such area of application, and others are found in the exercises.

Example D
It has been found that the human ear responds to sound on a scale which is approximately proportional to the logarithm of the intensity of the sound. Thus, the loudness of sound, measured in decibels, is defined by the equation $b = 10 \log (I/I_0)$, where I is the intensity of the sound and I_0 is the minimum intensity detectable.

A busy city street has a loudness of 70 dB, and riveting has a loudness of 100 dB. How many times greater is the intensity of the sound of riveting I_r than the sound of the city street I_c?

First, we substitute the decibel readings into the above definition. This gives us

$$70 = 10 \log(I_c/I_o) \qquad \text{and} \qquad 100 = 10 \log(I_r/I_o)$$

To solve these equations for I_c and I_r, we divide each side by 10 and then use the exponential form. Thus, we have

$$7.0 = \log(I_c/I_o) \qquad \text{and} \qquad 10 = \log(I_r/I_o)$$

$$\frac{I_c}{I_o} = 10^{7.0} \qquad\qquad\qquad \frac{I_r}{I_o} = 10^{10}$$

$$I_c = I_o(10^{7.0}) \qquad\qquad\qquad I_r = I_o(10^{10})$$

Since we want the number of times I_r is greater than I_c, we divide I_r by I_c. This gives us

$$\frac{I_r}{I_c} = \frac{I_o(10^{10})}{I_o(10^{7.0})} = \frac{10^{10}}{10^{7.0}} = 10^{3.0}$$

or

$$I_r = 10^{3.0}I_c = 1000 I_c$$

Thus, the sound of riveting is 1000 times as intense as the sound of the city street. This demonstrates that sound intensity levels are considerably greater than loudness levels. (See Exercise 28.)

The following examples illustrate the solution of other logarithmic equations.

Example E
Solve the equation $\log_2 7 - \log_2 14 = x$.

Using the basic properties of logarithms, we arrive at the following result:

$$\log_2\left(\tfrac{7}{14}\right) = x$$
$$\log_2\left(\tfrac{1}{2}\right) = x \qquad \text{or} \qquad \tfrac{1}{2} = 2^x$$

Thus, $x = -1$.

Example F
Solve the equation $2 \log x - 1 = \log(1 - 2x)$.

$$\log x^2 - \log(1 - 2x) = 1$$

$$\log \frac{x^2}{1 - 2x} = 1$$

$$\frac{x^2}{1 - 2x} = 10^1$$

$$x^2 = 10 - 20x$$

$$x^2 + 20x - 10 = 0$$

$$x = \frac{-20 \pm \sqrt{400 + 40}}{2} = -10 \pm \sqrt{110}$$

Since logarithms of negative numbers are not defined, we have the result that $x = \sqrt{110} - 10$.

Exercises 12–8

In Exercises 1 through 24 solve the given equations.

1. $2^x = 16$ 2. $3^x = \frac{1}{81}$

3. $5^x = 4$ 4. $6^x = 15$

5. $6^{x+1} = 10$ 6. $5^{x-1} = 2$

7. $4(3^x) = 5$ 8. $14^x = 40$

9. $0.8^x = 0.4$ 10. $0.6^x = 100$

11. $(15.6)^{x+2} = 23^x$ 12. $5^{x+2} = 3^{2x}$

13. $2 \log_2 x = 4$ 14. $3 \log_8 x = 1$

15. $3 \log_8 x = 2$ 16. $5 \log_{32} x = -3$

17. $2 \log(3 - x) = 1$ 18. $3 \log(2x - 1) = 1$

19. $\frac{1}{2} \log(x + 2) + \log 5 = 1$ 20. $\frac{1}{2} \log(x - 1) - \log x = 0$

21. $\log_5(x - 3) + \log_5 x = \log_5 4$ 22. $\log_7 x + \log_7(2x - 5) = \log_7 3$

23. $\log(2x - 1) + \log(x + 4) = 1$ 24. $\log_2 x + \log_2(x + 2) = 3$

In Exercises 25 through 32 determine the required quantities.

25. For a certain electric circuit, the current i is given by $i = 1.50e^{-200t}$. For what value of t (in seconds) is $i = 1.00$ A? (Use 2.718 to approximate e.)

26. The amount q of a certain radioactive substance remaining after t years is given by $q = 100(0.900)^t$. After how many years are there 50.0 mg of the substance remaining?

27. Referring to Example D, how many times I_0 is the intensity of sound of a jet plane which has a loudness of 110 dB?

28. Referring to Example D, show that if the difference in loudness of two sounds is d decibels, the louder sound is $10^{d/10}$ more intense than the quieter sound.

29. Measured on the Richter scale, the magnitude of an earthquake of intensity I is defined as $R = \log(I/I_0)$, where I_0 is a minimum level for comparison. How many times I_0 was the 1906 San Francisco earthquake whose magnitude was 8.25 on the Richter scale?

30. How many more times intense was the 1964 Alaska earthquake, $R = 7.5$, than the 1971 Los Angeles earthquake, $R = 6.7$? (See Exercise 29.)

31. In chemistry, the pH-value of a solution is a measure of its acidity. The pH-value is defined by the relation $pH = -\log (H^+)$, where H^+ is the hydrogen ion concentration. If the pH of a certain wine is 3.4065, find the hydrogen ion concentration. (If the pH-value is less than 7, the solution is acid. If the pH-value is above 7, the solution is basic.)

32. Referring to Exercise 31, find the hydrogen ion concentration for ammonia for which the pH is 10.8.

To solve more complicated problems, we may use graphical methods. For example, if we wish to solve the equation $2^x + 3^x = 50$, we can set up the function $y = 2^x + 3^x - 50$ and then determine its zeros graphically. Note that the given equation can be written as $2^x + 3^x - 50 = 0$, and therefore the zeros of the function which has been set up will give the desired solution. In Exercises 33 through 36 solve the given equations in this way.

33. $2^x + 3^x = 50$ 34. $3^{x+1} - 4^x = 1$

35. $3^x - 2x = 40$ 36. $4^x + x^2 = 25$

12–9 Graphs on Logarithmic and Semilogarithmic Paper

If, when we are graphing, the range of values of one variable is much greater than the corresponding range of values of the other variable, it is often convenient to use what is known as **semilogarithmic** paper. On this paper the y-axis (usually) is marked off in distances proportional to the logarithms of numbers. This means that the distances between numbers on this axis are not even, but this system does allow for a much greater range of values, and with much greater accuracy for many of the numbers. There is another advantage to this paper: Many equations which would exhibit more complex curves on ordinary graph paper will work out as straight lines on semilogarithmic paper. In many instances this makes the analysis of the curve easier.

If we wish to indicate a large range of values for each of the variables, we use what is known as **logarithmic** paper, or as **log-log** paper. Both axes are marked off with logarithmic scales. Again, the more complicated equations give simple curves or straight lines on this paper.

The following examples will illustrate the use of semilogarithmic and logarithmic paper.

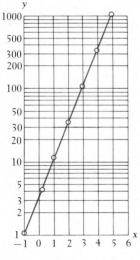

Figure 12–7

Example A

Construct the graph of $y = 4(3)^x$ on semilogarithmic paper.

First we construct a table of values.

x	-1	0	1	2	3	4	5
y	1.3	4	12	36	108	324	972

From the table we see that the range of y-values is large. If we plotted this curve on a regular coordinate system we would have large units for each interval along the y-axis. This would make the values of 1.3, 4, 12, and 36 appear at practically the same level. However, if we use semilogarithmic graph paper, we can label each axis such that all y-values are accurately plotted as well as the x-values.

The logarithmic scale is shown in cycles, and we must label the base line of the first cycle as 1 times a power of ten (0.01, 0.1, 1, 10, 100, etc.) with the following cycle labeled with the next power of ten. The lines between are labeled with 2, 3, 4, and so on, times the proper power of ten. See the vertical scale in Fig. 12–7. We now plot the points in the table on the graph. The resulting graph is a straight line, as we see in Fig. 12–7. Taking logarithms of both sides the equation, we have

$$\log y = \log 4 + x \log 3$$

However, since $\log y$ was plotted automatically (because we used semilogarithmic paper), the graph really represents

$$u = \log 4 + x \log 3$$

where $u = \log y$; $\log 3$ and $\log 4$ are constants, and therefore this equation is of the form $u = ax + b$, which is a straight line (see Section 4–1). If we had sketched this graph on regular coordinate paper, the scale would be so reduced that the values of 0.5, 1.3, 4, 12, and 36 would appear at practically the same level.

Example B

Construct the graph of $x^4y^2 = 1$ on logarithmic paper.

First we solve for y and then construct a table of values. Considering positive values of x and y, we have

$$y = \sqrt{\frac{1}{x^4}} = \frac{1}{x^2}$$

x	0.5	1	2	8	20
y	4	1	0.25	0.0156	0.0025

We now plot these values on log-log paper on which both scales are logarithmic, as shown in Fig. 12–8. We again note that we have a straight line. Taking logarithms of both sides of the equation, we have

$$4 \log x + 2 \log y = 0$$

If we let $u = \log y$ and $v = \log x$, we then have

$$4v + 2u = 0 \qquad \text{or} \qquad u = -2v$$

which is the equation of a straight line as shown in Fig. 12–8. It should be pointed out that not all graphs on logarithmic paper are straight lines.

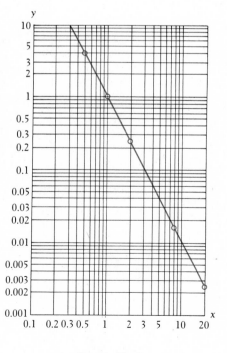

Figure 12–8

Example C

The deflection (in feet) of a certain cantilever beam as a function of the distance x from one end is

$$d = 0.0001(30x^2 - x^3)$$

If the beam is 20.0 ft long, plot a graph of d vs. x on log-log paper. Constructing a table of values we have

x (feet)	1.00	1.50	2.00	3.00	4.00	5.00	10.0	15.0	20.0
d (feet)	0.00290	0.00641	0.0112	0.0243	0.0416	0.0625	0.200	0.338	0.400

The graph is shown in Fig. 12−9.

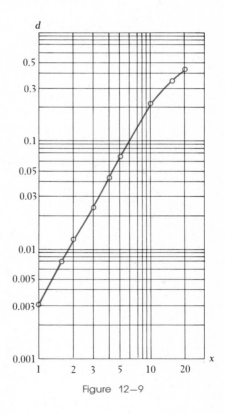

Figure 12−9

Logarithmic and semilogarithmic paper is often useful for plotting data derived from experimentation. Often the data cover too large a range of values to be plotted on ordinary graph paper. The following example illustrates how we use semilogarithmic paper to plot data.

Example D

The vapor pressure of water depends on the temperature. The following table gives the vapor pressure (in kilopascals) for corresponding values of temperature (in degrees Celsius).

Pressure	1.19	2.33	7.34	19.9	47.3	101	199	361	617
Temp.	10	20	40	60	80	100	120	140	160

These data are then plotted on semilogarithmic paper, as shown in Fig. 12–10. Intermediate values of temperature and pressure can then be read directly from the graph.

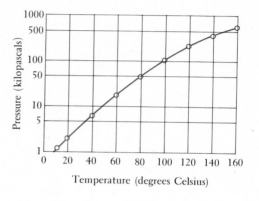

Figure 12–10

Exercises 12–9

In Exercises 1 through 12 plot the graphs of the given functions on semilogarithmic paper.

1. $y = 2^x$

2. $y = 5^x$

3. $y = 2(4^x)$

4. $y = 5(10^x)$

5. $y = 3^{-x}$

6. $y = 2^{-x}$

7. $y = x^3$

8. $y = x^5$

9. $y = 3x^2$

10. $y = 2x^4$

11. $y = 2x^3 + 4x$

12. $y = 4x^3 + 2x^2$

In Exercises 13 through 24 plot the graphs of the given functions on log-log paper.

13. $y = 0.01x^4$

14. $y = 0.02x^3$

15. $y = \sqrt{x}$

16. $y = x^{2/3}$

17. $y = x^2 + 2x$

18. $y = x + \sqrt{x}$

19. $xy = 4$

20. $xy^2 = 10$

21. $y^2x = 1$

22. $x^2y^3 = 1$

23. $x^2y^2 = 25$

24. $x^3y = 8$

In Exercises 25 through 30 plot the indicated graphs.

25. The atmospheric pressure p at a given height h is given by $p = p_0 e^{-kh}$, where p_0 and k are constants. On semilogarithmic paper plot p (in atmospheres) vs. h (in feet) for $0 \le h \le 10^5$. Use $e = 2.7$, $p_0 = 1$ atm, and $k = 10^{-5}$ per foot.

26. Strontium 90 decays according to the equation $N = N_0 e^{-0.028t}$, where N is the amount present after t years, and N_0 is the original amount. Plot N vs. t on semilogarithmic paper if $N_0 = 1000$ g.

27. A company estimates that the value of a piece of machinery is $V = 75000(2^{-0.15t})$, where V is the value (in dollars) t years after the purchase. Plot V vs. t on semilogarithmic paper.

28. At constant temperature, the relation between the volume V and pressure P of a gas is $PV = c$, where c is a constant. On logarithmic paper, plot the graph of P (in atmospheres) vs. V (in cubic feet) for $c = 4$ atm-ft³. Use values of $0.1 \leq P \leq 10$.

29. One end of a very hot steel bar is sprayed with a stream of cool water. The rate of cooling (in degrees Fahrenheit per second) as a function of the distance (in inches) from the end of the bar is then measured. The following results are obtained.

Cooling rate	600	190	100	72	46	29	17	10	6
Distance	0.063	0.13	0.19	0.25	0.38	0.50	0.75	1.0	1.5

Plot the data on logarithmic paper. Such experiments are made to determine the hardenability of steel.

30. The magnetic intensity H (in amperes per meter) and flux density B (in teslas) of annealed iron are given in the following table.

H	10	50	100	150	200	500	1000	10000	100000
B	0.0042	0.043	0.67	1.01	1.18	1.44	1.58	1.72	2.26

Plot H versus B on logarithmic paper.

12–10 Exercises for Chapter 12

In Exercises 1 through 12 determine the value of x.

1. $\log_{10} x = 4$
2. $\log_9 x = 3$
3. $\log_5 x = -1$
4. $\log_4 x = -\frac{1}{2}$
5. $\log_2 64 = x$
6. $\log_{12} 144 = x$
7. $\log_8 32 = x$
8. $\log_9 27 = x$
9. $\log_x 36 = 2$
10. $\log_x 243 = 5$
11. $\log_x 10 = \frac{1}{2}$
12. $\log_x 8 = \frac{3}{4}$

In Exercises 13 through 24 express each as a sum, difference, or multiple of logarithms. Wherever possible, evaluate logarithms of the result.

13. $\log_3 2x$
14. $\log_5 \left(\frac{7}{a}\right)$
15. $\log_5 (t^2)$
16. $\log_6 \sqrt{5}$
17. $\log_2 28$
18. $\log_7 98$
19. $\log_3 \left(\frac{9}{x}\right)$
20. $\log_6 \left(\frac{5}{36}\right)$
21. $\log_4 \sqrt{48}$
22. $\log_6 \sqrt{72y}$
23. $\log_{10} (1000x^4)$
24. $\log_3 (9^2 \cdot 6^3)$

In Exercises 25 through 28, solve for y in terms of x.

25. $\log_6 y = \log_6 4 - \log_6 x$
26. $\log_3 y = \frac{1}{2} \log_3 7 + \frac{1}{2} \log_3 x$
27. $\log_2 y + \log_2 x = 3$
28. $6 \log_4 y = 8 \log_4 4 - 3 \log_4 x$

In Exercises 29 through 32 graph the given functions.

29. $y = 0.5(5^x)$
30. $y = 3(2^x)$
31. $y = 0.5 \log_4 x$
32. $y = 10 \log_{16} x$

In Exercises 33 through 44 use logarithms to perform the indicated calculations.

33. $(13.60)(0.6930)$ 34. $(0.07255)(4320)$ 35. $\dfrac{9.826}{0.08004}$

36. $\dfrac{87.64}{108.2}$ 37. $(5.670)^{20}$ 38. $(0.9823)^{10}$

39. $\sqrt[4]{17.22}$ 40. $(0.006247)^{0.2}$ 41. $\dfrac{\sqrt{8645}}{19.49}$

42. $[(9.060)(13.45)]^{1/3}$ 43. $\dfrac{\sqrt[5]{22.46}\,(14.98)}{\sqrt[3]{0.8664}}$ 44. $(12.66)^{1.096}$

In Exercises 45 through 48 use logarithms to solve the given triangles.

45. $A = 36°20'$, $C = 90°0'$, $a = 15.60$ 46. $B = 14°50'$, $C = 90°0'$, $c = 4730$
47. $A = 45°0'$, $B = 67°10'$, $a = 76.50$ 48. $B = 123°0'$, $C = 15°43'$, $a = 0.9122$

In Exercises 49 through 52, by using logarithms to the base 10, find the natural logarithms of the given numbers.

49. 8.86 50. 33.0 51. 2.07 52. 0.542

In Exercises 53 through 56 solve the given equations.

53. $3^{x+2} = 5^x$ 54. $5^x = 10$
55. $\log_8(x + 2) + \log_8 2 = 2$ 56. $\log(x + 2) + \log x = 0.4771$

In Exercises 57 and 58 plot the graphs of the given functions on semilogarithmic paper. In Exercises 59 and 60 plot the graphs of the given functions on log-log paper.

57. $y = 6^x$ 58. $y = 5x^3$ 59. $y = \sqrt[3]{x}$ 60. $xy^4 = 16$

In Exercises 61 through 76 use logarithms to make any indicated calculations.

61. The vapor pressure P over a liquid may be related to temperature by the formula $\log P = a/T + b$, where a and b are constants. Solve for P.

62. The Beer–Lambert law of light absorption may be expressed as

$$\log \frac{I}{I_0} = -\alpha x$$

where I/I_0 is that fraction of the incident light beam which is transmitted, α is a constant, and x is the distance the light travels through the medium. Solve for I.

63. The edge of a cubical metal block expanded from 37.75 cm to 38.25 cm while being heated. What was the increase in volume?

64. The ratio of the rates of diffusion of two gases is given by the equation $r_1/r_2 = \sqrt{m_2}/\sqrt{m_1}$, where m_1 and m_2 are the masses of the molecules of the gases. Given that $m_1 = 31.44$ units of mass and $m_2 = 74.92$ units of mass, calculate the ratio of r_1 to r_2.

65. Under certain circumstances the efficiency of an internal combustion engine is given by

$$\text{eff (in percent)} = 100\left(1 - \frac{1}{(V_1/V_2)^{0.4}}\right)$$

where V_1 and V_2 are, respectively, the maximum and minimum volumes of air in a cylinder. The ratio V_1/V_2 is called the compression ratio. Compute the efficiency of an engine with a compression ratio of 6.550.

66. If P dollars are invested at an interest rate r which is compounded n times a year, the value A of the investment t years later is given by the formula $A = P(1 + r/n)^{nt}$. What is the value after 5 years of \$5636 invested at $5\frac{1}{2}\%$ and compounded quarterly?

67. Points A and B are on opposite sides of a lake. A third point C is found such that $AC = 402.5$ ft and $BC = 317.9$ ft. What is the distance AB if the angle BAC is $41°18'$?

68. The angle of depression of a fire noticed directly north of a 74.50-ft fire tower is $5°30'$. The angle of depression of a stream running east to west, and also north of the tower, is $13°0'$. How far is the fire from the stream?

69. Under certain conditions, the potential (in volts) due to a magnet is given by $V = -k \ln (1 + l/b)$, with l the length of the magnet and b the distance from the point where the potential is measured. Find V, if $k = 2$ units, $l = 5.00$ cm, and $b = 2.00$ cm.

70. The Nernst equation,

$$E = E_0 - \frac{0.05910}{n} \log Q$$

is used for oxidation-reduction reactions. In the equation, E and E_0 are voltages, n is the number of electrons involved in the reaction, and Q is a measure of the activity of reaction. Given that $E_0 = 1.1000$ V, $E = 1.1300$ V, and $n = 2$, what is the value of Q?

71. For first-order chemical reactions, concentration of a reacting chemical species is related to time by the expression

$$\log \frac{x_0}{x} = kt$$

where x_0 is the initial concentration and x is the concentration after time t. Determine the quantity of sucrose remaining after 3 h, if the initial concentration is 9.00 g-mol/L and $k = 0.00158$ per minute.

72. The power gain of an electronic device such as an amplifier is defined as $n = 10 \log (P_o/P_i)$, where n is measured in decibels, P_o is the power output, and P_i is the power input. If $P_o = 10.0$ W and $P_i = 0.125$ W, calculate the power gain. (See Example D of Section 12–8.)

73. In 1975 it was estimated that the total annual world demand for copper was $C = 9.0e^{0.08t}$, where C is in millions of tons of copper and t is the number of years after 1975. When will copper demand be 20 million tons?

74. The bacteria population in a certain culture is given by $N = 1000(1.5)^t$. How long does it take for the population to reach 10,000 if t is measured in hours?

75. Plot a semilogarithmic graph of N vs. t for the bacteria culture of Exercise 74.

76. The luminous efficiency (measured in lumens per watt) of a tungsten lamp as a function of its input power (in watts) is given by the following table. On semilogarithmic paper, plot efficiency versus power.

Efficiency	7.8	10.4	11.7	13.9	16.3	18.3	19.9	21.5
Power	10	25	40	60	100	200	500	1000

13

Additional Types of Equations and Systems of Equations

13-1 Graphical Solution of Systems of Equations

In Chapter 2 we learned how to graph a function as well as how to solve equations graphically. Since then we have dealt with methods for solving quadratic equations and systems of linear equations. Also, we have graphed the trigonometric, logarithmic, and exponential functions. In this section we shall introduce one more general type of equation: the general quadratic equation. We shall then discuss graphical solutions of systems of equations involving quadratic equations as well as other types of equations. Here again, as in solving systems of linear equations, we shall obtain the desired solution by finding the values of x and y which satisfy both equations in a system at the same time. From the standpoint of graphs, this means that we wish to find all points which the graphs of the given functions have in common.

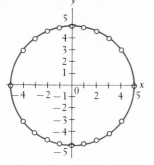

Figure 13—1

An equation of the form

$$ax^2 + bxy + cy^2 + dx + ey + f = 0 \qquad (13\text{—}1)$$

is called a **general quadratic equation in x and y.** We shall be interested primarily in some special cases of this equation. The graphs of the various possible forms of this equation result in curves known as **conic sections.** These curves are the circle, parabola, ellipse, and hyperbola. The following examples will illustrate these curves. A more complete discussion will be found in Chapter 20.

Example A
Plot the graph of the equation $x^2 + y^2 = 25$.

We first solve this equation for y, obtaining $y = \pm\sqrt{25 - x^2}$. We now assume values for x and find the corresponding values for y.

x	0	± 1	± 2	± 3	± 4	± 5
y	± 5	± 4.9	± 4.6	± 4	± 3	0

If we try values greater than 5, we have imaginary numbers. These cannot be plotted, for we assume that both x and y are real. (The complex plane is only for *numbers* of the form $a + bj$ and does not represent pairs of numbers representing two variables.) When we give the value $x = \pm 4$ when $y = \pm 3$, this is simply a short way of representing 4 points. These points are $(4, 3)$, $(4, -3)$, $(-4, 3)$, $(-4, -3)$. We note in Fig. 13—1 that the resulting curve is a **circle.** A circle always results from an equation of the form $x^2 + y^2 = r^2$, and r is the radius of the circle.

Example B
Plot the graph of the equation $y = 3x^2 - 6x$.

We plotted curves of this form in Section 2—3, and we follow the same method here.

x	-1	0	1	2	3
y	9	0	-3	0	9

This curve (Fig. 13—2) is called a **parabola.** A parabola always results if the equation is of the form $y = ax^2 + dx + f$.

Example C
Plot the graph of the equation $2x^2 + 5y^2 = 10$.

We first solve for y, then we construct the table of values.

$$y = \pm\sqrt{\frac{10 - 2x^2}{5}}$$

x	0	± 1	± 2	$\pm \sqrt{5} \ (= \pm 2.2)$
y	± 1.4	± 1.3	± 0.6	0

Values of x greater than $\sqrt{5}$ result in imaginary values of y. The curve (Fig. 13—3) is an **ellipse.** An ellipse results from an equation of the form $ax^2 + cy^2 = k$.

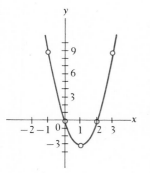

Figure 13—2

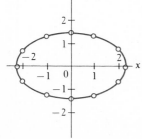

Figure 13—3

Example D

Plot the graph of the equation $xy = 4$.

Solving for y, we obtain $y = 4/x$. Now, constructing the table of values, we have the following points.

x	-8	-4	-2	-1	$-\frac{1}{2}$	$\frac{1}{2}$	1	2	4	8
y	$-\frac{1}{2}$	-1	-2	-4	-8	8	4	2	1	$\frac{1}{2}$

Plotting these points, we obtain the curve in Fig. 13–4. This curve is called a **hyperbola**. A hyperbola always results if the equation is of the form $xy = k$. We also obtain a hyperbola if the equation is of the form $ax^2 - cy^2 = k$.

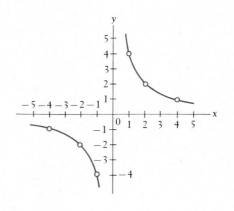

Figure 13–4

To solve any system of equations graphically, we need only graph the equations and then find the points of intersection. If the curves do not intersect, the system has no real solution.

Example E

Graphically solve the system of equations

$$2x^2 - y^2 = 4$$
$$x - 3y = 6$$

We should recognize the second equation as that of a straight line. Now constructing the tables, we solve $2x^2 - y^2 = 4$ for y and get $y = \pm\sqrt{2x^2 - 4}$. Therefore, we obtain the following table.

x	± 1.4	± 2	± 4	± 6
y	0	± 2	± 5.3	± 8.2

For the straight line we have the points

x	0	6	3
y	-2	0	-1

The solutions, as indicated on the graph in Fig. 13–5, are approximately $x = 1.8$, $y = -1.4$, and $x = -2.4$, $y = -2.8$.

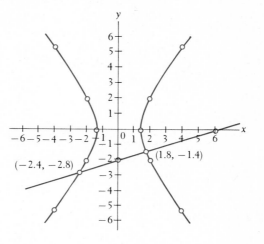

Figure 13–5

The following example illustrates the graphical solution of a system of equations in which one of the equations is not a general quadratic type.

Example F

Graphically solve the system of equations

$$9x^2 + 4y^2 = 36$$
$$y = 3^x$$

The first equation is of the form represented by an ellipse, as indicated in Example C. The second equation is an exponential function, as discussed in Chapter 12. Solving the first equation for y, we have $y = \pm\frac{1}{2}\sqrt{36 - 9x^2}$. Substituting values for x, we obtain the following table.

x	0	±1	±2
y	±3	±2.6	0

For the exponential function, we obtain the following table.

x	-3	-2	-1	0	1	2
y	$\frac{1}{27}$	$\frac{1}{9}$	$\frac{1}{3}$	1	3	9

We plot these curves as shown in Fig. 13–6. The points of intersection are approximately $x = -1.9$, $y = 0.1$, and $x = 0.9$, $y = 2.7$.

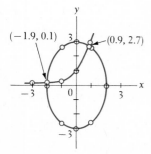

Figure 13–6

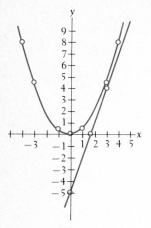

Figure 13–7

Example G

Graphically solve the system of equations

$$x^2 = 2y$$
$$3x - y = 5$$

We note that the two curves in this system are a parabola and a straight line. Solving the equation of the parabola for y, we obtain $y = \frac{1}{2}x^2$. We construct the following table.

x	0	± 1	± 2	± 3	± 4
y	0	$\frac{1}{2}$	2	$\frac{9}{2}$	8

For the straight line we have the following points.

x	0	$\frac{5}{3}$	3
y	-5	0	4

We plot these curves and see in Fig. 13–7 that they do not intersect, so we conclude that there are no real solutions to the system.

Exercises 13–1

In Exercises 1 through 20 solve the given systems of equations graphically.

1. $y = 2x$
   $x^2 + y^2 = 16$

2. $3x - y = 4$
   $y = 6 - 2x^2$

3. $x^2 + 2y^2 = 8$
   $x - 2y = 4$

4. $y = 3x - 6$
   $xy = 6$

5. $y = x^2 - 2$
   $4y = 12x - 17$

6. $x^2 + 4y^2 = 4$
   $2y = 12 - x$

7. $y = x^2$
   $xy = 4$

8. $y = -2x^2$
   $y = x^2 - 6$

9. $y = -x^2 + 4$
   $x^2 + y^2 = 9$

10. $y = 2x^2 - 1$
    $x^2 + 2y^2 = 16$

11. $x^2 - 4y^2 = 16$
    $x^2 + y^2 = 1$

12. $y = 2x^2 - 4x$
    $xy = -4$

13. $2x^2 + 3y^2 = 19$
    $x^2 + y^2 = 9$

14. $x^2 - y^2 = 4$
    $2x^2 + y^2 = 16$

15. $x^2 + y^2 = 1$
    $xy = \frac{1}{2}$

16. $x^2 + y^2 = 25$
    $x^2 - y^2 = 7$

17. $y = x^2$
    $y = \sin x$

18. $y = 2^x$
    $x^2 + y^2 = 4$

19. $x^2 - y^2 = 1$
    $y = \log_2 x$

20. $y = \cos x$
    $y = \log_3 x$

In Exercises 21 through 24 solve the indicated systems of equations graphically. In Exercises 23 and 24 the necessary systems of equations must be properly set up.

21. A rectangular field has a perimeter of 1140 m and an area of 75,600 m². Show that the two equations necessary to find the dimensions l and w are $l + w = 570$, $lw = 75600$. Graphically solve for l and w.

22. The diagonal of a rectangular metal plate is 10 in. and the area is 50 in.^{2}. Show that the two equations necessary to find the dimensions l and w are $l^2 + w^2 = 100$, $lw = 50$. Graphically solve for l and w.

23. The power developed in an electric resistor R is i^2R, where i is the current. If one current passes through a 2 Ω resistor, and the second current passes through a 3 Ω resistor, the total power produced is 12 W. The sum of the currents is 3 A. Find the currents.

24. A circular hole y cm in radius is cut from a square piece of wood x cm on a side, leaving an area of 10 cm^2. If $x - y = 4$ cm, find x and y graphically.

13–2 Algebraic Solution of Systems of Equations

Often the graphical method is the easiest way to solve a system of equations. However, this method does not usually give an exact answer. Using algebraic methods to find exact solutions for some systems of equations is either not possible or quite involved. There are some systems, however, which do lend themselves to relatively simple solutions by algebraic means. In this section we shall consider two useful methods, both of which we discussed before when we were studying systems of linear equations.

The first method is substitution. If we can solve one equation for one of its variables, we can substitute this solution into the other equation. We then have only one unknown in the resulting equation, and we can solve this equation by methods discussed in earlier chapters.

Example A
Solve by substitution the system of equations

$$2x - y = 4$$
$$x^2 - y^2 = 4$$

We solve the first equation for y, obtaining $y = 2x - 4$. We now substitute this into the second equation, getting $x^2 - (2x - 4)^2 = 4$. When simplified, this gives a quadratic equation.

$$x^2 - (4x^2 - 16x + 16) = 4$$
$$-3x^2 + 16x - 20 = 0$$

$$x = \frac{-16 \pm \sqrt{256 - 4(-3)(-20)}}{-6} = \frac{-16 \pm \sqrt{16}}{-6} = \frac{-16 \pm 4}{-6} = \frac{10}{3}, 2$$

We now find the corresponding values of y by substituting into $y = 2x - 4$. Thus, we have the solutions $x = \frac{10}{3}$, $y = \frac{8}{3}$, and $x = 2$, $y = 0$. By substitution, these values also satisfy the equation $x^2 - y^2 = 4$. (We do this as a check.)

Example B

Solve by substitution the system of equations

$$xy = -2$$
$$2x + y = 2$$

From the first equation we have $y = -2/x$. Substituting this into the second equation, we have

$$2x - \left(\frac{2}{x}\right) = 2$$

$$2x^2 - 2 = 2x$$
$$x^2 - x - 1 = 0$$
$$x = \frac{1 \pm \sqrt{1 + 4}}{2} = \frac{1 \pm \sqrt{5}}{2}$$

We find the corresponding values of y, and we have the solutions

$$x = \frac{1 + \sqrt{5}}{2}, \quad y = 1 - \sqrt{5} \quad \text{and} \quad x = \frac{1 - \sqrt{5}}{2}, \quad y = 1 + \sqrt{5}$$

Now let us use the other algebraic method of solution, that of addition or subtraction. This method can be used to great advantage if both equations have only squared terms and constants.

Example C

Solve, by addition or subtraction, the system of equations

$$2x^2 + y^2 = 9$$
$$x^2 - y^2 = 3$$

We note that if we add the two equations we get $3x^2 = 12$. Thus, $x = \pm 2$. For $x = 2$, we have two corresponding y-values, $y = \pm 1$. Also for $x = -2$, we have two corresponding y-values, $y = \pm 1$. Thus, we have four solutions: $x = 2$, $y = 1$; $x = 2$, $y = -1$; $x = -2$, $y = 1$; and $x = -2$, $y = -1$.

Example D

Solve, by addition or subtraction, the system of equations

$$3x^2 - 2y^2 = 5$$
$$x^2 + y^2 = 5$$

If we multiply the second equation by 2 and then add the two resulting equations, we get $5x^2 = 15$. Thus, $x = \pm \sqrt{3}$. The corresponding values of y for each value of x are $\pm \sqrt{2}$. Again we have four solutions: $x = \sqrt{3}$, $y = \sqrt{2}$; $x = \sqrt{3}$, $y = -\sqrt{2}$; $x = -\sqrt{3}$, $y = \sqrt{2}$; and $x = -\sqrt{3}$, $y = -\sqrt{2}$.

Example E

A certain number of machine parts cost $1000. If they cost $5 less per part, ten additional parts could be purchased for the same amount of money. What is the cost of each?

Since the cost of each part is required, we let $c =$ the cost per part. Also, we let $n =$ the number of parts. From the first statement of the problem, we see that $cn = 1000$. Also, from the second statement, we have $(c - 5)(n + 10) = 1000$. Therefore, we are to solve the system of equations

$$cn = 1000$$
$$(c - 5)(n + 10) = 1000$$

Solving the first equation for n, and multiplying out the second equation, we have

$$n = \frac{1000}{c}$$

$$cn + 10c - 5n - 50 = 1000$$

Now, substituting the expression for n into the second equation, we solve for c.

$$c\left(\frac{1000}{c}\right) + 10c - 5\left(\frac{1000}{c}\right) - 50 = 1000$$

$$1000 + 10c - \frac{5000}{c} - 50 = 1000$$

$$10c - \frac{5000}{c} - 50 = 0$$

$$10c^2 - 50c - 5000 = 0$$
$$c^2 - 5c - 500 = 0$$
$$(c + 20)(c - 25) = 0$$
$$c = -20, 25$$

Since a negative answer has no significance in this particular situation, we see that the solution is $c = \$25$ per part. Checking with the original statement of the problem, we see that this is correct.

Exercises 13–2

In Exercises 1 through 20 solve the given systems of equations algebraically.

1. $y = x + 1$
   $y = x^2 + 1$

2. $y = 2x - 1$
   $y = 2x^2 + 2x - 3$

3. $x + 2y = 3$
   $x^2 + y^2 = 26$

4. $y = x + 1$
   $x^2 + y^2 = 25$

5. $2x - y = 2$
   $2x^2 + 3y^2 = 4$

6. $6y - x = 6$
   $x^2 + 3y^2 = 36$

7. $xy = 3$
   $3x - 2y = -7$

8. $xy = -4$
   $2x + y = -2$

9. $y = x^2$
   $y = 3x^2 - 8$

10. $y = x^2 - 1$
    $2x^2 - y^2 = 2$

11. $x^2 - y = -1$
    $x^2 + y^2 = 5$

12. $x^2 + y = 5$
    $x^2 + y^2 = 25$

13. $x^2 - 1 = y$
    $x^2 - 2y^2 = 1$

14. $2y^2 - 4x = 7$
    $y^2 + 2x^2 = 3$

15. $x^2 + y^2 = 25$
    $x^2 - 2y^2 = 7$

16. $3x^2 - y^2 = 4$
    $x^2 + 4y^2 = 10$

17. $y^2 - 2x^2 = 6$
    $5x^2 + 3y^2 = 20$

18. $y^2 - 2x^2 = 17$
    $2y^2 + x^2 = 54$

19. $x^2 + 3y^2 = 37$
    $2x^2 - 9y^2 = 14$

20. $5x^2 - 4y^2 = 15$
    $3y^2 + 4x^2 = 12$

In Exercises 21 through 28 solve the indicated systems of equations algebraically. In Exercises 23 through 28 it is necessary to properly set up the systems of equations.

21. The vertical distance which a certain projectile travels from its starting point is given by $y = 60t - 16t^2$. When the horizontal distance it has traveled equals twice the vertical distance, $y = 40t$. Find the values of y (in feet) and t (in seconds) which satisfy these equations.

22. A 300-g block and a 200-g block collide. Using the physical laws of conservation of energy and conservation of momentum, along with certain given conditions, we can establish the following equations involving velocities of each block after collision:

$$150v_1{}^2 + 100v_2{}^2 = 1375000$$
$$300v_1 + 200v_2 = -5000$$

Find these velocities (in centimeters per second).

23. Find two positive numbers such that the sum of their squares is 233 and the difference between their squares is 105.

24. The length of a table is three times the width, and the area is 48 ft². Find the dimensions of the table.

25. Two ships leave a port, one traveling due south and the other due east. The ship going east travels twice as far as the other ship, at which time they are 10 km apart. How far does each travel?

26. To enclose a rectangular field of 11,200 ft² in area, 440 ft of fence are required. What are the dimensions of the field?

27. The radii of two spheres differ by 4 in., and the difference between the spherical surfaces is 320π in.². Find the radii. (The surface area of a sphere is $4\pi r^2$.)

28. Two cities are 2000 mi apart. If an airplane increases its usual speed between these two cities by 100 mi/h, the trip would take 1 h less. Find the normal speed of the plane and the normal time of the flight.

13–3 Equations in Quadratic Form

Often we encounter equations which can be solved by methods applicable to quadratic equations, even though these equations are not actually quadratic. They do have the property, however, that with a proper substitution they may be written in the form of a quadratic equation. All that is necessary is that the equation have terms including some quantity, its square, and perhaps a constant term. The following example illustrates these types of equations.

Example A

The equation $x - 2\sqrt{x} - 5 = 0$ is an equation in quadratic form, because if we let $y = \sqrt{x}$, we have the resulting equivalent equation $y^2 - 2y - 5 = 0$.

Other examples of equations in quadratic form are as follows:

$t^{-4} - 5t^{-2} + 3 = 0$;

by letting $y = t^{-2}$ we have $y^2 - 5y + 3 = 0$

$t^3 - 3t^{3/2} - 7 = 0$;

by letting $y = t^{3/2}$ we have $y^2 - 3y - 7 = 0$

$(x + 1)^4 - (x + 1)^2 - 1 = 0$;

by letting $y = (x + 1)^2$ we have $y^2 - y - 1 = 0$

$x^{10} - 2x^5 + 1 = 0$;

by letting $y = x^5$ we have $y^2 - 2y + 1 = 0$

$(x - 3) + \sqrt{x - 3} - 6 = 0$;

by letting $y = \sqrt{x - 3}$ we have $y^2 + y - 6 = 0$

The following examples illustrate the method of solving equations in quadratic form.

Example B

Solve the equation $x^4 - 5x^2 + 4 = 0$.

We first let $y = x^2$, and obtain the resulting equivalent equation $y^2 - 5y + 4 = 0$. This may be factored as $(y - 4)(y - 1) = 0$. Thus, we have the solutions $y = 4$ and $y = 1$. Therefore, $x^2 = 4$ and $x^2 = 1$, which means that we have $x = \pm 2$ and $x = \pm 1$. Substitution into the original equation verifies that each of these is a solution.

Example C

Solve the equation $x - \sqrt{x} - 2 = 0$.

By letting $y = \sqrt{x}$, we have the equivalent equation $y^2 - y - 2 = 0$. This is factorable into $(y - 2)(y + 1) = 0$. Therefore, we have $y = 2$ and $y = -1$. Since $y = \sqrt{x}$, we note that y cannot be negative, and this in turn tells us that $y = -1$ cannot lead to a solution. For $y = 2$ we have $x = 4$. Checking, we find that $x = 4$ satisfies the original equation. Thus, the only solution is $x = 4$.

Example C illustrates a very important point: *Whenever any operation involving the unknown is performed on an equation, this operation may introduce roots into a subsequent equation which are not roots of the original equation. Therefore, we must check all answers in the original equation.* Only operations involving constants—that is, adding, subtracting, multiplying by, or dividing by constants—are certain not to introduce these **extraneous roots.** Squaring both sides of an equation is a common way of introducing extraneous roots. We first encountered the concept of an extraneous root in Section 5–7, when we were discussing equations involving fractions.

Example D

Solve the equation $x^{-2} + 3x^{-1} + 1 = 0$.

By substituting $y = x^{-1}$, we have $y^2 + 3y + 1 = 0$. To solve this equation we may use the quadratic formula:

$$y = \frac{-3 \pm \sqrt{9 - 4}}{2} = \frac{-3 \pm \sqrt{5}}{2}$$

Thus, since $x = \frac{1}{y}$

$$x = \frac{2}{-3 + \sqrt{5}}, \quad \frac{2}{-3 - \sqrt{5}}$$

Rationalizing the denominators of the values of x, we have

$$x = \frac{-6 - 2\sqrt{5}}{4} = \frac{-3 - \sqrt{5}}{2} \quad \text{and} \quad x = \frac{-3 + \sqrt{5}}{2}$$

Checking these solutions, we have

$$\left(\frac{-3 - \sqrt{5}}{2}\right)^{-2} + 3\left(\frac{-3 - \sqrt{5}}{2}\right)^{-1} + 1 \overset{?}{=} 0 \quad \text{or} \quad 0 = 0$$

and

$$\left(\frac{-3 + \sqrt{5}}{2}\right)^{-2} + 3\left(\frac{-3 + \sqrt{5}}{2}\right)^{-1} + 1 \overset{?}{=} 0 \quad \text{or} \quad 0 = 0$$

Thus, these solutions check.

Example E

Solve the equation $(x^2 - x)^2 - 8(x^2 - x) + 12 = 0$.

By substituting $y = x^2 - x$, we have $y^2 - 8y + 12 = 0$. This is solved by factoring, which gives us the solutions $y = 2$ and $y = 6$. Thus, $x^2 - x = 2$ and $x^2 - x = 6$. Solving these, we find that $x = 2, -1, 3, -2$. Substituting these in the original equation, we find that all are solutions.

Example F illustrates a stated problem which leads to an equation in quadratic form.

Example F

A rectangular plate has an area of 60 cm². The diagonal of the plate is 13 cm. Find the length and width of the plate.

Since the required quantities are the length and width, let $l =$ the length of the plate and $w =$ the width of the plate. Now, since the area is 60 cm², $lw = 60$. Also, using the Pythagorean theorem and the fact that the diagonal is 13 cm, we have $l^2 + w^2 = 169$. Therefore, we are to solve the system of equations

$$lw = 60, \quad l^2 + w^2 = 169$$

Solving the first equation for l, we have $l = 60/w$. Substituting this expression into the second equation we have

$$\left(\frac{60}{w}\right)^2 + w^2 = 169$$

We now solve for w as follows:

$$\frac{3600}{w^2} + w^2 = 169$$

$$3600 + w^4 = 169w^2$$

$$w^4 - 169w^2 + 3600 = 0$$

Let $x = w^2$.

$$x^2 - 169x + 3600 = 0$$
$$(x - 144)(x - 25) = 0$$
$$x = 25, 144.$$

Therefore,

$$w^2 = 25, 144$$

Solving for w, we obtain $w = \pm 5$ or $w = \pm 12$. Only the positive values of w are meaningful in this problem. Therefore, if $w = 5$ cm, then $l = 12$ cm. Normally, we designate the length as the longer dimension. Checking in the original equation, we find that this solution is correct.

Exercises 13—3

In Exercises 1 through 16 solve the given equations.

1. $x^4 - 13x^2 + 36 = 0$
2. $x^4 - 20x^2 + 64 = 0$
3. $x^6 + 7x^3 - 8 = 0$
4. $x^6 - 19x^3 - 216 = 0$
5. $x^{-2} - 2x^{-1} - 8 = 0$
6. $10x^{-2} + 3x^{-1} - 1 = 0$
7. $x^{-4} + 2x^{-2} = 24$
8. $x^{-6} - 3x^{-3} - 10 = 0$
9. $x - 4\sqrt{x} + 3 = 0$
10. $2x + \sqrt{x} - 1 = 0$
11. $3\sqrt[3]{x} - 5\sqrt[6]{x} + 2 = 0$
12. $\sqrt{x} + 3\sqrt[4]{x} = 28$
13. $x^{2/3} - 2x^{1/3} - 15 = 0$
14. $x^3 + 2x^{3/2} - 80 = 0$
15. $(x - 1) - \sqrt{x - 1} - 2 = 0$
16. $(x + 1)^{-2/3} + 5(x + 1)^{-1/3} - 6 = 0$
17. $(x^2 - 2x)^2 - 11(x^2 - 2x) + 24 = 0$
18. $3(x^2 + 3x)^2 - 2(x^2 + 3x) - 5 = 0$
19. $x - 3\sqrt{x - 2} = 6$ (Let $y = \sqrt{x - 2}$.)
20. $(x^2 - 1)^2 + (x^2 - 1)^{-2} = 2$

In Exercises 21 through 24 solve the indicated equations. In Exercises 23 and 24 it is necessary to set up the required equation.

21. A manufacturer determines that the total profit P when producing x thousand television sets monthly is given by $P = 10,000(-x^4 + 8x^2 - 2)$, where P is measured in dollars. Determine the number of sets which can be produced for a profit of $140,000.

22. In optics, in the theory which deals with interferometers, the equation $\sqrt{F} = 2\sqrt{p}/(1 - p)$ is found. Solve for p if $F = 16$.

23. Find the dimensions of a rectangular area having a diagonal of 40 ft and an area of 768 ft².

24. A metal plate is in the shape of an isosceles triangle. The length of the base equals the square root of one of the equal sides. Determine the lengths of the sides if the perimeter of the plate is 55 cm.

13—4 Equations with Radicals

Equations with radicals in them are normally solved by squaring both sides of the equation, or by a similar operation. However, when we do this, we often introduce extraneous roots. Thus, it is very important that all solutions be checked in the original equation.

Example A
Solve the equation $\sqrt{x - 4} = 2$.
   By squaring both sides of the equation, we have

$$(\sqrt{x - 4})^2 = 2^2 \quad \text{or} \quad x - 4 = 4 \quad \text{or} \quad x = 8$$

This solution checks when put into the original equation.

Example B
Solve the equation $\sqrt{x - 1} = x - 3$.
   Squaring both sides of the equation, we have

$$(\sqrt{x - 1})^2 = (x - 3)^2$$

(Remember, we are squaring each *side* of the equation, not just the terms separately on each side.) Hence,

$$x - 1 = x^2 - 6x + 9$$
$$x^2 - 7x + 10 = 0$$
$$(x - 5)(x - 2) = 0$$
$$x = 5 \quad \text{or} \quad x = 2$$

The solution $x = 5$ checks, but the solution $x = 2$ gives $1 = -1$. Thus, the solution is $x = 5$, and $x = 2$ is an extraneous root.

Example C
Solve the equation $\sqrt[3]{x - 8} = 2$.
   Cubing both sides of the equation, we have $x - 8 = 8$. Thus $x = 16$, which checks.

Example D
Solve the equation $\sqrt{x + 1} + \sqrt{x - 4} = 5$.

This is most easily solved by first placing one of the radicals on the right side and then squaring both sides of the equation:

$$\sqrt{x+1} = 5 - \sqrt{x-4}$$
$$(\sqrt{x+1})^2 = (5 - \sqrt{x-4})^2$$
$$x + 1 = 25 - 10\sqrt{x-4} + (x-4)$$

Now, isolating the radical on one side of the equation and squaring again, we have

$$10\sqrt{x-4} = 20$$
$$\sqrt{x-4} = 2$$
$$x - 4 = 4$$
$$x = 8$$

This solution checks.

Example E
Solve the equation $\sqrt{x} - \sqrt[4]{x} = 2$.
    We can solve this most easily by handling it as an equation in quadratic form. By letting $y = \sqrt[4]{x}$, we have

$$y^2 - y - 2 = 0$$
$$(y - 2)(y + 1) = 0$$
$$y = 2 \quad \text{or} \quad y = -1$$
$$x = 16 \quad \text{or} \quad x = 1$$

The solution $x = 16$ checks, but the solution $x = 1$ does not. Thus, the only solution is $x = 16$.

Example F
The perimeter of a right triangle is 60 ft, and its area is 120 ft². Find the lengths of the three sides (see Fig. 13–8).
    If we let the two legs of the triangle be x and y, the perimeter can be expressed as $p = x + y + \sqrt{x^2 + y^2}$. Also, the area is $A = \frac{1}{2}xy$. In this way we arrive at the equations $x + y + \sqrt{x^2 + y^2} = 60$ and $xy = 240$. Solving the first of these for the radical, we then have $\sqrt{x^2 + y^2} = 60 - x - y$. Squaring both sides and combining terms, we have

$$0 = 3600 - 120x - 120y + 2xy$$

Solving the second of the original equations for y, we have $y = 240/x$. Substituting, we have

$$0 = 3600 - 120x - 120\left(\frac{240}{x}\right) + 480$$

Multiplying each side by x, dividing through by 120, and rearranging the terms, we have $x^2 - 34x + 240 = 0$, which may be factored into $(x - 10)(x - 24) = 0$. Thus, x can be either 10 or 24. From the equation $xy = 240$, if $x = 10$, then $y = 24$. This means that the two legs are 10 ft and 24 ft, and the hypotenuse is 26 ft. The same solution is found by using the value of 24 ft for x.

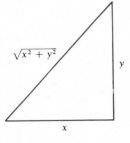

$\sqrt{x^2 + y^2}$ y

x

Figure 13–8

Exercises 13—4

In Exercises 1 through 24 solve the given equations.

1. $\sqrt{x-8} = 2$

2. $\sqrt{x+4} = 3$

3. $\sqrt{8-2x} = x$

4. $\sqrt{3x+4} = x$

5. $\sqrt{x-2} = x-2$

6. $\sqrt{5x-1} = x-3$

7. $\sqrt[3]{y-5} = 3$

8. $\sqrt[4]{5-x} = 2$

9. $\sqrt{x+12} = x$

10. $\sqrt{x+3} = 4x$

11. $5\sqrt{x+3} = 2x$

12. $4\sqrt{x} = x+3$

13. $\sqrt{x+4} = x-8$

14. $\sqrt{x+15} = x-5$

15. $2\sqrt{x+2} - \sqrt{3x+4} = 1$

16. $\sqrt{x-1} + \sqrt{x+2} = 3$

17. $\sqrt{5x+1} - 1 = 3\sqrt{x}$

18. $\sqrt{2x+1} + \sqrt{3x} = 11$

19. $\sqrt{2x-1} - \sqrt{x+11} = -1$

20. $\sqrt{5x-4} - \sqrt{x} = 2$

21. $\sqrt[3]{2x-1} = \sqrt[3]{x+5}$

22. $\sqrt[4]{x+10} = \sqrt{x-2}$

23. $\sqrt{x-2} = \sqrt[4]{x-2} + 12$

24. $\sqrt{3x + \sqrt{3x+4}} = 4$

In Exercises 25 through 28 solve the indicated equations for the indicated letter.

25. The velocity of an object falling under the influence of gravity in terms of its initial velocity v_0, the acceleration due to gravity g, and the height fallen, is given by $v = \sqrt{v_0^2 - 2gh}$. Solve this equation for h.

26. In measuring the velocity of water flowing through an opening under given conditions, the equation $v = \sqrt{2g(h_1 - h_2)}$ arises. Solve for h_1.

27. An equation used in analyzing a certain type of concrete beam is $k = \sqrt{2np + (np)^2} - np$. Solve for p.

28. The theory of relativity states that the mass m of an object increases with velocity v according to the relation

$$m = \frac{m_0}{\sqrt{1 - v^2/c^2}}$$

where m_0 is the "rest mass" and c is the velocity of light. Solve for v in terms of m.

In Exercises 29 through 32 set up the proper equations and solve them.

29. Find the dimensions of the rectangle for which the diagonal is 3 in. more than the longer side, which in turn is 3 in. longer than the shorter side.

30. The sides of a certain triangle are $\sqrt{x-1}$, $\sqrt{5x-1}$, and $x-1$. Find x when the perimeter of the triangle is 19.

31. An island is 3 mi offshore from the nearest point P on a straight beach. A person in a motorboat travels straight from the island to the beach x mi from P, and then travels 2 mi along the beach away from P. Find x if the person traveled a total of 8 mi.

32. The focal length f of a lens, in terms of its image distance q and object distance p, is given by

$$\frac{1}{f} = \frac{1}{p} + \frac{1}{q}$$

Find p and q if $f = 4$ cm and $p = \sqrt{q}$.

13–5 Exercises for Chapter 13

In Exercises 1 through 8 solve the given systems of equations graphically.

1. $x + 2y = 6$
$y = 4x^2$

2. $x + y = 3$
$x^2 + y^2 = 25$

3. $3x + 2y = 6$
$x^2 + 4y^2 = 4$

4. $x^2 - 2y = 0$
$y = 3x - 5$

5. $y = x^2 + 1$
$2x^2 + y^2 = 4$

6. $\dfrac{x^2}{4} + y^2 = 1$

$x^2 - y^2 = 1$

7. $y = 4 - x^2$
$y = 2x^2$

8. $xy = -2$
$y = 1 - 2x^2$

In Exercises 9 through 16 solve the given systems of equations algebraically.

9. $y = 4x^2$
$y = 8x$

10. $x + y = 2$
$xy = 1$

11. $4x^2 + y = 3$
$2x + 3y = 1$

12. $2x^2 + y^2 = 3$
$x + 2y = 1$

13. $4x^2 - 7y^2 = 21$
$x^2 + 2y^2 = 99$

14. $3x^2 + 2y^2 = 11$
$2x^2 - y^2 = 30$

15. $4x^2 + 3xy = 4$
$x + 3y = 4$

16. $\dfrac{6}{x} + \dfrac{3}{y} = 4$

$\dfrac{36}{x^2} + \dfrac{36}{y^2} = 13$

In Exercises 17 through 32 solve the given equations.

17. $x^4 - 20x^2 + 64 = 0$

18. $x^6 - 26x^3 - 27 = 0$

19. $x^{3/2} - 9x^{3/4} + 8 = 0$

20. $x^{1/2} + 3x^{1/4} - 28 = 0$

21. $x^{-2} + 4x^{-1} - 21 = 0$

22. $x^{-4} - 5x^{-2} - 36 = 0$

23. $2x - 3\sqrt{x} - 5 = 0$

24. $(x^2 + 5x)^2 - 5(x^2 + 5x) = 6$

25. $\sqrt{x + 5} = 4$

26. $\sqrt[3]{x - 2} = 3$

27. $x - 1 = \sqrt{5x + 9}$

28. $x + 2 = \sqrt{11x - 2}$

29. $\sqrt{x + 1} + \sqrt{x} = 2$

30. $\sqrt{3 + x} + \sqrt{3x - 2} = 1$

31. $\sqrt{3x + 4} + \sqrt{x + 2} = 8$

32. $\sqrt{3x - 2} - \sqrt{x + 7} = 1$

In Exercises 33 through 36 solve for the indicated quantities.

33. The formula for the lateral surface area of a cone can be stated as $S = \pi r \sqrt{r^2 + h^2}$. Solve for r.

34. Under certain conditions, the frequency ω of an RLC circuit is given by

$$\omega = \frac{\sqrt{R^2 + 4(L/C)} + R}{2L}$$

Solve for C.

35. In an experiment, an object is allowed to fall, stopped, and then falls for twice the initial time. The total distance the object falls is 45 ft. The equations relating the times t_1 and t_2, in seconds, of fall are $16t_1^2 + 16t_2^2 = 45$, and $t_2 = 2t_1$. Find the times of fall.

36. If two objects collide and the kinetic energy remains constant, the collision is termed perfectly elastic. Under these conditions, if an object of mass m_1 and initial velocity u_1 strikes a second object (initially at rest) of mass m_2, such that the velocities after collision are v_1 and v_2, the following equations are found:

$$m_1 u_1 = m_1 v_1 + m_2 v_2$$
$$\tfrac{1}{2}m_1 u_1^2 = \tfrac{1}{2}m_1 v_1^2 + \tfrac{1}{2}m_2 v_2^2$$

Solve these equations for m_2 in terms of u_1, v_1, and m_1.

In Exercises 37 through 40 set up the appropriate equations and solve them.

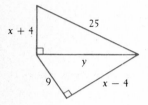

Figure 13—9

37. Find the values of x and y in Fig. 13–9.

38. The perimeter of a rectangle is 36 cm. The length is x cm and the width is $\sqrt{x + 2}$ cm. Find the dimensions of the rectangle.

39. An object is dropped from the top of a building. Six seconds later it is heard to hit the street below. How high is the building? (The velocity of sound is 1100 ft/s and the distance the object falls as a function of time is $s = 16t^2$.)

40. Two trains are approaching the same crossing on tracks which are at right angles to each other. Each is traveling at 60 km/h. If one is 6 km from the crossing when the other is 3 km from it, how much later will they be 4 km apart?

14

Equations of Higher Degree

14–1 The Remainder Theorem and the Factor Theorem

In previous chapters we have discussed methods of solving many kinds of equations. Except for special cases, however, we have not solved polynomial equations of degree higher than two (a polynomial equation of the first degree is a linear equation, and a polynomial equation of the second degree is a quadratic equation.) In this chapter we shall develop certain methods for solving polynomial equations, especially the higher-degree equations. Since we shall be discussing equations involving only polynomials, in this chapter $f(x)$ will be assumed to be a polynomial.

Any polynomial is a function of the form

$$f(x) = a_0 x^n + a_1 x^{n-1} + \cdots + a_n \qquad (14\text{–}1)$$

If we divide a polynomial by $x - r$, we find a result of the following form:

$$f(x) = (x - r)q(x) + R \qquad (14\text{–}2)$$

where $q(x)$ is the quotient and R is the remainder.

Example A
Divide $f(x) = 3x^2 + 5x - 8$ by $x - 2$.

$$
\begin{array}{r}
3x + 11 \\
x - 2 \overline{\smash{\big)}\ 3x^2 + 5x - 8} \\
\underline{3x^2 - 6x} \\
11x - 8 \\
\underline{11x - 22} \\
14
\end{array}
$$

Thus,

$$3x^2 + 5x - 8 = (x - 2)(3x + 11) + 14$$

If we now set $x = r$ in Eq. (14–2), we have

$$f(r) = q(r)(r - r) + R = R \qquad (14\text{–}3)$$

The equation above states that the remainder equals the function of r. This leads us to the **remainder theorem,** which states that *if a polynomial f(x) is divided by x − r until a constant remainder (R) is obtained, then f(r) = R.*

Example B
In Example A, $f(x) = 3x^2 + 5x - 8$, $R = 14$, $r = 2$.
  We find that

$$f(2) = 3(4) + 5(2) - 8 = 14$$

Thus, $f(2) = 14$ verifies that $f(r) = R$.

Example C
Using the remainder theorem, determine the remainder when we divide $3x^3 - x^2 - 20x + 5$ by $x + 4$.
  In using the remainder theorem, we determine the remainder when the function is divided by $x - r$ by evaluating the function for $x = r$. To have $x + 4$ in the proper form to identify r, we write it as $x - (-4)$. This means that $r = -4$, and we therefore are to evaluate the function $f(x) = 3x^3 - x^2 - 20x + 5$ for $x = -4$, or find $f(-4)$. Thus,

$$f(-4) = 3(-4)^3 - (-4)^2 - 20(-4) + 5 = -192 - 16 + 80 + 5$$
$$= -123$$

Thus, the remainder when $3x^3 - x^2 - 20x + 5$ is divided by $x + 4$ is -123.

  The remainder theorem leads immediately to another important theorem known as the **factor theorem.** The factor theorem states that *if f(r) = R = 0, then x − r is a factor of f(x).* Inspection of Eq. (14–2) justifies this theorem. It is also true that if $x - r$ is a factor of $f(x)$, then r is a zero of $f(x)$. (The zero of a function was first introduced in Chapter 2.)

Example D

Is $x + 1$ a factor of $f(x) = x^3 + 2x^2 - 5x - 6$?
 Here $r = -1$, and thus

$$f(-1) = -1 + 2 + 5 - 6 = 0$$

Therefore, since $f(-1) = 0$, $x + 1$ is a factor of $f(x)$.

Example E

The expression $x + 2$ is not a factor of the function in Example D, since

$$f(-2) = -8 + 8 + 10 - 6 = 4$$

But $x - 2$ is a factor, since $f(2) = 8 + 8 - 10 - 6 = 0$.

 We now have one way of determining whether or not an expression of the form $x - r$ is a factor of a function. By finding $f(r)$, we can determine whether or not $x - r$ is a factor and whether or not r is a zero of the function.

Exercises 14–1

In Exercises 1 through 8 find the remainder R by long division and by the remainder theorem.

1. $(x^3 + 2x^2 - x - 2) \div (x - 1)$ 2. $(x^3 - 3x^2 - x + 2) \div (x - 2)$
3. $(x^3 + 2x + 3) \div (x + 1)$ 4. $(x^4 - 4x^3 - x^2 + x - 100) \div (x + 3)$
5. $(2x^5 - x^2 + 8x + 44) \div (x + 2)$ 6. $(x^3 + 4x^2 - 25x - 98) \div (x - 5)$
7. $(2x^4 - 3x^3 - 4x^2 + 2x - 5) \div (x - 3)$
8. $(2x^4 - 10x^2 + 30x - 60) \div (x + 4)$

In Exercises 9 through 16 find the remainder using the remainder theorem.

9. $(x^3 + 2x^2 - 3x + 4) \div (x + 1)$ 10. $(2x^3 - 4x^2 + x - 1) \div (x + 2)$
11. $(x^4 + x^3 - 2x^2 - 5x + 3) \div (x + 4)$ 12. $(2x^4 - x^2 + 5x - 7) \div (x - 3)$
13. $(2x^4 - 7x^3 - x^2 + 8) \div (x - 3)$
14. $(x^4 - 5x^3 + x^2 - 2x + 6) \div (x + 4)$
15. $(x^5 - 3x^3 + 5x^2 - 10x + 6) \div (x - 2)$
16. $(3x^4 - 12x^3 - 60x + 4) \div (x - 5)$

In Exercises 17 through 24 use the factor theorem to determine whether or not the second expression is a factor of the first.

17. $x^2 - 2x - 3, x - 3$ 18. $3x^3 + 2x^2 - 3x - 2, x + 2$
19. $4x^3 + x^2 - 16x - 4, x - 2$ 20. $3x^3 + 14x^2 + 7x - 4, x + 4$
21. $5x^3 - 3x^2 + 4, x - 2$ 22. $x^5 - 2x^4 + 3x^3 - 6x^2 - 4x + 8, x - 2$
23. $x^6 + 1, x + 1$ 24. $x^7 - 128, x + 2$

In Exercises 25 through 28 determine whether or not the given numbers are zeros of the given functions.

25. $f(x) = x^3 - 2x^2 - 9x + 18$; 2
26. $f(x) = 2x^3 + 3x^2 - 8x - 12$; $-\frac{3}{2}$
27. $f(x) = 4x^4 - 4x^3 + 23x^2 + x - 6$; $\frac{1}{2}$
28. $f(x) = 2x^4 + 3x^3 - 12x^2 - 7x + 6$; -3

In Exercises 29 and 30 answer the given questions.

29. By division, show that $2x - 1$ is a factor of $f(x) = 4x^3 + 8x^2 - x - 2$. May we therefore conclude that $f(1) = 0$?

30. By division, show that $x^2 + 2$ is a factor of $f(x) = 3x^3 - x^2 + 6x - 2$. May we therefore conclude that $f(-2) = 0$?

14–2 Synthetic Division

We shall now develop a method which greatly simplifies the procedure for dividing a polynomial by an expression of the form $x - r$. Using **synthetic division**, which is an abbreviated form of long division, we can determine the coefficients of the quotient as well as the remainder. Of course, for some values of r, we can easily calculate $f(r)$ directly. However, if the degree of the equation is high, this requires finding and combining high powers of r. Synthetic division therefore allows us to find $f(r)$ easily by finding the remainder. The method is developed in the following example.

Example A
Divide $x^4 + 4x^3 - x^2 - 16x - 14$ by $x - 2$.
    We shall first perform this division in the usual manner.

$$
\begin{array}{r}
x^3 + 6x^2 + 11x + 6 \\
x - 2 \overline{\smash{\big)}\ x^4 + 4x^3 - x^2 - 16x - 14} \\
\underline{x^4 - 2x^3} \\
6x^3 - x^2 \\
\underline{6x^3 - 12x^2} \\
11x^2 - 16x \\
\underline{11x^2 - 22x} \\
6x - 14 \\
\underline{6x - 12} \\
-2
\end{array}
$$

We now note that, when we performed this division, we repeated many terms. Also, the only quantities of importance in the function being divided are the coefficients. There is no real need to put in the powers of x all the time. Therefore, we shall now write the above example without any x's and also eliminate the writing of identical terms:

$$
\begin{array}{r}
1 \quad\ 6 \quad\ 11 \quad\ 6 \\
-2 \overline{\smash{\big)}\ 1 \quad\ 4 \quad -1 \quad -16 \quad -14} \\
\underline{-2} \\
6 \\
\underline{-12} \\
11 \\
\underline{-22} \\
6 \\
\underline{-12} \\
-2
\end{array}
$$

All but the first of the numbers which represent coefficients of the quotient are repeated below. Also, all the numbers below the dividend may be written in two lines. Thus, we have the following form:

$$
\begin{array}{r|rrrr}
-2 & 1 & 4 & -1 & -16 & -14 \\
   &   & -2 & -12 & -22 & -12 \\
\hline
   &   & 6 & 11 & 6 & -2
\end{array}
$$

All the coefficients of the actual quotient appear except the first, so we shall now repeat the 1 in the bottom line. Also, we shall change -2 to 2, which is the actual value of r. Then, to conform to the normal practice of writing r to the right, we have the following form:

$$
\begin{array}{rrrrr|r}
1 & 4 & -1 & -16 & -14 & \underline{2} \\
  & -2 & -12 & -22 & -12 & \\
\hline
1 & 6 & 11 & 6 & -2 &
\end{array}
$$

In this form the 1, 6, 11, and 6 represent the coefficients of the x^3, x^2, x, and constant terms of the quotient. The -2 is the remainder. Finally, we find it easier to use addition rather than subtraction in the process, so we change the signs of the numbers in the middle row. Remember that originally the bottom line was found by subtraction. Thus, we have

$$
\begin{array}{rrrrr|r}
1 & 4 & -1 & -16 & -14 & \underline{2} \\
  & 2 & 12 & 22 & 12 & \\
\hline
1 & 6 & 11 & 6 & -2 &
\end{array}
$$

When we inspect this form we find the following: The 1 multiplied by the 2 (r) gives 2, which is the first number of the middle row. The 4 and 2 (of the middle row) added is 6, which is the second number in the bottom row. The 6 multiplied by 2 (r) is 12, which is the second number in the middle row. This 12 and the -1 give 11. The 11 multiplied by 2 is 22. The 22 added to -16 is 6. This 6 multiplied by 2 gives 12. this 12 added to -14 is -2. When this process is followed in general, the method is called synthetic division.

Generalizing on this last example, we have the following procedure: We write down the coefficients of $f(x)$, being certain that the powers are in descending order and that zeros are placed in for missing powers. We write the value of r to the right. We carry down the left coefficient, multiply this number by r, and place this product under the second coefficient of the top line. We add the two numbers in this second column and place the result below; then we multiply this number by r and place the result under the third coefficient of the top line. We continue until the bottom row has as many numbers as the top row. The last number in the bottom row is the remainder, the other numbers being the respective coefficients of the quotient. The first term of the quotient is of degree one less than the dividend.

Example B

By synthetic division, divide $x^5 + 2x^4 - 4x^2 + 3x - 4$ by $x + 3$.

In writing down the coefficients of $f(x)$, we must be certain to include a zero for the missing x^3 term. Also, since the divisor is $x + 3$, we must recognize that $r = -3$. The setup and synthetic division follow.

$$
\begin{array}{rrrrrr|r}
1 & 2 & 0 & -4 & 3 & -4 & \underline{-3} \\
  & -3 & 3 & -9 & 39 & -126 & \\
\hline
1 & -1 & 3 & -13 & 42 & -130 &
\end{array}
$$

Thus, the quotient is $x^4 - x^3 + 3x^2 - 13x + 42$ and the remainder is -140. Notice the degree of the dividend is 5 and the degree of the quotient is 4.

Example C

By synthetic division, divide $3x^4 - 5x + 6$ by $x - 4$.

$$
\begin{array}{rrrrr|r}
3 & 0 & 0 & -5 & 6 & \underline{4} \\
  & 12 & 48 & 192 & 748 & \\
\hline
3 & 12 & 48 & 187 & 754 &
\end{array}
$$

Thus, the quotient is $3x^3 + 12x^2 + 48x + 187$ and the remainder is 754.

Example D

By synthetic division, determine whether or not $x - 4$ is a factor of $x^4 + 2x^3 - 15x^2 - 32x - 16$.

$$
\begin{array}{rrrrr|r}
1 & 2 & -15 & -32 & -16 & \underline{4} \\
  & 4 & 24 & 36 & 16 & \\
\hline
1 & 6 & 9 & 4 & 0 &
\end{array}
$$

Since the remainder is zero, $x - 4$ is a factor. We may also conclude that $f(x) = (x - 4)(x^3 + 6x^2 + 9x + 4)$, since the bottom line gives us the coefficients in the quotient.

Example E

By using synthetic division, determine whether $2x - 3$ is a factor of $2x^3 - 3x^2 + 8x - 12$.

We first note that the coefficient of x in the possible factor is not 1. Thus, we cannot use $r = 3$, since the factor is not of the form $x - r$. However, $2x - 3 = 2(x - \frac{3}{2})$, which means that if $2(x - \frac{3}{2})$ is a factor of the function, $2x - 3$ is a factor. If we use $r = \frac{3}{2}$, and find that the remainder is zero, then $x - \frac{3}{2}$ is a factor.

$$
\begin{array}{rrrr|r}
2 & -3 & 8 & -12 & \underline{\frac{3}{2}} \\
  & 3 & 0 & 12 & \\
\hline
2 & 0 & 8 & 0 &
\end{array}
$$

Since the remainder is zero, $x - \frac{3}{2}$ is a factor. Also, the quotient is $2x^2 + 8$, which may be factored into $2(x^2 + 4)$. Thus, 2 is also a factor of the function. This means that $2(x - \frac{3}{2})$ is a factor of the function, and this in turn means that $2x - 3$ is a factor.

Example F

By synthetic division, determine whether or not $\frac{1}{3}$ is a zero of the function $3x^3 + 2x^2 - 4x + 1$.

This problem is equivalent to dividing the function by $x - \frac{1}{3}$. If the remainder is zero, $\frac{1}{3}$ is a zero of the function.

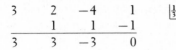

$$
\begin{array}{rrrr|r}
3 & 2 & -4 & 1 & \frac{1}{3} \\
  & 1 & 1 & -1 & \\
\hline
3 & 3 & -3 & 0 &
\end{array}
$$

Since the remainder is zero, we conclude that $\frac{1}{3}$ is a zero of the function.

$$3x^3 + 2x^2 - 4x + 1 = (x - \tfrac{1}{3})(3x^2 + 3x - 3)$$
$$= 3(x - \tfrac{1}{3})(x^2 + x - 1).$$

Exercises 14–2

In Exercises 1 through 20 perform the required divisions by synthetic division. Exercises 1 through 16 are the same as those of Section 14–1.

1. $(x^3 + 2x^2 - x - 2) \div (x - 1)$
2. $(x^3 - 3x^2 - x + 2) \div (x - 2)$
3. $(x^3 + 2x + 3) \div (x + 1)$
4. $(x^4 - 4x^3 - x^2 + x - 100) \div (x + 3)$
5. $(2x^5 - x^2 + 8x + 44) \div (x + 2)$
6. $(x^3 + 4x^2 - 25x - 98) \div (x - 5)$
7. $(2x^4 - 3x^3 - 4x^2 + 2x - 5) \div (x - 3)$
8. $(2x^4 - 10x^2 + 30x - 60) \div (x + 4)$
9. $(x^3 + 2x^2 - 3x + 4) \div (x + 1)$
10. $(2x^3 - 4x^2 + x - 1) \div (x + 2)$
11. $(x^4 + x^3 - 2x^2 - 5x + 3) \div (x + 4)$
12. $(2x^4 - x^2 + 5x - 7) \div (x - 3)$
13. $(2x^4 - 7x^3 - x^2 + 8) \div (x - 3)$
14. $(x^4 - 5x^3 + x^2 - 2x + 6) \div (x + 4)$
15. $(x^5 - 3x^3 + 5x^2 - 10x + 6) \div (x - 2)$
16. $(3x^4 - 12x^3 - 60x + 4) \div (x - 5)$
17. $(x^6 + 2x^2 - 6) \div (x - 2)$
18. $(x^5 + 4x^4 - 8) \div (x + 1)$
19. $(x^7 - 128) \div (x - 2)$
20. $(x^5 + 32) \div (x + 2)$

In Exercises 21 through 28 use the factor theorem and synthetic division to determine whether or not the second expression is a factor of the first.

21. $x^3 + x^2 - x + 2;\quad x + 2$
22. $x^3 + 6x^2 + 10x + 6;\quad x + 3$
23. $x^4 - 6x^2 - 3x - 2;\quad x - 3$
24. $2x^4 - 5x^3 - 24x^2 + 5;\quad x - 5$
25. $2x^4 - x^3 + 2x^2 - 3x + 1;\quad 2x - 1$
26. $6x^4 + 5x^3 - x^2 + 6x - 2;\quad 3x - 1$
27. $4x^4 + 2x^3 - 8x^2 + 3x + 12;\quad 2x + 3$
28. $3x^4 - 2x^3 + x^2 + 15x + 4;\quad 3x + 4$

In Exercises 29 through 32 use synthetic division to determine whether or not the given numbers are zeros of the given functions.

29. $x^4 - 5x^3 - 15x^2 + 5x + 14;\quad 7$
30. $x^4 + 7x^3 + 12x^2 + x + 4;\quad -4$
31. $9x^3 + 9x^2 - x + 2;\quad -\frac{2}{3}$
32. $2x^3 + 13x^2 + 10x - 4;\quad \frac{1}{2}$

14–3 The Roots of an Equation

In this section we shall present certain theorems which are useful in determining the number of roots in the equation $f(x) = 0$, and the nature of some of these roots. In dealing with polynomial equations of higher degree, it is helpful to have as much of this kind of information as is readily obtainable before proceeding to solve for the roots.

The first of these theorems is so important that it is called **the fundamental theorem of algebra**. It states that *every polynomial equation has at least one (real or complex) root.* The proof of this theorem is of an advanced nature, and therefore we must accept its validity at this time. However, using the fundamental theorem, we can show the validity of other useful theorems.

Let us now assume that we have a polynomial equation $f(x) = 0$, and that we are looking for its roots. By the fundamental theorem, we know that it has at least one root. Assuming that we can find this root by some means (the factor theorem, for example), we shall call this root r_1. Thus,

$$f(x) = (x - r_1)f_1(x)$$

where $f_1(x)$ is the polynomial quotient found by dividing $f(x)$ by $(x - r_1)$. However, since the fundamental theorem states that any polynomial equation has at least one root, this must apply to $f_1(x) = 0$ as well. Let us assume that $f_1(x) = 0$ has the root r_2. Therefore, this means that $f(x) = (x - r_1)(x - r_2)f_2(x)$. Continuing this process until one of the quotients is a constant a, we have

$$f(x) = a(x - r_1)(x - r_2) \cdots (x - r_n)$$

Note that one linear factor appears each time a root is found, and that the degree of the quotient is one less each time. Thus there are n factors, if the degree of $f(x)$ is n. This leads us to two theorems. The first of these states that *each polynomial of the nth degree can be factored into n linear factors.* The second theorem states that *each polynomial equation of degree n has exactly n roots.*

Example A

Consider the equation $f(x) = 2x^4 - 3x^3 - 12x^2 + 7x + 6 = 0$.

$$2x^4 - 3x^3 - 12x^2 + 7x + 6 = (x - 3)(2x^3 + 3x^2 - 3x - 2)$$
$$2x^3 + 3x^2 - 3x - 2 = (x + 2)(2x^2 - x - 1)$$
$$2x^2 - x - 1 = (x - 1)(2x + 1)$$
$$2x + 1 = 2(x + \tfrac{1}{2})$$

Therefore,

$$2x^4 - 3x^3 - 12x^2 + 7x + 6 = 2(x - 3)(x + 2)(x - 1)(x + \tfrac{1}{2}) = 0$$

The degree of $f(x)$ is 4. There are 4 linear factors: $(x - 3)$, $(x + 2)$, $(x - 1)$, and $(x + \frac{1}{2})$. There are 4 roots of the equation: 3, -2, 1, and $-\frac{1}{2}$. Thus, we have verified each of the theorems above for this example.

It is not necessary for each root of an equation to be different from the others. For example, the equation $(x - 1)^2 = 0$ has two roots, both of which are 1. Such roots are referred to as multiple roots.

When we solve the equation $x^2 + 1 = 0$, we get two roots, j and $-j$. In fact, if we have any equation for which the roots are complex, for every root of the form $a + bj$ $(b \neq 0)$, there is also a root of the form $a - bj$. This is so because any quadratic equation can be solved by the quadratic formula. The solutions from the quadratic formula (for an equation of the form $ax^2 + bx + c = 0$) are

$$\frac{-b + \sqrt{b^2 - 4ac}}{2a} \quad \text{and} \quad \frac{-b - \sqrt{b^2 - 4ac}}{2a}$$

and the only difference between these roots is the sign before the radical. Thus we have the following theorem. *If a complex number $a + bj$ is the root of $f(x) = 0$, its conjugate $a - bj$ is also a root.*

Example B

Consider the equation $f(x) = (x - 1)^3(x^2 + x + 1) = 0$.

We observe directly (since three factors of $x - 1$ are already indicated) that there is a triple root of 1. To find the other two roots, we use the quadratic formula on the *factor* $(x^2 + x + 1)$. This is permissible, because what we are actually finding are those values of x which make $x^2 + x + 1 = 0$. For this we have

$$x = \frac{-1 \pm \sqrt{1 - 4}}{2}$$

Thus,

$$x = \frac{-1 + \sqrt{3}j}{2} \quad \text{and} \quad x = \frac{-1 - \sqrt{3}j}{2}$$

Therefore, the roots of $f(x)$ are

$$1, \quad 1, \quad 1, \quad \frac{-1 + \sqrt{3}j}{2}, \quad \frac{-1 - \sqrt{3}j}{2}$$

One further observation can be made from Example B. *Whenever enough roots are known so that the remaining factor is quadratic, it is always possible to find the remaining roots from the quadratic formula.* This is true for finding real or complex roots. If there are n roots and if we find $n - 2$ of these roots, the solution may be completed by using the quadratic formula.

Example C

Solve the equation $3x^3 + 10x^2 - 16x - 32 = 0$ given that $-\frac{4}{3}$ is a root.

Using synthetic division and the given root we have

$$
\begin{array}{rrrr|r}
3 & 10 & -16 & -32 & \underline{-\frac{4}{3}} \\
  & -4 & -8 & 32 & \\
\hline
3 & 6 & -24 & 0 &
\end{array}
$$

Thus, $3x^3 + 10x^2 - 16x - 32 = (x + \frac{4}{3})(3x^2 + 6x - 24)$. We know that $x + \frac{4}{3}$ is a factor from the given root, and that $3x^2 + 6x - 24$ is a factor from the synthetic division. This second factor has a common factor of 3, which means that $3x^2 + 6x - 24 = 3(x^2 + 2x - 8)$. We now see that $x^2 + 2x - 8 = (x + 4)(x - 2)$. Thus,

$$3x^3 + 10x^2 - 16x - 32 = 3(x + \tfrac{4}{3})(x + 4)(x - 2)$$

This means the roots are $-\frac{4}{3}$, -4, and 2.

Example D

Solve the equation $x^4 + 3x^3 - 4x^2 - 10x - 4 = 0$, given that -1 and 2 are roots.

Using synthetic division and the root -1, we have

$$
\begin{array}{rrrrr|r}
1 & 3 & -4 & -10 & -4 & \underline{-1} \\
  & -1 & -2 & 6 & 4 & \\
\hline
1 & 2 & -6 & -4 & 0 &
\end{array}
$$

Therefore, we now know that

$$x^4 + 3x^3 - 4x^2 - 10x - 4 = (x + 1)(x^3 + 2x^2 - 6x - 4)$$

We now know that $x - 2$ must be a factor of $x^3 + 2x^2 - 6x - 4$, since it is a factor of the original function. Again, using synthetic division and this time the root 2, we have the following:

$$
\begin{array}{rrrr|r}
1 & 2 & -6 & -4 & \underline{2} \\
  & 2 & 8 & 4 & \\
\hline
1 & 4 & 2 & 0 &
\end{array}
$$

Thus,

$$x^4 + 3x^3 - 4x^2 - 10x - 4 = (x + 1)(x - 2)(x^2 + 4x + 2)$$

The roots from this last factor are now found by the quadratic formula:

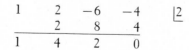

$$x = \frac{-4 \pm \sqrt{16 - 8}}{2} = \frac{-4 \pm 2\sqrt{2}}{2} = -2 \pm \sqrt{2}$$

Therefore, the roots are -1, 2, $-2 + \sqrt{2}$, $-2 - \sqrt{2}$.

Example E

Solve the equation $3x^4 - 26x^3 + 63x^2 - 36x - 20 = 0$, given that 2 is a double root.

Using synthetic division, we have

$$
\begin{array}{rrrrr|}
3 & -26 & 63 & -36 & -20 \quad \underline{|2} \\
& 6 & -40 & 46 & 20 \\
\hline
3 & -20 & 23 & 10 & 0
\end{array}
$$

Therefore, we know that

$$3x^4 - 26x^3 + 63x^2 - 36x - 20 = (x - 2)(3x^3 - 20x^2 + 23x + 10)$$

Also, since 2 is a double root, it must be a root of the quotient $3x^3 - 20x^2 + 23x + 10$. Using synthetic division again, we have

$$
\begin{array}{rrrr|}
3 & -20 & 23 & 10 \quad \underline{|2} \\
& 6 & -28 & -10 \\
\hline
3 & -14 & -5 & 0
\end{array}
$$

The quotient $3x^2 - 14x - 5$ factors into $(3x + 1)(x - 5)$. Therefore, the roots of the equation are 2, 2, $-\frac{1}{3}$, and 5.

Example F

Solve the equation $2x^4 - x^3 + 7x^2 - 4x - 4 = 0$, given that $2j$ is a root.

Since $2j$ is a root, we know that $-2j$ is also a root. Using synthetic division twice, we can then reduce the remaining factor to a quadratic function.

$$
\begin{array}{rrrrr|}
2 & -1 & 7 & -4 & -4 \quad \underline{|2j} \\
& 4j & -8 - 2j & 4 - 2j & 4 \\
\hline
2 & 4j - 1 & -1 - 2j & -2j & \quad \underline{|-2j} \\
& -4j & 2j & 2j \\
\hline
2 & -1 & -1
\end{array}
$$

The quadratic factor $2x^2 - x - 1$ factors into $(2x + 1)(x - 1)$. Therefore, the roots of the function are $2j$, $-2j$, 1, and $-\frac{1}{2}$.

Exercises 14—3

In Exercises 1 through 20 solve the given equations using synthetic division, given the roots indicated.

1. $x^3 + 2x^2 - x - 2 = 0$ $(r_1 = 1)$ 2. $x^3 + 2x^2 + x + 2 = 0$ $(r_1 = -2)$

3. $x^3 + x^2 - 8x - 12 = 0$ $(r_1 = -2)$ 4. $x^3 - 1 = 0$ $(r_1 = 1)$

5. $2x^3 + 11x^2 + 20x + 12 = 0$ $(r_1 = -\frac{3}{2})$

6. $2x^3 + 5x^2 - 11x + 4 = 0$ $(r_1 = \frac{1}{2})$

7. $3x^3 + 2x^2 + 3x + 2 = 0$ $(r_1 = j)$

8. $x^3 + 5x^2 + 9x + 5 = 0$ $(r_1 = -2 + j)$

9. $x^4 + x^3 - 2x^2 + 4x - 24 = 0$ $(r_1 = 2, r_2 = -3)$

10. $x^4 + 2x^3 - 4x^2 - 5x + 6 = 0$ $(r_1 = 1, r_2 = -2)$

11. $x^4 - 6x^2 - 8x - 3 = 0$ (-1 is a double root)
12. $4x^4 + 28x^3 + 61x^2 + 42x + 9 = 0$ (-3 is a double root)
13. $6x^4 + 5x^3 - 15x^2 + 4 = 0$ ($r_1 = -\frac{1}{2}, r_2 = \frac{2}{3}$)
14. $6x^4 - 5x^3 - 14x^2 + 14x - 3 = 0$ ($r_1 = \frac{1}{3}, r_2 = \frac{3}{2}$)
15. $2x^5 + 11x^4 + 16x^3 - 8x^2 - 32x - 16 = 0$ (-2 is a triple root)
16. $x^5 - 3x^4 + 4x^3 - 4x^2 + 3x - 1 = 0$ (1 is a triple root)
17. $2x^5 + x^4 - 15x^3 + 5x^2 + 13x - 6 = 0$ ($r_1 = 1, r_2 = -1, r_3 = \frac{1}{2}$)
18. $12x^5 - 7x^4 + 41x^3 - 26x^2 - 28x + 8 = 0$ ($r_1 = 1, r_2 = \frac{1}{4}, r_3 = -\frac{2}{3}$)
19. $x^6 + 2x^5 - 4x^4 - 10x^3 - 41x^2 - 72x - 36 = 0$ (-1 is a double root, $2j$ is a root)
20. $x^6 - x^5 - 2x^3 - 3x^2 - x - 2 = 0$ (j is a double root)

14–4 Rational Roots

If we form the product of the factors $(x + 2)(x - 4)(x + 3)$, we obtain $x^3 + x^2 - 14x - 24$. In forming this product, we find that the constant 24 which results is determined only by the numbers 2, 4, and 3. We note that these numbers represent the roots of the equation if the given function is set equal to zero. In fact, if we found all the integral roots of an equation, and represented the equation in the form

$$f(x) = (x - r_1)(x - r_2) \cdots (x - r_k) f_{k+1}(x) = 0$$

where all the roots indicated are integers, the constant term of $f(x)$ must have factors of $r_1, r_2, \ldots, r_k$. This leads us to the theorem which states that *if the coefficient of the highest power of x is 1, then any integral roots are factors of the constant term of the function.*

Example A
The equation $f(x) = x^5 - 4x^4 - 7x^3 + 14x^2 - 44x + 120 = 0$ can be written as

$$(x - 5)(x + 3)(x - 2)(x^2 + 4) = 0$$

We now note that $5(3)(2)(4) = 120$. Thus the roots 5, -3, and 2 are numerical factors of $|120|$. The theorem states nothing in regard to the signs involved.

If the coefficient of the highest-power term of $f(x)$ is not 1, then this coefficient can be factored from every term of $f(x)$. Thus any equation of the form $f(x) = a_0 x^n + a_1 x^{n-1} + \cdots + a_n = 0$ can be written in the form

$$f(x) = a_0 \left(x^n + \frac{a_1}{a_0} x^{n-1} + \cdots + \frac{a_n}{a_0} \right) = 0 \qquad (14\text{--}4)$$

This equation, along with the theorem above, now gives us another, more inclusive, theorem. *Any rational roots of a polynomial equation $f(x) = a_0 x^n + a_1 x^{n-1} + \cdots + a_n = 0$ must be integral factors of a_n divided* *by integral factors of a_0.* The same reasoning as previously stated, applied to the factor within parentheses of Eq. (14–4), leads us to this result.

Example B

If $f(x) = 4x^3 - 3x^2 - 25x - 6 = 0$, any rational roots, if they exist, must be integral factors of 6 divided by integral factors of 4. The integral factors of 6 are 1, 2, 3, and 6 and the integral factors of 4 are 1, 2, and 4. Forming all possible positive and negative quotients, any rational roots that exist will be found in the following list: ± 1, $\pm \frac{1}{2}$, $\pm \frac{1}{4}$, ± 2, ± 3, $\pm \frac{3}{2}$, $\pm \frac{3}{4}$, ± 6.

The roots of this equation are -2, 3, and $-\frac{1}{4}$.

There are 16 different possible rational roots in Example B. Since we have no way of telling which of these are the actual roots, we now present a rule which will help us to find these roots. This rule is known as **Descartes' rule of signs.** It states that *the number of positive roots of a polynomial equation $f(x) = 0$ cannot exceed the number of changes in sign in $f(x)$ in going from one term to the next in $f(x)$. The number of negative roots cannot exceed the number of sign changes in $f(-x)$.*

We can reason this way: If $f(x)$ has all positive terms, then any positive number substituted in $f(x)$ must give a positive value for the function. This indicates that the number substituted in the function is not a root. Thus, there must be at least one negative and one positive term in the function for any positive number to be a root. This is not a proof, but does indicate the type of reasoning which is used in developing the theorem.

Example C

By Descartes' rule of signs, determine the maximum number of positive and negative roots of $3x^3 - x^2 - x + 4 = 0$.

Here $f(x) = 3x^3 - x^2 - x + 4$. The first term is positive and the second negative, which indicates a change of sign. The third term is also negative; there is no change of sign from the second to the third term. The fourth term is positive, thus giving us a second change of sign, from the third to the fourth term. Hence there are two changes in sign, and therefore no more than two positive roots of $f(x) = 0$. Then we write

$$f(-x) = 3(-x)^3 - (-x)^2 - (-x) + 4 = -3x^3 - x^2 + x + 4$$

There is only one change of sign in $f(-x)$; therefore, there is one negative root. *When there is just one change of sign in $f(x)$ there is a positive root, and when there is just one change of sign in $f(-x)$ there is a negative root.*

Example D

For the equation $4x^5 - x^4 - 4x^3 + x^2 - 5x - 6 = 0$, we write

$$f(x) = 4x^5 - x^4 - 4x^3 + x^2 - 5x - 6$$

and

$$f(-x) = -4x^5 - x^4 + 4x^3 + x^2 + 5x - 6.$$

Thus, there are no more than three positive and two negative roots.

At this point let us summarize the information we can determine about the roots of a polynomial equation $f(x) = 0$ of degree n:

(1) There are n roots.

(2) Complex roots appear in conjugate pairs.

(3) Any rational roots must be factors of the constant term divided by factors of the coefficient of the highest-power term.

(4) The maximum number of positive roots is the number of sign changes in $f(x)$, and the maximum number of negative roots is the number of sign changes in $f(-x)$.

(5) Once we determine $n - 2$ of the roots, the remaining roots can be found by the quadratic formula.

Synthetic division is normally used to try possible roots. This is because synthetic division is relatively easy to perform, and when a root is found we have the quotient factor, which is of degree one less than the degree of the dividend. Each root we find makes the ensuing work simpler. The following examples indicate the complete method, as well as two other helpful rules.

Example E

Determine the roots of the equation $2x^3 + x^2 + 5x - 3 = 0$.

Since $n = 3$, there are three roots. If we can find one of these roots, we can use the quadratic formula to find the other two. We have $f(x) = 2x^3 + x^2 + 5x - 3$, and therefore there is one positive root. We also have $f(-x) = -2x^3 + x^2 - 5x - 3$, and therefore there are no more than two negative roots. The *possible* rational roots are ± 1, $\pm \frac{1}{2}$, $\pm \frac{3}{2}$, ± 3. Thus, using synthetic division, we shall try these. We first try the root 1 (always a possibility if there are positive roots).

$$
\begin{array}{rrrr|l}
2 & 1 & 5 & -3 & \underline{1} \\
  & 2 & 3 & 8 & \\
\hline
2 & 3 & 8 & 5 &
\end{array}
$$

Thus we see that 1 is not a root, but we have gained some information, if we observe closely. If we try any positive number larger than 1, the results in the last row will be larger positive numbers than we now have. The products will be larger, and therefore the sums will also be larger. Thus there is no positive root larger than 1. This leads to the following rule: *When we are trying a root, if the bottom row contains all positive numbers, then there are no roots larger than the value tried.* This rule tells us that there is no reason to try $+\frac{3}{2}$ and $+3$ as roots. Therefore, let us now try $+\frac{1}{2}$.

$$
\begin{array}{rrrr|l}
2 & 1 & 5 & -3 & \underline{\frac{1}{2}} \\
  & 1 & 1 & 3 & \\
\hline
2 & 2 & 6 & 0 &
\end{array}
$$

Hence $+\frac{1}{2}$ is a root, and the remaining factor is $2x^2 + 2x + 6$, which itself factors to $2(x^2 + x + 3)$. By the quadratic formula we find the remaining roots.

$$x = \frac{-1 \pm \sqrt{1 - 12}}{2} = \frac{-1 \pm \sqrt{11}j}{2}$$

The three roots are

$$\frac{1}{2}, \quad \frac{-1 + \sqrt{11}j}{2} \quad \text{and} \quad \frac{-1 - \sqrt{11}j}{2}$$

We note that there were actually no negative roots, because the non-positive roots are complex. Also, in proceeding in this way, we never found it necessary to try any negative roots. It must be admitted, however, that the solutions to all problems may not be so easily determined.

Example F

Determine the roots of the equation $x^4 - 7x^3 + 12x^2 + 4x - 16 = 0$.
We write

$$f(x) = x^4 - 7x^3 + 12x^2 + 4x - 16$$
$$f(-x) = x^4 + 7x^3 + 12x^2 - 4x - 16$$

We see that there are four roots; there are no more than three positive roots, and there is one negative root. The possible rational roots are ± 1, ± 2, ± 4, ± 8, ± 16. Since there is only one negative root, we shall look for this one first. Trying -2, we have

$$
\begin{array}{rrrrr|r}
1 & -7 & +12 & +4 & -16 & \underline{|-2} \\
 & -2 & +18 & -60 & +112 & \\
\hline
1 & -9 & +30 & -56 & +96 &
\end{array}
$$

If we were to try any negative roots less than -2 (remember, -3 is less than -2), we would find that the numbers would still alternate from term to term in the quotient. Thus, we have this rule: *If the signs alternate in the bottom row, then there are no roots less than the value tried.* So we next try -1.

$$
\begin{array}{rrrrr|r}
1 & -7 & +12 & +4 & -16 & \underline{|-1} \\
 & -1 & 8 & -20 & 16 & \\
\hline
1 & -8 & 20 & -16 & 0 &
\end{array}
$$

Thus, -1 is the negative root. Next we shall try $+1$.

$$
\begin{array}{rrrr|r}
1 & -8 & 20 & -16 & \underline{|1} \\
 & 1 & -7 & 13 & \\
\hline
1 & -7 & 13 & -3 &
\end{array}
$$

Since $+1$ is not a root, we next try $+2$.

$$
\begin{array}{rrrr|r}
1 & -8 & 20 & -16 & \underline{|2} \\
 & 2 & -12 & 16 & \\
\hline
1 & -6 & 8 & 0 &
\end{array}
$$

Thus $+2$ is a root. It is not necessary to find any more roots by trial and error. We now may use the quadratic formula on the remaining factor $x^2 - 6x + 8$, and find that the roots are 2 and 4. Thus, the roots are $-1, 2, 2,$ and 4. (Note that 2 is a double root.)

Exercises 14—4

In Exercises 1 through 20 solve the given equations.

1. $x^3 + 2x^2 - x - 2 = 0$ 2. $x^3 + x^2 - 5x + 3 = 0$
3. $x^3 + 2x^2 - 5x - 6 = 0$ 4. $x^3 + 1 = 0$
5. $2x^3 - 5x^2 - 28x + 15 = 0$ 6. $2x^3 - x^2 - 3x - 1 = 0$
7. $3x^3 + 11x^2 + 5x - 3 = 0$ 8. $4x^3 - 5x^2 - 23x + 6 = 0$
9. $x^4 - 11x^2 - 12x + 4 = 0$ 10. $x^4 + x^3 - 2x^2 - 4x - 8 = 0$
11. $x^4 - 2x^3 - 13x^2 + 14x + 24 = 0$ 12. $x^4 - x^3 + 2x^2 - 4x - 8 = 0$
13. $2x^4 - 5x^3 - 3x^2 + 4x + 2 = 0$ 14. $2x^4 + 7x^3 + 9x^2 + 5x + 1 = 0$
15. $12x^4 + 44x^3 + 21x^2 - 11x - 6 = 0$ 16. $9x^4 - 3x^3 + 34x^2 - 12x - 8 = 0$
17. $x^5 + x^4 - 9x^3 - 5x^2 + 16x + 12 = 0$ 18. $x^6 - x^4 - 14x^2 + 24 = 0$
19. $2x^5 - 5x^4 + 6x^3 - 6x^2 + 4x - 1 = 0$
20. $2x^5 + 5x^4 - 4x^3 - 19x^2 - 16x - 4 = 0$

In Exercises 21 through 26 determine the required quantities. In Exercises 25 and 26 it is necessary to set up equations of higher degree.

21. Under certain conditions, the velocity of an object as a function of time is given by $v = 2t^3 - 11t^2 - 28t - 15$. For what values of t is $v = 0$?

22. The deflection y of a beam at a horizontal distance x from one end is given by $y = k(x^4 - 2Lx^3 + L^3x)$, where L is the length of the beam and k is a constant. For what values of x is the deflection zero?

23. In the theory of the motion of a sphere moving through a fluid, the expression $4r^3 - 3ar^2 - a^3$ is found. In terms of a, solve for r if this expression is zero.

24. Three electric resistors are connected in parallel. The second resistor is 1 Ω more than the first, and the third resistor is 4 Ω more than the first. The total resistance of the combination is 1 Ω. To find the first resistance R, we must solve the equation

$$\frac{1}{R} + \frac{1}{R+1} + \frac{1}{R+4} = 1$$

Find the values of the resistances.

25. A rectangular box is made from a piece of cardboard 8 in. by 12 in., by cutting a square from each corner and bending up the sides. How large is the side of the square cut out, if the volume of the box is 64 in.³?

26. A slice 2 cm thick is cut off the side of a cube, leaving 75 cm³ in the remaining volume. Find the length of the edge of the cube.

14—5 Irrational Roots by Linear Interpolation

When a polynomial equation has more than two irrational roots, we cannot find these roots by the methods just presented. Therefore, we must have some method for finding irrational roots for those equations in which we cannot reduce the given function to quadratic factors. Many methods have been developed for this purpose, but we shall discuss only one: **linear interpolation.** The basic assumption is the same as that involved in finding values which lie between listed values in tables;

namely, that if two points are sufficiently close to each other, a straight line joining the points will very nearly approximate the actual curve between the two points. This method is basically a graphical one, and is illustrated in the following examples.

Example A

Using the method of linear interpolation, find the irrational root of the equation $x^3 + 2x^2 + 8x - 2 = 0$ which lies between 0 and 1.

We know that wherever a curve crosses the x-axis, that value of x is a root. We are told that the root we want is between 0 and 1. Normally we would then expect to find the function to be either positive or negative when $x = 0$, and to have the opposite sign when $x = 1$. To check this, the remainder theorem may be used. We find that $f(0) = -2$ and $f(1) = 9$. We now *assume* the curve between these points can be approximated by a straight line between these points. If this were exactly correct, as the magnified scale drawing in Fig. 14-1 shows, the root would lie between 0.1 and 0.2, very close to 0.2. Hence we shall try these values, using synthetic division, and rounding off to two significant digits for now.

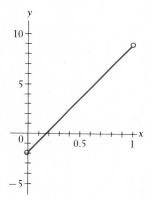

Figure 14-1

1	2	8	-2	$\underline{|0.1}$
	0.1	0.2	0.8	
1	2.1	8.2	-1.2	

1	2	8	-2	$\underline{|0.2}$
	0.2	0.4	1.7	
1	2.2	8.4	-0.3	

We note that the remainders for $x = 0.1$ and $x = 0.2$ are -1.2 and -0.3 respectively. Since the signs are the same, the root does not lie between 0.1 and 0.2. We do know, however, that it lies between 0.2 and 1. Thus we continue trying values of x nearer 1.

1	2	8	-2	$\underline{|0.3}$
	0.3	0.7	2.6	
1	2.3	8.7	0.6	

Since the sign of the remainder for $x = 0.3$ is positive, we now know that the root lies between 0.2 and 0.3. Again we make a scale drawing (Fig. 14-2) to approximate the hundredths digit. The root is apparently between 0.23 and 0.24. We shall try these values (rounding off to three significant digits).

1	2	8	-2	$\underline{|0.23}$
	0.23	0.51	1.96	
1	2.23	8.51	-0.04	

1	2	8	-2	$\underline{|0.24}$
	0.24	0.54	2.05	
1	2.24	8.54	0.05	

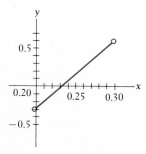

Figure 14-2

Thus the root is between 0.23 and 0.24. Since the remainder is numerically smaller for $x = 0.23$, we may conclude from linear interpolation that this is the value of the root to two significant digits. The process may be continued to obtain greater accuracy if necessary.

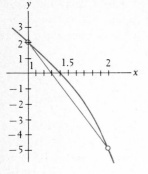

Figure 14–3

Example B

By linear interpolation, find the root between 1 and 2 of the equation $x^4 - 5x^3 + 6x^2 - 5x + 5 = 0$.

The method followed should be clear when we observe Fig. 14–3 and the steps shown.

$$
\begin{array}{rrrrr|l}
1 & -5 & 6 & -5 & 5 & \underline{1} \\
  & 1 & -4 & 2 & -3 & \\
\hline
1 & -4 & 2 & -3 & +2 &
\end{array}
$$

$$
\begin{array}{rrrrr|l}
1 & -5 & 6 & -5 & 5 & \underline{2} \\
  & 2 & -6 & 0 & -10 & \\
\hline
1 & -3 & 0 & -5 & -5 &
\end{array}
$$

$$
\begin{array}{rrrrr|l}
1 & -5 & 6 & -5 & 5 & \underline{1.2} \\
  & 1.2 & -4.6 & 1.7 & -4.0 & \\
\hline
1 & -3.8 & 1.4 & -3.3 & +1.0 &
\end{array}
$$

$$
\begin{array}{rrrrr|l}
1 & -5 & 6 & -5 & 5 & \underline{1.3} \\
  & 1.3 & -4.8 & 1.6 & -4.4 & \\
\hline
1 & -3.7 & 1.2 & -3.4 & +0.6 &
\end{array}
$$

$$
\begin{array}{rrrrr|l}
1 & -5 & 6 & -5 & 5 & \underline{1.4} \\
  & 1.4 & -5.0 & 1.4 & -5.04 & \\
\hline
1 & -3.6 & +1.0 & -3.6 & -0.04 &
\end{array}
$$

$$
\begin{array}{rrrrr|l}
1 & -5 & 6 & -5 & 5 & \underline{1.39} \\
  & 1.39 & -5.02 & 1.36 & -5.06 & \\
\hline
1 & -3.61 & 0.98 & -3.64 & -0.06 &
\end{array}
$$

$$
\begin{array}{rrrrr|l}
1 & -5 & 6 & -5 & 5 & \underline{1.38} \\
  & 1.38 & -5.00 & 1.38 & -4.996 & \\
\hline
1 & -3.62 & 1.00 & -3.62 & +0.004 &
\end{array}
$$

Thus $r = 1.38$ (to three significant digits).

If we must find the roots of an equation without any specific information as to the location of the roots, we first make an approximate graph. In this way we can know the integers between which the roots lie. Then linear interpolation can be used to approximate them more accurately. The following example outlines the method.

Example C

Find the roots of the equation $2x^4 - 3x^3 - 6x^2 + 2x - 15 = 0$.

First we calculate values as shown in the following table so that we might graph the function

$$y = 2x^4 - 3x^3 - 6x^2 + 2x - 15$$

and thereby locate the roots approximately.

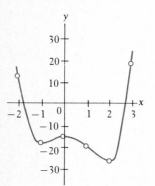

Figure 14–4

x	-2	-1	0	1	2	3
y	13	-18	-15	-20	-27	18

The graph is shown in Fig. 14−4. We note that the roots of the equation lie between $x = -2$ and $x = -1$, and between $x = 2$ and $x = 3$. By using linear interpolation these roots can be found more accurately. In this case, the roots are approximately $x = -1.79$ and $x = 2.79$.

Exercises 14−5

In Exercises 1 through 12 find by linear interpolation the irrational root (to two decimal places) between the indicated values of x.

1. $x^3 - 6x^2 + 10x - 4 = 0$ (0 and 1) 2. $x^3 - 3x^2 - 2x + 3 = 0$ (0 and 1)
3. $x^3 - 5x^2 + 7x - 2 = 0$ (0 and 1) 4. $x^3 + 5x^2 - 3x - 2 = 0$ (0 and 1)
5. $2x^3 + 2x^2 - 11x + 3 = 0$ (1 and 2) 6. $x^3 - 5x^2 + 3x + 4 = 0$ (1 and 2)
7. $3x^3 + 13x^2 + 3x - 4 = 0$ (−1 and 0)
8. $2x^4 - x^3 + 6x^2 - 4x - 8 = 0$ (−1 and 0)
9. $x^4 - x^3 - 3x^2 - x - 4 = 0$ (2 and 3)
10. $2x^4 - 2x^3 - 5x^2 - x - 3 = 0$ (2 and 3)
11. $x^4 - 2x^3 - 8x - 16 = 0$ (3 and 4)
12. $3x^4 - 3x^3 - 11x^2 - x - 4 = 0$ (−2 and −1)

In Exercises 13 through 16 find all of the real roots of the given equations to two decimal places.

13. $x^3 - 2x^2 - 5x + 4 = 0$ 14. $x^3 - 2x^2 - 2x - 7 = 0$
15. $x^4 - x^3 - 2x^2 - x - 3 = 0$ 16. $x^5 - 2x^4 + 4x^3 - 7x^2 + 4 = 0$

In Exercises 17 through 20 determine the required values. In Exercises 19 and 20 first set up the appropriate equation.

17. The ends of a 10-ft beam are supported at different levels. The deflection y of the beam is given by $y = kx^2(x^3 + 450x - 3500)$, where x is the horizontal distance from one end and k is a constant. Determine the values of x for which the deflection is zero.

18. In determining one of the dimensions d of the support columns of a building, the equation $3d^3 + 5d^2 - 400d - 3000 = 0$ is found. Determine, to one decimal place, this dimension (in inches).

19. A metal storage tank which holds 500 m³ is spherical, with an outside diameter of 10.0 m. What is the thickness (to three decimal places) of the metal of which the tank is made?

20. The sides of a rectangular box are 3, 5, and 6 ft. If each side is increased by the same amount, the volume is doubled. By how much should each side be increased to accomplish this?

14−6 Exercises for Chapter 14

In Exercises 1 through 4 find the remainder of the indicated division by the remainder theorem.

1. $(2x^3 - 4x^2 - x + 4) \div (x - 1)$ 2. $(x^3 - 2x^2 + 9) \div (x + 2)$
3. $(4x^3 + x + 4) \div (x + 3)$ 4. $(x^4 - 5x^3 + 8x^2 + 15x - 2) \div (x - 3)$

In Exercises 5 through 8 use the factor theorem to determine whether or not the second expression is a factor of the first.

5. $x^4 + x^3 + x^2 - 2x - 3$, $x + 1$ 6. $2x^3 - 2x^2 - 3x - 2$, $x - 2$

7. $x^4 + 4x^3 + 5x^2 + 5x - 6$, $x + 3$ 8. $9x^3 + 6x^2 + 4x + 2$, $3x + 1$

In Exercises 9 through 16 use synthetic division to perform the indicated divisions.

9. $(x^3 + 3x^2 + 6x + 1) \div (x - 1)$ 10. $(3x^3 - 2x^2 + 7) \div (x - 3)$

11. $(2x^3 - 3x^2 - 4x + 3) \div (x + 2)$ 12. $(3x^3 - 5x^2 + 7x - 6) \div (x + 4)$

13. $(x^4 - 2x^3 - 3x^2 - 4x - 8) \div (x + 1)$

14. $(x^4 - 6x^3 + x - 8) \div (x - 3)$ 15. $(2x^5 - 46x^3 + x^2 - 9) \div (x - 5)$

16. $(x^6 + 63x^3 + 5x^2 - 9x - 8) \div (x + 4)$

In Exercises 17 through 20 use synthetic division to determine whether or not the given numbers are zeros of the given functions.

17. $x^3 + 8x^2 + 17x - 6$; -3 18. $2x^3 + x^2 - 4x + 4$; -2

19. $2x^4 - x^3 + 2x^2 + x - 1$; $\frac{1}{2}$ 20. $6x^4 - 7x^3 + 2x^2 - 9x - 6$; $-\frac{2}{3}$

In Exercises 21 through 28 find all of the solutions of the given equations, with the aid of synthetic division and with the roots indicated.

21. $x^3 + 8x^2 + 17x + 6 = 0$ $(r_1 = -3)$

22. $2x^3 + 7x^2 - 6x - 8 = 0$ $(r_1 = -4)$

23. $3x^4 + 5x^3 + x^2 + x - 10 = 0$ $(r_1 = 1, r_2 = -2)$

24. $x^4 - x^3 - 5x^2 - x - 6 = 0$ $(r_1 = 3, r_2 = -2)$

25. $2x^4 + x^3 - 29x^2 - 34x + 24 = 0$ $(r_1 = -2, r_2 = \frac{1}{2})$

26. $x^4 + x^3 - 11x^2 - 9x + 18 = 0$ $(r_1 = -3, r_2 = 1)$

27. $x^5 + 3x^4 - x^3 - 11x^2 - 12x - 4 = 0$ $(-1$ is a triple root$)$

28. $24x^5 + 10x^4 + 7x^2 - 6x + 1 = 0$ $(r_1 = -1, r_2 = \frac{1}{4}, r_3 = \frac{1}{3})$

In Exercises 29 through 36 solve the given equations.

29. $x^3 + x^2 - 10x + 8 = 0$ 30. $x^3 - 8x^2 + 20x - 16 = 0$

31. $2x^3 - x^2 - 8x - 5 = 0$ 32. $2x^3 - 3x^2 - 11x + 6 = 0$

33. $6x^3 - x^2 - 12x - 5 = 0$ 34. $6x^3 + 19x^2 + 2x - 3 = 0$

35. $2x^4 + x^3 + 3x^2 + 2x - 2 = 0$

36. $2x^4 + 5x^3 - 14x^2 - 23x + 30 = 0$

In Exercises 37 through 40, find the indicated irrational root by linear interpolation. Find the value to two decimal places.

37. $x^3 - 3x^2 - x + 2 = 0$ (between 0 and 1)

38. $x^3 + 3x^2 - 6x - 2 = 0$ (between 1 and 2)

39. $3x^3 - x^2 - 8x - 2 = 0$ (between 1 and 2)

40. $x^4 + 3x^3 + 6x + 4 = 0$ (between -1 and 0)

In Exercises 41 through 48 determine the required quantities. Where appropriate, set up the required equations.

41. The total profit P a manufacturer makes in producing x units of a commodity is given by $P = 2x^3 - 3x^2 - 5x - 150$. Less than how many units of production result in a loss?

42. Three electric capacitors are connected in series. The capacitance of the second is 1 μF (microfarad) more than the first, and the third is 2 μF more than the second. The capacitance of the combination is 1.33 μF. The equation used to determine C, the capacitance of the first capacitor, is

$$\frac{1}{C} + \frac{1}{C+1} + \frac{1}{C+3} = \frac{3}{4}$$

Find the values of the capacitances.

43. Where does the graph of function $f(x) = 6x^4 - 14x^3 + 5x^2 + 5x - 2$ cross the x-axis?

44. The hypotenuse of a right triangle is 2 m longer than one of the legs. The area of the triangle is 24 m². Find the sides of the triangle.

45. The width of a rectangular box equals the depth, and the length is 4 ft more than the width. The volume of the box is 539 ft³. What are the dimensions of the box?

46. A certain sphere floating in water sinks to a depth y which is given by the equation $y^3 - 6y^2 + 16 = 0$. Find, to one decimal place, the depth (in centimeters) to which the sphere sinks.

47. The area of a segment of a circle is given approximately by the equation

$$A = \frac{h^3}{2L} + \frac{2Lh}{3}$$

where L is the length of the chord and h is the altitude of the segment. Find h when $L = 3$ and $A = 4$. (Evaluate to two decimal places.)

48. If the edge of a cube is increased by 1 mm, its volume is doubled. Find the edge of the cube to two decimal places.

15

Determinants and Matrices

15–1 Determinants: Expansion by Minors

In Chapter 4 we first met the concept of a determinant and saw how it is used to solve systems of linear equations. However, at that time we limited our discussion to second- and third-order determinants. In the first two sections of this chapter we shall show methods of evaluating higher-order determinants. In the remainder of the chapter we shall develop another related concept and its use in solving systems of linear equations.

From Section 4–6, we recall that a third-order determinant is defined by the equation

$$\begin{vmatrix} a_1 & b_1 & c_1 \\ a_2 & b_2 & c_2 \\ a_3 & b_3 & c_3 \end{vmatrix} = a_1 b_2 c_3 + a_3 b_1 c_2 + a_2 b_3 c_1 - a_3 b_2 c_1 - a_1 b_3 c_2 - a_2 b_1 c_3 \qquad (15\text{–}1)$$

If we rearrange the terms on the right and factor a_1, a_2, and a_3 from the terms in which they are contained, we have

$$\begin{vmatrix} a_1 & b_1 & c_1 \\ a_2 & b_2 & c_2 \\ a_3 & b_3 & c_3 \end{vmatrix} = a_1 (b_2 c_3 - b_3 c_2) - a_2 (b_1 c_3 - b_3 c_1) + a_3 (b_1 c_2 - b_2 c_1) \qquad (15\text{–}2)$$

Recalling the definition of a second-order determinant we have

$$\begin{vmatrix} a_1 & b_1 & c_1 \\ a_2 & b_2 & c_2 \\ a_3 & b_3 & c_3 \end{vmatrix} = a_1 \begin{vmatrix} b_2 & c_2 \\ b_3 & c_3 \end{vmatrix} - a_2 \begin{vmatrix} b_1 & c_1 \\ b_3 & c_3 \end{vmatrix} + a_3 \begin{vmatrix} b_1 & c_1 \\ b_2 & c_2 \end{vmatrix} \qquad (15-3)$$

In Eq. (15–3) we note that the third-order determinant is expanded with the terms of the expansion as products of the elements of the first column and specific second-order determinants. In each case the elements of the second-order determinant are those elements which are in neither the same row nor the same column as the element from the first column. These determinants are called **minors**.

In general, *the minor of a given element of a determinant is the determinant which results by deleting the row and the column in which the element lies.* Consider the following example.

Example A

Consider the determinant $\begin{vmatrix} 1 & 2 & 3 \\ 4 & 5 & 6 \\ 7 & 8 & 9 \end{vmatrix}$

We find the minor of the element 1 by deleting the elements in the first row and first column because the element 1 is located in the first row and in the first column. This minor is the determinant

$$\begin{vmatrix} 5 & 6 \\ 8 & 9 \end{vmatrix}$$

The minor for the element 2 is formed by deleting the elements in the first row and second column, for this is the location of the 2. The minor of 2 is the determinant

$$\begin{vmatrix} 4 & 6 \\ 7 & 9 \end{vmatrix}$$

The minor for the element 6 is the determinant

$$\begin{vmatrix} 1 & 2 \\ 7 & 8 \end{vmatrix}$$

The minor for the element 8 is the determinant

$$\begin{vmatrix} 1 & 3 \\ 4 & 6 \end{vmatrix}$$

We now see that Eq. (15–3) expresses the expansion of a third-order determinant as the sum of the products of the elements of the first column and their minors, with the second term assigned a minus sign.

Actually this is only one of several ways of expressing the expansion. However, it does lead to a general theorem regarding the expansion of a determinant of any order. The foregoing provides a basis for this theorem, although it cannot be considered as a proof. The theorem is as follows:

> *The value of a determinant of order n may be found by forming the n products of the elements of any column (or row) and their minors. A product is given a plus sign if the sum of the number of the column and the number of the row in which the element lies is even, and a minus sign if this sum is odd. The algebraic sum of the terms thus obtained is the value of the determinant.*

The following examples illustrate the expansion of determinants by minors in accordance with the theorem above.

Example B
Evaluate $\begin{vmatrix} 1 & -3 & -2 \\ 4 & -1 & 0 \\ 4 & 3 & -5 \end{vmatrix}$ by expansion by minors.

Since we may expand by any column or row, let us select the first row. The expansion is as follows:

$$\begin{vmatrix} 1 & -3 & -2 \\ 4 & -1 & 0 \\ 4 & 3 & -5 \end{vmatrix} = +(1)\begin{vmatrix} -1 & 0 \\ 3 & -5 \end{vmatrix} - (-3)\begin{vmatrix} 4 & 0 \\ 4 & -5 \end{vmatrix} + (-2)\begin{vmatrix} 4 & -1 \\ 4 & 3 \end{vmatrix}$$

The first term of the expansion is assigned a plus sign since the element 1 is in column 1, row 1 and $1 + 1 = 2$ (even). The second term is assigned a minus sign since the element -3 is in column 2 and row 1, and $2 + 1 = 3$ (odd). The third term is assigned a plus sign since the element -2 is in column 3 and row 1, and $3 + 1 = 4$ (even). Actually, once the first sign has been properly determined, the others are known since the signs alternate from term to term. Using the definition of a second-order determinant, we complete the evaluation.

$$\begin{vmatrix} 1 & -3 & -2 \\ 4 & -1 & 0 \\ 4 & 3 & -5 \end{vmatrix} = +(1)(5 - 0) - (-3)(-20 - 0) + (-2)[12 - (-4)]$$

$$= 1(5) + 3(-20) - 2(16) = 5 - 60 - 32 = -87$$

Expansion of this same determinant by the third column is as follows:

$$\begin{vmatrix} 1 & -3 & -2 \\ 4 & -1 & 0 \\ 4 & 3 & -5 \end{vmatrix} = +(-2)\begin{vmatrix} 4 & -1 \\ 4 & 3 \end{vmatrix} - (0)\begin{vmatrix} 1 & -3 \\ 4 & 3 \end{vmatrix} + (-5)\begin{vmatrix} 1 & -3 \\ 4 & -1 \end{vmatrix}$$

$$= -2(12 + 4) + 0 - 5(-1 + 12)$$

$$= -2(16) - 5(11) = -32 - 55 = -87$$

This expansion has one advantage: since one of the elements of the third column is zero, its minor does not have to be evaluated because zero times whatever the value of the determinant will give the product of zero.

Example C
Evaluate

$$\begin{vmatrix} 3 & -2 & 0 & 2 \\ 1 & 0 & -1 & 4 \\ -3 & 1 & 2 & -2 \\ 2 & -1 & 0 & -1 \end{vmatrix}$$

Expanding by the third column, we have

$$\begin{vmatrix} 3 & -2 & 0 & 2 \\ 1 & 0 & -1 & 4 \\ -3 & 1 & 2 & -2 \\ 2 & -1 & 0 & -1 \end{vmatrix} = +(0)\begin{vmatrix} 1 & 0 & 4 \\ -3 & 1 & -2 \\ 2 & -1 & -1 \end{vmatrix} - (-1)\begin{vmatrix} 3 & -2 & 2 \\ -3 & 1 & -2 \\ 2 & -1 & -1 \end{vmatrix}$$

$$+ (2)\begin{vmatrix} 3 & -2 & 2 \\ 1 & 0 & 4 \\ 2 & -1 & -1 \end{vmatrix} - (0)\begin{vmatrix} 3 & -2 & 2 \\ 1 & 0 & 4 \\ -3 & 1 & -2 \end{vmatrix}$$

It is not necessary to expand the minors in the first and fourth terms, since the element in each case is zero. The minors in the second and third terms can be expanded as third-order determinants or by minors. This illustrates well that expansion by minors effectively reduces the order of the determinant to be evaluated by one. Completing the evaluation by minors, we have

$$\begin{vmatrix} 3 & -2 & 0 & 2 \\ 1 & 0 & -1 & 4 \\ -3 & 1 & 2 & -2 \\ 2 & -1 & 0 & -1 \end{vmatrix} = \begin{vmatrix} 3 & -2 & 2 \\ -3 & 1 & -2 \\ 2 & -1 & -1 \end{vmatrix} + 2\begin{vmatrix} 3 & -2 & 2 \\ 1 & 0 & 4 \\ 2 & -1 & -1 \end{vmatrix}$$

$$= \left[3\begin{vmatrix} 1 & -2 \\ -1 & -1 \end{vmatrix} - (-3)\begin{vmatrix} -2 & 2 \\ -1 & -1 \end{vmatrix} + 2\begin{vmatrix} -2 & 2 \\ 1 & -2 \end{vmatrix} \right]$$

$$+ 2\left[-(-2)\begin{vmatrix} 1 & 4 \\ 2 & -1 \end{vmatrix} + 0\begin{vmatrix} 3 & 2 \\ 2 & -1 \end{vmatrix} - (-1)\begin{vmatrix} 3 & 2 \\ 1 & 4 \end{vmatrix} \right]$$

$$= [3(-1 - 2) + 3(2 + 2) + 2(4 - 2)] + 2[2(-1 - 8) + (12 - 2)]$$
$$= [-9 + 12 + 4] + 2[-18 + 10]$$
$$= +7 + 2(-8) = -9$$

We can use the expansion of determinants by minors to solve systems of linear equations. Cramer's rule for solving systems of equations, as stated in Section 4–6, is valid for any system of n equations in n unknowns. The following examples illustrate the solution of systems of equations.

Example D

The production of a particular computer component is done in three stages, taking a total of 7 h. The second stage is one hour less than the first, and the third stage is twice as long as the second stage. How long is each stage of production?

First, we let a = the number of hours of the first production stage, b = the number of hours of the second stage, and c = the number of hours of the third stage.

The total production time of 7 h gives us $a + b + c = 7$. Since the second stage is one hour less than the first, we then have $b = a - 1$. The fact that the third stage is twice as long as the second gives us $c = 2b$. Stating these equations in standard form for solution, we have

$$a + b + c = 7$$
$$a - b \quad = 1$$
$$2b - c = 0$$

Using Cramer's rule, we have

$$a = \frac{\begin{vmatrix} 7 & 1 & 1 \\ 1 & -1 & 0 \\ 0 & 2 & -1 \end{vmatrix}}{\begin{vmatrix} 1 & 1 & 1 \\ 1 & -1 & 0 \\ 0 & 2 & -1 \end{vmatrix}} = \frac{-(1)\begin{vmatrix} 1 & 1 \\ 2 & -1 \end{vmatrix} + (-1)\begin{vmatrix} 7 & 1 \\ 0 & -1 \end{vmatrix} - 0 \begin{vmatrix} 7 & 1 \\ 0 & 2 \end{vmatrix}}{-(1)\begin{vmatrix} 1 & 1 \\ 2 & -1 \end{vmatrix} + (-1)\begin{vmatrix} 1 & 1 \\ 0 & -1 \end{vmatrix} + 0 \begin{vmatrix} 1 & 1 \\ 0 & 2 \end{vmatrix}}$$

$$= \frac{-(-1-2) - (-7)}{-(-1-2) - (-1)} = \frac{3+7}{3+1} = \frac{10}{4} = \frac{5}{2}$$

Here we expanded each determinant by minors of the second row. Now using the second equation we have $\frac{5}{2} - b = 1$, or $b = \frac{3}{2}$. Using the third equation we have $2(\frac{3}{2}) - c = 0$, or $c = 3$. Thus,

$$a = \frac{5}{2} \text{ h}, \quad b = \frac{3}{2} \text{ h}, \quad \text{and} \quad c = 3 \text{ h}$$

This means that the first stage takes 2.5 h, the second stage takes 1.5 h, and the third stage takes 3 h. We see that these times agree with the given information.

Example E

Solve the following system of equations.

$$\begin{aligned} x + 2y + z &= 5 \\ 2x \quad\quad + z + 2t &= 1 \\ x - y + 3z + 4t &= -6 \\ 4x - y \quad\quad - 2t &= 0 \end{aligned}$$

$$x = \frac{\begin{vmatrix} 5 & 2 & 1 & 0 \\ 1 & 0 & 1 & 2 \\ -6 & -1 & 3 & 4 \\ 0 & -1 & 0 & -2 \end{vmatrix}}{\begin{vmatrix} 1 & 2 & 1 & 0 \\ 2 & 0 & 1 & 2 \\ 1 & -1 & 3 & 4 \\ 4 & -1 & 0 & -2 \end{vmatrix}}$$

$$= \frac{-(0)\begin{vmatrix} 2 & 1 & 0 \\ 0 & 1 & 2 \\ -1 & 3 & 4 \end{vmatrix} + (-1)\begin{vmatrix} 5 & 1 & 0 \\ 1 & 1 & 2 \\ -6 & 3 & 4 \end{vmatrix} - (0)\begin{vmatrix} 5 & 2 & 0 \\ 1 & 0 & 2 \\ -6 & -1 & 4 \end{vmatrix} + (-2)\begin{vmatrix} 5 & 2 & 1 \\ 1 & 0 & 1 \\ -6 & -1 & 3 \end{vmatrix}}{(1)\begin{vmatrix} 0 & 1 & 2 \\ -1 & 3 & 4 \\ -1 & 0 & -2 \end{vmatrix} - 2\begin{vmatrix} 2 & 1 & 2 \\ 1 & 3 & 4 \\ 4 & 0 & -2 \end{vmatrix} + (1)\begin{vmatrix} 2 & 0 & 2 \\ 1 & -1 & 4 \\ 4 & -1 & -2 \end{vmatrix} - (0)\begin{vmatrix} 2 & 0 & 1 \\ 1 & -1 & 3 \\ 4 & -1 & 0 \end{vmatrix}}$$

$$= \frac{-(-26) - 2(-14)}{1(0) - 2(-18) + 1(18)} = \frac{26 + 28}{36 + 18} = \frac{54}{54} = 1$$

In solving for x the determinant in the numerator was evaluated by expanding by the minors of the fourth row, since it contained two zeros. The determinant in the denominator was evaluated by expanding by the minors of the first row. Now we solve for y, and we again note two zeros in the fourth row of the determinant of the numerator.

$$y = \frac{\begin{vmatrix} 1 & 5 & 1 & 0 \\ 2 & 1 & 1 & 2 \\ 1 & -6 & 3 & 4 \\ 4 & 0 & 0 & -2 \end{vmatrix}}{54} = \frac{-4\begin{vmatrix} 5 & 1 & 0 \\ 1 & 1 & 2 \\ -6 & 3 & 4 \end{vmatrix} + (-2)\begin{vmatrix} 1 & 5 & 1 \\ 2 & 1 & 1 \\ 1 & -6 & 3 \end{vmatrix}}{54}$$

$$= \frac{-4(-26) - 2(-29)}{54} = \frac{104 + 58}{54} = \frac{162}{54} = 3$$

Substituting these values for x and y into the first equation, we can solve for z. This gives $z = -2$. Again, substituting the values for x and y into the fourth equation, we find $t = \frac{1}{2}$. Thus the required solution is $x = 1$, $y = 3$, $z = -2$, $t = \frac{1}{2}$. The solution can be checked by substituting these values into either the second or third equation.

Exercises 15—1

In Exercises 1 through 16 evaluate the given determinants by expansion by minors.

1. $\begin{vmatrix} 3 & 0 & 0 \\ -2 & 1 & 4 \\ 4 & -2 & 5 \end{vmatrix}$
2. $\begin{vmatrix} 10 & 0 & -3 \\ -2 & -4 & 1 \\ 3 & 0 & 2 \end{vmatrix}$
3. $\begin{vmatrix} -2 & -4 & 2 \\ 1 & 3 & 0 \\ -4 & 5 & 2 \end{vmatrix}$

4. $\begin{vmatrix} 5 & -1 & 2 \\ 8 & 3 & -4 \\ 0 & 2 & -6 \end{vmatrix}$
5. $\begin{vmatrix} -6 & -1 & 3 \\ 2 & -2 & -3 \\ 10 & 1 & -2 \end{vmatrix}$
6. $\begin{vmatrix} 9 & -3 & 1 \\ -1 & 2 & -1 \\ 2 & -1 & 3 \end{vmatrix}$

7. $\begin{vmatrix} -3 & -2 & 5 \\ 1 & 2 & -1 \\ 3 & -4 & 2 \end{vmatrix}$
8. $\begin{vmatrix} 4 & -3 & 3 \\ -3 & 5 & 6 \\ 2 & -1 & 2 \end{vmatrix}$

9. $\begin{vmatrix} 1 & 0 & 1 & 0 \\ 2 & 4 & -3 & 1 \\ 1 & 1 & 1 & 1 \\ 3 & 5 & 0 & 2 \end{vmatrix}$
10. $\begin{vmatrix} 2 & 0 & 3 & 1 \\ -1 & -1 & 4 & 0 \\ 1 & 2 & 1 & 2 \\ 3 & 3 & -2 & -1 \end{vmatrix}$
11. $\begin{vmatrix} 2 & -1 & 1 & -4 \\ 2 & 1 & 3 & -5 \\ 3 & -1 & -1 & 0 \\ 1 & 2 & 2 & 6 \end{vmatrix}$

12. $\begin{vmatrix} 3 & 6 & -2 & 4 \\ 2 & -5 & 2 & 6 \\ 5 & 3 & 4 & 0 \\ 1 & 2 & 0 & -1 \end{vmatrix}$
13. $\begin{vmatrix} 1 & 2 & -1 & -2 \\ 3 & 1 & 2 & 1 \\ -1 & 3 & -1 & 2 \\ 2 & 1 & 3 & -3 \end{vmatrix}$
14. $\begin{vmatrix} 3 & -1 & 2 & -5 \\ 1 & 4 & 2 & 5 \\ -1 & 1 & 1 & 3 \\ 1 & 2 & -1 & -2 \end{vmatrix}$

15. $\begin{vmatrix} 1 & 2 & 1 & 2 & 1 \\ 1 & 0 & 0 & 1 & 0 \\ 0 & 1 & 1 & 0 & 1 \\ 1 & 1 & 2 & 2 & 1 \\ 0 & 1 & 1 & 0 & 2 \end{vmatrix}$
16. $\begin{vmatrix} 3 & 1 & 1 & 1 & 2 \\ 1 & 1 & 0 & 0 & 1 \\ 1 & 1 & 2 & 2 & 3 \\ 0 & 2 & 1 & 0 & 3 \\ 1 & 1 & 0 & 1 & 0 \end{vmatrix}$

In Exercises 17 through 24 solve the given systems of equations by determinants. Evaluate the determinants by expansion by minors.

17. $2x + y + z = 6$
$x - 2y + 2z = 10$
$3x - y - z = 4$

18. $2x + y = -1$
$4x - 2y - z = 5$
$2x + 3y + 3z = -2$

19. $3x + 6y + 2z = -2$
    $x + 3y - 4z = 2$
    $2x - 3y - 2z = -2$

20. $x + 3y + z = 4$
    $2x - 6y - 3z = 10$
    $4x - 9y + 3z = 4$

21. $x + t = 0$
    $3x + y + z = -1$
    $2y - z + 3t = 1$
    $2z - 3t = 1$

22. $2x + y + z = 4$
    $2y - 2z - t = 3$
    $3y - 3z + 2t = 1$
    $6x - y + t = 0$

23. $x + 2y - z = 6$
    $y - 2z - 3t = -5$
    $3x - 2y + t = 2$
    $2x + y + z - t = 0$

24. $2x + 3y + z = 4$
    $x - 2y - 3z + 4t = -1$
    $3x + y + z - 5t = 3$
    $-x + 2y + z + 3t = 2$

In Exercises 25 through 28 solve the given problems by use of determinants, using methods of this section.

25. In applying Kirchhoff's laws (see Exercise 19 of Section 4–5) to the given electric circuit, the following equations are found. Determine the indicated currents in amperes (see Fig. 15–1).

$$I_A + I_B + I_C + I_D = 0$$
$$2I_A - I_B = -2$$
$$3I_C - 2I_D = 0$$
$$I_B - 3I_C = 6$$

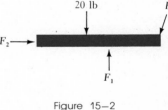

Figure 15–1

26. In analyzing the forces shown in Fig. 15–2, the following equations are derived:

$$F_1 = 20 + 0.8F_3$$
$$F_2 = 0.6F_3$$
$$3F_1 = 40 + 4F_3$$

Find forces F_1, F_2, and F_3.

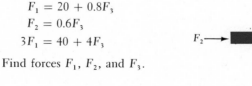

Figure 15–2

27. A 1% solution, a 5% solution, and a 10% solution of sulfuric acid are to be mixed in order to get 600 mL of a 6% solution. If the volume of the 5% solution equals the volume of the other two solutions together, how much of each is needed?

28. A company budgets $100,000 to buy a fleet of 20 cars, made up of four models costing $4000, $5000, $6000, and $9000 each, respectively. The budget calls for 15 of the $4000 and $5000 models. The total cost of the $5000 and $6000 models is $59,000. How many of each model are in the budget?

15–2 Some Properties of Determinants

Expansion of determinants by minors allows us to evaluate a determinant of any order. However, even for a fourth-order determinant, the amount of work necessary for the evaluation is usually excessive. There are a number of basic properties of determinants which allow us to perform the evaluation with considerably less work. We will present these properties here without proof, although each will be illustrated.

(1) *If each element below the principal diagonal of a determinant is zero, then the product of the elements of the principal diagonal is the value of the determinant.*

Example A

The value of the determinant

$$\begin{vmatrix} 2 & 1 & 5 & 8 \\ 0 & -5 & 7 & 9 \\ 0 & 0 & 4 & -6 \\ 0 & 0 & 0 & 3 \end{vmatrix}$$

equals the product $2(-5)(4)(3) = -120$. Since all of the elements below the principal diagonal are zero, there is no need to expand the determinant. It will be noted, however, that if the determinant is expanded by the first column, and successive determinants are expanded by their first columns, the same value is found. Performing the expansion we have

$$\begin{vmatrix} 2 & 1 & 5 & 8 \\ 0 & -5 & 7 & 9 \\ 0 & 0 & 4 & -6 \\ 0 & 0 & 0 & 3 \end{vmatrix} = 2 \begin{vmatrix} -5 & 7 & 9 \\ 0 & 4 & -6 \\ 0 & 0 & 3 \end{vmatrix}$$

$$= 2(-5) \begin{vmatrix} 4 & -6 \\ 0 & 3 \end{vmatrix} = 2(-5)(4)(3) = -120$$

(2) *If the corresponding rows and columns of a determinant are interchanged, the value of the determinant is unchanged.*

Example B

For the determinant

$$\begin{vmatrix} 1 & 3 & -1 \\ 2 & 0 & 4 \\ -2 & 5 & -6 \end{vmatrix}$$

if we interchange the first row and first column, the second row and second column, and the third row and third column, we obtain the determinant

$$\begin{vmatrix} 1 & 2 & -2 \\ 3 & 0 & 5 \\ -1 & 4 & -6 \end{vmatrix}$$

By expanding, we can show that the value of each is the same. We obtain very similar expansions if we expand the first by the first column and the second by the first row. These expansions are

$$\begin{vmatrix} 1 & 3 & -1 \\ 2 & 0 & 4 \\ -2 & 5 & -6 \end{vmatrix} = (1)\begin{vmatrix} 0 & 4 \\ 5 & -6 \end{vmatrix} - 2\begin{vmatrix} 3 & -1 \\ 5 & -6 \end{vmatrix} + (-2)\begin{vmatrix} 3 & -1 \\ 0 & 4 \end{vmatrix}$$

$$= (-20) - 2(-13) - 2(12) = -18$$

$$\begin{vmatrix} 1 & 2 & -2 \\ 3 & 0 & 5 \\ -1 & 4 & -6 \end{vmatrix} = (1)\begin{vmatrix} 0 & 5 \\ 4 & -6 \end{vmatrix} - 2\begin{vmatrix} 3 & 5 \\ -1 & -6 \end{vmatrix} + (-2)\begin{vmatrix} 3 & 0 \\ -1 & 4 \end{vmatrix}$$

$$= (-20) - 2(-13) - 2(12) = -18$$

Therefore, we see that $\begin{vmatrix} 1 & 3 & -1 \\ 2 & 0 & 4 \\ -2 & 5 & -6 \end{vmatrix} = \begin{vmatrix} 1 & 2 & -2 \\ 3 & 0 & 5 \\ -1 & 4 & -6 \end{vmatrix}$

(3) *If two columns (or rows) of a determinant are identical, the value of the determinant is zero.*

Example C

The value of the determinant

$$\begin{vmatrix} 3 & 5 & 2 \\ -4 & 6 & 9 \\ -4 & 6 & 9 \end{vmatrix}$$

is zero, since the second and third rows are identical. This is easily verified by expanding by the first row.

$$\begin{vmatrix} 3 & 5 & 2 \\ -4 & 6 & 9 \\ -4 & 6 & 9 \end{vmatrix} = 3\begin{vmatrix} 6 & 9 \\ 6 & 9 \end{vmatrix} - 5\begin{vmatrix} -4 & 9 \\ -4 & 9 \end{vmatrix} + 2\begin{vmatrix} -4 & 6 \\ -4 & 6 \end{vmatrix}$$

$$= 3(0) - 5(0) + 2(0) = 0$$

(4) *If two columns (or rows) of a determinant are interchanged, the value of the determinant is changed in sign.*

Example D
The values of the determinants

$$\begin{vmatrix} 3 & 0 & 2 \\ 1 & 1 & 5 \\ 2 & 1 & 3 \end{vmatrix} \quad \text{and} \quad \begin{vmatrix} 2 & 0 & 3 \\ 5 & 1 & 1 \\ 3 & 1 & 2 \end{vmatrix}$$

differ in sign, since the first and third columns are interchanged. We shall verify this by expanding each by the second column.

$$\begin{vmatrix} 3 & 0 & 2 \\ 1 & 1 & 5 \\ 2 & 1 & 3 \end{vmatrix} = -(0)\begin{vmatrix} 1 & 5 \\ 2 & 3 \end{vmatrix} + (1)\begin{vmatrix} 3 & 2 \\ 2 & 3 \end{vmatrix} - (1)\begin{vmatrix} 3 & 2 \\ 1 & 5 \end{vmatrix}$$

$$= 0 + (9 - 4) - (15 - 2) = 5 - 13 = -8$$

$$\begin{vmatrix} 2 & 0 & 3 \\ 5 & 1 & 1 \\ 3 & 1 & 2 \end{vmatrix} = -(0)\begin{vmatrix} 5 & 1 \\ 3 & 2 \end{vmatrix} + (1)\begin{vmatrix} 2 & 3 \\ 3 & 2 \end{vmatrix} - (1)\begin{vmatrix} 2 & 3 \\ 5 & 1 \end{vmatrix}$$

$$= 0 + (4 - 9) - (2 - 15) = -5 + 13 = 8$$

Therefore, $\begin{vmatrix} 3 & 0 & 2 \\ 1 & 1 & 5 \\ 2 & 1 & 3 \end{vmatrix} = - \begin{vmatrix} 2 & 0 & 3 \\ 5 & 1 & 1 \\ 3 & 1 & 2 \end{vmatrix}$

(5) *If all the elements of a column (or row) are multiplied by the same number k, the value of the determinant is multiplied by k.*

Example E
The value of the determinant

$$\begin{vmatrix} -1 & 0 & 6 \\ 2 & 1 & -2 \\ 0 & 5 & 3 \end{vmatrix}$$

is multiplied by 3 if the elements of the second row are multiplied by 3. That is,

$$\begin{vmatrix} -1 & 0 & 6 \\ 6 & 3 & -6 \\ 0 & 5 & 3 \end{vmatrix} = 3 \begin{vmatrix} -1 & 0 & 6 \\ 2 & 1 & -2 \\ 0 & 5 & 3 \end{vmatrix}$$

By expansion, we can show that

$$\begin{vmatrix} -1 & 0 & 6 \\ 2 & 1 & -2 \\ 0 & 5 & 3 \end{vmatrix} = 47 \quad \text{and} \quad \begin{vmatrix} -1 & 0 & 6 \\ 6 & 3 & -6 \\ 0 & 5 & 3 \end{vmatrix} = 141$$

The validity of this property can be seen by expanding each determinant by the second row. In each case one element is three times the other corresponding element, but the minors are the same. Look at the element in the second row, first column and its minor for each determinant.

$$2\begin{vmatrix} 0 & 6 \\ 5 & 3 \end{vmatrix} \quad \text{and} \quad 6\begin{vmatrix} 0 & 6 \\ 5 & 3 \end{vmatrix}$$

The element, 6, in the second determinant is three times the corresponding element, 2, in the first determinant, and the minors are the same.

(6) *If all the elements of any column (or row) are multiplied by the same number k, and the resulting numbers are added to the corresponding elements of another column (or row), the value of the determinant is unchanged.*

Example F

The value of the determinant

$$\begin{vmatrix} 4 & -1 & 3 \\ 2 & 2 & 1 \\ 1 & 0 & -3 \end{vmatrix}$$

is unchanged if we multiply each element of the first row by 2, and add these numbers to the corresponding elements of the second row. This gives

$$\begin{vmatrix} 4 & -1 & 3 \\ 2+8 & 2+(-2) & 1+6 \\ 1 & 0 & -3 \end{vmatrix} = \begin{vmatrix} 4 & -1 & 3 \\ 10 & 0 & 7 \\ 1 & 0 & -3 \end{vmatrix}$$

or

$$\begin{vmatrix} 4 & -1 & 3 \\ 10 & 0 & 7 \\ 1 & 0 & -3 \end{vmatrix} = \begin{vmatrix} 4 & -1 & 3 \\ 2 & 2 & 1 \\ 1 & 0 & -3 \end{vmatrix}$$

When each determinant is expanded, the value -37 is obtained. The great value in property 6 is that by its use zeros can be purposely placed in the resulting determinant.

With the use of the properties above, determinants of higher order can be evaluated much more readily. The technique is to obtain zeros in a given column (or row) in all positions except one. We can than expand by this column (or row), thereby reducing the order of the determinant. The following example illustrates the method.

Example G
Evaluate

$$\begin{vmatrix} 3 & 2 & -1 & 1 \\ -1 & 1 & 2 & 3 \\ 2 & 2 & 1 & 4 \\ 0 & -1 & -2 & 2 \end{vmatrix}$$

The evaluation is as follows. The small circled numbers above the equals signs refer to the explanations given below the setup.

$$\begin{vmatrix} 3 & 2 & -1 & 1 \\ -1 & 1 & 2 & 3 \\ 2 & 2 & 1 & 4 \\ 0 & -1 & -2 & 2 \end{vmatrix} \overset{①}{=} \begin{vmatrix} 0 & 5 & 5 & 10 \\ -1 & 1 & 2 & 3 \\ 2 & 2 & 1 & 4 \\ 0 & -1 & -2 & 2 \end{vmatrix}$$

$$\overset{②}{=} \begin{vmatrix} 0 & 5 & 5 & 10 \\ -1 & 1 & 2 & 3 \\ 0 & 4 & 5 & 10 \\ 0 & -1 & -2 & 2 \end{vmatrix}$$

$$\overset{③}{=} -(-1)\begin{vmatrix} 5 & 5 & 10 \\ 4 & 5 & 10 \\ -1 & -2 & 2 \end{vmatrix} \overset{④}{=} 5\begin{vmatrix} 1 & 1 & 2 \\ 4 & 5 & 10 \\ -1 & -2 & 2 \end{vmatrix}$$

$$\overset{⑤}{=} 5(2)\begin{vmatrix} 1 & 1 & 1 \\ 4 & 5 & 5 \\ -1 & -2 & 1 \end{vmatrix} \overset{⑥}{=} 10\begin{vmatrix} 1 & 1 & 1 \\ 0 & 1 & 1 \\ -1 & -2 & 1 \end{vmatrix}$$

$$\overset{⑦}{=} 10\begin{vmatrix} 1 & 1 & 1 \\ 0 & 1 & 1 \\ 0 & -1 & 2 \end{vmatrix} \overset{⑧}{=} 10(1)\begin{vmatrix} 1 & 1 \\ -1 & 2 \end{vmatrix}$$

$$\overset{⑨}{=} 10(2+1) = 30$$

① Each element of the second row is multiplied by 3, and the resulting numbers are added to the corresponding elements of the first row. Here we have used property 6. In this way a zero has been placed in column 1, row 1.

② Each element of the second row is multiplied by 2, and the resulting numbers are added to the corresponding elements of the third row. Again, we have used property 6. Also, a zero has been placed in the first column, third row. We now have three zeros in the first column.

③ Expand the determinant by the first column. We have now reduced the determinant to a third-order determinant.

④ Factor 5 from each element of the first row. Here we are using property 5.

⑤ Factor 2 from each element of the third column. Again we are using property 5. Also, by doing this we have reduced the size of the numbers, and the resulting numbers are somewhat easier to work with.

⑥ Each element of the first row is multiplied by −4, and the resulting numbers are added to the corresponding elements of the second row. Here we are using property 6. We have placed a zero in the first column, second row.

⑦ Each element of the first row is added to the corresponding element of the third row. Again, we have used property 6. A zero has been placed in the first column, third row. We now have two zeros in the first column.

⑧ Expand the determinant by the first column.

⑨ Expand the second-order determinant.

A somewhat more systematic method is to place zeros below the principal diagonal and then use property 1. However, all such techniques are essentially equivalent.

Exercises 15–2

In Exercises 1 through 8 evaluate each of the determinants by inspection. Careful observation will allow evaluation by the use of one or more of the basic properties of this section.

1. $\begin{vmatrix} 4 & -5 & 9 \\ 0 & 3 & -8 \\ 0 & 0 & -5 \end{vmatrix}$ 2. $\begin{vmatrix} 6 & 4 & 0 \\ 0 & -2 & 3 \\ 0 & 0 & -6 \end{vmatrix}$ 3. $\begin{vmatrix} -2 & 0 & 0 \\ 15 & 4 & 0 \\ 2 & -7 & 7 \end{vmatrix}$

4. $\begin{vmatrix} 3 & 0 & 0 \\ 0 & 10 & 0 \\ -9 & -1 & -5 \end{vmatrix}$ 5. $\begin{vmatrix} -2 & 0 & -1 \\ 5 & 0 & 3 \\ 3 & 0 & -4 \end{vmatrix}$ 6. $\begin{vmatrix} -6 & -3 & 1 \\ 1 & 2 & -5 \\ 0 & 0 & 0 \end{vmatrix}$

7. $\begin{vmatrix} 3 & -2 & 4 \\ 5 & -1 & 2 \\ 3 & -2 & 4 \end{vmatrix}$ 8. $\begin{vmatrix} -1 & -2 & -2 \\ 1 & 3 & 3 \\ -2 & 1 & 1 \end{vmatrix}$

In Exercises 9 through 20 evaluate the determinants using the properties given in this section. Do not evaluate directly more than one second-order determinant for each.

9. $\begin{vmatrix} 3 & 1 & 0 \\ -2 & 3 & -1 \\ 4 & 2 & 5 \end{vmatrix}$ 10. $\begin{vmatrix} 6 & -1 & 3 \\ 0 & 2 & -2 \\ -1 & 4 & 3 \end{vmatrix}$ 11. $\begin{vmatrix} 5 & -1 & -2 \\ 3 & -5 & -2 \\ 1 & 4 & 6 \end{vmatrix}$

12. $\begin{vmatrix} -4 & 3 & -2 \\ -2 & 2 & 4 \\ -1 & 5 & -3 \end{vmatrix}$

13. $\begin{vmatrix} 4 & 3 & 6 & 0 \\ 3 & 0 & 0 & 4 \\ 5 & 0 & 1 & 2 \\ 2 & 1 & 1 & 7 \end{vmatrix}$

14. $\begin{vmatrix} -2 & 1 & 3 & 0 \\ 1 & 3 & 0 & 0 \\ 0 & 2 & -3 & -1 \\ 4 & -1 & 2 & 1 \end{vmatrix}$

15. $\begin{vmatrix} 3 & 1 & 2 & -1 \\ 2 & -1 & 3 & -1 \\ 1 & 2 & 1 & 3 \\ 1 & -2 & -3 & 2 \end{vmatrix}$

16. $\begin{vmatrix} 6 & -3 & -6 & 3 \\ -2 & 1 & 2 & -1 \\ 18 & 7 & -1 & 5 \\ 0 & -1 & 10 & 10 \end{vmatrix}$

17. $\begin{vmatrix} 1 & 3 & -3 & 5 \\ 4 & 2 & 1 & 2 \\ 3 & 2 & -2 & 2 \\ 0 & 1 & 2 & -1 \end{vmatrix}$

18. $\begin{vmatrix} -2 & 2 & 1 & 3 \\ 1 & 4 & 3 & 1 \\ 4 & 3 & -2 & -2 \\ 3 & -2 & 1 & 5 \end{vmatrix}$

19. $\begin{vmatrix} 1 & 2 & 0 & 1 & 0 \\ 0 & 2 & 1 & 0 & 1 \\ 1 & 0 & -1 & 1 & -1 \\ -2 & 0 & -1 & 2 & 1 \\ 1 & 0 & 2 & -1 & -2 \end{vmatrix}$

20. $\begin{vmatrix} -1 & 3 & 5 & 0 & -5 \\ 0 & 1 & 7 & 3 & -2 \\ 5 & -2 & -1 & 0 & 3 \\ -3 & 0 & 2 & -1 & 3 \\ 6 & 2 & 1 & -4 & 2 \end{vmatrix}$

In Exercises 21 through 28, solve the given systems of equations by determinants. Evaluate the determinants by the properties of determinants given in this section.

21. $2x - y + z = 5$
$x + 2y + 3z = 10$
$3x + 3y + 2z = 5$

22. $2x + y + z = 5$
$x + 3y - 3z = -13$
$3x + 2y - z = -1$

23. $3x + 2y + z = 1$
$9x + 2z = 5$
$6x - 4y - z = 3$

24. $3x + y + 2z = 4$
$x - y + 4z = 2$
$6x + 3y - 2z = 10$

25. $2x + y + z = 2$
$3y - z + 2t = 4$
$y + 2z + t = 0$
$3x + 2z = 4$

26. $2x + y + z = 0$
$x - y + 2t = 2$
$2y + z + 4t = 2$
$5x + 2z + 2t = 4$

27. $x + y + 2z = 1$
$2x - y + t = -2$
$x - y - z - 2t = 4$
$2x - y + 2z - t = 0$

28. $3x + y + t = 0$
$3z + 2t = 8$
$6x + 2y + 2z + t = 3$
$3x - y - z - t = 0$

In Exercises 29 through 32 solve the given problems by determinants. In Exercises 30 through 32 the necessary equations must be set up.

29. In applying Kirchhoff's laws (see Exercise 19 of Section 4–5) to the circuit shown in Fig. 15–3, the following equations are found. Determine the indicated currents, in amperes.

$$I_A + I_B + I_C + I_D + I_E = 0$$
$$-2I_A + 3I_B = 0$$
$$3I_B - 3I_C = 6$$
$$-3I_C + I_D = 0$$
$$-I_D + 2I_E = 0$$

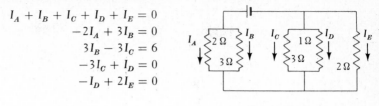

Figure 15—3

30. A land developer subdivides a tract of 100 acres into 120 building lots of 3 types. They have areas of $\frac{1}{2}$ acre, 1 acre, and 2 acres, to sell at $3000, $5000, and $8000, respectively. If all lots are sold, the gross income is $510,000. How many of each type are there in the development?

31. In testing for air pollution, a given air sample contained a total of 6 parts per million (ppm) of four pollutants, sulfur dioxide (SO_2), nitric oxide (NO), nitrogen dioxide (NO_2), and carbon monoxide (CO). The ppm of CO was ten times that of SO_2, which in turn equaled those of NO and NO_2. There was a total of 0.8 ppm of SO_2 and NO. How many ppm of each were present in the air sample?

32. A firm sells four types of appliances. Appliances A, B, C, and D respectively sell for $2, $3, $1, and $4 each. On a certain day it sold a total of 33 appliances, with receipts of $91. It sold twice as many of type B as type C, and twice as many of type D as type C. How many of each were sold on this day?

15—3 Matrices: Definitions and Basic Operations

Systems of linear equations occur in several areas of important technical and scientific applications. We indicated a few of these in Chapter 4 and in the first two sections of this chapter. Since a considerable amount of work is generally required to solve a system of equations, numerous methods have been developed for their solution.

Since the use of computers has been rapidly increasing in importance over the last several years, another mathematical concept which can be used to solve systems of equations is becoming used much more widely than in previous years. It is also used in numerous applications other than systems of equations, in such fields as business, economics, and psychology, as well as the scientific and technical areas. Since it is readily adaptable to use on a computer and is applicable to numerous areas, its importance will increase for some time to come. At this point, however, we shall only be able to introduce its definitions and basic operations.

A **matrix** *is an ordered rectangular array of numbers.* To distinguish such an array from a determinant, we shall enclose it within parentheses. As with a determinant, the individual numbers are called **elements** of the matrix.

Example A
Some examples of matrices are as follows:

$$\begin{pmatrix} 2 & 8 \\ 1 & 0 \end{pmatrix} \quad \begin{pmatrix} 2 & -4 & 6 \\ -1 & 0 & 5 \end{pmatrix} \quad \begin{pmatrix} 4 & 6 \\ 0 & -1 \\ -2 & 5 \\ 3 & 0 \end{pmatrix}$$

$$(-1 \quad 2 \quad 0 \quad 9) \quad \begin{pmatrix} -1 & 8 & 6 & 7 & 9 \\ 2 & 6 & 0 & 4 & 3 \\ 5 & -1 & 8 & 10 & 2 \end{pmatrix}$$

As we can see, it is not necessary for the number of columns and number of rows to be the same, although such is the case for a determinant. However, *if the number of rows does equal the number of columns, the matrix is called a* **square matrix**. We shall find that square matrices are of some special importance. *If all the elements of a matrix are zero, the matrix is called a* **zero matrix**. We shall find it convenient to designate a given matrix by a capital letter.

We must be careful to distinguish between a matrix and a determinant. *A matrix is simply any* **rectangular array** *of numbers, whereas a determinant is a specific value which is associated with a* **square** *matrix.*

Example B
Consider the following matrices:

$$A = \begin{pmatrix} 5 & 0 & -1 \\ 1 & 2 & 6 \\ 0 & -4 & -5 \end{pmatrix}, \quad B = \begin{pmatrix} 9 \\ 8 \\ 1 \\ 5 \end{pmatrix}, \quad C = (-1 \quad 6 \quad 8 \quad 9), \quad O = \begin{pmatrix} 0 & 0 \\ 0 & 0 \end{pmatrix}$$

Matrix A is an example of a square matrix, matrix B is an example of a matrix with one column, matrix C is an example of a matrix with one row, and matrix O is an example of a zero matrix.

To be able to refer to specific elements of a matrix, and to give a general representation, a double-subscript notation is usually employed. That is,

$$A = \begin{pmatrix} a_{11} & a_{12} & a_{13} \\ a_{21} & a_{22} & a_{23} \\ a_{31} & a_{32} & a_{33} \end{pmatrix}$$

We see that the first subscript refers to the row in which the element lies, and the second subscript refers to the column in which the element lies.

Two matrices are said to be equal if and only if they are identical. That is, they must have the same number of columns, the same number of rows, and the elements must respectively be equal. If these conditions are not satisfied, the matrices are not equal.

Example C

$$\begin{pmatrix} a_{11} & a_{12} & a_{13} \\ a_{21} & a_{22} & a_{23} \end{pmatrix} = \begin{pmatrix} 1 & -5 & 0 \\ 4 & 6 & -3 \end{pmatrix}$$

if and only if $a_{11} = 1$, $a_{12} = -5$, $a_{13} = 0$, $a_{21} = 4$, $a_{22} = 6$, and $a_{23} = -3$.

The matrices

$$\begin{pmatrix} 1 & 2 & 3 \\ -1 & -2 & -5 \end{pmatrix} \quad \text{and} \quad \begin{pmatrix} 1 & 2 & -5 \\ -1 & -2 & 3 \end{pmatrix}$$

are not equal, since the elements in the third column are reversed.

The matrices

$$\begin{pmatrix} 2 & 3 \\ -1 & 5 \end{pmatrix} \quad \text{and} \quad \begin{pmatrix} 2 & 3 \\ -1 & 5 \\ 0 & 0 \end{pmatrix}$$

are not equal, since the number of rows is different.

If two matrices have the same number of rows and the same number of columns, their **sum** *is defined as the matrix consisting of the sums of the corresponding elements.* If the number of rows or the number of columns of the two matrices is not equal, they cannot be added.

Example D

$$\begin{pmatrix} 8 & 1 & -5 & 9 \\ 0 & -2 & 3 & 7 \end{pmatrix} + \begin{pmatrix} -3 & 4 & 6 & 0 \\ 6 & -2 & 6 & 5 \end{pmatrix}$$

$$= \begin{pmatrix} 8 + (-3) & 1 + 4 & -5 + 6 & 9 + 0 \\ 0 + 6 & -2 + (-2) & 3 + 6 & 7 + 5 \end{pmatrix}$$

$$= \begin{pmatrix} 5 & 5 & 1 & 9 \\ 6 & -4 & 9 & 12 \end{pmatrix}$$

The matrices

$$\begin{pmatrix} 3 & -5 & 8 \\ 2 & 9 & 0 \\ 4 & -2 & 3 \end{pmatrix} \quad \text{and} \quad \begin{pmatrix} 3 & -5 & 8 & 0 \\ 2 & 9 & 0 & 0 \\ 4 & -2 & 3 & 0 \end{pmatrix}$$

cannot be added since the second matrix has one more column than the first matrix. The fact that the extra column contains only zeros does not matter.

The product of a number and a matrix is defined as the matrix whose elements are obtained by multiplying each element of the given matrix by the given number. That is, kA is the matrix obtained by multiplying the elements of matrix A by k. In this way $A + A$ and $2A$ will result in the same matrix.

Example E
For the matrix

$$A = \begin{pmatrix} -5 & 7 \\ 3 & 0 \end{pmatrix}$$

we have

$$2A = \begin{pmatrix} 2(-5) & 2(7) \\ 2(3) & 2(0) \end{pmatrix} = \begin{pmatrix} -10 & 14 \\ 6 & 0 \end{pmatrix}$$

Also,

$$5A = \begin{pmatrix} -25 & 35 \\ 15 & 0 \end{pmatrix} \quad \text{and} \quad -A = \begin{pmatrix} 5 & -7 \\ -3 & 0 \end{pmatrix}$$

By combining the definitions for the addition of matrices and for the multiplication of a matrix by a number, we can define the difference of matrices. That is, $A - B = A + (-B)$. Therefore, we would change the sign of each element of matrix B, and proceed as in addition.

By the preceding definitions we can see that the operations of addition, subtraction, and multiplication by a number on matrices are like those for real numbers. For these operations, we say that the algebra of matrices is like the algebra of real numbers. Although it is not our primary purpose to develop the algebra of matrices, we can see that the following laws hold for matrices.

$A + B = B + A$	(commutative law)	(15–4)
$A + (B + C) = (A + B) + C$	(associative law)	(15–5)
$k(A + B) = kA + kB$		(15–6)
$A + O = A$		(15–7)

Here we have let O represent the zero matrix. We shall find in the next section that not all laws for the operations with matrices are similar to those for real numbers.

Exercises 15–3

In Exercises 1 through 4 determine the value of the literal symbols.

1. $\begin{pmatrix} a & b \\ c & d \end{pmatrix} = \begin{pmatrix} 1 & -3 \\ 4 & 7 \end{pmatrix}$

2. $\begin{pmatrix} x & y & z \\ r & -s & -t \end{pmatrix} = \begin{pmatrix} -2 & 7 & -9 \\ 4 & -4 & 5 \end{pmatrix}$

3. $\begin{pmatrix} x \\ x + y \end{pmatrix} = \begin{pmatrix} 2 \\ 5 \end{pmatrix}$

4. $(x \quad x + y \quad x + y + z) = (5 \quad 6 \quad 8)$

In Exercises 5 through 8 find the indicated sums of matrices.

5. $\begin{pmatrix} 2 & 3 \\ -5 & 4 \end{pmatrix} + \begin{pmatrix} -1 & 7 \\ 5 & -2 \end{pmatrix}$ **6.** $\begin{pmatrix} 1 & 0 & 9 \\ 3 & -5 & -2 \end{pmatrix} + \begin{pmatrix} 4 & -1 & 7 \\ 2 & 0 & -3 \end{pmatrix}$

7. $\begin{pmatrix} 5 & -8 \\ -3 & 5 \\ -1 & 6 \end{pmatrix} + \begin{pmatrix} -5 & 8 \\ 4 & 1 \\ 2 & -6 \end{pmatrix}$ **8.** $\begin{pmatrix} 4 & 2 & -9 \\ -6 & 4 & 7 \\ -1 & 0 & 5 \end{pmatrix} + \begin{pmatrix} -4 & -9 & -2 \\ 3 & 0 & 0 \\ 5 & 10 & -1 \end{pmatrix}$

In Exercises 9 through 16 use the following matrices to determine the indicated matrices.

$$A = \begin{pmatrix} -1 & 4 & -7 & 0 \\ 2 & -6 & -1 & 2 \end{pmatrix}, \quad B = \begin{pmatrix} 1 & 5 & -6 & 3 \\ 4 & -1 & 8 & -2 \end{pmatrix}, \quad C = \begin{pmatrix} 3 & -6 & 9 \\ -4 & 1 & 2 \end{pmatrix}$$

9. $A + B$ **10.** $A - B$ **11.** $A + C$ **12.** $B + C$

13. $2A + B$ **14.** $2B + A$ **15.** $A - 2B$ **16.** $3A - B$

In Exercises 17 through 20 use the given matrices to verify the indicated laws.

$$A = \begin{pmatrix} -1 & 2 & 3 & 7 \\ 0 & -3 & -1 & 4 \\ 9 & -1 & 0 & -2 \end{pmatrix}, \quad B = \begin{pmatrix} 4 & -1 & -3 & 0 \\ 5 & 0 & -1 & 1 \\ 1 & 11 & 8 & 2 \end{pmatrix}$$

17. $A + B = B + A$ **18.** $A + 0 = A$

19. $-(A - B) = B - A$ **20.** $3(A + B) = 3A + 3B$

In Exercises 21 and 22 perform the indicated matrix operations.

21. The contractor of a housing development constructs four different types of houses, with either a carport, one-car garage, or a two-car garage. The following matrix shows the number of houses of each type, and the type of garage.

	Type A	Type B	Type C	Type D
Carport	8	6	0	0
1-car garage	5	4	3	0
2-car garage	0	3	5	6

If the contractor builds two additional identical developments, find the matrix showing the total number of each house-garage type he built.

22. In taking inventory, a firm finds that it has in one warehouse 6 pieces of 20-ft brass pipe, 8 pieces of 30-ft brass pipe, 11 pieces of 40-ft brass pipe, 5 pieces of 20-ft steel pipe, 10 pieces of 30-ft steel pipe, and 15 pieces of 40-ft steel pipe. This inventory can be represented by the matrix

$$A = \begin{pmatrix} 6 & 8 & 11 \\ 5 & 10 & 15 \end{pmatrix}$$

In each of two other warehouses, the inventory of the same items is represented by the matrix

$$B = \begin{pmatrix} 8 & 3 & 4 \\ 6 & 10 & 5 \end{pmatrix}$$

By matrix addition and multiplication by a constant, find the matrix which represents the total number of each item in the three warehouses.

15–4 Multiplication of Matrices

The definition for the multiplication of matrices does not have an intuitive basis. However, through the solution of a system of linear equations we can, at least in part, show why multiplication is defined as it is. First, let us consider the following example.

Example A

If we solve the system of equations

$$2x + y = 1$$
$$7x + 3y = 5$$

we obtain the solution $x = 2$, $y = -3$. In checking this solution in each of the equations, we obtain

$$2(2) + 1(-3) = 1$$
$$7(2) + 3(-3) = 5$$

Let us represent the coefficients of the equations by the matrix $\begin{pmatrix} 2 & 1 \\ 7 & 3 \end{pmatrix}$ and the solutions by the matrix $\begin{pmatrix} 2 \\ -3 \end{pmatrix}$

If we now multiply these matrices as

$$\begin{pmatrix} 2 & 1 \\ 7 & 3 \end{pmatrix} \begin{pmatrix} 2 \\ -3 \end{pmatrix} = \begin{pmatrix} 2(2) + 1(-3) \\ 7(2) + 3(-3) \end{pmatrix} = \begin{pmatrix} 1 \\ 5 \end{pmatrix}$$

we note that we obtain a matrix which properly represents the right-side values of the equations. (Note carefully how the products and sums in the resulting matrix are formed.)

Following reasons along the lines indicated in Example A, we shall now define the **multiplication of matrices**. If the number of columns in a first matrix equals the number of rows in a second matrix, the product of these matrices is formed as follows: *The element in a specified row and a specified column of the product matrix is the sum of the products formed by multiplying each element in the specified row of the first matrix by the corresponding element in the specific column of the second matrix.* The product matrix will have the same number of rows as the first matrix and the same number of columns as the second matrix. Consider the following examples.

Example B

Find the product AB, where

$$A = \begin{pmatrix} 2 & 1 \\ -3 & 0 \\ 1 & 2 \end{pmatrix} \quad \text{and} \quad B = \begin{pmatrix} -1 & 6 & 5 & -2 \\ 3 & 0 & 1 & -4 \end{pmatrix}$$

To find the element in the first row and first column of the product, we find the sum of the products of corresponding elements of the first row of A and first column of B. To find the element in the first row and second column of the product, we find the sum of the products of corresponding elements in the first row of A and the second column of B. We continue this process until we have found the three rows (the number of rows in A) and the four columns (the number of columns in B) of the product. The product is formed as follows.

$$\begin{pmatrix} 2 & 1 \\ -3 & 0 \\ 1 & 2 \end{pmatrix} \begin{pmatrix} -1 & 6 & 5 & -2 \\ 3 & 0 & 1 & -4 \end{pmatrix}$$

$$= \begin{pmatrix} 2(-1) + 1(3) & 2(6) + 1(0) & 2(5) + 1(1) & 2(-2) + 1(-4) \\ -3(-1) + 0(3) & -3(6) + 0(0) & -3(5) + 0(1) & -3(-2) + 0(-4) \\ 1(-1) + 2(3) & 1(6) + 2(0) & 1(5) + 2(1) & 1(-2) + 2(-4) \end{pmatrix}$$

$$= \begin{pmatrix} 1 & 12 & 11 & -8 \\ 3 & -18 & -15 & 6 \\ 5 & 6 & 7 & -10 \end{pmatrix}$$

If we attempt to form the product BA, we find that B has four columns and A has 3 rows. Since the number of columns in B does not equal the number of rows in A, the product BA cannot be formed. In this way we see that $AB \neq BA$, which means that matrix multiplication is not commutative (except in special cases). Therefore, matrix multiplication differs from the multiplication of real numbers.

Example C
Find the product

$$\begin{pmatrix} -1 & 9 & 3 & -2 \\ 2 & 0 & -7 & 1 \end{pmatrix} \begin{pmatrix} 6 & -2 \\ 1 & 0 \\ 3 & -5 \\ 3 & 9 \end{pmatrix}$$

We can find the product because the first matrix has four columns and the second matrix has four rows. The product is found as follows.

$$\begin{pmatrix} -1 & 9 & 3 & -2 \\ 2 & 0 & -7 & 1 \end{pmatrix} \begin{pmatrix} 6 & -2 \\ 1 & 0 \\ 3 & -5 \\ 3 & 9 \end{pmatrix}$$

$$= \begin{pmatrix} -1(6) + 9(1) + 3(3) + (-2)(3) & -1(-2) + 9(0) + 3(-5) + (-2)(9) \\ 2(6) + 0(1) + (-7)(3) + 1(3) & 2(-2) + 0(0) + (-7)(-5) + 1(9) \end{pmatrix}$$

$$= \begin{pmatrix} -6 + 9 + 9 - 6 & 2 + 0 - 15 - 18 \\ 12 + 0 - 21 + 3 & -4 + 0 + 35 + 9 \end{pmatrix} = \begin{pmatrix} 6 & -31 \\ -6 & 40 \end{pmatrix}$$

There are two special matrices of particular importance in the multiplication of matrices. The first of these is the **identity matrix I**, *which is a square matrix with 1's for elements on the principal diagonal, with all other elements zero.* It has the property that if it is multiplied by another square matrix with the same number of rows and columns, then the second matrix equals the product matrix.

Example D
Show that $AI = IA = A$ for the matrix

$$A = \begin{pmatrix} 2 & -3 \\ 4 & 1 \end{pmatrix}$$

Since A has two rows and two columns, we choose I with two rows and two columns. Therefore, for this case

$$I = \begin{pmatrix} 1 & 0 \\ 0 & 1 \end{pmatrix}$$

Forming the indicated products, we have results as follows.

$$AI = \begin{pmatrix} 2 & -3 \\ 4 & 1 \end{pmatrix}\begin{pmatrix} 1 & 0 \\ 0 & 1 \end{pmatrix}$$

$$= \begin{pmatrix} 2(1) + (-3)(0) & 2(0) + (-3)(1) \\ 4(1) + 1(0) & 4(0) + 1(1) \end{pmatrix} = \begin{pmatrix} 2 & -3 \\ 4 & 1 \end{pmatrix}$$

$$IA = \begin{pmatrix} 1 & 0 \\ 0 & 1 \end{pmatrix}\begin{pmatrix} 2 & -3 \\ 4 & 1 \end{pmatrix}$$

$$= \begin{pmatrix} 1(2) + 0(4) & 1(-3) + 0(1) \\ 0(2) + 1(4) & 0(-3) + 1(1) \end{pmatrix} = \begin{pmatrix} 2 & -3 \\ 4 & 1 \end{pmatrix}$$

Therefore, we see that $AI = IA = A$.

For a given square matrix A, its **inverse A^{-1}** is the other important special matrix. The matrix A and its inverse have the property that

$$AA^{-1} = A^{-1}A = I \tag{15–8}$$

If the product of two matrices equals the identity matrix, the matrices are called inverses of each other. Under certain conditions the inverse of a given square matrix may not exist, although for most square matrices the inverse does exist. In the next section we shall develop the procedure for finding the inverse of a square matrix, and the section which follows shows how the inverse is used in the solution of systems of equations. At this point we shall simply show that the product of certain matrices equals the identity matrix, and that therefore these matrices are inverses of each other.

Example E
For the given matrices A and B, show that $AB = BA = I$, and therefore that $B = A^{-1}$.

$$A = \begin{pmatrix} 1 & -3 \\ -2 & 7 \end{pmatrix} \qquad B = \begin{pmatrix} 7 & 3 \\ 2 & 1 \end{pmatrix}$$

Forming the products AB and BA, we have the following:

$$AB = \begin{pmatrix} 1 & -3 \\ -2 & 7 \end{pmatrix}\begin{pmatrix} 7 & 3 \\ 2 & 1 \end{pmatrix} = \begin{pmatrix} 7-6 & 3-3 \\ -14+14 & -6+7 \end{pmatrix} = \begin{pmatrix} 1 & 0 \\ 0 & 1 \end{pmatrix}$$

$$BA = \begin{pmatrix} 7 & 3 \\ 2 & 1 \end{pmatrix}\begin{pmatrix} 1 & -3 \\ -2 & 7 \end{pmatrix} = \begin{pmatrix} 7-6 & -21+21 \\ 2-2 & -6+7 \end{pmatrix} = \begin{pmatrix} 1 & 0 \\ 0 & 1 \end{pmatrix}$$

Since $AB = I$, $B = A^{-1}$.

The following example illustrates one kind of application of the multiplication of matrices.

Example F
A particular firm produces three types of machines parts. On a given day it produces 40 of type X, 50 of type Y, and 80 of type Z. Each of type X requires 4 units of material and 1 man-hour to produce; each of type Y requires 5 units of material and 2 man-hours to produce; each of type Z requires 3 units of material and 2 man-hours to produce. By representing the number of each type produced as the matrix $A = (40 \quad 50 \quad 80)$ and the material and time requirements by the matrix

$$B = \begin{pmatrix} 4 & 1 \\ 5 & 2 \\ 3 & 2 \end{pmatrix}$$

the product AB gives the total number of units of material and the total number of man-hours needed for the day's production in a one-row, two-column matrix.

$$AB = (40 \quad 50 \quad 80)\begin{pmatrix} 4 & 1 \\ 5 & 2 \\ 3 & 2 \end{pmatrix}$$

$$= (160 + 250 + 240 \quad 40 + 100 + 160) = (650 \quad 300)$$

Therefore, 650 units of material and 300 man-hours are required.

We now have seen how multiplication is defined for matrices. We see that *matrix multiplication is not commutative;* that is, $AB \neq BA$ in general. This is a major difference from the multiplication of real numbers. Another difference is that it is possible that $AB = 0$, even though neither A nor B is 0 (see Exercise 8, below). There are some similarities, however, in that $AI = A$, where we make I and the number 1 equivalent for the two types of multiplication. Also, the distributive property $A(B + C) = AB + AC$ holds for matrix multiplication. This points out some more of the properties of the algebra of matrices.

Exercises 15—4

In Exercises 1 through 12 perform the indicated matrix multiplications.

1. $(4 \quad -2)\begin{pmatrix} -1 & 0 \\ 2 & 6 \end{pmatrix}$

2. $(-1 \quad 5 \quad -2)\begin{pmatrix} 6 & 3 \\ 2 & -1 \\ 0 & 2 \end{pmatrix}$

3. $\begin{pmatrix} 2 & -3 \\ 5 & -1 \end{pmatrix}\begin{pmatrix} 3 & 0 & -1 \\ 7 & -5 & 8 \end{pmatrix}$

4. $\begin{pmatrix} -7 & 8 \\ 5 & 0 \end{pmatrix}\begin{pmatrix} -9 & 10 \\ 1 & 4 \end{pmatrix}$

5. $\begin{pmatrix} 2 & -3 & 1 \\ 0 & 7 & -3 \end{pmatrix}\begin{pmatrix} 9 \\ -2 \\ 5 \end{pmatrix}$

6. $\begin{pmatrix} 0 & -1 & 2 \\ 4 & 11 & 2 \end{pmatrix}\begin{pmatrix} 3 & -1 \\ 1 & 2 \\ 6 & 1 \end{pmatrix}$

7. $\begin{pmatrix} -1 & -5 \\ 4 & 0 \\ 2 & 10 \end{pmatrix}\begin{pmatrix} 2 & 0 \\ 1 & 1 \end{pmatrix}$

8. $\begin{pmatrix} 12 & -4 \\ 3 & -1 \\ 6 & -2 \end{pmatrix}\begin{pmatrix} 2 & -1 & 3 \\ 6 & -3 & 9 \end{pmatrix}$

9. $\begin{pmatrix} -1 & 7 \\ 3 & 5 \\ 10 & -1 \\ -5 & 12 \end{pmatrix}\begin{pmatrix} 2 & 1 & 0 \\ 5 & -3 & 1 \end{pmatrix}$

10. $\begin{pmatrix} 3 & -1 & 8 \\ 0 & 2 & -4 \\ -1 & 6 & 7 \end{pmatrix}\begin{pmatrix} 7 & -1 \\ 0 & 3 \\ 1 & -2 \end{pmatrix}$

11. $\begin{pmatrix} -9 & -1 & 4 \\ 6 & 9 & -1 \end{pmatrix}\begin{pmatrix} 6 & -5 \\ 4 & 1 \\ -1 & 6 \end{pmatrix}$

12. $\begin{pmatrix} 1 & 2 & -6 & 6 & 1 \\ -2 & 4 & 0 & 1 & 2 \end{pmatrix}\begin{pmatrix} 1 \\ -1 \\ 0 \\ 5 \\ 2 \end{pmatrix}$

In Exercises 13 through 16 find, if possible, AB and BA.

13.
$$A = (1 \quad -3 \quad 8) \quad B = \begin{pmatrix} -1 \\ 5 \\ 7 \end{pmatrix}$$

14.
$$A = \begin{pmatrix} -3 & 2 & 0 \\ 1 & -4 & 5 \end{pmatrix} \quad B = \begin{pmatrix} -2 & 0 \\ 4 & -6 \\ 5 & 1 \end{pmatrix}$$

15.
$$A = \begin{pmatrix} -1 & 2 & 3 \\ 5 & -1 & 0 \end{pmatrix} \quad B = \begin{pmatrix} 1 \\ -5 \\ 2 \end{pmatrix}$$

16.
$$A = \begin{pmatrix} -2 & 1 & 7 \\ 3 & -1 & 0 \\ 0 & 2 & -1 \end{pmatrix} \quad B = \begin{pmatrix} 4 & -1 & 5 \end{pmatrix}$$

In Exercises 17 through 20 show that $AI = IA = A$.

17.
$$A = \begin{pmatrix} 1 & 8 \\ -2 & 2 \end{pmatrix}$$

18.
$$A = \begin{pmatrix} -3 & 4 \\ 1 & 2 \end{pmatrix}$$

19.
$$A = \begin{pmatrix} 1 & 3 & -5 \\ 2 & 0 & 1 \\ 1 & -2 & 4 \end{pmatrix}$$

20.
$$A = \begin{pmatrix} -1 & 2 & 0 \\ 4 & -3 & 1 \\ 2 & 1 & 3 \end{pmatrix}$$

In Exercises 21 through 24 determine whether or not $B = A^{-1}$.

21.
$$A = \begin{pmatrix} 5 & -2 \\ -2 & 1 \end{pmatrix} \quad B = \begin{pmatrix} 1 & 2 \\ 2 & 5 \end{pmatrix}$$

22.
$$A = \begin{pmatrix} 3 & -4 \\ 5 & -7 \end{pmatrix} \quad B = \begin{pmatrix} 7 & -4 \\ 5 & -2 \end{pmatrix}$$

23.
$$A = \begin{pmatrix} 1 & -2 & 3 \\ 2 & -5 & 7 \\ -1 & 3 & -5 \end{pmatrix} \quad B = \begin{pmatrix} 4 & -1 & 1 \\ 3 & -2 & -1 \\ 1 & -1 & -1 \end{pmatrix}$$

24.
$$A = \begin{pmatrix} 1 & -1 & 3 \\ 3 & -4 & 8 \\ -2 & 3 & -4 \end{pmatrix} \quad B = \begin{pmatrix} 8 & -5 & -4 \\ 4 & -2 & -1 \\ -1 & 1 & 1 \end{pmatrix}$$

In Exercises 25 through 28 determine by matrix multiplication whether or not A is the proper matrix of solution values.

25. $3x - 2y = -1$
$4x + y = 6$ $\quad A = \begin{pmatrix} 1 \\ 2 \end{pmatrix}$

26. $4x + y = -5$
$3x + 4y = 6$ $\quad A = \begin{pmatrix} -2 \\ 3 \end{pmatrix}$

27. $3x + y + 2z = 1$
$x - 3y + 4z = -3 \quad A = \begin{pmatrix} -1 \\ 2 \\ 1 \end{pmatrix}$
$2x + 2y + z = 1$

28. $2x - y + z = 7$
$x - 3y + 2z = 6 \quad A = \begin{pmatrix} 3 \\ -2 \\ -1 \end{pmatrix}$
$3x + y - z = 8$

In Exercises 29 and 30 perform the indicated matrix multiplications.

29. The firm referred to in Exercise 22 of Section 15–3 can determine the total number of feet of brass pipe and of steel pipe in each warehouse by multiplying the matrices of that exercise by the matrix

$$C = \begin{pmatrix} 20 \\ 30 \\ 40 \end{pmatrix}$$

Determine the total number of feet of each type of pipe (a) in the first warehouse and (b) in all three warehouses by matrix multiplication.

30. In the theory related to the reproduction of color photography, the equations

$$\begin{pmatrix} X \\ Y \\ Z \end{pmatrix} = \begin{pmatrix} 1.0 & 0.1 & 0 \\ 0.5 & 1.0 & 0.1 \\ 0.3 & 0.4 & 1.0 \end{pmatrix} \begin{pmatrix} x \\ y \\ z \end{pmatrix}$$

are found. The X, Y, and Z represent the red, green, and blue densities of the reproductions, respectively, and the x, y, and z represent the red, green, and blue densities, respectively, of the subject. Give the equations relating X, Y, and Z and x, y, and z.

15–5 Finding the Inverse of a Matrix

In the last section we introduced the concept of the inverse of a matrix. In this section we shall show how the inverse is found, and in the following section we shall show how this inverse is used in the solution of a system of linear equations.

We shall first show two methods of finding the inverse of a two-row, two-column (2 × 2) matrix. The first method is as follows:

(1) *Interchange the elements on the principal diagonal.*
(2) *Change the signs of the off-diagonal elements.*
(3) *Divide each resulting element by the determinant of the given matrix.*

This is illustrated in the following example.

Example A
Find the inverse of the matrix

$$A = \begin{pmatrix} 2 & -3 \\ 4 & -7 \end{pmatrix}$$

First we interchange the elements on the principal diagonal and change the signs of the off-diagonal elements. This gives us the matrix

$$\begin{pmatrix} -7 & 3 \\ -4 & 2 \end{pmatrix}$$

Now we find the determinant of the original matrix, which means we evaluate

$$\begin{vmatrix} 2 & -3 \\ 4 & -7 \end{vmatrix} = -2$$

(Note again that the matrix is the array of numbers, whereas the determinant of the matrix has a value associated with it.) We now divide each element of the second matrix by -2. This gives

$$\frac{1}{-2}\begin{pmatrix} -7 & 3 \\ -4 & 2 \end{pmatrix} = \begin{pmatrix} \dfrac{-7}{-2} & \dfrac{3}{-2} \\ \dfrac{-4}{-2} & \dfrac{2}{-2} \end{pmatrix} = \begin{pmatrix} \dfrac{7}{2} & -\dfrac{3}{2} \\ 2 & -1 \end{pmatrix}$$

This last matrix is the inverse of matrix A. Therefore,

$$A^{-1} = \begin{pmatrix} \frac{7}{2} & -\frac{3}{2} \\ 2 & -1 \end{pmatrix}$$

Check by multiplication gives

$$AA^{-1} = \begin{pmatrix} 2 & -3 \\ 4 & -7 \end{pmatrix}\begin{pmatrix} \frac{7}{2} & -\frac{3}{2} \\ 2 & -1 \end{pmatrix} = \begin{pmatrix} 7-6 & -3+3 \\ 14-14 & -6+7 \end{pmatrix} = \begin{pmatrix} 1 & 0 \\ 0 & 1 \end{pmatrix} = I$$

The second method involves transforming the given matrix into the identity matrix, while at the same time transforming the identity matrix into the inverse. There are two types of steps allowable in making these transformations.

(1) *Every element in any row may be multiplied by any given number other than zero.*
(2) *Any row may be replaced by a row whose elements are the sum of a nonzero multiple itself and a nonzero multiple of another row.*

Some reflection shows that these operations are those which are performed in solving a system of equations by addition or subtraction. The following example illustrates the method.

Example B

Find the inverse of the matrix

$$A = \begin{pmatrix} 2 & -3 \\ 4 & -7 \end{pmatrix}$$

First we set up the given matrix along with the identity matrix in the following manner.

$$\begin{pmatrix} 2 & -3 & | & 1 & 0 \\ 4 & -7 & | & 0 & 1 \end{pmatrix}$$

The vertical line simply shows the separation of the two matrices.

We wish to transform the left matrix into the identity matrix. Therefore, the first requirement is a 1 for element a_{11}. Therefore, we divide all elements of the first row by 2. This gives the following setup.

$$\begin{pmatrix} 1 & -\frac{3}{2} & | & \frac{1}{2} & 0 \\ 4 & -7 & | & 0 & 1 \end{pmatrix}$$

Next we want to have a zero for element a_{21}. Therefore, we shall subtract 4 times each element of row 1 from the corresponding element in row 2, replacing the elements of row 2. This gives us the following setup.

$$\begin{pmatrix} 1 & -\frac{3}{2} & | & \frac{1}{2} & 0 \\ 4 - 4(1) & -7 - 4(-\frac{3}{2}) & | & 0 - 4(\frac{1}{2}) & 1 - 4(0) \end{pmatrix}$$

or

$$\begin{pmatrix} 1 & -\frac{3}{2} & | & \frac{1}{2} & 0 \\ 0 & -1 & | & -2 & 1 \end{pmatrix}$$

Next, we want to have 1, not -1, for element a_{22}. Therefore, we multiply each element of row two by -1. This gives

$$\begin{pmatrix} 1 & -\frac{3}{2} & | & \frac{1}{2} & 0 \\ 0 & 1 & | & 2 & -1 \end{pmatrix}$$

Finally, we want zero for element a_{12}. Therefore, we add $\frac{3}{2}$ times each element of row two to the corresponding elements of row one, replacing row one. This gives

$$\begin{pmatrix} 1 + \frac{3}{2}(0) & -\frac{3}{2} + \frac{3}{2}(1) & | & \frac{1}{2} + \frac{3}{2}(2) & 0 + \frac{3}{2}(-1) \\ 0 & 1 & | & 2 & -1 \end{pmatrix}$$

or

$$\begin{pmatrix} 1 & 0 & \Big| & \frac{7}{2} & -\frac{3}{2} \\ 0 & 1 & \Big| & 2 & -1 \end{pmatrix}$$

At this point, we have transformed the given matrix into the identity matrix, and the identity matrix into the inverse. Therefore, the matrix to the right of the vertical bar in the last setup is the required inverse. Thus,

$$A^{-1} = \begin{pmatrix} \frac{7}{2} & -\frac{3}{2} \\ 2 & -1 \end{pmatrix}$$

This is the same matrix and inverse as illustrated in Example A.

The idea to be noted most carefully in Example B is the order in which the zeros and ones were placed in transforming the given matrix to the identity matrix. We shall now give another example of finding the inverse for a 2×2 matrix, and then we shall find the inverse for a 3×3 matrix with the same method. This method is applicable for a square matrix of any number of rows or columns.

Example C
Find the inverse of the matrix $\begin{pmatrix} -3 & 6 \\ 4 & 5 \end{pmatrix}$.

$$\begin{pmatrix} -3 & 6 & \Big| & 1 & 0 \\ 4 & 5 & \Big| & 0 & 1 \end{pmatrix} \qquad \text{original setup}$$

$$\begin{pmatrix} 1 & -2 & \Big| & -\frac{1}{3} & 0 \\ 4 & 5 & \Big| & 0 & 1 \end{pmatrix} \qquad \text{row 1 divided by } -3$$

$$\begin{pmatrix} 1 & -2 & \Big| & -\frac{1}{3} & 0 \\ 0 & 13 & \Big| & \frac{4}{3} & 1 \end{pmatrix} \qquad -4 \text{ times row 1 added to row 2}$$

$$\begin{pmatrix} 1 & -2 & \Big| & -\frac{1}{3} & 0 \\ 0 & 1 & \Big| & \frac{4}{39} & \frac{1}{13} \end{pmatrix} \qquad \text{row 2 divided by 13}$$

$$\begin{pmatrix} 1 & 0 & \Big| & -\frac{5}{39} & \frac{2}{13} \\ 0 & 1 & \Big| & \frac{4}{39} & \frac{1}{13} \end{pmatrix} \qquad 2 \text{ times row 2 added to row 1}$$

Therefore, $A^{-1} = \begin{pmatrix} -\frac{5}{39} & \frac{2}{13} \\ \frac{4}{39} & \frac{1}{13} \end{pmatrix}$, which can be checked by multiplication.

Example D
Find the inverse of the matrix $\begin{pmatrix} 1 & 2 & -1 \\ 3 & 5 & -1 \\ -2 & -1 & -2 \end{pmatrix}$

$$\left(\begin{array}{ccc|ccc} 1 & 2 & -1 & 1 & 0 & 0 \\ 3 & 5 & -1 & 0 & 1 & 0 \\ -2 & -1 & -2 & 0 & 0 & 1 \end{array} \right)$$ original setup

$$\left(\begin{array}{ccc|ccc} 1 & 2 & -1 & 1 & 0 & 0 \\ 0 & -1 & 2 & -3 & 1 & 0 \\ -2 & -1 & -2 & 0 & 0 & 1 \end{array} \right)$$ -3 times row 1 added to row 2

$$\left(\begin{array}{ccc|ccc} 1 & 2 & -1 & 1 & 0 & 0 \\ 0 & -1 & 2 & -3 & 1 & 0 \\ 0 & 3 & -4 & 2 & 0 & 1 \end{array} \right)$$ 2 times row 1 added to row 3

$$\left(\begin{array}{ccc|ccc} 1 & 2 & -1 & 1 & 0 & 0 \\ 0 & 1 & -2 & 3 & -1 & 0 \\ 0 & 3 & -4 & 2 & 0 & 1 \end{array} \right)$$ row 2 multiplied by -1

$$\left(\begin{array}{ccc|ccc} 1 & 0 & 3 & -5 & 2 & 0 \\ 0 & 1 & -2 & 3 & -1 & 0 \\ 0 & 3 & -4 & 2 & 0 & 1 \end{array} \right)$$ -2 times row 2 added to row 1

$$\left(\begin{array}{ccc|ccc} 1 & 0 & 3 & -5 & 2 & 0 \\ 0 & 1 & -2 & 3 & -1 & 0 \\ 0 & 0 & 2 & -7 & 3 & 1 \end{array} \right)$$ -3 times row 2 added to row 3

$$\left(\begin{array}{ccc|ccc} 1 & 0 & 3 & -5 & 2 & 0 \\ 0 & 1 & -2 & 3 & -1 & 0 \\ 0 & 0 & 1 & -\frac{7}{2} & \frac{3}{2} & \frac{1}{2} \end{array} \right)$$ row 3 divided by 2

$$\left(\begin{array}{ccc|ccc} 1 & 0 & 3 & -5 & 2 & 0 \\ 0 & 1 & 0 & -4 & 2 & 1 \\ 0 & 0 & 1 & -\frac{7}{2} & \frac{3}{2} & \frac{1}{2} \end{array} \right)$$ 2 times row 3 added to row 2

$$\left(\begin{array}{ccc|ccc} 1 & 0 & 0 & \frac{11}{2} & -\frac{5}{2} & -\frac{3}{2} \\ 0 & 1 & 0 & -4 & 2 & 1 \\ 0 & 0 & 1 & -\frac{7}{2} & \frac{3}{2} & \frac{1}{2} \end{array} \right)$$ -3 times row 3 added to row 1

Therefore, the required inverse matrix is

$$\begin{pmatrix} \frac{11}{2} & -\frac{5}{2} & -\frac{3}{2} \\ -4 & 2 & 1 \\ -\frac{7}{2} & \frac{3}{2} & \frac{1}{2} \end{pmatrix}$$

which may be checked by multiplication.

In transforming a matrix into the identity matrix, we work on one column at a time, transforming the columns in order from left to right. It is generally wisest to make the element on the principal diagonal for the column 1 first, and then to make all the other elements in the column 0. Looking back to Example D, we see that this procedure has been systematically followed, first on column one, then on column two, and finally on column three.

There are other methods of finding the inverse of a matrix. One of these other methods is shown in Exercises 25 through 28 which follow.

Exercises 15–5

In Exercises 1 through 8 find the inverse of each of the given matrices by the method of Example A of this section.

1. $\begin{pmatrix} 2 & -5 \\ -2 & 4 \end{pmatrix}$ 2. $\begin{pmatrix} -6 & 3 \\ 3 & -2 \end{pmatrix}$ 3. $\begin{pmatrix} -1 & 5 \\ 4 & 10 \end{pmatrix}$ 4. $\begin{pmatrix} 8 & -1 \\ -4 & -5 \end{pmatrix}$

5. $\begin{pmatrix} 0 & -4 \\ 2 & 6 \end{pmatrix}$ 6. $\begin{pmatrix} 7 & -2 \\ -6 & 2 \end{pmatrix}$ 7. $\begin{pmatrix} -5 & -4 \\ 2 & 8 \end{pmatrix}$ 8. $\begin{pmatrix} 7 & -3 \\ -1 & -5 \end{pmatrix}$

In Exercises 9 through 24 find the inverse of each of the given matrices by transforming the identity matrix, as in Examples B through D.

9. $\begin{pmatrix} 1 & 2 \\ 2 & 3 \end{pmatrix}$ 10. $\begin{pmatrix} 1 & 5 \\ -1 & -4 \end{pmatrix}$ 11. $\begin{pmatrix} 2 & 4 \\ -1 & -1 \end{pmatrix}$

12. $\begin{pmatrix} -2 & 6 \\ 3 & -4 \end{pmatrix}$ 13. $\begin{pmatrix} 2 & 5 \\ -1 & 2 \end{pmatrix}$ 14. $\begin{pmatrix} -2 & 3 \\ -3 & 5 \end{pmatrix}$

15. $\begin{pmatrix} 2 & -1 \\ 4 & 6 \end{pmatrix}$ 16. $\begin{pmatrix} 1 & -3 \\ 7 & -5 \end{pmatrix}$ 17. $\begin{pmatrix} 1 & -3 & -2 \\ -2 & 7 & 3 \\ 1 & -1 & -3 \end{pmatrix}$

18. $\begin{pmatrix} 1 & 2 & -1 \\ 3 & 7 & -5 \\ -1 & -2 & 0 \end{pmatrix}$ 19. $\begin{pmatrix} 1 & -1 & -3 \\ 0 & -1 & -2 \\ 2 & 1 & -1 \end{pmatrix}$ 20. $\begin{pmatrix} 1 & 4 & 1 \\ -3 & -13 & -1 \\ 0 & -2 & 5 \end{pmatrix}$

21. $\begin{pmatrix} 1 & 3 & 2 \\ -2 & -5 & -1 \\ 2 & 4 & 0 \end{pmatrix}$ 22. $\begin{pmatrix} 1 & 3 & 4 \\ -1 & -4 & -2 \\ 4 & 9 & 20 \end{pmatrix}$ 23. $\begin{pmatrix} 2 & 4 & 0 \\ 3 & 4 & -2 \\ -1 & 1 & 2 \end{pmatrix}$

24. $\begin{pmatrix} -2 & 6 & 1 \\ 0 & 3 & -3 \\ 4 & -7 & 3 \end{pmatrix}$

In Exercises 25 through 28 find the inverse of each of the given matrices (same as those for Exercises 21 through 24) by use of the following information. For matrix A, its inverse A^{-1} is found from

$$A = \begin{pmatrix} a_{11} & a_{12} & a_{13} \\ a_{21} & a_{22} & a_{23} \\ a_{31} & a_{32} & a_{33} \end{pmatrix}, \quad A^{-1} = \frac{1}{|A|} \begin{pmatrix} \begin{vmatrix} a_{22} & a_{23} \\ a_{32} & a_{33} \end{vmatrix} & -\begin{vmatrix} a_{12} & a_{13} \\ a_{32} & a_{33} \end{vmatrix} & \begin{vmatrix} a_{12} & a_{13} \\ a_{22} & a_{23} \end{vmatrix} \\ -\begin{vmatrix} a_{21} & a_{23} \\ a_{31} & a_{33} \end{vmatrix} & \begin{vmatrix} a_{11} & a_{13} \\ a_{31} & a_{33} \end{vmatrix} & -\begin{vmatrix} a_{11} & a_{13} \\ a_{21} & a_{23} \end{vmatrix} \\ \begin{vmatrix} a_{21} & a_{22} \\ a_{31} & a_{32} \end{vmatrix} & -\begin{vmatrix} a_{11} & a_{12} \\ a_{31} & a_{32} \end{vmatrix} & \begin{vmatrix} a_{11} & a_{12} \\ a_{21} & a_{22} \end{vmatrix} \end{pmatrix}$$

25. $\begin{pmatrix} 1 & 3 & 2 \\ -2 & -5 & -1 \\ 2 & 4 & 0 \end{pmatrix}$ 26. $\begin{pmatrix} 1 & 3 & 4 \\ -1 & -4 & -2 \\ 4 & 9 & 20 \end{pmatrix}$

27. $\begin{pmatrix} 2 & 4 & 0 \\ 3 & 4 & -2 \\ -1 & 1 & 2 \end{pmatrix}$ 28. $\begin{pmatrix} -2 & 6 & 1 \\ 0 & 3 & -3 \\ 4 & -7 & 3 \end{pmatrix}$

15–6 Matrices and Linear Equations

As we stated earlier, matrices can be used to solve systems of equations. In this section we shall show one of the methods of how this is done. Let us consider the system of equations

$$a_1 x + b_1 y = c_1$$
$$a_2 x + b_2 y = c_2$$

Recalling the definition of equality of matrices, we can write this system directly in terms of matrices as

$$\begin{pmatrix} a_1 x + b_1 y \\ a_2 x + b_2 y \end{pmatrix} = \begin{pmatrix} c_1 \\ c_2 \end{pmatrix}$$

The left side of this equation can be written as the product of two matrices. If we let

$$A = \begin{pmatrix} a_1 & b_1 \\ a_2 & b_2 \end{pmatrix} \quad \text{and} \quad X = \begin{pmatrix} x \\ y \end{pmatrix} \tag{15–9}$$

then we have

$$AX = \begin{pmatrix} a_1 x + b_1 y \\ a_2 x + b_2 y \end{pmatrix} \tag{15–10}$$

Therefore, the system of equations in Eq. (15–10) can be written in terms of matrices as

$$AX = C \tag{15-11}$$

where $C = \begin{pmatrix} c_1 \\ c_2 \end{pmatrix}$.

If we now multiply each side of this matrix equation by A^{-1}, we have

$$A^{-1}AX = A^{-1}C$$

Since $A^{-1}A = I$, we have

$$IX = A^{-1}C$$

However, $IX = X$. Therefore,

$$X = A^{-1}C \tag{15-12}$$

Equation (15–12) states that *we can solve a system of linear equations by multiplying the one-column matrix of the constants on the right by the inverse of the matrix of the coefficients.* The result is a one-column matrix whose elements are the required values. The following examples illustrate the method.

Example A

Solve by matrices the system of equations

$$2x - y = 7$$
$$5x - 3y = 18$$

We set up the matrix of the coefficients as

$$A = \begin{pmatrix} 2 & -1 \\ 5 & -3 \end{pmatrix}$$

By either of the methods of the previous section, we can determine the inverse of this matrix to be

$$A^{-1} = \begin{pmatrix} 3 & -1 \\ 5 & -2 \end{pmatrix}$$

We now form the matrix product $A^{-1}C$, where $C = \begin{pmatrix} 7 \\ 18 \end{pmatrix}$. This gives

$$A^{-1}C = \begin{pmatrix} 3 & -1 \\ 5 & -2 \end{pmatrix}\begin{pmatrix} 7 \\ 18 \end{pmatrix} = \begin{pmatrix} 21 - 18 \\ 35 - 36 \end{pmatrix} = \begin{pmatrix} 3 \\ -1 \end{pmatrix}$$

Since $X = A^{-1}C$, this means that

$$\begin{pmatrix} x \\ y \end{pmatrix} = \begin{pmatrix} 3 \\ -1 \end{pmatrix}$$

Therefore, the required solution is $x = 3$ and $y = -1$.

Example B

Solve by matrices the system of equations

$$2x - y = 3$$
$$6x + 4y = -5$$

Setting up matrices A and C, we have

$$A = \begin{pmatrix} 2 & -1 \\ 6 & 4 \end{pmatrix} \quad \text{and} \quad C = \begin{pmatrix} 3 \\ -5 \end{pmatrix}$$

We now find the inverse of A to be

$$A^{-1} = \begin{pmatrix} \frac{2}{7} & \frac{1}{14} \\ -\frac{3}{7} & \frac{1}{7} \end{pmatrix}$$

Therefore,

$$A^{-1}C = \begin{pmatrix} \frac{2}{7} & \frac{1}{14} \\ -\frac{3}{7} & \frac{1}{7} \end{pmatrix}\begin{pmatrix} 3 \\ -5 \end{pmatrix} = \begin{pmatrix} \frac{6}{7} - \frac{5}{14} \\ -\frac{9}{7} - \frac{5}{7} \end{pmatrix} = \begin{pmatrix} \frac{1}{2} \\ -2 \end{pmatrix}$$

Therefore, the required solution is $x = \frac{1}{2}$ and $y = -2$.

Example C

Solve by matrices the system of equations

$$x + 4y - z = 4$$
$$x + 3y + z = 8$$
$$2x + 6y + z = 13$$

Setting up matrices A and C, we have

$$A = \begin{pmatrix} 1 & 4 & -1 \\ 1 & 3 & 1 \\ 2 & 6 & 1 \end{pmatrix} \quad \text{and} \quad C = \begin{pmatrix} 4 \\ 8 \\ 13 \end{pmatrix}$$

To give another example of finding the inverse of a 3×3 matrix, we shall briefly show the steps for finding A^{-1}.

$$\left(\begin{array}{ccc|ccc} 1 & 4 & -1 & 1 & 0 & 0 \\ 1 & 3 & 1 & 0 & 1 & 0 \\ 2 & 6 & 1 & 0 & 0 & 1 \end{array}\right) \qquad \left(\begin{array}{ccc|ccc} 1 & 4 & -1 & 1 & 0 & 0 \\ 0 & -1 & 2 & -1 & 1 & 0 \\ 2 & 6 & 1 & 0 & 0 & 1 \end{array}\right)$$

$$\left(\begin{array}{ccc|ccc} 1 & 4 & -1 & 1 & 0 & 0 \\ 0 & -1 & 2 & -1 & 1 & 0 \\ 0 & -2 & 3 & -2 & 0 & 1 \end{array}\right) \qquad \left(\begin{array}{ccc|ccc} 1 & 4 & -1 & 1 & 0 & 0 \\ 0 & 1 & -2 & 1 & -1 & 0 \\ 0 & -2 & 3 & -2 & 0 & 1 \end{array}\right)$$

$$\left(\begin{array}{ccc|ccc} 1 & 0 & 7 & -3 & 4 & 0 \\ 0 & 1 & -2 & 1 & -1 & 0 \\ 0 & -2 & 3 & -2 & 0 & 1 \end{array}\right) \qquad \left(\begin{array}{ccc|ccc} 1 & 0 & 7 & -3 & 4 & 0 \\ 0 & 1 & -2 & 1 & -1 & 0 \\ 0 & 0 & -1 & 0 & -2 & 1 \end{array}\right)$$

$$\begin{pmatrix} 1 & 0 & 7 & -3 & 4 & 0 \\ 0 & 1 & -2 & 1 & -1 & 0 \\ 0 & 0 & 1 & 0 & 2 & -1 \end{pmatrix} \qquad \begin{pmatrix} 1 & 0 & 7 & -3 & 4 & 0 \\ 0 & 1 & 0 & 1 & 3 & -2 \\ 0 & 0 & 1 & 0 & 2 & -1 \end{pmatrix}$$

$$\begin{pmatrix} 1 & 0 & 0 & -3 & -10 & 7 \\ 0 & 1 & 0 & 1 & 3 & -2 \\ 0 & 0 & 1 & 0 & 2 & -1 \end{pmatrix} \qquad \text{Thus, } A^{-1} = \begin{pmatrix} -3 & -10 & 7 \\ 1 & 3 & -2 \\ 0 & 2 & -1 \end{pmatrix}$$

Therefore,

$$A^{-1}C = \begin{pmatrix} -3 & -10 & 7 \\ 1 & 3 & -2 \\ 0 & 2 & -1 \end{pmatrix} \begin{pmatrix} 4 \\ 8 \\ 13 \end{pmatrix} = \begin{pmatrix} -1 \\ 2 \\ 3 \end{pmatrix}$$

This means that $x = -1$, $y = 2$, $z = 3$.

Example D

Solve by matrices the system of equations

$$x + 2y - z = -4$$
$$3x + 5y - z = -5$$
$$-2x - y - 2z = -5$$

Setting up matrices A and C, we have

$$A = \begin{pmatrix} 1 & 2 & -1 \\ 3 & 5 & -1 \\ -2 & -1 & -2 \end{pmatrix} \qquad \text{and} \qquad C = \begin{pmatrix} -4 \\ -5 \\ -5 \end{pmatrix}$$

We now find the inverse of A to be

$$A^{-1} = \begin{pmatrix} \frac{11}{2} & -\frac{5}{2} & -\frac{3}{2} \\ -4 & 2 & 1 \\ -\frac{7}{2} & \frac{3}{2} & \frac{1}{2} \end{pmatrix}$$

(see Example D of Section 15–5). Therefore,

$$A^{-1}C = \begin{pmatrix} \frac{11}{2} & -\frac{5}{2} & -\frac{3}{2} \\ -4 & 2 & 1 \\ -\frac{7}{2} & \frac{3}{2} & \frac{1}{2} \end{pmatrix} \begin{pmatrix} -4 \\ -5 \\ -5 \end{pmatrix} = \begin{pmatrix} -2 \\ 1 \\ 4 \end{pmatrix}$$

This means that the solution is $x = -2$, $y = 1$, $z = 4$.

After having solved systems of equations in this manner, the reader may feel that the method is much longer and more tedious than previously developed techniques. The principal problem with this method is that a great deal of numerical computation is generally required. However, methods such as this one are easily programmed for use on a computer, which can do the arithmetic work very rapidly. Recalling that matrices are of particular importance in connection with computers, it is the method of solving the system of equations which is of primary importance.

Exercises 15—6

In Exercises 1 through 8 solve the given systems of equations by using the inverse of the coefficient matrix. The numbers in parentheses refer to exercises from Section 15–5 where the inverses may be checked.

1. $2x - 5y = -14$ (No. 1)
   $-2x + 4y = 11$

2. $-x + 5y = 4$ (No. 3)
   $4x + 10y = -4$

3. $2x + 4y = -9$ (No. 11)
   $-x - y = 2$

4. $2x + 5y = -6$ (No. 13)
   $-x + 2y = -6$

5. $x - 3y - 2z = -8$ (No. 17)
   $-2x + 7y + 3z = 19$
   $x - y - 3z = -3$

6. $x - y - 3z = -1$ (No. 19)
   $-y - 2z = -2$
   $2x + y - z = 2$

7. $x + 3y + 2z = 5$ (No. 21)
   $-2x - 5y - z = -1$
   $2x + 4y = -2$

8. $2x + 4y = -2$ (No. 23)
   $3x + 4y - 2z = -6$
   $-x + y + 2z = 5$

In Exercises 9 through 20 solve the given systems of equations by using the inverse of the coefficient matrix.

9. $2x + 7y = 16$
   $x + 4y = 9$

10. $4x - 3y = -13$
    $-3x + 2y = 9$

11. $2x - 3y = 3$
    $4x - 5y = 4$

12. $x + 2y = 3$
    $3x + 4y = 11$

13. $5x - 2y = -14$
    $3x + 4y = -11$

14. $4x - 3y = -1$
    $8x + 3y = 4$

15. $2x - y = 6$
    $4x + 3y = -10$

16. $4x - y = 3$
    $6x - 3y = 5$

17. $x + 2y + 2z = -4$
    $4x + 9y + 10z = -18$
    $-x + 3y + 7z = -7$

18. $x - 4y - 2z = -7$
    $-x + 5y + 5z = 18$
    $3x - 7y + 10z = 38$

19. $2x + 4y + z = 5$
    $-2x - 2y - z = -6$
    $-x + 2y + z = 0$

20. $4x + y = 2$
    $-2x - y + 3z = -18$
    $2x + y - z = 8$

In Exercises 21 through 24 solve the indicated systems of equations by using the inverse of the coefficient matrix. In Exercises 23 and 24 it is necessary to set up the appropriate equations.

21. Three forces F_1, F_2, and F_3 are acting on a certain beam. The forces (in pounds) can be found by solving the following equations.

$$F_1 + F_2 + F_3 = 30$$
$$4F_1 + F_2 - 4F_3 = 0$$
$$5F_2 - 3F_3 = 4$$

Determine these forces.

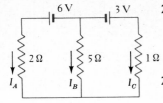

Figure 15–4

22. In applying Kirchhoff's laws (see Exercise 19 of Section 4–5) to the circuit shown in Fig. 15–4, the following equations are found. Determine the indicated currents, in amperes.

$$I_A + I_B + I_C = 0, \qquad 2I_A - 5I_B = 6, \qquad 5I_B - I_C = -3$$

23. Type A doors cost \$10 each and type B doors cost \$14 each. A builder was billed \$220 for a shipment of these doors. He found that had he reversed the number of each on his order, he would have been billed \$212. How many of each did he actually receive?

24. Fifty shares of stock A and 30 shares of stock B cost \$2600. Thirty shares of stock A and 40 shares of stock B cost \$2000. What is the price per share of each stock?

15–7 Exercises for Chapter 15

In Exercises 1 through 8 evaluate the given determinants by expansion by minors.

1. $\begin{vmatrix} 1 & 2 & -1 \\ 4 & 1 & -3 \\ -3 & -5 & 2 \end{vmatrix}$
2. $\begin{vmatrix} 3 & -1 & 2 \\ 7 & -1 & 4 \\ 2 & 1 & -3 \end{vmatrix}$
3. $\begin{vmatrix} -1 & 3 & -7 \\ 0 & 5 & 4 \\ 4 & -3 & -2 \end{vmatrix}$

4. $\begin{vmatrix} 6 & -5 & -7 \\ -1 & 2 & 4 \\ 2 & -3 & 1 \end{vmatrix}$
5. $\begin{vmatrix} 2 & 6 & 2 & 5 \\ 2 & 0 & 4 & -1 \\ 4 & -3 & 6 & 1 \\ 3 & -1 & 0 & -2 \end{vmatrix}$
6. $\begin{vmatrix} 1 & -2 & 2 & 4 \\ 0 & 1 & 2 & 3 \\ 3 & 2 & 2 & 5 \\ 2 & 1 & -2 & 0 \end{vmatrix}$

7. $\begin{vmatrix} 1 & 3 & -2 & 4 \\ 2 & 0 & 3 & -2 \\ 5 & -1 & 5 & -3 \\ -6 & 4 & -1 & 2 \end{vmatrix}$
8. $\begin{vmatrix} 2 & 3 & -1 & -1 \\ -3 & -2 & 5 & -6 \\ 2 & 1 & -3 & 2 \\ 4 & 0 & -2 & 1 \end{vmatrix}$

In Exercises 9 through 16 evaluate the determinants of Exercises 1 through 8 by using the basic properties of determinants.

In Exercises 17 through 20 evaluate the given determinants by using the basic properties of determinants.

17. $\begin{vmatrix} 1 & 0 & -3 & -2 \\ 1 & -1 & 2 & 0 \\ -1 & 1 & 1 & 1 \\ 5 & -1 & 2 & -1 \end{vmatrix}$
18. $\begin{vmatrix} 2 & 6 & -2 & 4 \\ -2 & 2 & -3 & 3 \\ 3 & 2 & 2 & -2 \\ 2 & -6 & 4 & 1 \end{vmatrix}$

19. $\begin{vmatrix} 1 & -1 & 3 & 0 & 2 \\ 4 & 0 & 4 & -2 & 2 \\ 0 & 4 & 0 & -1 & -1 \\ -2 & 2 & -1 & 4 & 0 \\ 1 & -1 & 2 & 0 & 1 \end{vmatrix}$
20. $\begin{vmatrix} 1 & 4 & -3 & 3 & 0 \\ 3 & 1 & -1 & 2 & 2 \\ 1 & 2 & 1 & 1 & 1 \\ -3 & -5 & -5 & 0 & -6 \\ 2 & 2 & -2 & 3 & -2 \end{vmatrix}$

In Exercises 21 through 28 use the given matrices and perform the indicated operations.

$$A = \begin{pmatrix} 2 & -3 \\ 4 & 1 \\ -5 & 0 \\ 2 & -3 \end{pmatrix}, \quad B = \begin{pmatrix} -1 & 0 \\ 4 & -6 \\ -3 & -2 \\ 1 & -7 \end{pmatrix}, \quad C = \begin{pmatrix} 5 & -6 \\ 2 & 8 \\ 0 & -2 \end{pmatrix}$$

21. $A + B$
22. $2C$
23. $-3B$
24. $B - A$
25. $A - C$
26. $2C - B$
27. $2A - 3B$
28. $2(A - B)$

In Exercises 29 through 32 perform the indicated matrix multiplications.

29. $\begin{pmatrix} 5 & -1 \\ 3 & 2 \end{pmatrix} \begin{pmatrix} 1 \\ -8 \end{pmatrix}$

30. $\begin{pmatrix} 6 & -4 & 1 & 0 \\ 2 & 0 & -4 & 3 \end{pmatrix} \begin{pmatrix} 7 & -1 & 6 \\ 4 & 0 & 1 \\ 3 & -2 & 5 \\ 9 & 1 & 0 \end{pmatrix}$

31. $\begin{pmatrix} -1 & 7 \\ 2 & 0 \\ 4 & -1 \end{pmatrix} \begin{pmatrix} 1 & -4 & 5 \\ 5 & 1 & 0 \end{pmatrix}$

32. $\begin{pmatrix} 0 & -1 & 6 \\ 8 & 1 & 4 \\ 7 & -2 & -1 \end{pmatrix} \begin{pmatrix} 5 & -1 & 7 & 1 & 5 \\ 0 & 1 & 0 & 4 & 1 \\ 1 & -2 & 3 & 0 & 1 \end{pmatrix}$

In Exercises 33 through 40 find the inverses of the given matrices.

33. $\begin{pmatrix} 2 & -5 \\ 2 & -4 \end{pmatrix}$

34. $\begin{pmatrix} -1 & -6 \\ 2 & 10 \end{pmatrix}$

35. $\begin{pmatrix} 7 & -1 \\ 4 & 8 \end{pmatrix}$

36. $\begin{pmatrix} 5 & -1 \\ 4 & -8 \end{pmatrix}$

37. $\begin{pmatrix} 1 & 1 & -2 \\ -1 & -2 & 1 \\ 0 & 3 & 4 \end{pmatrix}$

38. $\begin{pmatrix} -1 & -1 & 2 \\ 2 & 3 & 0 \\ 1 & 4 & 1 \end{pmatrix}$

39. $\begin{pmatrix} 2 & -4 & 3 \\ 4 & -6 & 5 \\ -2 & 1 & -1 \end{pmatrix}$

40. $\begin{pmatrix} 3 & 1 & -4 \\ -3 & 1 & -2 \\ -6 & 0 & 3 \end{pmatrix}$

In Exercises 41 through 48 solve the given systems of equations using the inverse of the coefficient matrix.

41. $2x - 3y = -9$
    $4x - y = -13$

42. $5x - 7y = 62$
    $6x + 5y = -6$

43. $3x + 5y = 29$
    $4x - 7y = -57$

44. $4x - 2y = 1$
    $8x + 2y = 5$

45. $2x - 3y + 2z = 7$
    $3x + y - 3z = -6$
    $x + 4y + z = -13$

46. $2x + 2y - z = 8$
    $x + 4y + 2z = 5$
    $3x - 2y + z = 17$

47. $x + 2y + 3z = 1$
$3x - 4y - 3z = 2$
$7x - 6y + 6z = 2$

48. $3x + 2y + z = 2$
$2x + 3y - 6z = 3$
$x + 3y + 3z = 1$

In Exercises 49 through 52 solve the given systems of equations by determinants. Use the basic properties of determinants.

49. $3x - 2y + z = 6$
$2x + 3z = 3$
$4x - y + 5z = 6$

50. $7x + y + 2z = 3$
$4x - 2y + 4z = -2$
$2x + 3y - 6z = 3$

51. $2x - 3y + z - t = -8$
$4x + 3z + 2t = -3$
$2y - 3z - t = 12$
$x - y - z + t = 3$

52. $3x + 2y - 2z - 2t = 0$
$5y + 3z + 4t = 3$
$6y - 3z + 4t = 9$
$6x - y + 2z - 2t = -3$

In Exercises 53 through 56 solve the given systems of equations by any appropriate method of this chapter.

53. To find the forces F_1 and F_2 shown in Fig. 15–5, it is necessary to solve the following equations.

$$F_1 + F_2 = 21$$
$$3F_1 - 4F_2 = 0$$

Find F_1 and F_2.

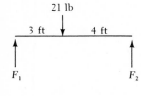

21 lb

3 ft　　4 ft

F_1　　　　F_2

Figure 15–5

54. Two electric resistors, R_1 and R_2, are tested with currents and voltages such that the following equations are found.

$$2R_1 + 3R_2 = 26$$
$$3R_1 + 2R_2 = 24$$

Find the resistances R_1 and R_2 (in ohms).

55. A business executive, in pricing three different products, determines that a certain total income should be made on given combinations of sales of these products. Thus, if she sets prices p_1, p_2, and p_3, each respectively, she will arrive at the following equations.

$$p_1 + p_2 + p_3 = 200$$
$$p_1 + 2p_2 + 3p_3 = 430$$
$$4p_1 + 2p_2 + p_3 = 430$$

What are the prices necessary to meet her goals?

56. To find the electric currents (in amperes) indicated in Fig. 15–6, it is necessary to solve the following equations.

$$I_A + I_B + I_C = 0$$
$$5I_A - 2I_B = -4$$
$$2I_B - I_C = 0$$

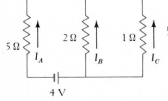

5 Ω　2 Ω　1 Ω

I_A　I_B　I_C

4 V

Figure 15–6

Find I_A, I_B, and I_C.

In Exercises 57 through 60 set up systems of linear equations and solve by any appropriate method illustrated in this chapter.

57. By mass three alloys have the following percentages of lead, zinc, and copper.

	Lead	Zinc	Copper
Alloy A	60%	30%	10%
Alloy B	40%	30%	30%
Alloy C	30%	70%	

How many grams of each of alloys A, B, and C must be mixed to get 100 g of an alloy which is 44% lead, 38% zinc, and 18% copper?

58. A sum of $9000 is invested, part at 6%, part at 5%, and part at 4%. The annual income from these investments is $460. The 5% investment yields $50 more than the 4% investment. How much is invested at each rate?

59. The angles A, B, C, and D of a quadrilateral are related in the following way. Angles B and C are supplementary; four times angle A equals 10° less than the sum of angles B, C, and D; six times angle A plus three times angle C equals twice the sum of all four angles. Find the angles.

60. In setting up salaries for personnel in a certain company, the following criteria were used. The total annual budget for salaries of the 3 managers, 15 research persons, 25 technicians, and 40 production workers was $1,230,000. Each manager receives $5000 more than each research person, $10,000 more than each technician, and $13,000 more than each production worker. What salary does each position pay?

In Exercises 61 and 62 perform the indicated operations on the required matrices.

61. An automobile maker has two assembly plants at which cars with 4 cylinders, 6 cylinders, or 8 cylinders, and with either standard transmission or automatic transmission are assembled. The annual production at the first plant of cars with number of cylinders-transmission type (standard-automatic) is as follows: 4—15,000, 10,000; 6—20,000, 18,000; 8—8,000, 30,000. At the second plant the production is 4—18,000, 12,000; 6—30,000, 22,000; 8—12,000, 40,000. Set up matrices for this information, and by matrix addition find the matrix for total production by the number of cylinders and type of transmission.

62. Set up a matrix representing the information given in Exercise 57. A given shipment contains 500 g of alloy A, 800 g of alloy B, and 700 g of alloy C. Set up a matrix for this information. By multiplying these matrices, obtain a matrix which gives the total weight of lead, zinc, and copper in the shipment.

16

Inequalities

16—1 Properties of Inequalities

Until now we have devoted a great deal of time to the solution of equations. Equation-solving does play an extremely important role in mathematics, but there are also times when we wish to solve inequalities. For example, we have often been faced with the problem of whether or not a given number is real or complex. We determine this from the quadratic formula, by observing the sign of the expression $b^2 - 4ac$. If this expression is positive, the resulting number is real, and if it is negative, the resulting number is complex. This is one of the important uses of inequalities. In this chapter we shall discuss some of the important properties of inequalities and methods of solving inequalities, and illustrate some of their applications in various fields of technology.

In Chapter 1 we first came across the signs of inequality. The expression $a < b$ is read as "a is less than b," and the expression $a > b$ is read as "a is greater than b." *These signs define what is known as the* **sense** *(indicated by the direction of the sign) of the inequality.* Two inequalities are said to have the same sense if the signs of inequality point in the same direction. They are said to have the opposite sense if the signs of inequality point in opposite directions. *The two sides of the inequality are called* **members** *of the inequality.*

Example A

The inequalities $x + 3 > 2$ and $x + 1 > 0$ have the same sense, as do the inequalities $3x - 1 < 4$ and $x^2 - 1 < 3$.

The inequalities $x - 4 < 0$ and $x > -4$ have the opposite sense, as do the inequalities $2x + 4 > 1$ and $3x^2 - 7 < 1$.

The **solution** *of an inequality consists of those values of the variable for which the inequality is satisfied.* Most inequalities with which we shall deal are known as **conditional inequalities.** That is, there are some values of the variable which satisfy the inequality, and also there are some values which do not satisfy it. Some inequalities are satisfied for all values of the variable. These are called **absolute inequalities.** Also, a solution of an inequality may consist of only real numbers, as the terms "greater than" and "less than" have not been defined for complex numbers.

Example B

The inequality $x + 1 > 0$ is satisfied by all values of x greater than -1. Thus, the values of x which satisfy this inequality are written as $x > -1$. This illustrates the difference between the solution of an equation and the solution of an inequality. The solution to an equation normally consists of a few specific numbers, whereas *the solution to an inequality normally consists of a range of values of the variable.* Any and all values within this range are termed the solution of the inequality.

Example C

The inequality $x^2 + 1 > 0$ is true for all values of x, since x^2 is never negative. This is an absolute inequality. The inequality shown in Example B is a conditional inequality.

There are occasions when it is convenient to combine an inequality with an equality. For such purposes, the symbols $\leq$, read "less than or equal to," and $\geq$, read "greater than or equal to," are used.

Example D

If we wish to state that x is positive, we would write $x > 0$. However, the value zero is not included in the solution. If we wished to state that x is not negative, that is, that zero is included as a part of the solution, we can write $x \geq 0$. In order to state that x is less than or equal to -5, we write $x \leq -5$.

We shall now present the basic operations performed on inequalities. These operations are the same as those performed on equations, but in certain cases the results take on a different form. The following are referred to as the **properties of inequalities:**

(1) *The sense of an inequality is not changed when the same number is added to—or subtracted from—both members of the inequality.* Symbolically this may be stated as "if $a > b$, then $a + c > b + c$, or $a - c > b - c$."

Example E

$9 > 6$; thus, $9 + 4 > 6 + 4$, or $13 > 10$. Also, $9 - 12 > 6 - 12$ or $-3 > -6$.

(2) *The sense of an inequality is not changed if both members are multiplied or divided by the same positive number.* Symbolically this is stated as, "if $a > b$, then $ac > bc$, or $a/c > b/c$, provided that $c > 0$."

Example F

$8 < 15$; thus, $8(2) < 15(2)$ or $16 < 30$. Also, $\frac{8}{2} < \frac{15}{2}$ or $4 < \frac{15}{2}$.

(3) *The sense of an inequality is reversed if both members are multiplied or divided by the same negative number.* Symbolically this is stated as, "if $a > b$, then $ac < bc$, or $a/c < b/c$, provided that $c < 0$." Be very careful to note the *we obtain different results, depending on whether both members are multiplied by a positive or by a negative number.*

Example G

$4 > -2$; thus, $4(-3) < (-2)(-3)$, or $-12 < 6$. Also,

$$\frac{4}{-2} < \frac{-2}{-2} \qquad \text{or} \qquad -2 < 1$$

(4) *If both members of an inequality are positive numbers and n is a positive integer, then the inequality formed by taking the nth power of each member, or the nth root of each member, is in the same sense as the given inequality.* Symbolically this is stated as, "if $a > b$, then $a^n > b^n$, or $\sqrt[n]{a} > \sqrt[n]{b}$, provided that $n > 0$, $a > 0$, $b > 0$."

Example H

$16 > 9$; thus, $16^2 > 9^2$ or $256 > 81$; also, $\sqrt{16} > \sqrt{9}$ or $4 > 3$.

Many inequalities have more than two members. In fact, inequalities with three members are very common. All the operations stated above hold for inequalities with more than two members. Some care must be used, however, in stating inequalities with more than two members.

Example I

In order to state that 5 is less than 6, and also greater than 2, which says that 5 is between 2 and 6, we may write $2 < 5 < 6$, or $6 > 5 > 2$. However, generally the form with the *less than* inequality signs is preferred.

In order to state that a number x may be equal to or greater than 2, and also less than 6, we write $2 \leq x < 6$.

By writing $2 \leq x \leq 6$ we are stating that x is greater than or equal to 2, and at the same time less than or equal to 6.

By writing $x \leq -5$, $x > 7$ we are stating that x is less than or equal to -5, or greater than 7. This may not be stated as $7 < x \leq -5$, for this shows x as being less than -5, while at the same time greater than 7, and no such numbers exist.

Example J

The inequality $x^2 - 3x + 2 > 0$ is satisfied if x is either greater than 2 or less than 1. This would be written as $x > 2$ or $x < 1$, but it would be incorrect to state it as $1 > x > 2$. (If we wrote it this way, we would be saying that the same value of x is less than 1 and at the same time greater than 2. Of course, as we noted for this type of situation in Example I, no such number exists.) Any inequality must be valid for all values satisfying it. However, we could say that the inequality is not satisfied for $1 \leq x \leq 2$, which means those values of x between or equal to 1 and 2.

We shall now present two examples of other kinds of problems in which the basic properties of inequalities are used.

Example K

If $0 < x < 1$, prove that $x^2 < x$.

From the given inequality we see that x is a positive number less than 1. Thus, if we multiply the members of the given inequality by x, we have $0 < x^2 < x$, which gives the desired result if we consider the middle and right members. Note the meaning of this inequality. The square of any positive number less than 1 is less than the number itself.

Example L

State, by means of an inequality, the conditions that x must satisfy if a point in the xy-plane lies between the lines $x = 1$ and $x = 5$.

The x-coordinate of any point in this part of the plane is greater than 1, but at the same time less than 5. Thus we have $1 < x < 5$. See Fig. 16–1.

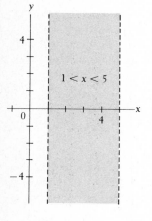

Figure 16–1

On occasion it is necessary to define a function in a different way for some values of the independent variable than for other values. Inequalities can then be used to denote the intervals over which the different definitions of the function are valid. The following example illustrates this use of inequalities, and includes a graphical representation.

Example M

The electrical intensity within a charged spherical conductor is zero. The intensity on the surface and outside of the sphere is equal to a constant divided by the square of the distance from the center of the sphere. State these relations by using inequalities, and make a graphical representation.

Let a = the radius of the sphere, r = the distance from the center of the sphere, and E = the electrical intensity.

The first statement may be written as $E = 0$ if $0 \leq r < a$, since this would be read as "the electric intensity is 0 if the distance from the center is less than the radius." Negative values of r are meaningless, which is the reason for saying that r is greater than or equal to zero. The second statement may be written as $E = k/r^2$ if $a \leq r$. Making a table of values for this equation, we have the following points:

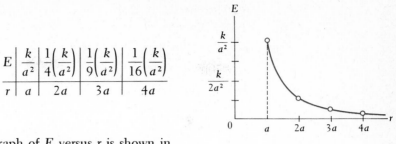

$$E \quad \begin{array}{c|c|c|c|c} & \dfrac{k}{a^2} & \dfrac{1}{4}\!\left(\dfrac{k}{a^2}\right) & \dfrac{1}{9}\!\left(\dfrac{k}{a^2}\right) & \dfrac{1}{16}\!\left(\dfrac{k}{a^2}\right) \\ \hline r & a & 2a & 3a & 4a \end{array}$$

The graph of E versus r is shown in Fig. 16–2.

Figure 16–2

Exercises 16–1

In Exercises 1 through 8, for the inequality $4 < 9$, state the inequality resulting when the operations given are performed on both members.

1. Add 3.
2. Subtract 6.
3. Multiply by 5.
4. Multiply by -2.
5. Divide by -1.
6. Divide by 2.
7. Square both.
8. Take square roots.

In Exercises 9 through 16 give the inequalities which are equivalent to the following statements about a number x.

9. Greater than -2
10. Less than 7
11. Less than or equal to 4
12. Greater than or equal to -6
13. Greater than 1 and less than 7
14. Greater than or equal to -2 and less than 6
15. Less than -9, or greater than or equal to -4
16. Less than or equal to 8, or greater than or equal to 12

In Exercises 17 through 24 state the condition in terms of an inequality that x must satisfy to describe the location of the given point.

17. The point (x, y) lies to the right of the y-axis.
18. The point (x, y) lies to the right of the line $x = 1$.
19. The point (x, y) lies on or to the left of the y-axis.
20. The point (x, y) lies on or to the right of the line $x = -2$.
21. The point (x, y) lies outside of the region between the lines $x = -1$ and $x = 1$.
22. The point (x, y) lies in the region between the lines $x = -1$ and $x = 1$.
23. The point (x, y) lies on or to the right of the line $x = 2$ or to the left of the line $x = 6$.
24. The point (x, y) lies to the left of the line $x = -4$ or to the right of the line $x = 3$.

In Exercises 25 through 28 state the conditions in terms of inequalities that x, or y, or both, must satisfy to describe the location of the given point.

25. The point (x, y) lies in the first quadrant.

26. The point (x, y) lies in the region bounded by the lines $x = 1$, $x = 4$, $y = -3$, and $y = -1$.

27. The point (x, y) lies above the line $x = y$.

28. The point (x, y) lies within three units of the origin. [*Hint:* Use the Pythagorean theorem.]

In Exercises 29 through 32 prove the given inequalities.

29. If $x > 1$, prove that $x^2 > x$.   30. If $x > y > 0$, prove that $1/y > 1/x$.

31. If $0 < x < y$, prove that $\sqrt{xy} < y$.

32. If $x > x^2$, prove that $\sqrt{3x + 1} > x + 1$.

In Exercises 33 through 36 some applications of inequalities are shown.

33. A certain projectile is above 200 m from 3.5 s after it is launched until 15.3 s after it is launched. Express this statement in terms of inequalities in terms of the time t and height h.

34. An earth satellite put into orbit near the earth's surface will have an elliptic orbit if its velocity v is between 18,000 mi/h and 25,000 mi/h. State this as an inequality.

35. The electric potential V inside a charged spherical conductor equals a constant k divided by the radius a of the sphere. The potential on the surface of and outside the sphere equals the same constant k divided by the distance r from the center of the sphere. State these relations by the use of inequalities and make a graphical representation of V versus r.

36. A semiconductor diode, an electronic device, has the property that an electric current can flow through it in only one direction. Thus, if a diode is in a circuit with an alternating-current source, the current in the circuit exists only during the half-cycle when the direction is correct for the diode. If a source of current given by $i = 2 \sin 120\pi t$ milliamperes is connected in series with a diode, write the inequalities which are appropriate for the first four half-cycles and graph the resulting current versus the time. Assume that the diode allows a positive current to flow.

16–2 Graphical Solution of Inequalities

Equations can be solved by graphical and by algebraic means. This is also true of inequalities. In this section we shall take up graphical solutions, and in the following section we shall develop algebraic methods. The graphical method is shown in the following examples.

Example A
Graphically solve the inequality $3x - 2 > 4$.

   This means that we want to locate all those values of x which make the left member of this inequality greater than the right member. By subtracting 4 from each member, we have the equivalent inequality $3x - 6 > 0$.

   If we find the graph of $y = 3x - 6$, all those values of x for which y is positive would satisfy the inequality $3x - 6 > 0$. Thus, we graph the equation $y = 3x - 6$, and find those values of x for which y is positive. From the graph in Fig. 16–3, we see that values of $x > 2$ correspond to $y > 0$. Thus, the values of x which satisfy the inequality are given by $x > 2$.

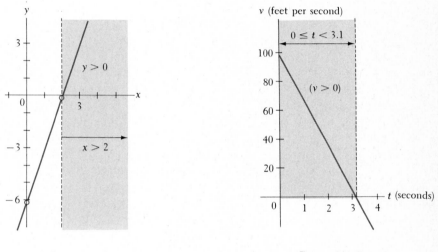

Figure 16–3   Figure 16–4

Example B
The velocity v (in feet per second) of a certain projectile in terms of the time t (in seconds) is given by $v = 100 - 32t$. For how long is the velocity positive? (This can be interpreted as "how long is the projectile moving upward?")

   In terms of inequalities, we would like to know for what values of t is $v > 0$, or in other terms, solve the inequality $100 - 32t > 0$. Therefore, we graph the function $v = 100 - 32t$ as shown in Fig. 16–4. From the graph, we see that the values of t which correspond to $v > 0$ are $0 \le t < 3.1$ s, which are therefore the required values of t. The last value is approximated from the graph.

Example C
Graphically solve the inequality $2x^2 < x + 3$.

Finding the equivalent inequality, with 0 for a right-hand member, we have $2x^2 - x - 3 < 0$. Thus, those values of x for which y is negative for the function $y = 2x^2 - x - 3$ will satisfy the inequality. So we graph the equation $y = 2x^2 - x - 3$, from the values given in the following table:

x	-3	-2	-1	0	1	2	3
y	18	7	0	-3	-2	3	12

From the graph in Fig. 16–5, we can see that the inequality is satisfied for the values $-1 < x < 1.5$.

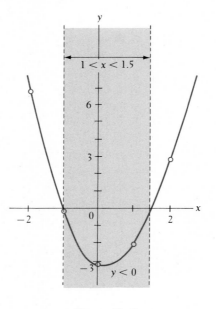

Figure 16–5

Summarizing the method for the graphical solution of an inequality, we see that we first write the inequality in an equivalent form with zero on the right. Next we set y equal to the left member and graph the resulting equation. Those values of x corresponding to the proper values of y (either above or below the x-axis) are those values which satisfy the inequality.

Example D
Graphically solve the inequality $x^3 > x^2 - 3$.

Finding the equivalent inequality with 0 on the right, we then have $x^3 - x^2 + 3 > 0$. By letting $y = x^3 - x^2 + 3$, we may solve the inequality by finding those values of x for which y is positive.

x	-2	-1	0	1	2
y	-9	1	3	3	7

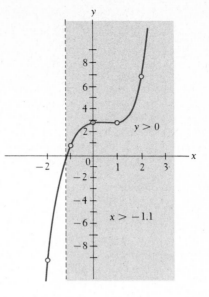

Figure 16–6

Approximating the root of the function to be -1.1, the values which satisfy the inequality are given by $x > -1.1$ (Fig. 16–6). If greater accuracy is required, the methods of Section 14–5 may be used to find the root. This example also points out the usefulness of graphical methods, since this inequality would prove to be beyond elementary methods if an algebraic solution were required.

Exercises 16–2

In Exercises 1 through 24 solve the given inequalities graphically.

1. $2x > 4$

2. $3x < -6$

3. $5x - 1 > 3x$

4. $2x - 3 < x$

5. $7x - 5 < 4x + 3$

6. $2x > 6x - 2$

7. $5x < 6x - 1$

8. $6 - x < x$

9. $x^2 > 2x$

10. $x^2 < x$

11. $2x + 3 < x^2$

12. $x - 1 < x^2$

13. $x^2 - 5x < -4$

14. $7x - 3 < -6x^2$

15. $3x^2 - 2x - 8 > 0$

16. $4x^2 - 2x > 5$

17. $x^3 > 1$

18. $x^3 > x + 4$

19. $x^4 < x^2 - 2x - 1$

20. $x^4 - 6x^3 + 7x^2 > 18 - 12x$

21. $2^x > 0$

22. $\log x > 1$

23. $\sin x < 0$ (limit the graph to the values $0 \le x \le 2\pi$)

24. $\cos 2x > 0$ (limit the graph as in Exercise 23)

In Exercises 25 through 28 answer the given questions by solving appropriate inequalities graphically.

25. A salesman receives $300 monthly plus a 10% commission on sales. Therefore, his monthly income I in terms of his sales s is $I = 300 + 0.1s$. How much must his sales for the month be in order that his income is at least $500?

26. The basic maintenance on a certain machine is $10 per day. It also costs $2 per hour while in operation. Therefore, the total cost C to operate this machine in terms of the number of hours t that it operates in a given day is $C = 10 + 2t$. How many hours can it operate without the cost exceeding $30 for the day?

27. The electrical resistance R of a certain material depends on the temperature, according to the relation $R = 40 + 0.1T + 0.01T^2$. For what values of the temperature $(T > 0°C)$ is the resistance over 42 Ω?

28. The height s of a certain object is given by $s = 140 + 60t - 16t^2$, where t is the time (in seconds). For what values of t is $s > 180$ ft?

16—3 Algebraic Solution of Inequalities

We learned that one important step in solving inequalities by graphical means was to set up an equivalent inequality with zero as the right member. This enabled us to find the values which satisfied the inequality by simply determining the *sign* of the function which was set up. A similar procedure is useful when we solve inequalities algebraically.

A linear function is either negative or positive for *all* values to the left of a particular value of x, and has the opposite sign for *all* values to the right of the same value of x. *This value of x which divides the positive and negative intervals is called the* **critical value.** *This critical value is found where the function is zero.* Thus, to determine where a linear function is positive and where it is negative, we need to find only this critical value, and then determine the *sign* of the function to the left and to the right of this value.

Example A
Solve the inequality $2x - 5 > 1$.

We first find the equivalent inequality with zero on the right. This is done by subtracting 1 from each member. Thus, we have $2x - 6 > 0$. We now set the left member *equal* to zero to find the critical value. Thus, the critical value is 3. We know that the function $2x - 6$ is of one sign for $x < 3$ and has the opposite sign for $x > 3$. Testing values in these intervals, we find that for $x > 3$, $2x - 6 > 0$. Thus, the values which satisfy the inequality are those for which $x > 3$.

It is possible, and appropriate, to solve linear inequalities such as this one just as we would solve an equation. That is, we could isolate x by adding 5 to each side, obtaining $2x > 6$, and then dividing both sides by 2, obtaining $x > 3$. However, the method used above is much more generally applicable. It can be used with higher-degree expressions and fractional expressions, as well as with linear expressions.

Example B
Solve the inequality $\frac{1}{2}x - 3 \leq \frac{1}{3} - x$.

We note that this is an inequality combined with an equality. However, the solution proceeds essentially the same as with an inequality.

Multiplying by 6, we have $3x - 18 \leq 2 - 6x$. Subtracting $2 - 6x$ from each member, we have $9x - 20 \leq 0$. The critical value is $\frac{20}{9}$. If $x \leq \frac{20}{9}$, $9x - 20 \leq 0$. Thus, the values which satisfy the inequality are given by $x \leq \frac{20}{9}$.

The preceding analysis is especially useful for solving inequalities involving higher-degree functions or involving fractions with x in the denominator as well as in the numerator. When the equivalent inequality with zero on the right has been found, this inequality is then factored into linear factors (and those quadratic factors which lead to complex roots). Each linear factor can change sign only at its critical value, as all possible values of x are considered. Thus, the function on the left can change sign only where one of its factors changes sign. The function will have the same sign for all values of x less than the leftmost critical value. The sign of the function will also be the same within any given interval between two critical values. All values to the right of the rightmost critical value will also give the function the same sign. *Therefore, we must find all of the critical values and then determine the sign of the function to the left of the leftmost critical value, between the critical values, and to the right of the rightmost critical value. Those intervals in which we have the proper sign will satisfy the given inequality.*

Example C
Solve the inequality $x^2 - 3 > 2x$.

We first find the equivalent inequality with zero on the right. Thus, we have $x^2 - 2x - 3 > 0$. We then factor the left member, and have

$$(x - 3)(x + 1) > 0$$

We find the critical value for each of the factors, for these are the only values for which the function $x^2 - 2x - 3$ is zero. The left critical value is -1, and the right critical value is 3. All values of x to the left of -1 give the same sign for the function. All values of x between -1 and 3 give the function the same sign. All values of x to the right of 3 give the same sign to the function. Therefore, we must determine the sign for $x < -1$, $-1 < x < 3$, and $x > 3$. For the interval $x < -1$, we find that each of the factors is negative. However, the product of two negative numbers gives a positive number. Therefore, if $x < -1$, then $(x - 3)(x + 1) > 0$.

For the interval $-1 < x < 3$, we find that the left factor is negative, but the right factor is positive. The product of a negative and positive number gives a negative number. Thus, for the interval $-1 < x < 3$, $(x - 3)(x + 1) < 0$. For the interval $x > 3$, both factors are positive, making $(x - 3)(x + 1) > 0$. We tabulate the results.

If	$x < -1$	$(x - 3)(x + 1) > 0$
If	$-1 < x < 3$	$(x - 3)(x + 1) < 0$
If	$x > 3$	$(x - 3)(x + 1) > 0$

Thus, the inequality is satisfied for $x < -1$ or $x > 3$.

Example D

Solve the inequality $x^3 - 4x^2 + x + 6 < 0$.

By methods developed in Chapter 14, we factor the function of the left and obtain $(x + 1)(x - 2)(x - 3) < 0$. The critical values are -1, 2, 3. We wish to determine the sign of the left member for the intervals $x < -1$, $-1 < x < 2$, $2 < x < 3$, and $x > 3$. This is tabulated here, with the sign of the factors in each case indicated.

Interval	$(x + 1)$	$(x - 2)$	$(x - 3)$	Sign of $(x + 1)(x - 2)(x - 3)$
$x < -1$	$-$	$-$	$-$	$-$
$-1 < x < 2$	$+$	$-$	$-$	$+$
$2 < x < 3$	$+$	$+$	$-$	$-$
$x > 3$	$+$	$+$	$+$	$+$

Thus, the inequality is satisfied for $x < -1$ or $2 < x < 3$.

Example E

Solve the inequality $\dfrac{x - 3}{x + 4} \geq 0$.

The critical values are found from the factors, whether they are in the numerator or in the denominator. Thus, the critical values are -4 and 3. Considering now the *greater than* part of the $\geq$ sign, we set up the following table.

Interval	$\dfrac{x - 3}{x + 4}$	Sign of $\dfrac{x - 3}{x + 4}$
$x < -4$	$\dfrac{-}{-}$	$+$
$-4 < x < 3$	$\dfrac{-}{+}$	$-$
$x > 3$	$\dfrac{+}{+}$	$+$

Thus, the values which satisfy the greater than part of the problem are those for which $x < -4$ or for which $x > 3$. Now considering the equality part of the $\geq$ sign, we note that $x = 3$ is valid, for the fraction is zero. However, if $x = -4$, we have division by zero, and thus x may not equal -4. Therefore, the inequality is satisfied for $x < -4$ or $x \geq 3$.

Example F

Solve the inequality $x^3 - x^2 + x - 1 > 0$.

This leads to $(x^2 + 1)(x - 1) > 0$. There is only one linear factor with a critical value. The factor $x^2 + 1$ is never negative. The inequality is satisfied for $x > 1$.

Example G

Solve the inequality

$$\frac{(x - 2)^2(x + 3)}{4 - x} < 0$$

The critical values are -3, 2, and 4. Thus, we have the following table.

Interval	$\dfrac{(x - 2)^2(x + 3)}{4 - x}$	Sign of $\dfrac{(x - 2)^2(x + 3)}{4 - x}$
$x < -3$	$\dfrac{+ \quad -}{+}$	$-$
$-3 < x < 2$	$\dfrac{+ \quad +}{+}$	$+$
$2 < x < 4$	$\dfrac{+ \quad +}{+}$	$+$
$x > 4$	$\dfrac{+ \quad +}{-}$	$-$

The inequality is satisfied for $x < -3$ or $x > 4$.

Exercises 16–3

In Exercises 1 through 32 solve the given inequalities.

1. $x + 3 > 0$
2. $2x - 7 < 0$
3. $6x - 4 < 8 - x$

4. $2x - 6 < x + 4$
5. $3x - 7 \leq x + 1$
6. $7 - x \geq x - 1$

7. $\frac{1}{3}(x - 6) > 4 - x$
8. $\frac{x}{4} - 7 > \frac{x}{2} + 3$

9. $x^2 - 1 < 0$
10. $x^2 - 4x - 5 > 0$

11. $3x^2 + 5x \geq 2$
12. $2x^2 - 12 \leq -5x$

13. $6x^2 + 1 < 5x$
14. $9x^2 + 6x > -1$

15. $x^2 + 4 > 0$
16. $x^4 + 2 < 1$

17. $x^3 + x^2 - 2x > 0$
18. $x^3 - 2x^2 + x > 0$

19. $x^3 + 2x^2 - x - 2 > 0$
20. $x^4 - 2x^3 - 7x^2 + 8x + 12 < 0$

21. $\frac{x - 8}{3 - x} < 0$
22. $\frac{x + 5}{x - 1} > 0$
23. $\frac{2x - 3}{x + 6} \leq 0$

24. $\frac{3x + 1}{x - 3} \geq 0$
25. $\frac{2}{x^2 - x - 2} < 0$
26. $\frac{-5}{2x^2 + 3x - 2} < 0$

27. $\frac{x^2 - 6x - 7}{x + 5} > 0$
28. $\frac{4 - x}{3 + 2x - x^2} > 0$

29. $\frac{6 - x}{3 - x - 4x^2} > 0$
30. $\frac{(x - 2)^2(5 - x)}{(4 - x)^3} < 0$

31. $\frac{x^4(9 - x)(x - 5)(2 - x)}{(4 - x)^5} > 0$
32. $\frac{x^3(1 - x)(x - 2)(3 - x)(4 - x)}{(5 - x)^2(x - 6)^3} < 0$

In Exercises 33 through 36 determine the values of x for which the given radicals represent real numbers.

33. $\sqrt{(x-1)(x+2)}$

34. $\sqrt{x^2 - 3x}$

35. $\sqrt{-x - x^2}$

36. $\sqrt{\dfrac{x^3 + 6x^2 + 8x}{3 - x}}$

In Exercises 37 through 40 answer the given questions by solving the appropriate inequalities.

37. The velocity (in feet per second) of a certain object in terms of the time t (in seconds) is given by $v = 120 - 32t$. For what values of t is the object ascending $(v > 0)$?

38. The relationship between Fahrenheit degrees and Celsius degrees is $F = \frac{9}{5}C + 32$. For what values of C is $F \geq 98.6$ (normal body temperature)?

39. Determine the values of T for which the resistor of Exercise 27 of Section 16–2 has a resistance between 41 and 42 Ω.

40. The deflection y of a certain beam 9 ft long is given by the equation $y = k(x^3 - 243x + 1458)$. For which values of x (the distance from one end of the beam) is the quantity y/k greater than 216 units?

16–4 Inequalities Involving Absolute Values

If we wish to write the inequality $|x| > 1$ without absolute-value signs, we must note that we are considering values of x which are *numerically* larger than 1. Thus we may write this inequality in the equivalent form $x < -1$ or $x > 1$. We now note that the original inequality, with an absolute value sign, can be written in terms of two equivalent inequalities, neither involving absolute values. If we are asked to write the inequality $|x| < 1$ without the absolute-value signs, we write $-1 < x < 1$ since we are considering values of x which are numerically less than 1.

Following reasoning similar to the above, whenever absolute values are involved in inequalities, the following two relations allow us to write equivalent inequalities without absolute values.

If $\|f(x)\| > n$, then $f(x) < -n$ or $f(x) > n$.	(16–1)
If $\|f(x)\| < n$, then $-n < f(x) < n$.	(16–2)

The use of these relations is indicated in the following examples.

Example A

Solve the inequality $|x - 3| < 2$.

Inspection of this inequality shows that we wish to find the values of x which are within 2 units of $x = 3$. Of course, such values are given by $1 < x < 5$. Let us now see how Eq. (16–2) gives us this result.

By using Eq. (16–2), we have

$$-2 < x - 3 < 2$$

By adding 3 to all three members of this inequality, we have

$$1 < x < 5$$

which is the proper interval.

Example B

Solve the inequality $|2x - 1| > 5$.

By using Eq. (16–1), we have

$$2x - 1 < -5 \quad \text{or} \quad 2x - 1 > 5$$

Completing the solution, we have

$$2x < -4 \quad \text{or} \quad 2x > 6$$
$$x < -2 \quad \text{or} \quad x > 3$$

This means that the given inequality is satisfied for $x < -2$ or for $x > 3$.

Example C

Solve the inequality $|3x + 2| \leq 4$.

Although there is a sign of equality involved, we may solve this inequality in the same way as indicated in Eq. (16–2). Since $f(x)$ is linear (and therefore no division by a factor containing x is involved), we may include the equals sign throughout the solution. Therefore, we have

$$-4 \leq 3x + 2 \leq 4$$
$$-6 \leq 3x \leq 2$$
$$-2 \leq x \leq \frac{2}{3}$$

We note that for $x = -2$ and for $x = \frac{2}{3}$, $|3x + 2| = 4$. Thus, the last inequality shown gives the values of x which satisfy the given inequality.

Example D

Solve the inequality $|x^2 + x - 4| > 2$.

By Eq. (16–1), we have $x^2 + x - 4 < -2$ or $x^2 + x - 4 > 2$, which means we want values of x which satisfy *either* of these inequalities. The first inequality becomes

$$x^2 + x - 2 < 0$$
$$(x + 2)(x - 1) < 0$$

which is satisfied for $-2 < x < 1$. The second inequality becomes

$$x^2 + x - 6 > 0$$
$$(x + 3)(x - 2) > 0$$

which is satisfied for $x < -3$ or for $x > 2$. Thus, the original inequality is satisfied for $x < -3$, or for $-2 < x < 1$, or for $x > 2$.

Example E
Solve the inequality $|x^2 + x - 4| < 2$.

By Eq. (16–2), we have $-2 < x^2 + x - 4 < 2$, which we can write as $x^2 + x - 4 > -2$ and $x^2 + x - 4 < 2$, as long as we remember that we want values of x which satisfy *both* of these at the same time. The first inequality can be written as

$$x^2 + x - 4 > -2$$
$$x^2 + x - 2 > 0$$
$$(x + 2)(x - 1) > 0$$

which is satisfied for $x < -2$ or for $x > 1$. The second inequality is

$$x^2 + x - 4 < 2$$
$$x^2 + x - 6 < 0$$

or

$$(x + 3)(x - 2) < 0$$

which is satisfied for $-3 < x < 2$. The values of x which satisfy both of the inequalities are those between -3 and -2 and those between 1 and 2. Thus, the original inequality is satisfied for $-3 < x < -2$ or for $1 < x < 2$.

Exercises 16—4

In Exercises 1 through 16 solve the given inequalities.

1. $|x - 4| < 1$ 2. $|x + 1| < 3$ 3. $|3x - 5| > 2$
4. $|2x - 1| > 1$ 5. $|6x - 5| \leq 4$ 6. $|3 - x| \leq 2$
7. $|4x + 3| > 3$ 8. $|3x + 1| > 2$ 9. $|x + 4| < 6$
10. $|5x - 10| < 2$ 11. $|2 - 3x| \geq 5$ 12. $|3 - 2x| \geq 6$
13. $|x^2 + 3x - 1| < 3$ 14. $|x^2 - 5x - 1| < 5$
15. $|x^2 + 3x - 1| > 3$ 16. $|x^2 - 5x - 1| > 5$

In Exercises 17 through 20 use inequalities involving absolute values to solve the given problems.

17. The deflection y at a horizontal distance x from the left end of a beam is less than $\frac{1}{4}$ ft within 2 ft of a point 6 ft from the left end. State this with the use of an inequality involving absolute values.

18. A given projectile is at an altitude h between 40 and 60 m for the time between $t = 3$ s and $t = 5$ s. Write this using two inequalities involving absolute values.

19. An object is oscillating at the end of a spring which is suspended from a support. The distance x of the object from the support is given by the equation $|x - 8| < 3$. By solving this inequality, determine the distances (in inches) from the support of the extreme positions of the object.

20. The production p (in barrels) of an oil refinery for the coming month is estimated at $|p - 2,000,000| < 200,000$. By solving this inequality, determine the production which is anticipated.

16—5 Graphical Solution of Inequalities with Two Variables

To this point we have considered inequalities with one variable and certain methods of solving them. We may also graphically solve inequalities involving two variables, such as x and y. In this section we consider the solution of such inequalities, as well as one important type of application.

Let us consider the function $y = f(x)$. We know that the coordinates of points on the graph satisfy the equation $y = f(x)$. However, for points above the graph of the function, we have $y > f(x)$, and for points below the graph of the function we have $y < f(x)$. Consider the following example.

Example A

Consider the linear function $y = 2x - 1$. This equation is satisfied for points on the line. For example, the point $(2,3)$ is on the line and we have $3 = 2(2) - 1 = 3$. Therefore, for points on the line we have $y = 2x - 1$, or $y - 2x + 1 = 0$. The point $(2, 4)$ is above the line, since we have $4 > 2(2) - 1$, or $4 > 3$. Therefore, for points above the line we have $y > 2x - 1$, or $y - 2x + 1 > 0$. In the same way, for points below the line, $y < 2x - 1$ or $y - 2x + 1 < 0$. We note this is true for the point $(2,1)$, since $1 < 2(2) - 1$, or $1 < 3$. The line for which $y = 2x + 1$, and the regions for which $y > 2x - 1$, and for which $y < 2x - 1$ are shown in Fig. 16−7.

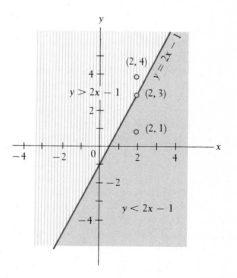

Figure 16—7

The illustration of Example A leads us to the graphical method of indicating the points which satisfy an inequality with two variables. First we solve the inequality for y and then determine the graph of the function $y = f(x)$. If we wish to solve the inequality $y > f(x)$, we indicate the appropriate points by shading in the region above the curve. For the inequality $y < f(x)$, we indicate the appropriate points by shading in the region below the curve. We note that the complete solution to the inequality consists of all points in an entire region of the plane.

Example B

Draw a sketch of the graph of the inequality $y < x + 3$.

First we graph the function $y = x + 3$, as shown in Fig. 16–8. Since we wish to find the points which satisfy the inequality $y < x + 3$, we show these points by shading in the region below the line. The line itself is shown as a dashed line since points on it do not satisfy the inequality.

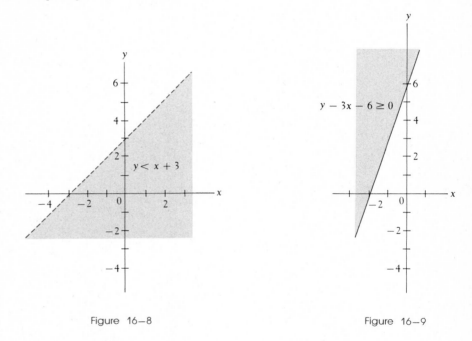

Figure 16—8   Figure 16—9

Example C

Draw a sketch of the graph of the inequality $y - 3x - 6 \geq 0$.

First we state the inequality as $y \geq 3x + 6$. Next the graph of the line $y = 3x + 6$ is drawn, as in Fig. 16–9. The points which satisfy the inequality consist of all points above the line and those points which are on the line. Therefore, we show the line as a solid line.

Example D

Draw a sketch of the graph of the inequality $y > x^2 - 4$.

Although the graph of $y = x^2 - 4$ is not a straight line, the method of solution is the same. We graph the function $y = x^2 - 4$ as shown in Fig. 16–10. We then shade in the region above the curve to indicate the points which satisfy the inequality.

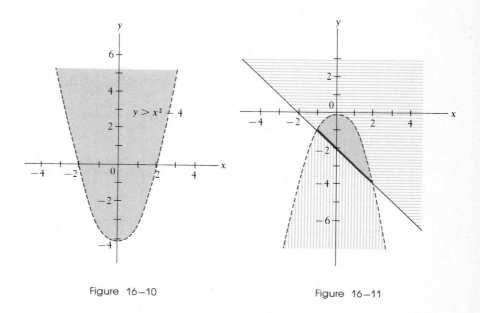

Figure 16–10   Figure 16–11

Example E

Draw a sketch of the region which is defined by the system of inequalities $y \geq -x - 2$ and $y + x^2 < 0$.

In this case we sketch the graph of both inequalities, and then determine the region common to both graphs. First we draw the graph of $y = -x - 2$ (the straight line), and shade in the region above the line. See Fig. 16–11. Next we have $y < -x^2$ and draw the graph of $y = -x^2$, shading the region below it. The sketch of the region which is defined by this system of inequalities is the darkly shaded region below the parabola which is above and on the line.

An important area in which graphs of inequalities with two or more variables are used is the branch of mathematics known as **linear programming** (in this context, "programming" has no relation to computer programming). This subject is widely applied in industry, business, economics, and technology. The analysis of many social problems can also be made by the use of linear programming.

Linear programming is used to analyze problems such as those related to maximizing profit, minimizing costs, or the use of materials, with certain constraints of production. The following serves as an example of the use of linear programming.

Example F

A company makes two types of stereo speaker systems, their good quality system and their highest quality system. The production of the systems requires assembly of the speaker system itself and the production of the cabinets in which they are installed. The good quality system requires 3 worker-hours for speaker assembly and 2 worker-hours for cabinet production for each complete system. The highest quality system requires 4 worker-hours for speaker assembly and 6 worker-hours for cabinet production for each complete system. Available skilled labor allows for a maximum of 480 worker-hours per week for speaker assembly and a maximum of 540 worker-hours per week for cabinet production. It is anticipated that all systems will be sold and that the profit will be $10 for each good quality system and $25 for each highest quality system. How many of each should be produced to provide the greatest profit?

First, let $x =$ the number of good quality systems and $y =$ the number of highest quality systems made in one week. Thus, the profit p is given by

$$p = 10x + 25y$$

We know that negative numbers are not valid for either x or y, and therefore we have $x \geq 0$ and $y \geq 0$. Also, the number of available worker-hours per week for each part of the production restricts the number of systems which can be made. Both speaker assembly and cabinet production are required for all systems. The number of worker-hours needed to produce the x good quality systems is $3x$ in the speaker assembly shop. Also, $4y$ worker-hours are required in the speaker assembly shop for the highest quality systems. Thus,

$$3x + 4y \leq 480$$

since no more than 480 worker-hours are available in the speaker assembly shop. In the cabinet shop, we have

$$2x + 6y \leq 540$$

since no more than 540 worker-hours are available in the cabinet shop.

Therefore, we wish to maximize the profit p under the **constraints**

$$x \geq 0, \quad y \geq 0$$
$$3x + 4y \leq 480$$
$$2x + 6y \leq 540$$

In order to do this we sketch the region of points which satisfy this system of inequalities. From the previous examples, we see that the appropriate region is in the first quadrant (since $x \geq 0$ and $y \geq 0$) and under both lines. See Fig. 16–12.

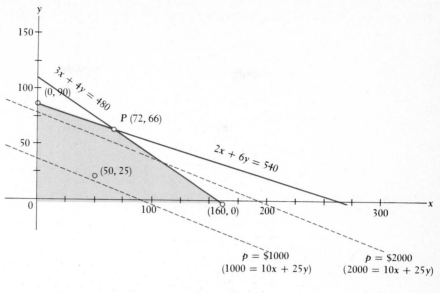

Figure 16–12

Any point in the shaded region which is defined by the preceding system of inequalities is known as a **feasible point**. In this case it means that it is possible to produce the number of systems of each type according to the coordinates of the point. For example, the point (50,25) is in the region, which means that it is possible to produce 50 good quality systems and 25 highest quality systems under the given constraints of available skilled labor. However, we wish to find the point which indicates the number of each kind of system which produces the greatest profit.

If we assume values for the profit, the resulting equations are straight lines. Thus, by finding the greatest value of p for which the line passes through a feasible point, we may solve the given problem. If $p = \$1000$, or if $p = \$2000$, we have the lines shown. Both are possible with various combinations of speaker systems being produced. However, we note the line for $p = \$2000$ passes through feasible points farther from the origin. It is also clear, since these lines are parallel, that the greatest profit attainable is given by the line passing through P, where $3x + 4y = 480$ and $2x + 6y = 540$ intersect. The coordinates of P are (72,66). Thus, the production should be 72 good quality systems and 66 highest quality systems to produce a weekly profit of $p = 10(72) + 25(66) = \$2370$.

For this type of problem, the solution will be given by one of the vertices of the region. However, it could be any one of them, which means it is possible that only one type of product should be produced. (See Exercise 27.) Thus, we can solve the problem by finding the appropriate region and then testing the coordinates of the vertex points. Here the vertex points are (160,0) which indicates a profit of $1600, (0,90) which indicates a profit of $2250, and (72,66) which indicates a profit of $2370.

In Exercises 1 through 20 draw a sketch of the graph of the given inequality.

1. $y > x - 1$ 2. $y < 3x - 2$

3. $y \geq 2x + 5$ 4. $y \leq 3 - x$

5. $2x + y < 5$ 6. $4x - y > 1$

7. $3x + 2y + 6 > 0$ 8. $x + 4y - 8 < 0$

9. $y < x^2$ 10. $y > -2x^2$

11. $y \geq 1 - x^2$ 12. $y \leq 2x^2 - 3$

13. $x^2 + 2x + y < 0$ 14. $2x^2 - 4x - y > 0$

15. $4x^2 - x - 2y > 0$ 16. $3x^2 + 6x + 2y < 0$

17. $y \leq x^3$ 18. $y \geq 3x - x^3$

19. $y > x^4 - 8$ 20. $y < 32x - x^4$

In Exercises 21 through 24 draw a sketch of the graph of the region in which the points satisfy the given system of inequalities.

21. $y > x$ 22. $y \leq 2x$ 23. $y \leq 2x^2$ 24. $y > x^2$

$y > 1 - x$ $y \geq x - 1$ $y > x - 2$ $y < x + 4$

In Exercises 25 through 28 solve the given linear programming problems.

25. A manufacturer makes two types of calculators, a business model and a scientific model. Each model is assembled in two sets of operations, where each operation is in production 8 h each day. The average time required for a business model in the first operation is 3 min, and 6 min is required in the second operation. The scientific model averages 6 min in the first operation and 4 min in the second operation. All calculators can be sold; the profit for a business model is $8, and the profit for a scientific model is $10. How many of each model should be made each day in order to maximize profit?

26. A company makes brands A and B of breakfast cereal, both of which are enriched with vitamins P and Q. The necessary information about these cereals is given in the following table.

	Cereal A	Cereal B	Min. daily requirement
Vitamin P (units/oz)	1	2	10
Vitamin Q (units/oz)	5	3	30
Cost per ounce	2¢	3¢	

Find the number of ounces of each cereal which together satisfies the minimum daily requirement of vitamins P and Q at the lowest cost. (Note: We wish to *minimize* cost; be careful in determining the feasible region.)

27. Using the information of Example F, with the single exception that the profit on each good quality system is $20, how many of each system should be made?

28. A company in competition with the company of Exercise 25 uses identical production methods. However, the profit it receives on its business calculators is only $4, although its profit on its scientific calculators is $10. How many of each type should this company make in order to maximize profit?

16—6 Exercises for Chapter 16

In Exercises 1 through 20 solve the given inequalities algebraically.

1. $2x - 12 > 0$

2. $5 - 3x < 0$

3. $3x + 5 \leq 0$

4. $\frac{1}{4}x - 2 \geq 3x$

5. $x^2 + 2x > 63$

6. $6x^2 - x > 35$

7. $x^3 + 4x^2 - x > 4$

8. $2x^3 + 4 \leq x^2 + 8x$

9. $\frac{x - 8}{2x + 1} \leq 0$

10. $\frac{3x + 2}{x - 3} > 0$

11. $\frac{(2x - 1)(3 - x)}{x + 4} > 0$

12. $\frac{(3 - x)^2}{2x + 7} \leq 0$

13. $x^4 + x^2 \leq 0$

14. $3x^3 + 7x^2 - 20x < 0$

15. $\frac{1}{x} < 2$

16. $\frac{1}{x - 2} < \frac{1}{4}$

17. $|x - 2| > 3$

18. $|2x - 1| > 5$

19. $|3x + 2| \leq 4$

20. $|4 - 3x| \leq 1$

In Exercises 21 through 28 solve the given inequalities graphically.

21. $6x - 3 < 0$

22. $5 - 8x > 0$

23. $3x - 2 > x$

24. $4 - 5x < 2$

25. $x^2 + 2x + 4 > 0$

26. $3x^2 + 5 > 16x$

27. $x^3 + x + 1 < 0$

28. $\frac{1}{x} > 2$

In Exercises 29 through 32 determine the values of x for which the given radicals represent real numbers.

29. $\sqrt{3 - x}$

30. $\sqrt{x + 5}$

31. $\sqrt{x^2 + 4x}$

32. $\sqrt{\frac{x - 1}{x + 2}}$

In Exercises 33 through 40 draw a sketch of the graph of the given inequality.

33. $y > 4 - x$

34. $y < \frac{1}{2}x + 2$

35. $2y - 3x - 4 \leq 0$

36. $3y - x + 6 \geq 0$

37. $y > x^2 + 1$

38. $y < 4x - x^2$

39. $y - x^3 + 1 < 0$

40. $2y + 2x^3 + 6x - 3 > 0$

In Exercises 41 through 44 prove the given inequalities.

41. If $x > 0$ and $y < 0$, prove that $\frac{1}{x} > \frac{1}{y}$.

42. If $x < -1$, prove that $\frac{1 - x}{x^2 + 1} > 0$.

43. If $y > 0$ and $x > y + 1$, prove that $\frac{x}{y} > \frac{y + 1}{x - 1}$.

44. If $x \neq y$, prove that $x^2 + y^2 > 2xy$.

In Exercises 45 through 52 solve the given problems using inequalities.

45. A piece of wire 100 ft long is to have a piece at least 20 ft cut from it. What lengths may the remaining piece be?

46. After conducting tests, it was determined that the stopping distance x (in feet) of a car traveling 60 mi/h was $|x - 290| \leq 35$. Express this inequality without absolute values, and determine the interval of stopping distances which were found in the tests.

47. One leg of a right triangle is 14 in. longer than the other leg. If the hypotenuse is to be greater than 34 in., what values of the other side are permissible?

48. The length of a rectangular lot is 20 m more than its width. If the area is to be at least 4800 m², what values may the width be?

49. Two resistors have a combined resistance of 8 Ω when connected in series. What are the permissible values if they are to have a combined resistance of at least $\frac{3}{2}$ Ω when connected in parallel? (See Exercise 41 of Section 6–1.)

50. City A is 300 mi from city B. One car starts from A for B one hour before a second car. The first car averages 45 mi/h and the second car averages 60 mi/h for the trip. For what times after the first car starts is the second car ahead of the first car?

51. For 1 g of ice to be melted, then heated to boiling water, and finally vaporized into steam, the relation between the temperature T (in degrees Celsius) and the number of joules absorbed Q is given by $T = 0$ if $Q < 335$, $T = Q - 335$ if $335 < Q < 750$, and $T = 100$ if $750 < Q < 3010$. Plot the graph of T (along the y-axis) versus Q (along the x-axis) if 3010 J of heat are absorbed by 1 g of ice originally at 0°C.

52. A company produces two types of cameras, the regular model and the deluxe model. For each regular model produced there is a profit of $8, and for each deluxe model the profit is $15. The same amount of materials is used to make each model, but the supply is sufficient only for 450 cameras per day. The deluxe model requires twice the time to produce as the regular model. If only regular models were made, there would be time enough to produce 600 per day. Assuming all models will be sold, how many of each model should be produced if the profit is to be a maximum?

17

Variation

17—1 Ratio and Proportion

In mathematics and its applications, we often come across the terms "ratio" and "proportion." In fact, in Chapter 3 when we first introduced the trigonometric functions of angles, we used ratios which had a specific meaning. In general, *a* **ratio** *of a number a to a number b* ($b \neq 0$) *is the quotient a/b.* Thus, a fraction is a ratio.

Any measurement made is the ratio of the measured magnitude to an accepted unit of measurement. For example, when we say that an object is five feet long, we are saying that the length of that object is five times as long as an accepted unit of length, the foot. Other examples of ratios are density (weight/volume), relative density (density of object/density of water), and pressure (force/area). As these examples illustrate, ratios may compare quantities of the same kind, or they may express a division of magnitudes of different quantities.

Example A

The approximate airline distance from New York to San Francisco is 2500 mi, and the approximate airline distance from New York to Minneapolis is 1000 mi. The ratio of these distances is

$$\frac{2500 \text{ mi}}{1000 \text{ mi}} = \frac{5}{2}$$

Since the units in both are miles, the resulting ratio is a dimensionless number.

If a jet travels from New York to San Francisco in 4 h, its average speed is

$$\frac{2500 \text{ mi}}{4 \text{ h}} = 625 \text{ mi/h}$$

In this case we must attach the proper units to the resulting ratio.

As we noted in Example A, we must be careful to attach the proper units to the resulting ratio. Generally, the ratio of measurements of the same kind should be expressed as a dimensionless number. Consider the following example.

Example B

The length of a certain room is 24 ft, and the width of the room is 18 ft. Therefore, the ratio of the length to the width is $\frac{24}{18}$ or $\frac{4}{3}$.

If the width of the room were expressed as 6 yd, we should not express the ratio as 24 ft/6 yd = 4 ft/1 yd. It is much better and more meaningful to first change the units of one of the measurements. Changing the length from 6 yd to 18 ft, we express the ratio as $\frac{4}{3}$, as we saw above. From this ratio we can easily see that the length is $\frac{4}{3}$ as long as the width.

A *statement of equality between two ratios is called a* **proportion**. One way of denoting a proportion is $a:b = c:d$, which is read "a is to b as c is to d." (Another notation used for a proportion is $a:b::c:d$.) Of course, by the definition, $a/b = c/d$, which means that a proportion is an equation. Any operation applicable to an equation is also applicable to a proportion.

Example C

On a certain map 1 in. represents 10 mi. Thus on this map we have a ratio of 1 in./10 mi. To find the distance represented by 3.5 in., we can set up the proportion

$$\frac{3.5 \text{ in.}}{x \text{ mi}} = \frac{1 \text{ in.}}{10 \text{ mi}}$$

From this proportion we find the value of $x = 35$ mi.

Example D

The magnitude of an electric field E is defined as the ratio between the force F on a charge q and the magnitude of q. This can be written as $E = F/q$. If we know the force exerted on a particular charge at some point in the field, we can determine the force which would be exerted on another charge placed at the same point. For example, if we know that a force of 10 nN is exerted on a charge of 4 nC, we can then determine the force which would be exerted on a charge of 6 nC by the proportion

$$\frac{10 \times 10^{-9}}{4 \times 10^{-9}} = \frac{F}{6 \times 10^{-9}}$$

or

$$F = 1.5 \times 10^{-8}\,\text{N} = 15\ \text{nN}$$

Example E

A certain alloy is 5 parts tin and 3 parts lead. How many grams of each are there in 40 g of the alloy?

First, we let $x =$ the number of grams of tin in the given amount of the alloy. Next we note that there are 8 total parts of alloy, of which 5 are tin. Thus, 5 is to 8 as x is to 40. This gives the equation

$$\frac{5}{8} = \frac{x}{40}$$

Multiplying each side by 40, we then find that $x = 25$ g. Therefore, there are 25 g of tin and 15 g of lead, and the ratio of 25 to 15 is the same as 5 to 3.

Exercises 17–1

In Exercises 1 through 8 express the ratios in the simplest form.

1. 18 V to 3 V
2. 27 ft to 18 ft
3. 48 in. to 3 ft
4. 120 s to 4 min
5. 20 qt to 25 gal
6. 4 lb to 8 oz
7. 14 kg to 350 g
8. 200 mm to 5 cm

In Exercises 9 through 16 find the required ratios.

9. A virus 3.0×10^{-5} cm long appears to be 1.2 cm long through a microscope. What is the *magnification* (ratio of image length to object length) of the microscope?

10. The efficiency of an engine is defined as the ratio of output to input. Find the efficiency, in percent, of an engine for which the input is 6000 W and output is 4500 W.

11. The ratio of the density of an object to the density of water is known as the *relative density* of the object. If the density of gold is 1200 lb/ft³ and the density of water is 62.4 lb/ft³, what is the relative density of gold?

12. The *atomic mass* of an atom of carbon is defined to be 12 u. The ratio of the atomic mass of an atom of oxygen to that of an atom of carbon is $\frac{4}{3}$. What is the atomic mass of an atom of oxygen? (The symbol u represents the *unified atomic mass unit*, where $1 \text{ u} = 1.66 \times 10^{-27}$ kg.)

13. A certain body of water exerts a force of 18,000 lb on an area of 20 in.². Find the pressure (force per unit area) on this area.

14. The electric current in a given circuit is the ratio of the voltage to the resistance. What is the current ($1 \text{ V}/1 \text{ } \Omega = 1$ A) for a circuit where the voltage is 24.0 V and the resistance is 10.0 Ω?

15. A student finds that 8 divisions can be done on a calculator in 20.0 s. What is the student's rate, in calculations per minute, in doing such division problems?

16. The *heat of vaporization* of a substance is the amount of heat required to change one unit amount of the substance from liquid to vapor. Experimentation shows that 7910 J are needed to change 3.50 g of water to steam. What is the heat of vaporization of water?

In Exercises 17 through 20 find the required quantities from the given proportions.

17. In an electric instrument called a "Wheatsone bridge" electric resistances are related by

$$\frac{R_1}{R_2} = \frac{R_3}{R_4}$$

Find R_2 if $R_1 = 6.00$ Ω, $R_3 = 62.5$ Ω, and $R_4 = 15.0$ Ω.

18. For two connected gears, the relation

$$\frac{d_1}{d_2} = \frac{N_1}{N_2}$$

holds, where d is the diameter of the gear and N is the number of teeth. Find N_1 if $d_1 = 2.60$ in., $d_2 = 11.7$ in., and $N_2 = 45$.

19. For two pulleys connected by a belt, the relation

$$\frac{d_1}{d_2} = \frac{n_1}{n_2}$$

holds, where d is the diameter of the pulley and n is the number of revolutions per unit time it makes. Find n_2 if $d_1 = 4.60$ in., $d_2 = 8.30$ in., and $n_1 = 18.0$ r/min.

20. In a transformer, an electric current in one coil of wire induces a current in a second coil. For a transformer

$$\frac{i_1}{i_2} = \frac{t_2}{t_1}$$

where i is the current and t is the number of windings in each coil, find i_2 for $i_1 = 0.0350$ A, $t_1 = 560$, and $t_2 = 1500$.

In Exercises 21 through 32 answer the given questions by setting up and solving the appropriate proportions.

21. If 1 lb = 454 g, what weight in grams is 20.0 lb?

22. If 9 ft² = 1 yd², what area in square yards is 45.0 ft²?

23. How many meters per second are equivalent to 45.0 km/h?

24. How many gallons per hour are equivalent to 500 quarts per minute?

25. The length of a picture is 48.0 in., and its width is 36.0 in. In a reproduction of the picture the length is 36.0 in. What is the width of the reproduction?

26. A car will travel 93.0 mi on 6.00 gal of gasoline. How far will it travel on 10.0 gal of gasoline?

27. In physics, power is defined as the time rate at which work is done. If a given motor does 6000 ft-lb of work in 20.0 s, what work will it do in 4.00 min?

28. It is known that 98.0 kg of sulfuric acid are required to neutralize 80.0 kg of sodium hydroxide. Given 37.0 kg of sulfuric acid, determine the amount of sodium hydroxide which will be neutralized.

29. A physician has 220 mg of medication, which is sufficient for just 2 dosages. The amount given to a patient should be proportional to the patient's weight. For persons of weights of 60 kg and 72 kg, what should be the dosages?

30. A person pays $4500 in state and federal income taxes. Find the amount paid for each if the state taxes were 30% of the taxes paid.

31. A board 10.0 ft long is cut into two pieces, the lengths of which are in the ratio 2:3. Find the lengths of the pieces.

32. A total of 322 bolts are in two containers. The ratio of the number in one container to the number in the other container is 5:9. How many are in each container?

17—2 Variation

Scientific laws are often stated in terms of ratios and proportions. For example, Charles' law can be stated as "for a perfect gas under constant pressure, the ratio of any two volumes this gas may occupy equals the ratio of the absolute temperatures." Symbolically this could be stated as $V_1/V_2 = T_1/T_2$. Thus, if the ratio of the volumes and one of the values of the temperature are known, we can easily find the other temperature.

By multiplying both sides of the proportion of Charles' law by V_2/T_1, we can change the form of the proportion to $V_1/T_1 = V_2/T_2$. This statement says that the ratio of the volume to the temperature (for constant pressure) is constant. Thus, if any pair of values of volume and temperature is known, this ratio of V_1/T_1 can be calculated. This ratio of V_1/T_1 can be called a constant k, which means that Charles' law can be written as $V/T = k$. We now have the statement that the ratio of the volume to temperature is always constant; or, as it is normally stated, "the volume is proportional to the temperature." Therefore, we write $V = kT$, the clearest and most informative statement of Charles' law.

Thus, for any two quantities always in the same proportion, we say that one *is proportional to* (or *varies directly as*) the second, and in general this is written as $y = kx$, where k is the **constant of proportionality**. This type of relationship is known as **direct variation**.

Example A
The circumference of a circle is proportional to (varies directly as) the radius. We write this symbolically as $C = kr$, where (in this case) $k = 2\pi$.

Example B
The fact that the electric resistance of a wire varies directly as (is proportional to) its length is stated as $R = kL$.

It is very common that, when two quantities are related, the product of the two quantities remains constant. In such a case $yx = k$, or $y = k/x$. This is stated as "*y varies inversely as x,*" or "*y is inversely proportional to x.*" This type of relationship is known as **inverse variation**.

Example C
Boyle's law states that "at a given temperature, the pressure of a gas varies inversely as the volume." This we write symbolically as $P = k/V$.

For many relationships, one quantity varies as a specified power of another. The terms "varies directly" and "varies inversely" are used in the following examples with the specified power of the relation.

Example D
The statement that the volume of a sphere varies directly as the cube of its radius is written as $V = kr^3$. In this case we know that $k = \frac{4}{3}\pi$.

Example E
The fact that the gravitational force of attraction between two bodies varies inversely as the square of the distance between them is written as $F = k/d^2$.

Finally, one quantity may vary as the product of two or more other quantities. Such variation is termed **joint variation**. Also, some quantities are related such that a combination of variations is involved.

Example F
The cost of sheet metal varies jointly as the area of the sheet and the cost per unit area of the metal. This we write as $C = kAc$.

Example G
Newton's law of gravitation states that "the force of gravitation between two objects varies jointly as the product of the masses of the objects, and inversely as the square of the distance between their centers." We write this symbolically as $F = km_1 m_2 / d^2$.

Once we know how to express the given statement in terms of the variables and the constant of proportionality, we may compute the value of k if one set of values of the variables is known. This value of k can then be used to compute values of one variable, when given the others.

Example H

If y varies inversely as x, and $x = 15$ when $y = 4$, find the value of y when $x = 12$.

First we write $y = k/x$ to denote that y varies inversely as x. Next we substitute $x = 15$ and $y = 4$ into the equation. This leads to

$$4 = \frac{k}{15}$$

or $k = 60$. Thus, for our present discussion the constant of proportionality is 60, and this may be substituted into $y = k/x$, giving

$$y = \frac{60}{x}$$

as the equation between y and x. Now, for any given value of x, we may find the value of y. For $x = 12$, we have

$$y = \frac{60}{12} = 5$$

Example I

The distance an object falls under the influence of gravity varies directly as the square of the time of fall. If an object falls 64.0 ft in 2.00 s, how far will it fall in 3.00 s?

We first write the relation $d = kt^2$. Then we use the given fact that $d = 64.0$ ft for $t = 2.00$ s. This gives $64.0 = 4.00k$. In this way we find that $k = 16.0$ ft/s². We now know a general relation between d and t, which is $d = 16.0t^2$. Now we put in the value 3.00 s for t, so that we can find d for this particular value for the time. This gives us $d = 16.0(9.00) = 144$ ft. We also note in this problem that k will normally have a certain set of units associated with it.

Example J

The kinetic energy of a moving object varies jointly as the mass of the object and the square of its velocity. If a 5.00-kg object, traveling at 10.0 m/s, has a kinetic energy of 250 J, find the kinetic energy of an 8.00-kg object traveling at 50.0 m/s.

We first write the relation KE $= kmv^2$. Then we use the known set of values to find k. We write $250 = k(5.00)(100)$ giving

$$k = 0.500 \, \frac{\text{J}}{\text{kg(m/s)}^2}$$

[actually 1 J $= 1$ kg (m/s)², which means that $k = 0.500$ with no physical units.] Next we find the desired value for KE by substituting the other given values, and the value of k, in the original relation:

$$\text{KE} = 0.500 \, mv^2 = 0.500(8.00)(2500) = 10,000 \text{ J}$$

Example K

The heat developed in a resistor varies jointly as the time and the square of the current in the resistor. If the heat developed in t_0 seconds with a current i_0 passing through the resistor is H_0, how much heat is developed if both the time and current are doubled?

First we set up the relation $H = kti^2$, where t is the time and i is the current. From the given information we can write $H_0 = kt_0 i_0^2$. Thus $k = H_0/t_0 i_0^2$, and the original equation becomes $H = H_0 ti^2/t_0 i_0^2$. We now let $t = 2t_0$ and $i = 2i_0$, so that we can find H when the time and current are doubled. With these values we obtain

$$H = \frac{H_0(2t_0)(2i_0)^2}{t_0 i_0^2} = \frac{8H_0 t_0 i_0^2}{t_0 i_0^2} = 8H_0$$

This tells us that the heat developed is eight times as much as for the original values of i and t.

Exercises 17–2

In Exercises 1 through 4 express the given statements as equations.

1. y varies directly as z.
2. s varies inversely as the square of t.
3. w varies jointly as x and the cube of y.
4. q varies as the square of r and inversely as the fourth power of t.

In Exercises 5 through 8 give the equation relating the variables after evaluating the constant of proportionality for the given set of values.

5. r varies inversely as y, and $r = 2$ when $y = 8$.
6. y varies directly as the square root of x, and $y = 2$ when $x = 64$.
7. p is proportional to q and inversely proportional to the cube of r, and $p = 6$ when $q = 3$ and $r = 2$.
8. v is proportional to t and the square of s, and $v = 80$ when $s = 2$ and $t = 5$.

In Exercises 9 through 16 find the required value by setting up the general equation and then evaluating.

9. Find y when $x = 10$ if y varies directly as x and $y = 20$ when $x = 8$.
10. Find y when $x = 5$ if y varies directly as the square of x and $y = 6$ when $x = 8$.
11. Find s when $t = 10$ if s is inversely proportional to t and $s = 100$ when $t = 5$.
12. Find p for $q = 0.8$ if p is inversely proportional to the square of q and $p = 18$ when $q = 0.2$.
13. Find y for $x = 6$ and $z = 5$ if y varies directly as x and inversely as z and $y = 60$ when $x = 4$ and $z = 10$.
14. Find r when $n = 16$ if r varies directly as the square root of n and $r = 4$ when $n = 25$.
15. Find f when $p = 2$ and $c = 4$ if f varies jointly as p and the cube of c and $f = 8$ when $p = 4$ and $c = 0.1$.

16. Find v when $r = 2$, $s = 3$, and $t = 4$ if v varies jointly as r and s and inversely as the square of t and $v = 8$ when $r = 2$, $s = 6$, and $t = 6$.

In Exercises 17 through 36 solve the given applied problems.

17. Hooke's law states that the force needed to stretch a spring is proportional to the amount the spring is stretched. If 10.0 lb stretches a certain spring 4.00 in., how much will the spring be stretched by a force of 6.00 lb?

18. In modern physics we learn that the energy of a photon (a "particle" of light) is directly proportional to its frequency f. Given that the constant of proportionality is 6.63×10^{-34} J·s (this is known as *Planck's constant*), what is the energy of a photon whose frequency is 3.00×10^{15} Hz?

19. A particular type of automobile engine produces p cm³ of carbon monoxide proportional to the time t that it idles. Find the equation relating p and t if $p = 60,000$ cm³ for $t = 2.00$ min.

20. In biology it is found that under certain circumstances the rate of increase v of bacteria is proportional to the number N of bacteria present. If $v = 800$ bacteria/h when $N = 4000$ bacteria, what is v when $N = 7500$ bacteria?

21. The heat loss through rockwool insulation is inversely proportional to the thickness of the rockwool. If the loss through 6.00 in. of rockwool is 3200 BTU/h, find the loss through 2.50 in. of rockwool.

22. In economics it is often found that the demand D for a product varies inversely as the price P. If the demand is 500 units per week at a cost of $8.00, what would the demand be if the price were $10.00 each?

23. The illuminance of a light source varies inversely as the square of the distance from the source. Given that the illuminance is 25.0 units at a distance of 200 cm, find the general relation between the illuminance and distance for this light source.

24. The rate of emission of radiant energy from the surface of a body is proportional to the fourth power of the thermodynamic temperature. Given that a 25.0 W (the rate of emission) lamp has an operating temperature of 2500 K, what is the operating temperature of a similar 40.0 W lamp?

25. The electric resistance of a wire varies directly as its length and inversely as its cross-sectional area. Find the relation between resistance, length, and area for a wire which has a resistance of 0.200 Ω for a length of 200 ft and cross-sectional area of 0.0500 in.².

26. The general gas law states that the pressure of an ideal gas varies directly as the thermodynamic temperature and inversely as the volume. By first finding the relation between P, T, and V, find V for $P = 400$ kPa and $T = 400$ K, given that $P = 600$ kPa for $V = 10.0$ cm³ and $T = 300$ K.

27. The frequency of vibration of a wire varies directly as the square root of the tension on the wire. Express the relation between f and T. If $f = 400$ Hz when $T = 1.00$ N, find f when $T = 3.40$ N.

28. The period of a pendulum is directly proportional to the square root of its length. Given that a pendulum 2.00 ft long has a period of $\pi/2$ s, what is the period of a pendulum 4.00 ft long?

29. The distance s that an object falls due to gravity varies jointly as the acceleration due to gravity g and the square of the time t of fall. On Earth $g = 32.0$ ft/s² and on the moon $g = 5.50$ ft/s². On Earth an object falls 144 ft in 3.00 s. How far does an object fall in 7.00 s on the moon?

30. The power of an electric current varies jointly as the resistance and the square of the current. Given that the power is 10.0 W when the current is 0.500 A and the resistance is 40.0 Ω, find the power if the current is 2.00 A and the resistance is 20.0 Ω.

31. Under certain conditions the velocity of an object is proportional to the logarithm of the square root of the time elapsed. Given that $v = 18.0$ cm/s after 4.00 s, what is the velocity after 6.00 s?

32. The level of intensity of a sound wave is proportional to the logarithm of the ratio of the sound intensity to an arbitrary reference intensity, normally defined as 10^{-12} W/m². Assuming that the intensity level is 100 dB for $I = 10^{-2}$ W/m², what is the constant of proportionality?

33. When the volume of a gas changes very rapidly, an approximate relation is that the pressure varies inversely as the $\frac{3}{2}$ power of the volume. Express P as a function of V. Given the $P = 300$ kPa when $V = 100$ cm³, find P when $V = 25.0$ cm³.

34. The x-component of the velocity of an object moving around a circle with constant angular velocity ω varies jointly as ω and $\sin \omega t$. Given that ω is constant at $\pi/6$ rad/s, and the x-component of the velocity is -4π ft/s when $t = 1.00$ s, find the x-component of the velocity when $t = 9.00$ s.

35. The acceleration in the x-direction of the object referred to in Exercise 34 varies jointly as $\cos \omega t$ and the square of ω. Under the same conditions as stated in Exercise 34, calculate the x-component of the acceleration.

36. Under certain conditions, the natural logarithm of the ratio of an electric current at time t to the current at time $t = 0$ is proportional to the time. Given that the current is $1/e$ of its initial value after 0.100 s, what is its value after 0.200 s?

17–3 Exercises for Chapter 17

In Exercises 1 through 4 find the indicated ratios.

1. 1 km to 1 mm   2. 1 mL to 1 L

3. The area of the world needed for food production is about 5×10^{13} m², and the area needed for housing and industry is about 7×10^{12} m². Find the ratio of the food production area to that for housing and industry.

4. The capacitance C of a capacitor is defined as the ratio of its charge to the voltage. What is the capacitance of a capacitor (in farads) for which the charge is 5.00×10^{-6} C and the voltage is 200 V? (1 F = 1 C/1 V.)

In Exercises 5 through 12 answer the given questions by setting up and solving the appropriate proportions.

5. On a certain map, 1.00 in. represents 16.0 mi. What distance on the map represents 52.0 mi?

6. Given that 1.00 m equals 39.4 in., what length in inches is 2.45 m?

7. Given that 1.00 L equals 61.0 in.³, how many liters is 105 in.³?

8. Given that 1.00 BTU equals 1060 J, how many BTU equal 8190 J?

9. An electronic data-processing card sorter can sort 45,000 cards in 20.0 min. How many cards can it sort in 5.00 h?

10. A given machine can produce 80 bolts in 5.00 min. How many bolts can it produce in an hour?

11. Assuming that 195 g of zinc sulfide are used to produce 128 g of sulfur dioxide, how many grams of sulfur dioxide are produced by the use of 750 g of zinc sulfide?

12. Given that 32.0 lb of oxygen are required to burn 20.0 lb of a certain fuel gas, how much air (which can be assumed to be 21% oxygen) is required to burn 100 lb of the fuel gas?

In Exercises 13 through 16 give the equation relating the variables after evaluating the constant of proportionality for the given set of values.

13. y varies directly as the square of x, and $y = 27$ when $x = 3$.
14. f varies inversely as l, and $f = 5$ when $l = 8$.
15. v is directly proportional to x and inversely proportional to the cube of y, and $v = 10$ when $x = 5$ and $y = 4$.
16. r varies jointly as u, v, and the square of w, and $r = 8$ when $u = 2$, $v = 4$, and $w = 3$.

In Exercises 17 through 36 solve the given applied problems.

17. On a certain blueprint a measurement of 25.0 ft is represented by 2.00 in. What is the actual distance between two points if they are 5.75 in. apart on the blueprint?

18. A certain gasoline company sells regular gas and lead-free gas in the ratio of 7 to 2. If, in a month, the company sells a total of 18,000,000 gal, how many of each type were sold?

19. For a lever balanced at the fulcrum, the relation

$$\frac{F_1}{F_2} = \frac{L_2}{L_1}$$

holds, where F_1 and F_2 are forces on opposite sides of the fulcrum at distances L_1 and L_2, respectively. If $F_1 = 4.50$ lb, $F_2 = 6.75$ lb, and $L_1 = 17.5$ in., find L_2.

20. A company finds that the volume V of sales of a certain item and the price P of the item are related by

$$\frac{P_1}{P_2} = \frac{V_2}{V_1}$$

Find V_2 if $P_1 = \$8.00$, $P_2 = \$6.00$, and $V_1 = 3000$ per week.

21. The power of a gas engine is proportional to the area of the piston. If an engine with a piston area of 8.00 in.² can develop 30.0 hp, what power is developed by an engine with a piston area of 6.00 in.²?

22. Ohm's law states that the voltage across a given resistor is proportional to the current i in the resistor. Given that 18.0 V are across a certain resistor in which a current of 8.00 A is flowing, express the general relationship between voltage and current for this resistor.

23. An apartment owner charges rent R proportional to the floor area A of the apartment. Find the equation used relating R and A if an apartment of 900 ft² rents for $250 per month.

24. A manufacturer determines that the number r of aluminum cans that can be made by recycling n used cans is proportional to n. How many cans can be made from 50,000 used cans if $r = 115$ cans for $n = 125$ cans?

25. The surface area of a sphere varies directly as the square of its radius. The surface area of a certain sphere is 36π square units when the radius is 3.00 units. What is the surface area when the radius is 4.00 units?

26. The difference in pressure in a fluid between that at the surface and that at a point below varies jointly as the density of the fluid and the depth of the point. The density of water is 1000 kg/m³, and the density of alcohol is 800 kg/m³. This difference in pressure at a point 0.200 m below the surface of water is 1.96 kPa. What is the difference in pressure at a point 0.300 m below the surface of alcohol?

27. The velocity of a pulse traveling in a string varies directly as the square root of the tension of the string. Given that the velocity in a certain string is 450 ft/s when the tension is 20.0 lb, determine the velocity if the tension were 30.0 lb.

28. The velocity of a jet of fluid flowing from an opening in the side of a container is proportional to the square root of the depth of the opening. If the velocity of the jet from an opening at a depth of 4.00 ft is 16.0 ft/s, what is the velocity of a jet from an opening at a depth of 25.0 ft?

29. The crushing load of a pillar varies as the fourth power of its radius and inversely as the square of its length. Express L in terms of r and l for a pillar 20.0 ft tall and 1.00 ft in diameter which is crushed by a load of 20.0 tons.

30. The acoustical intensity of a sound wave is proportional to the square of the pressure amplitude and inversely proportional to the velocity of the wave. Given that the intensity is 0.474 W/m² for a pressure amplitude of 20.0 Pa and a velocity of 346 m/s, what is the intensity if the pressure amplitude is 15.0 Pa and the velocity is 320 m/s?

31. In any given electric circuit containing an inductance and capacitance, the resonant frequency is inversely proportional to the square root of the capacitance. If the resonant frequency in a circuit is 25.0 Hz and the capacitance is 100 μF, what is the resonant frequency of this circuit if the capacitance is 25.0 μF?

32. The safe uniformly distributed load on a horizontal beam, supported at both ends, varies jointly as the width and the square of the depth and inversely as the distance between supports. Given that one beam has double the dimensions of another, how many times heavier is the safe load it can support than the first can support?

33. Kepler's third law of planetary motion states that the square of the period of any planet is proportional to the cube of the mean radius (about the sun) of that planet, with the constant of proportionality being the same for all planets. Using the fact that the period of the earth is one year and its mean radius is 93.0 million mi, calculate the mean radius for Venus, given that its period is 7.38 months.

34. The amount of heat per unit of time passing through a wall t units thick is proportional to the temperature difference ΔT and the area A, and is inversely proportional to t. The constant of proportionality is called the coefficient of conductivity. Calculate the coefficient of conductivity of a 0.210-m-thick concrete wall if 0.419 J/s pass through an area of 0.0105 m² when the temperature difference is 10.5°C.

35. The percentage error in determining an electric current due to a small error in reading a galvanometer is proportional to $\tan \theta + \cot \theta$, where θ is the angular deflection of the galvanometer. Given that the percentage error is 2.00% when $\theta = 4.0°$, determine the percentage error as a function of θ.

36. Newton's law of gravitation is stated in Example G of Section 17–2. Here k is the same for any two objects. A spacecraft is traveling the 240,000 mi from the earth to the moon, whose mass is $\frac{1}{81}$ that of the earth. How far from the earth is the gravitational force of the earth on the spacecraft equal to the gravitational force of the moon on the spacecraft?

18

Progressions and
the Binomial Theorem

18–1 Arithmetic Progressions

In this chapter we are going to consider briefly the properties of certain sequences of numbers. In itself a sequence is some set of numbers arranged in some specified manner. The kinds of sequences we shall consider are those which form what are known as arithmetic progressions, those which form geometric progressions, and those which are used in the expansion of a binomial to a power. Applications of progressions can be found in many areas, including interest calculations and certain areas in physics. Also, progressions and binomial expansions are of importance in developing mathematical topics which in themselves have wide technical application.

An **arithmetic progression** *(AP) is a sequence of numbers in which each number after the first can be obtained from the preceding one by adding to it a fixed number called the* **common difference.**

Example A
The sequence 2, 5, 8, 11, 14, . . . is an AP with a common difference of 3. The sequence 7, 2, −3, −8, . . . is an AP with a common difference of −5.

If we know the first term of an AP, we can find any other term in the progression by successively adding the common difference enough times for the desired term to be obtained. This, however, is a very inefficient method, and we can learn more about the progression if we establish a general way of finding any particular term.

In general, if a is the first term and d the common difference, the second term is $a + d$, the third term is $a + 2d$, and so forth. If we are looking for the nth term, we note that we need only add d to the first term $n − 1$ times. Thus, the nth term l of an AP is given by

$$l = a + (n − 1)d \tag{18–1}$$

Occasionally l is referred to as the last term of an AP, but this is somewhat misleading. In reality there is no actual limit to the possible number of terms in an AP, although we may be interested only in a particular number of them. For this reason it is clearer to call l the nth term, rather than the last term. Also, this is the reason for writing three dots after the last indicated term of an AP. These dots indicate that the progression may continue.

Example B
Find the tenth term of the progression 2, 5, 8, ...

By subtracting any given term from the following term, we find that the common difference is $d = 3$. From the terms given, we know that the first term is $a = 2$. From the statement of the problem, the desired term is the tenth, or $n = 10$. Thus, we may find the tenth term l by

$$l = 2 + (10 − 1)3 = 2 + 9 \cdot 3 = 29$$

Example C
Find the number of terms in the progression for which $a = 5$, $l = −119$, and $d = −4$.

Substitution into Eq. (18–1) gives

$$−119 = 5 + (n − 1)(−4)$$

which leads to

$$−124 = −4n + 4$$
$$4n = 128$$
$$n = 32$$

Example D

How many numbers between 10 and 1000 are divisible by 6?

We must first find the smallest and the largest numbers in this range which are divisible by 6. These numbers are 12 and 996. Obviously the common difference between all multiples of 6 is 6. Thus, $a = 12$, $l = 996$, and $d = 6$. Therefore,

$$996 = 12 + (n - 1)6$$
$$6n = 990$$
$$n = 165$$

Thus there are 165 numbers between 10 and 1000 which are divisible by 6.

Another important quantity concerning an AP is the sum s of the first n terms. We can indicate this sum by either of the two equations,

$$s = a + (a + d) + (a + 2d) + \cdots + (l - d) + l$$

or

$$s = l + (l - d) + (l - 2d) + \cdots + (a + d) + a$$

If we now add these equations, we have

$$2s = (a + l) + (a + l) + (a + l) + \cdots + (a + l) + (a + l)$$

There is one factor $(a + l)$ for each term, and there are n terms. Thus,

$$s = \frac{n}{2}(a + l) \tag{18–2}$$

Example E

Find the sum of the first 1000 positive integers.

Here $a = 1$, $l = 1000$, and $n = 1000$. Thus,

$$s = \frac{1000}{2}(1 + 1000) = 500(1001) = 500{,}500$$

Example F

Find the sum of the AP for which $n = 10$, $a = 4$, and $d = -5$.

We first find the nth term. We write

$$l = 4 + (10 - 1)(-5) = 4 - 45 = -41$$

Now we can solve for s:

$$s = \frac{10}{2}(4 - 41) = 5(-37) = -185$$

Example G

For an AP, given that $a = 2$, $d = \frac{3}{2}$, and $s = 72$, find n and l.

First we substitute the given values into Eqs. (18–1) and (18–2) in order to identify what is known and how we may proceed. Substituting $a = 2$ and $d = \frac{3}{2}$ in Eq. (18–1), we obtain

$$l = 2 + (n - 1)\left(\frac{3}{2}\right)$$

Substituting $s = 72$ and $a = 2$ in Eq. (18–2), we obtain

$$72 = \frac{n}{2}(2 + l)$$

We note that n and l appear in both equations, which means that we must solve them simultaneously. Substituting the expression for l from the first equation into the second equation we proceed with the solution.

$$72 = \frac{n}{2}\left[2 + 2 + (n - 1)\left(\frac{3}{2}\right)\right]$$

$$72 = 2n + \frac{3n(n - 1)}{4}$$

$$288 = 8n + 3n^2 - 3n$$

$$3n^2 + 5n - 288 = 0$$

$$n = \frac{-5 \pm \sqrt{25 - 4(3)(-288)}}{6} = \frac{-5 \pm \sqrt{3481}}{6} = \frac{-5 \pm 59}{6}$$

Since n must be a positive integer we find that $n = \frac{-5 + 59}{6} = 9$. Using this value in the expression for l, we find

$$l = 2 + (9 - 1)\left(\frac{3}{2}\right) = 14$$

Therefore, $n = 9$ and $l = 14$.

Example H

Each swing of a pendulum is measured to be 3.00 in. shorter than the preceding swing. If the first swing is 10.0 ft, determine the total distance traveled by the pendulum bob in the first five swings.

In this problem each of the terms of the progression represents the distance traveled in each respective swing. This means that $a = 10.0$. Also, since 3.00 in. = 0.25 ft, we see that $d = -0.25$. Using these values, we find the distance traversed in the fifth swing to be

$$l = 10.0 + 4(-0.25) = 9.00$$

The total distance traversed is

$$s = \frac{5}{2}(10.0 + 9.00) = 47.5 \text{ ft}$$

Exercises 18—1

In Exercises 1 through 4 write five terms of the AP with the given values.

1. $a = 4, d = 2$ 2. $a = 6, d = -\frac{1}{2}$
3. Third term $= 5$, fifth term $= -3$
4. Second term $= -2$, fifth term $= 7$

In Exercises 5 through 12 find the nth term of the AP with the given values.

5. $1, 4, 7, \ldots n = 8$ 6. $-6, -4, -2, \ldots n = 10$
7. $18, 13, 8, \ldots n = 17$ 8. $2, \frac{1}{2}, -1, \ldots n = 25$
9. $a = -7, d = 4, n = 12$ 10. $a = \frac{3}{2}, d = \frac{1}{6}, n = 50$
11. $a = b, d = 2b, n = 25$ 12. $a = -c, d = 3c, n = 30$

In Exercises 13 through 16 find the indicated sum of the terms of the AP.

13. $n = 20, a = 4, l = 40$ 14. $n = 8, a = -12, l = -26$
15. $n = 10, a = -2, d = -\frac{1}{2}$ 16. $n = 40, a = 3, d = \frac{1}{3}$

In Exercises 17 through 28 find any of the values of a, d, l, n, or s that are missing.

17. $a = 5, d = 8, l = 45$ 18. $a = -2, n = 60, l = 28$
19. $a = \frac{5}{3}, n = 20, s = \frac{40}{3}$ 20. $a = 0.1, l = -5.9, s = -8.7$
21. $d = 3, n = 30, s = 1875$ 22. $d = 9, l = 86, s = 455$
23. $a = 74, d = -5, l = -231$ 24. $a = -\frac{9}{7}, n = 19, l = -\frac{36}{7}$
25. $a = -5, d = \frac{1}{2}, s = \frac{23}{2}$ 26. $d = -2, n = 50, s = 0$

27. $a = -c, l = \dfrac{b}{2}, s = 2b - 4c$ 28. $a = 3b, n = 7, d = \dfrac{b}{3}$

In Exercises 29 through 40 find the indicated quantities.

29. Sixth term $= 56$, tenth term $= 72$ (find a, d, s for $n = 10$).
30. Seventeenth term $= -91$, second term $= -73$ (find a, d, s for $n = 40$).
31. Fourth term $= 2$, tenth term $= 0$ (find a, d, s for $n = 10$)
32. Third term $= 1$, sixth term $= -8$ (find a, d, s for $n = 12$)
33. Find the sum of the first 100 integers.
34. Find the sum of the first 100 odd integers.
35. Find the sum of the first 200 multiples of 5.
36. Find the number of multiples of 8 between 99 and 999.
37. A man accepts a position which pays $8200 per year, and receives a raise of $450 each year. During what year of his association with the firm will his salary be $16,300?
38. A body falls 16.0 ft during the first second, 48.0 ft during the second second, 80.0 ft during the third second, etc. How far will it fall in the twentieth second?
39. For the object in Exercise 38, what is the total distance fallen in the first 20 s?
40. A well-driller charges $3 for drilling the first foot of a well, and for every foot thereafter he charges 1¢ more than the preceding foot. How much does he charge for drilling a 500-ft well?

18–2 Geometric Progressions

A second type of sequence is the **geometric progression.** *A geometric progression* (GP) *is a sequence of numbers in which each number after the first can be obtained from the preceding one by multiplying it by a fixed number called the* **common ratio.** One important application of geometric progressions is in computing interest on savings accounts. Other applications can be found in biology and physics.

Example A
The sequence 2, 4, 8, 16, . . . forms a GP with a common ratio of 2. The sequence 9, 3, 1, $\frac{1}{3}$, . . . forms a GP with a common ratio of $\frac{1}{3}$.

If we know the first term, we can then find any other desired term by multiplying by the common ratio a sufficient number of times. When we do this for a general GP, we can determine the nth term in terms of the first term a, the common ratio r, and n. Thus, the second term is ra, the third term is r^2a, and so forth. In general, the expression for the nth term is

$$l = ar^{n-1}$$

(18–3)

Example B
Find the eighth term of the GP 8, 4, 2, ...
Here $a = 8$, $r = \frac{1}{2}$, and $n = 8$. The eighth term is given by

$$l = 8\left(\frac{1}{2}\right)^{8-1} = \frac{8}{2^7} = \frac{1}{16}$$

Example C
Find the tenth term of a GP when the second term is 3, the fourth term is 9, and $r > 0$.
We can find r, if we let $a = 3$, $l = 9$, and $n = 3$ (we are at this time considering the progression made up of 3, the next number, and 9). Thus,

$$9 = 3r^2 \qquad \text{or} \qquad r = \sqrt{3}$$

We now can find a, by using just two terms (a and 3) for a progression:

$$3 = a(\sqrt{3})^{2-1} \qquad \text{or} \qquad a = \sqrt{3}$$

We now can find the tenth term directly:

$$l = \sqrt{3}(\sqrt{3})^{10-1} = \sqrt{3}(\sqrt{3})^9 = \sqrt{3}(3^4\sqrt{3}) = 3^5 = 243$$

We could have shortened this procedure one step by letting the second term be the first term of a new progression of 9 terms. If the first term is of no importance in itself, this is perfectly acceptable.

Example D

Under certain circumstances, 20% of a substance changes chemically each 10.0 min. If there are originally 100 g of a substance, how much will remain after an hour?

Let P = the portion of the substance remaining after each minute. From the statement of the problem, $r = 0.8$ (80% remains after each 10-min period), $a = 100$, and n represents the number of minutes elapsed. This means $P = 100(0.8)^{n/10}$. It is necessary to divide n by 10 because the ratio is given for a 10-min period. In order to find P when $n = 60$, we write

$$P = 100(0.8)^6$$
$$= 100(0.262)$$
$$= 26.2 \text{ g}$$

This means that 26.2 g are left after an hour.

A general expression for the sum of the first n terms of a geometric progression may be found by directly forming the sum and multiplying this equation by r. By doing this, we have

$$s = a + ar + ar^2 + \cdots + ar^{n-1}$$
$$rs = ar + ar^2 + ar^3 + \cdots + ar^n$$

If we now subtract the first of these equations from the second, we have $rs - s = ar^n - a$. All other terms cancel by subtraction. Solving this equation for s and writing both the numerator and the denominator in the final solution in the form generally used, we obtain

$$s = \frac{a(1 - r^n)}{1 - r} \qquad (r \neq 1) \tag{18-4}$$

Example E

Find the sum of the first 7 terms of the GP 2, 1, $\frac{1}{2}$, ...

Here $a = 2$, $r = \frac{1}{2}$, and $n = 7$. Hence

$$s = \frac{2(1 - (\frac{1}{2})^7)}{1 - \frac{1}{2}} = \frac{2(1 - \frac{1}{128})}{\frac{1}{2}} = 4\left(\frac{127}{128}\right) = \frac{127}{32}$$

Example F

If $100 is invested each year at 5% interest compounded annually, what would be the total amount of the investment after 10 years (before the eleventh deposit is made)?

After one year the amount invested will have added to it the interest for the year. Thus, for the last $100 invested, its value will become $100(1 + 0.05) = $100(1.05) = 105. The next to last $100 will have interest added twice. After one year its value becomes $100(1.05)$, and after two years its value becomes $[\$100(1.05)](1.05) = \$100(1.05)^2$. In the same way, the value of the first $100 becomes $100(1.05)^{10}$, since it will have interest added 10 times. This means we are asked to sum the progression

$$100(1.05) + 100(1.05)^2 + 100(1.05)^3 + \cdots + 100(1.05)^{10}$$

or

$$100[1.05 + (1.05)^2 + (1.05)^3 + \cdots + (1.05)^{10}]$$

For the progression in the brackets we have $a = 1.05$, $r = 1.05$, and $n = 10$. Thus,

$$s = \frac{1.05[1 - (1.05)^{10}]}{1 - 1.05} = \frac{1.05}{-0.05}(1 - 1.628895) = 13.2068$$

(This value is obtained by use of a calculator. If 4-place logarithms are used we would obtain 13.21.) Therefore, the total value of these $100 investments is $100(13.2068) = \$1320.68$. We see that $320.68 of interest has been earned.

Exercises 18–2

In Exercises 1 through 4 write down the first five terms of the GP with the given values.

1. $a = 45$, $r = \frac{1}{3}$ **2.** $a = 9$, $r = -\frac{2}{3}$

3. $a = 2$, $r = 3$ **4.** $a = -3$, $r = 2$

In Exercises 5 through 12 find the nth term of the GP which has the given values.

5. $\frac{1}{2}, 1, 2, \ldots$ $(n = 6)$ **6.** $10, 1, 0.1, \ldots$ $(n = 8)$

7. $125, -25, 5, \ldots$ $(n = 7)$ **8.** $0.1, 0.3, 0.9, \ldots$ $(n = 5)$

9. $a = -27$, $r = -\frac{1}{3}$, $n = 6$ **10.** $a = 48$, $r = \frac{1}{2}$, $n = 9$

11. $a = 2$, $r = 10$, $n = 7$ **12.** $a = -2$, $r = 2$, $n = 6$

In Exercises 13 through 16 find the sum of the n terms of the GP with the given values.

13. $a = 8$, $r = 2$, $n = 5$ **14.** $a = 162$, $r = -\frac{1}{3}$, $n = 6$

15. $a = 192$, $l = 3$, $n = 4$ **16.** $a = 9$, $l = -243$, $n = 4$

In Exercises 17 through 20 find any of the values of a, r, l, n, or s that are missing.

17. $l = 27$, $n = 4$, $s = 40$ **18.** $a = 3$, $n = 5$, $l = 48$

19. $a = 75$, $r = \frac{1}{5}$, $l = \frac{3}{25}$ **20.** $r = -2$, $n = 6$, $s = 42$

In Exercises 21 through 36 find the indicated quantities.

21. Find the tenth term of a GP if the fourth term is 8 and the seventh term 16.

22. Find the sum of the first 8 terms of the geometric progression for which the fifth term is 5, the seventh term is 10, and $r > 0$.

23. What is the value of an investment of $100 after 20 yr, if it draws interest of 4% annually?

24. What is the value of an investment of $10,000 after 10 years if it earns 6% annual interest, compounded semiannually. (6% annual interest compounded semiannually means that 3% interest is added each six months.)

25. A person invests $100 each year for 5 years. How much is the investment worth if the interest is 6% compounded annually?

26. A person invests $1000 each year for 8 years. How much is the investment worth if the interest is 8% compounded quarterly? (See Exercise 24.)

27. If the population of a certain town increases 20% each year, how long will it take for the population to double?

28. If you decided to save money by putting away 1¢ on a given day, 2¢ one week later, 4¢ a week later, etc., how much would you have to put aside one year later?

29. A ball is dropped from a height of 8.00 ft, and on each rebound it rises $\frac{1}{2}$ of the height it last fell. What is the total distance the ball has traveled when it hits the ground for the fourth time?

30. How many direct ancestors (parents, grandparents, etc.) does a person have in the 10 generations which preceded him?

31. The American Wire Gauge standard of wire diameters is based on a geometric progression. The ratio of one diameter to the next is the 39th root of 92. If the diameter of No. 30 wire is 0.0100 in., what is the diameter of the wire which is 10 sizes larger (No. 20 wire)?

32. A certain object, after being heated, cools at such a rate that its temperature decreases 10% each minute. If the object is originally heated to 100°C, what is its temperature 10.0 min later?

33. The half-life of tungsten 176 is 80.0 min. This means that half of a given amount will disintegrate in 80.0 min. After 160 min three-fourths will have disintegrated. How much will disintegrate in 120 min?

34. The power on a satellite is supplied by a radioactive isotope. On a given satellite the power decreases by 0.2% each day. What percent of the initial power remains after one year?

35. Derive a formula for s in terms of a, r, and l.

36. Write down several terms of a general GP. Then verify the statement that, if the logarithm of each term is taken, the resulting sequence is an AP.

18–3   Geometric Progressions with Infinitely Many Terms

If we consider the sum of the first n terms of the GP with terms $1, \frac{1}{2}, \frac{1}{4}, \ldots$, we find that we get the values in the following table.

n	2	3	4	5	6	7	8	9	10
s	$\frac{3}{2}$	$\frac{7}{4}$	$\frac{15}{8}$	$\frac{31}{16}$	$\frac{63}{32}$	$\frac{127}{64}$	$\frac{255}{128}$	$\frac{511}{256}$	$\frac{1023}{512}$

We see that as n gets larger, the numerator of each fraction becomes more nearly twice the denominator. In fact, we would find that if we continued to compute s as n becomes larger, s can be found as close to the value 2 as desired, although it will never actually reach the value 2. For example, if $n = 100$, $s = 2 - 1.6 \times 10^{-30}$, which could be written as

$$1.99999999999999999999999999999984$$

to 32 significant figures. In the formula for the sum of n terms of a GP,

$$s = a\frac{1 - r^n}{1 - r}$$

the term r^n becomes exceedingly small, and if we consider n as being sufficiently large, we can see that this term is effectively zero. *If* this term were *exactly* zero, then the sum would be

$$s = 1\frac{1 - 0}{1 - \frac{1}{2}} = 2$$

The only problem is that we cannot find any number large enough for n to make $(\frac{1}{2})^n$ zero. There is, however, an accepted notation for this. This notation is

$$\lim_{n \to \infty} r^n = 0 \qquad (\text{if } |r| < 1)$$

and it is read as "the limit, as n *approaches* infinity, of r to the nth power is zero."

The symbol ∞ is read as **infinity**, but it must not be thought of as a number. It is simply a symbol which stands for a *process* of considering numbers which become large without bound. The number which is called the **limit** of the sums is simply the number which the sums get closer and closer to, as n is considered to approach infinity. This notation and terminology are of particular importance in the calculus.

If we consider values of r such that $|r| < 1$, and let the values of n become unbounded, we find that $\lim_{n \to \infty} r^n = 0$. The formula for the sum of a geometric progression with infinitely many terms then becomes

$$s = \frac{a}{1 - r} \tag{18–5}$$

(If $r \geq 1$, s is unbounded in value.)

Example A
Find the sum of the geometric progession for which $a = 4$, $r = \frac{1}{8}$, and for which n increases without bound.

$$s = \frac{4}{1 - \frac{1}{8}} = \frac{4}{1} \cdot \frac{8}{7} = \frac{32}{7}$$

Example B

Find the fraction which has as its decimal form 0.44444444 . . . .

This decimal form can be thought of as being

$$0.4 + 0.04 + 0.004 + 0.0004 + \cdots$$

which means that it can also be thought of as the sum of a GP with infinitely many terms, where $a = 0.4$ and $r = 0.1$. With these considerations, we have

$$s = \frac{0.4}{1 - 0.1} = \frac{0.4}{0.9} = \frac{4}{9}$$

Thus, the fraction $\frac{4}{9}$ and the decimal 0.4444 . . . represent the same number.

Example C

Find the fraction which has as its decimal form 0.121212 . . . .

This decimal form can be considered as being

$$0.12 + 0.0012 + 0.000012 + \cdots$$

which means that we have a GP with infinitely many terms, and that $a = 0.12$ and $r = 0.01$. Thus

$$s = \frac{0.12}{1 - 0.01} = \frac{0.12}{0.99} = \frac{4}{33}$$

Therefore, the decimal 0.121212 . . . and the fraction $\frac{4}{33}$ represent the same number.

The decimals in Examples B and C are called **repeating decimals,** because the numbers in the decimal form appear over and over again in a particular order. These two examples verify the theorem that any repeating decimal represents a rational number. However, all repeating decimals do not necessarily start repeating immediately. If numbers never do repeat, the decimal represents an irrational number. For example, there is no repeating decimal which represents π or $\sqrt{2}$.

Example D

Find the fraction which has as its decimal form the repeating decimal 0.50345345345 . . . .

We first separate the decimal into the beginning, nonrepeating part, and the infinite repeating decimal which follows. Thus we have 0.50 + 0.00345345345 . . . . This means that we are to add $\frac{50}{100}$ to the fraction which represents the sum of the terms of the GP 0.00345 + 0.00000345 + $\cdots$. For this GP, $a = 0.00345$ and $r = 0.001$. We find the sum of this GP to be

$$s = \frac{0.00345}{1 - 0.001} = \frac{0.00345}{0.999} = \frac{115}{33300} = \frac{23}{6660}$$

Therefore,

$$0.50345345\ldots = \frac{5}{10} + \frac{23}{6660} = \frac{5(666) + 23}{6660} = \frac{3353}{6660}$$

Example E

Each swing of a certain pendulum bob is 95% as long as the preceding swing. How far does the bob travel in coming to rest if the first swing is 40.0 in. long?

We are to find the sum of a geometric progression with infinitely many terms, for which $a = 40.0$ and $r = 95\% = \frac{19}{20}$. Substituting these values into Eq. (18–5), we obtain

$$s = \frac{40.0}{1 - \frac{19}{20}} = \frac{40.0}{\frac{1}{20}} = (40.0)(20) = 800 \text{ in.}$$

Therefore, the pendulum bob travels 800 in. (about 67 ft) in coming to rest.

Exercises 18–3

In Exercises 1 through 12 find the sum of the given geometric progressions.

1. $4, 2, 1, \frac{1}{2}, \ldots$

2. $6, -2, \frac{2}{3}, \ldots$

3. $5, 1, 0.2, 0.04, \ldots$

4. $2, \sqrt{2}, 1, \ldots$

5. $20, -1, 0.05, \ldots$

6. $9, 8.1, 7.29, \ldots$

7. $1, \frac{7}{8}, \frac{49}{64}, \ldots$

8. $6, -4, \frac{8}{3}, \ldots$

9. $1, 0.0001, 0.00000001, \ldots$

10. $30, -9, 2.7, \ldots$

11. $2 + \sqrt{3}, 1, 2 - \sqrt{3}, \ldots$

12. $1 + \sqrt{2}, -1, \sqrt{2} - 1, \ldots$

In Exercises 13 through 24 find the fractions equal to the given decimals.

13. $0.33333\ldots$

14. $0.55555\ldots$

15. $0.404040\ldots$

16. $0.070707\ldots$

17. $0.181818\ldots$

18. $0.272727\ldots$

19. $0.273273273\ldots$

20. $0.792792792\ldots$

21. $0.366666\ldots$

22. $0.66424242\ldots$

23. $0.100841841841\ldots$

24. $0.184561845618456\ldots$

In Exercises 25 and 26 solve the given problems by use of the sum of a geometric progression with infinitely many terms.

25. If the ball in Exercise 29 of Section 18–2 is allowed to bounce indefinitely, what is the total distance it will travel?

26. An object suspended on a spring is oscillating up and down. If the first oscillation is 10.0 cm and each oscillation thereafter is nine-tenths of the preceding one, find the total distance the object travels.

18—4 The Binomial Theorem

If we wished to find the roots of the equation $(x + 2)^5 = 0$, we note that there are five factors of $x + 2$, which in turn tells us the only root is $x = -2$. However, if we wished to expand the expression $(x + 2)^5$, a number of repeated multiplications would be needed. This would be a relatively tedious operation. In this section we shall develop the **binomial theorem,** by which it is possible to expand binomials to any given power without direct multiplication. Such direct expansion can be helpful and labor-saving in developing certain mathematical topics. We may also expand certain expressions where direct multiplication is not actually possible. Also, the binomial theorem is used to develop the necessary expressions for use in certain technical applications.

By direct multiplication, we may obtain the following expansions of the binomial $a + b$.

$$(a + b)^0 = 1$$
$$(a + b)^1 = a + b$$
$$(a + b)^2 = a^2 + 2ab + b^2$$
$$(a + b)^3 = a^3 + 3a^2b + 3ab^2 + b^3$$
$$(a + b)^4 = a^4 + 4a^3b + 6a^2b^2 + 4ab^3 + b^4$$
$$(a + b)^5 = a^5 + 5a^4b + 10a^3b^2 + 10a^2b^3 + 5ab^4 + b^5$$

An inspection indicates certain properties which these expansions have, and which we shall assume are valid for the expansion of $(a + b)^n$, where n is any positive integer. These properties are as follows:

(1) There are $n + 1$ terms.
(2) The first term is a^n and the final term is b^n.
(3) Progressing from the first term to the last, the exponent of a decreases by 1 from term to term, the exponent of b increases by 1 from term to term, and the sum of the exponents of a and b in each term is n.
(4) The coefficients of terms equidistant from the ends are equal.
(5) If the coefficient of any term is multiplied by the exponent of a in that term, and this product is divided by the number of that term, we obtain the coefficient of the next term.

Example A
Using the above properties we shall develop the expansion for $(a + b)^5$.

From property (1) we know that there are 6 terms. From property (2) we know that the first term is a^5 and the final term is b^5. From property (3) we know that the factors of a and b in terms 2, 3, 4, and 5 are a^4b, a^3b^2, a^2b^3, and ab^4, respectively.

From property (5) we obtain the coefficients of terms 2, 3, 4, and 5. In the first term, a^5, the coefficient is 1. Multiplying by 5, the power of a, and dividing by 1, the number of the term, we obtain 5, which is the coefficient of the second term. Thus, the second term is $5a^4b$. Again using property (5) we obtain the coefficient of the third term. The coefficient of the second term is 5. Multiplying by 4, and dividing by 2, we obtain 10. This means that the third term is $10a^3b^2$.

From property (4) we know that the coefficient of the fifth term is the same as the second, and the coefficient of the fourth term is the same as the third. Thus,

$$(a + b)^5 = a^5 + 5a^4b + 10a^3b^2 + 10a^2b^3 + 5ab^4 + b^5$$

It is not necessary to use the above properties directly to expand a given binomial. If they are applied to $(a + b)^n$ we may obtain a general formula for the expansion of a binomial. Thus, the binomial theorem states that the following **binomial formula** is valid for all values of n (the binomial theorem is proven through advanced methods).

$$(a + b)^n = a^n + na^{n-1}b + \frac{n(n-1)}{2!}a^{n-2}b^2 + \frac{n(n-1)(n-2)}{3!}a^{n-3}b^3 + \cdots + b^n \tag{18-6}$$

The notation $n!$ is read as "n **factorial**". It denotes the product of the first n integers. Thus, $2! = 1 \cdot 2$, $3! = 1 \cdot 2 \cdot 3$, $4! = 1 \cdot 2 \cdot 3 \cdot 4$, and so on. Evaluating these products we see that $2! = 2$, $3! = 6$, $4! = 24$, and so on.

Example B

By use of the binomial formula expand $(2x + 3)^6$.

In using the binomial formula for $(2x + 3)^6$ we use $2x$ for a, 3 for b, and 6 for n. Thus,

$$(2x + 3)^6 = (2x)^6 + 6(2x)^5(3) + \frac{(6)(5)}{2}(2x)^4(3^2)$$

$$+ \frac{(6)(5)(4)}{(2)(3)}(2x)^3(3^3) + \frac{(6)(5)(4)(3)}{(2)(3)(4)}(2x)^2(3^4)$$

$$+ \frac{(6)(5)(4)(3)(2)}{(2)(3)(4)(5)}(2x)(3^5) + 3^6$$

$$= 64x^6 + 576x^5 + 2160x^4 + 4320x^3 + 4860x^2 + 2916x + 729$$

For the first few integral powers of a binomial, the coefficients can be obtained by setting them up in the following pattern, known as **Pascal's triangle.**

$n = 0$							1						
$n = 1$						1		1					
$n = 2$					1		2		1				
$n = 3$				1		3		3		1			
$n = 4$			1		4		6		4		1		
$n = 5$		1		5		10		10		5		1	
$n = 6$	1		6		15		20		15		6		1

We note that the first and last coefficient shown in each row is 1, and the second and next-to-last coefficients are equal to n. Other coefficients are obtained by adding the two nearest coefficients in the row above. This pattern may be continued indefinitely, although the use of Pascal's triangle is cumbersome for high values of n.

Example C
By use of Pascal's triangle expand $(5s - 2t)^4$.
Here we note that $n = 4$. Thus, the coefficients of the five terms are 1, 4, 6, 4, and 1, respectively. Also, here we use $5s$ for a and $-2t$ for b. We are expanding this as $[(5s) + (-2t)]^4$. Therefore,

$$(5s - 2t)^4 = (5s)^4 + 4(5s)^3(-2t) + 6(5s)^2(-2t)^2 + 4(5s)(-2t)^3 + (-2t)^4$$
$$= 625s^4 - 1000s^3t + 600s^2t^2 - 160st^3 + 16t^4$$

In certain uses of a binomial expansion it is not necessary to obtain all terms. Only the first few terms are required. The following example illustrates finding the first four terms of an expansion.

Example D
Find the first four terms of the expansion of $(x + 7)^{12}$.
Here we use x for a, 7 for b, and 12 for n. Thus, from the binomial formula we have

$$(x + 7)^{12} = x^{12} + 12x^{11}(7) + \frac{(12)(11)}{2}x^{10}(7^2) + \frac{(12)(11)(10)}{(2)(3)}x^9(7^3) + \cdots$$

$$= x^{12} + 84x^{11} + 3234x^{10} + 75460x^9 + \cdots$$

If we let $a = 1$ and $b = x$ in the binomial formula, we obtain the **binomial series**

$$(1 + x)^n = 1 + nx + \frac{n(n-1)}{2!}x^2 + \frac{n(n-1)(n-2)}{3!}x^3 + \cdots \qquad (18\text{--}7)$$

which through advanced methods can be shown to be valid for any real number n if $|x| < 1$. When n is either negative or a fraction, we obtain an infinite series. In such a case, we calculate as many terms as may be needed although such a series is not obtainable through direct multiplication. The binomial series may be used to find numerical approximations and to develop important expressions which are used in applications.

Example E

Approximate the value of $\sqrt[3]{1006}$ to five decimal places.

This approximation can be made by use of the first three terms of the binomial expansion if we write $\sqrt[3]{1006} = \sqrt[3]{1000(1.006)} = 10\sqrt[3]{1.006} = 10\sqrt[3]{1 + 0.006}$. By expanding $(1 + 0.006)^{1/3}$, we have

$$(1 + 0.006)^{1/3} = 1 + \frac{1}{3}(0.006) + \frac{(\frac{1}{3})(-\frac{2}{3})}{2}(0.006)^2 + \cdots$$

$$= 1 + 0.002 - 0.000004$$

$$= 1.001996$$

Therefore, $\sqrt[3]{1006} = 10(1.001996) = 10.01996$. The use of additional terms of the expansion will not affect the first five decimal places. The use of this type of approximation is helpful if a calculator is not available, or if accuracy beyond that available on the calculator is required.

Exercises 18—4

In Exercises 1 through 8 expand and simplify the given expressions by use of the binomial formula.

1. $(t + 1)^3$ 2. $(3x - 2)^3$ 3. $(2x - 1)^4$ 4. $(x^2 + 3)^4$

5. $(x + 2)^5$ 6. $(xy - z)^5$ 7. $(2a - b^2)^6$ 8. $(\frac{a}{x} + x)^6$

In Exercises 9 through 12 expand and simplify the given expressions by use of Pascal's triangle.

9. $(5x - 3)^4$ 10. $(b + 4)^5$ 11. $(2a + 1)^6$ 12. $(x - 3)^7$

In Exercises 13 through 16 find the first four terms of the indicated expansions.

13. $(x + 2)^{10}$ 14. $(x - 3)^8$ 15. $(1 - x)^{-2}$ 16. $(1 + x)^{-1/3}$

In Exercises 17 through 24 approximate the values of the given expressions to three decimal places by use of three terms of the appropriate binomial series.

17. $\sqrt{1.1}$ 18. $\sqrt{0.9}$ 19. $\sqrt[3]{994}$ (see Example E)

20. $\sqrt[3]{9}$ ($\sqrt[3]{9} = \sqrt[3]{8 + 1} = \sqrt[3]{8(1 + \frac{1}{8})} = 2\sqrt[3]{1 + \frac{1}{8}}$)

21. $\sqrt[4]{82}$ 22. $\sqrt[4]{15}$ 23. $(1.02)^{-4}$ 24. $(0.97)^{-2}$

In Exercises 25 through 28 find the indicated terms by use of the following information. The $r + 1$ term of the expansion of $(a + b)^n$ is given by

$$\frac{n(n - 1)(n - 2) \cdots (n - r + 1)}{r!} a^{n-r}b^r$$

25. The term involving b^5 in $(a + b)^8$.

26. The term involving y^6 in $(x + y)^{10}$.

27. The fifth term of $(2x - 3b)^{12}$.

28. The sixth term of $(a - b)^{14}$.

In Exercises 29 through 32 find the indicated expansions.

29. In determining the change of the rate of emission of energy from the surface of a body at temperature T, the expression $(T + h)^4$ is used. Expand this expression.

30. In determining the probability of a given number of heads or tails when 8 coins are tossed, the expression $(H + T)^8$ can be used. The various coefficients give the number of chances in 256 that a certain number of heads and tails will result. For example, the coefficient of the H^2T^6 term gives the chances in 256 that 2 heads and 6 tails will result. Expand this expression.

31. In the theory associated with the magnetic field due to an electric current, the expression $1 - \dfrac{x}{\sqrt{a^2 + x^2}}$ is found. By expanding $(a^2 + x^2)^{-1/2}$ find the first three nonzero terms which could be used to approximate the given expression.

32. Find the first four terms of the expansion of $(1 + x)^{-1}$ and then divide $1 + x$ into 1. Compare the results.

18—5 Exercises for Chapter 18

In Exercises 1 through 8 find the indicated term of each progression.

1. $1, 6, 11, \ldots$ (17th)
2. $1, -3, -7, \ldots$ (21st)
3. $\frac{1}{2}, 0.1, 0.02, \ldots$ (9th)
4. $0.025, 0.01, 0.004, \ldots$ (7th)
5. $8, \frac{7}{2}, -1, \ldots$ (16th)
6. $-1, -\frac{5}{3}, -\frac{7}{3}, \ldots$ (25th)
7. $\frac{3}{4}, \frac{1}{2}, \frac{1}{3}, \ldots$ (7th)
8. $\frac{2}{3}, 1, \frac{3}{2}, \ldots$ (7th)

In Exercises 9 through 12 find the sum of each progression with the indicated values.

9. $a = -4, n = 15, l = 17$ (AP)
10. $a = 3, d = -\frac{2}{3}, n = 10$
11. $a = 16, r = -\frac{1}{2}, n = 10$
12. $a = 64, l = 729, n = 7$ (GP, $r > 0$)

In Exercises 13 through 20 find the indicated quantities for the appropriate progressions.

13. $a = 17, d = -2, n = 9, s = ?$
14. $d = \frac{4}{3}, a = -3, l = 17, n = ?$
15. $a = 18, r = \frac{1}{2}, n = 6, l = ?$
16. $l = \frac{49}{8}, r = -\frac{2}{7}, s = \frac{17199}{288}, a = ?$
17. $a = -1, l = 32, n = 12, s = ?$ (AP)
18. $a = 1, l = 64, s = 325, n = ?$ (AP)
19. $a = 1, n = 7, l = 64, s = ?$
20. $a = \frac{1}{4}, n = 6, l = 8, s = ?$

In Exercises 21 through 28 find the fractions equal to the given decimals.

21. $0.77777\ldots$
22. $0.030303\ldots$
23. $0.757575\ldots$
24. $0.484848\ldots$
25. $0.123123123\ldots$
26. $0.0727272\ldots$
27. $0.166666\ldots$
28. $0.25399399399\ldots$

In Exercises 29 through 36 expand and simplify the given expressions. In Exercises 33 through 36 find the first four terms of the appropriate expansion.

29. $(x - 2)^4$ **30.** $(s + 2t)^4$ **31.** $(x^2 + 1)^5$ **32.** $(3n - a)^6$

33. $\sqrt{1 - a^2}$ **34.** $\sqrt{1 + b^4}$ **35.** $(1 - 2x)^{-3}$ **36.** $(1 + 4x)^{-1/4}$

In Exercises 37 through 40 approximate the values of the given expressions to three decimal places by use of three terms of the appropriate binomial series.

37. $\sqrt{908}$ **38.** $\sqrt[3]{61}$ **39.** $(8.04)^{-1}$ **40.** $(4.06)^{-1/2}$

In Exercises 41 through 52 solve the given problems by use of an appropriate progression or expansion.

41. Find the sum of the first 1000 positive even integers.

42. How many numbers divisible by 4 lie between 23 and 121?

43. Fifteen layers of logs are so piled that there are 20 logs in the bottom layer, and each layer contains one log less than the layer below it. How many logs are in the pile?

44. A contractor employed in the construction of a building was penalized for taking more time than the contract allowed. She forfeited $150 for the first day late, $225 for the second day, $300 for the third day, and so forth. If she forfeited a total of $6750, how many additional days did she require to complete the building?

45. What is the value after 20 years of an investment of $2500, if it draws interest at 5% compounded annually?

46. A person invests $1000 each year for 20 years. How much is the total invest-ment worth if the annual interest is 6% and it is compounded quarterly?

47. A business estimates that the salvage value of a piece of machinery de-creases by 20% each year. If the machinery is purchased for $80,000, what is its value after 10 years?

48. A tank contains 100 L of a given chemical. Thirty liters are drawn off and replaced with water. Then 30 L of the resulting solution are drawn off and replaced with water. If this operation is performed a total of 5 times, how much of the original chemical remains?

49. A ball, starting from rest, rolls down a uniform incline so that it covers 10 in. during the first second, 30 in. during the second second, 50 in. during the third second, and so on. How long will it take to cover $333\frac{1}{3}$ ft?

50. The successive distances traveled by a pendulum bob are 90 cm, 60 cm, 40 cm, ... Find the total distance the bob travels before it comes to rest.

51. In finding the partial pressure P_F of fluorine gas under certain conditions, the equation

$$P_F = \frac{(1 + 2 \times 10^{-10}) - \sqrt{1 + 4 \times 10^{-10}}}{2}\,\text{atm}$$

is found. By using three terms of the expansion for $\sqrt{1 + x}$ approximate the value of this expression.

52. The terms a, $a + 12$, $a + 24$ form an AP, and the terms a, $a + 24$, $a + 12$ form a GP. Find these progressions.

19

Additional Topics in Trigonometry

19–1 Fundamental Trigonometric Identities

The definitions of the trigonometric functions were first introduced in Section 3–2, and were again summarized in Section 7–1. If we take a close look at these definitions, we find that there are many relationships among the various functions. For example, the definition of the sine of an angle is $\sin \theta = y/r$, and the definition of the cosecant of an angle is $\csc \theta = r/y$. But we know that $1/(r/y) = y/r$, which means that $\sin \theta = 1/\csc \theta$. In writing this down we made no reference to any particular angle, and since the definitions hold for *any* angle, this relation between the $\sin \theta$ and $\csc \theta$ also holds for any angle. A *relation* such as this, *which holds for any value of the variable, is called an* **identity**. Of course, specific values where division by zero would be indicated are excluded.

Such trigonometric identities are important for a number of reasons. We have already actually made limited use of some of them in Section 9–4 when we graphed certain trigonometric functions. We also used an important identity in deriving the Law of Cosines in Chapter 8. When we consider equations with trigonometric functions later in this chapter, we will find that the solution of such equations depends on the proper use of identities. In the study of calculus, there are certain types of problems which require the use of trigonometric identities for solution (even problems in which trigonometric functions do not appear). Also, they are used in developing expressions and solving equations in certain technical areas.

Several important identities exist among the six trigonometric functions, and we shall develop these identities in this section. We shall also show how we can use the basic identities to verify other identities among the functions.

By the definitions, we have

$$\sin \theta \csc \theta = \frac{y}{r} \cdot \frac{r}{y} = 1 \quad \text{or} \quad \sin \theta = \frac{1}{\csc \theta} \quad \text{or} \quad \csc \theta = \frac{1}{\sin \theta}$$

$$\cos \theta \sec \theta = \frac{x}{r} \cdot \frac{r}{x} = 1 \quad \text{or} \quad \cos \theta = \frac{1}{\sec \theta} \quad \text{or} \quad \sec \theta = \frac{1}{\cos \theta}$$

$$\tan \theta \cot \theta = \frac{y}{x} \cdot \frac{x}{y} = 1 \quad \text{or} \quad \tan \theta = \frac{1}{\cot \theta} \quad \text{or} \quad \cot \theta = \frac{1}{\tan \theta}$$

$$\frac{\sin \theta}{\cos \theta} = \frac{y/r}{x/r} = \frac{y}{x} = \tan \theta; \qquad \frac{\cos \theta}{\sin \theta} = \frac{x/r}{y/r} = \frac{x}{y} = \cot \theta$$

Also, by the definitions and the Pythagorean theorem in the form of $x^2 + y^2 = r^2$, we arrive at the following identities:

By dividing the Pythagorean relation through by r^2, we have

$$\left(\frac{x}{r}\right)^2 + \left(\frac{y}{r}\right)^2 = 1 \quad \text{which leads us to } \cos^2\theta + \sin^2\theta = 1$$

By dividing the Pythagorean relation by x^2, we have

$$1 + \left(\frac{y}{x}\right)^2 = \left(\frac{r}{x}\right)^2 \quad \text{which leads us to } 1 + \tan^2\theta = \sec^2\theta$$

By dividing the Pythagorean relation by y^2, we have

$$\left(\frac{x}{y}\right)^2 + 1 = \left(\frac{r}{y}\right)^2 \quad \text{which leads us to } \cot^2\theta + 1 = \csc^2\theta$$

The term $\cos^2 \theta$ is the common way of writing $(\cos \theta)^2$, and thus it means to square the value of the cosine of the angle. Obviously the same holds true for the other functions.

Summarizing these results, we have the following important identities among the trigonometric functions:

(19–1)	$\sin \theta = \dfrac{1}{\csc \theta}$	$\cos \theta = \dfrac{1}{\sec \theta}$ (19–2)
(19–3)	$\tan \theta = \dfrac{1}{\cot \theta}$	$\tan \theta = \dfrac{\sin \theta}{\cos \theta}$ (19–4)
(19–5)	$\cot \theta = \dfrac{\cos \theta}{\sin \theta}$	$\sin^2\theta + \cos^2\theta = 1$ (19–6)
(19–7)	$1 + \tan^2\theta = \sec^2\theta$	$1 + \cot^2\theta = \csc^2\theta$ (19–8)

In using these identities, θ may stand for any angle or number or expression representing an angle or number.

Example A

$$\sin (x + 1) = \frac{1}{\csc (x + 1)}$$

$$\tan 157° = \frac{\sin 157°}{\cos 157°}, \quad 1 + \tan^2\!\left(\frac{\pi}{6}\right) = \sec^2\!\left(\frac{\pi}{6}\right)$$

Example B
We shall verify three of the identities for particular values of θ.
   From Table 3, we find that $\cos 53° = 0.6018$ and $\sec 53° = 1.662$. Using Eq. (19–2), and dividing, we find that

$$\cos 53° = \frac{1}{\sec 53°} = \frac{1}{1.662} = 0.6018$$

and this value checks.
   Using Table 3, we find that $\sin 157° = 0.3907$ and $\cos 157° = -0.9205$. Using Eq. (19–4), and dividing, we find that

$$\tan 157° = \frac{\sin 157°}{\cos 157°} = \frac{0.3907}{-0.9205} = -0.4245$$

Checking with Table 3, we see that this value checks.
   From Section 3–3, we recall that

$$\sin 45° = \frac{1}{\sqrt{2}} = \frac{\sqrt{2}}{2} \quad \text{and} \quad \cos 45° = \frac{\sqrt{2}}{2}$$

Using Eq. (19–6), we have

$$\sin^2 45° + \cos^2 45° = \left(\frac{\sqrt{2}}{2}\right)^2 + \left(\frac{\sqrt{2}}{2}\right)^2 = \frac{1}{2} + \frac{1}{2} = 1$$

We see that this identity checks for these values.

A great many identities exist among the trigonometric functions. We are going to use the basic identities already developed in Eqs. (19–1) through (19–8), along with a few additional ones developed in later sections, to prove the validity of still other identities. **The ability to prove such identities depends to a large extent on being *very* familiar with the basic identities,** so that you can recognize them in somewhat different forms. If you do not learn these basic identities and learn them well, you will have difficulty in following the examples and doing the exercises. The more readily you recognize these forms, the more easily you will be able to prove such identities.

In proving identities, we should look for combinations which appear in, or are very similar to, those in the basic identities. Consider the following examples.

Example C

In proving the identity

$$\sin x = \frac{\cos x}{\cot x}$$

we know that $\cot x = \dfrac{\cos x}{\sin x}$. Since $\sin x$ appears on the left, substituting for $\cot x$ on the right will eliminate $\cot x$ and introduce $\sin x$. This should help us proceed in proving the identity. Thus,

$$\sin x = \frac{\cos x}{\cot x}$$

$$= \frac{\cos x}{\dfrac{\cos x}{\sin x}} = \frac{\cos x}{1} \cdot \frac{\sin x}{\cos x}$$

$$= \sin x$$

By showing that the right side may be changed exactly to $\sin x$, the expression on the left side, we have proved the identity.

Some important points should be made in relation to the proof of the identity of Example C. We must recognize what basic identities may be useful. The proof of an identity requires the use of basic algebraic operations, and these must be done carefully and correctly. Although in Example C we changed the right side to the form on the left, we could have changed the left to the form on the right. From this, and the fact that various substitutions are possible, we see that there is a variety of procedures which can be used to prove any given identity.

Example D

Prove that $\tan\theta\csc\theta = \sec\theta$.

   In proving this identity we know that $\tan\theta = \dfrac{\sin\theta}{\cos\theta}$ and also that $\dfrac{1}{\cos\theta} = \sec\theta$. Thus, by substituting for $\tan\theta$ we introduce $\cos\theta$ in the denominator, which is equivalent to introducing $\sec\theta$ in the numerator. Therefore, changing only the left side, we have

$$\tan\theta\,\csc\theta = \sec\theta$$

$$\frac{\sin\theta}{\cos\theta}\csc\theta = \sec\theta$$

$$\frac{1}{\cos\theta}\sin\theta\,\csc\theta = \sec\theta$$

$$\sec\theta\,\sin\theta\,\frac{1}{\sin\theta} = \sec\theta$$

$$\sec\theta = \sec\theta$$

Many variations of the preceding steps are possible. Also, we could have changed only the right side to obtain the form on the left. For example,

$$\tan\theta\,\csc\theta = \sec\theta$$

$$= \frac{1}{\cos\theta} = \frac{\sin\theta}{\cos\theta\,\sin\theta} = \frac{\sin\theta}{\cos\theta}\frac{1}{\sin\theta}$$

$$= \tan\theta\,\csc\theta$$

   In proving the identities of Examples C and D we have shown that the expression on one side of the equals sign can be changed into the expression on the other side. Although making the restriction that we change only one side is not entirely necessary, *we shall restrict the method of proof to changing only one side into the same form as the other side.* In this way, we know precisely what form we are to change to, and therefore by looking ahead we are better able to make the proper changes.

   There is no set procedure which can be stated for working with identities. The most important factors are to be able to *recognize the proper forms*, to be able to *see what effect any change may have* before we actually perform it, and then *perform it correctly.* Normally *it is easier to change the more complicated side of an identity to the same form as the less complicated side.* If the two sides are of approximately the same complexity, a close look at each side usually suggests steps which will lead to the solution.

Example E

Prove the identity $\dfrac{\cos x \, \csc x}{\cot^2 x} = \tan x$.

First, we note that the lefthand side has several factors and the right-hand side has only one. Therefore, let us transform the lefthand side. Next, we note that we want tan x as the final result. We know that cot $x = 1/\tan x$. Thus

$$\frac{\cos x \, \csc x}{\cot^2 x} = \frac{\cos x \, \csc x}{1/\tan^2 x} = \cos x \, \csc x \, \tan^2 x$$

At this point, we have two factors of tan x on the left. Since we want only one, let us factor out one. Therefore,

$$\cos x \, \csc x \, \tan^2 x = \tan x (\cos x \, \csc x \, \tan x)$$

Now, replacing tan x within the parentheses by sin x/cos x, we have

$$\tan x (\cos x \, \csc x \, \tan x) = \frac{\tan x (\cos x \, \csc x \, \sin x)}{\cos x}$$

Now we may cancel cos x. Also, csc x sin $x = 1$ from Eq. (19–1). Finally,

$$\frac{\tan x (\cos x \, \csc x \, \sin x)}{\cos x} = \tan x \left(\frac{\cos x}{\cos x}\right)(\csc x \, \sin x)$$

$$= \tan x (1)(1) = \tan x$$

Since we have transformed the lefthand side into tan x, we have proven the identity. Of course, it is not necessary to rewrite expressions as we did in this example. This was done here only to include the explanations between steps.

Example F

Prove the identity $\sin^4 x - \cos^4 x = \sin^2 x - \cos^2 x$.

We note that either side of this identity may be factored, but that one of the factors of the left side is the expression which appears on the right. Therefore, by factoring, and the use of Eq. (19–6), we have (changing only the form of the left side)

$$\sin^4 x - \cos^4 x = \sin^2 x - \cos^2 x$$
$$(\sin^2 x - \cos^2 x)(\sin^2 x + \cos^2 x) = \sin^2 x - \cos^2 x$$
$$(\sin^2 x - \cos^2 x)(1) = \sin^2 x - \cos^2 x$$
$$\sin^2 x - \cos^2 x = \sin^2 x - \cos^2 x$$

Example G

Prove the identity $\dfrac{\sec^2 y}{\cot y} - \tan^3 y = \tan y.$

Here we shall simplify the left side. We note that we can remove cot y from the denominator since tan $y = 1/\cot y$. Also, the presence of $\sec^2 y$ suggests the use of Eq. (19–7). Therefore, we have

$$\frac{\sec^2 y}{\cot y} - \tan^3 y = \frac{\sec^2 y}{1/\tan y} - \tan^3 y = \sec^2 y \tan y - \tan^3 y$$

$$= \tan y (\sec^2 y - \tan^2 y) = \tan y (1) = \tan y$$

or

$$\frac{\sec^2 y}{\cot y} - \tan^3 y = \tan y$$

Here we have used Eq. (19–7) in the form $\sec^2 y - \tan^2 y = 1$.

Example H

Prove the identity $\dfrac{1 - \sin x}{\sin x \cot x} = \dfrac{\cos x}{1 + \sin x}.$

The combination $1 - \sin x$ also suggests $1 - \sin^2 x$, since multiplying $(1 - \sin x)$ by $(1 + \sin x)$ gives $1 - \sin^2 x$, which can then be replaced by $\cos^2 x$. Thus, changing only the left side we have

$$\frac{(1 - \sin x)}{\sin x \cot x} = \frac{\cos x}{1 + \sin x}$$

$$\frac{(1 - \sin x)(1 + \sin x)}{\sin x \cot x (1 + \sin x)} = \frac{\cos x}{1 + \sin x}$$

$$\frac{1 - \sin^2 x}{\sin x \left(\dfrac{\cos x}{\sin x}\right)(1 + \sin x)} = \frac{\cos x}{1 + \sin x}$$

$$\frac{\cos^2 x}{\cos x (1 + \sin x)} = \frac{\cos x}{1 + \sin x}$$

$$\frac{\cos x}{1 + \sin x} = \frac{\cos x}{1 + \sin x}$$

Example I

Prove the identity $\sec^2 x + \csc^2 x = \sec^2 x \csc^2 x.$

Here we note the presence of $\sec^2 x$ and $\csc^2 x$ on each side. This suggests the possible use of the square relationships. By replacing the $\sec^2 x$ on the righthand side by $1 + \tan^2 x$, we can create $\csc^2 x$ plus another term. The lefthand side is the $\csc^2x$ plus another term, so this procedure should help. Thus, changing only the right side,

$$\sec^2x + \csc^2x = \sec^2x\,\csc^2x$$
$$= (1 + \tan^2x)(\csc^2x)$$
$$= \csc^2x + \tan^2x\,\csc^2x$$

Now we note that $\tan x = \sin x/\cos x$ and $\csc x = 1/\sin x$. Thus,

$$\sec^2x + \csc^2x = \csc^2x + \left(\frac{\sin^2x}{\cos^2x}\right)\left(\frac{1}{\sin^2x}\right)$$

$$= \csc^2x + \frac{1}{\cos^2x}$$

$$= \csc^2x + \sec^2x$$

We could have used many other variations of this procedure, and they would have been perfectly valid.

Example J

Prove the identity $\dfrac{\csc x}{\tan x + \cot x} = \cos x$.

Here we shall simplify the lefthand side until we have the expression which appears on the righthand side.

$$\frac{\csc x}{\tan x + \cot x} = \frac{\csc x}{\tan x + \dfrac{1}{\tan x}} = \frac{\csc x}{\dfrac{\tan^2x + 1}{\tan x}}$$

$$= \frac{\csc x\,\tan x}{\tan^2x + 1} = \frac{\csc x\,\tan x}{\sec^2x}$$

$$= \frac{\dfrac{1}{\sin x}\cdot\dfrac{\sin x}{\cos x}}{\dfrac{1}{\cos^2x}} = \frac{1}{\sin x}\cdot\frac{\sin x}{\cos x}\cdot\frac{\cos^2x}{1}$$

$$= \cos x$$

Therefore, we have shown that $\dfrac{\csc x}{\tan x + \cot x} = \cos x$ which proves the identity.

Exercises 19–1

In Exercises 1 through 4 verify the indicated basic identities for the given angles.

1. Verify Eq. (19–3) for $\theta = 56°$

2. Verify Eq. (19–5) for $\theta = 80°$

3. Verify Eq. (19–6) for $\theta = \dfrac{2\pi}{3}$

4. Verify Eq. (19–8) for $\theta = \dfrac{7\pi}{6}$

In Exercises 5 through 48 prove the given identities.

5. $\dfrac{\cot \theta}{\cos \theta} = \csc \theta$ 6. $\dfrac{\tan y}{\sin y} = \sec y$ 7. $\dfrac{\sin x}{\tan x} = \cos x$ 8. $\dfrac{\csc \theta}{\sec \theta} = \cot \theta$

9. $\sin y \cot y = \cos y$ 10. $\cos x \tan x = \sin x$ 11. $\sin x \sec x = \tan x$

12. $\cot \theta \sec \theta = \csc \theta$ 13. $\csc^2 x (1 - \cos^2 x) = 1$ 14. $\cos^2 x (1 + \tan^2 x) = 1$

15. $\sin x (1 + \cot^2 x) = \csc x$ 16. $\sec \theta (1 - \sin^2 \theta) = \cos \theta$

17. $\sin x (\csc x - \sin x) = \cos^2 x$ 18. $\cos y (\sec y - \cos y) = \sin^2 y$

19. $\tan y (\cot y + \tan y) = \sec^2 y$ 20. $\csc x (\csc x - \sin x) = \cot^2 x$

21. $\sin x \tan x + \cos x = \sec x$ 22. $\sec x \csc x - \cot x = \tan x$

23. $\cos \theta \cot \theta + \sin \theta = \csc \theta$ 24. $\csc x \sec x - \tan x = \cot x$

25. $\sec \theta \tan \theta \csc \theta = \tan^2 \theta + 1$ 26. $\sin x \cos x \tan x = 1 - \cos^2 x$

27. $\cot \theta \sec^2 \theta - \cot \theta = \tan \theta$ 28. $\sin y + \sin y \cot^2 y = \csc y$

29. $\tan x + \cot x = \sec x \csc x$ 30. $\tan x + \cot x = \tan x \csc^2 x$

31. $\cos^2 x - \sin^2 x = 1 - 2\sin^2 x$ 32. $\tan^2 y \sec^2 y - \tan^4 y = \tan^2 y$

33. $\dfrac{\sin x}{1 - \cos x} = \csc x + \cot x$ 34. $\dfrac{1 + \cos x}{\sin x} = \dfrac{\sin x}{1 - \cos x}$

35. $\dfrac{\sec x + \csc x}{1 + \tan x} = \csc x$ 36. $\dfrac{\cot x + 1}{\cot x} = 1 + \tan x$

37. $\tan^2 x \cos^2 x + \cot^2 x \sin^2 x = 1$ 38. $\cos^3 x \csc^3 x \tan^3 x = \csc^2 x - \cot^2 x$

39. $4\sin x + \tan x = \dfrac{4 + \sec x}{\csc x}$ 40. $\dfrac{1 + \tan x}{\sin x} - \sec x = \csc x$

41. $\sec x + \tan x + \cot x = \dfrac{1 + \sin x}{\cos x \sin x}$

42. $\sec x (\sec x - \cos x) + \dfrac{\cos x - \sin x}{\cos x} + \tan x = \sec^2 x$

43. $2\sin^4 x - 3\sin^2 x + 1 = \cos^2 x (1 - 2\sin^2 x)$ 44. $\dfrac{\sin^4 x - \cos^4 x}{1 - \cot^4 x} = \sin^4 x$

45. $\dfrac{\cot 2y}{\sec 2y - \tan 2y} - \dfrac{\cos 2y}{\sec 2y + \tan 2y} = \sin 2y + \csc 2y$

46. $\dfrac{1}{2} \sin 5y \left(\dfrac{\sin 5y}{1 - \cos 5y} + \dfrac{1 - \cos 5y}{\sin 5y} \right) = 1$

47. $1 + \sin^2 x + \sin^4 x + \cdots = \sec^2 x$ 48. $1 - \tan^2 x + \tan^4 x - \cdots = \cos^2 x$

In Exercises 49 through 52 prove the identities which arise in the given area of application.

49. For an object of weight w on an inclined plane the coefficient of friction μ, related to the frictional force between the plane and object, can be found from the equation $\mu w \cos \theta = w \sin \theta$, where θ is the angle between the plane and horizontal. Solve for μ and show that $\mu = \tan \theta$.

50. In finding the change in $\tan^2 x$ for a given change in x, the expression $2\tan x \sec^2 x$ is used. Show that this expression is equal to $2\sin x \sec^3 x$.

51. In determining the rate of radiation by an accelerated electric charge, it is necessary to show that $\sin^3 \theta = \sin \theta - \cos^2 \theta \sin \theta$. Show that this is valid, by transforming the lefthand side.

52. In determining the path of least time between two points under certain circumstances, it is necessary to show that

$$\sqrt{\frac{1 + \cos \theta}{1 - \cos \theta}} \sin \theta = (1 + \cos \theta)$$

Show this by transforming the lefthand side.

19–2 Sine and Cosine of the Sum and Difference of Two Angles

There are other important relations among the trigonometric functions. The most important and useful relations are those which involve twice an angle and half an angle. To obtain these relations, we shall first derive the expressions for the sine and cosine of the sum and difference of two angles. These expressions will lead directly to the desired relations of double and half angles.

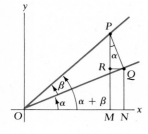

Figure 19–1

In Fig. 19–1, the angle α is in standard position, and the angle β has as its initial side the terminal side of α. Thus the angle of interest, $\alpha + \beta$, is in standard position. From a point P, on the terminal side of $\alpha + \beta$, perpendiculars are dropped to the x-axis and to the terminal side of α, at the points M and Q respectively. Then perpendiculars are dropped from Q to the x-axis and to the line MP at points N and R respectively. By this construction, $\angle RPQ$ is equal to $\angle \alpha$. ($\angle RQO = \angle \alpha$ by alternate interior angles; $\angle RQO + \angle RQP = 90°$ by construction; $\angle RQP + \angle RPQ = 90°$ by the sum of the angles of a triangle being $180°$. Thus, $\angle \alpha = \angle RPQ$.) By definition,

$$\sin(\alpha + \beta) = \frac{MP}{OP} = \frac{MR + RP}{OP} = \frac{NQ}{OP} + \frac{RP}{OP}$$

These last two fractions do not define any function of either α or β, and therefore we multiply the first fraction (numerator and denominator) by OQ and the second fraction by QP. When we do this and rearrange the fractions, we have functions of α and β:

$$\sin(\alpha + \beta) = \frac{NQ}{OP} + \frac{RP}{OP} = \frac{NQ}{OQ} \cdot \frac{OQ}{OP} + \frac{RP}{QP} \cdot \frac{QP}{OP}$$

$$= \sin \alpha \cos \beta + \cos \alpha \sin \beta$$

Using the same figure, we can also obtain the expression for $\cos(\alpha + \beta)$. Thus we have the relations

$$\sin(\alpha + \beta) = \sin \alpha \cos \beta + \cos \alpha \sin \beta \tag{19–9}$$

and

$$\cos(\alpha + \beta) = \cos \alpha \cos \beta - \sin \alpha \sin \beta \tag{19–10}$$

Example A
Find sin 75° from sin 75° = sin(45° + 30°).

$$\sin 75° = \sin(45° + 30°) = \sin 45° \cos 30° + \cos 45° \sin 30°$$

$$= \frac{\sqrt{2}}{2} \cdot \frac{\sqrt{3}}{2} + \frac{\sqrt{2}}{2} \cdot \frac{1}{2} = \frac{\sqrt{6}}{4} + \frac{\sqrt{2}}{4} = \frac{\sqrt{6} + \sqrt{2}}{4}$$

$$= 0.9659$$

Example B
Verify that sin 90° = 1, by finding sin(60° + 30°).

$$\sin 90° = \sin(60° + 30°) = \sin 60° \cos 30° + \cos 60° \sin 30°$$

$$= \frac{\sqrt{3}}{2} \cdot \frac{\sqrt{3}}{2} + \frac{1}{2} \cdot \frac{1}{2} = \frac{3}{4} + \frac{1}{4} = 1$$

[It should be obvious from this example that $\sin(\alpha + \beta)$ is *not* equal to $\sin \alpha + \sin \beta$, something which many students assume before they are familiar with the formulas and ideas of this section. If we used such a formula, we would get $\sin 90° = \frac{1}{2}\sqrt{3} + \frac{1}{2} = 1.366$ for the combination (60° + 30°). This is not possible, since the values of the sine never exceed 1 in value. Also, if we used the combination (45° + 45°), we would get 1.414, a different value for the same number, sin 90°.]

From Eq. (19–9) and (19–10), we can easily find expressions for $\sin(\alpha - \beta)$ and $\cos(\alpha - \beta)$. This is done by finding $\sin(\alpha + (-\beta))$ and $\cos(\alpha + (-\beta))$. Thus, we have

$$\sin(\alpha - \beta) = \sin(\alpha + (-\beta)) = \sin \alpha \cos(-\beta) + \cos \alpha \sin(-\beta)$$

Since $\cos(-\beta) = \cos \beta$ and $\sin(-\beta) = -\sin \beta$ (see Exercise 61 of Section 7–2), we have

$$\sin(\alpha - \beta) = \sin \alpha \cos \beta - \cos \alpha \sin \beta \qquad (19–11)$$

In the same manner we find that

$$\cos(\alpha - \beta) = \cos \alpha \cos \beta + \sin \alpha \sin \beta \qquad (19–12)$$

Example C
Find cos 15° from cos(45° − 30°).

$$\cos 15° = \cos(45° - 30°) = \cos 45° \cos 30° + \sin 45° \sin 30°$$

$$= \frac{\sqrt{2}}{2} \cdot \frac{\sqrt{3}}{2} + \frac{\sqrt{2}}{2} \cdot \frac{1}{2} = \frac{\sqrt{6} + \sqrt{2}}{4} = 0.9659$$

We get the same result as in Example A, which should be the case since sin 75° = cos 15°. (See Section 3–4.)

By using Eqs. (19–9) and (19–10), we can determine expressions for $\tan(\alpha + \beta)$, $\cot(\alpha + \beta)$, $\sec(\alpha + \beta)$, and $\csc(\alpha + \beta)$. These expressions are less applicable than those for the sine and cosine, and therefore we shall not derive them here, although the expression for $\tan(\alpha + \beta)$ is found in the exercises at the end of this section. By using Eqs. (19–11) and (19–12), we can find similar expressions for the functions of $(\alpha - \beta)$.

Certain trigonometric identities can also be worked out by using the formulas derived in this section. The following examples illustrate the use of these formulas in identities.

Example D

Prove that $\sin(180° + x) = -\sin x$.

By using Eq. (19–9) we have

$$\sin(180° + x) = \sin 180° \cos x + \cos 180° \sin x$$

Since $\sin 180° = 0$ and $\cos 180° = -1$, we have

$$\sin 180° \cos x + \cos 180° \sin x = (0) \cos x + (-1) \sin x$$

or

$$\sin(180° + x) = -\sin x$$

Example E

Show that $\dfrac{\sin(\alpha - \beta)}{\sin \alpha \sin \beta} = \cot \beta - \cot \alpha$.

By using Eq. (19–11), we have

$$\frac{\sin(\alpha - \beta)}{\sin \alpha \sin \beta} = \frac{\sin \alpha \cos \beta - \cos \alpha \sin \beta}{\sin \alpha \sin \beta} = \frac{\sin \alpha \cos \beta}{\sin \alpha \sin \beta} - \frac{\cos \alpha \sin \beta}{\sin \alpha \sin \beta}$$

$$= \frac{\cos \beta}{\sin \beta} - \frac{\cos \alpha}{\sin \alpha} = \cot \beta - \cot \alpha$$

Example F

Show that

$$\sin\left(\frac{\pi}{4} + x\right)\cos\left(\frac{\pi}{4} + x\right) = \frac{1}{2}(\cos^2 x - \sin^2 x)$$

$$\sin\left(\frac{\pi}{4} + x\right)\cos\left(\frac{\pi}{4} + x\right)$$

$$= \left(\sin\frac{\pi}{4}\cos x + \cos\frac{\pi}{4}\sin x\right)\left(\cos\frac{\pi}{4}\cos x - \sin\frac{\pi}{4}\sin x\right)$$

$$= \sin\frac{\pi}{4}\cos\frac{\pi}{4}\cos^2 x - \sin^2\frac{\pi}{4}\sin x \cos x + \cos^2\frac{\pi}{4}\sin x \cos x - \sin^2 x \sin\frac{\pi}{4}\cos\frac{\pi}{4}$$

$$= \frac{\sqrt{2}}{2}\frac{\sqrt{2}}{2}\cos^2 x - \left(\frac{\sqrt{2}}{2}\right)^2 \sin x \cos x + \left(\frac{\sqrt{2}}{2}\right)^2 \sin x \cos x - \frac{\sqrt{2}}{2}\frac{\sqrt{2}}{2}\sin^2 x$$

$$= \frac{1}{2}\cos^2 x - \frac{1}{2}\sin^2 x = \frac{1}{2}(\cos^2 x - \sin^2 x)$$

Example G

Show that $\sin(x + y) \cos y - \cos(x + y) \sin y = \sin x$.

If we let $x + y = z$, we note that the lefthand side of the above expression becomes $\sin z \cos y - \cos z \sin y$, which is the proper form for $\sin(z - y)$. By replacing z with $x + y$, we obtain $\sin(x + y - y)$, which is $\sin x$. Therefore, the above expression has been shown to be true. We again see that proper recognition of a basic form leads to the solution.

Exercises 19—2

In Exercises 1 through 4 determine the values of the given functions as indicated.

1. Find $\sin 105°$ by using $105° = 60° + 45°$.
2. Find $\cos 75°$ by using $75° = 30° + 45°$.
3. Find $\cos 15°$ by using $15° = 60° - 45°$.
4. Find $\sin 15°$ by using $15° = 45° - 30°$.

In Exercises 5 through 8 evaluate the indicated functions with the following given information: $\sin \alpha = \frac{4}{5}$ (in first quadrant), and $\cos \beta = -\frac{12}{13}$ (in second quadrant).

5. $\sin(\alpha + \beta)$ 6. $\cos(\beta - \alpha)$ 7. $\cos(\alpha + \beta)$ 8. $\sin(\alpha - \beta)$

In Exercises 9 through 12 reduce each of the given expressions to a single term. Expansion of any term is not necessary; proper recognition of the form of the expression leads to the proper result.

9. $\sin x \cos 2x + \sin 2x \cos x$
10. $\sin 3x \cos x - \sin x \cos 3x$
11. $\cos(x + y)\cos y + \sin(x + y)\sin y$
12. $\cos(2x - y)\cos y - \sin(2x - y)\sin y$

In Exercises 13 through 24 prove the given identities.

13. $\sin(270° - x) = -\cos x$ 14. $\sin(90° + x) = \cos x$

15. $\cos\left(\dfrac{\pi}{2} - x\right) = \sin x$ 16. $\cos\left(\dfrac{3\pi}{2} + x\right) = \sin x$

17. $\cos(30° + x) = \dfrac{\sqrt{3}\cos x - \sin x}{2}$ 18. $\sin(120° - x) = \dfrac{\sqrt{3}\cos x + \sin x}{2}$

19. $\sin\left(\dfrac{\pi}{4} + x\right) = \dfrac{\sin x + \cos x}{\sqrt{2}}$ 20. $\cos\left(\dfrac{\pi}{3} + x\right) = \dfrac{\cos x - \sqrt{3}\sin x}{2}$

21. $\sin(x + y)\sin(x - y) = \sin^2 x - \sin^2 y$
22. $\cos(x + y)\cos(x - y) = \cos^2 x - \sin^2 y$
23. $\cos(\alpha + \beta) + \cos(\alpha - \beta) = 2 \cos \alpha \cos \beta$
24. $\cos(x - y) + \sin(x + y) = (\cos x + \sin x)(\cos y + \sin y)$

In Exercises 25 through 28 additional trigonometric identities are shown. Derive these in the indicated manner. Equations (19–13), (19–14), and (19–15) are known as the product formulas.

25. By dividing Eq. (19–9) by Eq. (19–10), show that

$$\tan(\alpha + \beta) = \frac{\tan \alpha + \tan \beta}{1 - \tan \alpha \tan \beta}$$

[*Hint:* Divide numerator and denominator by $\cos \alpha \cos \beta$.]

26. By adding Eqs. (19–9) and (19–11), derive the equation

$$\sin \alpha \cos \beta = \tfrac{1}{2}[\sin (\alpha + \beta) + \sin (\alpha - \beta)] \qquad (19\text{–}13)$$

27. By adding Eqs. (19–10) and (19–12), derive the equation

$$\cos \alpha \cos \beta = \tfrac{1}{2}[\cos (\alpha + \beta) + \cos (\alpha - \beta)] \qquad (19\text{–}14)$$

28. By subtracting Eq. (19–10) from Eq. (19–12), derive

$$\sin \alpha \sin \beta = \tfrac{1}{2}[\cos (\alpha - \beta) - \cos (\alpha + \beta)] \qquad (19\text{–}15)$$

In Exercises 29 through 32 additional trigonometric identities are shown. Derive them by letting $\alpha + \beta = x$ and $\alpha - \beta = y$, which leads to $\alpha = \tfrac{1}{2}(x + y)$ and $\beta = \tfrac{1}{2}(x - y)$. The resulting equations are known as the factor formulas.

29. Use Eq. (19–13) and the substitutions above to derive the equation

$$\sin x + \sin y = 2 \sin \tfrac{1}{2}(x + y) \cos \tfrac{1}{2}(x - y) \qquad (19\text{–}16)$$

30. Use Eqs. (19–9) and (19–11) and the substitutions above to derive the equation

$$\sin x - \sin y = 2 \sin \tfrac{1}{2}(x - y) \cos \tfrac{1}{2}(x + y) \qquad (19\text{–}17)$$

31. Use Eq. (19–14) and the substitutions above to derive the equation

$$\cos x + \cos y = 2 \cos \tfrac{1}{2}(x + y) \cos \tfrac{1}{2}(x - y) \qquad (19\text{–}18)$$

32. Use Eq. (19–15) and the substitutions above to derive the equation

$$\cos x - \cos y = -2 \sin \tfrac{1}{2}(x + y) \sin \tfrac{1}{2}(x - y) \qquad (19\text{–}19)$$

In Exercises 33 through 36 use the equations of this section to solve the given problems.

33. In determining the motion of an object, the expression $\cos \alpha \sin (\omega t + \phi) - \sin \alpha \cos (\omega t + \phi)$ is found. Simplify this expression.

34. Under certain conditions, the current in an electric circuit is given by

$$i = I_m[\sin(\omega t + \alpha) \cos \phi + \cos(\omega t + \alpha) \sin \phi]$$

Simplify the expression on the right.

35. The displacements y_1 and y_2 of two waves traveling through the same medium are given by the equations $y_1 = A \sin 2\pi(t/T - x/\lambda)$ and $y_2 = A \sin 2\pi(t/T + x/\lambda)$. Find an expression for the displacement $y_1 + y_2$ of the combination of the waves.

36. In the analysis of the angles of incidence i and reflection r of a light ray subject to certain conditions, the following expression is found:

$$E_2\left(\frac{\tan r}{\tan i} + 1\right) = E_1\left(\frac{\tan r}{\tan i} - 1\right)$$

Show that an equivalent expression is

$$E_2 = E_1 \frac{\sin(r - i)}{\sin(r + i)}$$

19–3 Double-Angle Formulas

If we let $\beta = \alpha$ in Eqs. (19–9) and (19–10), we can derive the important double-angle formulas. Thus, by making this substitution in Eq. (19–9), we have

$$\sin(\alpha + \alpha) = \sin(2\alpha) = \sin\alpha\cos\alpha + \cos\alpha\sin\alpha = 2\sin\alpha\cos\alpha$$

Using the same substitution in Eq. (19–10), we have

$$\cos(\alpha + \alpha) = \cos\alpha\cos\alpha - \sin\alpha\sin\alpha = \cos^2\alpha - \sin^2\alpha$$

By using the basic identity (19–6), other forms of this last equation may be derived. Thus, summarizing these formulas, we have

$\sin 2\alpha = 2\sin\alpha\cos\alpha$	(19–20)
$\cos 2\alpha = \cos^2\alpha - \sin^2\alpha$	(19–21)
$= 2\cos^2\alpha - 1$	(19–22)
$= 1 - 2\sin^2\alpha$	(19–23)

We should note carefully that these equations give expressions for the sine and cosine of twice an angle in terms of functions of the angle. They can be used any time we have expressed one angle as twice another. These double-angle formulas are widely used in applications of trigonometry, especially in the calculus. They should be known and recognized quickly in any of the various forms.

Example A
If $\alpha = 30°$, we have $\cos 2(30°) = \cos 60° = \cos^2 30° - \sin^2 30°$.
If $\alpha = 3x$, we have $\sin 2(3x) = \sin 6x = 2\sin 3x\cos 3x$.
If $2\alpha = x$, we may write $\alpha = x/2$, which means that

$$\sin 2\left(\frac{x}{2}\right) = \sin x = 2\sin\frac{x}{2}\cos\frac{x}{2}$$

Example B
Using the double-angle formulas, simplify the expression

$$\cos^2 2x - \sin^2 2x$$

By using Eq. (19–21) and letting $\alpha = 2x$, we have

$$\cos^2 2x - \sin^2 2x = \cos 2(2x) = \cos 4x$$

Example C

Verify the values of sin 90° and cos 90° by use of the functions of 45°.

$$\sin 90° = \sin 2(45°) = 2 \sin 45° \cos 45° = 2\left(\frac{\sqrt{2}}{2}\right)\left(\frac{\sqrt{2}}{2}\right) = 1$$

$$\cos 90° = \cos 2(45°) = \cos^2 45° - \sin^2 45° = \left(\frac{\sqrt{2}}{2}\right)^2 - \left(\frac{\sqrt{2}}{2}\right)^2 = 0$$

Example D

Given that $\cos \alpha = \frac{3}{5}$ (in the fourth quadrant), find sin 2α.

Knowing that $\cos \alpha = \frac{3}{5}$ for an angle in the fourth quadrant, we then determine that

$$\sin \alpha = -\frac{4}{5}$$

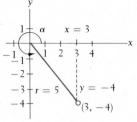

Figure 19–2

(see Fig. 19–2). Thus,

$$\sin 2\alpha = 2\left(-\frac{4}{5}\right)\left(\frac{3}{5}\right) = -\frac{24}{25}$$

Example E

Prove the identity $\dfrac{2}{1 + \cos 2x} = \sec^2 x$.

$$\frac{2}{1 + \cos 2x} = \frac{2}{1 + (2 \cos^2 x - 1)} = \frac{2}{2 \cos^2 x} = \sec^2 x$$

Example F

Show that $\dfrac{\sin 3x}{\sin x} + \dfrac{\cos 3x}{\cos x} = 4 \cos 2x$.

The first step is to combine the two fractions on the left, so that we can see if any usable forms will emerge:

$$\frac{\sin 3x \cos x + \cos 3x \sin x}{\sin x \cos x} \stackrel{?}{=} 4 \cos 2x$$

We now note that the numerator is of the form sin $(A + x)$, where $A = 3x$. Also, the denominator is $\frac{1}{2} \sin 2x$. Making these substitutions, we have

$$\frac{\sin(3x + x)}{\frac{1}{2} \sin 2x} = \frac{2 \sin 4x}{\sin 2x} \stackrel{?}{=} 4 \cos 2x$$

By expanding sin 4x into 2 sin 2x cos 2x, we obtain

$$\frac{2(2 \sin 2x \cos 2x)}{\sin 2x} = 4 \cos 2x$$

Therefore, the expression is shown to be valid.

Exercises 19–3

In Exercises 1 through 4 determine the values of the indicated functions in the given manner.

1. Find $\sin 60°$ by using the functions of $30°$.
2. Find $\sin 120°$ by using the functions of $60°$.
3. Find $\cos 120°$ by using the functions of $60°$.
4. Find $\cos 60°$ by using the functions of $30°$.

In Exercises 5 through 8 evaluate the indicated functions with the given information.

5. Find $\sin 2x$ if $\cos x = \frac{4}{5}$ (in first quadrant).
6. Find $\cos 2x$ if $\sin x = -\frac{12}{13}$ (in third quadrant).
7. Find $\cos 2x$ if $\tan x = \frac{1}{2}$ (in third quadrant).
8. Find $\sin 4x$ if $\sin x = \frac{3}{5}$ (in first quadrant) $[4x = 2(2x)]$.

In Exercises 9 through 12 reduce the given expressions to a single term. Expansion of any term is not necessary; proper recognition of the form of the expression leads to the proper result.

9. $4 \sin 4x \cos 4x$
10. $4 \sin^2 x \cos^2 x$
11. $1 - 2 \sin^2 4x$
12. $\sin^2 4x - \cos^2 4x$

In Exercises 13 through 20 prove the given identities.

13. $\cos^2\alpha - \sin^2\alpha = 2 \cos^2\alpha - 1$
14. $\cos^2\alpha - \sin^2\alpha = 1 - 2 \sin^2\alpha$
15. $\cos^4 x - \sin^4 x = \cos 2x$
16. $(\sin x + \cos x)^2 = 1 + \sin 2x$

17. $2 \csc 2x \tan x = \sec^2 x$
18. $2 \sin x + \sin 2x = \dfrac{2 \sin^3 x}{1 - \cos x}$

19. $\dfrac{\sin 3x}{\sin x} - \dfrac{\cos 3x}{\cos x} = 2$
20. $\dfrac{\sin 3x}{\sin x} + \dfrac{\cos 3x}{\cos x} = 4 \cos 2x$

In Exercises 21 and 22 prove the given identities by letting $3x = 2x + x$.

21. $\sin 3x = 3 \cos^2 x \sin x - \sin^3 x$
22. $\cos 3x = \cos^3 x - 3 \sin^2 x \cos x$

In Exercises 23 through 26 solve the given problems.

23. In Exercise 25 of Section 19–2, let $\beta = \alpha$, and show that

$$\tan 2\alpha = \frac{2 \tan \alpha}{1 - \tan^2\alpha}$$

24. Given that $x = \cos 2\theta$ and $y = \sin \theta$, find the relation between x and y by eliminating θ.

25. The equation for the displacement of a certain object at the end of a spring is $y = A \sin 2t + B \cos 2t$. Show that this equation may be written as $y = C \sin(2t + \alpha)$ where $C = \sqrt{A^2 + B^2}$ and $\tan \alpha = B/A$. [*Hint:* Let $A/C = \cos \alpha$ and $B/C = \sin \alpha$.]

26. To find the horizontal range R of a projectile, the equation $R = vt \cos \alpha$ is used, where α is the angle between the line of fire and the horizontal, v is the initial velocity of the projectile, and t is the time of flight. It can be shown that $t = (2v \sin \alpha)/g$, where g is the acceleration due to gravity. Show that $R = (v^2 \sin 2\alpha)/g$.

19—4 Half-Angle Formulas

If we let $\theta = \alpha/2$ in the identity $\cos 2\theta = 1 - 2\sin^2\theta$ and then solve for $\sin(\alpha/2)$, we obtain

$$\sin \frac{\alpha}{2} = \pm \sqrt{\frac{1 - \cos \alpha}{2}} \tag{19-24}$$

Also, with the same substitution in the identity $\cos 2\theta = 2\cos^2\theta - 1$, which is then solved for $\cos(\alpha/2)$, we have

$$\cos \frac{\alpha}{2} = \pm \sqrt{\frac{1 + \cos \alpha}{2}} \tag{19-25}$$

In each of Eqs. (19–24) and (19–25), the sign chosen depends on the quadrant in which $\alpha/2$ lies.

We can use these half-angle formulas to find values of the functions of angles which are half of those for which the functions are known. Examples A through F which follow illustrate how these identities are used in evaluations and in identities.

Example A
We can find $\sin 15°$ by using the relation

$$\sin 15° = \sqrt{\frac{1 - \cos 30°}{2}} = \sqrt{\frac{1 - 0.8660}{2}} = 0.2588$$

Here the plus sign is used, since $15°$ is in the first quadrant.

Example B
We can find $\cos 165°$ by use of the relation

$$\cos 165° = -\sqrt{\frac{1 + \cos 330°}{2}} = -\sqrt{\frac{1 + 0.8660}{2}} = -0.9659$$

Here the minus sign is used, since $165°$ is in the second quadrant, and the cosine of a second-quadrant angle is negative.

Example C
Simplify the expression $\sqrt{18 - 18\cos 4x}$.

First we factor the 18 from each of the terms under the radical, and note that $18 = 9(2)$ and 9 is a perfect square. This leads to

$$\sqrt{18 - 18\cos 4x} = \sqrt{9(2)(1 - \cos 4x)} = 3\sqrt{2(1 - \cos 4x)}$$

This last expression is very similar to that for $\sin(\alpha/2)$, except that no 2 appears in the denominator. Therefore, multiplying the numerator and the denominator under the radical by 2 leads to the solution.

$$3\sqrt{2(1 - \cos 4x)} = 3\sqrt{\frac{4(1 - \cos 4x)}{2}} = 6\sqrt{\frac{1 - \cos 4x}{2}} = 6\sin\frac{4x}{2} = 6\sin 2x$$

Example D

Prove the identity $\sec\dfrac{\alpha}{2} + \csc\dfrac{\alpha}{2} = \dfrac{2\left(\sin\dfrac{\alpha}{2} + \cos\dfrac{\alpha}{2}\right)}{\sin\alpha}$

By expressing $\sin\alpha$ as $2\sin\frac{\alpha}{2}\cos\frac{\alpha}{2}$, we have

$$\frac{2\left(\sin\dfrac{\alpha}{2} + \cos\dfrac{\alpha}{2}\right)}{2\sin\dfrac{\alpha}{2}\cos\dfrac{\alpha}{2}} = \frac{1}{\cos\dfrac{\alpha}{2}} + \frac{1}{\sin\dfrac{\alpha}{2}} = \sec\dfrac{\alpha}{2} + \csc\dfrac{\alpha}{2}$$

Example E

We can find relations for the other functions of $\alpha/2$ by expressing these functions in terms of $\sin(\alpha/2)$ and $\cos(\alpha/2)$. For example:

$$\sec\frac{\alpha}{2} = \frac{1}{\cos\dfrac{\alpha}{2}} = \pm\frac{1}{\sqrt{\dfrac{1 + \cos\alpha}{2}}} = \pm\sqrt{\frac{2}{1 + \cos\alpha}}$$

Example F

Show that $2\cos^2\dfrac{x}{2} - \cos x = 1$.

The first step is to substitute for $\cos(x/2)$, which will result in each term containing x on the left being in terms of x, and no $x/2$ terms will exist. This might allow us to combine terms. So we perform this operation, and we have

$$2\left(\frac{1 + \cos x}{2}\right) - \cos x = 1$$

Combining terms, we can complete the proof:

$$1 + \cos x - \cos x = 1$$

Exercises 19—4

In Exercises 1 through 4 use the half-angle formulas to evaluate the given functions.

1. $\cos 15°$ 2. $\sin 22.5°$ 3. $\sin 75°$ 4. $\cos 112.5°$

In Exercises 5 through 8 use the half-angle formulas to simplify the given expressions.

5. $\sqrt{\dfrac{1 - \cos 6\alpha}{2}}$ 6. $\sqrt{\dfrac{4 + 4\cos 8\beta}{2}}$

7. $\sqrt{8 + 8\cos 4x}$ 8. $\sqrt{2 - 2\cos 16x}$

In Exercises 9 through 12 evaluate the indicated functions with the information given.

9. Find the value of $\sin(\alpha/2)$, if $\cos \alpha = \frac{12}{13}$ (in first quadrant).
10. Find the value of $\cos(\alpha/2)$, if $\sin \alpha = -\frac{4}{5}$ (in third quadrant).
11. Find the value of $\cos(\alpha/2)$, if $\tan \alpha = -\frac{7}{24}$ (in second quadrant).
12. Find the value of $\sin(\alpha/2)$, if $\cos \alpha = \frac{8}{17}$ (in fourth quadrant).

In Exercises 13 through 16 derive the required expressions.

13. Derive an expression for $\csc(\alpha/2)$ in terms of $\cos \alpha$.
14. Derive an expression for $\sec(\alpha/2)$ in terms of $\sec \alpha$.
15. Derive an expression for $\tan(\alpha/2)$ in terms of $\sin \alpha$ and $\cos \alpha$.
16. Derive an expression for $\cot(\alpha/2)$ in terms of $\sin \alpha$ and $\cos \alpha$.

In Exercises 17 through 20 prove the given identities.

17. $\sin \dfrac{\alpha}{2} = \dfrac{1 - \cos \alpha}{2 \sin \dfrac{\alpha}{2}}$

18. $2 \cos \dfrac{x}{2} = (1 + \cos x)\sec \dfrac{x}{2}$

19. $2 \sin^2 \dfrac{\alpha}{2} - \cos^2 \dfrac{\alpha}{2} = \dfrac{1 - 3 \cos \alpha}{2}$

20. $\tan \dfrac{\alpha}{2} = \dfrac{\sin \alpha}{1 + \cos \alpha}$

In Exercises 21 and 22 use the half-angle formulas to solve the given problems.

21. In the kinetic theory of gases, the expression

$$\sqrt{(1 - \cos \alpha)^2 + \sin^2 \alpha \cos^2 \beta + \sin^2 \alpha \sin^2 \beta}$$

is found. Show that this expression equals $2 \sin \frac{\alpha}{2}$.

22. The index of refraction n, the angle of a prism A, and the minimum angle of refraction ϕ are related by

$$n = \frac{\sin \dfrac{A + \phi}{2}}{\sin \dfrac{A}{2}}$$

Show that an equivalent expression is

$$n = \sqrt{\frac{1 + \cos \phi}{2}} + \left(\cot \frac{A}{2}\right)\sqrt{\frac{1 - \cos \phi}{2}}$$

19—5 Trigonometric Equations

One of the most important uses of the trigonometric identities is in the solution of equations involving the trigonometric functions. When equations are written in terms of more than one function, the identities provide a way of transforming many of them to equations or factors involving only one function of the same angle. If we can accomplish this we can employ algebraic methods from then on to complete the solution. No general methods exist for the solution of such equations, but the following examples illustrate methods which prove to be useful.

Example A

Solve the equation $2 \cos \theta - 1 = 0$ for all values of θ such that $0 \leq \theta < 2\pi$.

Solving the equation for $\cos \theta$, we obtain $\cos \theta = \frac{1}{2}$. The problem asks for all values of θ between 0 and 2π that satisfy the equation. We know that the cosine of angles in the first and fourth quadrants is positive. Also, we know that $\cos (\pi/3) = \frac{1}{2}$. Therefore, $\theta = \pi/3$ and $\theta = 5\pi/3$.

Example B

Solve the equation $2 \cos^2 x - \sin x - 1 = 0$ $(0 \leq x < 2\pi)$.

By use of the identity $\sin^2 x + \cos^2 x = 1$, this equation may be put in terms of $\sin x$ only. Thus, we have

$$2(1 - \sin^2 x) - \sin x - 1 = 0$$

$$-2 \sin^2 x - \sin x + 1 = 0$$
$$2 \sin^2 x + \sin x - 1 = 0$$

or

$$(2 \sin x - 1)(\sin x + 1) = 0$$

Just as in solving algebraic equations, we can set each factor equal to zero to find valid solutions. Thus, $\sin x = \frac{1}{2}$ and $\sin x = -1$. For the range between 0 and 2π, the value $\sin x = \frac{1}{2}$ gives values of x as $\pi/6$ and $5\pi/6$, and $\sin x = -1$ gives the value $x = 3\pi/2$. Thus, the complete solution is $x = \pi/6$, $x = 5\pi/6$, and $x = 3\pi/2$.

Example C

Solve the equation $\sec^2 x + 2 \tan x - 6 = 0$ $(0 \leq x < 2\pi)$.

By use of the identity $1 + \tan^2 x = \sec^2 x$ we may express this equation in terms of $\tan x$ only. Therefore,

$$\tan^2 x + 1 + 2 \tan x - 6 = 0$$
$$\tan^2 x + 2 \tan x - 5 = 0$$

We note that this expression is not factorable. Therefore, using the quadratic formula, we obtain the following solution:

$$\tan x = \frac{-2 \pm \sqrt{4 + 20}}{2} = \frac{-2 \pm 4.899}{2}$$

Therefore, $\tan x = \frac{2.899}{2} = 1.450$ and $\tan x = \frac{-6.899}{2} = -3.450$. Expressing the results in radians, we find that $\tan x = 1.450$ for $x = 0.967$.

Since tan x is also positive in the third quadrant, we also have $x = 4.11$. In the same way, using tan $x = -3.450$, we obtain $x = 1.85$ and 4.99. Therefore, the correct solutions are $x = 0.967$, $x = 1.85$, $x = 4.11$, and $x = 4.99$.

Example D

Solve the equation sin $2x$ + sin $x = 0$ $(0 \leq x < 2\pi)$.

By using the double-angle formula for sin $2x$, we can write the equation in the form

$$2 \sin x \cos x + \sin x = 0 \qquad \text{or} \qquad \sin x(2 \cos x + 1) = 0$$

The first factor gives $x = 0$ or $x = \pi$. The second factor, for which cos $x = -\frac{1}{2}$, gives $x = 2\pi/3$ and $x = 4\pi/3$. Thus, the complete solution is $x = 0$, $x = 2\pi/3$, $x = \pi$, and $x = 4\pi/3$.

Example E

Solve the equation $\cos \dfrac{x}{2} = 1 + \cos x$ $(0 \leq x < 2\pi)$.

By using the half-angle formula for cos $(x/2)$ and then squaring both sides of the resulting equation, this equation can be solved.

$$\pm\sqrt{\frac{1 + \cos x}{2}} = 1 + \cos x$$

$$\frac{1 + \cos x}{2} = 1 + 2 \cos x + \cos^2 x$$

Simplifying this last equation, we have

$$2 \cos^2 x + 3 \cos x + 1 = 0$$
$$(2 \cos x + 1)(\cos x + 1) = 0$$

The values of the cosine which come from these factors are cos $x = -\frac{1}{2}$ and cos $x = -1$. Thus, the values of x which satisfy the last equation are $x = 2\pi/3$, $x = 4\pi/3$, and $x = \pi$. However, when we solved this equation, we squared both sides of it. In doing this we may have introduced extraneous solutions (see Section 13–3). Thus, we must check each solution in the original equation to see if it is valid. Hence,

$$\cos\frac{\pi}{3} \stackrel{?}{=} 1 + \cos\frac{2\pi}{3} \qquad \text{or} \qquad \frac{1}{2} \stackrel{?}{=} 1 + \left(-\frac{1}{2}\right) \qquad \text{or} \qquad \frac{1}{2} = \frac{1}{2}$$

$$\cos\frac{2\pi}{3} \stackrel{?}{=} 1 + \cos\frac{4\pi}{3} \qquad \text{or} \qquad -\frac{1}{2} \stackrel{?}{=} 1 + \left(-\frac{1}{2}\right) \qquad \text{or} \qquad -\frac{1}{2} \neq \frac{1}{2}$$

$$\cos\frac{\pi}{2} \stackrel{?}{=} 1 + \cos \pi \qquad \text{or} \qquad 0 \stackrel{?}{=} 1 - 1 \qquad \text{or} \qquad 0 = 0$$

Thus, the apparent solution $x = 4\pi/3$ is not a solution of the original equation. The correct solutions are $x = 2\pi/3$ and $x = \pi$.

Example F

Solve the equation $\tan 3\theta - \cot 3\theta = 0$ $(0 \leq \theta < 2\pi)$.

$$\tan 3\theta - \frac{1}{\tan 3\theta} = 0 \quad \text{or} \quad \tan^2 3\theta = 1 \quad \text{or} \quad \tan 3\theta = \pm 1$$

Thus,

$$3\theta = \frac{\pi}{4}, \frac{3\pi}{4}, \frac{5\pi}{4}, \frac{7\pi}{4}, \frac{9\pi}{4}, \frac{11\pi}{4}, \frac{13\pi}{4}, \frac{15\pi}{4}, \frac{17\pi}{4}, \frac{19\pi}{4}, \frac{21\pi}{4}, \frac{23\pi}{4}$$

Here we must include values of angles which when divided by 3 give angles between 0 and 2π. Thus, values of 3θ from 0 to 6π are necessary. The solutions are

$$\theta = \frac{\pi}{12}, \frac{\pi}{4}, \frac{5\pi}{12}, \frac{7\pi}{12}, \frac{3\pi}{4}, \frac{11\pi}{12}, \frac{13\pi}{12}, \frac{5\pi}{4}, \frac{17\pi}{12}, \frac{19\pi}{12}, \frac{7\pi}{4}, \frac{23\pi}{12}$$

It is noted that these values satisfy the original equation. Since we multiplied through by $\tan 3\theta$ in the solution, any value of θ which leads to $\tan 3\theta = 0$ would not be valid, since this would indicate division by zero in the original equation.

Example G

Solve the equation $\cos 3x \cos x + \sin 3x \sin x = 1$ $(0 \leq x < 2\pi)$.

The left side of this equation is of the general form $\cos(A - x)$, where $A = 3x$. Therefore,

$$\cos 3x \cos x + \sin 3x \sin x = \cos(3x - x) = \cos 2x$$

The original equation becomes

$$\cos 2x = 1$$

This equation is satisfied if $2x = 0$ and $2x = 2\pi$. The solutions are $x = 0$ and $x = \pi$. Only through recognition of the proper trigonometric form can we readily solve this equation.

Exercises 19–5

In Exercises 1 through 28 solve the given trigonometric equations for values of x so that $0 \leq x < 2\pi$.

1. $\sin x - 1 = 0$

2. $2 \sin x + 1 = 0$

3. $\tan x + 1 = 0$

4. $2 \cos x + 1 = 0$

5. $4 \cos^2 x - 1 = 0$

6. $\sin^2 x - 1 = 0$

7. $4 \sin^2 x - 3 = 0$

8. $3 \tan^2 x - 1 = 0$

9. $2 \sin^2 x - \sin x = 0$

10. $3 \cos x - 4 \cos^2 x = 0$

11. $\sin 4x - \cos 2x = 0$

12. $\sin 4x - \sin 2x = 0$

13. $\sin 2x \sin x + \cos x = 0$

14. $\cos 2x + \sin^2 x = 0$

15. $2 \sin x - \tan x = 0$

16. $\sin x - \sin \dfrac{x}{2} = 0$

17. $2 \cos^2 x - 2 \cos 2x - 1 = 0$

18. $2 \cos^2 2x + 1 = 3 \cos 2x$

19. $\sin^2 x - 2 \sin x - 1 = 0$

20. $\tan^2 x - 5 \tan x + 6 = 0$

21. $4 \tan x - \sec^2 x = 0$

22. $\tan^2 x - 2 \sec^2 x + 4 = 0$

23. $\sin 2x \cos x - \cos 2x \sin x = 0$

24. $\cos 3x \cos x - \sin 3x \sin x = 0$

25. $\sin 2x + \cos 2x = 0$

26. $2 \sin 4x + \csc 4x = 3$

27. $\tan x + 3 \cot x = 4$

28. $\sin x \sin \frac{1}{2} x = 1 - \cos x$

In Exercises 29 through 32 solve the indicated equations.

29. In finding the dimensions of the largest cylinder which can be inscribed in a sphere, the equation $\sin \theta - 3 \sin \theta \cos^2\theta = 0$ must be solved for θ, for $0 < \theta < \pi/2$. Solve for the value of θ which satisfies the equation.

30. Vectors of magnitudes 3 and 2 are directed at an angle θ, such that the vertical component of the first vector equals the horizontal component of the second vector. Find the angle θ, such that $0 < \theta < \pi$.

31. The angular displacement θ of a certain pendulum in terms of the time t is given by $\theta = e^{-0.1t}(\cos 2t + 3 \sin 2t)$. What is the smallest value of t for which the displacement is zero?

32. The vertical displacement y of an object at the end of a spring, which itself is being moved up and down, is given by $y = 2 \cos 4t + \sin 2t$. Find the smallest value of t (in seconds) for which $y = 0$.

In Exercises 33 through 36 solve the given equations graphically.

33. $\sin 2x = x$

34. $\cos 2x = 4 - x^2$

35. In the study of light diffraction, the equation $\tan \theta = \theta$ is found. Solve this equation for $0 \leq \theta < 2\pi$.

36. An equation used in astronomy is $\theta - e \sin \theta = M$. Solve for θ for $e = 0.25$ and $M = 0.75$.

19–6 Introduction to the Inverse Trigonometric Functions

When we studied logarithms, we found that we often wished to change a given expression from exponential to logarithmic form, or from logarithmic to exponential form. Each of these forms has its advantages for particular purposes. We found that the exponential function $y = b^x$ can also be written in logarithmic form with x as a function of y, or $x = \log_b y$. We then represented both of these functions as y in terms of x, saying that the letter used for the dependent and independent variables did not matter, when we wished to express a functional relationship. Since y is normally the dependent variable, we wrote the logarithmic function as $y = \log_b x$.

These two functions, the exponential function $y = b^x$ and the logarithmic function $y = \log_b x$, are called **inverse functions**. This means that if we solve for the independent variable in terms of the dependent variable in one, we will arrive at the functional relationship expressed by the other. It also means that, for every value of x, there is only one corresponding value of y.

Just as we are able to solve $y = b^x$ for the exponent by writing it in logarithmic form, there are times when it is necessary to solve for the independent variable (the angle) in trigonometric functions. Therefore, we define the **inverse sine of x** by the relation

$$y = \arcsin x \quad \text{(the notation } y = \sin^{-1} x \text{ is also used)} \qquad (19\text{--}26)$$

Similar relations exist for the other inverse trigonometric relations. In Eq. (19–26), x is the value of the sine of the angle y, and therefore the most meaningful way of reading it is "y is the angle whose sine is x."

Example A

$y = \arccos x$ would be read as "y is the angle whose cosine is x."

The equation $y = \arctan 2x$ would be read as "y is the angle whose tangent is $2x$."

It is important to emphasize that $y = \arcsin x$ and $x = \sin y$ express the same relationship between x and y. The advantage of having both forms is that a trigonometric relation may be expressed in terms of a function of an angle or in terms of the angle itself.

If we consider closely the equation $y = \arcsin x$ and possible values of x, we note that there are an unlimited number of possible values of y for a given value of x. Consider the following example.

Example B

For $y = \arcsin x$, if $x = \frac{1}{2}$, we have $y = \arcsin \frac{1}{2}$. This means that we are to find an angle whose sine is $\frac{1}{2}$. We know that $\sin (\pi/6) = \frac{1}{2}$. Therefore, $y = \pi/6$.

However, we also know that $\sin (5\pi/6) = \frac{1}{2}$. Therefore, $y = 5\pi/6$ is also a proper value. If we consider negative angles, such as $-7\pi/6$, or angles generated by additional rotations, such as $13\pi/6$, we conclude that there are an unlimited number of possible values for y.

To have a properly defined **function** *in mathematics, there must be only one value of the dependent variable for a given value of the independent variable. A* **relation,** *on the other hand, may have more than one such value.* Therefore, we see that $y = \arcsin x$ is not really a function, although it is properly a relation. It is necessary to restrict the values of y in order to define the **inverse trigonometric functions,** and this is done in the following section. It is the purpose of this section to introduce the necessary notation and to develop an understanding of the basic concept. The following examples further illustrate the meaning of the notation.

Example C

If $y = \arccos 0$, y is the angle whose cosine is zero. The smallest positive angle for which this is true is $\pi/2$. Therefore, $y = \pi/2$ is an acceptable value.

If $y = \arctan 1$, an acceptable value for y is $\pi/4$. This is the same as saying $\tan \pi/4 = 1$.

Example D
Given that $y = \sec 2x$, solve for x.

We first express the inverse relation as $2x = \text{arcsec } y$. Then we solve for x by dividing through by 2. Thus, we have $x = \frac{1}{2} \text{arcsec } y$. Note that we first wrote the inverse relation by writing the expression for the angle, which in this case was $2x$. Just as $\sec 2x$ and $2 \sec x$ are different relations, so are the arcsec $2x$ and 2 arcsec x.

Example E
Given that $4y = \text{arccot } 2x$, solve for x.

Writing this as the cotangent of $4y$ (since the given expression means "$4y$ is the angle whose cotangent is $2x$"), we have

$$2x = \cot 4y \qquad \text{or} \qquad x = \frac{1}{2} \cot 4y$$

Example F
Given that $\pi - y = \text{arccsc } \frac{1}{3}x$, solve for x.

$$\frac{1}{3}x = \csc(\pi - y) \qquad \text{or} \qquad x = 3 \csc y$$

[since $\csc(\pi - y) = \csc y$].

Exercises 19—6

In Exercises 1 through 8 write down the meaning of each of the given equations. See Example A.

1. $y = \arctan x$ 2. $y = \text{arcsec } x$ 3. $y = \text{arccot } 3x$

4. $y = \text{arccsc } 4x$ 5. $y = 2 \arcsin x$ 6. $y = 3 \arctan x$

7. $y = 5 \arccos 2x$ 8. $y = 4 \arcsin 3x$

In Exercises 9 through 20 find the smallest positive angle (in terms of π) for each of the given expressions.

9. $\arccos \dfrac{1}{2}$ 10. $\arcsin 1$ 11. $\text{arcsec}(-\sqrt{2})$

12. $\arccos \dfrac{\sqrt{2}}{2}$ 13. $\arctan(-1)$ 14. $\text{arccsc}(-1)$

15. $\arctan \sqrt{3}$ 16. $\text{arcsec } 2$ 17. $\text{arccot}(-\sqrt{3})$

18. $\arcsin\left(-\dfrac{\sqrt{3}}{2}\right)$ 19. $\text{arccsc } \sqrt{2}$ 20. $\text{arccot } \dfrac{\sqrt{3}}{3}$

In Exercises 21 through 28 solve the given equations for x.

21. $y = \sin 3x$ 22. $y = \cos(x - \pi)$

23. $y = \arctan\left(\dfrac{x}{4}\right)$ 24. $y = 2 \arcsin\left(\dfrac{x}{6}\right)$

25. $y = 1 + \sec 3x$ 26. $4y = 5 - \csc 8x$

27. $1 - y = \arccos(1 - x)$ 28. $2y = \text{arccot } 3x - 5$

In Exercises 29 through 32 determine the required quadrants.

29. In which quadrants is arcsin x if $0 < x < 1$?
30. In which quadrants is arctan x if $0 < x < 1$?
31. In which quadrants is arccos x if $-1 < x < 0$?
32. In which quadrants is arcsin x if $-1 < x < 0$?

In Exercises 33 through 36 solve the given problems with the use of the inverse trigonometric relations.

33. A body is moving along a straight line in such a way that its acceleration is directed toward a fixed point, and is proportional to its distance from that point. Its position is given by $x = A \cos t \sqrt{k/m}$. Solve for k.
34. Under certain conditions the magnetic potential V at a distance r from a circuit with a current I is given by

$$V = \frac{kI \cos \theta}{r^2}$$

where k is a constant and θ is the angle between the radius vector r and the direction perpendicular to the plane of the circuit. Solve for θ.
35. The magnitude of a certain ray of polarized light is given by the equation $E = E_0 \cos \theta \sin \theta$. Solve for θ.
36. The equation for the displacement of a certain object oscillating at the end of a spring is given by $y = A \sin 2t + B \cos 2t$. Solve for t. [*Hint:* See Exercise 25 of Section 19–3.]

19–7 The Inverse Trigonometric Functions

We noted in the preceding section that we could find many values of y if we assumed some value for x in the relation $y = \arcsin x$. As these relations were defined, any one of the various possibilities would be considered correct. This, however, does not meet a basic requirement for a function, and it also leads to ambiguity. In order to define the **inverse trigonometric functions** properly, so this ambiguity does not exist, there must be only a single value of y for any given value of x. Therefore, the following values are defined for the given functions.

$$-\frac{\pi}{2} \le \text{Arcsin } x \le \frac{\pi}{2}, \quad 0 \le \text{Arccos } x \le \pi, \quad -\frac{\pi}{2} < \text{Arctan } x < \frac{\pi}{2}$$

$$0 < \text{Arccot } x < \pi, \quad 0 \le \text{Arcsec } x \le \pi, \quad -\frac{\pi}{2} \le \text{Arccsc } x \le \frac{\pi}{2}$$

(19–27)

This means that when we are looking for a value of y to correspond to a given value for x, we must use a value of y as defined in Eqs. (19–27). The capital letter designates the use of the inverse trigonometric *function*.

Example A

$$\text{Arcsin}\left(\frac{1}{2}\right) = \frac{\pi}{6}$$

This is the only value of the function which lies within the defined range. The value $5\pi/6$ is not correct, since it lies outside the defined range of values.

Example B

$$\text{Arccos}\left(-\frac{1}{2}\right) = \frac{2\pi}{3}$$

Other values such as $4\pi/3$ and $-2\pi/3$ are not correct, since they are not within the defined range of values for the function Arccos x.

Example C

$$\text{Arctan}(-1) = -\frac{\pi}{4}$$

This is the only value within the defined range for the function Arctan x. We must remember that when x is negative for Arcsin x and Arctan x, the value of y is a fourth-quadrant angle, expressed as a *negative angle*. This is a direct result of the definition.

Example D

$$\text{Arcsin}\left(-\frac{\sqrt{3}}{2}\right) = -\frac{\pi}{3} \qquad \text{Arccos}(-1) = \pi$$

$$\text{Arctan}\ 0 = 0 \qquad\qquad \text{Arcsin}(-0.1564) = -\frac{\pi}{20}$$

$$\text{Arccos}(-0.8090) = \frac{4\pi}{5} \qquad \text{Arctan}(\sqrt{3}) = \frac{\pi}{3}$$

One might logically ask why these values are chosen when there are so many different possibilities. The values are so chosen that, if x is positive, the resulting answer gives an angle in the first quadrant. We must, however, account for the possibility that x might be negative. We could not choose second-quadrant angles for Arcsin x. Since the sine of a second-quadrant angle is also positive, this then would lead to ambiguity. The sine is negative for fourth-quadrant angles, and to have a continuous range of values we must express the fourth-quadrant angles in the form of negative angles. This range is also chosen for Arctan x, for similar reasons. However, Arccos x cannot be chosen in this way, since the cosine of fourth-quadrant angles is also positive. Thus, again to keep a continuous range of values for Arccos x, the second-quadrant angles are chosen for negative values of x.

As for the values for the other functions, we chose values such that if x is positive, the result is also an angle in the first quadrant. As for negative values of x, it rarely makes any difference, since either positive values of x arise, or we can use one of the other functions. Our definitions, however, are those which are generally used.

The graphs of the inverse trigonometric relations can be used to show the fact that many values of y correspond to a given value of x. We can also show the ranges used in defining the inverse trigonometric functions, and that these ranges are specific sections of the curves.

Since $y = \arcsin x$ and $x = \sin y$ are equivalent equations, we can obtain the graph of the inverse sine by sketching the sine curve *along the y-axis.* In Figs. (19–3), (19–4), and (19–5), the graphs of three inverse trigonometric relations are shown, with the heavier portions indicating the graphs of the inverse trigonometric functions. The graphs of the other inverse relations are found in the same way.

If we know the value of x for one of the inverse functions, we can find the trigonometric functions of the angle. If general relations are desired, a representative triangle is very useful. The following examples illustrate these methods.

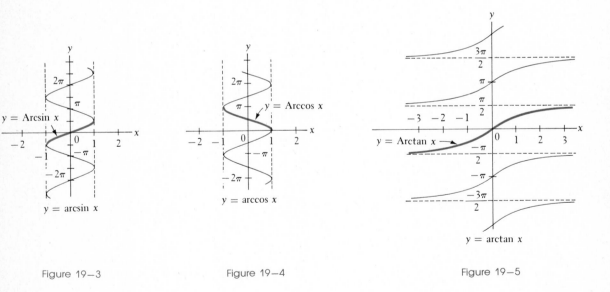

Figure 19–3   Figure 19–4   Figure 19–5

Example E

Find cos(Arcsin 0.5). [Remember again: the inverse functions yield *angles.*]

We know Arcsin 0.5 is a first-quadrant angle, since 0.5 is positive. Thus we find Arcsin $0.5 = \pi/6$. The problem now becomes one of finding $\cos(\pi/6)$. This is, of course, $\sqrt{3}/2$ or 0.8660.

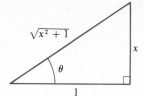

Figure 19–6

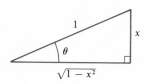

Figure 19–7

Example F

$$\sin(\text{Arccot } 1) = \sin\frac{\pi}{4} = \frac{\sqrt{2}}{2} = 0.7071$$

$$\tan[\text{Arccos}(-1)] = \tan\pi = 0$$

Example G

Find $\sin(\text{Arctan } x)$.

We know that Arctan x is another way of stating "the angle whose tangent is x." Thus, let us draw a right triangle (as in Fig. 19–6) and label one of the acute angles θ, the side opposite θ as x, and the side adjacent to θ as 1. In this way we see that, by definition, $\tan\theta = x/1$, or $\theta = \text{Arctan } x$, which means θ is the desired angle. By the Pythagorean theorem, the hypotenuse of this triangle is $\sqrt{x^2 + 1}$. Now we find that the $\sin\theta$, which is the same as $\sin(\text{Arctan } x)$, is $x/\sqrt{x^2 + 1}$, from the definition of the sine. Thus,

$$\sin(\text{Arctan } x) = \frac{x}{\sqrt{x^2 + 1}}$$

Example H

Find $\cos(2\text{ Arcsin } x)$.

From Fig. 19–7, we see that $\theta = \text{Arcsin } x$. From the double-angle formulas, we have $\cos 2\theta = 1 - 2\sin^2\theta$. Thus, since $\sin\theta = x$, we have

$$\cos(2\text{ Arcsin } x) = 1 - 2x^2$$

Exercises 19–7

In Exercises 1 through 24 evaluate the given expressions.

1. $\text{Arccos}(\frac{1}{2})$
2. $\text{Arcsin}(1)$
3. $\text{Arcsin } 0$
4. $\text{Arccos } 0$
5. $\text{Arctan}(-\sqrt{3})$
6. $\text{Arcsin}(-\frac{1}{2})$

7. $\text{Arcsec } 2$
8. $\text{Arccot } \sqrt{3}$
9. $\text{Arctan}\left(\frac{\sqrt{3}}{3}\right)$

10. $\text{Arctan } 1$
11. $\text{Arcsin}\left(-\frac{\sqrt{2}}{2}\right)$
12. $\text{Arccos}\left(-\frac{\sqrt{3}}{2}\right)$
13. $\text{Arccsc } \sqrt{2}$
14. $\text{Arccot } 1$
15. $\text{Arctan}(-3.732)$

16. $\text{Arccos}(-0.5878)$
17. $\sin(\text{Arctan } \sqrt{3})$
18. $\tan\left(\text{Arcsin }\frac{\sqrt{2}}{2}\right)$

19. $\cos[\text{Arctan}(-1)]$
20. $\sec[\text{Arccos}(-\frac{1}{2})]$
21. $\tan[\text{Arccos}(-0.6561)]$
22. $\cot[\text{Arcsin}(-0.3827)]$
23. $\cos(2\text{ Arcsin } 1)$
24. $\sin(2\text{ Arctan } 2)$

In Exercises 25 through 32 find an algebraic expression for each of the expressions given.

25. $\tan(\text{Arcsin } x)$
26. $\sin(\text{Arccos } x)$
27. $\cos(\text{Arcsec } x)$
28. $\cot(\text{Arccot } x)$
29. $\sec(\text{Arccsc } 3x)$
30. $\tan(\text{Arcsin } 2x)$
31. $\sin(2\text{ Arcsin } x)$
32. $\cos(2\text{ Arctan } x)$

In Exercises 33 and 34, prove that the given expressions are equal. This can be done by use of the relation for $\sin(\alpha + \beta)$ and by showing that the sine of the sum of angles on the left equals the sine of the angle on the right.

33. $\operatorname{Arcsin} \frac{3}{5} + \operatorname{Arcsin} \frac{5}{13} = \operatorname{Arcsin} \frac{56}{65}$ **34.** $\operatorname{Arctan} \frac{1}{3} + \operatorname{Arctan} \frac{1}{2} = \frac{\pi}{4}$

In Exercises 35 and 36 derive the given expressions.

35. For the triangle in Fig. 19–8, show that $\alpha = \operatorname{Arctan}(a + \tan \beta)$.

36. Show that the length of the pulley belt indicated in Fig. 19–9 is given by the expression

$$L = 24 + 11\pi + 10 \operatorname{Arcsin}\left(\frac{5}{13}\right).$$

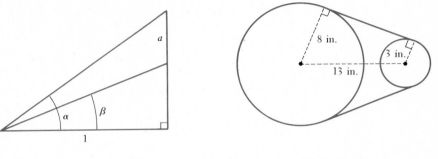

Figure 19–8   Figure 19–9

19–8 Exercises for Chapter 19

In Exercises 1 through 8 determine the values of the indicated functions in the given manner.

1. Find $\sin 120°$ by using $120° = 90° + 30°$.
2. Find $\cos 30°$ by using $30° = 90° - 60°$.
3. Find $\sin 135°$ by using $135° = 180° - 45°$.
4. Find $\cos 225°$ by using $225° = 180° + 45°$.
5. Find $\cos 180°$ by using $180° = 2(90°)$.
6. Find $\sin 180°$ by using $180° = 2(90°)$.
7. Find $\sin 45°$ by using $45° = \frac{1}{2}(90°)$.
8. Find $\cos 45°$ by using $45° = \frac{1}{2}(90°)$.

In Exercises 9 through 16 reduce each of the given expressions to a single term. Expansion of any term is not necessary; proper recognition of the form of the expression leads to the proper result.

9. $\sin 2x \cos 3x + \cos 2x \sin 3x$

10. $\cos 7x \cos 3x + \sin 7x \sin 3x$

11. $8 \sin 6x \cos 6x$

12. $10 \sin 5x \cos 5x$

13. $2 - 4 \sin^2 6x$

14. $\cos^2 2x - \sin^2 2x$

15. $\sqrt{2 + 2 \cos 2x}$

16. $\sqrt{32 - 32 \cos 4x}$

In Exercises 17 through 24 evaluate the given expressions.

17. $\text{Arcsin}(-1)$

18. $\text{Arcsec } \sqrt{2}$

19. $\text{Arccos}(0.9659)$

20. $\text{Arctan}(-0.6249)$

21. $\tan[\text{Arcsin}(-\tfrac{1}{2})]$

22. $\cos[\text{Arctan}(-\sqrt{3})]$

23. $\text{Arcsin}(\tan \pi)$

24. $\text{Arccos}\left[\tan\left(-\dfrac{\pi}{4}\right)\right]$

In Exercises 25 through 48 prove the given identities.

25. $\dfrac{\sec y}{\csc y} = \tan y$

26. $\cos \theta \csc \theta = \cot \theta$

27. $\sin x(\csc x - \sin x) = \cos^2 x$

28. $\cos y(\sec y - \cos y) = \sin^2 y$

29. $\dfrac{1}{\sin \theta} - \sin \theta = \cot \theta \cos \theta$

30. $\sin \theta \sec \theta \csc \theta \cos \theta = 1$

31. $\cos \theta \cot \theta + \sin \theta = \csc \theta$

32. $\dfrac{\sin x \cot x + \cos x}{\cot x} = 2 \sin x$

33. $\dfrac{\sec^4 x - 1}{\tan^2 x} = 2 + \tan^2 x$

34. $\cos^2 y - \sin^2 y = \dfrac{1 - \tan^2 y}{1 + \tan^2 y}$

35. $2 \csc 2x \cot x = 1 + \cot^2 x$

36. $\cos^8 x - \sin^8 x = (\cos^4 x + \sin^4 x)\cos 2x$

37. $\sin\dfrac{\theta}{2} \cos\dfrac{\theta}{2} = \dfrac{\sin \theta}{2}$

38. $\sin\dfrac{x}{2} = \dfrac{\sec x - 1}{2 \sec x \sin\left(\dfrac{x}{2}\right)}$

39. $\sec x + \tan x = \dfrac{\cos x}{1 - \sin x}$

40. $\dfrac{\cos \theta - \sin \theta}{\cos \theta + \sin \theta} = \dfrac{\cot \theta - 1}{\cot \theta + 1}$

41. $\cos(x - y)\cos y - \sin(x - y)\sin y = \cos x$

42. $\sin 3y \cos 2y - \cos 3y \sin 2y = \sin y$

43. $\sin 4x(\cos^2 2x - \sin^2 2x) = \dfrac{\sin 8x}{2}$

44. $\csc 2x + \cot 2x = \cot x$

45. $\dfrac{\sin x}{\csc x - \cot x} = 1 + \cos x$

46. $\cos x - \sin\dfrac{x}{2} = \left(1 - 2 \sin\dfrac{x}{2}\right)\left(1 + \sin\dfrac{x}{2}\right)$

47. $\dfrac{\sin(x + y) + \sin(x - y)}{\cos(x + y) + \cos(x - y)} = \tan x$

48. $\sec\dfrac{x}{2} + \csc\dfrac{x}{2} = \dfrac{2\left(\sin\dfrac{x}{2} + \cos\dfrac{x}{2}\right)}{\sin x}$

In Exercises 49 through 52 solve for x.

49. $y = 2 \cos 2x$

50. $y - 2 = 2 \tan\left(x - \dfrac{\pi}{2}\right)$

51. $y = \dfrac{\pi}{4} - 3 \arcsin 5x$

52. $2y = \text{arcsec } 4x - 2$

In Exercises 53 through 60 solve the given equations for x such that $0 \le x < 2\pi$.

53. $\cos^2 2x - 1 = 0$

54. $2 \sin 2x + 1 = 0$

55. $4 \cos^2 x - 3 = 0$

56. $\cos 2x = \sin x$

57. $\sin^2 x - \cos^2 x + 1 = 0$

58. $\cos 3x \cos x + \sin 3x \sin x = 0$

59. $\sin^2\left(\dfrac{x}{2}\right) - \cos x + 1 = 0$

60. $\sin x + \cos x = 1$

In Exercises 61 through 64 find an algebraic expression for each of the expressions.

61. $\tan(\text{Arccot } x)$

62. $\cos(\text{Arccsc } x)$

63. $\sin(2 \text{ Arccos } x)$

64. $\cos(\pi - \text{Arctan } x)$

In Exercises 65 through 76 use the formulas and methods of this chapter to solve the given problems.

65. In finding the area between a section of the curve of $y = \cos^3 x$ and the x-axis, it is necessary to transform $\cos^3 x$ to $\cos x - \sin^2 x \cos x$. Show that this is valid.

66. In the theory dealing with the motion of fluid in cylinders, the expression

$$4 \sin^2\alpha \cos^2\alpha + (\cos^2\alpha - \sin^2\alpha)^2$$

is found. Simplify this expression.

67. If the area bounded by $y = \sin x$ between 0 and π and the x-axis is rotated about the x-axis, a volume is generated. In finding this volume it is necessary to change $\sin^2 x$ into $\frac{1}{2}(1 - \cos 2x)$. Show that this change is valid.

68. In surveying, when determining an azimuth (a measure used for reference purposes), it might be necessary to simplify the expression

$$\frac{1}{2 \cos \alpha \cos \beta} - \tan \alpha \tan \beta$$

Perform this operation by expressing it in the simplest possible form when $\alpha = \beta$.

69. An object is under the influence of a central force (an example of one type of central force is the attraction of the sun for the earth). The y-coordinate of its path is given by $y = 20 \sin \frac{1}{3}t$. Solve for t.

70. In finding the pressure exerted by soil on a retaining wall, the expression $1 - \cos 2\varphi - \sin 2\varphi \tan \alpha$ is found. Show that this expression can also be written as $2 \sin \varphi(\sin \varphi - \cos \varphi \tan \alpha)$.

71. In the theory dealing with the reflection of light, the expression

$$\frac{\cos (\phi + \alpha)}{\cos (\phi - \alpha)}$$

is found. Express this in terms of functions of α if $\phi = 2\alpha$.

72. In developing an expression for the power in an alternating-current circuit, the expression $\sin \omega t \sin(\omega t + \phi)$ is found. Show that this expression can be written as $\frac{1}{2}[\cos \phi - \cos(2\omega t + \phi)]$.

73. In the theory of interference of light, the expression $1 - 2r^2\cos \beta + r^4$ is found. Show that this expression can be written as $(1 - r^2)^2 + 4r^2\sin^2(\beta/2)$.

74. In the theory of diffraction of light, an equation found is

$$y = R \sin 2\pi\left(\frac{t}{T} - \frac{a}{\lambda}\right)\cos \alpha - R \cos 2\pi\left(\frac{t}{T} - \frac{a}{\lambda}\right)\sin \alpha$$

Show that

$$y = R \sin 2\pi\left(\frac{t}{T} - \frac{a}{\lambda} - \frac{\alpha}{2\pi}\right)$$

75. If a plane surface inclined at angle θ moves horizontally, the angle for which the lifting force of the air is a maximum is found by solving the equation $2 \sin \theta \cos^2\theta - \sin^3\theta = 0$, where $0 < \theta < 90°$. Solve for θ.

76. The electric current as a function of the time for a particular circuit is given by $i = 8e^{-20t}(\sqrt{3} \cos 10t - \sin 10t)$. Find the time in seconds when the current is first zero.

20

Plane Analytic Geometry

20—1 Basic Definitions

We first introduced the graph of a function in Chapter 2, and since that time we have made extensive use of graphs for representing functions. We have used graphs to represent the trigonometric functions, the exponential and logarithmic functions, and the inverse trigonometric functions. We have also seen how graphs may be used in solving equations and systems of equations. In this chapter we shall consider certain basic principles relating to the graphs of functions. We shall also show how certain graphs can be constructed by recognizing the form of the equation.

It is necessary when studying many of the concepts of the calculus to have the ability to recognize certain curves and their basic characteristics. Also, curves have many technical applications, many of which are illustrated or indicated in the examples and exercises in this chapter.

The underlying principle of analytic geometry is the relationship of geometry to algebra. A great deal can be learned about a geometric figure if we can find the function which represents its graph. Also, by analyzing certain characteristics of a function, we can obtain useful information as to the nature of its graph. In this section we shall develop certain basic concepts which will be needed for future use in establishing the proper relationships between an equation and a curve.

The first of these concepts involves the distance between any two points in the coordinate plane. If these two points lie on a line parallel

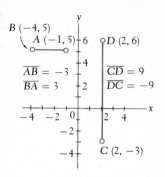

$B(-4, 5)$

$A(-1, 5)$

$\overline{AB} = -3$
$\overline{BA} = 3$

$\overline{CD} = 9$
$\overline{DC} = -9$

$D(2, 6)$

$C(2, -3)$

Figure 20–1

to the x-axis, the **directed distance** from the first point $A(x_1, y)$ to the second point $B(x_2, y)$ is denoted as $\overline{AB}$ and is defined as $x_2 - x_1$. We can see that $\overline{AB}$ *is positive if B is to the right of A, and it is negative if B is to the left of A.* Similarly, the directed distance between two points $C(x, y_1)$ and $D(x, y_2)$ on a line parallel to the y-axis is $y_2 - y_1$. We see that $\overline{CD}$ *is positive if D is above C, and it is negative if D is below C.*

Example A

The line segment joining $A(-1, 5)$ and $B(-4, 5)$ in Fig. 20–1 is parallel to the x-axis. Therefore, the directed distance $\overline{AB} = -4 - (-1) = -3$, and the directed distance $\overline{BA} = -1 - (-4) = 3$.

   Also in Fig. 20–1, the line segment joining $C(2, -3)$ and $D(2, 6)$ is parallel to the y-axis. The directed distance $\overline{CD} = 6 - (-3) = 9$, and the directed distance $\overline{DC} = -3 - 6 = -9$.

   We now wish to find the length of a line segment joining any two points in the plane. If these points are on a line which is not parallel to either of the axes (Fig. 20–2), we must use the Pythagorean theorem to find the distance between them. By making a right triangle with the line segment joining the two points as the hypotenuse, and line segments parallel to the axes as the legs, we have the formula which gives the distance between any two points in the plane. This formula, called the **distance formula,** is

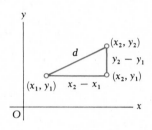

Figure 20–2

$$d = \sqrt{(x_2 - x_1)^2 + (y_2 - y_1)^2} \qquad (20\text{–}1)$$

Here we choose the positive square root since we are concerned only with the magnitude of the length of the line segment.

Example B

The distance between $(3, -1)$ and $(-2, -5)$ is given by

$$d = \sqrt{[(-2) - 3]^2 + [(-5) - (-1)]^2}$$
$$= \sqrt{(-5)^2 + (-4)^2} = \sqrt{25 + 16} = \sqrt{41}$$

It makes no difference which point is chosen as (x_1, y_1) and which is chosen as (x_2, y_2), since the difference in the x-coordinates (and y-coordinates) is squared. We also obtain $\sqrt{41}$ if we set up the distance as

$$d = \sqrt{[3 - (-2)]^2 + [(-1) - (-5)]^2}$$

   Another important quantity which is defined for a line is its **slope.** *The slope gives a measure of the direction of a line, and is defined as the vertical directed distance from one point to another on the same straight line, divided by the horizontal directed distance from the first point to the second.* Thus, using the letter m to represent slope, we have

$$m = \frac{y_2 - y_1}{x_2 - x_1} \qquad (20\text{–}2)$$

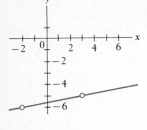

Figure 20–3

Example C

The slope of the line joining $(3, -5)$ and $(-2, -6)$ is

$$m = \frac{-6 - (-5)}{-2 - 3} = \frac{-6 + 5}{-5} = \frac{1}{5}$$

See Fig. 20–3. Again we may interpret either of the points as (x_1, y_1) and the other as (x_2, y_2). We can also obtain the slope of this same line from

$$m = \frac{-5 - (-6)}{3 - (-2)} = \frac{1}{5}$$

The larger the numerical value of the slope of a line, the more nearly vertical is the line. Also, a line rising to the right has a positive slope, and a line falling to the right has a negative slope.

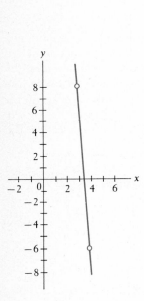

Figure 20–4

Example D

The line through the two points in Example C has a positive slope, which is numerically small. From Fig. 20–3 it can be seen that the line rises slightly to the right.

The line joining $(3, 8)$ and $(4, -6)$ has a slope of -14. This line falls sharply to the right (see Fig. 20–4).

From the definition of slope, we may conclude that the slope of a line parallel to the *y*-axis cannot be defined (the *x*-coordinates of any two points on the line would be the same, which would then necessitate division by zero). This, however, does not prove to be of any trouble.

If a given line is extended indefinitely in either direction, it must cross the *x*-axis at some point unless it is parallel to the *x*-axis. *The angle measured from the x-axis in a positive direction to the line is called the* **inclination** *of the line* (see Fig. 20–5). The inclination of a line parallel to the *x*-axis is defined to be zero. An alternative definition of slope, in terms of the inclination, is

$$m = \tan \alpha, \qquad 0° \leq \alpha < 180° \tag{20–3}$$

where α is the inclination. This can be seen from the fact that the slope can be defined in terms of any two points on the line. Thus, if we choose as one of these points that point where the line crosses the *x*-axis and any other point, we see from the definition of the tangent of an angle that Eq. (20–3) is in agreement with Eq. (20–2).

Figure 20–5

Example E

The slope of a line with an inclination of 45° is $m = \tan 45° = 1.000$. The slope of a line having an inclination of 120° is $m = \tan 120° = -\sqrt{3} = -1.732$. See Fig. 20–6.

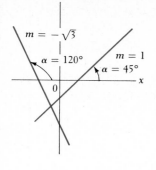

$$m = -\sqrt{3}$$

$$\alpha = 120°$$

$$m = 1$$
$$\alpha = 45°$$

Figure 20–6

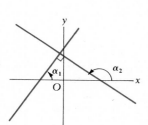

Figure 20–7

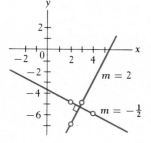

$$m = 2$$

$$m = -\tfrac{1}{2}$$

Figure 20–8

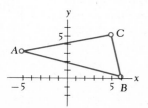

Figure 20–9

Any two parallel lines crossing the x-axis will have the same inclination. Therefore, *the slopes of parallel lines are equal.* This can be stated as

$$m_1 = m_2 \qquad \text{for} \parallel \text{lines} \tag{20–4}$$

If two lines are perpendicular, this means that there must be 90° between their inclinations (Fig. 20–7). The relation between their inclinations is

$$\alpha_2 = \alpha_1 + 90°$$

which can be written as

$$90° - \alpha_2 = -\alpha_1$$

Taking the tangent of each of the angles in this last relation, we have

$$\tan(90° - \alpha_2) = \tan(-\alpha_1)$$

or

$$\cot \alpha_2 = -\tan \alpha_1$$

since a function of the complement of an angle is equal to the cofunction of that angle (see Section 3–4), and since $\tan(-\alpha) = -\tan \alpha$ (see Exercise 61 of Section 7–2). But $\cot \alpha = 1/\tan \alpha$, which means that $1/\tan \alpha_2 = -\tan \alpha_1$. Using the inclination definition of slope, we may write, as the relation between slopes of perpendicular lines,

$$m_2 = -\frac{1}{m_1} \qquad \text{or} \qquad m_1 m_2 = -1 \qquad \text{for} \perp \text{lines} \tag{20–5}$$

Example F

The line through $(3, -5)$ and $(2, -7)$ has a slope of 2. The line through $(4, -6)$ and $(2, -5)$ has a slope of $-\tfrac{1}{2}$. These lines are perpendicular. See Fig. 20–8.

Using the formulas for distance and slope, we can show certain basic geometric relations. The following examples illustrate the use of the formulas, and thus show the use of algebra in solving problems which are basically geometric. This illustrates the methods of analytic geometry.

Example G

Show that line segments joining $A(-5, 3)$, $B(6, 0)$, and $C(5, 5)$ form a right triangle (see Fig. 20–9).

If these points are vertices of a right triangle, the slopes of two of the sides must be negative reciprocals. This would show perpendicularity. Thus, we find the slopes of the three lines to be

$$m_{AB} = \frac{3 - 0}{-5 - 6} = -\frac{3}{11}, \qquad m_{AC} = \frac{3 - 5}{-5 - 5} = \frac{1}{5}, \qquad m_{BC} = \frac{0 - 5}{6 - 5} = -5$$

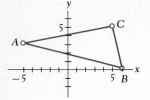

Figure 20—9

We see that the slopes of AC and BC are negative reciprocals, which means that $AC \perp BC$. From this we can conclude that the triangle is a right triangle.

Example H

Find the area of the triangle in Example G.

Since the right angle is at C, the legs of the triangle are AC and BC. The area is one-half the product of the lengths of the legs of a right triangle. The lengths of the legs are

$$d_{AC} = \sqrt{(-5 - 5)^2 + (3 - 5)^2} = \sqrt{104} = 2\sqrt{26}$$

and

$$d_{BC} = \sqrt{(6 - 5)^2 + (0 - 5)^2} = \sqrt{26}$$

Therefore, the area is

$$A = \frac{1}{2}(2\sqrt{26})(\sqrt{26}) = 26$$

Exercises 20—1

In Exercises 1 through 8 find the distances between the given pairs of points.

1. $(3, 8)$ and $(-1, -2)$ 2. $(-1, 3)$ and $(-8, -4)$
3. $(4, -5)$ and $(4, -8)$ 4. $(-3, 7)$ and $(2, 10)$
5. $(-1, 0)$ and $(5, -7)$ 6. $(15, -1)$ and $(-11, 1)$
7. $(-4, -3)$ and $(3, -3)$ 8. $(-2, 5)$ and $(-2, -2)$

In Exercises 9 through 16 find the slopes of the lines through the points in Exercises 1 through 8.

In Exercises 17 through 20 find the slopes of the lines with the given inclinations.

17. $30°$ 18. $60°$ 19. $150°$ 20. $135°$

In Exercises 21 through 24 find the inclinations of the lines with the given slopes.

21. 0.3640 22. 0.8243 23. -6.691 24. -1.428

In Exercises 25 through 28 determine whether the lines through the two pairs of points are parallel or perpendicular.

25. $(6, -1)$ and $(4, 3)$, and $(-5, 2)$ and $(-7, 6)$
26. $(-3, 9)$ and $(4, 4)$, and $(9, -1)$ and $(4, -8)$
27. $(-1, -4)$ and $(2, 3)$, and $(-5, 2)$ and $(-19, 8)$
28. $(-1, -2)$ and $(3, 6)$, and $(2, -6)$ and $(5, 0)$

In Exercises 29 through 32 determine the value of k.

29. The distance between $(-1, 3)$ and $(11, k)$ is 13.
30. The distance between $(k, 0)$ and $(0, 2k)$ is 10.

31. The points $(6, -1)$, $(3, k)$, and $(-3, -7)$ are all on the same line.

32. The points in Exercise 31 are the vertices of a right triangle, with the right angle at $(3, k)$.

In Exercises 33 through 36 show that the given points are vertices of the indicated geometric figures.

distance 33. Show that the points $(2, 3)$, $(4, 9)$, and $(-2, 7)$ are the vertices of an isosceles triangle.

slope 34. Show that $(-1, 3)$, $(3, 5)$, and $(5, 1)$ are the vertices of a right triangle.

slope 35. Show that $(3, 2)$, $(7, 3)$, $(-1, -3)$, and $(3, -2)$ are the vertices of a parallelogram.

36. Show that $(-5, 6)$, $(0, 8)$, $(-3, 1)$, and $(2, 3)$ are the vertices of a square.

In Exercises 37 and 38 find the indicated areas.

37. Find the area of the triangle of Exercise 34.

38. Find the area of the square of Exercise 36.

20—2 The Straight Line

Using the definition of slope, we can derive the equation which always represents a straight line. This is another basic method of analytic geometry. That is, equations of a particular form can be shown to represent a particular type of curve. When we recognize the form of the equation, we know the kind of curve it represents. This can be of great assistance in sketching the graph.

A straight line can be defined as a "curve" with constant slope. By this we mean that for any two different points chosen on a given line, if the slope is calculated, the same value is always found. Thus, if we consider one point (x_1, y_1) on a line to be fixed (Fig. 20–10), and another point $P(x, y)$ which can *represent* any other point on the line, we have

$$m = \frac{y - y_1}{x - x_1}$$

which can be written as

$$y - y_1 = m(x - x_1) \tag{20–6}$$

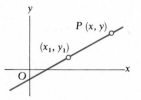

Figure 20–10

Equation (20–6) is known as the **point-slope form** of the equation of a straight line. It is useful when we know the slope of a line and some point through which the line passes. Direct substitution can then give us the equation of the line. Such information is often available about a given line.

Example A
Find the equation of the line which passes through $(-4, 1)$ with a slope of -2.

By using Eq. (20–6), we find that

$$y - 1 = (-2)(x + 4)$$

which can be simplified to

$$y + 2x + 7 = 0$$

This line is shown in Fig. 20–11.

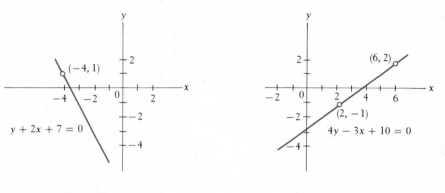

Figure 20–11   Figure 20–12

Example B
Find the equation of the line through $(2, -1)$ and $(6, 2)$.

We first find the slope of the line through these points:

$$m = \frac{2 + 1}{6 - 2} = \frac{3}{4}$$

Then, by using either of the two known points and Eq. (20–6), we can find the equation of the line:

$$y + 1 = \frac{3}{4}(x - 2)$$

or

$$4y + 4 = 3x - 6$$

or

$$4y - 3x + 10 = 0$$

This line is shown in Fig. 20–12.

Equation (20–6) can be used for any line except one parallel to the y-axis. Such a line has an undefined slope. However, it does have the property that all points have the same x-coordinate, regardless of the y-coordinate. We represent a line parallel to the y-axis as

$$\underline{x = a}\qquad\qquad(20\text{--}7)$$

A line parallel to the x-axis has a slope of 0. From Eq. (20–6), we can find its equation to be $y = y_1$. To keep the same form as Eq. (20–7), we normally write this as

$$\underline{y = b}\qquad\qquad(20\text{--}8)$$

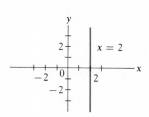

Figure 20—13

Example C
The line $x = 2$ is a line parallel to the y-axis and two units to the right of it. This line is shown in Fig. 20–13.

Example D
The line $y = -4$ is a line parallel to the x-axis and 4 units below it. This line is shown in Fig. 20–14.

If we choose the special point $(0, b)$, which is the y-intercept of the line, as the point to use in Eq. (20–6), we have

$$y - b = m(x - 0)$$

or

$$\underline{y = mx + b}\qquad\qquad(20\text{--}9)$$

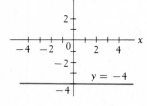

Figure 20—14

Equation (20–9) is known as the **slope-intercept form** of the equation of a straight line. Its usefulness lies in the fact that once we find the equation of a line and then write it in slope-intercept form, we know that the slope of the line is the coefficient of the x-term and that it crosses the y-axis with the coordinate indicated by the constant term.

Example E
Find the slope and the y-intercept of the straight line whose equation is $2y + 4x - 5 = 0$.
   We write this equation in slope-intercept form:

$$2y = -4x + 5$$

$$y = -2x + \frac{5}{2}$$

Since the coefficient of x in this form is -2, the slope of the line is -2. The constant on the right is $\frac{5}{2}$, which means that the y-intercept is $\frac{5}{2}$.

From Eqs. (20–6) and (20–9), and from the examples of this section, we see that the equation of the straight line has certain characteristics: we have a term in y, a term in x, and a constant term if we simplify as much as possible. This form is represented by the equation

$$Ax + By + C = 0 \qquad (20\text{--}10)$$

which is known as the **general form** of the equation of the straight line. We have seen this form before in Chapter 4. Now we have shown why it represents a straight line.

Example F
What are the intercepts of the line $3x - 4y - 12 = 0$?
We know that the intercepts of a curve are those points where it crosses each of the axes. At the point where any curve crosses the x-axis, the y-coordinate must be 0. Thus, by letting $y = 0$ in the equation above, we solve for x and obtain $x = 4$. Hence one intercept is (4, 0). By letting $x = 0$, we find the other intercept as (0, -3).

In many physical situations a linear relationship exists between variables. A few examples of situations where such relationships exist are between (1) the distance traveled by an object and the elapsed time, when the velocity is constant, (2) the amount a spring stretches and the force applied, (3) the change in electric resistance and the change in temperature, (4) the force applied to an object and the resulting acceleration, and (5) the pressure at a certain point within a liquid and the depth of the point. The following example illustrates the use of a straight line in dealing with an applied problem.

Example G
Under the condition of constant acceleration, the velocity of an object varies linearly with the time. If after 1 s a certain object has a velocity of 40 ft/s, and 3 s later it has a velocity of 55 ft/s, find the equation relating the velocity and time, and graph this equation. From the graph determine the initial velocity (the velocity when $t = 0$) and the velocity after 6 s.
If we treat the velocity v as the dependent variable, and the time t as the independent variable, the slope of the straight line is

$$m = \frac{v_2 - v_1}{t_2 - t_1}$$

Using the information given in the problem, we have

$$m = \frac{55 - 40}{4 - 1} = 5$$

Then, using the point-slope form of the equation of a straight line, we have $v - 40 = 5(t - 1)$, or $v = 5t + 35$, which is the required equation (see Fig. 20–15). For purposes of graphing the line, the values given

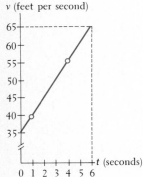

v (feet per second)

t (seconds)

Figure 20–15

are sufficient. Of course, there is no need to include negative values of t, since these have no physical meaning. From the graph we see that the line crosses the v-axis at 35. This means that the initial velocity is 35 ft/s. Also, when $t = 6$ we see that $v = 65$ ft/s.

Exercises 20—2

In Exercises 1 through 16 find the equation of each of the lines with the given properties.

1. Passes through $(-3, 8)$ with a slope of 4
2. Passes through $(-2, -1)$ with a slope of -2
3. Passes through $(-2, -5)$ and $(4, 2)$
4. Passes through $(-3, -5)$ and $(-2, 3)$
5. Passes through $(1, 3)$ and has an inclination of $45°$
6. Has a y-intercept of -2 and an inclination of $120°$
7. Passes through $(6, -3)$ and is parallel to the x-axis
8. Passes through $(-4, -2)$ and is perpendicular to the x-axis
9. Is parallel to the y-axis and is 3 units to the left of it
10. Is parallel to the x-axis and is 5 units below it
11. Has an x-intercept of 4 and a y-intercept of -6
12. Has an x-intercept of -3 and a slope of 2
13. Is perpendicular to a line with a slope of 3 and passes through $(1, -2)$
14. Is perpendicular to a line with a slope of -4 and has a y-intercept of 3
15. Is perpendicular to the line joining $(4, 2)$ and $(3, -5)$ and passes through $(4, 2)$
16. Is parallel to the line $2y - 6x - 5 = 0$ and passes through $(-4, -5)$

In Exercises 17 through 20 draw the lines with the given equations.

17. $4x - y = 8$
18. $2x - 3y - 6 = 0$
19. $3x + 5y - 10 = 0$
20. $4y = 6x - 9$

In Exercises 21 through 24 reduce the equations to slope-intercept form and determine the slope and y-intercept.

21. $3x - 2y - 1 = 0$
22. $4x + 2y - 5 = 0$
23. $5x - 2y + 5 = 0$
24. $6x - 3y - 4 = 0$

In Exercises 25 through 28 determine the value of k.

25. What is the value of k if the lines $4x - ky = 6$ and $6x + 3y + 2 = 0$ are to be parallel?
26. What must k equal in Exercise 25, if the given lines are to be perpendicular?
27. What must be the value of k if the lines $3x - y = 9$ and $kx + 3y = 5$ are to be perpendicular?
28. What must k equal in Exercise 27, if the given lines are to be parallel?

In Exercises 29 and 30 show that the given lines are parallel. In Exercises 31 and 32 show that the given lines are perpendicular.

29. $3x - 2y + 5 = 0$ and $4y = 6x - 1$
30. $3y - 2x = 4$ and $6x - 9y = 5$

31. $6x - 3y - 2 = 0$ and $x + 2y - 4 = 0$

32. $4x - y + 2 = 0$ and $2x + 8y - 1 = 0$

In Exercises 33 through 36 find the equations of the given lines.

33. The line which has an x-intercept of 4 and a y-intercept the same as the line $2y - 3x - 4 = 0$

34. The line which is perpendicular to the line $8x + 2y - 3 = 0$ and has the same x-intercept as this line

35. The line with a slope of -3 which also passes through the intersection of the lines $5x - y = 6$ and $x + y = 12$

36. The line which passes through the point of intersection of $2x + y - 3 = 0$ and $x - y - 3 = 0$ and through the point $(4, -3)$

In Exercises 37 through 50 some applications and methods involving straight lines are shown.

37. The average velocity of an object is defined as the change in displacement s divided by the corresponding change in time t. Find the equation relating the displacement s and time t for an object for which the average velocity is 50 m/s and $s = 10$ m when $t = 0$ s.

38. The acceleration of an object is defined as the change in velocity v divided by the corresponding change in time t. Find the equation relating the velocity v and time t for an object for which the acceleration is 20 ft/s² and $v = 5.0$ ft/s when $t = 0$ s.

39. Within certain limits, the amount which a spring stretches varies linearly with the amount of force applied. If a spring whose natural length is 15 in. stretches 2.0 in. when 3.0 lb of force are applied, find the equation relating the length of the spring and the applied force.

40. The electric resistance of a certain resistor increases by 0.005 Ω for every increase of 1°C. Given that its resistance is 2.000 Ω at 0°C, find the equation relating the resistance and temperature. From the equation find the resistance when the temperature is 50°C.

41. The amount of heat required to raise the temperature of water varies linearly with the increase in temperature. However, a certain quantity of heat is required to change ice (at 0°C) into water without a change in temperature. An experiment is performed with 10 g of ice at 0°C. It is found that ice requires 4.19 kJ to change it into water at 20°C. Another 1.26 kJ is required to warm the water to 50°C. How many kilojoules are required to melt the ice at 0°C into water at 0°C?

42. The pressure at a point below the surface of a body of water varies linearly with the depth of the water. If the pressure at a depth of 10.0 m is 199 kPa and the pressure at a depth of 30.0 m is 395 kPa, what is the pressure at the surface? (This is the atmospheric pressure of the air above the water.)

43. A survey of the traffic on a particular highway showed that the number of cars passing a particular point each minute varied linearly from 6:30 AM to 8:30 AM on workday mornings. The study showed that an average of 45 cars passed the point in one minute at 7 AM, and that 115 cars passed in one minute at 8 AM. If n is the number of cars passing the point in one minute and t is the number of minutes after 6:30 AM, find the equation relating n and t, and graph the equation. From the graph, determine n at 6:30 AM and at 8:30 AM.

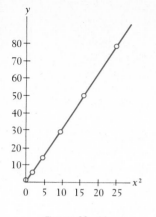

Figure 20–16

44. The total fixed cost for a company to operate a certain plant is $400 per day. It also costs $2 for each unit produced in the plant. Find the equation relating the total cost C of operating the plant and the number of units n produced each day. Graph the equation, assuming that $n \leq 300$.

45. Sometimes it is desirable to treat a nonlinear function as a linear function. For example, if $y = 2 + 3x^2$, this can be plotted as a straight line by plotting y vs. x^2. A table of values for this graph is

x	0	1	2	3	4	5
x^2	0	1	4	9	16	25
y	2	5	14	29	50	77

and the graph appears in Fig. 20–16. Using this method, sketch the function $y = 1 + \sqrt{x}$. That is, plot y vs. $\sqrt{x}$.

46. Using the method of Exercise 45, sketch the function $C = 10/E$ as a linear function. This is the equation between the voltage across a capacitor and the capacitance, assuming the charge on the capacitor is constant.

47. Another method of treating a nonlinear function as a linear one is to use logarithms. In Section 12–9 we noted that curves plotted on logarithmic and semilogarithmic paper often come out as straight lines. Since distances corresponding to log y and log x are plotted automatically if the graph is logarithmic in the respective directions, many nonlinear functions are linear when plotted on this paper. A function of the form $y = ax^n$ is straight when plotted on logarithmic paper, since log y = log a + n log x is in the form of a straight line. The variables are log y and log x; the slope can be found from (log y − log a)/log x = n, and the intercept is a. (To get the slope from the graph, it is necessary to measure vertical and horizontal distances between two points. The log y intercept is found where log x = 0, and this occurs when $x = 1$.) Plot $y = 3x^4$ on logarithmic paper to verify this analysis.

48. A function of the form $y = a(b^x)$ is a straight line on semilogarithmic paper, since log y = log a + x log b is in the form of a straight line. The variables are log y and x, the slope is log b, and the intercept is a. [To get the slope from the graph, we must calculate (log y − log a)/x for some set of values x and y. The intercept is read directly off the graph where $x = 0$.] Plot $y = 3(2^x)$ on semilogarithmic paper to verify this analysis.

49. If experimental data are plotted on logarithmic paper and the points lie on a straight line, it is possible to determine the function (see Exercise 47). The following data come from an experiment to determine the functional relationship between the tension in a string and the velocity of a wave in the string. From the graph on logarithmic paper, determine v as a function of T.

v (meters per second)	16.0	32.0	45.3	55.4	64.0
T (newtons)	0.100	0.400	0.800	1.20	1.60

50. If experimental data are plotted on semilogarithmic paper, and the points lie on a straight line, it is possible to determine the function (see Exercise 48). The following data come from an experiment designed to determine the relationship between the voltage across an inductor and the time, after the switch is opened. Determine v as a function of t.

v (volts)	40	15	5.6	2.2	0.8
t (milliseconds)	0.0	20	40	60	80

20–3 The Circle

We have found that we can obtain a general equation which represents a straight line by considering a fixed point on the line and then a general point $P(x, y)$ which can represent any other point on the same line. Mathematically we can state this as "the line is the **locus** of a point $P(x, y)$ which *moves* along the line." That is, the point $P(x, y)$ can be considered as a variable point which moves along the line.

In this way we can define a number of important curves. *The* **circle** *is defined as the locus of a point* $P(x, y)$ *which moves so that it is always equidistant from a fixed point. This fixed distance we call the* **radius**, *and the fixed point is called the* **center** *of the circle.* Thus, using this definition, calling the fixed point (h, k) and the radius r, we have

$$\sqrt{(x - h)^2 + (y - k)^2} = r$$

or, by squaring both sides, we have

$$(x - h)^2 + (y - k)^2 = r^2 \tag{20–11}$$

Equation (20–11) is called the **standard equation** of a circle with center at (h, k) and radius r (Fig. 20–17).

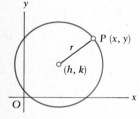

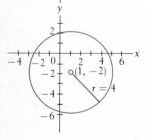

Figure 20–17

Figure 20–18

Example A

The equation $(x - 1)^2 + (y + 2)^2 = 16$ represents a circle with center at $(1, -2)$ and a radius of 4. We determine these values by considering the equation of this circle to be in the form of Eq. (20–11) as $(x - 1)^2 + (y - (-2))^2 = 4^2$. Note carefully the way in which we find the y-coordinate of the center. This circle is shown in Fig. 20–18.

If the center of the circle is at the origin, which means that the coordinates of the center are $(0, 0)$, the equation of the circle becomes

$$x^2 + y^2 = r^2 \tag{20–12}$$

A circle of this type clearly exhibits an important property of the graphs of many equations. It is **symmetrical** to the x-axis and also to the y-axis. Symmetry to the x-axis can be thought of as meaning that the lower half of the curve is a reflection of the upper half, and conversely. It can be shown that *if* $-y$ *can replace* y *in an equation without changing the equation, the graph of the equation is symmetrical to the* x-*axis.* Symmetry to the y-axis has a similar meaning, so *if* $-x$ *can replace* x *in the equation without changing the equation, the graph is symmetrical to the* y-*axis.*

This type of circle is symmetrical to the origin as well as being symmetrical to both axes. The meaning of symmetry to the origin is that the origin is the midpoint of any two points (x, y) and $(-x, -y)$ which are on the curve. Thus, *if −x can replace x, and −y replace y at the same time, without changing the equation, the graph of the equation is symmetrical to the origin.*

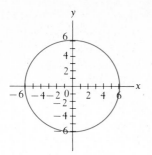

Figure 20–19

Example B

The equation of the circle with its center at the origin and with a radius of 6 is $x^2 + y^2 = 36$.

The symmetry of this circle can be shown analytically by the substitutions mentioned above. Replacing x by $−x$, we obtain $(−x)^2 + y^2 = 36$. Since $(−x)^2 = x^2$, this equation can be rewritten as $x^2 + y^2 = 36$. Since this substitution did not change the equation, the graph is symmetrical to the y-axis.

Replacing y by $−y$, we obtain $x^2 + (−y)^2 = 36$, which is the same as $x^2 + y^2 = 36$. This means that the curve is symmetrical to the x-axis.

Replacing x by $−x$, and simultaneously replacing y by $−y$, we obtain $(−x)^2 + (−y)^2 = 36$, which is the same as $x^2 + y^2 = 36$. This means that the curve is symmetrical to the origin. The circle is shown in Fig. 20–19.

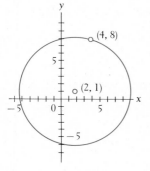

Figure 20–20

Example C

Find the equation of the circle with center at (2, 1) and which passes through (4, 8).

In Eq. (20–11), we can determine the equation if we can find h, k, and r for this circle. From the given information, $h = 2$ and $k = 1$. To find r, we use the fact that *all points on the circle must satisfy the equation of the circle.* The point (4, 8) must satisfy Eq. (20–11), with $h = 2$ and $k = 1$. Thus, $(4 − 2)^2 + (8 − 1)^2 = r^2$. From this relation we find $r^2 = 53$. The equation of the circle is

$$(x − 2)^2 + (y − 1)^2 = 53$$

This circle is shown in Fig. 20–20.

If we multiply out each of the terms in Eq. (20–11), we may combine the resulting terms to obtain

$$x^2 − 2hx + h^2 + y^2 − 2ky + k^2 = r^2$$
$$x^2 + y^2 − 2hx − 2ky + (h^2 + k^2 − r^2) = 0 \qquad (20\text{–}13)$$

Since each of h, k, and r is constant for any given circle, the coefficients of x and y and the term within parentheses in Eq. (20–13) are constants. Equation (20–13) can then be written as

$$x^2 + y^2 + Dx + Ey + F = 0 \qquad (20\text{–}14)$$

Equation (20–14) is called the **general equation** of the circle. It tells us that any equation which can be written in that form will represent a circle.

Example D
Find the center and radius of the circle

$$x^2 + y^2 - 6x + 8y - 24 = 0$$

We can find this information if we write the given equation in standard form. To do so, we must complete the square in the x-terms and also in the y-terms. This is done by first writing the equation in the form

$$(x^2 - 6x \quad) + (y^2 + 8y \quad) = 24$$

To complete the square of the x-terms, we take half of 6, which is 3, square it, and add the result, 9, to each side of the equation. In the same way, we complete the square of the y-terms by adding 16 to each side of the equation, which gives

$$(x^2 - 6x + 9) + (y^2 + 8y + 16) = 24 + 9 + 16$$
$$(x - 3)^2 + (y + 4)^2 = 49$$

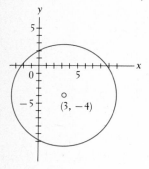

Figure 20—21

Thus, the center is $(3, -4)$, and the radius is 7 (see Fig. 20–21).

Example E
The equation $3x^2 + 3y^2 + 6x - 20 = 0$ can be seen to represent a circle by writing it in general form. This is done by dividing through by 3. In this way we have

$$x^2 + y^2 + 2x - \frac{20}{3} = 0$$

To determine the center and radius for this circle, we write the equation in standard form and then complete the necessary squares. This leads to

$$(x^2 + 2x + 1) + y^2 = \frac{20}{3} + 1$$

$$(x + 1)^2 + y^2 = \frac{23}{3}$$

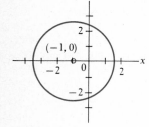

Figure 20—22

Thus, the center is $(-1, 0)$; the radius is $\sqrt{23/3} = 2.77$ (see Fig. 20–22).
We can also see that this circle is symmetrical to the x-axis, but it is not symmetrical to the y-axis or to the origin. If we replace y by $-y$, the equation does not change, but if we replace x by $-x$, the $6x$ term in the original equation becomes negative, and the equation *does* change.

Exercises 20—3

In Exercises 1 through 4 determine the center and radius of each circle.

1. $(x - 2)^2 + (y - 1)^2 = 25$ 2. $(x - 3)^2 + (y + 4)^2 = 49$
3. $(x + 1)^2 + y^2 = 4$ 4. $x^2 + (y + 6)^2 = 64$

In Exercises 5 through 16 find the equation of each of the circles from the given information.

5. Center at $(0, 0)$, radius 3   6. Center at $(0, 0)$, radius 1
7. Center at $(2, 2)$, radius 4   8. Center at $(0, 2)$, radius 2

9. Center at $(-2, 5)$, radius $\sqrt{5}$ 10. Center at $(-3, -5)$, radius 8
11. Center at $(2, 1)$, passes through $(4, -1)$
12. Center at $(-1, 4)$, passes through $(-2, 3)$
13. Center $(-3, 5)$, tangent to the x-axis
14. Tangent to both axes, radius 4, and in the second quadrant
15. Center on the line $5x = 2y$, radius 5, tangent to the x-axis
16. The points $(3, 8)$ and $(-3, 0)$ are the ends of a diameter.

In Exercises 17 through 24 determine the center and radius of each circle. Sketch each circle.

17. $x^2 + y^2 - 25 = 0$ 18. $x^2 + y^2 - 9 = 0$
19. $x^2 + y^2 - 2x - 8 = 0$ 20. $x^2 + y^2 - 4x - 6y - 12 = 0$
21. $x^2 + y^2 + 8x - 10y - 8 = 0$ 22. $x^2 + y^2 + 8x + 6y = 0$
23. $2x^2 + 2y^2 - 4x - 8y - 1 = 0$ 24. $3x^2 + 3y^2 - 12x + 4 = 0$

In Exercises 25 through 28 determine whether the circles with the given equations are symmetrical to either axis or the origin.

25. $x^2 + y^2 = 100$ 26. $x^2 + y^2 - 4x - 5 = 0$
27. $x^2 + y^2 + 8y - 9 = 0$ 28. $x^2 + y^2 - 2x + 4y - 3 = 0$

In Exercises 29 through 36 find the indicated quantities.

29. Determine where the circle $x^2 - 6x + y^2 - 7 = 0$ crosses the x-axis.
30. Find the points of intersection of the circle $x^2 + y^2 - x - 3y = 0$ and the line $y = x - 1$.
31. Find the locus of a point $P(x, y)$ which moves so that its distance from $(2, 4)$ is twice its distance from $(0, 0)$. Describe the locus.
32. Find the equation of the locus of a point $P(x, y)$ which moves so that the line joining it and $(2, 0)$ is always perpendicular to the line joining it and $(-2, 0)$. Describe the locus.
33. If an electrically charged particle enters a magnetic field of flux density B with a velocity v at right angles to the field, the path of the particle is a circle. The radius of the path is given by $R = mv/Bq$, where m is the mass of the particle and q is its charge. If a proton ($m = 1.67 \times 10^{-27}$ kg, $q = 1.60 \times 10^{-19}$ C) enters a magnetic field of flux density 1.50 T (tesla: $V \cdot s/m^2$) with a velocity of 2.40×10^8 m/s, find the equation of the path of the proton. (The fact that a charged particle travels in a circular path in a magnetic field is an important basis for the construction of a cyclotron.)
34. For a constant (magnitude) impedance and capacitive reactance, sketch the graph of resistance versus inductive reactance (see Section 11–7).
35. A cylindrical oil tank, 4.00 ft in diameter, is on its side. A circular hole, with center 18.0 in. below the center of the end of the tank, has been drilled in the end of the tank. If the radius of the hole is 3.00 in., what is the equation of the circle of the end of the tank and the equation of the circle of the hole? Use the center of the end of the tank as the origin.
36. A draftsman is drawing a friction drive in which two circular disks are in contact with each other. They are represented by circles in his drawing. The first has a radius of 10.0 cm and the second has a radius of 12.0 cm. What is the equation of each circle if the origin is at the center of the first circle and the x-axis passes through the center of the second circle?

20—4 The Parabola

Another important curve is the parabola. We have come across this curve several times in the past. In this section we shall find the form of the equation of the parabola and see that this is a familiar form.

The **parabola** *is defined as the locus of a point P(x, y) which moves so that it is always equidistant from a given line and a given point. The given line is called the* **directrix,** *and the given point is called the* **focus.** The line through the focus which is perpendicular to the directrix is called the **axis** of the parabola. The point midway between the directrix and focus is the **vertex** of the parabola. Using the definition, we shall find the equation of the parabola for which the focus is the point $(p, 0)$ and the directrix is the line $x = -p$. By choosing the focus and directrix in this manner, we shall be able to find a general representation of the equation of a parabola with its vertex at the origin.

According to the definition of the parabola, the distance from a point $P(x, y)$ on the parabola to the focus $(p, 0)$ must equal the distance from $P(x, y)$ to the directrix $x = -p$. The distance from P to the focus can be found by use of the distance formula. The distance from P to the directrix is the perpendicular distance, and this can be found as the distance between two points on a line parallel to the x-axis. These distances are indicated in Fig. 20–23.

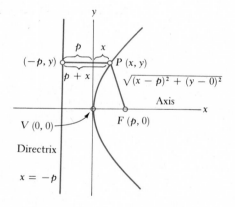

Figure 20—23

Thus, we have

$$\sqrt{(x - p)^2 + (y - 0)^2} = x + p$$

Squaring both sides of this equation, we have

$$(x - p)^2 + y^2 = (x + p)^2$$

or

$$x^2 - 2px + p^2 + y^2 = x^2 + 2px + p^2$$

Simplifying, we obtain

$$y^2 = 4px \qquad (20-15)$$

Equation (20–15) is called the **standard form** of the equation of a parabola with its axis along the x-axis and the vertex at the origin. Its symmetry to the x-axis can be proven since $(-y)^2 = 4px$ is the same as $y^2 = 4px$.

Example A

Find the coordinates of the focus, the equation of the directrix, and sketch the graph of the parabola $y^2 = 12x$.

From the form of the equation, we know that the vertex is at the origin (Fig. 20–24). The coefficient 12 tells us that the focus is (3, 0), since $p = \frac{12}{4}$ [note that the coefficient of x in Eq. (20–15) is $4p$]. Also, this means that the directrix is the line $x = -3$.

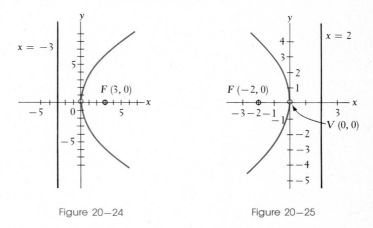

Figure 20—24   Figure 20—25

Example B

If the focus is to the left of the origin, with the directrix an equal distance to the right, the coefficient of the x-term will be negative. This tells us that the parabola opens to the left, rather than to the right, as is the case when the focus is to the right of the origin. For example, the parabola $y^2 = -8x$ has its vertex at the origin, its focus at $(-2, 0)$, and the line $x = 2$ as its directrix. This is consistent with Eq. (20–15), in that $4p = -8$, or $p = -2$. The parabola opens to the left as shown in Fig. 20–25.

If we chose the focus as the point $(0, p)$ and the directrix as the line $y = -p$, we would find that the resulting equation is

$$x^2 = 4py \qquad (20-16)$$

This is the standard form of the equation of a parabola with the y-axis as its axis and the vertex at the origin. Its symmetry to the y-axis can be proven since $(-x)^2 = 4py$ is the same as $x^2 = 4py$. We note that the difference between this equation and Eq. (20–15) is that x is squared and y appears to the first power in Eq. (20–16), rather than the reverse, as in Eq. (20–15).

Example C

The parabola $x^2 = 4y$ has its vertex at the origin, focus at the point $(0, 1)$, and its directrix the line $y = -1$. The graph is shown in Fig. 20–26, and we see in this case that the parabola opens up.

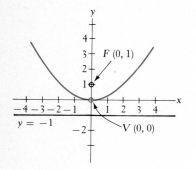

Figure 20–26

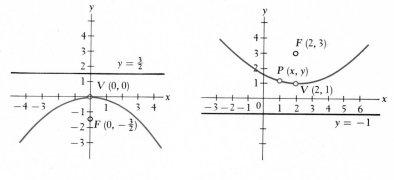

Figure 20–27   Figure 20–28

Example D

The parabola $x^2 = -6y$ has its vertex at the origin, its focus at the point $(0, -\frac{3}{2})$, and its directrix the line $y = \frac{3}{2}$. This parabola opens down, as Fig. 20–27 shows.

Equations (20–15) and (20–16) give us the general form of the equation of a parabola with its vertex at the origin and its focus on one of the coordinate axes. The following example illustrates the use of the definition of the parabola to find the equation of a parabola which has its vertex at a point other than at the origin.

Example E

Using the definition of the parabola, determine the equation of the parabola with its focus at $(2, 3)$ and its directrix the line $y = -1$ (see Fig. 20–28).

Choosing a general point $P(x, y)$ on the parabola, and equating the distances from this point to $(2, 3)$ and to the line $y = -1$, we have

$$\sqrt{(x - 2)^2 + (y - 3)^2} = y + 1$$

Squaring both sides of this equation and simplifying, we have

$$(x - 2)^2 + (y - 3)^2 = (y + 1)^2$$
$$x^2 - 4x + 4 + y^2 - 6y + 9 = y^2 + 2y + 1$$

or

$$8y = 12 - 4x + x^2$$

When we see it in this form, we note that this type of equation has appeared numerous times in earlier chapters. The x-term and the constant (12 in this case) are characteristic of a parabola which does not have its vertex at the origin if the directrix is parallel to the x-axis.

Thus we can conclude that a parabola is characterized by the presence of the square of either (but not both) x or y, and a first-power term in the other. In this way we can recognize a parabola by inspecting the equation.

Exercises 20—4

In Exercises 1 through 12 determine the coordinates of the focus and the equation of the directrix of each of the given parabolas. Sketch each curve.

1. $y^2 = 4x$
2. $y^2 = 16x$
3. $y^2 = -4x$
4. $y^2 = -16x$
5. $x^2 = 8y$
6. $x^2 = 10y$
7. $x^2 = -4y$
8. $x^2 = -12y$
9. $y^2 = 2x$
10. $x^2 = 14y$
11. $y = x^2$
12. $x = 3y^2$

In Exercises 13 through 20 find the equations of the parabolas satisfying the given conditions.

13. Focus $(3, 0)$, directrix $x = -3$
14. Focus $(-2, 0)$, directrix $x = 2$
15. Focus $(0, 4)$, vertex $(0, 0)$
16. Focus $(-3, 0)$, vertex $(0, 0)$
17. Vertex $(0, 0)$, directrix $y = -1$
18. Vertex $(0, 0)$, directrix $y = \frac{1}{2}$
19. Vertex at $(0, 0)$, axis along the y-axis, passes through $(-1, 8)$
20. Vertex at $(0, 0)$, axis along the x-axis, passes through $(2, -1)$

In Exercises 21 through 24 use the definition of the parabola to find the equations of the parabolas satisfying the given conditions. Sketch each curve.

21. Focus $(6, 1)$, directrix $x = 0$
22. Focus $(1, -4)$, directrix $x = 2$
23. Focus $(1, 1)$, vertex $(1, 3)$
24. Vertex $(-2, -4)$, directrix $x = 3$

In Exercises 25 through 32 find the indicated quantities.

25. In calculus it can be shown that a light ray emanating from the focus of a parabola will be reflected off parallel to the axis of the parabola. Suppose that a light ray from the focus of a parabolic reflector described by the equation $y^2 = 8x$ strikes the reflector at the point $(2, 4)$. Along what line does the incident ray move, and along what line does the reflected ray move?

26. The rate of development of heat H (measured in watts) in a resistor of resistance R (measured in ohms) of an electric circuit is given by $H = Ri^2$, where i is the current (measured in amperes) in the resistor. Sketch the graph of H versus i, if $R = 6.0\ \Omega$.

27. Under certain conditions, a cable which hangs between two supports can be closely approximated as being parabolic. Assuming that this cable hangs in the shape of a parabola, find its equation if a point 10 ft horizontally from its lowest point is 1.0 ft above its lowest point. Choose the lowest point as the origin of the coordinate system.

28. A wire is fastened 36.0 ft up on each of two telephone poles which are 200 ft apart. Halfway between the poles the wire is 30.0 ft above the ground. Assuming the wire is parabolic, find the height of the wire 50.0 ft from either pole.

29. The period T (measured in seconds) of the oscillation for resonance in an electric circuit is given by $T = 2\pi\sqrt{LC}$, where L is the inductance (in henrys) and C is the capacitance (in farads). Sketch the graph of the period versus capacitance for a constant inductance of 1 H. Assume values of C from 1 μF to 250 μF for this is a common range of values.

30. The velocity v of a jet of water flowing from an opening in the side of a certain container is given by $v = 8\sqrt{h}$, where h is the depth of the opening. Sketch a graph of v (in feet per second) vs. h (in feet).

31. A small island is 4 km from a straight shoreline. A ship channel is equidistant between the island and the shoreline. Write an equation for the channel.

32. Under certain circumstances, the maximum power P in an electric circuit varies as the square of the voltage of the source E_0 and inversely as the internal resistance R_i of the source. If 10 W is the maximum power for a source of 2.0 V and internal resistance of 0.10 Ω, sketch the graph of P versus E_0, if R_i remains constant.

20–5 The Ellipse

The next important curve we shall discuss is the ellipse. *The ellipse is defined as the locus of a point* $P(x, y)$ *which moves so that the sum of its distances from two fixed points is constant.* These two fixed points are called the **foci** of the ellipse. Letting this fixed sum equal $2a$ and the foci be the points $(c, 0)$ and $(-c, 0)$, we have (see Fig. 20–29) from the definition of the ellipse

$$\sqrt{(x - c)^2 + y^2} + \sqrt{(x + c)^2 + y^2} = 2a$$

From the section on solving equations involving radicals (Section 13–4), we find that we should remove one of the radicals to the right side, and then square each side. Thus we have the following steps:

$$\sqrt{(x + c)^2 + y^2} = 2a - \sqrt{(x - c)^2 + y^2}$$
$$(x + c)^2 + y^2 = 4a^2 - 4a\sqrt{(x - c)^2 + y^2} + (\sqrt{(x - c)^2 + y^2})^2$$
$$x^2 + 2cx + c^2 + y^2 = 4a^2 - 4a\sqrt{(x - c)^2 + y^2} + x^2 - 2cx + c^2 + y^2$$
$$4a\sqrt{(x - c)^2 + y^2} = 4a^2 - 4cx$$
$$a\sqrt{(x - c)^2 + y^2} = a^2 - cx$$
$$a^2(x^2 - 2cx + c^2 + y^2) = a^4 - 2a^2cx + c^2x^2$$
$$(a^2 - c^2)x^2 + a^2y^2 = a^2(a^2 - c^2)$$

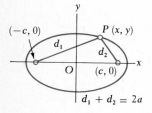

Figure 20–29

At this point we define (and the usefulness of this definition will be shown presently) $a^2 - c^2 = b^2$. This substitution gives us

$$b^2x^2 + a^2y^2 = a^2b^2$$

Dividing through by a^2b^2, we have

$$\frac{x^2}{a^2} + \frac{y^2}{b^2} = 1 \qquad (20\text{--}17)$$

If we let $y = 0$, we find that the x-intercepts are $(-a, 0)$ and $(a, 0)$. We see that the distance $2a$, originally chosen as the sum of the distances in the derivation of Eq. (20–17), is the distance between the x-intercepts. *These two points are known as the* **vertices** *of the ellipse, and the line between them is known as the* **major axis** *of the ellipse. Thus, a is called the* **semi-major axis.**

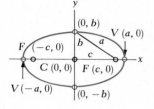

Figure 20—30

If we now let $x = 0$, we find the y-intercepts to be $(0, -b)$ and $(0, b)$. *The line joining these two intercepts is called the* **minor axis** *of the ellipse* (Fig. 20–30) *which means b is called the* **semi-minor axis.** The point $(0, b)$ is on the ellipse, and is also equidistant from $(-c, 0)$ and $(c, 0)$. Since the sum of the distances from these points to $(0, b)$ equals $2a$, the distance from $(c, 0)$ to $(0, b)$ must be a. Thus, we have a right triangle formed by line segments of lengths a, b, and c, with a as the hypotenuse. From this we have the relation

$$a^2 = b^2 + c^2 \qquad (20\text{--}18)$$

between the distances a, b, and c. This equation also shows us why b was defined as it was in the derivation.

Equation (20–17) is called the **standard equation** of the ellipse with its major axis along the x-axis and its center at the origin.

If we choose points on the y-axis as the foci, the standard equation of the ellipse, with its center at the origin and its major axis along the y-axis, is

$$\frac{y^2}{a^2} + \frac{x^2}{b^2} = 1 \qquad (20\text{--}19)$$

In this case the vertices are $(0, a)$ and $(0, -a)$, the foci are $(0, c)$ and $(0, -c)$, and the ends of the minor axis are $(b, 0)$ and $(-b, 0)$.

The symmetry of the ellipses given by Eqs. (20–17) and (20–19) to each of the axes and the origin can be proven since each of x and y can be replaced by its negative in these equations without changing the equations.

Example A
The ellipse

$$\frac{x^2}{25} + \frac{y^2}{9} = 1$$

has vertices at $(5, 0)$ and $(-5, 0)$. Its minor axis extends from $(0, 3)$ to $(0, -3)$, as we see in Fig. 20–31. This information is directly obtainable from this form of the equation, since the 25 tells us that $a^2 = 25$, or $a = 5$. In the same way we have $b = 3$. Since we know both a^2 and b^2, we can find c^2 from the relation $c^2 = a^2 - b^2$. Thus, $c^2 = 16$, or $c = 4$. This in turn tells us that the foci of this ellipse are at $(4, 0)$ and $(-4, 0)$.

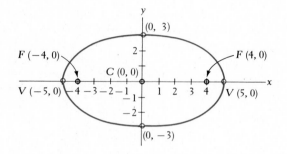

Figure 20–31

Example B
The ellipse

$$\frac{x^2}{4} + \frac{y^2}{9} = 1$$

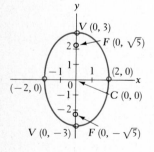

Figure 20–32

has vertices at $(0, 3)$ and $(0, -3)$. The minor axis extends from $(2, 0)$ to $(-2, 0)$. This we can find directly from the equation, since $a^2 = 9$ and $b^2 = 4$. One might ask how we chose $a^2 = 9$ in this example and $a^2 = 25$ in the preceding example. Since $a^2 = b^2 + c^2$, a is always larger than b. Thus, we can tell which axis (x or y) the major axis is along by seeing which number (in the denominator) is larger, when the equation is written in standard form. The larger one stands for a^2. In this example, the foci are $(0, \sqrt{5})$ and $(0, -\sqrt{5})$ (see Fig. 20–32).

Example C
Find the coordinates of the vertices, the ends of the minor axis, and the foci of the ellipse $4x^2 + 16y^2 = 64$.

This equation must be put in standard form first, which we do by dividing through by 64. When this is done, we obtain

$$\frac{x^2}{16} + \frac{y^2}{4} = 1$$

Thus, $a = 4$, $b = 2$, and $c = 2\sqrt{3}$. The vertices are at $(4, 0)$ and $(-4, 0)$. The ends of the minor axis are $(0, 2)$ and $(0, -2)$, and the foci are $(2\sqrt{3}, 0)$ and $(-2\sqrt{3}, 0)$ (see Fig. 20–33).

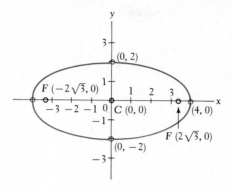

Figure 20–33

Example D
Find the equation of the ellipse for which the center is at the origin, the major axis is along the *y*-axis, the minor axis is 6 units long, and there are 8 units between foci.

Directly we know that $2b = 6$, or $b = 3$. Also $2c = 8$, or $c = 4$. Thus, we find that $a = 5$. Since the major axis is along the *y*-axis, we have the equation

$$\frac{y^2}{25} + \frac{x^2}{9} = 1$$

This ellipse is shown in Fig. 20–34.

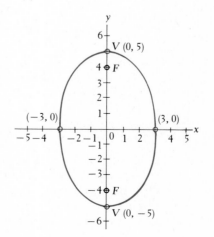

Figure 20–34

Equations (20–17) and (20–19) give us the standard form of the equation of an ellipse with its center at the origin and its foci on one of the coordinate axes. The following example illustrates the use of the definition of the ellipse to find the equation of an ellipse with its center at a point other than the origin.

Example E

Using the definition, find the equation of the ellipse with foci at (1, 3) and (9, 3), with a major axis of 10.

Using the same method as in the derivation of Eq. (20–17), we have the following steps. (Remember, the sum of distances in the definition equals the length of the major axis.)

$$\sqrt{(x-1)^2 + (y-3)^2} + \sqrt{(x-9)^2 + (y-3)^2} = 10$$
$$\sqrt{(x-1)^2 + (y-3)^2} = 10 - \sqrt{(x-9)^2 + (y-3)^2}$$
$$(x-1)^2 + (y-3)^2 = 100 - 20\sqrt{(x-9)^2 + (y-3)^2}$$
$$+ (\sqrt{(x-9)^2 + (y-3)^2})^2$$
$$x^2 - 2x + 1 + y^2 - 6y + 9 = 100 - 20\sqrt{(x-9)^2 + (y-3)^2}$$
$$+ x^2 - 18x + 81 + y^2 - 6y + 9$$
$$20\sqrt{(x-9)^2 + (y-3)^2} = 180 - 16x$$
$$5\sqrt{(x-9)^2 + (y-3)^2} = 45 - 4x$$
$$25(x^2 - 18x + 81 + y^2 - 6y + 9) = 2025 - 360x + 16x^2$$
$$25x^2 - 450x + 2250 + 25y^2 - 150y = 2025 - 360x + 16x^2$$
$$9x^2 - 90x + 25y^2 - 150y + 225 = 0$$

The additional x- and y-terms are characteristic of the equation of an ellipse whose center is not at the origin (see Fig. 20–35).

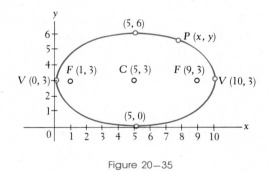

Figure 20–35

We can conclude that the equation of an ellipse is characterized by the presence of both an x^2- and a y^2-term, having different coefficients (in value but not in sign). The difference between the equation of an ellipse and that of a circle is that the coefficients of the squared terms in the equation of the circle are the same, whereas those of the ellipse differ.

Exercises 20—5

In Exercises 1 through 12 find the coordinates of the vertices and foci of the given ellipses. Sketch each curve.

1. $\dfrac{x^2}{4} + \dfrac{y^2}{1} = 1$

2. $\dfrac{x^2}{100} + \dfrac{y^2}{64} = 1$

3. $\dfrac{x^2}{25} + \dfrac{y^2}{36} = 1$

4. $\dfrac{x^2}{49} + \dfrac{y^2}{81} = 1$

5. $4x^2 + 9y^2 = 36$

6. $x^2 + 36y^2 = 144$

7. $49x^2 + 4y^2 = 196$

8. $25x^2 + y^2 = 25$

9. $8x^2 + y^2 = 16$

10. $2x^2 + 3y^2 = 6$

11. $4x^2 + 25y^2 = 25$

12. $9x^2 + 4y^2 = 9$

In Exercises 13 through 20 find the equations of the ellipses satisfying the given conditions. The center of each is at the origin.

13. Vertex $(15, 0)$, focus $(9, 0)$

14. Minor axis 8, vertex $(0, -5)$

15. Focus $(0, 2)$, major axis 6

16. Semi-minor axis 2, focus $(3, 0)$

17. Vertex $(8, 0)$, passes through $(2, 3)$

18. Focus $(0, 2)$, passes through $(-1, \sqrt{3})$

19. Passes through $(2, 2)$ and $(1, 4)$

20. Passes through $(-2, 2)$ and $(1, \sqrt{6})$

In Exercises 21 through 24 find the equations of the ellipses with the given properties by use of the definition of an ellipse.

21. Foci at $(-2, 1)$ and $(4, 1)$, a major axis of 10

22. Foci at $(-3, -2)$ and $(-3, 8)$, major axis 26

23. Vertices at $(1, 5)$ and $(1, -1)$, foci at $(1, 4)$ and $(1, 0)$

24. Vertices at $(-2, 1)$ and $(-2, 5)$, foci at $(-2, 2)$ and $(-2, 4)$

In Exercises 25 through 32 solve the given problems.

25. Show that the ellipse $2x^2 + 3y^2 - 8x - 4 = 0$ is symmetrical to the x-axis.

26. Show that the ellipse $5x^2 + y^2 - 3y - 7 = 0$ is symmetrical to the y-axis.

27. The arch of a bridge across a stream is in the form of half an ellipse above the water level. If the span of the arch at water level is 100 ft and the maximum height of the arch above water level is 30 ft, what is the equation of the arch? Choose the origin of the coordinate system at the most convenient point.

28. An elliptical gear (Fig. 20—36) which rotates about its center is kept continually in mesh with a circular gear which is free to move horizontally. If the equation of the ellipse of the gear (with the origin of the coordinate system at its center) in its present position is $3x^2 + 7y^2 = 20$, how far does the center of the circular gear move going from one extreme position to the other? (Assume the units are centimeters.)

29. An artificial satellite of the earth has a minimum altitude of 500 mi and a maximum altitude of 2000 mi. If the path of the satellite about the earth is an ellipse with the center of the earth at one focus, what is the equation of its path? (Assume the radius of the earth is 4000 mi.)

Figure 20—36

30. An electric current is caused to flow in a loop of wire rotating in a magnetic field. In a study of this phenomenon, a piece of wire is cut into two pieces, one of which is bent into a circle and the other into a square. If the sum of areas of the circle and square is always π units, find the relation between the radius r of the circle and the side x of the square. Sketch the graph of r versus x.

31. A vertical pipe 6.0 in. in diameter is to pass through a roof inclined at 45°. What are the dimensions of the elliptical hole which must be cut in the roof for the pipe?

32. The ends of a horizontal tank 20.0 ft long are ellipses, which can be described by the equation $9x^2 + 20y^2 = 180$, where x and y are measured in feet. The area of an ellipse is $A = \pi ab$. Find the volume of the tank.

20—6 The Hyperbola

The final curve we shall discuss in detail is the hyperbola. *The hyperbola is defined as the locus of a point $P(x, y)$ which moves so that the difference of the distances from two fixed points is a constant. These fixed points are the foci of the hyperbola.* Assuming that the foci of the hyperbola are the points $(c, 0)$ and $(-c, 0)$ (see Fig. 20–37) and the constant difference is $2a$, we have

$$\sqrt{(x + c)^2 + y^2} - \sqrt{(x - c)^2 + y^2} = 2a$$

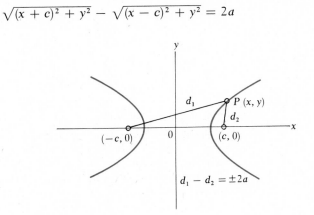

Figure 20—37

Following this same procedure as in the preceding section, we find the equation of the hyperbola to be

$$\frac{x^2}{a^2} - \frac{y^2}{b^2} = 1 \qquad\qquad (20\text{--}20)$$

When we derive this equation, we have a definition of the relation between a, b, and c which is different from that for the ellipse. This relation is

$$c^2 = a^2 + b^2 \qquad (20\text{--}21)$$

An analysis of Eq. (20–20) will reveal the significance of a and b. First, by letting $y = 0$, we find that the x-intercepts are $(a, 0)$ and $(-a, 0)$, just as they are for the ellipse. These points are called the **vertices** of the hyperbola. By letting $x = 0$, we find that we have imaginary solutions for y, which means that there are no points on the curve which correspond to a value of $x = 0$.

To find the significance of b, we shall solve Eq. (20–20) for y in a particular form. First we have

$$\frac{y^2}{b^2} = \frac{x^2}{a^2} - 1$$

$$= \frac{x^2}{a^2} - \frac{a^2 x^2}{a^2 x^2}$$

$$= \frac{x^2}{a^2}\left(1 - \frac{a^2}{x^2}\right)$$

Multiplying through by b^2 and then taking the square root of each side, we have

$$y^2 = \frac{b^2 x^2}{a^2}\left(1 - \frac{a^2}{x^2}\right)$$

$$y = \pm\frac{bx}{a}\sqrt{1 - \frac{a^2}{x^2}} \qquad (20\text{--}22)$$

We note that, if large values of x are assumed in Eq. (20–22), the quantity under the radical becomes approximately 1. In fact, the larger x becomes, the nearer 1 this expression becomes, since the x^2 in the denominator of a^2/x^2 makes this term nearly zero. Thus, for large values of x, Eq. (20–22) is approximately

$$y = \pm\frac{bx}{a} \qquad (20\text{--}23)$$

Equation (20–23) can be seen to represent the equations for two straight lines, each of which passes through the origin. One has a slope of b/a and the other a slope of $-b/a$. These lines are called the **asymptotes** of the hyperbola. An asymptote is a line which a curve approaches as one of the variables approaches some particular value. The tangent curve also has asymptotes, as we can see in Fig. 9–17. We can designate this limiting procedure with notation introduced in Chapter 18, by saying that

$$y \to \frac{bx}{a} \text{ as } x \to \infty$$

Since straight lines are easily sketched, the easiest way to sketch a hyperbola is to draw its asymptotes and then to draw the hyperbola so that it comes closer and closer to these lines as x becomes larger numerically. To draw in the asymptotes, the usual procedure is to first draw a small rectangle, $2a$ by $2b$, with the origin in the center. Then straight lines are drawn through opposite vertices. These lines are the asymptotes (see Fig. 20–38). Thus we see that the significance of the value of b lies in the slope of the asymptotes of the hyperbola.

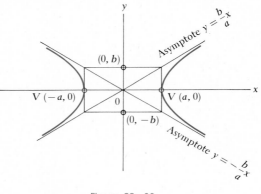

Figure 20–38

Equation (20–20) is called the **standard equation** of the hyperbola with its center at the origin. *It has a* **transverse axis** *of length 2a along the x-axis and a* **conjugate axis** *of length 2b along the y-axis.* This means that a represents the length of the semi-transverse axis, and b represents the length of the semi-conjugate axis. The relation between a, b, and c is given in Eq. (20–21).

If the transverse axis is along the y-axis and the conjugate axis is along the x-axis, the equation of a hyperbola with its center at the origin is

$$\frac{y^2}{a^2} - \frac{x^2}{b^2} = 1 \tag{20–24}$$

The symmetry of the hyperbolas given by Eqs. (20–20) and (20–24) to each of the axes and to the origin can be proven since each of x and y can be replaced by its negative in these equations without changing the equations.

Example A
The hyperbola

$$\frac{x^2}{16} - \frac{y^2}{9} = 1$$

has vertices at $(4, 0)$ and $(-4, 0)$. Its transverse axis extends from one vertex to the other. Its conjugate axis extends from $(0, 3)$ to $(0, -3)$. Since $c^2 = a^2 + b^2$, we find that $c = 5$, which means the foci are the points $(5, 0)$ and $(-5, 0)$. Drawing in the rectangle and then the asymptotes (Fig. 20–39), we draw the hyperbola from each vertex toward the asymptotes. Thus, the curve is sketched.

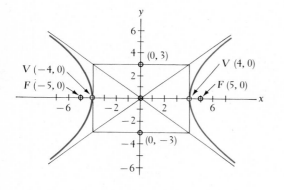

Figure 20–39

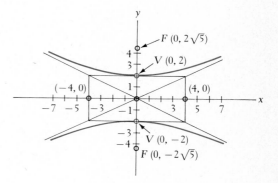

Figure 20–40

Example B
The hyperbola

$$\frac{y^2}{4} - \frac{x^2}{16} = 1$$

has vertices at $(0, 2)$ and $(0, -2)$. Its conjugate axis extends from $(4, 0)$ to $(-4, 0)$. The foci are $(0, 2\sqrt{5})$ and $(0, -2\sqrt{5})$. Since, with 1 on the right side of the equation, the y^2-term is the positive term, this hyperbola is in the form of Eq. (20–24). [Example A illustrates a hyperbola of the type of Eq. (20–20), since the x^2-term is the positive term.] Since $2a$ extends along the y-axis, we see that the equations of the asymptotes are $y = \pm(a/b)x$. This is not a contradiction of Eq. (20–23), but an extension of it for the case of a hyperbola with its transverse axis along the y-axis. The ratio a/b simply expresses the slope of the asymptote (see Fig. 20–40).

Example C
Determine the coordinates of the vertices and foci of the hyperbola
$4x^2 - 9y^2 = 36$.

First, by dividing through by 36, we can put this equation in standard form. Thus, we have

$$\frac{x^2}{9} - \frac{y^2}{4} = 1$$

The transverse axis is along the x-axis with vertices at $(3, 0)$ and $(-3, 0)$, since $c^2 = a^2 + b^2$ and $c = \sqrt{13}$. This means that the foci are at $(\sqrt{13}, 0)$ and $(-\sqrt{13}, 0)$ (see Fig. 20–41).

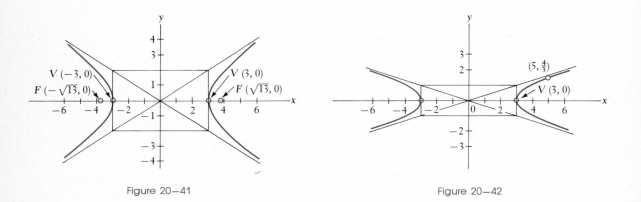

Figure 20–41   Figure 20–42

Example D
Find the equation of the hyperbola with its center at the origin, a vertex at $(3, 0)$, and which passes through $(5, \frac{4}{3})$.

When we know that the hyperbola has its center at the origin and a vertex at $(3, 0)$, we know that the standard form of its equation is given by Eq. (20–20). This also tells us that $a = 3$. By using the fact that the coordinates of the point $(5, \frac{4}{3})$ must satisfy the equation, we are able to find the value of b^2. Substituting, we have

$$\frac{25}{9} - \frac{(16/9)}{b^2} = 1$$

from which we find $b^2 = 1$. Therefore, the equation of the hyperbola is

$$\frac{x^2}{9} - \frac{y^2}{1} = 1$$

or

$$x^2 - 9y^2 = 9$$

This hyperbola is shown in Fig. 20–42.

x	y
-8	$-\frac{1}{2}$
-4	-1
-1	-4
$-\frac{1}{2}$	-8
$\frac{1}{2}$	8
1	4
4	1
8	$\frac{1}{2}$

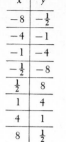

Figure 20—43

Equations (20—20) and (20—24) give us the standard form of the equation of the hyperbola with its center at the origin and its foci on one of the coordinate axes. There is one other important equation form which respresents a hyperbola, and that is

$$xy = c \qquad (20\text{—}25)$$

The asymptotes of this hyperbola are the coordinate axes, and the foci are on the line $y = x$, or on the line $y = -x$, if c is negative. This hyperbola is symmetrical to the origin, for if $-x$ replaces x, and $-y$ replaces y at the same time, we have $(-x)(-y) = c$, or $xy = c$. The equation remains unchanged. However, if either $-x$ replaces x, or if $-y$ replaces y, but not both, the sign on the left is changed. Therefore, it is not symmetrical to either axis. The c here represents a constant and is not related to the focus. The following example illustrates this type of hyperbola.

Example E

Plot the graph of the equation $xy = 4$.

We find the values of the table at the left, and then plot the appropriate points. Here it is permissible to use a limited number of points, since we know that the equation represents a hyperbola (Fig. 20—43). Thus, using $y = 4/x$, we obtain the values in the table.

We conclude that the equation of a hyperbola is characterized by the presence of both an x^2- and a y^2-term, having different signs, or by the presence of an xy-term with no squared terms.

Exercises 20—6

In Exercises 1 through 12 find the coordinates of the vertices and the foci of the given hyperbolas. Sketch each curve.

1. $\dfrac{x^2}{25} - \dfrac{y^2}{144} = 1$ 2. $\dfrac{x^2}{16} - \dfrac{y^2}{4} = 1$ 3. $\dfrac{y^2}{9} - \dfrac{x^2}{1} = 1$

4. $\dfrac{y^2}{2} - \dfrac{x^2}{2} = 1$ 5. $2x^2 - y^2 = 4$ 6. $3x^2 - y^2 = 9$

7. $2y^2 - 5x^2 = 10$ 8. $3y^2 - 2x^2 = 6$ 9. $4x^2 - y^2 + 4 = 0$
10. $9x^2 - y^2 - 9 = 0$ 11. $4x^2 - 9y^2 = 16$ 12. $y^2 - 9x^2 = 25$

In Exercises 13 through 20 find the equations of the hyperbolas satisfying the given conditions. The center of each is at the origin.

13. Vertex $(3, 0)$, focus $(5, 0)$ 14. Vertex $(0, 1)$, focus $(0, \sqrt{3})$
15. Conjugate axis $= 12$, vertex $(0, 10)$ 16. Focus $(8, 0)$, transverse axis $= 4$
17. Passes through $(2, 3)$, focus $(2, 0)$ 18. Passes through $(8, \sqrt{3})$, vertex $(4, 0)$
19. Passes through $(5, 4)$ and $(3, \frac{4}{5}\sqrt{5})$ 20. Passes through $(1, 2)$ and $(2, 2\sqrt{2})$

In Exercises 21 through 24 sketch the graphs of the hyperbolas given.

21. $xy = 2$ 22. $xy = 10$ 23. $xy = -2$ 24. $xy = -4$

In Exercises 25 through 28 find the equations of the hyperbolas with the given properties by use of the definition of the hyperbola.

25. Foci at (1, 2) and (11, 2), with a transverse axis of 8
26. Vertices (−2, 4) and (−2, −2), with conjugate axis of 4
27. Center at (2, 0), vertex at (3, 0), conjugate axis of 6
28. Center at (1, −1), focus at (1, 4), vertex at (1, 2)

In Exercises 29 through 34 solve the given problems.

29. Sketch the graph of impedance versus resistance if the reactance $X_L - X_C$ of a given electric circuit is constant at 60 Ω (see Section 11–7).
30. One statement of Boyle's law is that the product of the pressure and volume, for constant temperature, remains a constant for a perfect gas. If one set of values for a perfect gas under the condition of constant temperature is that the pressure is 300 kPa for a volume of 8.0 L, sketch a graph of pressure versus volume.
31. The relationship between the frequency f, wavelength λ, and the velocity v of a wave is given by $v = f\lambda$. The velocity of light is a constant, being 3.0×10^{10} cm/s. The visible spectrum ranges in wavelength from about 4.0×10^{-5} cm (violet) to about 7.0×10^{-5} cm (red). Sketch a graph of frequency f (in Hertz) as a function of wavelength for the visible spectrum.
32. Wavelengths of gamma rays vary from about 10^{-8} cm to about 10^{-13} cm, but the gamma rays have the same velocity as light. On logarithmic paper, plot the graph of frequency versus wavelength for gamma rays. What type of curve results when this type of hyperbola is plotted on logarithmic paper?
33. An electronic instrument located at point P records the sound of a rifle shot and the impact of the bullet striking the target at the same instant. Show that P lies on a branch of a hyperbola.
34. Two concentric hyperbolas are called conjugate hyperbolas if the transverse and conjugate axes of one are respectively the conjugate and transverse axes of the other. What is the equation of the hyperbola conjugate to the hyperbola of Exercise 14?

20–7 Translation of Axes

Until now, the equations considered for the parabola, the ellipse, and the hyperbola have been restricted to the particular cases in which the vertex of the parabola is at the origin and the center of the ellipse or hyperbola is at the origin. In this section we shall consider the equations of these curves for the cases in which the axis of the curve is parallel to one of the coordinate axes. This is done by **translation of axes.**

We choose a point (h, k) in the xy-coordinate plane and let this point be the origin of another coordinate system, the $x'y'$-coordinate system. The x'-axis is parallel to the x-axis and the y'-axis is parallel to the y-axis.

Every point in the plane now has two sets of coordinates associated with it, (x, y) and (x', y'). From Fig. 20–44 we see that

$$x = x' + h \qquad \text{and} \qquad y = y' + k \tag{20–26}$$

Equations (20–26) can also be written in the form

$$x' = x - h \qquad \text{and} \qquad y' = y - k \tag{20–27}$$

The following examples illustrate the use of Eqs. (20–27) in the analysis of equations of the parabola, ellipse, and hyperbola.

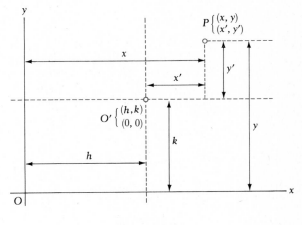

Figure 20–44

Example A

Describe the locus of the equation

$$\frac{(x - 3)^2}{25} + \frac{(y + 2)^2}{9} = 1$$

In this equation, given that $h = 3$ and $k = -2$, we have $x' = x - 3$ and $y' = y + 2$. In terms of x' and y', the equation is

$$\frac{(x')^2}{25} + \frac{(y')^2}{9} = 1$$

We recognize this equation as that of an ellipse (see Fig. 20–45) with a semi-major axis of 5 and a semi-minor axis of 3. The center of the ellipse is at $(3, -2)$ since this was the choice of h and k to make the equation fit a standard form.

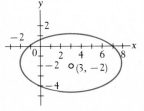

Figure 20–45

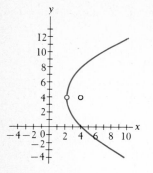

Figure 20—46

Example B
Find the equation of the parabola with vertex at (2, 4) and focus at (4, 4).

If we let the origin of the $x'y'$-coordinate system be the point (2, 4), the point (4, 4) would be the point (2, 0) in the $x'y'$-system. This means that $p = 2$ and $4p = 8$ (Fig. 20–46). In the $x'y'$-system, the equation is

$$(y')^2 = 8(x')$$

Since (2, 4) is the origin of the $x'y'$-system, this means that $h = 2$ and $k = 4$. Using Eq. (20–27), we have

$$(y - 4)^2 = 8(x - 2)$$

as the equation of the parabola in the xy-coordinate system. If this equation is multiplied out, and like terms are combined, we obtain

$$y^2 - 8x - 8y + 32 = 0$$

Example C
Find the center of the hyperbola $2x^2 - y^2 - 4x - 4y - 4 = 0$.

To analyze this curve, we first complete the square in the x-terms and in the y-terms. This will allow us to recognize properly the choice of h and k.

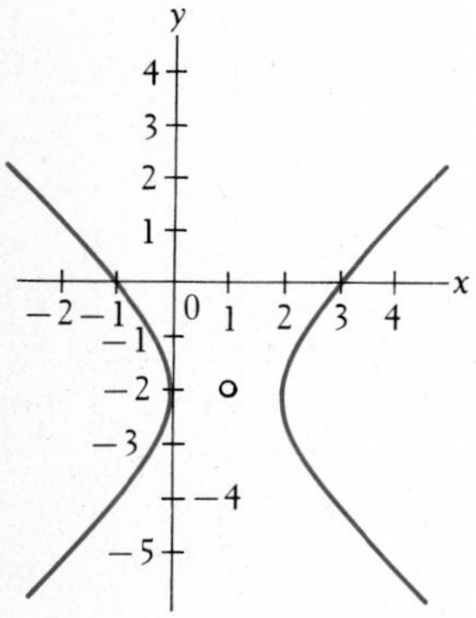

$$2x^2 - 4x - y^2 - 4y = 4$$
$$2(x^2 - 2x \quad) - (y^2 + 4y \quad) = 4$$
$$2(x^2 - 2x + 1) - (y^2 + 4y + 4) = 4 + 2 - 4$$
$$2(x - 1)^2 - (y + 2)^2 = 2$$

$$\frac{(x - 1)^2}{1} - \frac{(y + 2)^2}{2} = 1$$

Thus, if we let $h = 1$ and $k = -2$, the equation in the $x'y'$-system becomes

$$\frac{(x')^2}{1} - \frac{(y')^2}{2} = 1$$

This means that the center is at $(1, -2)$, since this point corresponds to the origin of the $x'y'$-coordinate system (see Fig. 20–47).

Figure 20—47

Example D
Find the vertex of the parabola $2x^2 - 12x - 3y + 15 = 0$.

First, we complete the square in the x terms, placing all other resulting terms on the right. By factoring the resulting expression on the right, we may determine the values of h and k.

$$2x^2 - 12x = 3y - 15$$
$$2(x^2 - 6x \quad) = 3y - 15$$
$$2(x^2 - 6x + 9) = 3y - 15 + 18$$
$$2(x - 3)^2 = 3(y + 1)$$

$$(x - 3)^2 = \frac{3}{2}(y + 1)$$

$$x'^2 = \frac{3}{2}y'$$

Therefore, the vertex is at $(3, -1)$, since this point corresponds to the origin of the $x'y'$-coordinate system. See Fig. 20–48.

Example E

Glass beakers are to be made with a height of 3 in. Express the surface area of the beakers in terms of the radius of the base. Sketch the graph of area versus radius.

The total surface area of a beaker is the sum of the area of the base and the lateral surface area of the side. In general, this surface area S in terms of the radius r of the base and the height h of the side is

$$S = \pi r^2 + 2\pi r h$$

Since h is constant at 3 in., we have

$$S = \pi r^2 + 6\pi r$$

which is the desired relationship.

For the purposes of sketching the graph of S and r, we now complete the square of the r terms:

$$S = \pi(r^2 + 6r)$$
$$S + 9\pi = \pi(r + 6r + 9)$$
$$S + 9\pi = \pi(r + 3)^2$$
$$(r + 3)^2 = \frac{1}{\pi}(S + 9\pi)$$

We note that this equation represents a parabola with vertex at $(-3, -9\pi)$ for its coordinates (r, S). Since $4p = \frac{1}{\pi}$, $p = \frac{1}{4\pi}$ and the focus of this parabola is at $(-3, \frac{1}{4\pi} - 9\pi)$. Only positive values for S and r have meaning, and therefore the part of the graph for negative r is shown as a dashed curve (see Fig. 20–49).

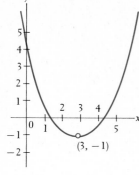

Figure 20–48

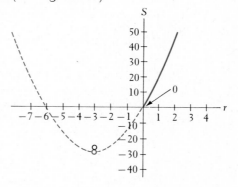

Figure 20–49

Exercises 20—7

In Exercises 1 through 8 describe the locus of each of the given equations. Identify the type of curve and its center (vertex if it is a parabola). Sketch each curve.

1. $(y - 2)^2 = 4(x + 1)$

2. $\dfrac{(x + 4)^2}{4} + \dfrac{(y - 1)^2}{1} = 1$

3. $\dfrac{(x - 1)^2}{4} - \dfrac{(y - 2)^2}{9} = 1$

4. $(y + 5)^2 = -8(x - 2)$

5. $\dfrac{(x + 1)^2}{1} + \dfrac{y^2}{9} = 1$

6. $\dfrac{(y - 4)^2}{16} - \dfrac{(x + 2)^2}{4} = 1$

7. $(x + 3)^2 = -12(y - 1)$

8. $\dfrac{x^2}{16} + \dfrac{(y + 1)^2}{1} = 1$

In Exercises 9 through 16 find the equation of each of the curves described by the given information.

9. Parabola: vertex $(-1, 3)$, $p = 4$, axis parallel to x-axis
10. Parabola: vertex $(2, -1)$, directrix $y = 3$
11. Parabola: vertex $(-3, 2)$, focus $(-3, 3)$
12. Parabola: focus $(2, 4)$, directrix $x = 6$
13. Ellipse: center $(-2, 2)$, focus $(-5, 2)$, vertex $(-7, 2)$
14. Ellipse: center $(0, 3)$, focus $(12, 3)$, major axis 26 units
15. Hyperbola: vertices $(2, 1)$ and $(-4, 1)$, focus $(-6, 1)$
16. Hyperbola: center $(1, -4,)$ focus $(1, 1)$, transverse axis 8 units

In Exercises 17 through 24 determine the center (or vertex if the curve is a parabola) of the given curves. Sketch each curve.

17. $x^2 + 2x - 4y - 3 = 0$
18. $y^2 - 2x - 2y - 9 = 0$
19. $4x^2 + 9y^2 + 24x = 0$
20. $2x^2 + 9y^2 + 8x - 72y + 134 = 0$
21. $9x^2 - y^2 + 8y - 7 = 0$
22. $5x^2 - 4y^2 + 20x + 8y = 4$
23. $2x^2 - 4x = 9y - 2$
24. $4x^2 + 16x = y - 20$

In Exercises 25 through 28 find the required equations.

25. Find the equation of the hyperbola with asymptotes $x - y = -1$ and $x + y = -3$, and vertex $(3, -1)$.

26. The circle $x^2 + y^2 + 4x - 5 = 0$ passes through the foci and the ends of the minor axis of an ellipse which has its major axis along the x-axis. Find the equation of the ellipse.

27. A first parabola has its vertex at the focus of a second parabola, and its focus at the vertex of the second parabola. If the equation of the second parabola is $y^2 = 4x$, find the equation of the first parabola.

28. Verify each of the following equations as being the standard form as indicated. Parabola, vertex at (h, k), axis parallel to the x-axis:

$$(y - k)^2 = 4p(x - h)$$

Parabola, vertex at (h, k), axis parallel to the y-axis:

$$(x - h)^2 = 4p(y - k)$$

Ellipse, center at (h, k), major axis parallel to the x-axis:

$$\frac{(x - h)^2}{a^2} + \frac{(y - k)^2}{b^2} = 1$$

Ellipse, center at (h, k), major axis parallel to the y-axis:

$$\frac{(y - k)^2}{a^2} + \frac{(x - h)^2}{b^2} = 1$$

Hyperbola, center at (h, k), transverse axis parallel to the x-axis:

$$\frac{(x - h)^2}{a^2} - \frac{(y - k)^2}{b^2} = 1$$

Hyperbola, center at (h, k), transverse axis parallel to the y-axis:

$$\frac{(y - k)^2}{a^2} - \frac{(x - h)^2}{b^2} = 1$$

In Exercises 29 through 32 solve the given problems.

29. The power supplied to a circuit by a battery with a voltage E and an internal resistance r is given by $P = EI - rI^2$, where P is the power (in watts) and I is the current (in amperes). Sketch the graph of P vs. I for a 6.0 V battery with an internal resistance of 0.30 Ω.

30. A calculator company determined that its total income I from the sale of a particular type of calculator is given by $I = 100x - x^2$, where x is the selling price of the calculator. Sketch a graph of I vs. x.

31. The planet Pluto moves about the sun in an elliptical orbit, with the sun at one focus. The closest that Pluto approaches the sun is 2.8 billion miles, and the farthest it gets from the sun is 4.6 billion miles. If the sun is at the origin of a coordinate system and the other focus is on the positive x-axis, what is the equation of the path of Pluto?

32. A rectangular tract of land is to have a perimeter of 800 m. Express the area in terms of its width and sketch the graph.

20—8 The Second-Degree Equation

The equations of the circle, parabola, ellipse, and hyperbola are all special cases of the same general equation. In this section we shall discuss this general equation and how to identify the particular form it takes when it represents a specific type of curve.

Each of these curves can be represented by a **second-degree equation** of the form

$$Ax^2 + Bxy + Cy^2 + Dx + Ey + F = 0 \qquad (20\text{–}28)$$

[This equation is the same as Eq. (13–1).] The coefficients of the second-degree terms determine the type of curve which results. Recalling the discussions of the general forms of the equations of the circle, parabola, ellipse, and hyperbola from the previous sections of this chapter, we have the following results.

Equation (20–28) represents the indicated curve for the given conditions for A, B, and C.

(1) If $A = C$, $B = 0$, a circle.
(2) If $A \neq C$ (but they have the same sign), $B = 0$, an ellipse.
(3) If A and C have different signs, $B = 0$, a hyperbola.
(4) If $A = 0$, $C = 0$, $B \neq 0$, a hyperbola.
(5) If either $A = 0$ or $C = 0$ (but not both), $B = 0$, a parabola.
   (Special cases, such as a single point or no real locus, can also result.)

Another conclusion about Eq. (20–28) is that, if either $D \neq 0$ or $E \neq 0$ (or both), the center (or vertex of a parabola) of the curve is not at the origin. If $B \neq 0$, the axis of the curve has been rotated. We have considered only one such case (the hyperbola $xy = c$) in this chapter.

Example A

The equation $3x^2 = 6x - y^2 + 3$ represents an ellipse. Before we analyze the equation, we should put it in the form of Eq. (20–28). For the given equation, this form is

$$3x^2 + y^2 - 6x - 3 = 0$$

Here we see that $B = 0$ and $A \neq C$. Therefore, it is an ellipse. The $-6x$ term indicates that the center of the ellipse is not at the origin.

Example B

The equation $2(x + 3)^2 = y^2 + 2x^2$ represents a parabola. Putting it in the form of Eq. (20–28), we have

$$2(x^2 + 6x + 9) = y^2 + 2x^2$$
$$2x^2 + 12x + 18 = y^2 + 2x^2$$
$$y^2 - 12x - 18 = 0$$

We now note that $A = 0$, $B = 0$, and $C \neq 0$. This indicates that the equation represents a parabola. Here, the -18 term indicates that the vertex is not at the origin.

Example C

Identify the curve represented by the equation $2x^2 + 12x = y^2 - 14$. Determine the appropriate important quantities associated with the curve, and sketch the graph.

Writing this equation in the form of Eq. (20–28), we have

$$2x^2 - y^2 + 12x + 14 = 0$$

In this form we identify the equation as representing a hyperbola, since

A and C have different signs, and $B = 0$. We now write it in the standard form of a hyperbola.

$$2x^2 + 12x - y^2 = -14$$
$$2(x^2 + 6x \quad) - y^2 = -14$$
$$2(x^2 + 6x + 9) - y^2 = -14 + 18$$
$$2(x + 3)^2 - y^2 = 4$$

$$\frac{(x + 3)^2}{2} - \frac{y^2}{4} = 1$$

$$\frac{x'^2}{2} - \frac{y'^2}{4} = 1$$

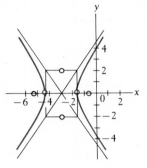

Figure 20–50

Thus, we see that the center (h, k) of the hyperbola is the point $(-3, 0)$. Also, $a = \sqrt{2}$ and $b = 2$. This means that the vertices are $(-3 + \sqrt{2}, 0)$ and $(-3 - \sqrt{2}, 0)$, and the conjugate axis extends from $(-3, 2)$ to $(-3, -2)$. Also, $c^2 = 2 + 4 = 6$, which means that $c = \sqrt{6}$. The foci are $(-3 + \sqrt{6}, 0)$ and $(-3 - \sqrt{6}, 0)$. The graph is shown in Fig. 20–50.

Example D

Identify the curve represented by the equation $4y^2 - 23 = 4(4x + 3y)$. Determine the appropriate important quantities associated with the curve, and sketch the graph.

Writing this equation in the form of Eq. (20–28), we have

$$4y^2 - 23 = 16x + 12y$$
$$4y^2 - 16x - 12y - 23 = 0$$

Therefore, we recognize the equation as representing a parabola, since $A = 0$ and $B = 0$. Now writing the equation in the standard form of a parabola, we have

$$4y^2 - 12y = 16x + 23$$
$$4(y^2 - 3y \quad) = 16x + 23$$

$$4\left(y^2 - 3y + \frac{9}{4}\right) = 16x + 23 + 9$$

$$4\left(y - \frac{3}{2}\right)^2 = 16(x + 2)$$

$$\left(y - \frac{3}{2}\right)^2 = 4(x + 2)$$

$$y'^2 = 4x'$$

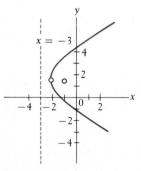

Figure 20–51

We now note that the vertex is the point $(-2, \frac{3}{2})$ and that $p = 1$. Also, it is symmetric to the x' axis. Therefore, the focus is $(-1, \frac{3}{2})$ and the directrix is $x = -3$. The graph is shown in Fig. 20–51.

In Chapter 13, when these curves were first introduced, they were referred to as **conic sections.** If a plane is passed through a cone, the intersection of the plane and the cone results in one of these curves, the curve formed depends on the angle of the plane with respect to the axis of the cone. This is indicated in Fig. 20–52.

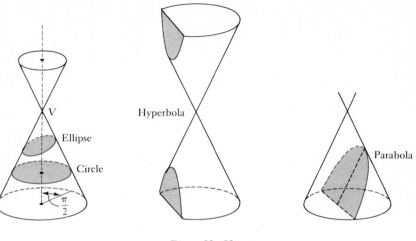

Figure 20–52

Exercises 20–8

In Exercises 1 through 16 identify each of the equations as representing either a circle, parabola, ellipse, or hyperbola.

1. $2x^2 + 2y^2 - 3y - 1 = 0$

2. $x^2 - 2y^2 - 3x - 1 = 0$

3. $2x^2 - x - y = 1$

4. $2x^2 + 4y^2 - y - 2x = 4$

5. $x^2 = y^2 - 1$

6. $3x^2 = 2y - 4y^2$

7. $x^2 = y - y^2$

8. $y = 3 - 6x^2$

9. $x(y + 3x) = x^2 + xy - y^2 + 1$

10. $x(2 - x) = y^2$

11. $2xy + x - 3y = 6$

12. $(y + 1)^2 = x^2 + y^2 - 1$

13. $2x(x - y) = y(3 - y - 2x)$

14. $2x^2 = x(x - 1) + 4y^2$

15. $y(3 - 2y) = 2(x^2 - y^2)$

16. $4x(x - 1) = 2x^2 - 2y^2 + 3$

In Exercises 17 through 24 identify the curve represented by each of the given equations. Determine the appropriate important quantities associated with the curve, and sketch the graph.

17. $x^2 = 8(y - x - 2)$

18. $x^2 = 6x - 4y^2 - 1$

19. $y^2 = 2(x^2 - 2x - 2y)$

20. $4x^2 + 4 = 9 - 8x - 4y^2$

21. $y^2 + 42 = 2x(10 - x)$

22. $x^2 - 4y = y^2 + 4(1 - x)$

23. $4(y^2 - 4x - 2) = 5(4y - 5)$

24. $2(2x^2 - y) = 8 - y^2$

In Exercises 25 through 28 set up the necessary equation and then determine the type of curve it represents.

25. For a given alternating-current circuit the resistance and capacitive reactance are constant. What type of curve is represented by the equation relating impedance and inductive reactance? (See Section 11–7.)

26. A room is 8.0 ft high, and the length is 6.5 ft longer than the width. Express the volume V of the (rectangular) room in terms of the width w. What type of curve is represented by the equation?

27. The sides of a rectangle are $2x$ and y, and the digaonal is $x + 5$. What type of curve is represented by the equation relating x and y?

28. The legs of a right triangle are x and y and the hypotenuse is $x + 2$. What type of curve is represented by the equation relating x and y?

20—9 Polar Coordinates

Thus far we have graphed all curves in one coordinate system. This system, the rectangular coordinate system, is probably the most useful and widely applicable system. However, for certain types of curves, other coordinate systems prove to be better adapted. These coordinate systems are widely used, especially when certain applications of higher mathematics are involved. We shall discuss one of these systems here.

Instead of designating a point by its x- and y-coordinates, we can specify its location by its radius vector and the angle which the radius vector makes with the x-axis. Thus, the r and θ that are used in the definitions of the trigonometric functions can also be used as the coordinates of points in the plane. The important aspect of choosing coordinates is that, for each set of values, there must be only one point which corresponds to this set. We can see that this condition is satisfied by the use of r and θ as coordinates. *In* **polar coordinates** *the origin is called the* **pole,** *and the positive x-axis is called the* **polar axis** (see Fig. 20—53).

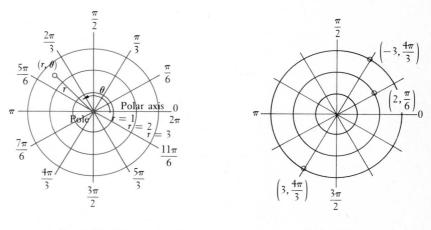

Figure 20—53   Figure 20—54

Example A

If $r = 2$ and $\theta = \pi/6$, we have the point as indicated in Fig. 20—54. The coordinates (r, θ) of this point are written as $(2, \pi/6)$ when polar coordinates are used. This point corresponds to $(\sqrt{3}, 1)$ in rectangular coordinates.

One difference between rectangular coordinates and polar coordinates is that, for each point in the plane, there are limitless possibilities for the polar coordinates of that point. For example, the point $(2, \pi/6)$ can also be represented by $(2, 13\pi/6)$ since the angles $\pi/6$ and $13\pi/6$ are coterminal. We also remove one restriction on r that we imposed in the definitions of the trigonometric functions. That is, r is allowed to take on positive and negative values. If r is considered negative, then the point is found on the opposite side of the pole from that on which it is positive.

Example B

The coordinates $(3, 4\pi/3)$ and $(3, -2\pi/3)$ represent the same point. However, the point $(-3, 4\pi/3)$ is on the opposite side of the pole, three units from the pole. Another possible set of coordinates for $(-3, 4\pi/3)$ is $(3, \pi/3)$ (see Fig. 20–54).

The relationships between the polar coordinates of a point and the rectangular coordinates of the same point come directly from the definitions of the trigonometric functions. Those most commonly used are

$$x = r \cos \theta, \qquad y = r \sin \theta \qquad\qquad (20\text{–}29)$$

and

$$\tan \theta = \frac{y}{x}, \qquad r = \sqrt{x^2 + y^2} \qquad\qquad (20\text{–}30)$$

The following examples show the use of Eqs. (20–29) and (20–30) in changing coordinates in one system to coordinates in the other system. Also, they are used to transform equations from one system to the other.

Example C

Using Eqs. (20–29), we can transform the polar coordinates of $(4, \pi/4)$ into the rectangular coordinates $(2\sqrt{2}, 2\sqrt{2})$, since

$$x = 4 \cos \frac{\pi}{4} = 4\left(\frac{\sqrt{2}}{2}\right) = 2\sqrt{2}$$

and

$$y = 4 \sin \frac{\pi}{4} = 4\left(\frac{\sqrt{2}}{2}\right) = 2\sqrt{2}$$

Example D

Using Eqs. (20–30), we can transform the rectangular coordinates $(3, -5)$ into polar coordinates.

$$\tan \theta = -\frac{5}{3} = -1.667, \qquad \theta = 5.25 \quad (\text{or} -1.03)$$

$$r = \sqrt{3^2 + (-5)^2} = \sqrt{34} = 5.83$$

We know that θ is a fourth-quadrant angle since x is positive and y is negative. Therefore, the point $(3, -5)$ in rectangular coordinates can be expressed as the point $(5.83, 5.25)$ in polar coordinates. Other polar coordinates for the point are also possible.

Example E
Find the polar equation of the circle $x^2 + y^2 = 2x$.
   Here we are given the equation of a circle in rectangular coordinates x and y and are to change it into an equation expressed in polar coordinates r and θ. Since

$$r^2 = x^2 + y^2 \quad \text{and} \quad x = r \cos \theta$$

we have

$$r^2 = 2r \cos \theta$$

or

$$r = 2 \cos \theta$$

as the appropriate polar equation.

Example F
Find the rectangular equation of the "rose" $r = 4 \sin 2\theta$.
   Using the relation $2 \sin \theta \cos \theta = \sin 2\theta$, we have $r = 8 \sin \theta \cos \theta$. Then, using Eqs. (20–29) and (20–30), we have

$$\sqrt{x^2 + y^2} = 8\left(\frac{y}{r}\right)\left(\frac{x}{r}\right) = \frac{8xy}{r^2} = \frac{8xy}{x^2 + y^2}$$

Squaring both sides, we obtain

$$x^2 + y^2 = \frac{64x^2 y^2}{(x^2 + y^2)^2} \quad \text{or} \quad (x^2 + y^2)^3 = 64x^2 y^2$$

From this example we can see that plotting the graph from the rectangular equation would be complicated.

Exercises 20–9

In Exercises 1 through 12 plot the given points on polar coordinate paper.

1. $\left(3, \frac{\pi}{6}\right)$ 2. $(2, \pi)$ 3. $\left(\frac{5}{2}, -\frac{2\pi}{5}\right)$ 4. $\left(5, -\frac{\pi}{3}\right)$

5. $\left(-2, \frac{7\pi}{6}\right)$ 6. $\left(-5, \frac{\pi}{4}\right)$ 7. $\left(-3, -\frac{5\pi}{4}\right)$ 8. $\left(-4, -\frac{5\pi}{3}\right)$

9. $\left(0.5, -\frac{8\pi}{3}\right)$ 10. $(2.2, -6\pi)$ 11. $(2, 2)$ 12. $(-1, -1)$

In Exercises 13 through 16 find a set of polar coordinates for each of the given points expressed in rectangular coordinates.

13. $(\sqrt{3}, 1)$ 14. $(-1, -1)$ 15. $\left(-\frac{\sqrt{3}}{2}, -\frac{1}{2}\right)$ 16. $(-5, 4)$

In Exercises 17 through 20 find the rectangular coordinates corresponding to the points for which the polar coordinates are given.

17. $\left(8, \dfrac{4\pi}{3}\right)$ 18. $(-4, -\pi)$ 19. $\left(3, -\dfrac{\pi}{8}\right)$ 20. $(-1, -1)$

In Exercises 21 through 28 find the polar equation of the given rectangular equations.

21. $x = 3$ 22. $y = 2$ 23. $x^2 + y^2 = a^2$
24. $x^2 + y^2 = 4y$ 25. $y^2 = 4x$ 26. $x^2 - y^2 = a^2$
27. $x^2 + 4y^2 = 4$ 28. $y = x^2$

In Exercises 29 through 36 find the rectangular equation of each of the given polar equations.

29. $r = \sin\theta$ 30. $r = 4\cos\theta$ 31. $r\cos\theta = 4$
32. $r\sin\theta = -2$ 33. $r = 2(1 + \cos\theta)$ 34. $r = 1 - \sin\theta$
35. $r^2 = \sin 2\theta$ 36. $r^2 = 16\cos 2\theta$

In Exercises 37 through 40 find the required equations.

37. If we refer back to Eqs. (7–10) and (7–11), we see that the length along the arc of a circle and the area within a circular sector vary with two variables. These variables are those which we refer to as the polar coordinates. Express the arc length s and the area A in terms of rectangular coordinates. (How must we express θ?)

38. Under certain conditions, the x- and y-components of a magnetic field B are given by the equations

$$B_x = \frac{-ky}{x^2 + y^2} \quad \text{and} \quad B_y = \frac{kx}{x^2 + y^2}$$

Write these equations in terms of polar coordinates.

39. Express the equation of the cable (see Exercise 27 of Section 20–4) in polar coordinates.

40. The polar equation of the path of an artificial satellite of the earth is

$$r = \frac{4800}{1 + 0.14\cos\theta}$$

where r is measured in miles. Find the rectangular equation of the path of this satellite. The path is an ellipse, with the earth at one of the foci.

20–10 Curves in Polar Coordinates

The basic method for finding a curve in polar coordinates is the same as in rectangular coordinates. We assume values of θ and then find the corresponding values of r. These points are plotted and joined, thus forming the curve which represents the function. The following examples illustrate the method.

Example A

The graph of the polar equation $r = 3$ is a circle of radius 3, with center at the pole. This is the case since $r = 3$, regardless of the value of θ. It is not really necessary to find specific points for this circle. See Fig. 20–55.

The graph of $\theta = \pi/6$ is a straight line through the pole. It represents all points for which $\theta = \pi/6$, regardless of the value of r, positive or negative. See Fig. 20–55.

Example B

Plot the graph of $r = 1 + \cos \theta$.

We find the following table of values of r corresponding to the assumed values of θ.

θ	0	$\dfrac{\pi}{4}$	$\dfrac{\pi}{2}$	$\dfrac{3\pi}{4}$	π	$\dfrac{5\pi}{4}$	$\dfrac{3\pi}{2}$	$\dfrac{7\pi}{4}$	2π
r	2	1.7	1	0.3	0	0.3	1	1.7	2

We now see that the points on the curve start repeating, and it is unnecessary to find additional points. This curve is called a **cardioid** and is shown in Fig. 20–56.

Example C

Plot the graph of $r = 1 - 2 \sin \theta$.

θ	0	$\dfrac{\pi}{4}$	$\dfrac{\pi}{2}$	$\dfrac{3\pi}{4}$	π	$\dfrac{5\pi}{4}$	$\dfrac{3\pi}{2}$	$\dfrac{7\pi}{4}$	2π
r	1	−0.4	−1	−0.4	1	2.4	3	2.4	1

Particular care should be taken in plotting the points for which r is negative. This curve is known as a **limaçon** and is shown in Fig. 20–57.

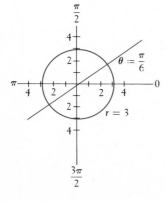

Figure 20–55

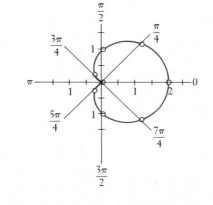

Figure 20–56

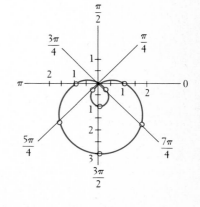

Figure 20–57

Example D
Plot the graph of $r = 2 \cos 2\theta$.

θ	0	$\dfrac{\pi}{12}$	$\dfrac{\pi}{6}$	$\dfrac{\pi}{4}$	$\dfrac{\pi}{3}$	$\dfrac{5\pi}{12}$	$\dfrac{\pi}{2}$	$\dfrac{7\pi}{12}$	$\dfrac{2\pi}{3}$	$\dfrac{3\pi}{4}$	$\dfrac{5\pi}{6}$	$\dfrac{11\pi}{12}$	π
r	2	1.7	1	0	-1	-1.7	-2	-1.7	-1	0	1	1.7	2

For the values of θ from π to 2π, the values of r repeat. We have a four-leaf **rose** (Fig. 20–58).

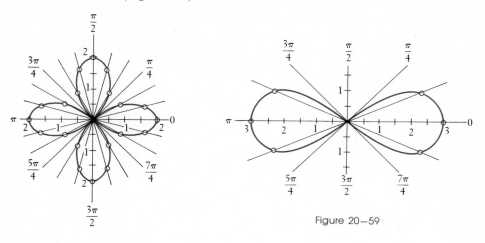

Figure 20–58

Figure 20–59

Example E
Plot the graph of $r^2 = 9 \cos 2\theta$.

θ	0	$\dfrac{\pi}{8}$	$\dfrac{\pi}{4}$	$\cdots$	$\dfrac{3\pi}{4}$	$\dfrac{7\pi}{8}$	π
r	± 3	± 2.5	0		0	± 2.5	± 3

There are no values of r corresponding to values of θ in the range $\pi/4 < \theta < 3\pi/4$, since twice these angles are in the second and third quadrants, and the cosine is negative for such angles. The value of r^2 cannot be negative. Also, the values of r repeat for $\theta > \pi$. The figure is called a **lemniscate** (Fig. 20–59).

Exercises 20–10

In Exercises 1 through 24 plot the given curves in polar coordinates.

1. $r = 4$ 2. $r = 2$ 3. $\theta = \dfrac{3\pi}{4}$ 4. $\theta = \dfrac{5\pi}{3}$

5. $r = 4 \sec \theta$ 6. $r = 4 \csc \theta$ 7. $r = 2 \sin \theta$ 8. $r = 3 \cos \theta$

9. $r = 1 - \cos \theta$ (cardioid)   10. $r = \sin \theta - 1$ (cardioid)

11. $r = 2 - \cos \theta$ (limaçon)   12. $r = 2 + 3 \sin \theta$ (limaçon)

13. $r = 4 \sin 2\theta$ (rose)   14. $r = 2 \sin 3\theta$ (rose)

15. $r^2 = 4 \sin 2\theta$ (lemniscate)

16. $r^2 = 2 \sin \theta$

17. $r = 2^\theta$ (spiral)

18. $r = 10^\theta$ (spiral)

19. $r = -4 \sin 4\theta$ (rose)

20. $r = -\cos 3\theta$ (rose)

21. $r = \dfrac{1}{2 - \cos \theta}$ (ellipse)

22. $r = \dfrac{1}{1 - \cos \theta}$ (parabola)

23. $r = 3 - \sin 3\theta$

24. $r = 4 \tan \theta$

In Exercises 25 through 28 sketch the indicated graphs.

25. The charged particle (see Exercise 33 of Section 20–3) is originally travel-ing along the line $\theta = \pi$ toward the pole. When it reaches the pole it enters the magnetic field. Its path is then described by the polar equation $r = 2a \sin \theta$, where a is the radius of the circle. Sketch the graph of this path.

26. A cam is shaped such that the equation of the edge of the upper "half" is given by $r = 2 + \cos \theta$, and the equation of the edge of the lower "half" by $r = 3/(2 - \cos \theta)$. Plot the curve which represents the shape of the cam.

27. A satellite at a height proper to make one revolution per day around the earth will have for an excellent approximation of its projection on the earth of its path the curve

$$r^2 = R^2 \cos 2\left(\theta + \frac{\pi}{2}\right)$$

where R is the radius of the earth. Sketch the path of the projection.

28. Sketch the graph of the rectangular equation

$$4(x^6 + 3x^4y^2 + 3x^2y^4 + y^6 - x^4 - 2x^2y^2 - y^4) + y^2 = 0$$

[*Hint:* The equation can be written as $4(x^2 + y^2)^3 - 4(x^2 + y^2)^2 + y^2 = 0$. Transform to polar coordinates, and then sketch the curve.]

20—11 Exercises for Chapter 20

In Exercises 1 through 12 find the equation of the indicated curve subject to the given conditions. Sketch each curve.

1. Straight line: passes through $(1, -7)$ with a slope of 4

2. Straight line: passes through $(-1, 5)$ and $(-2, -3)$

3. Straight line: perpendicular to $3x - 2y + 8 = 0$ and has a y-intercept of -1

4. Straight line: parallel to $2x - 5y + 1 = 0$ and has an x-intercept of 2

5. Circle: center at $(1, -2)$, passes through $(4, -3)$

6. Circle: tangent to the line $x = 3$, center at $(5, 1)$

7. Parabola: focus $(3, 0)$, vertex $(0, 0)$

8. Parabola: directrix $y = -5$, vertex $(0, 0)$

9. Ellipse: vertex $(10, 0)$, focus $(8, 0)$, center $(0, 0)$

10. Ellipse: center $(0, 0)$, passes through $(0, 3)$ and $(2, 1)$

11. Hyperbola: vertex $(0, 13)$, center $(0, 0)$, conjugate axis of 24

12. Hyperbola: foci $(0, 10)$ and $(0, -10)$, vertex $(0, 8)$

In Exercises 13 through 24 find the indicated quantities for each of the given equations. Sketch each curve.

13. $x^2 + y^2 + 6x - 7 = 0$, center and radius

14. $x^2 + y^2 - 4x + 2y - 20 = 0$, center and radius

15. $x^2 = -20y$, focus and directrix

16. $y^2 = 24x$, focus and directrix

17. $16x^2 + y^2 = 16$, vertices and foci

18. $2y^2 - 9x^2 = 18$, vertices and foci

19. $2x^2 - 5y^2 = 8$, vertices and foci

20. $2x^2 + 25y^2 = 50$, vertices and foci

21. $x^2 - 8x - 4y - 16 = 0$, vertex and focus

22. $y^2 - 4x + 4y + 24 = 0$, vertex and directrix

23. $4x^2 + y^2 - 16x + 2y + 13 = 0$, center

24. $x^2 - 2y^2 + 4x + 4y + 6 = 0$, center

In Exercises 25 through 32 plot the given curves in polar coordinates.

25. $r = 4(1 + \sin \theta)$ 26. $r = 1 + 2 \cos \theta$

27. $r = 4 \cos 3\theta$ 28. $r = -3 \sin \theta$

29. $r = \cot \theta$ 30. $r = \dfrac{1}{2(\sin \theta - 1)}$

31. $r = 2 \sin \left(\dfrac{\theta}{2}\right)$ 32. $r = \theta$

In Exercises 33 through 36 find the polar equation of each of the given rectangular equations.

33. $y = 2x$ 34. $2xy = 1$ 35. $x^2 - y^2 = 16$ 36. $x^2 + y^2 = 7 - 6y$

In Exercises 37 through 40 find the rectangular equation of each of the given polar equations.

37. $r = 2 \sin 2\theta$ 38. $r^2 = \sin \theta$

39. $r = \dfrac{4}{2 - \cos \theta}$ 40. $r = \dfrac{2}{1 - \sin \theta}$

In Exercises 41 through 68 solve the given problems.

41. Find the points of intersection of the ellipses $25x^2 + 4y^2 = 100$ and $4x^2 + 9y^2 = 36$.

42. Find the points of intersection of the hyperbola $y^2 - x^2 = 1$ and the ellipse $x^2 + 25y^2 = 25$.

43. In two ways show that the line segments joining $(-3, 11)$, $(2, -1)$, and $(14, 4)$ form a right triangle.

44. Show that the altitudes of the triangle with vertices $(2, -4)$, $(3, -1)$, and $(-2, 5)$ meet at a single point.

45. By means of the definition of a parabola, find the equation of the parabola with focus at $(3, 1)$ and directrix the line $y = -3$. Find the same equation by the method of translation of axes.

46. Repeat the instructions of Exercise 45 for the parabola with focus at $(0, 2)$ and directrix the line $y = 4$.

47. In an electric circuit the voltage V equals the product of the current I and the resistance R. Sketch the graph of V (in volts) vs. I (in amperes) for a circuit in which $R = 3\ \Omega$.

48. An airplane touches down when landing at 100 mi/h. Its velocity v while coming to a stop is given by $v = 100 - 20000t$, where t is the time in hours. Sketch the graph of v vs. t.

49. In a certain electric circuit, two resistors having resistances R_1 and R_2 respectively, act as a voltage divider. The relation between them is $\alpha = R_1/(R_1 + R_2)$, where α is a constant less than 1. Sketch the curve of R_1 vs. R_2 (both in ohms), if $\alpha = \frac{1}{2}$.

50. Let C and F denote corresponding Celsius and Fahrenheit temperature readings. If the equation relating the two is linear, determine this equation given that $C = 0$ when $F = 32$ and $C = 100$ when $F = 212$.

51. The arch of a small bridge across a stream is parabolic. If, at water level, the span of the arch is 80 ft and the maximum height of the span above water level is 20 ft, what is the equation of the arch? Choose the most convenient point for the origin of the coordinate system.

52. If a source of light is placed at the focus of a parabolic reflector, the reflected rays are parallel. Where is the focus of a parabolic reflector which is 8 cm across and 6 cm deep?

53. Sketch the curve of the total surface area of a right circular cylinder as a function of its radius, if the height is always 10 units.

54. At very low temperatures certain metals have an electric resistance of zero. This phenomenon is called superconductivity. A magnetic field also affects the superconductivity. A certain level of magnetic field, the threshold field, is related to the temperature T by

$$\frac{H_T}{H_0} = 1 - \left(\frac{T}{T_0}\right)^2$$

where H_0 and T_0 are specificially defined values of magnetic field and temperature. Sketch H_T/H_0 vs. T/T_0.

55. The vertical position of a projectile is given by $y = 120t - 16t^2$, and its hozizontal position is given by $x = 60t$. By eliminating the time t, determine the path of the projectile. Sketch this path for the length of time it would need to strike the ground, assuming level terrain.

56. The rate r in grams per second at which a substance is formed in a chemical reaction is given by $r = 10.0 - 0.010t^2$. Sketch the graph of r vs. t.

57. The inside of the top of an arch is a semi-ellipse with a major axis (width) of 26 ft and a minor axis of 10 ft. The arch is 7 ft thick at all points. Is the outside of the arch a portion of an ellipse? (*Hint:* Check the equation of the outer "ellipse" 1 ft to the right of center.)

58. The earth moves about the sun in an elliptical path. If the closest the earth gets to the sun is 90.5 million miles, and the farthest it gets from the sun is 93.5 million miles, find the equation of the path of the earth. The sun is at one focus of the ellipse. Assume the major axis to be along the x-axis and that the center of the ellipse is at the origin.

59. Soon after reaching the vicinity of the moon, Apollo 11 (the first spacecraft to land a man on the moon) went into an elliptical lunar orbit. The closest the craft was to the moon in this orbit was 70 mi, and the farthest it was

from the moon was 190 mi. What was the equation of the path if the moon was at one of the foci of the ellipse? Assume the major axis to be along the x-axis and that the center of the ellipse is at the origin. The radius of the moon is 1080 mi.

60. A machine-part designer wishes to make a model for an elliptical cam by placing two pins in her design board, putting a loop of string over the pins, and marking off the outline by keeping the string taut. (Note that she is using the definition of the ellipse.) If the cam is to measure 10 cm by 6 cm, how long should the loop of string be and how far apart should the pins be?

61. Under certain conditions the work W done on a wire by increasing the tension from T_1 to T_2 is given by $W = k(T_2^2 - T_1^2)$, where k is a constant depending on the properties of the wire. If the work is constant for various sets of initial and final tensions, sketch a graph of T_2 vs. T_1.

62. In order to study the relationship between velocity and pressure of a stream of water, a pipe is constructed such that its cross-section is a hyperbola. If the pipe is 10 ft long, 1 ft in diameter at the narrow point (middle) and 2 ft in diameter at the ends, what is the equation of the cross-section of the pipe? (In physics it is shown that where the velocity of a fluid is greatest, the pressure is the least.)

63. A hallway 16 ft wide has a ceiling whose cross-section is a semi-ellipse. The ceiling is 10 ft high at the walls and 14 ft high at the center. Find the height of the ceiling 4 ft from each wall.

64. A 60-ft rope passes over a pulley 10 ft above the ground and an object on the ground is attached at one end. A man holds the other end at a level of 4 ft above the ground. If the man walks away from the pulley, express the height of the object above the ground in terms of the distance the man is from directly below the object. Sketch the graph of distance vs. height.

65. Express the equation of the artificial satellite (see Exercise 29 of Section 20–5) in polar coordinates.

66. The x- and y-coordinates of the position of a certain moving object as functions of time are given by $x = 2t$ and $y = \sqrt{8t^2 + 1}$. Find the polar equation of the path of the object.

67. Under a force which varies inversely as the square of the distance from an attracting object (such as the force the sun exerts on the earth), it can be shown that the equation that an object follows is given in general by

$$\frac{1}{r} = a + b \cos \theta$$

where a and b are constant for a particular path. By transforming this equation to rectangular coordinates, show that this equation represents one of the conic sections, the particular section depending on the values of a and b. It is through this kind of analysis that we know the paths of the planets and comets are conic sections.

68. The sound produced by a jet engine was measured at a distance of 100 m in all directions. The loudness of the sound (in decibels) was found to be $d = 115 + 10 \cos \theta$, where the 0° line for the angle θ is directed in front of the engine. Sketch the graph of d vs. θ in polar coordinates (use d as r).

21

Introduction to Statistics
and Empirical Curve Fitting

21—1 Probability

Decisions which we make about the course of action to be taken now or in the future are based on knowledge which involves at least some uncertainty as to the outcome. For example, a decision as to whether to play golf would normally be based on the probability of good weather. In the same way, knowledge of events in the past is usually incomplete, for not every fact about such events is obtainable. This can be illustrated in the statement that "from available information, the age of the Earth is estimated to be about four billion years." Also, events in recorded history often have contradictions and varied interpretations as to actual happenings.

The basic concepts of probability are widely used, at least in an intuitive way. In this section we deal with making determinations as to possible outcomes of events. We will consider certain basic types of situations in which the probability of outcomes can be determined by the nature of the event, or on what is known from past experience.

In the study of probability, a numerical value is given to the likelihood of some particular event actually happening. In determining such a value, we assume that all events are equally likely to occur, unless we have special knowledge to the contrary.

Example A

In considering the possible outcomes of the toss of a coin, we assume that the coin will land either heads or tails, and that either of these possibilities is equally likely.

When considering the drawing of a card from a deck of cards, we assume that the deck is thoroughly shuffled, and that any of the cards in the deck is as likely to be chosen as any other.

When a die is tossed, it is assumed that any of the six faces will come up on top with equal likelihood.

Example B

If a study were made of the percentages of usable and defective parts produced by a particular machine, it would normally be expected that the machine would not turn out as many defective as usable parts. Thus, by studying a random group of parts, we can count the number of defective parts produced. This number would then form a basis of the probable percentage of defective parts which the machine would produce.

Probability, as used in this chapter, is defined as follows: *If an event can turn out in any one of n equally likely ways, and s of these would be successful, then the probability of the event occurring successfully is*

$$P = \frac{s}{n}$$
(21–1)

If the number of equally likely ways an event may turn out cannot be determined from theoretical considerations and N trials are made, of which S are successful, the probability of success is given by

$$P = \frac{S}{N}$$
(21–2)

If the events are equally likely, as expressed in Eq. (21–1), the probability is called an *a priori* probability. This means that probabilities of possible outcomes are determined without any experimentation, and are based on a knowledge of the nature of the event. If the probability is based on past experience, as expressed in Eq. (21–2), the probability is termed **empirical probability.**

Example C

When a card is drawn from a bridge deck (the standard 52-card deck), the probability that this card is a diamond is $\frac{1}{4}$. Here we know that of the 52 cards, 13 of them are diamonds, and that the drawing of a diamond is a success. This in turn means that $n = 52$ and $s = 13$. Thus, for this case,

$$P = \frac{13}{52} = \frac{1}{4}$$

In the same way, the probability of drawing an ace is $\frac{1}{13}$, since there are 4 aces in the 52 cards. For this case, $n = 52$ and $s = 4$, which means

$$P = \frac{4}{52} = \frac{1}{13}$$

Example D

If a particular machine produced 20 defective parts from a lot of 1000, the empirical probability of a defective part being produced is $\frac{1}{50}$. In this case $N = 1000$ and $S = 20$. Thus,

$$P = \frac{20}{1000} = \frac{1}{50}$$

It should be pointed out here that the larger the number inspected and counted, the more accurate is the empirical probability. However, the number sampled must not be so large that it is impractical.

It should be noted that when we have calculated the probability of a certain event occurring, there is no assurance that it will, or will not occur as indicated by the value of the probability. For example, in Example D, we should not expect that exactly one of every fifty parts will be defective. However, we should expect that the more parts we consider, the more likely that the ratio of defective parts to total parts will be approximately $\frac{1}{50}$.

We can see from the definitions and examples that the value of a particular probability can extend from 0 (impossible) to 1 (the sure thing). A probability of $\frac{1}{2}$ expresses equal likelihood of success or failure.

There are cases in which it is more practical to compute the probability of the failure of an event, in order to calculate the probability of its success. This is based on the fact that the probability of failure is

$$F = 1 - \frac{s}{n}$$

Thus, the probability of success, in terms of the probability of failure, is

$$P = 1 - F \tag{21-3}$$

Example E

A bag contains 3 red balls, 4 white balls, and 7 black balls. What is the probability of drawing a red or a black ball?

This can be computed directly, or it can be computed by first determining the probability of drawing a white ball, which would be the probability of failure.

Computing directly, we know that there are 10 balls which are either red or black. Thus, $s = 10$ and $n = 14$, which means that

$$P = \frac{10}{14} = \frac{5}{7}$$

Now, computing the probability of failure first, we know that there are 4 balls (the white ones) which would not be successful draws. Thus,

$$F = \frac{4}{14} = \frac{2}{7}$$

Using Eq. (21–3), we now have

$$P = 1 - \frac{2}{7} = \frac{5}{7}$$

We see that the results agree.

So far we have considered only the probability of success of a single event. The following examples illustrate how the probability of success of a combination of events is found.

Example F

What is the probability of a coin turning up heads in each of two successive tosses?

We can use the definition of probability to determine this result. On the first toss there are two possibilities. On the second toss there are also two possibilities, which means there are, in all, four possible ways in which the coin may fall in two successive tosses. These are HH, HT, TT, TH. Only one of these is successful (heads on two successive tosses). Thus, the probability is $\frac{1}{4}$. This is equivalent to multiplying the probability of success of the first toss by the probability of success of the second toss, or $(\frac{1}{2})(\frac{1}{2}) = \frac{1}{4}$. When we use this multiplication method it is not necessary to figure out all possibilities, a procedure which is often very lengthy, or even impossible from a practical point of view. This multiplication may be stated roughly as "there is a probability of $\frac{1}{2}$ (the second toss) of a probability of $\frac{1}{2}$ (the first toss) of success."

Based on the discussion and results of Example F, the probability of success of a compound event is given in terms of the probabilities of the separate events by

$$P_{1 \text{ and } 2} = P_1 P_2 \qquad (21-4)$$

Example G
Two cards are drawn from a deck of bridge cards. If the first card is not replaced before the second is drawn, what is the probability that both will be hearts?

The probability of drawing a heart on the first draw is $\frac{13}{52}$, or $\frac{1}{4}$. If this first card is a heart, there are only 12 hearts of 51 remaining cards for the second draw. Thus, the probability of success on the second draw is $\frac{12}{51}$. Multiplying these results, we have the probability of success for both, or

$$P = \left(\frac{1}{4}\right)\left(\frac{12}{51}\right) = \frac{1}{17}$$

This means there is a 1-in-17 chance of drawing two successive hearts in this manner.

Example H
In Example G determine the probability that both cards are hearts if the first card is replaced in the deck before the second card is drawn.

Again, the probability of drawing a heart on the first draw is $\frac{1}{4}$. However, since this card is replaced in the deck before the second draw is made, the probability that the second card is a heart is also $\frac{1}{4}$. Thus, the probability that both cards will be hearts is

$$P = \left(\frac{1}{4}\right)\left(\frac{1}{4}\right) = \frac{1}{16}$$

As we should expect, the probability of drawing two hearts in this way is slightly better than when the first card is not replaced.

Example I
In three tosses of a single die, what is the probability of tossing at least one 2?

Instead of calculating the various combinations, it is easier to calculate the probability of failure to get a 2, and subtract that from 1. This is due to the fact that the probability of failure is $\frac{5}{6}$ each time, and this must occur three times successively for failure of the compound event. Thus,

$$F = \left(\frac{5}{6}\right)\left(\frac{5}{6}\right)\left(\frac{5}{6}\right) = \frac{125}{216} \qquad \text{or} \qquad P = 1 - \frac{125}{216} = \frac{91}{216}$$

Example J

In eight tosses of a coin, what is the probability of tossing at least one head?

Again, it is easier to calculate the probability of failure to obtain the result. The probability of failure (tails) is $\frac{1}{2}$ for each toss. This must occur 8 successive times in order that a head does not appear. Thus,

$$F = \left(\frac{1}{2}\right)^8 = \frac{1}{256}$$

which means that

$$P = 1 - F = 1 - \frac{1}{256} = \frac{255}{256}$$

One misconception is often encountered when we are talking about probability: *In dealing with the probability that a single event will occur, we should remember that the occurrence of this event in the past does not alter the probability of the event occurring in the future.*

Example K

If a coin is tossed 7 times and it comes up tails each time, the probability that it will come up heads on the next toss is still $\frac{1}{2}$. On any given toss, the probability is $\frac{1}{2}$. In the previous example we showed that the probability of heads coming up at least once in 8 tosses is $\frac{255}{256}$. This, however, is a different problem from that of finding the probability of heads coming up on a particular toss of the coin.

The discussion of probability here has been restricted to certain basic cases. The probability of numerous other types of events can be determined. For example, it is possible to determine the probability of heads coming up exactly three times in five tosses of a coin. The general analysis of such cases, other than by specifying all possibilities, is beyond the scope of this discussion.

Exercises 21–1

In Exercises 1 through 8 consider a bag which contains 5 red balls, 6 white balls, and 9 black balls. What is the probability of drawing each of the following?

1. A red ball
2. A white ball
3. A white or black ball
4. A red or white ball
5. Two red balls on successive draws, if the first ball is replaced before the second draw is made
6. Two white balls on successive draws, if the first ball is replaced before the second draw is made
7. Two red balls on successive draws if the first ball is not replaced before the second draw is made
8. A red ball and then a white ball if the first ball is not replaced before the second draw is made

In Exercises 9 through 16 assume that we are tossing a single die. What is the probability of tossing the following?

9. A 4

10. A 2 or 4

11. Other than a 4

12. Other than a 2 or 4

13. Two successive 4's

14. Three successive 4's

15. At least one 4 in two successive tosses

16. At least one 4 in four successive tosses

In Exercises 17 through 24 assume that we are tossing two dice. An analysis of the possibilities shows that there are 36 different ways in which the dice may fall. What is the probability of tossing the following totals on the dice?

17. 2

18. 3

19. 7   20. 10

21. 7 or 11

22. 10, 11, or 12

23. 7 on two successive tosses

24. At least one 7 in two successive tosses

In Exercises 25 through 28 use the following information. An insurance company, in compiling mortality tables, found that of 10,000 10-year olds, 6,900 lived to be 60, and 4,700 lived to be 70.

25. What is the probability of a 10-year-old living to the age of 70?

26. What is the probability of a 60-year-old living to the age of 70?

27. What is the probability of two 10-year-old people living to the age of 60?

28. What is the probability of two 60-year-old people living to the age of 70?

In Exercises 29 through 32 use the following information:

The assembly of a certain product is done in three stages by machines A, B, and C. If any machine breaks down, the assembly cannot be done. The probabilities that the machines will not break down in a year are $\frac{4}{5}$, $\frac{9}{10}$, and $\frac{19}{20}$, respectively. Find the probabilities that production will cease at some point in a year due to breakdowns in the indicated machines.

29. A or B   30. B or C   31. A or C   32. Any of the machines

In Exercises 33 through 40 solve the given problems in probability.

33. What is the probability of drawing an ace on each of two successive draws from a standard bridge deck of cards, if the first card is not replaced before drawing the second card?

34. What is the probability of drawing at least one ace in two draws, if the first card is not replaced before drawing the second card?

35. For the machine in Example D, how many defective parts should we expect to find in 300 total parts?

36. A certain college, which accepts students only from the upper quarter of the high-school graduating class, finds that 12% of its students attain an average of 3.0 or better (based on a highest attainable score of 4.0). If all the graduates from a particular high school were to apply to this college, what is the probability of a particular one of them attaining an average of 3.0 or better in his classes at the college?

37. One of the first three trials in a series of complicated scientific experiments was unsuccessful due to a failure in a piece of equipment. Based on these three trials, what is the probability of success of the next two successive trials?

38. In Exercise 37, if the fourth trial is successful, what is the probability at this point of the fifth trial being successful?

39. In a random test of newly manufactured transistors, if there are two defective transistors in a particular group of 20, and two of the 20 are tested, what is the probability that at least one of those tested will be defective?

40. How many of the transistors of Exercise 39 would have to be tested in order for there to be a 50% chance of testing one of the defective ones?

21–2 Frequency Distributions and Measures of Central Tendency

When a mathematician wishes to state the relation between the area of a circle and its radius, he or she writes $A = \pi r^2$, and knows that this relation is true for all circles. When an engineer wishes to find the safe load which a particular cable is able to support, he or she cannot so simply write an equation for the relation, because the load which a cable may support depends on the diameter of the cable, the material of which it is made, the quality of material in the particular cable, any possible defects in its manufacture, and anything else which could make this cable different from all other cables. Thus, to determine the load which a cable can support, an engineer may test many cables of particular specifications. He or she will find that most of the cables can support approximately the same load, but that there is some variation, and occasionally perhaps a great variation for some reason or other. Any conclusions the person may draw will, by the nature of their source, yield probable knowledge of the cable.

The engineer, in testing a number of cables and thereby selecting a certain type of cable, is making use of the basic methods of **statistics.** That is, the engineer (1) collects data, (2) analyzes this data, and (3) interprets this data. In this section and the following section, we will discuss some of the methods of tabulating and analyzing this type of statistical information.

In statistics we are dealing with various sets of numbers. These could be measurements of length, test scores, weights of objects, or numerous other possibilities. We could deal with the entire set of numbers, but this is often too large to be practical. In such a case we deal with a selected (assumed to be representative) sample.

Example A
A company produces a machine part which is designed to be 3.80 cm long. If 10,000 are produced daily, it could be impractical to test each one to determine if it meets specifications. Therefore, it might be decided to test every tenth, or every hundredth, part.

If only ten such parts were produced daily, it might be possible to test each one for specifications.

One way of organizing data in order to develop some understanding of it is to tabulate the number of occurrences for each particular value within the set. This is called a **frequency distribution.**

Example B

A test station measured the loudness of the sound of jet aircraft taking off from a certain airport. The decibel readings of the first twenty jets were as follows: 110, 95, 100, 115, 105, 110, 120, 110, 115, 105, 90, 95, 105, 110, 100, 115, 105, 120, 95, 110.

We can see that it is difficult to determine any pattern to the readings. Therefore, we set up the following table to show the frequency distribution.

Decible reading	90	95	100	105	110	115	120
Frequency	1	3	2	4	5	3	2

We note that the distribution and pattern of readings is clearer in this form.

Just as graphs are useful in representing algebraic functions, so also are they a very convenient method of representing frequency distributions. There are several useful methods of graphing such distributions, among which the most important are the **histogram** and the **frequency polygon.** The following examples illustrate these graphical representations.

Example C

A histogram represents a particular set of data by use of rectangles. The width of the base of each rectangle is the same, and is labeled for one of the readings. The height of the rectangle represents the number of values of a given reading. In Fig. 21–1 a histogram representing the data of the frequency distribution of Example B is shown.

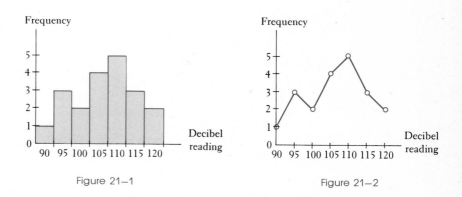

Figure 21–1   Figure 21–2

Example D

The frequency polygon is used to represent a set of data by plotting as abscissas (*x*-values) the values of the readings, and as ordinates (*y*-values) the number of occurrences of each reading (the frequency). The resulting points are joined by straight-line segments. Figure 21–2 shows a frequency polygon of the data of Example B.

Often the number of measurements is sufficiently large that it is not feasible to tabulate the number of occurrences for a particular value. In other cases such a table does not give a clear idea of the distribution. In these cases we may designate certain intervals, and tabulate the number of values within each interval. Frequency distributions, histograms, and frequency polygons can be used to represent data tabulated in this way.

Example E

A certain mathematics course had 80 students enrolled in it. After all the tests and exams were recorded, the instructors determined a numerical average (based on 100) for each student. The following is a list of the numerical grades, with the number of students receiving each.

22−1, 37−1, 40−2, 44−1, 47−1, 53−1, 55−3, 56−1, 60−3, 61−1, 63−4, 65−2, 66−1, 67−5, 68−2, 70−2, 71−4, 72−3, 74−5, 75−4, 77−7, 78−4, 79−1, 81−2, 82−4, 84−1, 85−1, 86−3, 87−2, 88−1, 90−2, 92−1, 93−2, 95−1, 97−1.

We can observe from this listing that it is difficult to see just how the grades were distributed. Therefore the instructors grouped the grades into intervals, which included five possible grades in each interval. This led to the following table.

Interval	20–24	25–29	30–34	35–39	40–44	45–49	50–54	55–59
Number in interval	1	0	0	1	3	1	1	4
Interval	60–64	65–69	70–74	75–79	80–84	85–89	90–94	95–99
Number in interval	8	10	14	16	7	7	5	2

We can see that the distribution of grades becomes much clearer in the above table. Finally, since the school graded students only with the letters A, B, C, D, and F, the instructors then grouped the grades in intervals below 60, from 60–69, from 70–79, from 80–89, and from 90–100, and assigned the appropriate letter grade to each numerical grade within each interval. This led to the following table.

Grade	A	B	C	D	F
Number receiving this grade	7	14	30	18	11

Thus, we can see the distribution according to letter grades. We can also note that, if the number of intervals were reduced much further, it would be difficult to draw any reasonable conclusions regarding the distribution of grades.

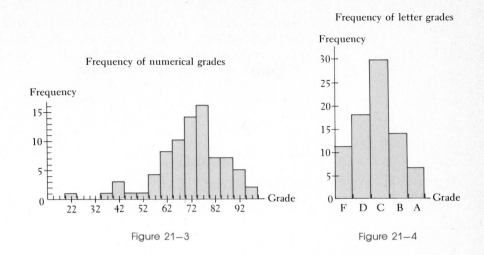

Figure 21—3

Figure 21—4

Histograms showing the frequency of numerical grades and letter grades are shown in Figs. 21–3 and 21–4. In Fig. 21–3, each interval is represented by one number, the middle number. In Fig. 21–5 a frequency polygon of numerical grades is shown, also with each interval represented by the middle number.

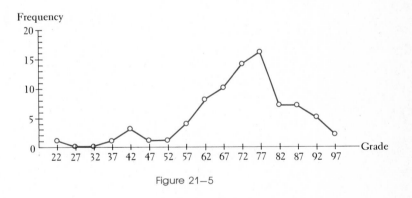

Figure 21—5

We can see from Example E that care must be taken in grouping data. If the number of intervals is too small, important characteristics of the data may not be apparent. If the number of intervals is too large, it may be difficult to analyze the data to determine the distribution and patterns.

Tables and graphical representations give a general description of data. However, it is often profitable and convenient to find representative values for the location of the center of distribution, and other numbers to give a measure of the deviation from this central value. In this way we can obtain an arithmetical description of the data. We shall now discuss the values commonly used to measure the location of the center of the distribution. These are referred to as "measures of central tendency."

The first of these measures of central tendency is the **median**. *The median is the middle number, that number for which there are as many above it as below it in the distribution.* If there is no middle number, the median is that number halfway between the two numbers nearest the middle of the distribution.

Example F

Given the numbers 5, 2, 6, 4, 7, 4, 7, 2, 8, 9, 4, 11, 9, 1, 3, we first arrange them in numerical order. This arrangement is

$$1, 2, 2, 3, 4, 4, 4, 5, 6, 7, 7, 8, 9, 9, 11.$$

Since there are 15 numbers, the middle number is the eighth. Since the eighth number is 5, the median is 5.

If the number 11 is not included in this set of numbers, and there are only 14 numbers in all, the median is that number halfway between the seventh and eighth numbers. Since the seventh is 4 and the eighth is 5, the median is 4.5.

Example G

In the distribution of grades given in Example E of this section, the median is 74. There are 80 grades in all, and if they are listed in numerical order we find that the 39th through the 43rd grade is 74. This means that the 40th and 41st grades are both 74. The number halfway between the 40th and 41st grades would be the median. The fact that both are 74 means that the median is also 74.

Another, and very widely applied, measure of central tendency is the **arithmetic mean**. *The mean is calculated by finding the sum of all the values and then dividing by the number of values.*

Example H

The arithmetic mean of the numbers given in Example F is found by finding the sum of all the numbers and dividing by 15. Thus, letting $\bar{x}$ (read as "x bar") represent the mean, we have

$$\bar{x} = \frac{5 + 2 + 6 + 4 + 7 + 4 + 7 + 2 + 8 + 9 + 4 + 11 + 9 + 1 + 3}{15}$$

$$= \frac{82}{15} = 5.5$$

Thus, the mean is 5.5.

If we wish to find the arithmetic mean of a large number of values, and if some of them appear more than once, the calculation can be somewhat simplified. By multiplying each number by its frequency, adding these results, and then dividing by the total number of values considered, the mean can be calculated. Letting $\bar{x}$ represent the mean of the values $x_1, x_2, \ldots, x_n$, which occur $f_1, f_2, \ldots, f_n$ times, respectively, we have

$$\bar{x} = \frac{x_1 f_1 + x_2 f_2 + \cdots + x_n f_n}{f_1 + f_2 + \cdots + f_n} \qquad (21\text{–}5)$$

(This notation can be simplified by letting

$$x_1 f_1 + x_2 f_2 + \cdots + x_n f_n = \sum_{i=1}^{n} x_i f_i$$

and

$$f_1 + f_2 + \cdots + f_n = \sum_{i=1}^{n} f_i$$

This notation is often used to indicate a sum, where Σ is known as the **summation sign**.)

Example I
Using Eq. (21–5) to find the arithmetic mean of the numbers of Example F, we have

$$\bar{x} = \frac{1(1) + 2(2) + 3(1) + 4(3) + 5(1) + 6(1) + 7(2) + 8(1) + 9(2) + 11(1)}{15}$$

$$= \frac{82}{15} = 5.5$$

Example J
We find the arithmetic mean of the grades in Example E by

$$\bar{x} = \frac{22(1) + (37)(1) + (40)(2) + \cdots + (67)(5) + \cdots + (97)(1)}{80}$$

$$= \frac{5733}{80} = 71.7$$

Exercises 21—2

In Exercises 1 through 24 use the following sets of numbers.

A: 3, 6, 4, 2, 5, 4, 7, 6, 3, 4, 6, 4, 5, 7, 3
B: 25, 26, 23, 24, 25, 28, 26, 27, 23, 28, 25
C: 48, 53, 49, 45, 55, 49, 47, 55, 48, 57, 51, 46
D: 105, 108, 103, 108, 106, 104, 109, 104, 110, 108, 108, 104, 113, 106, 107, 106, 107, 109, 105, 111, 109, 108

In Exercises 1 through 4 set up a frequency distribution table, indicating the frequency of each number given in the indicated set.

1. Set A   2. Set B   3. Set C   4. Set D

In Exercises 5 through 8 set up a frequency distribution table, indicating the frequency of numbers for the given intervals of the given sets.

5. Intervals 2–3, 4–5, and 6–7 for set A.
6. Intervals 22–24, 25–27, and 28–30 for set B.
7. Intervals 43–45, 46–48, 49–51, 52–54, and 55–57 for set C.
8. Intervals 101–105, 106–110, and 111–115 for set D.

In Exercises 9 through 12 draw histograms for the data in the given exercise.

9. Exercise 1   10. Exercise 4   11. Exercise 7   12. Exercise 8

In Exercises 13 through 16 draw frequency polygons for the data in the given exercise.

13. Exercise 1   14. Exercise 4   15. Exercise 7   16. Exercise 8

In Exercises 17 through 20 determine the median of the numbers of the given set.

17. Set A   18. Set B   19. Set C   20. Set D

In Exercises 21 through 24 determine the arithmetic mean of the numbers of the given set.

21. Set A   22. Set B   23. Set C   24. Set D

In Exercises 25 through 36 find the indicated quantities.

25. Form a histogram for the data given in the following table, which was compiled when a particular type of cable was being tested for its breaking load.

Load interval, pounds	830–839	840–849	850–859	860–869	870–879	880–889	890–899
Number of cables breaking	4	14	48	531	85	22	2

26. Form a frequency polygon for the data given in Exercise 25.

27. A researcher, testing an electric circuit, found the following values for the current (in milliamperes) in the circuit on successive trials: 3.44, 3.46, 3.39, 3.44, 3.48, 3.40, 3.29, 3.46, 3.41, 3.37, 3.45, 3.47, 3.43, 3.38, 3.50, 3.41, 3.42, 3.47. Form a histogram for the intervals 3.25–3.29, 3.30–3.34, etc.

28. Form a histogram for the data given in Exercise 27 for the intervals 3.21–3.30, 3.31–3.40, etc.

29. Find the median of the data given in Exercise 27.

30. Find the mean of the data given in Exercise 27.

31. One hundred motorists were asked to maintain a miles per gallon record for their cars, all the same model. The records which were reported are shown in the following table.

Miles per gallon	19.0–19.4	19.5–19.9	20.0–20.4	20.5–20.9
Number reporting	4	9	14	24

Miles per gallon	21.0–21.4	21.5–21.9	22.0–22.4	22.5–22.9
Number reporting	28	16	4	1

Draw a histogram for this data.

32. Draw a frequency polygon for the data of Exercise 31.

33. Determine the arithmetic mean of the data of Exercise 31.

34. Determine the median of the data of Exercise 31.

35. Take two dice and toss them 100 times, recording at each toss the sum which appears. Draw a frequency polygon of the sum and the frequency with which it occurred. Compare this with the expected frequency as based on probability.

36. From the financial section of a newspaper, record (to the nearest dollar) the closing price of the first 50 stocks listed. Form a frequency table with intervals 0–9, 10–19, and so forth. Form a histogram of these data. Finally, find the median price.

In Exercises 37 through 40 use the following information. The **mode** of a frequency distribution, another measure of central tendency, is defined as the measure with the maximum frequency, if there is one. A set of numbers may have more than one mode. Using this definition, find the mode of the numbers in the indicated sets of numbers at the beginning of this exercise set.

37. Set A 38. Set B 39. Set C 40. Set D

21—3 Standard Deviation

In the preceding section we discussed measures of central tendency of sets of data. However, regardless of the measure which may be used, it does not tell us whether the data are grouped closely together or spread over a large range of values. Therefore, we also need some measure of the deviation, or dispersion, of the values from the median or mean. If the dispersion is small and the numbers are grouped closely together, the measure of central tendency is more reliable and descriptive of the data than the case in which the spread is greater.

There are several measures of dispersion, and we discuss in this section one which is very widely used. It is called the **standard deviation.**

The standard deviation of a set of numbers is given by the equation

$$s = \sqrt{(x - \bar{x})^2} \qquad (21-6)$$

The definition of s indicates that the following steps are to be taken in computing its value.

(1) Find the arithmetic mean $\bar{x}$ of the set of numbers.
(2) Subtract the mean from each of the numbers of the set.
(3) Square these differences.
(4) Find the arithmetic mean of these squares. (Note that a bar over any quantity signifies the mean of the set of values of that quantity.)
(5) Find the square root of this last arithmetic mean.

Defined in this way, s must be a positive number, and thus indicates a deviation from the mean, regardless of whether or not individual numbers are greater or less than the mean.

Example A

Find the standard deviation of the numbers 1, 5, 4, 2, 6, 2, 1, 1, 5, 3. The most efficient method of finding s is to make a table in which Steps (1) to (4) are indicated.

x	$x - \bar{x}$	$(x - \bar{x})^2$
1	-2	4
5	2	4
4	1	1
2	-1	1
6	3	9
2	-1	1
1	-2	4
1	-2	4
5	2	4
3	0	0
30		32

$$\bar{x} = \frac{30}{10} = 3$$

$$\overline{(x - \bar{x})^2} = \frac{32}{10} = 3.2$$

$$s = \sqrt{3.2} = 1.8$$

Example B

Find the standard deviation of the numbers given in Example F of Section 21–2.

Since several of the numbers appear more than once, it is helpful to use the frequency of each number in the table. Therefore, we have the following table and calculations.

x	f	fx	$x - \bar{x}$	$(x - \bar{x})^2$	$f(x - \bar{x})^2$
1	1	1	-4.5	20.25	20.25
2	2	4	-3.5	12.25	24.50
3	1	3	-2.5	6.25	6.25
4	3	12	-1.5	2.25	6.75
5	1	5	-0.5	0.25	0.25
6	1	6	0.5	0.25	0.25
7	2	14	1.5	2.25	4.50
8	1	8	2.5	6.25	6.25
9	2	18	3.5	12.25	24.50
11	1	11	5.5	30.25	30.25
	15	82			123.75

$$\bar{x} = \frac{82}{15} = 5.5$$

$$\overline{f(x - \bar{x})^2} = \frac{123.75}{15} = 8.25$$

$$s = \sqrt{8.25} = 2.9$$

We can see from Examples A and B that there is a great deal of calculational work required to find the standard deviation of a set of numbers. It is possible to reduce this work somewhat, and we now show how this may be done.

To find the mean of the sum of two sets of data, x_i and y_i, where the number of values in each set is the same, we can determine the mean of the x's and the mean of the y's and add the results. That is

$$\overline{x + y} = \overline{x} + \overline{y} \tag{21-7}$$

This is true by the meaning of the definition of the arithmetic mean.

$$\overline{x + y} = \frac{x_1 + x_2 + \cdots + x_n + y_1 + y_2 + \cdots + y_n}{n}$$

$$= \frac{x_1 + x_2 + \cdots + x_n}{n} + \frac{y_1 + y_2 + \cdots y_n}{n} = \overline{x} + \overline{y}$$

Also, when we find the arithmetic mean, if all the numbers contain a constant factor, this number can be factored before the mean is found. That is,

$$\overline{kx} = k\overline{x} \tag{21-8}$$

If we multiply out the quantity under the radical in Eq. (21–6), and then apply Eq. (21–7), we obtain

$$\overline{x^2 - 2x\overline{x} + \overline{x}^2} = \overline{x^2} - \overline{2x\overline{x}} + \overline{\overline{x}^2}$$

In this equation the number 2 and $\overline{x}$ are constants for any given problem. Thus, by using Eq. (21–8), we have

$$\overline{x^2} - \overline{2x\overline{x}} + \overline{\overline{x}^2} = \overline{x^2} - 2\overline{x}(\overline{x}) + \overline{x}^2(1) = \overline{x^2} - \overline{x}^2$$

Substituting this last result into Eq. (21–6), we have

$$s = \sqrt{\overline{x^2} - \overline{x}^2} \tag{21-9}$$

Equation (21–9) shows us that the standard deviation s may be found by finding the mean of the squares of the x's, subtracting the square of $\overline{x}$, and then finding the square root. This eliminates the step of subtracting $\overline{x}$ from each x, a step required by the original definition.

Example C

By using Eq. (21–9), find s for the numbers in Example A. Again, a table is the most convenient form.

x	x^2
1	1
5	25
4	16
2	4
6	36
2	4
1	1
1	1
5	25
3	9
30	122

$$\bar{x} = \frac{30}{10} = 3, \qquad \bar{x}^2 = 9$$

$$\overline{x^2} = \frac{122}{10} = 12.2$$

$$\overline{x^2} - \bar{x}^2 = 12.2 - 9 = 3.2$$

$$s = \sqrt{3.2} = 1.8$$

Example D

In an ammeter, two resistances are connected in parallel. Most of the current passing through the meter goes through the one called the shunt. In order to determine the accuracy of the resistance of shunts being made for ammeters, a manufacturer tested a sample of 100 shunts. The resistance of each, to the nearest hundredth of an ohm, is indicated in the following table. Calculate the standard deviation of the resistances of the shunts.

R (ohms)	f	fR	fR^2
0.200	1	0.200	0.0400
0.210	3	0.630	0.1323
0.220	5	1.100	0.2420
0.230	10	2.300	0.5290
0.240	17	4.080	0.9792
0.250	40	10.000	2.5000
0.260	13	3.380	0.8788
0.270	6	1.620	0.4374
0.280	3	0.840	0.2352
0.290	2	0.580	0.1682
	100	24.730	6.1421

$$\bar{R} = \frac{\Sigma fR}{\Sigma f} = \frac{24.73}{100} = 0.2473$$

$$\bar{R}^2 = 0.06116$$

$$\overline{R^2} = \frac{\Sigma fR^2}{\Sigma f} = \frac{6.142}{100} = 0.06142$$

$$\overline{R^2} - \bar{R}^2 = 0.00026$$

$$s = \sqrt{0.00026} = 0.016$$

The arithmetic mean of the resistances is 0.247 Ω, with a mean deviation of 0.016 Ω.

Example E

Find the standard deviation of the grades in Example E of Section 21–2. Use the frequency distribution as grouped in intervals 20–24, 25–29, and so forth, and then assume that each value in the interval is equal to the representative value (middle value) of the interval. (This method is not exact, but when a problem involves a large number of values, the method provides a very good approximation and eliminates a great deal of arithmetic work.)

x	f	fx	fx²
22	1	22	484
27	0	0	0
32	0	0	0
37	1	37	1,369
42	3	126	5,292
47	1	47	2,209
52	1	52	2,704
57	4	228	12,996
62	8	496	30,752
67	10	670	44,890
72	14	1,008	72,576
77	16	1,232	94,864
82	7	574	47,068
87	7	609	52,983
92	5	460	42,320
97	2	194	18,818
	80	5,755	429,325

$$\bar{x} = \frac{\Sigma fx}{\Sigma f} = \frac{5,755}{80} = 71.9$$

$$\bar{x}^2 = 5,170$$

$$\overline{x^2} = \frac{\Sigma fx^2}{80} = \frac{429,325}{80} = 5,367$$

$$\overline{x^2} - \bar{x}^2 = 197$$

$$s = \sqrt{197} = 14.0$$

We have seen that the standard deviation is a measure of the dispersion of a set of data. Generally, if we make a great many measurements of a given type, we would expect to find a majority of them near the arithmetic mean. If this is the case, the distribution probably follows, at least to a reasonable extent, the **normal distribution curve**. See Fig. 21–6. This curve gives a theoretical distribution about the arithmetic mean, assuming that the number of values in the distribution becomes infinite, and its equation is

$$y = \frac{1}{\sqrt{2\pi}}e^{-x^2/2} \tag{21–10}$$

An important feature of the standard deviation is that in a normal distribution, about 68% of the values are found within the interval $\bar{x} - s$ to $\bar{x} + s$.

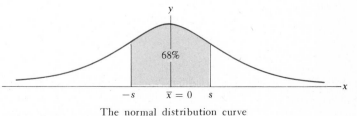

The normal distribution curve

Figure 21–6

Example F

In Example B, 9 of the 15 values, or 60%, are between 2.6 and 8.4. Here $\bar{x} = 5.5$ and $s = 2.9$. Thus, $\bar{x} - s = 2.6$ and $\bar{x} + s = 8.4$. Therefore, we see that the percentage in this interval is slightly less than in a normal distribution.

In Example E, using $\bar{x} = 72$ and $s = 14$, we have $\bar{x} - s = 58$ and $\bar{x} + s = 86$. We also note that 59 of the 80 values are in the interval from 58 to 86, which means that 74% of the values are in this interval.

Exercises 21—3

In Exercises 1 through 20 use the following sets of numbers. They are the same as those used in Exercises 21–2.

A: 3, 6, 4, 2, 5, 4, 7, 6, 3, 4, 6, 4, 5, 7, 3

B: 25, 26, 23, 24, 25, 28, 26, 27, 23, 28, 25

C: 48, 53, 49, 45, 55, 49, 47, 55, 48, 57, 51, 46

D: 105, 108, 103, 108, 106, 104, 109, 104, 110, 108, 108, 104, 113, 106, 107, 106, 107, 109, 105, 111, 109, 108

In Exercises 1 through 4 use Eq. (21–6) to find the standard deviation s for the indicated sets of numbers.

1. Set A   2. Set B   3. Set C   4. Set D

In Exercises 5 through 8 use Eq. (21–9) to find the standard deviation s for the indicated sets of numbers.

5. Set A   6. Set B   7. Set C   8. Set D

In Exercises 9 through 12 find the standard deviation s for the indicated sets of numbers.

9. The weekly salaries (in dollars) for the workers in a small factory are as follows: 250, 350, 275, 225, 175, 300, 200, 350, 275, 400, 300, 225, 250, 300.

10. The measurements of electric current in Exercise 27 of Exercises 21–2

11. The measurements of cable breaking loads in Exercise 25 of Exercises 21–2

12. The measurements of miles per gallon in Exercise 31 of Exercises 21–2

In Exercises 13 through 20 find the percentage of values in the interval $\bar{x} - s$ to $\bar{x} + s$ for the indicated sets of numbers.

13. Set A   14. Set B   15. Set C   16. Set D

17. The salaries of Exercise 9

18. The measurements of electric current in Exercise 27 of Exercises 21–2

19. The measurements of cable breaking loads in Exercise 25 of Exercises 21–2

20. The measurements of miles per gallon in Exercises 31 of Exercises 21–2

21—4 Fitting a Straight Line to a Set of Points

We have considered statistical methods for dealing with one variable. We have discussed methods of tabulating, graphing, measuring the central tendency and the deviations from this value for one variable. We now shall discuss how to obtain a relationship between two variables for which a set of points is known.

In this section we shall show a method of "fitting" a straight line to a given set of points. In the following section fitting suitable nonlinear curves to given sets of points will be discussed. Some of the reasons for doing this are (1) to express a concise relationship between the variables, (2) to use the equation for the purpose of predicting certain fundamental results, (3) to determine the reliability of certain sets of data, and (4) to use the data for testing theoretical concepts.

We shall assume for the examples and exercises of the remainder of this chapter that there is some relationship between the variables. Often when we are analyzing statistics for variables between which we think a relationship might exist, the points are so scattered as to give no reasonable idea regarding the possible functional relationship. We shall assume here that such combinations of variables have been discarded in the analysis.

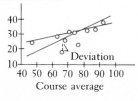

Entrance test

40
30
20
10
  40 50 60 70 80 90 100
Course average

Figure 21—7

Example A

All the students enrolled in the mathematics course referred to in Example E of Section 21–2 took an entrance test in mathematics. To study the reliability of this test, an instructor tabulated the test scores of 10 students (selected at random), along with their course average, and made a graph of these figures (see table below, and Fig. 21–7).

Student	Entrance test score based on 40	Course average based on 100
A	29	63
B	33	88
C	22	77
D	17	67
E	26	70
F	37	93
G	30	72
H	32	81
I	23	47
J	30	74

We now ask whether or not there is a functional relationship between the test scores and the course grades. Certainly no clear-cut relationship exists, but in general we see that the higher the test score, the higher the course grade. This leads to the possibility that there might be some straight line, from which none of the points would vary too significantly. If such a line could be found, then it could be the basis of predictions as to the possible success a student might have in the course, on the basis of his or her grade on the entrance test. Assuming that such a straight line exists, the problem is to find the equation of this line. Figure 21–8 shows two such possible lines.

Entrance test

40
30
20
10
  40 50 60 70 80 90 100
  Deviation
Course average

Figure 21—8

There are various methods of determining the line which best fits the given points. We shall employ the one which is most widely used: the **method of least squares.** *The basic principle of this method is that the sum of the squares of the deviation of all points from the best line (in accordance with this method) is the least it can be.* By **deviation** we mean *the difference between the y-value of the line and the y-value for the point (of original data) for a particular value of x.*

Example B

In Fig. 21–8 the deviation of one point is indicated. The point (67, 17) (student D of Example A) has a deviation of 8 from the indicated line of Fig. 21–8. Thus we square the value of this deviation to obtain 64. The method of least squares requires that the sum of all such squares be a minimum in order to determine the line which fits best.

Therefore, in applying this method, it is necessary to use the equation of a straight line and the coordinates of the points of the data. The deviation of these is indicated and squared. The problem then arises as to the method of determining the constants m and b in the equation of the line $y = mx + b$ for which these squares are a minimum. Since we are dealing with squared quantities, the problem is one of finding the minimum of a quadratic-type function. The following example indicates the method employed.

Example C

For what value of x is the quadratic function

$$y = x^2 - 8x + 19 \quad \text{a minimum?}$$

By inspection we see that this equation represents a parabola. From the properties of this type of parabola, we know that the minimum value of y will occur at the vertex. Thus, we are to find the x-coordinate of the vertex. To do this, we complete the square of the x-terms. And so we have

$$y = (x^2 - 8x + 16) + 3 \quad \text{or} \quad y = (x - 4)^2 + 3$$

We now see that if $x = 4$, $y = 3$. If x is anything other than 4, $y > 3$, since $(x - 4)$ is squared and is always positive for values other than $x = 4$. Therefore, the minimum value of this function is 3, and it occurs for $x = 4$.

The previous discussion indicates the type of reasoning used in developing the equations for the best straight line to fit a set of data. However, it is not a derivation, as a complete derivation requires more advanced mathematical methods.

By finding the deviations, squaring, and then applying the method above for finding the minimum of the sum of the squares, the equation of the **least-squares line,**

$$y = mx + b \qquad (21\text{–}11)$$

can be found by the values

$$m = \frac{\overline{xy} - \overline{x}\,\overline{y}}{s_x^2} \qquad (21\text{–}12)$$

and

$$b = \overline{y} - m\overline{x} \qquad (21\text{–}13)$$

In Eqs. (21–12) and (21–13), the x's and y's are those of the points in the data and s_x is the standard deviation of the x-values.

Example D

Find the least-squares line of the data of Example A.

Here the y-values will be the entrance-test scores, and the x-values the course averages. The results are best obtained by tabulating the necessary quantities, as we do in the following table.

x	y	xy	x^2
63	29	1,830	3,970
88	33	2,900	7,740
77	22	1,690	5,930
67	17	1,140	4,490
70	26	1,820	4,900
93	37	3,440	8,650
72	30	2,160	5,180
81	32	2,590	6,560
47	23	1,080	2,210
74	30	2,220	5,480
732	279	20,870	55,110

$$\overline{x} = \frac{732}{10} = 73.2, \quad \overline{x}^2 = 5358$$

$$\overline{y} = \frac{279}{10} = 27.9, \quad \overline{x}\,\overline{y} = 2042$$

$$\overline{xy} = \frac{20,870}{10} = 2087, \quad \overline{x^2} = \frac{55,110}{10} = 5511$$

$$s_x^2 = \overline{x^2} - \overline{x}^2 = 153$$

$$m = \frac{\overline{xy} - \overline{x}\,\overline{y}}{s_x^2} = \frac{2087 - 2042}{153}$$

$$= \frac{45}{153} = 0.294$$

$$b = \overline{y} - m\overline{x} = 27.9 - (0.294)(73.2) = 27.9 - 21.5 = 6.4$$

$$y = 0.294x + 6.4$$

Thus, the equation of the line is $y = 0.294x + 6.4$. This is the line indicated in Fig. 21–9.

We note that when plotting the least-squares line, we know two points on it. These are $(0, b)$ and $(\bar{x}, \bar{y})$. We can see that $(\bar{x}, \bar{y})$ satisfies the equation from the solution for b [Eq. (21–13)].

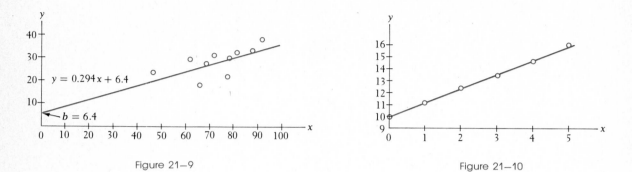

Figure 21–9   Figure 21–10

Example E

In an experiment to determine the relation between the load on a spring and the length of the spring, the following data were found.

Load (pounds)	0.0	1.0	2.0	3.0	4.0	5.0
Length (inches)	10.0	11.2	12.3	13.4	14.6	15.9

Find the least-squares line for this data which expresses the length as a function of the load.

x	y	xy	x^2
0.0	10.0	0.0	0.0
1.0	11.2	11.2	1.0
2.0	12.3	24.6	4.0
3.0	13.4	40.2	9.0
4.0	14.6	58.4	16.0
5.0	15.9	79.5	25.0
15.0	77.4	213.9	55.0

$$\bar{x} = \frac{15.0}{6} = 2.50, \quad \bar{x}^2 = 6.25$$

$$\bar{y} = \frac{77.4}{6} = 12.9, \quad \bar{x}\,\bar{y} = 32.25$$

$$\overline{xy} = \frac{213.9}{6} = 35.65, \quad \overline{x^2} = \frac{55.0}{6} = 9.17$$

$$s_x^2 = \overline{x^2} - \bar{x}^2 = 9.17 - 6.25 = 2.92$$

$$m = \frac{35.65 - 32.25}{2.92} = 1.16, \quad b = 12.9 - (1.16)(2.50) = 10.0$$

Therefore, the least-squares line in this case is

$$y = 1.16x + 10.0$$

where y is the length of the spring and x is the load. In Fig. 21–10, the line shown is the least-squares line, and the points are the experimental data points.

Exercises 21—4

In Exercises 1 through 8 find the equation of the least-squares line for the given data. In each case graph the line and the data points on the same graph.

1. The points in the following table:

x	4	6	8	10	12
y	1	4	5	8	9

2. The points in the following table:

x	1	2	3	4	5	6	7
y	10	17	28	37	49	56	72

3. The points in the following table:

x	20	26	30	38	48	60
y	160	145	135	120	100	90

4. The points in the following table:

x	1	3	6	5	8	10	4	7	3	8
y	15	12	10	8	9	2	11	9	11	7

5. In an electrical experiment, the following data were found for the values of current and voltage for a particular element of the circuit. Find the voltage as a function of the current.

Voltage (volts)	3.00	4.10	5.60	8.00	10.50
Current (milliamperes)	15.0	10.8	9.30	3.55	4.60

6. The velocity of a falling object was found each second by use of an electric device as shown. Find the velocity as a function of time.

Velocity (meters per second)	9.70	19.5	29.5	39.4	49.2	58.9	68.6
Time (seconds)	1.00	2.00	3.00	4.00	5.00	6.00	7.00

7. In an experiment on the photoelectric effect, the frequency of the light being used was measured as a function of the stopping potential (the voltage just sufficient to stop the photoelectric current) with the results given below. Find the least-squares line for V as a function of f. The frequency for $V = 0$ is known as the *threshold frequency*. From the graph, determine the threshold frequency.

V (volts)	0.350	0.600	0.850	1.10	1.45	1.80
f (petahertz)	0.550	0.605	0.660	0.735	0.805	0.880

8. If a gas is cooled under conditions of constant volume, it is noted that the pressure falls nearly proportionally as the temperature. If this were to happen until there was no pressure, the theoretical temperature for this case is referred to as *absolute zero*. In an elementary experiment, the following data were found for pressure and temperature for a gas under constant volume.

P (kilopascals)	133	143	153	162	172	183
T (degrees Celsius)	0.0	20	40	60	80	100

Find the least-squares line for P as a function of T, and, from the graph, determine the value of absolute zero found in this experiment.

The linear coefficient of correlation, a measure of the relatedness of two variables, is defined by $r = m(s_x/s_y)$. Due to its definition, the values of r lie in the range $-1 \leq r \leq 1$. If r is near 1, the correlation is considered good. For values of r between $-\frac{1}{2}$ and $+\frac{1}{2}$, the correlation is poor. If r is near -1, the variables are said to be negatively correlated; that is, one increases while the other decreases.

In Exercises 9 through 12 compute r for the given sets of data.

9. Exercise 1   10. Exercise 2   11. Exercise 4   12. Example A

21–5 Fitting Nonlinear Curves to Data

If the experimental points do not appear to be on a straight line, but we recognize them as being approximately on some other type of curve, the method of least squares can be extended to use on these other curves. For example, if the points are apparently on a parabola, we could use the function $y = a + bx^2$. To use the above method, we shall extend the least-squares line to

$$y = m[f(x)] + b \qquad (21\text{–}14)$$

Here, $f(x)$ must be calculated first, and then the problem can be treated as a least-squares line to find the values of m and b. Some of the functions $f(x)$ which may be considered for use are x^2, $1/x$, and 10^x.

Example A

Find the least-squares curve $y = mx^2 + b$ for the points in the following table.

y	1	5	12	24	53	76
x	0	1	2	3	4	5

The necessary quantities are tabulated for purposes of calculation.

x	y	$f(x) = x^2$	yx^2	$(x^2)^2$
0	1	0	0	0
1	5	1	5	1
2	12	4	48	16
3	24	9	216	81
4	53	16	848	256
5	76	25	1900	625
	171	55	3017	979

$$\overline{x^2} = \frac{55}{6} = 9.17, \quad \overline{x^{2^2}} = 84.1$$

$$\overline{y} = \frac{171}{6} = 28.5, \quad \overline{x^2}\,\overline{y} = 261$$

$$\overline{yx^2} = \frac{3017}{6} = 503, \quad \overline{(x^2)^2} = \frac{979}{6} = 163.2$$

$$s^2_{(x^2)} = 163.2 - 84.1 = 79.1$$

$$m = \frac{503 - 261}{79.1} = \frac{242}{79.1} = 3.06 \qquad b = 28.5 - (3.06)(9.17) = 0.40$$

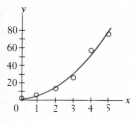

Figure 21–11

Therefore, the desired equation is $y = 3.06x^2 + 0.40$. The graph of this equation and the data points are shown in Fig. 21–11.

Example B

In a physics experiment designed to measure the pressure and volume of a gas at constant temperature, the following data were found. When the

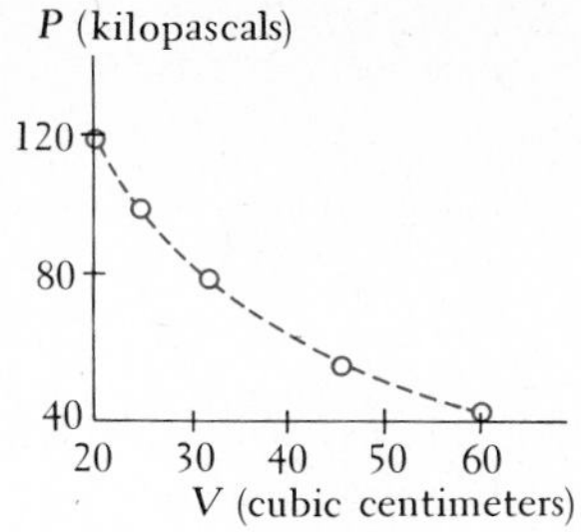

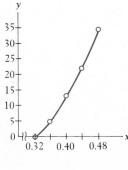

P (kilopascals)

V (cubic centimeters)

Figure 21–12

points were plotted, they were seen to approximate the hyperbola $y = c/x$. Find the least-squares approximation to this hyperbola $[y = m(1/x) + b]$ (see Fig. 21–12).

P(kPa)	V(cm³)	$x(=V)$	$y(=P)$	$f(x) = \dfrac{1}{x}$	$y\left(\dfrac{1}{x}\right)$	$\left(\dfrac{1}{x}\right)^2$
120.0	21.0	21.0	120.0	0.04762	5.714	0.002268
99.2	25.0	25.0	99.2	0.04000	3.968	0.001600
81.3	31.8	31.8	81.3	0.03145	2.557	0.000989
60.6	41.1	41.1	60.6	0.02433	1.474	0.000592
42.7	60.1	60.1	42.7	0.01664	0.711	0.000277
			403.8	0.16004	14.424	0.005726

$$\overline{\frac{1}{x}} = 0.03201 \qquad \overline{\left(\frac{1}{x}\right)^2} = 0.001025 \qquad \overline{y} = 80.76 \qquad \overline{\frac{1}{x}}\overline{y} = 2.585$$

$$\overline{y\left(\frac{1}{x}\right)} = 2.885 \qquad \left(\overline{\frac{1}{x}}\right)^2 = 0.001145 \qquad s^2_{(1/x)} = 0.001145 - 0.001025$$
$$= 0.000120$$

$$m = \frac{2.885 - 2.585}{0.000120} = 2500 \qquad b = 80.76 - 2500(0.03201)$$
$$= 0.74$$

y (=P)

x (=V)

Figure 21–13

Thus the equation of the hyperbola $y = m(1/x) + b$ is

$$y = \frac{2500}{x} + 0.74$$

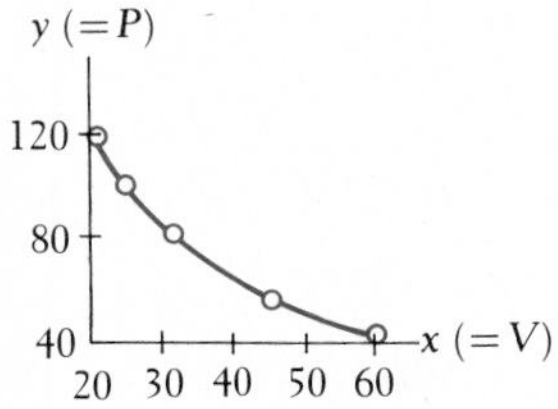

The graph of this hyperbola and the points representing the data are shown in Fig. 21–13.

Example C

It has been found experimentally that the tensile strength of brass (a copper-zinc alloy) increases (within certain limits) with the percentage of zinc. The following table indicates the values which have been found (also see Fig. 21–14).

Tensile strength (10^5 lb/in.²)	0.32	0.36	0.40	0.44	0.48
Percentage of zinc	0	5	13	22	34

Fit a curve of the form $y = m(10^x) + b$ to the data. Let $x =$ tensile strength ($\times 10^5$) and $y =$ percentage of zinc.

Figure 21–14

x	y	$f(x) = 10^x$	$y(10^x)$	$(10^x)^2$
0.32	0	2.09	0.0	4.37
0.36	5	2.29	11.4	5.25
0.40	13	2.51	32.6	6.31
0.44	22	2.75	60.5	7.59
0.48	34	3.02	102.7	9.12
	74	12.66	207.2	32.64

To find $f(x) = 10^x$, we may use either a calculator or logarithms. Using logarithms $x = 0.32$, $10^{0.32}$ is found by looking up the number for which 0.32 is the logarithm. This is due to the definition of a logarithm. Values of $(10^x)^2$ are found in the same manner. When $x = 0.32$, $(10^{0.32})^2 = (10)^{0.64}$, and the antilogarithm of 0.64 is required.

$$\overline{10^x} = 2.53 \qquad\qquad \overline{10^x \bar{y}} = 37.4$$
$$\overline{10^{x^2}} = 6.40 \qquad\qquad \overline{y(10^x)} = 41.4$$
$$\bar{y} = 14.8 \qquad\qquad \overline{(10^x)^2} = 6.53$$
$$s^2_{(10^x)} = 6.53 - 6.40 = 0.13$$
$$m = \frac{41.4 - 37.4}{0.13} = 31$$
$$b = 14.8 - 31(2.53) = -64$$

The equation of the curve is $y = 31(10^x) - 64$. It must be remembered that for practical purposes y must be positive. The graph of the equation is shown in Fig. 21–15, with the solid portion denoting the meaningful part of the curve. The points of the data are also shown.

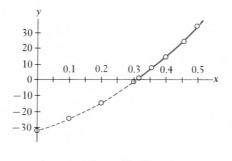

Figure 21–15

Exercises 21–5

In each of the following exercises find the indicated least-squares curve. Sketch the curve and plot the data points on the same graph.

1. For the points in the following table, find the least-squares curve $y = mx^2 + b$.

x	2	4	6	8	10
y	12	38	72	135	200

2. For the points in the following table, find the least-squares curve $y = m\sqrt{x} + b$.

x	0	4	8	12	16
y	1	9	11	14	15

3. For the points in the following table, find the least-squares curve $y = m(1/x) + b$.

x	1.10	2.45	4.04	5.86	6.90	8.54
y	9.85	4.50	2.90	1.75	1.48	1.30

4. For the points in the following table, find the least-squares curve $y = m(10^x) + b$.

x	0.00	0.200	0.500	0.950	1.325
y	6.00	6.60	8.20	14.0	26.0

5. The following data were found for the distance y that an object rolled down an inclined plane in time t. Determine the least-squares curve $y = mt^2 + b$.

y (centimeters)	6.0	23	55	98	148
t (seconds)	1.0	2.0	3.0	4.0	5.0

6. The increase in length of a certain metallic rod was measured in relation to particular increases in temperature. If y represents the increase in length for the corresponding increase in temperature x, find the least-squares curve $y = m(x^2) + b$ for these data.

x (degrees Celsius)	50.0	100	150	200	250
y (centimeters)	1.00	4.40	9.40	16.4	24.0

7. Use the data of Exercise 6 and determine the least-squares curve $y = m(10^z) + b$ where $z = x/1000$.

8. Measurements were made of the current in an electric circuit as a function of time. The circuit contained a resistance of 5 Ω and an inductance of 10 H. The following data were found.

i (amperes)	0.00	2.52	3.45	3.80	3.92
t (seconds)	0.00	2.00	4.00	6.00	8.00

Find the least-squares curve $i = m(e^{-0.5t}) + b$ for this data. Natural logarithms may be used. From the equation, determine the value the current approaches as t approaches infinity.

9. The resonant frequency of an electric circuit containing a 4μF capacitor was measured as a function of an inductance in the circuit. The following data were found.

f (hertz)	490	360	250	200	170
L (henrys)	1.0	2.0	4.0	6.0	9.0

Find the least-squares curve $f = m(1/\sqrt{L}) + b$.

10. The displacement of a pendulum bob from its equilibrium position as a function of time gave the following results.

Displacement (centimeters)	0.00	7.80	10.0	8.10	0.00
Time (seconds)	0.00	0.90	1.60	2.20	3.15

Find the least-squares curve of the form $y = m(\sin x) + b$, expressing the displacement as y and the time as x.

21—6 Exercises for Chapter 21

In Exercises 1 through 4 assume two dice are being tossed.

1. What is the probability of tossing a number greater than 4?
2. What is the probability of tossing a 6 or a 7?
3. What is the probability of tossing a 7 and then an 11 in successive tosses?
4. What is the probability of tossing a 2, a 3, and a 4 in successive tosses?

In Exercises 5 through 8 consider a person who has 6 pennies, 10 nickels, and 8 dimes in a drawer. Determine the probability of the person drawing at random from these coins:

5. Two pennies on successive draws, if the first coin is not replaced before the second is drawn
6. Two pennies on successive draws, if the first coin is replaced before the second is drawn
7. A nickel and then a dime, if the first coin is not replaced before the second coin is drawn
8. A penny, then a nickel, and then a dime, if the first and second coins are replaced before the following draw is made

In Exercises 9 through 12 use the following set of numbers:

$$2.3, \ 2.6, \ 4.2, \ 3.6, \ 3.5, \ 4.1, \ 4.8, \ 2.5, \ 3.0, \ 4.1, \ 3.8$$

9. Determine the median of the set of numbers.
10. Determine the arithmetic mean of the set of numbers.
11. Determine the standard deviation of the set of numbers.
12. Construct a frequency table with intervals 2.0–2.9, 3.0–3.9, and 4.0–4.9.

In Exercises 13 through 16 use the following data:

An important property of oil is its coefficient of viscosity, which gives a measure of how well it flows. In order to determine the viscosity of a certain motor oil, a refinery took samples from 12 different storage tanks and tested them at 50°C. The results (in pascal-seconds) were 0.24, 0.28, 0.29, 0.26, 0.27, 0.26, 0.25, 0.27, 0.28, 0.26, 0.26, 0.25.

13. Determine the arithmetic mean.   14. Determine the median.
15. Determine the standard deviation.   16. Make a histogram.

In Exercises 17 through 20 use the following data:

Two machine parts are considered satisfactorily assembled if their total thickness (to the nearest one-hundredth of an inch) is between or equal to 0.92 and 0.94 in. One hundred sample assemblies are tested, and the thicknesses, to the nearest one-hundredth of an inch, are given in the following table:

Total thickness	0.90	0.91	0.92	0.93	0.94	0.95	0.96
Number	3	9	31	38	12	5	2

17. Determine the arithmetic mean.   18. Determine the median.
19. Determine the standard deviation.   20. Make a frequency polygon.

In Exercises 21 through 24 use the following data:

A Geiger counter records the presence of high-energy nuclear particles. Even though no apparent radioactive source is present, a certain number of particles will be recorded. These are primarily cosmic rays, which are caused by very high-energy particles from outer space. In an experiment to measure the amount of cosmic radiation, the number of counts were recorded during 200 5-s intervals. The following table gives the number of counts, and the number of 5-s intervals having this number of counts. Draw a frequency curve for this data.

Counts	0	1	2	3	4	5	6	7	8	9	10
Intervals	3	10	25	45	29	39	26	11	7	2	3

21. Determine the median.

22. Determine the arithmetic mean.

23. Make a histogram.

24. Make a frequency polygon.

In Exercises 25 through 28 solve the given problems in probability.

25. An integer n, where $10 < n < 20$, is chosen at random. What is the probability that n is even?

26. What is the probability of drawing both red aces from a standard bridge deck of cards in two draws, if the first card is not replaced before drawing the second card?

27. A manufacturer finds that 3% of the parts produced by a certain machine are defective. A testing machine fails to operate properly in its determination of a defective part 0.1% of the time. What is the probability of a defective part not being detected by the testing machine?

28. A certain team won 12 of its first 20 games. Using the complete past record to determine the probability of winning a next game, what is the probability of this team winning the next two games?

In Exercises 29 through 34 find the indicated least-squares curves.

29. In a certain experiment, the resistance of a certain resistor was measured as a function of the temperature. The data found were as follows:

R (ohms)	25.0	26.8	28.9	31.2	32.8	34.7
T (degrees Celsius)	0.0	20.0	40.0	60.0	80.0	100

Find the least-squares line for this data, expressing R as a function of T. Sketch the line and data points on the same graph.

30. The solubility of sodium chloride (table salt) (in kilograms per cubic meter of water) as a function of temperature (degrees Celsius) is measured as follows:

Solubility	357	360	366	373	384
Temperature	0.0	20.0	40.0	60.0	80.0

Find the least-squares straight line for these data.

31. The coefficient of friction of an object sliding down an inclined plane was measured as a function of the angle of incline of the plane. The following results were obtained.

Coefficient of friction	0.16	0.34	0.55	0.85	1.24	1.82	2.80
Angle (degrees)	10.0	20.0	30.0	40.0	50.0	60.0	70.0

Find the least-squares curve of the form $y = m(\tan x) + b$, expressing the coefficient of friction as y and the angle as x.

32. An electric device recorded the total distance (in centimeters) which an object fell at 0.1 s intervals. Following are the data which were found.

Distance	4.90	19.5	44.0	78.1	122.0
Time	0.100	0.200	0.300	0.400	0.500

Find the least-squares curve of the form $y = mx^2 + b$, using y to represent distance and x to represent time.

33. The period of a pendulum as a function of its length was measured, giving the following results.

Period (seconds)	1.10	1.90	2.50	2.90	3.30
Length (feet)	1.00	3.00	5.00	7.00	9.00

Find the least-squares curve of the form $y = m\sqrt{x} + b$, which expresses the period as a function of the length.

34. In an elementary experiment which measured the wavelength of sound as a function of the frequency, the following results were obtained.

Wavelength (centimeters)	140	107	81.0	70.0	60.0
Frequency (hertz)	240	320	400	480	560

Find the least-squares curve of the form $y = m(1/x) + b$ for this data, expressing wavelength as y and frequency as x.

Appendix A

Study Aids

A–1 Introduction

The primary objective of this text is to give you an understanding of mathematics so that you can use it effectively as a tool in your technology. Without understanding of the basic methods, knowledge is usually short-lived. However, if you do understand, you will find your work much more enjoyable and rewarding. This is true in any course you may take, be it in mathematics or in any other field.

Mathematics is an indispensable tool in almost all scientific fields of study. You will find it used to a greater and greater degree as you work in your chosen field. Generally, in the introductory portions of allied courses, it is enough to have a grasp of elementary concepts in algebra and geometry. However, as you develop in your field, the need for more mathematics will be apparent. This text is designed to develop these necessary tools so they will be available in your allied courses. You cannot derive the full benefit from your mathematics course unless you devote the necessary amount of time to developing a sound understanding of the subject.

It is assumed in this text that you have a background which includes geometry and some algebra. Therefore, many of the topics covered in this book may seem familiar to you, especially in the earlier chapters. However, it is likely that your background in some of these areas is not complete, either because you have not studied mathematics for a year or two or because you did not understand the topics when you first encountered them. If a topic is familiar, do not reason that there is no sense in studying it again, but take the opportunity to clarify any points on which you are not certain. In almost every topic you will probably find certain points which can use further study. If the topic is new, use your time effectively to develop an understanding of the methods involved, and do not simply memorize problems of a certain type.

There is only one good way to develop the understanding and working knowledge necessary in any course, and that is to *work with it*. Many students consider mathematics difficult. They will tell you that it is their lack of mathematical ability and the complexity of the material itself which make it difficult. Some topics in mathematics, especially in the more advanced areas, do require a certain aptitude for full comprehension. However, a large proportion of poor grades in elementary mathematics courses result from the fact that the student is not willing to put in the necessary time to develop the understanding. The student takes a quick glance through the material, tries a few exercises, is largely unsuccessful, and then decides that the material is "impossible." A detailed reading of the text, a careful following of the illustrative examples, and then solving the exercises would lead to more success and therefore would make the work much more enjoyable and rewarding. No matter what text is used or what methods are used in the course or what other variables may be introduced, if you do not put in an adequate amount of time for studying, you will not derive the proper results. More detailed suggestions for study are included in the following section.

If you consider these suggestions carefully, and follow good study habits, you should enjoy a successful learning experience in this as well as in other courses.

A–2 Suggestions for Study

When you are studying the material presented in this text, the following suggestions may help you to derive full benefit from the time you devote to it.

(1) Before attempting to do the exercises, read through the material preceding them.

(2) Follow the illustrative examples carefully, being certain that you know how to proceed from step to step. You should then have a good idea of the methods involved.

(3) Work through the exercises, spending a reasonable amount of time on each problem. If you cannot solve a certain problem in a reasonable amount of time, leave it and go to the next. Return to this problem later. If you find many problems difficult, you should reread the explanatory material and the examples to determine what point or points you have not understood.

(4) When you have completed the exercises, or at least most of them, glance back through the explanatory material to be sure you understand the methods and principles.

(5) If you have gone through the first four steps and certain points still elude you, ask to have these points clarified in class. Do not be afraid to ask questions; only be sure that you have made a sincere effort on your own before you ask them.

Some study habits which are useful not only here but in all of your other subjects are the following:

(1) Put in the time required to develop the material fully, being certain that you are making effective use of your time. A good place to study helps immeasurably.

(2) Learn the *methods and principles* being presented. Memorize as little as possible, for although there are certain basic facts which are more expediently learned by memorization, these should be kept to a minimum.

(3) Keep up with the material in all of your courses. Do not let yourself get so behind in your studies that it becomes difficult to make up the time. Usually the time is never really made up. Studying only before tests is a poor way of learning, and is usually rather ineffective.

(4) When you are taking examinations, always read each question carefully before attempting the solution. Solve those you find easiest first, and do not spend too much time on any one problem. Also, use all the time available for the examination. If you finish early, use the remainder of the time to check your work.

A—3 Problem Analysis

Drill-type problems require a working knowledge of the methods presented. However, they do not require, in general, much analysis before being put in proper form for solution. Stated problems, on the other hand, do require proper interpretation before they can be put in a form for solution. The remainder of this section is devoted to some suggestions for solving stated problems.

We have to put stated problems in symbolic form before we attempt to solve them. It is this step which most students find difficult. Because such problems require the student to do more than merely go through a certain routine, they demand more analysis and thus appear more "difficult." There are several reasons for the student's difficulty, some of them being: (1) unsuccessful previous attempts at solving such problems, leading the student to believe that all stated problems are "impossible"; (2) failure to read the problem carefully; (3) a poorly organized approach to the solution; and (4) improper and incomplete interpretation of the statements given. The first two of these can be overcome only with the proper attitude and care.

There are over 70 completely worked examples of stated problems (as well as many other problems which indicate a similar analysis) throughout this text, illustrating proper interpretations and approaches to these problems. Therefore, we shall not include specific examples here. However, we shall set forth the method of analysis of any stated problem. Such an analysis generally follows these steps:

(1) Read the problem carefully.
(2) Carefully identify known and unknown quantities.
(3) Draw a figure when appropriate (which is quite often the case).
(4) Write, in symbols, the relations given in the statements.
(5) Solve for the desired quantities.

If you follow this step-by-step method, and write out the solution neatly, you should find that stated problems lend themselves to solution more readily than you had previously found.

Appendix B

Units of Measurement
and Approximate Numbers

B—1 Units of Measurement; the Metric System

The solution of most technical problems involves the use of the basic operations on numbers, where many of these numbers represent some sort of measurement or calculation. Therefore, associated with these numbers are *units of measurement*, and for the calculations to be meaningful, we must know these units. For example, if we measure the length of an object to be 12, we must know whether it is being measured in feet, yards, or some other specified unit of length.

Certain universally accepted **base units** *are used to measure fundamental quantities*. The units for numerous other quantities are expressed in terms of the base units. Fundamental quantities for which base units are defined are (1) length, (2) mass or force, depending on the system of units being used, (3) time, (4) electric current, (5) temperature, (6) amount of substance, and (7) luminous intensity. *Other units, referred to as* **derived units,** *are expressible in terms of the units for these quantities.*

Even though all other quantities can be expressed in terms of the fundamental ones, many have units which are given a specified name. This is done primarily for those quantities which are used very commonly, although it is not done for all such quantities. For example, the volt is defined as a meter^2-kilogram/second^3-ampere, which is in terms of (a unit of length)^2(a unit of mass)/(a unit of time)^3(a unit of electric current). The unit for acceleration has no special name, and is left in terms of the base units; for example, feet/second². For convenience, special symbols are usually used to designate units. The units for acceleration would be written as ft/s².

Although two basic systems of units, the **metric system** and the **British system,** are in use today, nearly every country in the world is either using or in the process of converting to the metric system. This includes the United States and all of the other countries which now use or previously used the British system. In the United States the conversion is presently coordinated by a national committee, but it is voluntary. However, most major United States' industrial firms will have completed the conversion for their products by the mid 1980s. In most of the other countries in the process of converting, specific timetables of completing various phases of the conversion have been set up.

Therefore, for the present, both systems are of importance although the metric system will eventually be used almost universally. For that reason, where units are used, some of the exercises and examples have

Table B—1. Quantities and Their Associated Units

| Quantity | Quantity Symbol | Unit | | | | |
| | | British | | Metric (SI) | | |
		Name	Symbol	Name	Symbol	In terms of other SI units
Length	s	foot	ft	**meter**	m	
Mass	m	slug		**kilogram**	kg	
Force	F	pound	lb	newton	N	$m \cdot kg/s^2$
Time	t	second	s	**second**	s	
Area	A		ft²		m²	
Volume	V		ft³		m³	
Capacity	V	gallon	gal	liter	L	$(1 \text{ L} = 1 \text{ dm}^3)$
Velocity	v		ft/s		m/s	
Acceleration	a		ft/s²		m/s²	
Density	d, ρ		lb/ft³		kg/m³	
Pressure	p		lb/ft²	pascal	Pa	N/m²
Energy, work	E, W		ft · lb	joule	J	N · m
Power	P	horsepower	hp	watt	W	J/s
Period	T		s		s	
Frequency	f		1/s	hertz	Hz	1/s
Angle	θ	radian	rad	radian	rad	

Special Notes:
1. The SI base units are shown in boldface type.
2. The units symbols shown above are those which are used in the text. Many of them were adopted with the adoption of the SI system. This means, for example, that we use s rather than sec for seconds, and A rather than amp for amperes. Also, other units such as volt are not spelled out, a common practice in the past. When a given unit is used with both systems, we use the SI symbol for the unit.
3. The liter and degree Celsius are not actually SI units. However, they are recognized for use with the SI system due to their practical importance. Also, the symbol for liter has several variations. Presently L is recognized for use in the United States and Canada, l is recognized by the International Committee of Weights and Measures, and *l* is also recognized for use in several countries.

metric units and others have British units. Technicians and engineers need to have some knowledge of both systems.

Although more than one system has been developed in which metric units are used, the system which is now becoming accepted as the metric system is the **International System of Units (SI)**. This was established in 1960, and uses some different definitions for base units than the previously developed metric units. However, the measurement of the base units in the SI system is more accessible, and the differences are very slight. *Therefore, when we refer to the metric system, we are using SI units.*

As we have stated, in each system the base units are specified, and all other units are then expressible in terms of these. Table B-1 lists the fundamental quantities, as well as many other commonly used quantities, along with the symbols and names of units used to represent each quantity shown.

Table B—1. Continued

		Unit				
		British		*Metric (SI)*		
Quantity	*Quantity Symbol*	*Name*	*Symbol*	*Name*	*Symbol*	*In terms of other SI units*
Electric current	I, i	ampere	A	**ampere**	A	
Electric charge	q	coulomb	C	coulomb	C	$A \cdot s$
Electric potential	V, E	volt	V	volt	V	$J/A \cdot s$
Capacitance	C	farad	F	farad	F	s/Ω
Inductance	L	henry	H	henry	H	$\Omega \cdot s$
Resistance	R	ohm	Ω	ohm	Ω	V/A
Thermodynamic Temperature	T			**kelvin**	K	
Temperature	T	Fahrenheit degree	°F	degree Celsius	°C	$(1°C = 1 \ K)$
Quantity of heat	Q	British thermal unit	Btu	joule	J	
Amount of substance	n			**mole**	mol	
Luminous intensity	I	candlepower	cp	**candela**	cd	

4. Other units of time, along with their symbols, which are recognized for use with the SI system and are used in this text are: minute, min; hour, h; day, d.
5. There are many additional specialized units which are used with the SI system. However, most of those which appear in this text are shown in the table. A few of the specialized units are noted when used in the text. One which is frequently used is that for revolution, r.
6. Other common British units which are used in the text are as follows: inch, in.; yard, yd; mile, mi; ounce, oz.; ton; quart, qt; acre.
7. There are a number of units which were used with the metric system prior to the development of the SI system. However, many of these are not to be used with the SI system. Among these which were commonly used are the dyne, erg, and calorie.

In the British system, the base unit of length is the foot, and that of force is the pound. In the metric system, the base unit of length is the meter, and that of mass is the kilogram. Here, we see a difference in the definition of the systems which causes some difficulty when units are converted from one system to the other. That is, a base unit in the British system is a unit of force, and a base unit in the metric system is a unit of mass.

The distinction between mass and force is very significant in physics, and the weight of an object is the force with which it is attracted to the earth. Weight, which is therefore a force, is different from mass, which is a measure of the inertia an object exhibits. Although they are different quantities, mass and weight are however very closely related. In fact, the weight of an object equals its mass multiplied by the acceleration due to gravity. Near the surface of the earth the acceleration due to gravity is nearly constant, although it decreases as the distance from the earth increases. Therefore, near the surface of the earth the weight of an object is directly proportional to its mass. However, at great distances from the earth the weight of an object will be zero, whereas its mass does not change.

Since force and mass are different, it is not strictly correct to convert pounds to kilograms. However, since the pound is the base unit in the British system, and the kilogram is the base unit in the metric system, at the earth's surface 1 kg corresponds to 2.21 lb, in the sense that the force of gravity on a 1 kg mass is 2.21 lb.

When designating units for weight, we use pounds in the British system. In the metric system, although kilograms are used for weight, it is preferable to specify the mass of an object in kilograms. The force of gravity on an object is designated in newtons, and the use of the term weight is avoided unless its meaning is completely clear.

As for the other fundamental quantities, both systems use the second as the base unit of time. In the SI system the ampere is defined as the base unit of electric current, and this can also be used in the British system. As for temperature, degrees Fahrenheit are used with the British system, and degrees Celsius (formerly Centigrade) are used with the metric system (actually, the kelvin is defined as the base unit, where the temperature in kelvins is the temperature in degrees Celsius plus 273.16). In the SI system, the base unit for the amount of a substance is the mole, and the base unit of luminous intensity is the candela. These last two are of limited importance to our use in this text.

Due to greatly varying sizes of certain quantities, the metric system employs certain prefixes to units to denote different orders of magnitude. These prefixes, with their meanings and symbols, are shown in Table B–2 on the following page.

Table B—2. Metric Prefixes

Prefix	Factor	Symbol	Prefix	Factor	Symbol
exa	10^{18}	E	deci	10^{-1}	d
peta	10^{15}	P	centi	10^{-2}	c
tera	10^{12}	T	milli	10^{-3}	m
giga	10^{9}	G	micro	10^{-6}	μ
mega	10^{6}	M	nano	10^{-9}	n
kilo	10^{3}	k	pico	10^{-12}	p
hecto	10^{2}	h	femto	10^{-15}	f
deca	10^{1}	da	atto	10^{-18}	a

Example A

Some of the more commonly used units which use the prefixes in Table B—2, along with their meanings, are shown below.

Unit	Symbol	Meaning	Unit	Symbol	Meaning
megohm	MΩ	10^{6} ohms	milligram	mg	10^{-3} gram
kilometer	km	10^{3} meters	microfarad	μF	10^{-6} farad
centimeter	cm	10^{-2} meter	nanosecond	ns	10^{-9} second

(Mega is shortened to meg when used with "ohm.")

When designating units of area or volume, where square or cubic units are used, we use exponents in the designation. For example, we use m^2 rather than sq m, or in.^{3} rather than cu in.

When we are working with numbers that represent units of measurement (referred to as **denominate numbers**), it is sometimes necessary to change from one set of units to another. A change within a given system is called a **reduction,** and a change from one system to another is called a **conversion.** Table B—3 gives some basic reduction and conversion factors. It should be noted that some calculators are programmed to do conversions.

Table B—3. Reduction and Conversion Factors

1 in. = 2.54 cm (exact)	1 ft^3 = 28.32 L
1 km = 0.6214 mi	1 L = 1.057 qt
1 lb = 453.6 g	1 Btu = 778.0 ft · lb
1 kg = 2.205 lb	1 hp = 550 ft · lb/s (exact)
1 lb = 4.448 N	1 hp = 746.0 W

The advantages of the metric system should be evident. Reductions within the system are made by use of powers of ten, which amounts to moving the decimal point. Reductions in the British system have numerous different multiples that must be used. Thus, comparisons and changes within the metric system are much simpler than in the British system.

To change a given number of one set of units into another set of units, *we perform algebraic operations with units in the same manner as we do with any algebraic symbol.* Consider the following example.

Example B

If we had a number representing feet per second to be multiplied by another number representing seconds per minute, as far as the units are concerned, we have

$$\frac{ft}{s} \times \frac{s}{min} = \frac{ft \times s}{s \times min} = \frac{ft}{min}$$

This means that the final result would be in feet per minute.

In changing a number of one set of units to another set of units, we use reduction and conversion factors and the principle illustrated in Example B. The convenient way to use the values in the tables is in the form of fractions. Since the given values are equal to each other, their quotient is 1. For example, since 1 in. = 2.54 cm,

$$\frac{1 \text{ in.}}{2.54 \text{ cm}} = 1 \qquad \text{or} \qquad \frac{2.54 \text{ cm}}{1 \text{ in.}} = 1$$

since each represents the division of a certain length by itself. Multiplying a quantity by 1 does not change its value. The following examples illustrate reduction and conversion of units.

Example C

Reduce 20 kg to milligrams.

$$20 \text{ kg} = 20 \text{ kg}\left(\frac{10^3 \text{ g}}{1 \text{ kg}}\right)\left(\frac{10^3 \text{ mg}}{1 \text{ g}}\right)$$

$$= 20 \times 10^6 \text{ mg}$$

$$= 2.0 \times 10^7 \text{ mg}$$

We note that this result is found essentially by moving the decimal point three places when changing from kilograms to grams, and another three places when changing from grams to milligrams.

Example D

Change 30 mi/h to feet per second.

$$30\frac{mi}{h} = \left(30\frac{mi}{h}\right)\left(\frac{5280 \text{ ft}}{1 \text{ mi}}\right)\left(\frac{1 \text{ h}}{60 \text{ min}}\right)\left(\frac{1 \text{ min}}{60 \text{ s}}\right) = \frac{(30)(5280) \text{ ft}}{(60)(60) \text{ s}} = 44\frac{ft}{s}$$

Note that the only units remaining after the division are those required.

Example E

Change 575 g/cm³ to kilograms per cubic meter.

$$575\frac{g}{cm^3} = \left(575\frac{g}{cm^3}\right)\left(\frac{100\ cm}{1\ m}\right)^3\left(\frac{1\ kg}{1000\ g}\right)$$

$$= \left(575\frac{g}{cm^3}\right)\left(\frac{10^6\ cm^3}{1\ m^3}\right)\left(\frac{1\ kg}{10^3\ g}\right)$$

$$= 575 \times 10^3\frac{kg}{m^3} = 5.75 \times 10^5\frac{kg}{m^3}$$

Example F

Change 62.8 lb/in.² to newtons per square meter.

$$62.8\frac{lb}{in.^2} = \left(62.8\frac{lb}{in.^2}\right)\left(\frac{4.448\ N}{1\ lb}\right)\left(\frac{1\ in.}{2.54\ cm}\right)^2\left(\frac{100\ cm}{1\ m}\right)^2$$

$$= \left(62.8\frac{lb}{in.^2}\right)\left(\frac{4.448\ N}{1\ lb}\right)\left(\frac{1\ in.^2}{2.54^2\ cm^2}\right)\left(\frac{10^4\ cm^2}{1\ m^2}\right)$$

$$= \frac{(62.8)(4.448)(10^4)}{(2.54)^2}\frac{N}{m^2} = 4.33 \times 10^5\frac{N}{m^2}$$

Exercises B—1

In Exercises 1 through 4 give the symbol and meaning for the given unit.

1. megahertz   2. kilowatt   3. millimeter   4. picosecond

In Exercises 5 through 8 give the name and meaning for the units whose symbols are given.

5. kV   6. GΩ   7. mA   8. pF

In Exercises 9 through 38 make the indicated reductions or conversions.

9. Reduce 1 km to centimeters   10. Reduce 1 kg to milligrams
11. Reduce 1 mi to inches   12. Reduce 1 gal to pints (2 pt = 1 qt)
13. Convert 5.25 in. to centimeters   14. Convert 6.50 kg to pounds
15. Convert 15.7 qt to liters   16. Convert 100 km to miles
17. Reduce 1 ft² to square inches   18. Reduce 1 yd³ to cubic feet
19. Reduce 250 mm² to square meters   20. Reduce 30.8 kL to milliliters
21. Convert 4.50 lb to grams   22. Convert 0.360 in. to meters
23. Convert 829 in.³ to liters
24. Convert 0.0680 kL to cubic feet
25. Convert 1 hp to kilogram centimeters per second
26. Convert 8.75 Btu to joules
27. Convert 75.0 W to horsepower
28. Convert 300 mL to quarts
29. An Atlas rocket weighed 260,000 lb at takeoff. How many tons is this?
30. An airplane is flying at 37,000 ft. What is its altitude in miles?
31. The speedometer of a car is calibrated in kilometers per hour. If the speedometer of such a car reads 60, how fast in miles per hour is the car traveling?

32. The acceleration due to gravity is about 980 cm/s². Convert this to feet per second squared.

33. The speed of sound is about 1130 ft/s. Change this speed to miles per hour.

34. The density of water is about 62.4 lb/ft³. Convert this to kilograms per cubic meter.

35. The average density of the earth is about 5.52 g/cm³. Convert this to pounds per cubic foot.

36. The moon travels about 1,500,000 miles in about 28 d in one rotation about the earth. Express its velocity in feet per second.

37. At sea level, atmospheric pressure is about 14.7 lb/in.². Express this pressure in pascals.

38. The earth's surface receives energy from the sun at the rate of 1.35 kW/m². Reduce this to joules per second square centimeter.

B—2 Approximate Numbers and Significant Digits

When we perform calculations on numbers, we must consider the accuracy of these numbers, since this affects the accuracy of the results obtained. Most of the numbers involved in technical and scientific work are *approximate*, having been arrived at through some process of measurement. However, certain other numbers are *exact*, having been arrived at through some definition or counting process. We can determine whether or not a number is approximate or exact if we know how the number was determined.

Example A

If we measure the length of a rope to be 15.3 ft, we know that the 15.3 is approximate. A more precise measuring device may cause us to determine the length as 15.28 ft. However, regardless of the method of measurement used, we shall not be able to determine this length exactly.

If a voltage shown on a voltmeter is read as 116 V, the 116 is approximate. A more precise voltmeter may show the voltage as 115.7 V. However, this voltage cannot be determined exactly.

Example B

If a computer counts the cards it has processed and prints this number as 837, this 837 is exact. We know the number of cards was not 836 or 838. Since 837 was determined through a counting process, it is exact.

When we say that 60 s = 1 min, the 60 is exact, since this is a definition. By this definition there are exactly sixty seconds in one minute.

When we are writing approximate numbers we often have to include some zeros so that the decimal point will be properly located. However, except for these zeros, all other digits are considered to be **significant digits.** When we make computations with approximate numbers, we must know the number of significant digits. The following example illustrates how we determine this.

Example C

All numbers in this example are assumed to be approximate.

34.7 has three significant digits.

8900 has two significant digits. We assume that the two zeros are place holders (unless we have specific knowledge to the contrary.)

0.039 has two significant digits. The zeros are for proper location of the decimal point.

706.1 has four significant digits. The zero is not used for the location of the decimal point. It shows specifically the number of tens in the number.

5.90 has three significant digits. The zero is not necessary as a place holder, and should not be written unless it is significant.

Other approximate numbers with the proper number of significant digits are listed below.

96000	two	0.0709	three	1.070	four
30900	three	6.000	four	700.00	five
4.006	four	0.0005	one	20008	five

Note from the example above that *all nonzero digits are significant. Zeros, other than those used as place holders for proper positioning of the decimal point, are also significant.*

In computations involving approximate numbers, the position of the decimal point as well as the number of significant digits is important. *The* **precision** *of a number refers directly to the decimal position of the last significant digit, whereas the* **accuracy** *of a number refers to the number of significant digits in the number.* Consider the illustrations in the following example.

Example D

Suppose that you are measuring an electric current with two ammeters. One ammeter reads 0.031 A and the second ammeter reads 0.0312 A. The second reading is more precise, in that the last significant digit is the number of ten-thousandths, and the first reading is expressed only to thousandths. The second reading is also more accurate, since it has three significant digits rather than two.

A machine part is measured to be 2.5 cm long. It is coated with a film 0.025 cm thick. The thickness of the film has been measured to a greater precision, although the two measurements have the same accuracy: two significant digits.

A segment of a newly completed highway is 9270 ft long. The concrete surface is 0.8 ft thick. Of these two numbers, 9270 is more accurate, since it contains three significant digits, and 0.8 is more precise, since it is expressed to tenths.

The last significant digit of an approximate number is known not to be completely accurate. It has usually been determined by estimation or **rounding off.** However, we do know that it is at most in error by one-half of a unit in its place value.

Example E

When we measure the length of the rope referred to in Example A to be 15.3 ft, we are saying that the length is at least 15.25 ft and no longer than 15.35 ft. Any value between these two, rounded off to tenths, would be expressed as 15.3 ft.

In converting the fraction $\frac{2}{3}$ to the decimal form 0.667, we are saying that the value is between 0.6665 and 0.6675.

The principle of rounding off a number is to write the closest approximation, with the last significant digit in a specified position, or with a specified number of significant digits. We shall now formalize the process of rounding off as follows: If we want a certain number of significant digits, we examine the digit in the next place to the right. If this digit is less than 5, we accept the digit in the last place. If the next digit is 5 or greater, we increase the digit in the last place by 1, and this resulting digit becomes the final significant digit of the approximation. If necessary, we use zeros to replace other digits in order to locate the decimal point properly. Except when the next digit is a 5, and no other nonzero digits are discarded, we have the closest possible approximation with the desired number of significant digits.

Example F

70360 rounded off to three significant digits is 70400.
70430 rounded off to three significant digits is 70400.
187.35 rounded off to four significant digits is 187.4.
71500 rounded off to two significant digits is 72000.

With the advent of computers and calculators, another method of reducing numbers to a specified number of significant digits is used. This is the process of **truncation,** in which the digits beyond a certain place are discarded. For example, 3.17482 truncated to thousandths is 3.174. For our purposes in this text, when working with approximate numbers, we have used only rounding off.

Exercises B—2

In Exercises 1 through 8 determine whether the numbers given are exact or approximate.

1. There are 24 hours in one day.
2. The velocity of light is 186,000 mi/s.
3. The 3-stage rocket took 74.6 hours to reach the moon.
4. A man bought 5 lb of nails for $1.56.
5. The melting point of gold is 1063°C.
6. The 21 students had an average test grade of 81.6.
7. A building lot 100 ft by 200 ft cost $3200.
8. In a certain city 5% of the people have their money in a bank that pays 5% interest.

In Exercises 9 through 16 determine the number of significant digits in the given approximate numbers.

9. 37.2; 6844   10. 3600; 730   11. 107; 3004   12. 0.8735; 0.0075

13. 6.80; 6.08   **14.** 90050; 105040   **15.** 30000; 30000.0 **16.** 1.00; 0.01

In Exercises 17 through 24 determine which of each pair of approximate numbers is (a) more precise and (b) more accurate.

17. 3.764, 2.81   **18.** 0.041, 7.673   **19.** 30.8, 0.01   **20.** 70,370, 50,400
21. 0.1, 78.0   **22.** 7040, 37.1   **23.** 7000, 0.004   **24.** 50.060, 8.914

In Exercises 25 through 32 round off each of the given approximate numbers (a) to three significant digits, and (b) to two significant digits.

25. 4.933   **26.** 80.53   **27.** 57893   **28.** 30490
29. 861.29   **30.** 9555   **31.** 0.30505   **32.** 0.7350

B—3 Arithmetic Operations with Approximate Numbers

When performing arithmetic operations on approximate numbers we must be careful not to express the result to a precision or accuracy which is not warranted. The following two examples illustrate how a false indication of the accuracy of a result could be obtained when using approximate numbers.

Example A

A pipe is made in two sections. The first is measured to be 16.3 ft long and the second is measured to be 0.927 ft long. A plumber wants to know what the total length will be when the two sections are put together.

At first, it appears we might simply add the numbers as follows to obtain the necessary result.

$$\begin{array}{r} 16.3 \ \ \text{ft} \\ \underline{0.927 \ \text{ft}} \\ 17.227 \ \text{ft} \end{array}$$

However, the first length is precise only to tenths, and the digit in this position was obtained by rounding off. It might have been as small as 16.25 ft or as large as 16.35 ft. If we consider only the precision of this first number, the total length might be as small as 17.177 ft or as large as 17.277 ft. These two values agree when rounded off to two significant digits (17). They vary by 0.1 when rounded off to tenths (17.2 and 17.3). When rounded to hundredths, they do not agree at all, since the third significant digit is different (17.18 and 17.28). Therefore there is no agreement at all in the digits after the third when these two numbers are rounded off to a precision beyond tenths. This may also be deemed reasonable, since the first length is not expressed beyond tenths. The second number does not further change the precision of the result, since it is expressed to thousandths. Therefore we may conclude that the result must be rounded off at least to tenths, the precision of the first number.

Example B

We can find the area of a rectangular piece of land by multiplying the length, 207.54 ft, by the width, 81.4 ft. Performing the multiplication, we find the area to be (207.54 ft)(81.4 ft) = 16893.756 ft².

However, we know this length and width were found by measurement and that the least each could be is 207.535 ft and 81.35 ft. Multiplying these values, we find the least value for the area to be

$$(207.535 \text{ ft})(81.35 \text{ ft}) = 16882.97225 \text{ ft}^2$$

The greatest possible value for the area is

$$(207.545 \text{ ft})(81.45 \text{ ft}) = 16904.54025 \text{ ft}^2$$

We now note that the least possible and greatest possible values of the area agree when rounded off to three significant digits (16900 ft²) and there is no agreement in digits beyond this if the two values are rounded off to a greater accuracy. Therefore we can conclude that the accuracy of the result is good to three significant digits, or certainly no more than four. We also note that the width was accurate to three significant digits, and the length to five significant digits.

The following rules are based on reasoning similar to that in Examples A and B; we go by these rules when we perform the basic arithmetic operations on approximate numbers.

(1) When approximate numbers are added or subtracted, the result is expressed with the precision of the least precise number.

(2) When approximate numbers are multiplied or divided, the result is expressed with the accuracy of the least accurate number.

(3) When the root of an approximate number is found, the result is accurate to the accuracy of the number.

(4) Before and during the calculation all numbers except the least precise or least accurate may be rounded off to one place beyond that of the least precise or least accurate. This procedure is helpful when a calculator is not used. It need not be followed when a calculator is used.

Example C

Add the approximate numbers 73.2, 8.0627, 93.57, 66.296.

The least precise of these numbers is 73.2. Therefore, before performing the addition we may round off the other number to hundredths. If we are using a calculator, this need not be done. In either case, after the addition we round off the result to tenths. This leads to

73.2		73.2
8.06	or	8.0627
93.57		93.57
66.30		66.296
241.13		241.1287

Therefore, the final result is 241.1.

Example D

If we multiply 2.4832 by 30.5, we obtain 75.7376. However, since 30.5 has only three significant digits, we express the product and result as $(2.4832)(30.5) = 75.7$.

To find the square root of 3.7, we may express the result only to two significant digits. Thus, $\sqrt{3.7} = 1.9$.

The rules stated in this section are usually sufficiently valid for the computations encountered in technical work. They are intended only as good practical rules for working with approximate numbers. It was recognized in Examples A and B that the last significant digit obtained by these rules is subject to some possible error. Therefore it is possible that the most accurate result is not obtained by their use, although this is not often the case.

If an exact number is included in a calculation, there is no limitation to the number of decimal positions it may take on. The accuracy of the result is limited only by the approximate numbers involved.

Exercises B—3

In Exercises 1 through 4 add the given approximate numbers.

1. 3.8	**2.** 26	**3.** 0.36294	**4.** 56.1
0.154	5.806	0.086	3.0645
47.26	147.29	0.5056	127.38
		0.74	0.055

In Exercises 5 through 8 subtract the given approximate numbers.

5. 468.14	**6.** 1.03964	**7.** 57.348	**8.** 8.93
36.7	0.69	26.5	6.8947

In Exercises 9 through 12 multiply the given approximate numbers.

9. $(3.64)(17.06)$ **10.** $(0.025)(70.1)$

11. $(704.6)(0.38)$ **12.** $(0.003040)(6079.52)$

In Exercises 13 through 16 divide the given approximate numbers.

13. $608 \div 3.9$ **14.** $0.4962 \div 827$

15. $\dfrac{596000}{22}$ **16.** $\dfrac{53.267}{0.3002}$

In Exercises 17 through 20 find the indicated square roots of the given approximate numbers.

17. $\sqrt{32}$ **18.** $\sqrt{6.5}$ **19.** $\sqrt{19.3}$ **20.** $\sqrt{0.0694}$

In Exercises 21 through 24 evaluate the given expression. All numbers are approximate.

21. $3.862 + 14.7 - 8.3276$ **22.** $(3.2)(0.386) + 6.842$

23. $\dfrac{8.60}{0.46} + (0.9623)(3.86)$ **24.** $9.6 - 0.1962(7.30)$

In Exercises 25 through 28 perform the indicated operations. The first number given is approximate and the second number is exact.

25. $3.62 + 14$

26. $17.382 - 2.5$

27. $(0.3142)(60)$

28. $8.62 \div 1728$

In Exercises 29 through 38 the solution to some of the problems will require the use of reduction and conversion factors.

29. Two forces, 18.6 lb and 2.382 lb, are acting on an object. What is the sum of these forces?

30. Three sections of a bridge are measured to be 52.3 ft, 36.38 ft, and 38 ft, respectively. What is the total length of these three sections?

31. Two planes are reported to have flown at speeds of 938 mi/h and 1400 km/h, respectively. Which plane is faster, and by how many miles per hour?

32. The density of a certain type of iron is 7.10 g/cm³. The density of a type of tin is 448 lb/ft³. Which is greater?

33. If the temperature of water is raised from 4°C to 30°C, its density reduces by 0.420%. If the density of water at 4°C is 62.4 lb/ft³, what is its density at 30°C?

34. The power (in watts) developed in an electric circuit is found by multiplying the current (in amperes) by the voltage. In a certain circuit the current is 0.0125 A and the voltage is 12.68 V. What is the power that is developed?

35. A certain ore is 5.3% iron. How many tons of ore must be refined to obtain 45,000 lb of iron?

36. An electric data-processing card sorter sorts 32,000 cards, by count, in 10.25 min. At what rate does the sorter operate?

37. In order to find the velocity (in feet per second) of an object which has fallen a certain height, we calculate the square root of the product of 64.4 (an approximate number) and the height in feet. What is the velocity of an object which has fallen 63 m?

38. A student reports the current in a certain experiment to be 0.02 A at one time and later notes that it is 0.023 A. He then states that the change in current is 0.003 A. What is wrong with his conclusion?

Appendix C

The Scientific Calculator

C—1 Introduction

Until the early 1970s the personal calculational device of many technicians and scientists was the slide rule. However, with the development of the microprocessor chip, the pocket scientific electronic calculator has become readily available. Since the calculator is easier to use, and has much greater accuracy and calculational ability than the slide rule, it is now the personal calculational device of technicians and scientists, as well as many others.

The scientific calculator can be used for any of the calculations which may be found in this text. Many of the more sophisticated models can also perform many types of calculations beyond the needs of this text. However, the calculator which performs only the basic arithmetic operations is in itself not sufficient for many of the calculations which are encountered.

There are a great many types and models of calculators. However, the discussions in this appendix are based on the operations which can be performed by use of the basic keys of a scientific, or slide-rule, calculator, and are general enough to apply to most such calculators. Some of the variations and special features which may be found are noted. Nearly all calculators come with a manual that can be used to learn the operations of the calculator, or to supplement this material on the variations and special features which a given calculator may have.

In this appendix we discuss the calculator keys and operations which are used for data entry, arithmetic operations, special functions (squares, square roots, reciprocals, powers and roots), trigonometric and inverse trigonometric functions, exponential and logarithmic functions, and calculator memory.

Many models of calculators use individual keys for each number and function. Other models use many of the keys for more than one purpose. However, the difference in operation is generally minor. Also, the labeling of many keys varies from one model to another. Some of these variations which are used are noted.

When a number is entered, or a result calculated, it shows on the display at the top of the calculator. We will use an eight-digit display, as well as a possible display of the exponent of ten for scientific notation, in our discussion of the calculator. Many calculators do display ten or more digits, although the operation is essentially the same. If the result contains more significant digits than the display can show, the result shown will be truncated or rounded off. We will use a rounded off display.

In making entries or calculations, it is possible that a number with too many digits or one which is too large or too small cannot be entered. Also, certain operations do not have defined results. If such an entry or calculation is attempted, the calculator will make an error indication such as E, ⊓, or a flashing display. Operations which can result in an error indication include division by zero, square root of a negative number, logarithm of a negative number, and the inverse trigonometric function of a value outside of the appropriate interval.

Also, some calculators will give a special display when batteries need charging or replacement. The user should become acquainted with any special displays the calculator may use.

The way in which a calculator must be used for various types of calculations depends on the type of calculation and the logic used by the particular calculator. The logic refers to the order in which entries and operations must be made in order to obtain the required result. Some discussion of this is found in the final section of this appendix, but *the user must become acquainted with the logic of the particular calculator being used.*

C—2 Calculator Data Entry and Function Keys

Following is a listing of certain basic keys which may be found on a scientific calculator, and which can be of use in performing calculations for the exercises in this text. There are other keys and other calculational capabilities which are also found on many calculators. Along with each key is a description and an illustration of its basic use. In the examples shown at the right, to perform the indicated entry or calculation, use the given sequence of entries and operations. The final display is also shown.

It should be emphasized that not all the keys which will probably be found on a given calculator are discussed, but that a scientific calculator will have most of the keys which are described. It should be noted that the use of many of the keys may be beyond the scope of the reader until the appropriate text material has been covered.

Keys	Examples
$\boxed{0}$, $\boxed{1}$, . . . , $\boxed{9}$ **Digit Keys** These keys are used to enter the digits 0 through 9 in the display, or to enter an exponent of 10 when scientific notation is used.	To enter: 37514 Sequence: $\boxed{3}$, $\boxed{7}$, $\boxed{5}$, $\boxed{1}$, $\boxed{4}$ Display: 37514.
$\boxed{\cdot}$ **Decimal Point Key** This key is used to enter a decimal point.	To enter: 375.14 Sequence: $\boxed{3}$, $\boxed{7}$, $\boxed{5}$, $\boxed{\cdot}$, $\boxed{1}$, $\boxed{4}$ Display: 375.14
$\boxed{+/-}$ **Change Sign Key** This key is used to change the sign of the number on the display, or to change the sign of the exponent when scientific notation is used. (May be designated as $\boxed{\text{CHS}}$.)	To enter: -375.14 Sequence: $\boxed{3}$, $\boxed{7}$, $\boxed{5}$, $\boxed{\cdot}$, $\boxed{1}$, $\boxed{4}$, $\boxed{+/-}$ Display: -375.14 (From here on the entry of a number will be shown as one operation.)
$\boxed{\pi}$ **Pi Key** This key is used to enter π to the number of digits of the display.	To enter: π Sequence: $\boxed{\pi}$ Display: 3.1415927 (For calculators with dual purpose keys, see $\boxed{\text{F}}$ key.)
$\boxed{\text{EE}}$ **Enter Exponent Key** This key is used to enter an exponent when scientific notation is used. After the key is pressed, the exponent is entered. For a negative exponent, the $\boxed{+/-}$ key is pressed after the exponent is entered. (May be designated as $\boxed{\text{E EX}}$.)	To enter: 2.936×10^8 Sequence: 2.936, $\boxed{\text{EE}}$, 8 Display: 2.936 08 To enter: -2.936×10^{-8} Sequence: 2.936, $\boxed{+/-}$, $\boxed{\text{EE}}$, 8, $\boxed{+/-}$ Display: $-2.936 \; -08$
$\boxed{=}$ **Equals Key** This key is used to complete a calculation to give the required result.	See the following examples for illustrations of the use of this key.

Keys	Examples
☐+☐ **Add Key** This key is used to add the next entry to the previous entry or result.	Evaluate: 37.56 + 241.9 Sequence: 37.56, ☐+☐, 241.9, ☐=☐ Display: 279.46
☐−☐ **Subtract Key** This key is used to subtract the next entry from the previous entry or result.	Evaluate: 37.56 − 241.9 Sequence: 37.56, ☐−☐, 241.9, ☐=☐ Display: −204.34
☐×☐ **Multiply Key** This key is used to multiply the previous entry or result by the next entry.	Evaluate: 8.75 × 30.92 Sequence: 8.75, ☐×☐, 30.92, ☐=☐ Display: 270.55
☐÷☐ **Divide Key** This key is used to divide the previous entry or result by the next entry.	Evaluate: 8.75 ÷ 30.92 Sequence: 8.75, ☐÷☐, 30.92, ☐=☐ Display: 0.2829884 (truncated or rounded off)
☐CE☐ **Clear Entry Key** This key is used to clear the last entry. Its use will not affect any other part of a calculation. On some calculators one press of the ☐C/CE☐ or ☐CL☐ key is used for this purpose.	Evaluate: 37.56 + 241.9, with an improper entry of 242.9 Sequence: 37.56, ☐+☐, 242.9, ☐CE☐, 241.9, = Display: 279.46
☐C☐ **Clear Key** This key is used to clear the display and information being calculated (not including memory), so that a new calculation may be started. For calculators with a ☐C/CE☐ or ☐C☐ key, and no ☐CE☐ key, a second press on these keys is used for this purpose.	To clear previous calculation Sequence: ☐C☐ Display: 0.
☐F☐ **Function Key** This key is used on calculators on which many of the keys serve dual purposes. It is pressed before the second key functions are activated.	Evaluate: 37.4^2 on a calculator where x^2 is a second use of a key Sequence: 37.4, ☐F☐, ☐x^2☐ Display: 1398.76

Keys	Examples
$\boxed{x^2}$ **Square Key** This key is used to square the number on the display.	Evaluate: 37.4^2 Sequence: 37.4, $\boxed{x^2}$ Display: 1398.76
$\boxed{\sqrt{x}}$ **Square Root Key** This key is used to find the square root of the number on the display.	Evaluate: $\sqrt{37.4}$ Sequence: 37.4, $\boxed{\sqrt{x}}$ Display: 6.1155539
$\boxed{1/x}$ **Reciprocal Key** This key is used to find the reciprocal of the number on the display.	Evaluate: $\dfrac{1}{37.4}$ Sequence: 37.4, $\boxed{1/x}$ Display: 0.0267380
$\boxed{x^y}$ **x to the y Power Key** This key is used to raise x, the first entry, to the y power, the second entry.	Evaluate: $3.73^{1.5}$ Sequence: 3.73, $\boxed{x^y}$, 1.5, $\boxed{=}$ Display: 7.2038266
$\boxed{\text{RD DG}}$ **Degree-Radian Switch** This switch is used to designate a displayed angle as being measured in degrees or in radians.	This switch should be on the appropriate angle measurement before the calculation is started.
$\boxed{\text{SIN}}$ **Sine Key** This key is used to find the sine of the angle on the display.	Evaluate: sin 37.4° Sequence: $\boxed{\text{RD } ⓓⒼ}$, 37.4, $\boxed{\text{SIN}}$ Display: 0.6073758
$\boxed{\text{COS}}$ **Cosine Key** This key is used to find the cosine of the angle on the display.	Evaluate: cos 2.475 (rad) Sequence: $\boxed{ⓇⒹ \text{ DG}}$, 2.475, $\boxed{\text{COS}}$ Display: -0.7859330
$\boxed{\text{TAN}}$ **Tangent Key** This key is used to find the tangent of the angle on the display.	Evaluate: $\tan(-24.9°)$ Sequence: $\boxed{\text{RD } ⓓⒼ}$, 24.9, $\boxed{+/-}$, $\boxed{\text{TAN}}$ Display: -0.4641845
Cotangent, Secant, Cosecant These functions are found through their reciprocal relation with the tangent, cosine, and sine functions, respectively. See Section 19–1.	Evaluate: cot 2.841 (rad) Sequence: $\boxed{ⓇⒹ \text{ DG}}$, 2.841, $\boxed{\text{TAN}}$, $\boxed{1/x}$ Display: -3.2259549

Keys	Examples
ARC **Inverse Trigonometric** or **INV** **Function Key** This key is used (prior to the appropriate trigonometric function key) to find the angle whose trigonometric function is on the display. Some calculators have separate **SIN⁻¹** , **COS⁻¹**, **TAN⁻¹** keys for this purpose.	Evaluate: Arcsin 0.1758 (the angle whose sine is 0.1758) in degrees Sequence: RD DG , .1758, ARC , SIN Display: 10.125217
LOG **Common Logarithm Key** This key is used to find the logarithm to the base 10 of the number on the display.	Evaluate: log 37.45 Sequence: 37.45, LOG Display: 1.5734518
LN **Natural Logarithm Key** This key is used to find the logarithm to the base e of the number on the display.	Evaluate: ln 0.8421 Sequence: 0.8421, LN Display: −0.1718565
10ˣ **10 to the x Power Key** This key is used to find anti-logarithms (base 10) of the number on the display. (The x^y key can be used for this purpose, if the calculator does not have this key.)	Evaluate: Antilog 0.7265 (or $10^{0.7265}$) Sequence: .7265, 10ˣ Display: 5.3272122
eˣ **e to the x Power Key** This key is used to raise e to the power on the display.	Evaluate: $e^{-4.05}$ Sequence: 4.05, +/− , eˣ Display: 0.0174224
STO **Store in Memory Key** This key is used to store the number on the display in the memory.	Store in memory: 56.02 Sequence: 56.02, STO
RCL **Recall from Memory Key** This key is used to recall the number in the memory to the display. (May be designated as **MR**.)	Recall from memory: 56.02 Sequence: RCL Display: 56.02

Keys

$\boxed{M}$ **Other Memory Keys**
Some calculators use an $\boxed{M}$ key
to store a number in the memory.
It also may add the entry to the
number in the memory. On such
calculators $\boxed{CM}$ (Clear Memory)
is used to clear the memory.
There are also keys for other
operations on the number in the
memory.

C—3 Combined Operations

Throughout the text there are numerous exercises in which numerical calculations are required. The use of a calculator can save a great deal of time in making these calculations. Many of them require only a basic two- or three-step use of the calculator, and a knowledge of the basic use of the keys is generally sufficient to make such calculations.

There are also many types of problems which require more extensive calculations for their solutions, and for many of these problems a calculator is the only practical way of making the necessary calculations. In this section we discuss some of these calculations which require a combination of operations, and how they may be solved on a calculator. However, it is not possible to cover all such types of calculations, since there are too many types, and there are many variations in calculator logic.

In the illustrations which are presented a sequence of calculator entries and operations is given. Due to the variations in calculator logic which are used in different models, it is not possible to give a sequence which is usable on all models. Therefore, a simple algebraic logic is assumed, and the sequences shown can be used, at least to a great extent, on most models. It is possible that a knowledge of the logic of a given calculator would allow for a reduction in the number of steps, and a change in the order of some of the steps, needed to complete a given calculation.

It should be noted that some of the following examples may be beyond the scope of the reader until the appropriate text material has been covered.

Example A
Evaluate $(30.45 + 75.76) \div 8.27 \times 10^7$

On calculations involving arithmetic operations, *we will assume that calculator logic is such that multiplications and divisions are performed before additions and subtractions, until the* $\boxed{=}$ *key is pressed.* This is generally referred to as *algebraic logic*. Therefore, in this illustration, it is necessary to use the $\boxed{=}$ key after summing 30.45 and 75.76. Thus, the sequence is

30.45, $\boxed{+}$, 75.76, $\boxed{=}$, $\boxed{\div}$, 8.27, $\boxed{EE}$, 7, $\boxed{=}$
Display: 1.2842805 −06

If the $\boxed{=}$ key had not been pressed after 75.76, the evaluation being made would have been 30.45 + (75.76 ÷ 8.27 × 10^7). It should be carefully noted, however, that on many calculators it is not necessary to press the $\boxed{=}$ key after 75.76 in order to perform the above evaluation. On such calculators one arithmetic operation is completed when another is entered. Therefore *check the manual of the calculator being used to determine the type of logic the calculator uses, and how such calculations should be entered.*

Example B
Given $f(x) = \sqrt{x^4 - 3x}$, evaluate $f(2.37)$.

$$f(2.37) = \sqrt{2.37^4 - 3(2.37)}$$

Sequence: 2.37, $\boxed{x^y}$, 4, $\boxed{-}$, 3, $\boxed{\times}$, 2.37, $\boxed{=}$, $\boxed{\sqrt{x}}$
Display: 4.9436389

Therefore, $f(2.37) = 4.94$. Normally, the result is expressed to the number of significant digits of the given data. See Appendix B.

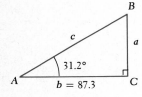

Figure C–1

Example C
Solve the right triangle with $b = 87.3$, $A = 31.2°$. Use Figure C–1.

$$B = 90.0° - 31.2°$$

$$\frac{a}{87.3} = \tan 31.2°, \qquad a = 87.3 \tan 31.2°$$

$$\frac{87.3}{c} = \cos 31.2°, \qquad c = \frac{87.3}{\cos 31.2°}$$

Sequences: for B: 90, $\boxed{-}$, 31.2, $\boxed{=}$
Display: 58.8

for a: $\boxed{\text{RD} \enspace \text{DG}}$, 31.2, $\boxed{TAN}$, $\boxed{\times}$, 87.3, $\boxed{=}$
Display: 52.870759

for c: $\boxed{\text{RD} \enspace \text{DG}}$, 31.2, $\boxed{COS}$, $\boxed{\div}$, 87.3, $\boxed{=}$, $\boxed{1/x}$
Display: 102.06178

Therefore, $B = 58.8°$, $a = 52.9$, $c = 102$. Again, we should carefully note the number of significant digits in the given data. In this case three significant digits are used. Therefore, we should write $a = 52.9$ (not 52.870759) and $c = 102$ (not 102.06178) in giving the results.

Example D
Solve $2x^2 - 3x - 7 = 0$ by the quadratic formula.

$$x = \frac{3 \pm \sqrt{3^2 - 4(2)(-7)}}{4}$$

Sequence: 3, $\boxed{x^2}$, $\boxed{-}$, 4, $\boxed{\times}$, 2, $\boxed{\times}$, 7, $\boxed{+/-}$,

$\boxed{=}$, $\boxed{\sqrt{x}}$, $\boxed{\text{STO}}$ (the value of $\sqrt{3^2 - 4(2)(-7)}$ is now in memory).

for first root: $\boxed{+}$, 3, $\boxed{=}$, $\boxed{\div}$, 4, $\boxed{=}$

Display: 2.7655644

for second root: 3, $\boxed{-}$, $\boxed{\text{RCL}}$, $\boxed{=}$, $\boxed{\div}$, 4, $\boxed{=}$

Display: −1.2655644

Therefore, the roots are (to four significant digits) 2.766 and −1.266.

Example E
Convert 123.7° to radians.

$$123.7° = \frac{(123.7)(\pi)}{180} \text{ rad}$$

Sequence: 123.7, $\boxed{\times}$, $\boxed{\pi}$, $\boxed{\div}$, 180, $\boxed{=}$
Display: 2.1589723

Therefore, 123.7° = 2.159 rad.

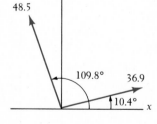

Figure C–2

Example F
Add the vectors shown in Figure C–2.

We are to find the magnitude and direction of vector **R**, with magnitude R, and components of R_x and R_y.

$$R_x = 36.9 \cos 10.4° + 48.5 \cos 109.8°$$
$$R_y = 36.9 \sin 10.4° + 48.5 \sin 109.8°$$
$$R = \sqrt{R_x^2 + R_y^2}$$

$$\tan \theta = \frac{R_y}{R_x} \quad \text{or} \quad \theta = \text{Arctan} \frac{R_y}{R_x}$$

Sequences: $\boxed{\text{RD} \ \ \textcircled{\text{DG}}}$ for all calculations

for R_x: 10.4, $\boxed{\text{COS}}$, $\boxed{\times}$, 36.9, $\boxed{+}$, 109.8, $\boxed{\text{COS}}$, $\boxed{\times}$, 48.5, $\boxed{=}$

Display: 19.864998

for R_y: 10.4, $\boxed{\text{SIN}}$, $\boxed{\times}$, 36.9, $\boxed{+}$, 109.8, $\boxed{\text{SIN}}$, $\boxed{\times}$, 48.5, $\boxed{=}$

Display: 52.293874

for R: 19.87, $\boxed{x^2}$, $\boxed{+}$, 52.29, $\boxed{x^2}$, $\boxed{=}$, $\boxed{\sqrt{x}}$

Display: 55.938010

for θ: 52.29, $\boxed{\div}$, 19.86, $\boxed{=}$, $\boxed{\text{ARC}}$, $\boxed{\text{TAN}}$

Display: 69.202976

Therefore, $R = 55.9$ and $\theta = 69.2°$

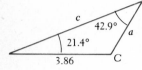

Figure C–3

Example G
Solve the triangle in Fig. C–3 by the law of sines.

$$C = 180° - (21.4° + 42.9°)$$

$$\frac{a}{\sin 21.4°} = \frac{3.86}{\sin 42.9°} = \frac{c}{\sin 115.7°}$$

$$a = \frac{3.86 \sin 21.4°}{\sin 42.9°}, \qquad c = \frac{3.86 \sin 115.7°}{\sin 42.9°}$$

Sequences: for C: 180, $\boxed{-}$, 21.4, $\boxed{-}$, 42.9, $\boxed{=}$

Display: 115.7

for a: $\boxed{\text{RD} \;\text{(DG)}}$, 3.86, $\boxed{\div}$, 42.9, $\boxed{\text{SIN}}$, $\boxed{=}$

$\boxed{\text{STO}}$ (the quotient 3.86/sin 42.9° is now in memory), $\boxed{\times}$, 21.4, $\boxed{\text{SIN}}$, $\boxed{=}$

Display: 2.0690190

for c: 115.7, $\boxed{\text{SIN}}$, $\boxed{\times}$, $\boxed{\text{RCL}}$, $\boxed{=}$

Display: 5.1095206

Therefore, $a = 2.07$, $c = 5.11$, $C = 115.7°$

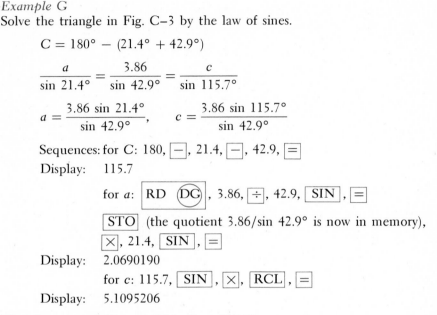

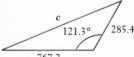

Figure C–4

Example H
Solve for side c in the triangle shown in Fig. C–4 by the law of cosines.

$$c = \sqrt{285.4^2 + 767.2^2 - 2(285.4)(767.2)\cos 121.3°}$$

Sequence: 285.4, $\boxed{x^2}$, $\boxed{+}$, 767.2, $\boxed{x^2}$, $\boxed{-}$, $\boxed{\text{RD}\;\text{(DG)}}$, 121.3, $\boxed{\text{COS}}$, $\boxed{\times}$, 2, $\boxed{\times}$, 285.4, $\boxed{\times}$, 767.2, $\boxed{=}$, $\boxed{\sqrt{x}}$

Display: 947.39413

Therefore, $c = 947.4$.

Example I
Evaluate $(709.6)^{2/7}$.

Sequence: 2, $\boxed{\div}$, 7, $\boxed{=}$, $\boxed{\text{STO}}$, 709.6, $\boxed{x^y}$, $\boxed{\text{RCL}}$, $\boxed{=}$

Display: 6.5249219

Therefore, $(709.6)^{2/7} = 6.525$.

Example J

Change the complex number $8.62 + 5.67j$ to exponential form.

$$r = \sqrt{8.62^2 + 5.67^2}; \qquad \tan\theta = \frac{5.67}{8.62}, \qquad \theta = \text{Arctan}\frac{5.67}{8.62}$$

Sequences: for r: 8.62, $\boxed{x^2}$, $\boxed{+}$, 5.67, $\boxed{x^2}$, $\boxed{=}$, $\boxed{\sqrt{x}}$

Display: 10.317621

for θ: 5.67, $\boxed{\div}$, 8.62, $\boxed{=}$, $\boxed{\text{RD}}\ \text{DG}$, $\boxed{\text{ARC}}$, $\boxed{\text{TAN}}$

Display: 0.5818199

Therefore, the exponential form of $8.62 + 5.67j$ is $10.3e^{0.582j}$.

Example K

Solve for x: $2^{x+2} = 7$.

$$(x + 2)\log 2 = \log 7,$$

$$x = \frac{\log 7}{\log 2} - 2.$$

Sequence: 7, $\boxed{\text{LOG}}$, $\boxed{\div}$, 2, $\boxed{\text{LOG}}$, $\boxed{=}$, $\boxed{-}$, 2, $\boxed{=}$

Display: 0.8073549

Therefore, to four significant digits, $x = 0.8074$.

Example L

Find the sum of the geometric progression for which $a = 175$, $r = 1.05$, $n = 20$.

$$s = \frac{175[1 - (1.05)^{20}]}{1 - 1.05} = \frac{175[1 - (1.05)^{20}]}{-0.05}$$

Sequence: 1.05, $\boxed{x^y}$, 20, $\boxed{=}$, $\boxed{-}$, 1, $\boxed{=}$, $\boxed{+/-}$, $\boxed{\times}$, 175, $\boxed{\div}$, .05, $\boxed{+/-}$, $\boxed{=}$

Display: 5786.5420

The number of significant digits which are kept in the result depends on the meaning of a, r, and n.

We can see from the above illustrations that a calculator is especially valuable in trigonometry problems where we use the Pythagorean theorem and the trigonometric and inverse trigonometric functions. Also, it is of great value in other problems where special functions, such as square roots, exponentials, and logarithms are used.

The calculator is also valuable in many calculations which are primarily arithmetic. Some are illustrated in the previous examples, but there are many others. In fact, there are some exercises in which the calculator plays an important role in developing a concept. Without the calculator it is difficult to make such calculations quickly and easily.

With a little practice, which with a calculator usually is interesting and enjoyable, you will find that a scientific calculator will save you a great deal of time in making necessary calculations. However, it is still necessary to learn the mathematics which is required to set up and understand a given problem.

C–4 Exercises for Appendix C

In Exercises 1 through 36, perform all calculations on a scientific calculator.

1. $47.08 + 8.94$
2. $654.1 + 407.7$
3. $4724 - 561.9$
4. $0.9365 - 8.077$
5. 0.0396×471
6. 26.31×0.9393
7. $76.7 \div 194$
8. $52060 \div 75.09$
9. 3.76^2
10. 0.986^2
11. $\sqrt{0.2757}$
12. $\sqrt{60.36}$
13. $\dfrac{1}{0.0749}$
14. $\dfrac{1}{607.9}$
15. $(19.66)^{2.3}$
16. $(8.455)^{1.75}$
17. $\sin 47.3°$
18. $\sin 1.15$
19. $\cos 3.85$
20. $\cos 119.1°$
21. $\tan 306.8°$
22. $\tan 0.537$
23. $\sec 6.11$
24. $\csc 242.0°$
25. Arcsin 0.6607 (in degrees)
26. Arccos(-0.8311) (in radians)
27. Arctan(-2.441) (in radians)
28. Arcsin 0.0737 (in degrees)
29. $\log 3.857$
30. $\log 0.9012$
31. $\ln 808$
32. $\ln 70.5$
33. $10^{0.545}$
34. $10^{-0.0915}$
35. $e^{-5.17}$
36. $e^{1.672}$

In Exercises 37 through 90, perform all calculations on a scientific calculator. In these exercises some of the combined operations which are encountered in certain types of problems are given. For specific types of applications, such as those demonstrated in Section C–3, solve problems from the appropriate sections of the text.

37. $(4.38 + 9.07) \div 6.55$
38. $(382 + 964) \div 844$
39. $4.38 + (9.07 \div 6.55)$
40. $382 + (964 \div 844)$
41. $\dfrac{5.73 \times 10^{11}}{20.61 - 7.88}$
42. $\dfrac{7.09 \times 10^{23}}{284 + 839}$
43. $50.38\pi^2$
44. $\dfrac{5\pi}{14.6}$
45. $\sqrt{1.65^2 + 6.44^2}$
46. $\sqrt{0.735^2 + 0.409^2}$
47. $3(3.5)^4 - 4(3.5)^2$
48. $\dfrac{3(-1.86)}{(-1.86)^2 + 1}$
49. $29.4 \cos 72.5°$
50. $\dfrac{477}{\sin 58.7°}$
51. $\dfrac{4 + \sqrt{(-4)^2 - 4(3)(-9)}}{2(3)}$
52. $\dfrac{-5 - \sqrt{5^2 - 4(4)(-7)}}{2(4)}$
53. $\dfrac{0.176(180)}{\pi}$
54. $\dfrac{209.6\pi}{180}$
55. $\dfrac{1}{2}\left(\dfrac{51.4\pi}{180}\right)(7.06)^2$

56. $\dfrac{1}{2}\left(\dfrac{148.2\pi}{180}\right)(49.13)^2$ 57. $\text{Arcsin}\dfrac{27.3 \sin 36.5°}{46.8}$ 58. $\dfrac{0.684 \sin 76.1°}{\sin 39.5°}$

59. $\sqrt{3924^2 + 1762^2 - 2(3924)(1762)\cos 106.2°}$

60. $\text{Arccos}\dfrac{8.09^2 + 4.91^2 - 9.81^2}{2(8.09)(4.91)}$ 61. $\sqrt{5.81 \times 10^8} + \sqrt[3]{7.06 \times 10^{11}}$

62. $(6.074 \times 10^{-7})^{2/5} - (1.447 \times 10^{-5})^{4/9}$

63. $\dfrac{3}{2\sqrt{7} - \sqrt{6}}$ 64. $\dfrac{7\sqrt{5}}{4\sqrt{5} - \sqrt{11}}$ 65. $\text{Arctan}\dfrac{7.37}{5.06}$ 66. $\text{Arctan}\dfrac{46.3}{-25.5}$

67. $2 + \dfrac{\log 12}{\log 7}$ 68. $\dfrac{10^{0.4115}}{\pi}$

69. $\dfrac{26}{2}(-1.450 + 2.075)$ 70. $\dfrac{4.55(1 - 1.08^{15})}{1 - 1.08}$

71. $\sin^2\left(\dfrac{\pi}{7}\right) + \cos^2\left(\dfrac{\pi}{7}\right)$ 72. $\sec^2\left(\dfrac{2}{9}\pi\right) - \tan^2\left(\dfrac{2}{9}\pi\right)$

73. $\sin 31.6° \cos 58.4° + \sin 58.4° \cos 31.6°$

74. $\cos^2 296.7° - \sin^2 296.7°$ 75. $\sqrt{(1.54 - 5.06)^2 + (-4.36 - 8.05)^2}$

76. $\sqrt{(7.03 - 2.94)^2 + (3.51 - 6.44)^2}$ 77. $\dfrac{(4.001)^2 - 16}{4.001 - 4}$

78. $\dfrac{(2.001)^2 + 3(2.001) - 10}{2.001 - 2}$ 79. $\dfrac{4\pi}{3}(8.01^3 - 8.00^3)$

80. $4\pi(76.3^2 - 76.0^2)$

81. $0.01\left(\dfrac{1}{2}\sqrt{2} + \sqrt{2.01} + \sqrt{2.02} + \dfrac{1}{2}\sqrt{2.03}\right)$

82. $0.2\left[\dfrac{1}{2}(3.5)^2 + 3.7^2 + 3.9^2 + \dfrac{1}{2}(4.1)^2\right]$

83. $\dfrac{e^{0.45} - e^{-0.45}}{e^{0.45} + e^{-0.45}}$ 84. $\ln \sin 2e^{-0.055}$

85. $\ln\dfrac{2 - \sqrt{2}}{2 - \sqrt{3}}$ 86. $\sqrt{\dfrac{9}{2} + \dfrac{9 \sin 0.2\pi}{8\pi}}$

87. $2 + \dfrac{0.3}{4} - \dfrac{(0.3)^2}{64} + \dfrac{(0.3)^3}{512}$ 88. $\dfrac{1}{2} + \dfrac{\pi\sqrt{3}}{360} - \dfrac{1}{4}\left(\dfrac{\pi}{180}\right)^2$

89. $160(1 - e^{-1.50})$ 90. $e^{-3.60}(\cos 1.20 + 2 \sin 1.20)$

Appendix D

Review of Geometry

D—1 Basic Geometric Figures and Definitions

In this appendix we shall present geometric terminology and formulas that are related to the basic geometric figures. It is intended only as a brief summary of basic geometry.

Geometry deals with the properties and measurement of angles, lines, surfaces, and volumes, and the basic figures that are formed. We shall restrict our attention in this appendix to the basic figures and concepts which are related to these figures.

Repeating the definition in Section 3–1, an **angle** is generated by rotating a half-line about its endpoint from an initial position to a terminal position. One complete rotation of a line about a point is defined to be an angle of 360 **degrees**, written as 360°. A **straight angle** contains 180°, and a **right angle** contains 90°. If two lines meet so that the angle between them is 90°, the lines are said to be **perpendicular**.

An angle less than 90° is an **acute angle**. An angle greater than 90°, but less than 180°, is an **obtuse angle**. **Supplementary angles** are two angles whose sum is 180°, and **complementary angles** are two angles whose sum equals 90°.

In a plane, if a line crosses two **parallel** or nonparallel lines, it is called a **transversal**. If a transversal crosses a pair of parallel lines, certain pairs of equal angles result. In Fig. D–1, the **corresponding angles** are equal. (That is, $\angle 1 = \angle 5$, $\angle 2 = \angle 6$, $\angle 3 = \angle 7$, $\angle 4 = \angle 8$.) Also, the **alternate interior angles** are equal ($\angle 3 = \angle 6$ and $\angle 4 = \angle 5$).

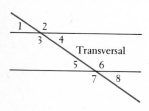

Figure D–1

Adjacent angles have a common vertex and a side common to them. For example, in Fig. D–1, ∠ 5 and 6 are adjacent angles. **Vertical angles** are equal angles formed "across" the point of intersection of two intersecting lines. In Fig. D–1, ∠ 5 and 8 are vertical angles.

When a part of the plane is bounded and closed by straight line segments, it is called a **polygon**. In general, polygons are named according to the number of sides they contain. A **triangle** has three sides, a **quadrilateral** has four sides, a **pentagon** has five sides, and so on. In a **regular polygon,** all of the sides are equal in length, and all of the interior angles are equal.

There are several important types of triangles. In an **equilateral triangle** the three sides are equal, and the three angles are also equal, each being 60°. In an **isosceles triangle** two of the sides are equal, as are the two **base angles** (the angles opposite the equal sides). In a **scalene triangle** no two sides are equal, and none of the angles is a right angle. In a **right triangle** one of the angles is a right angle. The side opposite the right angle is called the **hypotenuse.**

There are certain basic properties of triangles which we shall mention here. One very important property is that **the sum of the three angles of any triangle is** *180°.* Also, the three **medians** (line segments drawn from a vertex to the **midpoint** of the opposite side) meet at a single point. This point of intersection of the medians is called the **centroid** of the triangle. It is also true that the three **angle bisectors** meet at a common point, as do the three **altitudes** (heights) which are drawn from a vertex perpendicular to the opposite side (or the extension of the opposite side).

Of particular importance is the **Pythagorean theorem,** which states that **in a right triangle, the square of the length of the hypotenuse equals the sum of the squares of the lengths of the other two sides.**

Two triangles are said to be **congruent** if corresponding angles are equal and if corresponding sides are equal. Two triangles are said to be **similar** if corresponding angles are equal. In similar triangles corresponding sides are proportional.

A **quadrilateral** is a plane figure having four sides and therefore four interior angles. A **parallelogram** is a quadrilateral with opposite sides **parallel** (extension of the sides will not intersect). Also opposite sides and opposite angles of a parallelogram are equal. A **rectangle** is a parallelogram with intersecting sides perpendicular, which means that all four angles are right angles. It also means that opposite sides of a rectangle are equal and parallel. A **square** is a rectangle all sides of which are equal. A **trapezoid** is a quadrilateral with two of the sides parallel. These parallel sides are called the **bases** of the trapezoid. A **rhombus** is a parallelogram all four sides of which are equal.

All of the points on a **circle** are the same distance from a fixed point in the plane. This point is the **center** of the circle. The distance from the center to a point on the circle is the **radius** of the circle. The distance between two points on the circle and on a line passing through the center of the circle is the **diameter** of the circle. Thus the diameter is twice the radius.

Also associated with the circle is the **chord**, which is a line segment having its endpoints on the circle. A **tangent** is a line that touches a circle (does not pass through) at one point. A **secant** is a line that passes through two points of a circle. An **arc** is a part of the circle. When two radii form an angle at the center, the angle is called a **central angle**. An **inscribed angle** of an arc is one for which the endpoints of the arc are points on the sides of the angle, and for which the vertex is a point of the arc, although not an endpoint.

There are two important properties of a circle which we shall mention here.

(1) *A tangent to a circle is perpendicular to the radius drawn to the point of contact.*

(2) *An angle inscribed in a semicircle is a right angle.*

D–2 Basic Geometric Formulas

For the indicated figures, the following symbols are used: A = area, B = area of base, c = circumference, S = lateral area, V = volume.

1. **Triangle.** $A = \frac{1}{2}bh$ (Fig. D–2)
2. **Pythagorean theorem.** $c^2 = a^2 + b^2$ (Fig. D–3)
3. **Parallelogram.** $A = bh$ (Fig. D–4)
4. **Trapezoid.** $A = \frac{1}{2}(a + b)h$ (Fig. D–5)
5. **Circle.** $A = \pi r^2$, $c = 2\pi r$ (Fig. D–6)
6. **Rectangular solid.** $A = 2(lw + lh + wh)$, $V = lwh$ (Fig. D–7)
7. **Cube.** $A = 6e^2$, $V = e^3$ (Fig. D–8)
8. **Any cylinder or prism with parallel bases.** $V = Bh$ (Fig. D–9)
9. **Right circular cylinder.** $S = 2\pi rh$, $V = \pi r^2 h$ (Fig. D–10)
10. **Any cone or pyramid.** $V = \frac{1}{3}Bh$ (Fig. D–11)
11. **Right circular cone.** $S = \pi rs$, $V = \frac{1}{3}\pi r^2 h$ (Fig. D–12)
12. **Sphere.** $A = 4\pi r^2$, $V = \frac{4}{3}\pi r^3$ (Fig. D–13)

Also, the **perimeter** of a plane figure is the distance around it. For example, the perimeter p of the triangle in Fig. D–3 is $p = a + b + c$. (∟ denotes a right angle.)

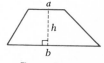

Figure D–2

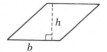

Figure D–3

Figure D–4

Figure D–5

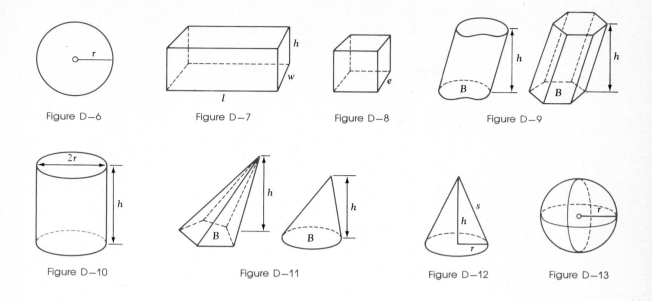

Figure D–6   Figure D–7   Figure D–8   Figure D–9

Figure D–10   Figure D–11   Figure D–12   Figure D–13

D–3 Exercises for Appendix D

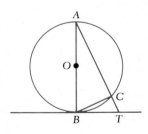

Figure D–14

In Exercises 1 through 4 refer to Fig. D–14, in which AOP and KOT are straight lines. $\angle TOP = 40°$, $\angle OBC = 90°$, and $\angle AOL = 55°$. Determine the indicated angles.

1. $\angle LOT$ 2. $\angle POL$ 3. $\angle KOP$ 4. $\angle KCB$

In Exercises 5 through 8 refer to Fig. D–15, where AB is a diameter, line TB is tangent to the circle at B, and $\angle ABC = 65°$. Determine the indicated angles.

5. $\angle CBT$ 6. $\angle BCT$ 7. $\angle CAB$ 8. $\angle BTC$

In Exercises 9 through 12, refer to Figs. D–16 and D–17. In each $ABCD$ is a parallelogram. In Fig. D–16, $\triangle BEC$ is isosceles, and $\angle BCE = 40°$. In Fig. D–17, $\angle FED = 34°$. Determine the indicated angles.

9. In Fig. D–16, $\angle CEB$ 10. In Fig. D–16, $\angle ADC$
11. In Fig. D–17, $\angle EDF$ 12. In Fig. D–17, $\angle DCB$

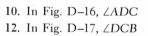

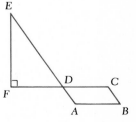

Figure D–15

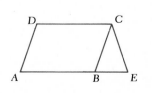

Figure D–16   Figure D–17

In Exercises 13 through 24 use the Pythagorean theorem to solve for the unknown side of the right triangle. In each case c is the hypotenuse. If the answer is not exact, round off to three digits.

	a	b	c			a	b	c
13.	3	4	?		14.	9	12	?
15.	8	15	?		16.	24	10	?
17.	6	?	10		18.	2	?	4
19.	5	?	7		20.	3	?	9
21.	?	12	16		22.	?	10	18
23.	?	15	32		24.	?	5	36

In Exercises 25 through 28 determine the required values. In Fig. D–18, $AD = 9$ and $AC = 12$.

25. Two triangles are similar, and the sides of the larger triangle are 3.0 in., 5.0 in., and 6.0 in., and the shortest side of the other triangle is 2.0 in. Find the remaining sides of the smaller triangle.

26. Two triangles are similar. The angles of the smaller triangle are 50°, 100°, and 30°, and the sides of the smaller triangle are 7.00 in., 9.00 in., and 4.57 in. The longest side of the larger triangle is 15.00 in. Find the other two sides and the three angles of the larger triangle.

27. In Fig. D–18, find AB

28. In Fig. D–18, find BC

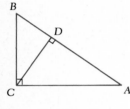

Figure D–18

In Exercises 29 through 40 find the perimeters (or circumferences) of the indicated figures.

29. A triangle with sides 6 ft, 8 ft, and 11 ft

30. A quadrilateral with sides 3 in., 4 in., 6 in., and 9 in.

31. An isosceles triangle whose equal sides are 3 yd long and whose third side is 4 yd long

32. An equilateral triangle whose sides are 7 ft long

33. A rectangle 5.14 in. long and 4.09 in. wide

34. A parallelogram whose longer side is 13.7 mm and whose shorter side is 11.9 mm

35. A square of side 8.18 cm

36. A rhombus of side 15.6 m

37. A trapezoid whose longer base is 74.2 cm, whose shorter base is 46.8 cm, and whose other sides are equal to the shorter base

38. A trapezoid whose bases are 17.8 in. and 7.4 in., and whose other sides are each 8.1 in.

39. A circle of radius 10.0 ft

40. A circle of diameter 7.06 cm

In Exercises 41 through 48 find the areas of the indicated figures.

41. A parallelogram of base 7.0 in. and height 4.0 in.

42. A rectangle of base 8.2 ft and height 2.5 ft

43. A triangle of base 6.3 yd and height 4.1 yd

44. A triangle of base 14.2 cm and height 6.83 cm

45. A trapezoid of bases 3.0 m and 9.0 m and height 4.0 m

46. A trapezoid of bases 18.5 in. and 26.3 in. and height 10.5 in.

47. A circle of radius 7.00 in.

48. A semicircle of diameter 8.24 cm

In Exercises 49 through 60 evaluate the volume of the indicated figures.

49. A rectangular solid of length 9.00 ft, width 6.00 ft, and height 4.00 ft

50. A cube of edge 7.15 ft

51. Prism, square base of side 2.0 mm, altitude 5.0 mm

52. Prism, trapezoidal base (bases 4.0 in. and 6.0 in. and height 3.0 in.), altitude 6.0 in.

53. Cylinder, radius of base 7.00 in., altitude 6.00 in.

54. Cylinder, diameter of base 6.36 cm, altitude 18.0 cm

55. Pyramid, rectangular base 12.5 in. by 8.75 in., altitude 4.20 in.

56. Pyramid, equilateral triangular base of side 3.00 in., altitude 4.25 in.

57. Cone, radius of base 2.66 ft, altitude 1.22 yd

58. Cone, diameter of base 16.3 cm, altitude 18.4 cm

59. Sphere, radius 5.48 m

60. Sphere, diameter 15.7 yd

In Exercises 61 through 68 find the total surface area of the indicated figure for the given values.

61. Prism, rectangular base 4.00 in. by 8.00 in., altitude 6.00 in.

62. Prism, parallelogram base (base 16.0 in., height 4.25 in., perimeter 42.0 in.), altitude 6.45 in.

63. Cylinder, radius of base 8.58 m, altitude 1.38 m

64. Cylinder, diameter of base 12.5 ft, altitude 4.60 ft

65. Sphere, radius 16.0 ft

66. Sphere, diameter 15.3 in.

67. Cone, radius of base 7.05 cm, slant height 8.45 cm

68. Cone, diameter of base 76.2 mm, altitude 22.1 mm

Appendix E

Tables

Table 1   A—39

Table 1. Powers and Roots

No.	Sq.	Sq. Root	Cube	Cube Root	No.	Sq.	Sq. Root	Cube	Cube Root
1	1	1.000	1	1.000	51	2,601	7.141	132,651	3.708
2	4	1.414	8	1.260	52	2,704	7.211	140,608	3.733
3	9	1.732	27	1.442	53	2,809	7.280	148,877	3.756
4	16	2.000	64	1.587	54	2,916	7.348	157,464	3.780
5	25	2.236	125	1.710	55	3,025	7.416	166,375	3.803
6	36	2.449	216	1.817	56	3,136	7.483	175,616	3.826
7	49	2.646	343	1.913	57	3,249	7.550	185,193	3.849
8	64	2.828	512	2.000	58	3,364	7.616	195,112	3.871
9	81	3.000	729	2.080	59	3,481	7.681	205,379	3.893
10	100	3.162	1,000	2.154	60	3,600	7.746	216,000	3.915
11	121	3.317	1,331	2.224	61	3,721	7.810	226,981	3.936
12	144	3.464	1,728	2.289	62	3,844	7.874	238,328	3.958
13	169	3.606	2,197	2.351	63	3,969	7.937	250,047	3.979
14	196	3.742	2,744	2.410	64	4,096	8.000	262,144	4.000
15	225	3.873	3,375	2.466	65	4,225	8.062	274,625	4.021
16	256	4.000	4,096	2.520	66	4,356	8.124	287,496	4.041
17	289	4.123	4,913	2.571	67	4,489	8.185	300,763	4.062
18	324	4.243	5,832	2.621	68	4,624	8.246	314,432	4.082
19	361	4.359	6,859	2.668	69	4,761	8.307	328,509	4.102
20	400	4.472	8,000	2.714	70	4,900	8.367	343,000	4.121
21	441	4.583	9,261	2.759	71	5,041	8.426	357,911	4.141
22	484	4.690	10,648	2.802	72	5,184	8.485	373,248	4.160
23	529	4.796	12,167	2.844	73	5,329	8.544	389,017	4.179
24	576	4.899	13,824	2.884	74	5,476	8.602	405,224	4.198
25	625	5.000	15,625	2.924	75	5,625	8.660	421,875	4.217
26	676	5.099	17,576	2.962	76	5,776	8.718	438,976	4.236
27	729	5.196	19,683	3.000	77	5,929	8.775	456,533	4.254
28	784	5.292	21,952	3.037	78	6,084	8.832	474,552	4.273
29	841	5.385	24,389	3.072	79	6,241	8.888	493,039	4.291
30	900	5.477	27,000	3.107	80	6,400	8.944	512,000	4.309
31	961	5.568	29,791	3.141	81	6,561	9.000	531,441	4.327
32	1,024	5.657	32,768	3.175	82	6,724	9.055	551,368	4.344
33	1,089	5.745	35,937	3.208	83	6,889	9.110	571,787	4.362
34	1,156	5.831	39,304	3.240	84	7,056	9.165	592,704	4.380
35	1,225	5.916	42,875	3.271	85	7,225	9.220	614,125	4.397
36	1,296	6.000	46,656	3.302	86	7,396	9.274	636,056	4.414
37	1,369	6.083	50,653	3.332	87	7,569	9.327	658,503	4.431
38	1,444	6.164	54,872	3.362	88	7,744	9.381	681,472	4.448
39	1,521	6.245	59,319	3.391	89	7,921	9.434	704,969	4.465
40	1,600	6.325	64,000	3.420	90	8,100	9.487	729,000	4.481
41	1,681	6.403	68,921	3.448	91	8,281	9.539	753,571	4.498
42	1,764	6.481	74,088	3.476	92	8,464	9.592	778,688	4.514
43	1,849	6.557	79,507	3.503	93	8,649	9.644	804,357	4.531
44	1,936	6.633	85,184	3.530	94	8,836	9.695	830,584	4.547
45	2,025	6.708	91,125	3.557	95	9,025	9.747	857,375	4.563
46	2,116	6.782	97,336	3.583	96	9,216	9.798	884,736	4.579
47	2,209	6.856	103,823	3.609	97	9,409	9.849	912,673	4.595
48	2,304	6.928	110,592	3.634	98	9,604	9.899	941,192	4.610
49	2,401	7.000	117,649	3.659	99	9,801	9.950	970,299	4.626
50	2,500	7.071	125,000	3.684	100	10,000	10.000	1,000,000	4.642

Table 2. Four-Place Logarithms of Numbers

N	0	1	2	3	4	5	6	7	8	9
10	0000	0043	0086	0128	0170	0212	0253	0294	0334	0374
11	0414	0453	0492	0531	0569	0607	0645	0682	0719	0755
12	0792	0828	0864	0899	0934	0969	1004	1038	1072	1106
13	1139	1173	1206	1239	1271	1303	1335	1367	1399	1430
14	1461	1492	1523	1553	1584	1614	1644	1673	1703	1732
15	1761	1790	1818	1847	1875	1903	1931	1959	1987	2014
16	2041	2068	2095	2122	2148	2175	2201	2227	2253	2279
17	2304	2330	2355	2380	2405	2430	2455	2480	2504	2529
18	2553	2577	2601	2625	2648	2672	2695	2718	2742	2765
19	2788	2810	2833	2856	2878	2900	2923	2945	2967	2989
20	3010	3032	3054	3075	3096	3118	3139	3160	3181	3201
21	3222	3243	3263	3284	3304	3324	3345	3365	3385	3404
22	3424	3444	3464	3483	3502	3522	3541	3560	3579	3598
23	3617	3636	3655	3674	3692	3711	3729	3747	3766	3784
24	3802	3820	3838	3856	3874	3892	3909	3927	3945	3962
25	3979	3997	4014	4031	4048	4065	4082	4099	4116	4133
26	4150	4166	4183	4200	4216	4232	4249	4265	4281	4298
27	4314	4330	4346	4362	4378	4393	4409	4425	4440	4456
28	4472	4487	4502	4518	4533	4548	4564	4579	4594	4609
29	4624	4639	4654	4669	4683	4698	4713	4728	4742	4757
30	4771	4786	4800	4814	4829	4843	4857	4871	4886	4900
31	4914	4928	4942	4955	4969	4983	4997	5011	5024	5038
32	5051	5065	5079	5092	5105	5119	5132	5145	5159	5172
33	5185	5198	5211	5224	5237	5250	5263	5276	5289	5302
34	5315	5328	5340	5353	5366	5378	5391	5403	5416	5428
35	5441	5453	5465	5478	5490	5502	5514	5527	5539	5551
36	5563	5575	5587	5599	5611	5623	5635	5647	5658	5670
37	5682	5694	5705	5717	5729	5740	5752	5763	5775	5786
38	5798	5809	5821	5832	5843	5855	5866	5877	5888	5899
39	5911	5922	5933	5944	5955	5966	5977	5988	5999	6010
40	6021	6031	6042	6053	6064	6075	6085	6096	6107	6117
41	6128	6138	6149	6160	6170	6180	6191	6201	6212	6222
42	6232	6243	6253	6263	6274	6284	6294	6304	6314	6325
43	6335	6345	6355	6365	6375	6385	6395	6405	6415	6425
44	6435	6444	6454	6464	6474	6484	6493	6503	6513	6522
45	6532	6542	6551	6561	6571	6580	6590	6599	6609	6618
46	6628	6637	6646	6656	6665	6675	6684	6693	6702	6712
47	6721	6730	6739	6749	6758	6767	6776	6785	6794	6803
48	6812	6821	6830	6839	6848	6857	6866	6875	6884	6893
49	6902	6911	6920	6928	6937	6946	6955	6964	6972	6981
50	6990	6998	7007	7016	7024	7033	7042	7050	7059	7067
51	7076	7084	7093	7101	7110	7118	7126	7135	7143	7152
52	7160	7168	7177	7185	7193	7202	7210	7218	7226	7235
53	7243	7251	7259	7267	7275	7284	7292	7300	7308	7316
54	7324	7332	7340	7348	7356	7364	7372	7380	7388	7396

Table 2 A—41

Table 2. Continued

N	0	1	2	3	4	5	6	7	8	9
55	7404	7412	7419	7427	7435	7443	7451	7459	7466	7474
56	7482	7490	7497	7505	7513	7520	7528	7536	7543	7551
57	7559	7566	7574	7582	7589	7597	7604	7612	7619	7627
58	7634	7642	7649	7657	7664	7672	7679	7686	7694	7701
59	7709	7716	7723	7731	7738	7745	7752	7760	7767	7774
60	7782	7789	7796	7803	7810	7818	7825	7832	7839	7846
61	7853	7860	7868	7875	7882	7889	7896	7903	7910	7917
62	7924	7931	7938	7945	7952	7959	7966	7973	7980	7987
63	7993	8000	8007	8014	8021	8028	8035	8041	8048	8055
64	8062	8069	8075	8082	8089	8096	8102	8109	8116	8122
65	8129	8136	8142	8149	8156	8162	8169	8176	8182	8189
66	8195	8202	8209	8215	8222	8228	8235	8241	8248	8254
67	8261	8267	8274	8280	8287	8293	8299	8306	8312	8319
68	8325	8331	8338	8344	8351	8357	8363	8370	8376	8382
69	8388	8395	8401	8407	8414	8420	8426	8432	8439	8445
70	8451	8457	8463	8470	8476	8482	8488	8494	8500	8506
71	8513	8519	8525	8531	8537	8543	8549	8555	8561	8567
72	8573	8579	8585	8591	8597	8603	8609	8615	8621	8627
73	8633	8639	8645	8651	8657	8663	8669	8675	8681	8686
74	8692	8698	8704	8710	8716	8722	8727	8733	8739	8745
75	8751	8756	8762	8768	8774	8779	8785	8791	8797	8802
76	8808	8814	8820	8825	8831	8837	8842	8848	8854	8859
77	8865	8871	8876	8882	8887	8893	8899	8904	8910	8915
78	8921	8927	8932	8938	8943	8949	8954	8960	8965	8971
79	8976	8982	8987	8993	8998	9004	9009	9015	9020	9025
80	9031	9036	9042	9047	9053	9058	9063	9069	9074	9079
81	9085	9090	9096	9101	9106	9112	9117	9122	9128	9133
82	9138	9143	9149	9154	9159	9165	9170	9175	9180	9186
83	9191	9196	9201	9206	9212	9217	9222	9227	9232	9238
84	9243	9248	9253	9258	9263	9269	9274	9279	9284	9289
85	9294	9299	9304	9309	9315	9320	9325	9330	9335	9340
86	9345	9350	9355	9360	9365	9370	9375	9380	9385	9390
87	9395	9400	9405	9410	9415	9420	9425	9430	9435	9440
88	9445	9450	9455	9460	9465	9469	9474	9479	9484	9489
89	9494	9499	9504	9509	9513	9518	9523	9528	9533	9538
90	9542	9547	9552	9557	9562	9566	9571	9576	9581	9586
91	9590	9595	9600	9605	9609	9614	9619	9624	9628	9633
92	9638	9643	9647	9652	9657	9661	9666	9671	9675	9680
93	9685	9689	9694	9699	9703	9708	9713	9717	9722	9727
94	9731	9736	9741	9745	9750	9754	9759	9763	9768	9773
95	9777	9782	9786	9791	9795	9800	9805	9809	9814	9818
96	9823	9827	9832	9836	9841	9845	9850	9854	9859	9863
97	9868	9872	9877	9881	9886	9890	9894	9899	9903	9908
98	9912	9917	9921	9926	9930	9934	9939	9943	9948	9952
99	9956	9961	9965	9969	9974	9978	9983	9987	9991	9996

Table 3. Four-Place Values of Functions and Radians
Angle θ in Degrees and Minutes

Degrees	Radians	Sin θ	Cos θ	Tan θ	Cot θ	Sec θ	Csc θ		
0°00′	0.0000	0.0000	1.0000	0.0000	—	1.000	—	1.5708	90°00′
10	0.0029	0.0029	1.0000	0.0029	343.8	1.000	343.8	1.5679	50
20	0.0058	0.0058	1.0000	0.0058	171.9	1.000	171.9	1.5650	40
30	0.0087	0.0087	1.0000	0.0087	114.6	1.000	114.6	1.5621	30
40	0.0116	0.0116	0.9999	0.0116	85.94	1.000	85.95	1.5592	20
50	0.0145	0.0145	0.9999	0.0145	68.75	1.000	68.76	1.5563	10
1°00′	0.0175	0.0175	0.9998	0.0175	57.29	1.000	57.30	1.5533	89°00′
10	0.0204	0.0204	0.9998	0.0204	49.10	1.000	49.11	1.5504	50
20	0.0233	0.0233	0.9997	0.0233	42.96	1.000	42.98	1.5475	40
30	0.0262	0.0262	0.9997	0.0262	38.19	1.000	38.20	1.5446	30
40	0.0291	0.0291	0.9996	0.0291	34.37	1.000	34.38	1.5417	20
50	0.0320	0.0320	0.9995	0.0320	31.24	1.001	31.26	1.5388	10
2°00′	0.0349	0.0349	0.9994	0.0349	28.64	1.001	28.65	1.5359	88°00′
10	0.0378	0.0378	0.9993	0.0378	26.43	1.001	26.45	1.5330	50
20	0.0407	0.0407	0.9992	0.0407	24.54	1.001	24.56	1.5301	40
30	0.0436	0.0436	0.9990	0.0437	22.90	1.001	22.93	1.5272	30
40	0.0465	0.0465	0.9989	0.0466	21.47	1.001	21.49	1.5243	20
50	0.0495	0.0494	0.9988	0.0495	20.21	1.001	20.23	1.5213	10
3°00′	0.0524	0.0523	0.9986	0.0524	19.08	1.001	19.11	1.5184	87°00′
10	0.0553	0.0552	0.9985	0.0553	18.07	1.002	18.10	1.5155	50
20	0.0582	0.0581	0.9983	0.0582	17.17	1.002	17.20	1.5126	40
30	0.0611	0.0610	0.9981	0.0612	16.35	1.002	16.38	1.5097	30
40	0.0640	0.0640	0.9980	0.0641	15.60	1.002	15.64	1.5068	20
50	0.0669	0.0669	0.9978	0.0670	14.92	1.002	14.96	1.5039	10
4°00′	0.0698	0.0698	0.9976	0.0699	14.30	1.002	14.34	1.5010	86°00′
10	0.0727	0.0727	0.9974	0.0729	13.73	1.003	13.76	1.4981	50
20	0.0756	0.0756	0.9971	0.0758	13.20	1.003	13.23	1.4952	40
30	0.0785	0.0785	0.9969	0.0787	12.71	1.003	12.75	1.4923	30
40	0.0814	0.0814	0.9967	0.0816	12.25	1.003	12.29	1.4893	20
50	0.0844	0.0843	0.9964	0.0846	11.83	1.004	11.87	1.4864	10
5°00′	0.0873	0.0872	0.9962	0.0875	11.43	1.004	11.47	1.4835	85°00′
10	0.0902	0.0901	0.9959	0.0904	11.06	1.004	11.10	1.4806	50
20	0.0931	0.0929	0.9957	0.0934	10.71	1.004	10.76	1.4777	40
30	0.0960	0.0958	0.9954	0.0963	10.39	1.005	10.43	1.4748	30
40	0.0989	0.0987	0.9951	0.0992	10.08	1.005	10.13	1.4719	20
50	0.1018	0.1016	0.9948	0.1022	9.788	1.005	9.839	1.4690	10
6°00′	0.1047	0.1045	0.9945	0.1051	9.514	1.006	9.567	1.4661	84°00′
10	0.1076	0.1074	0.9942	0.1080	9.255	1.006	9.309	1.4632	50
20	0.1105	0.1103	0.9939	0.1110	9.010	1.006	9.065	1.4603	40
30	0.1134	0.1132	0.9936	0.1139	8.777	1.006	8.834	1.4573	30
40	0.1164	0.1161	0.9932	0.1169	8.556	1.007	8.614	1.4544	20
50	0.1193	0.1190	0.9929	0.1198	8.345	1.007	8.405	1.4515	10
7°00′	0.1222	0.1219	0.9925	0.1228	8.144	1.008	8.206	1.4486	83°00′
10	0.1251	0.1248	0.9922	0.1257	7.953	1.008	8.016	1.4457	50
20	0.1280	0.1276	0.9918	0.1287	7.770	1.008	7.834	1.4428	40
30	0.1309	0.1305	0.9914	0.1317	7.596	1.009	7.661	1.4399	30
40	0.1338	0.1334	0.9911	0.1346	7.429	1.009	7.496	1.4370	20
50	0.1367	0.1363	0.9907	0.1376	7.269	1.009	7.337	1.4341	10
8°00′	0.1396	0.1392	0.9903	0.1405	7.115	1.010	7.185	1.4312	82°00′
		Cos θ	Sin θ	Cot θ	Tan θ	Csc θ	Sec θ	Radians	Degrees

Table 3   A—43

Table 3. Continued

Degrees	Radians	Sin θ	Cos θ	Tan θ	Cot θ	Sec θ	Csc θ		
8°00′	0.1396	0.1392	0.9903	0.1405	7.115	1.010	7.185	1.4312	82°00′
10	0.1425	0.1421	0.9899	0.1435	6.968	1.010	7.040	1.4283	50
20	0.1454	0.1449	0.9894	0.1465	6.827	1.011	6.900	1.4254	40
30	0.1484	0.1478	0.9890	0.1495	6.691	1.011	6.765	1.4224	30
40	0.1513	0.1507	0.9886	0.1524	6.561	1.012	6.636	1.4195	20
50	0.1542	0.1536	0.9881	0.1554	6.435	1.012	6.512	1.4166	10
9°00′	0.1571	0.1564	0.9877	0.1584	6.314	1.012	6.392	1.4137	81°00′
10	0.1600	0.1593	0.9872	0.1614	6.197	1.013	6.277	1.4108	50
20	0.1629	0.1622	0.9868	0.1644	6.084	1.013	6.166	1.4079	40
30	0.1658	0.1650	0.9863	0.1673	5.976	1.014	6.059	1.4050	30
40	0.1687	0.1679	0.9858	0.1703	5.871	1.014	5.955	1.4021	20
50	0.1716	0.1708	0.9853	0.1733	5.769	1.015	5.855	1.3992	10
10°00′	0.1745	0.1736	0.9848	0.1763	5.671	1.015	5.759	1.3963	80°00′
10	0.1774	0.1765	0.9843	0.1793	5.576	1.016	5.665	1.3934	50
20	0.1804	0.1794	0.9838	0.1823	5.485	1.016	5.575	1.3904	40
30	0.1833	0.1822	0.9833	0.1853	5.396	1.017	5.487	1.3875	30
40	0.1862	0.1851	0.9827	0.1883	5.309	1.018	5.403	1.3846	20
50	0.1891	0.1880	0.9822	0.1914	5.226	1.018	5.320	1.3817	10
11°00′	0.1920	0.1908	0.9816	0.1944	5.145	1.019	5.241	1.3788	79°00′
10	0.1949	0.1937	0.9811	0.1974	5.066	1.019	5.164	1.3759	50
20	0.1978	0.1965	0.9805	0.2004	4.989	1.020	5.089	1.3730	40
30	0.2007	0.1994	0.9799	0.2035	4.915	1.020	5.016	1.3701	30
40	0.2036	0.2022	0.9793	0.2065	4.843	1.021	4.945	1.3672	20
50	0.2065	0.2051	0.9787	0.2095	4.773	1.022	4.876	1.3643	10
12°00′	0.2094	0.2079	0.9781	0.2126	4.705	1.022	4.810	1.3614	78°00′
10	0.2123	0.2108	0.9775	0.2156	4.638	1.023	4.745	1.3584	50
20	0.2153	0.2136	0.9769	0.2186	4.574	1.024	4.682	1.3555	40
30	0.2182	0.2164	0.9763	0.2217	4.511	1.024	4.620	1.3526	30
40	0.2211	0.2193	0.9757	0.2247	4.449	1.025	4.560	1.3497	20
50	0.2240	0.2221	0.9750	0.2278	4.390	1.026	4.502	1.3468	10
13°00′	0.2269	0.2250	0.9744	0.2309	4.331	1.026	4.445	1.3439	77°00′
10	0.2298	0.2278	0.9737	0.2339	4.275	1.027	4.390	1.3410	50
20	0.2327	0.2306	0.9730	0.2370	4.219	1.028	4.336	1.3381	40
30	0.2356	0.2334	0.9724	0.2401	4.165	1.028	4.284	1.3352	30
40	0.2385	0.2363	0.9717	0.2432	4.113	1.029	4.232	1.3323	20
50	0.2414	0.2391	0.9710	0.2462	4.061	1.030	4.182	1.3294	10
14°00′	0.2443	0.2419	0.9703	0.2493	4.011	1.031	4.134	1.3265	76°00′
10	0.2473	0.2447	0.9696	0.2524	3.962	1.031	4.086	1.3235	50
20	0.2502	0.2476	0.9689	0.2555	3.914	1.032	4.039	1.3206	40
30	0.2531	0.2504	0.9681	0.2586	3.867	1.033	3.994	1.3177	30
40	0.2560	0.2532	0.9674	0.2617	3.821	1.034	3.950	1.3148	20
50	0.2589	0.2560	0.9667	0.2648	3.776	1.034	3.906	1.3119	10
15°00′	0.2618	0.2588	0.9659	0.2679	3.732	1.035	3.864	1.3090	75°00′
10	0.2647	0.2616	0.9652	0.2711	3.689	1.036	3.822	1.3061	50
20	0.2676	0.2644	0.9644	0.2742	3.647	1.037	3.782	1.3032	40
30	0.2705	0.2672	0.9636	0.2773	3.606	1.038	3.742	1.3003	30
40	0.2734	0.2700	0.9628	0.2805	3.566	1.039	3.703	1.2974	20
50	0.2763	0.2728	0.9621	0.2836	3.526	1.039	3.665	1.2945	10
16°00′	0.2793	0.2756	0.9613	0.2867	3.487	1.040	3.628	1.2915	74°00′
		Cos θ	Sin θ	Cot θ	Tan θ	Csc θ	Sec θ	Radians	Degrees

Table 3. Continued

Degrees	Radians	Sin θ	Cos θ	Tan θ	Cot θ	Sec θ	Csc θ		
16°00′	0.2793	0.2756	0.9613	0.2867	3.487	1.040	3.628	1.2915	74°00′
10	0.2822	0.2784	0.9605	0.2899	3.450	1.041	3.592	1.2886	50
20	0.2851	0.2812	0.9596	0.2931	3.412	1.042	3.556	1.2857	40
30	0.2880	0.2840	0.9588	0.2962	3.376	1.043	3.521	1.2828	30
40	0.2909	0.2868	0.9580	0.2994	3.340	1.044	3.487	1.2799	20
50	0.2938	0.2896	0.9572	0.3026	3.305	1.045	3.453	1.2770	10
17°00′	0.2967	0.2924	0.9563	0.3057	3.271	1.046	3.420	1.2741	73°00′
10	0.2996	0.2952	0.9555	0.3089	3.237	1.047	3.388	1.2712	50
20	0.3025	0.2979	0.9546	0.3121	3.204	1.048	3.356	1.2683	40
30	0.3054	0.3007	0.9537	0.3153	3.172	1.049	3.326	1.2654	30
40	0.3083	0.3035	0.9528	0.3185	3.140	1.049	3.295	1.2625	20
50	0.3113	0.3062	0.9520	0.3217	3.108	1.050	3.265	1.2595	10
18°00′	0.3142	0.3090	0.9511	0.3249	3.078	1.051	3.236	1.2566	72°00′
10	0.3171	0.3118	0.9502	0.3281	3.047	1.052	3.207	1.2537	50
20	0.3200	0.3145	0.9492	0.3314	3.018	1.053	3.179	1.2508	40
30	0.3229	0.3173	0.9483	0.3346	2.989	1.054	3.152	1.2479	30
40	0.3258	0.3201	0.9474	0.3378	2.960	1.056	3.124	1.2450	20
50	0.3287	0.3228	0.9465	0.3411	2.932	1.057	3.098	1.2421	10
19°00′	0.3316	0.3256	0.9455	0.3443	2.904	1.058	3.072	1.2392	71°00′
10	0.3345	0.3283	0.9446	0.3476	2.877	1.059	3.046	1.2363	50
20	0.3374	0.3311	0.9436	0.3508	2.850	1.060	3.021	1.2334	40
30	0.3403	0.3338	0.9426	0.3541	2.824	1.061	2.996	1.2305	30
40	0.3432	0.3365	0.9417	0.3574	2.798	1.062	2.971	1.2275	20
50	0.3462	0.3393	0.9407	0.3607	2.773	1.063	2.947	1.2246	10
20°00′	0.3491	0.3420	0.9397	0.3640	2.747	1.064	2.924	1.2217	70°00′
10	0.3520	0.3448	0.9387	0.3673	2.723	1.065	2.901	1.2188	50
20	0.3549	0.3475	0.9377	0.3706	2.699	1.066	2.878	1.2159	40
30	0.3578	0.3502	0.9367	0.3739	2.675	1.068	2.855	1.2130	30
40	0.3607	0.3529	0.9356	0.3772	2.651	1.069	2.833	1.2101	20
50	0.3636	0.3557	0.9346	0.3805	2.628	1.070	2.812	1.2072	10
21°00′	0.3665	0.3584	0.9336	0.3839	2.605	1.071	2.790	1.2043	69°00′
10	0.3694	0.3611	0.9325	0.3872	2.583	1.072	2.769	1.2014	50
20	0.3723	0.3638	0.9315	0.3906	2.560	1.074	2.749	1.1985	40
30	0.3752	0.3665	0.9304	0.3939	2.539	1.075	2.729	1.1956	30
40	0.3782	0.3692	0.9293	0.3973	2.517	1.076	2.709	1.1926	20
50	0.3811	0.3719	0.9283	0.4006	2.496	1.077	2.689	1.1897	10
22°00′	0.3840	0.3746	0.9272	0.4040	2.475	1.079	2.669	1.1868	68°00′
10	0.3869	0.3773	0.9261	0.4074	2.455	1.080	2.650	1.1839	50
20	0.3898	0.3800	0.9250	0.4108	2.434	1.081	2.632	1.1810	40
30	0.3927	0.3827	0.9239	0.4142	2.414	1.082	2.613	1.1781	30
40	0.3956	0.3854	0.9228	0.4176	2.394	1.084	2.595	1.1752	20
50	0.3985	0.3881	0.9216	0.4210	2.375	1.085	2.577	1.1723	10
23°00′	0.4014	0.3907	0.9205	0.4245	2.356	1.086	2.559	1.1694	67°00′
10	0.4043	0.3934	0.9194	0.4279	2.337	1.088	2.542	1.1665	50
20	0.4072	0.3961	0.9182	0.4314	2.318	1.089	2.525	1.1636	40
30	0.4102	0.3987	0.9171	0.4348	2.300	1.090	2.508	1.1606	30
40	0.4131	0.4014	0.9159	0.4383	2.282	1.092	2.491	1.1577	20
50	0.4160	0.4041	0.9147	0.4417	2.264	1.093	2.475	1.1548	10
24°00′	0.4189	0.4067	0.9135	0.4452	2.246	1.095	2.459	1.1519	66°00′
		Cos θ	Sin θ	Cot θ	Tan θ	Csc θ	Sec θ	Radians	Degrees

Table 3 A—45

Table 3. Continued

Degrees	Radians	Sin θ	Cos θ	Tan θ	Cot θ	Sec θ	Csc θ		
24°00′	0.4189	0.4067	0.9135	0.4452	2.246	1.095	2.459	1.1519	66°00′
10	0.4218	0.4094	0.9124	0.4487	2.229	1.096	2.443	1.1490	50
20	0.4247	0.4120	0.9112	0.4522	2.211	1.097	2.427	1.1461	40
30	0.4276	0.4147	0.9100	0.4557	2.194	1.099	2.411	1.1432	30
40	0.4305	0.4173	0.9088	0.4592	2.177	1.100	2.396	1.1403	20
50	0.4334	0.4200	0.9075	0.4628	2.161	1.102	2.381	1.1374	10
25°00′	0.4363	0.4226	0.9063	0.4663	2.145	1.103	2.366	1.1345	65°00′
10	0.4392	0.4253	0.9051	0.4699	2.128	1.105	2.352	1.1316	50
20	0.4422	0.4279	0.9038	0.4734	2.112	1.106	2.337	1.1286	40
30	0.4451	0.4305	0.9026	0.4770	2.097	1.108	2.323	1.1257	30
40	0.4480	0.4331	0.9013	0.4806	2.081	1.109	2.309	1.1228	20
50	0.4509	0.4358	0.9001	0.4841	2.066	1.111	2.295	1.1199	10
26°00′	0.4538	0.4384	0.8988	0.4877	2.050	1.113	2.281	1.1170	64°00′
10	0.4567	0.4410	0.8975	0.4913	2.035	1.114	2.268	1.1141	50
20	0.4596	0.4436	0.8962	0.4950	2.020	1.116	2.254	1.1112	40
30	0.4625	0.4462	0.8949	0.4986	2.006	1.117	2.241	1.1083	30
40	0.4654	0.4488	0.8936	0.5022	1.991	1.119	2.228	1.1054	20
50	0.4683	0.4514	0.8923	0.5059	1.977	1.121	2.215	1.1025	10
27°00′	0.4712	0.4540	0.8910	0.5095	1.963	1.122	2.203	1.0996	63°00′
10	0.4741	0.4566	0.8897	0.5132	1.949	1.124	2.190	1.0966	50
20	0.4771	0.4592	0.8884	0.5169	1.935	1.126	2.178	1.0937	40
30	0.4800	0.4617	0.8870	0.5206	1.921	1.127	2.166	1.0908	30
40	0.4829	0.4643	0.8857	0.5243	1.907	1.129	2.154	1.0879	20
50	0.4858	0.4669	0.8843	0.5280	1.894	1.131	2.142	1.0850	10
28°00′	0.4887	0.4695	0.8829	0.5317	1.881	1.133	2.130	1.0821	62°00′
10	0.4916	0.4720	0.8816	0.5354	1.868	1.134	2.118	1.0792	50
20	0.4945	0.4746	0.8802	0.5392	1.855	1.136	2.107	1.0763	40
30	0.4974	0.4772	0.8788	0.5430	1.842	1.138	2.096	1.0734	30
40	0.5003	0.4797	0.8774	0.5467	1.829	1.140	2.085	1.0705	20
50	0.5032	0.4823	0.8760	0.5505	1.816	1.142	2.074	1.0676	10
29°00′	0.5061	0.4848	0.8746	0.5543	1.804	1.143	2.063	1.0647	61°00′
10	0.5091	0.4874	0.8732	0.5581	1.792	1.145	2.052	1.0617	50
20	0.5120	0.4899	0.8718	0.5619	1.780	1.147	2.041	1.0588	40
30	0.5149	0.4924	0.8704	0.5658	1.767	1.149	2.031	1.0559	30
40	0.5178	0.4950	0.8689	0.5696	1.756	1.151	2.020	1.0530	20
50	0.5207	0.4975	0.8675	0.5735	1.744	1.153	2.010	1.0501	10
30°00′	0.5236	0.5000	0.8660	0.5774	1.732	1.155	2.000	1.0472	60°00′
10	0.5265	0.5025	0.8646	0.5812	1.720	1.157	1.990	1.0443	50
20	0.5294	0.5050	0.8631	0.5851	1.709	1.159	1.980	1.0414	40
30	0.5323	0.5075	0.8616	0.5890	1.698	1.161	1.970	1.0385	30
40	0.5352	0.5100	0.8601	0.5930	1.686	1.163	1.961	1.0356	20
50	0.5381	0.5125	0.8587	0.5969	1.675	1.165	1.951	1.0327	10
31°00′	0.5411	0.5150	0.8572	0.6009	1.664	1.167	1.942	1.0297	59°00′
10	0.5440	0.5175	0.8557	0.6048	1.653	1.169	1.932	1.0268	50
20	0.5469	0.5200	0.8542	0.6088	1.643	1.171	1.923	1.0239	40
30	0.5498	0.5225	0.8526	0.6128	1.632	1.173	1.914	1.0210	30
40	0.5527	0.5250	0.8511	0.6168	1.621	1.175	1.905	1.0181	20
50	0.5556	0.5275	0.8496	0.6208	1.611	1.177	1.896	1.0152	10
32°00′	0.5585	0.5299	0.8480	0.6249	1.600	1.179	1.887	1.0123	58°00′
		Cos θ	Sin θ	Cot θ	Tan θ	Csc θ	Sec θ	Radians	Degrees

Table 3. Continued

Degrees	Radians	Sin θ	Cos θ	Tan θ	Cot θ	Sec θ	Csc θ		
32°00′	0.5585	0.5299	0.8480	0.6249	1.600	1.179	1.887	1.0123	58°00′
10	0.5614	0.5324	0.8465	0.6289	1.590	1.181	1.878	1.0094	50
20	0.5643	0.5348	0.8450	0.6330	1.580	1.184	1.870	1.0065	40
30	0.5672	0.5373	0.8434	0.6371	1.570	1.186	1.861	1.0036	30
40	0.5701	0.5398	0.8418	0.6412	1.560	1.188	1.853	1.0007	20
50	0.5730	0.5422	0.8403	0.6453	1.550	1.190	1.844	0.9977	10
33°00′	0.5760	0.5446	0.8387	0.6494	1.540	1.192	1.836	0.9948	57°00′
10	0.5789	0.5471	0.8371	0.6536	1.530	1.195	1.828	0.9919	50
20	0.5818	0.5495	0.8355	0.6577	1.520	1.197	1.820	0.9890	40
30	0.5847	0.5519	0.8339	0.6619	1.511	1.199	1.812	0.9861	30
40	0.5876	0.5544	0.8323	0.6661	1.501	1.202	1.804	0.9832	20
50	0.5905	0.5568	0.8307	0.6703	1.492	1.204	1.796	0.9803	10
34°00′	0.5934	0.5592	0.8290	0.6745	1.483	1.206	1.788	0.9774	56°00′
10	0.5963	0.5616	0.8274	0.6787	1.473	1.209	1.781	0.9745	50
20	0.5992	0.5640	0.8258	0.6830	1.464	1.211	1.773	0.9716	40
30	0.6021	0.5664	0.8241	0.6873	1.455	1.213	1.766	0.9687	30
40	0.6050	0.5688	0.8225	0.6916	1.446	1.216	1.758	0.9657	20
50	0.6080	0.5712	0.8208	0.6959	1.437	1.218	1.751	0.9628	10
35°00′	0.6109	0.5736	0.8192	0.7002	1.428	1.221	1.743	0.9599	55°00′
10	0.6138	0.5760	0.8175	0.7046	1.419	1.223	1.736	0.9570	50
20	0.6167	0.5783	0.8158	0.7089	1.411	1.226	1.729	0.9541	40
30	0.6196	0.5807	0.8141	0.7133	1.402	1.228	1.722	0.9512	30
40	0.6225	0.5831	0.8124	0.7177	1.393	1.231	1.715	0.9483	20
50	0.6254	0.5854	0.8107	0.7221	1.385	1.233	1.708	0.9454	10
36°00′	0.6283	0.5878	0.8090	0.7265	1.376	1.236	1.701	0.9425	54°00′
10	0.6312	0.5901	0.8073	0.7310	1.368	1.239	1.695	0.9396	50
20	0.6341	0.5925	0.8056	0.7355	1.360	1.241	1.688	0.9367	40
30	0.6370	0.5948	0.8039	0.7400	1.351	1.244	1.681	0.9338	30
40	0.6400	0.5972	0.8021	0.7445	1.343	1.247	1.675	0.9308	20
50	0.6429	0.5995	0.8004	0.7490	1.335	1.249	1.668	0.9279	10
37°00′	0.6458	0.6018	0.7986	0.7536	1.327	1.252	1.662	0.9250	53°00′
10	0.6487	0.6041	0.7969	0.7581	1.319	1.255	1.655	0.9221	50
20	0.6516	0.6065	0.7951	0.7627	1.311	1.258	1.649	0.9192	40
30	0.6545	0.6088	0.7934	0.7673	1.303	1.260	1.643	0.9163	30
40	0.6574	0.6111	0.7916	0.7720	1.295	1.263	1.636	0.9134	20
50	0.6603	0.6134	0.7898	0.7766	1.288	1.266	1.630	0.9105	10
38°00′	0.6632	0.6157	0.7880	0.7813	1.280	1.269	1.624	0.9076	52°00′
10	0.6661	0.6180	0.7862	0.7860	1.272	1.272	1.618	0.9047	50
20	0.6690	0.6202	0.7844	0.7907	1.265	1.275	1.612	0.9018	40
30	0.6720	0.6225	0.7826	0.7954	1.257	1.278	1.606	0.8988	30
40	0.6749	0.6248	0.7808	0.8002	1.250	1.281	1.601	0.8959	20
50	0.6778	0.6271	0.7790	0.8050	1.242	1.284	1.595	0.8930	10
39°00′	0.6807	0.6293	0.7771	0.8098	1.235	1.287	1.589	0.8901	51°00′
		Cos θ	Sin θ	Cot θ	Tan θ	Csc θ	Sec θ	Radians	Degrees

Table 3   A—47

Table 3. Continued

Degrees	Radians	Sin θ	Cos θ	Tan θ	Cot θ	Sec θ	Csc θ		
39°00′	0.6807	0.6293	0.7771	0.8098	1.235	1.287	1.589	0.8901	51°00′
10	0.6836	0.6316	0.7753	0.8146	1.228	1.290	1.583	0.8872	50
20	0.6865	0.6338	0.7735	0.8195	1.220	1.293	1.578	0.8843	40
30	0.6894	0.6361	0.7716	0.8243	1.213	1.296	1.572	0.8814	30
40	0.6923	0.6383	0.7698	0.8292	1.206	1.299	1.567	0.8785	20
50	0.6952	0.6406	0.7679	0.8342	1.199	1.302	1.561	0.8756	10
40°00′	0.6981	0.6428	0.7660	0.8391	1.192	1.305	1.556	0.8727	50°00′
10	0.7010	0.6450	0.7642	0.8441	1.185	1.309	1.550	0.8698	50
20	0.7039	0.6472	0.7623	0.8491	1.178	1.312	1.545	0.8668	40
30	0.7069	0.6494	0.7604	0.8541	1.171	1.315	1.540	0.8639	30
40	0.7098	0.6517	0.7585	0.8591	1.164	1.318	1.535	0.8610	20
50	0.7127	0.6539	0.7566	0.8642	1.157	1.322	1.529	0.8581	10
41°00′	0.7156	0.6561	0.7547	0.8693	1.150	1.325	1.524	0.8552	49°00′
10	0.7185	0.6583	0.7528	0.8744	1.144	1.328	1.519	0.8523	50
20	0.7214	0.6604	0.7509	0.8796	1.137	1.332	1.514	0.8494	40
30	0.7243	0.6626	0.7490	0.8847	1.130	1.335	1.509	0.8465	30
40	0.7272	0.6648	0.7470	0.8899	1.124	1.339	1.504	0.8436	20
50	0.7301	0.6670	0.7451	0.8952	1.117	1.342	1.499	0.8407	10
42°00′	0.7330	0.6691	0.7431	0.9004	1.111	1.346	1.494	0.8378	48°00′
10	0.7359	0.6713	0.7412	0.9057	1.104	1.349	1.490	0.8348	50
20	0.7389	0.6734	0.7392	0.9110	1.098	1.353	1.485	0.8319	40
30	0.7418	0.6756	0.7373	0.9163	1.091	1.356	1.480	0.8290	30
40	0.7447	0.6777	0.7353	0.9217	1.085	1.360	1.476	0.8261	20
50	0.7476	0.6799	0.7333	0.9271	1.079	1.364	1.471	0.8232	10
43°00′	0.7505	0.6820	0.7314	0.9325	1.072	1.367	1.466	0.8203	47°00′
10	0.7534	0.6841	0.7294	0.9380	1.066	1.371	1.462	0.8174	50
20	0.7563	0.6862	0.7274	0.9435	1.060	1.375	1.457	0.8145	40
30	0.7592	0.6884	0.7254	0.9490	1.054	1.379	1.453	0.8116	30
40	0.7621	0.6905	0.7234	0.9545	1.048	1.382	1.448	0.8087	20
50	0.7650	0.6926	0.7214	0.9601	1.042	1.386	1.444	0.8058	10
44°00′	0.7679	0.6947	0.7193	0.9657	1.036	1.390	1.440	0.8029	46°00′
10	0.7709	0.6967	0.7173	0.9713	1.030	1.394	1.435	0.7999	50
20	0.7738	0.6988	0.7153	0.9770	1.024	1.398	1.431	0.7970	40
30	0.7767	0.7009	0.7133	0.9827	1.018	1.402	1.427	0.7941	30
40	0.7796	0.7030	0.7112	0.9884	1.012	1.406	1.423	0.7912	20
50	0.7825	0.7050	0.7092	0.9942	1.006	1.410	1.418	0.7883	10
45°00′	0.7854	0.7071	0.7071	1.000	1.000	1.414	1.414	0.7854	45°00′
		Cos θ	Sin θ	Cot θ	Tan θ	Csc θ	Sec θ	Radians	Degrees

Table 4. Four-Place Values of Trigonometric Functions
Angle θ in Degrees and Tenths

Degrees	Sin θ	Cos θ	Tan θ	Cot θ		Degrees	Sin θ	Cos θ	Tan θ	Cot θ	
0.0	0.0000	1.0000	0.0000	—	90.0	5.0	0.0872	0.9962	0.0875	11.43	85.0
.1	0.0017	1.0000	0.0017	573.0	.9	.1	0.0889	0.9960	0.0892	11.20	.9
.2	0.0035	1.0000	0.0035	286.4	.8	.2	0.0906	0.9959	0.0910	10.99	.8
.3	0.0052	1.0000	0.0052	191.0	.7	.3	0.0924	0.9957	0.0928	10.78	.7
.4	0.0070	1.0000	0.0070	143.2	.6	.4	0.0941	0.9956	0.0945	10.58	.6
.5	0.0087	1.0000	0.0087	114.6	.5	.5	0.0958	0.9954	0.0963	10.39	.5
.6	0.0105	0.9999	0.0105	95.49	.4	.6	0.0976	0.9952	0.0981	10.20	.4
.7	0.0122	0.9999	0.0122	81.85	.3	.7	0.0993	0.9951	0.0998	10.02	.3
.8	0.0140	0.9999	0.0140	71.62	.2	.8	0.1011	0.9949	0.1016	9.845	.2
.9	0.0157	0.9999	0.0157	63.66	.1	.9	0.1028	0.9947	0.1033	9.677	.1
1.0	0.0175	0.9998	0.0175	57.29	89.0	6.0	0.1045	0.9945	0.1051	9.514	84.0
.1	0.0192	0.9998	0.0192	52.08	.9	.1	0.1063	0.9943	0.1069	9.357	.9
.2	0.0209	0.9998	0.0209	47.74	.8	.2	0.1080	0.9942	0.1086	9.205	.8
.3	0.0227	0.9997	0.0227	44.07	.7	.3	0.1097	0.9940	0.1104	9.058	.7
.4	0.0244	0.9997	0.0244	40.92	.6	.4	0.1115	0.9938	0.1122	8.915	.6
.5	0.0262	0.9997	0.0262	38.19	.5	.5	0.1132	0.9936	0.1139	8.777	.5
.6	0.0279	0.9996	0.0279	35.80	.4	.6	0.1149	0.9934	0.1157	8.643	.4
.7	0.0297	0.9996	0.0297	33.69	.3	.7	0.1167	0.9932	0.1175	8.513	.3
.8	0.0314	0.9995	0.0314	31.82	.2	.8	0.1184	0.9930	0.1192	8.386	.2
.9	0.0332	0.9995	0.0332	30.14	.1	.9	0.1201	0.9928	0.1210	8.264	.1
2.0	0.0349	0.9994	0.0349	28.64	88.0	7.0	0.1219	0.9925	0.1228	8.144	83.0
.1	0.0366	0.9993	0.0367	27.27	.9	.1	0.1236	0.9923	0.1246	8.028	.9
.2	0.0384	0.9993	0.0384	26.03	.8	.2	0.1253	0.9921	0.1263	7.916	.8
.3	0.0401	0.9992	0.0402	24.90	.7	.3	0.1271	0.9919	0.1281	7.806	.7
.4	0.0419	0.9991	0.0419	23.86	.6	.4	0.1288	0.9917	0.1299	7.700	.6
.5	0.0436	0.9990	0.0437	22.90	.5	.5	0.1305	0.9914	0.1317	7.596	.5
.6	0.0454	0.9990	0.0454	22.02	.4	.6	0.1323	0.9912	0.1334	7.495	.4
.7	0.0471	0.9989	0.0472	21.20	.3	.7	0.1340	0.9910	0.1352	7.396	.3
.8	0.0488	0.9988	0.0489	20.45	.2	.8	0.1357	0.9907	0.1370	7.300	.2
.9	0.0506	0.9987	0.0507	19.74	.1	.9	0.1374	0.9905	0.1388	7.207	.1
3.0	0.0523	0.9986	0.0524	19.08	87.0	8.0	0.1392	0.9903	0.1405	7.115	82.0
.1	0.0541	0.9985	0.0542	18.46	.9	.1	0.1409	0.9900	0.1423	7.026	.9
.2	0.0558	0.9984	0.0559	17.89	.8	.2	0.1426	0.9898	0.1441	6.940	.8
.3	0.0576	0.9983	0.0577	17.34	.7	.3	0.1444	0.9895	0.1459	6.855	.7
.4	0.0593	0.9982	0.0594	16.83	.6	.4	0.1461	0.9893	0.1477	6.772	.6
.5	0.0610	0.9981	0.0612	16.35	.5	.5	0.1478	0.9890	0.1495	6.691	.5
.6	0.0628	0.9980	0.0629	15.89	.4	.6	0.1495	0.9888	0.1512	6.612	.4
.7	0.0645	0.9979	0.0647	15.46	.3	.7	0.1513	0.9885	0.1530	6.535	.3
.8	0.0663	0.9978	0.0664	15.06	.2	.8	0.1530	0.9882	0.1548	6.460	.2
.9	0.0680	0.9977	0.0682	14.67	.1	.9	0.1547	0.9880	0.1566	6.386	.1
4.0	0.0698	0.9976	0.0699	14.30	86.0	9.0	0.1564	0.9877	0.1584	6.314	81.0
.1	0.0715	0.9974	0.0717	13.95	.9	.1	0.1582	0.9874	0.1602	6.243	.9
.2	0.0732	0.9973	0.0734	13.62	.8	.2	0.1599	0.9871	0.1620	6.174	.8
.3	0.0750	0.9972	0.0752	13.30	.7	.3	0.1616	0.9869	0.1638	6.107	.7
.4	0.0767	0.9971	0.0769	13.00	.6	.4	0.1633	0.9866	0.1655	6.041	.6
.5	0.0785	0.9969	0.0787	12.71	.5	.5	0.1650	0.9863	0.1673	5.976	.5
.6	0.0802	0.9968	0.0805	12.43	.4	.6	0.1668	0.9860	0.1691	5.912	.4
.7	0.0819	0.9966	0.0822	12.16	.3	.7	0.1685	0.9857	0.1709	5.850	.3
.8	0.0837	0.9965	0.0840	11.91	.2	.8	0.1702	0.9854	0.1727	5.789	.2
.9	0.0854	0.9963	0.0857	11.66	.1	.9	0.1719	0.9851	0.1745	5.730	.1
5.0	0.0872	0.9962	0.0875	11.43	85.0	10.0	0.1736	0.9848	0.1763	5.671	80.0
	Cos θ	Sin θ	Cot θ	Tan θ	Degrees		Cos θ	Sin θ	Cot θ	Tan θ	Degrees

Table 4   A—49

Table 4. Continued

Degrees	Sin θ	Cos θ	Tan θ	Cot θ		Degrees	Sin θ	Cos θ	Tan θ	Cot θ	
10.0	0.1736	0.9848	0.1763	5.671	80.0	15.0	0.2588	0.9659	0.2679	3.732	75.0
.1	0.1754	0.9845	0.1781	5.614	.9	.1	0.2605	0.9655	0.2698	3.706	.9
.2	0.1771	0.9842	0.1799	5.558	.8	.2	0.2622	0.9650	0.2717	3.681	.8
.3	0.1788	0.9839	0.1817	5.503	.7	.3	0.2639	0.9646	0.2736	3.655	.7
.4	0.1805	0.9836	0.1835	5.449	.6	.4	0.2656	0.9641	0.2754	3.630	.6
.5	0.1822	0.9833	0.1853	5.396	.5	.5	0.2672	0.9636	0.2773	3.606	.5
.6	0.1840	0.9829	0.1871	5.343	.4	.6	0.2689	0.9632	0.2792	3.582	.4
.7	0.1857	0.9826	0.1890	5.292	.3	.7	0.2706	0.9627	0.2811	3.558	.3
.8	0.1874	0.9823	0.1908	5.242	.2	.8	0.2723	0.9622	0.2830	3.534	.2
.9	0.1891	0.9820	0.1926	5.193	.1	.9	0.2740	0.9617	0.2849	3.511	.1
11.0	0.1908	0.9816	0.1944	5.145	79.0	16.0	0.2756	0.9613	0.2867	3.487	74.0
.1	0.1925	0.9813	0.1962	5.097	.9	.1	0.2773	0.9608	0.2886	3.465	.9
.2	0.1942	0.9810	0.1980	5.050	.8	.2	0.2790	0.9603	0.2905	3.442	.8
.3	0.1959	0.9806	0.1998	5.005	.7	.3	0.2807	0.9598	0.2924	3.420	.7
.4	0.1977	0.9803	0.2016	4.959	.6	.4	0.2823	0.9593	0.2943	3.398	.6
.5	0.1994	0.9799	0.2035	4.915	.5	.5	0.2840	0.9588	0.2962	3.376	.5
.6	0.2011	0.9796	0.2053	4.872	.4	.6	0.2857	0.9583	0.2981	3.354	.4
.7	0.2028	0.9792	0.2071	4.829	.3	.7	0.2874	0.9578	0.3000	3.333	.3
.8	0.2045	0.9789	0.2089	4.787	.2	.8	0.2890	0.9573	0.3019	3.312	.2
.9	0.2062	0.9785	0.2107	4.745	.1	.9	0.2907	0.9568	0.3038	3.291	.1
12.0	0.2079	0.9781	0.2126	4.705	78.0	17.0	0.2924	0.9563	0.3057	3.271	73.0
.1	0.2096	0.9778	0.2144	4.665	.9	.1	0.2940	0.9558	0.3076	3.251	.9
.2	0.2113	0.9774	0.2162	4.625	.8	.2	0.2957	0.9553	0.3096	3.230	.8
.3	0.2130	0.9770	0.2180	4.586	.7	.3	0.2974	0.9548	0.3115	3.211	.7
.4	0.2147	0.9767	0.2199	4.548	.6	.4	0.2990	0.9542	0.3134	3.191	.6
.5	0.2164	0.9763	0.2217	4.511	.5	.5	0.3007	0.9537	0.3153	3.172	.5
.6	0.2181	0.9759	0.2235	4.474	.4	.6	0.3024	0.9532	0.3172	3.152	.4
.7	0.2198	0.9755	0.2254	4.437	.3	.7	0.3040	0.9527	0.3191	3.133	.3
.8	0.2215	0.9751	0.2272	4.402	.2	.8	0.3057	0.9521	0.3211	3.115	.2
.9	0.2233	0.9748	0.2290	4.366	.1	.9	0.3074	0.9516	0.3230	3.096	.1
13.0	0.2250	0.9744	0.2309	4.331	77.0	18.0	0.3090	0.9511	0.3249	3.078	72.0
.1	0.2267	0.9740	0.2327	4.297	.9	.1	0.3107	0.9505	0.3269	3.060	.9
.2	0.2284	0.9736	0.2345	4.264	.8	.2	0.3123	0.9500	0.3288	3.042	.8
.3	0.2300	0.9732	0.2364	4.230	.7	.3	0.3140	0.9494	0.3307	3.024	.7
.4	0.2317	0.9728	0.2382	4.198	.6	.4	0.3156	0.9489	0.3327	3.006	.6
.5	0.2334	0.9724	0.2401	4.165	.5	.5	0.3173	0.9483	0.3346	2.989	.5
.6	0.2351	0.9720	0.2419	4.134	.4	.6	0.3190	0.9478	0.3365	2.971	.4
.7	0.2368	0.9715	0.2438	4.102	.3	.7	0.3206	0.9472	0.3385	2.954	.3
.8	0.2385	0.9711	0.2456	4.071	.2	.8	0.3223	0.9466	0.3404	2.937	.2
.9	0.2402	0.9707	0.2475	4.041	.1	.9	0.3239	0.9461	0.3424	2.921	.1
14.0	0.2419	0.9703	0.2493	4.011	76.0	19.0	0.3256	0.9455	0.3443	2.904	71.0
.1	0.2436	0.9699	0.2512	3.981	.9	.1	0.3272	0.9449	0.3463	2.888	.9
.2	0.2453	0.9694	0.2530	3.952	.8	.2	0.3289	0.9444	0.3482	2.872	.8
.3	0.2470	0.9690	0.2549	3.923	.7	.3	0.3305	0.9438	0.3502	2.856	.7
.4	0.2487	0.9686	0.2568	3.895	.6	.4	0.3322	0.9432	0.3522	2.840	.6
.5	0.2504	0.9681	0.2586	3.867	.5	.5	0.3338	0.9426	0.3541	2.824	.5
.6	0.2521	0.9677	0.2605	3.839	.4	.6	0.3355	0.9421	0.3561	2.808	.4
.7	0.2538	0.9673	0.2623	3.812	.3	.7	0.3371	0.9415	0.3581	2.793	.3
.8	0.2554	0.9668	0.2642	3.785	.2	.8	0.3387	0.9409	0.3600	2.778	.2
.9	0.2571	0.9664	0.2661	3.758	.1	.9	0.3404	0.9403	0.3620	2.762	.1
15.0	0.2588	0.9659	0.2679	3.732	75.0	20.0	0.3420	0.9397	0.3640	2.747	70.0
	Cos θ	Sin θ	Cot θ	Tan θ	Degrees		Cos θ	Sin θ	Cot θ	Tan θ	Degrees

Table 4. Continued

Degrees	Sin θ	Cos θ	Tan θ	Cot θ		Degrees	Sin θ	Cos θ	Tan θ	Cot θ	
20.0	0.3420	0.9397	0.3640	2.747	70.0	25.0	0.4226	0.9063	0.4663	2.145	65.0
.1	0.3437	0.9391	0.3659	2.733	.9	.1	0.4242	0.9056	0.4684	2.135	.9
.2	0.3453	0.9385	0.3679	2.718	.8	.2	0.4258	0.9048	0.4706	2.125	.8
.3	0.3469	0.9379	0.3699	2.703	.7	.3	0.4274	0.9041	0.4727	2.116	.7
.4	0.3486	0.9373	0.3719	2.689	.6	.4	0.4289	0.9033	0.4748	2.106	.6
.5	0.3502	0.9367	0.3739	2.675	.5	.5	0.4305	0.9026	0.4770	2.097	.5
.6	0.3518	0.9361	0.3759	2.660	.4	.6	0.4321	0.9018	0.4791	2.087	.4
.7	0.3535	0.9354	0.3779	2.646	.3	.7	0.4337	0.9011	0.4813	2.078	.3
.8	0.3551	0.9348	0.3799	2.633	.2	.8	0.4352	0.9003	0.4834	2.069	.2
.9	0.3567	0.9342	0.3819	2.619	.1	.9	0.4368	0.8996	0.4856	2.059	.1
21.0	0.3584	0.9336	0.3839	2.605	69.0	26.0	0.4384	0.8988	0.4877	2.050	64.0
.1	0.3600	0.9330	0.3859	2.592	.9	.1	0.4399	0.8980	0.4899	2.041	.9
.2	0.3616	0.9323	0.3879	2.578	.8	.2	0.4415	0.8973	0.4921	2.032	.8
.3	0.3633	0.9317	0.3899	2.565	.7	.3	0.4431	0.8965	0.4942	2.023	.7
.4	0.3649	0.9311	0.3919	2.552	.6	.4	0.4446	0.8957	0.4964	2.014	.6
.5	0.3665	0.9304	0.3939	2.539	.5	.5	0.4462	0.8949	0.4986	2.006	.5
.6	0.3681	0.9298	0.3959	2.526	.4	.6	0.4478	0.8942	0.5008	1.997	.4
.7	0.3697	0.9291	0.3979	2.513	.3	.7	0.4493	0.8934	0.5029	1.988	.3
.8	0.3714	0.9285	0.4000	2.500	.2	.8	0.4509	0.8926	0.5051	1.980	.2
.9	0.3730	0.9278	0.4020	2.488	.1	.9	0.4524	0.8918	0.5073	1.971	.1
22.0	0.3746	0.9272	0.4040	2.475	68.0	27.0	0.4540	0.8910	0.5095	1.963	63.0
.1	0.3762	0.9265	0.4061	2.463	.9	.1	0.4555	0.8902	0.5117	1.954	.9
.2	0.3778	0.9259	0.4081	2.450	.8	.2	0.4571	0.8894	0.5139	1.946	.8
.3	0.3795	0.9252	0.4101	2.438	.7	.3	0.4586	0.8886	0.5161	1.937	.7
.4	0.3811	0.9245	0.4122	2.426	.6	.4	0.4602	0.8878	0.5184	1.929	.6
.5	0.3827	0.9239	0.4142	2.414	.5	.5	0.4617	0.8870	0.5206	1.921	.5
.6	0.3843	0.9232	0.4163	2.402	.4	.6	0.4633	0.8862	0.5228	1.913	.4
.7	0.3859	0.9225	0.4183	2.391	.3	.7	0.4648	0.8854	0.5250	1.905	.3
.8	0.3875	0.9219	0.4204	2.379	.2	.8	0.4664	0.8846	0.5272	1.897	.2
.9	0.3891	0.9212	0.4224	2.367	.1	.9	0.4679	0.8838	0.5295	1.889	.1
23.0	0.3907	0.9205	0.4245	2.356	67.0	28.0	0.4695	0.8829	0.5317	1.881	62.0
.1	0.3923	0.9198	0.4265	2.344	.9	.1	0.4710	0.8821	0.5340	1.873	.9
.2	0.3939	0.9191	0.4286	2.333	.8	.2	0.4726	0.8813	0.5362	1.865	.8
.3	0.3955	0.9184	0.4307	2.322	.7	.3	0.4741	0.8805	0.5384	1.857	.7
.4	0.3971	0.9178	0.4327	2.311	.6	.4	0.4756	0.8796	0.5407	1.849	.6
.5	0.3987	0.9171	0.4348	2.300	.5	.5	0.4772	0.8788	0.5430	1.842	.5
.6	0.4003	0.9164	0.4369	2.289	.4	.6	0.4787	0.8780	0.5452	1.834	.4
.7	0.4019	0.9157	0.4390	2.278	.3	.7	0.4802	0.8771	0.5475	1.827	.3
.8	0.4035	0.9150	0.4411	2.267	.2	.8	0.4818	0.8763	0.5498	1.819	.2
.9	0.4051	0.9143	0.4431	2.257	.1	.9	0.4833	0.8755	0.5520	1.811	.1
24.0	0.4067	0.9135	0.4452	2.246	66.0	29.0	0.4848	0.8746	0.5543	1.804	61.0
.1	0.4083	0.9128	0.4473	2.236	.9	.1	0.4863	0.8738	0.5566	1.797	.9
.2	0.4099	0.9121	0.4494	2.225	.8	.2	0.4879	0.8729	0.5589	1.789	.8
.3	0.4115	0.9114	0.4515	2.215	.7	.3	0.4894	0.8721	0.5612	1.782	.7
.4	0.4131	0.9107	0.4536	2.204	.6	.4	0.4909	0.8712	0.5635	1.775	.6
.5	0.4147	0.9100	0.4557	2.194	.5	.5	0.4924	0.8704	0.5658	1.767	.5
.6	0.4163	0.9092	0.4578	2.184	.4	.6	0.4939	0.8695	0.5681	1.760	.4
.7	0.4179	0.9085	0.4599	2.174	.3	.7	0.4955	0.8686	0.5704	1.753	.3
.8	0.4195	0.9078	0.4621	2.164	.2	.8	0.4970	0.8678	0.5727	1.746	.2
.9	0.4210	0.9070	0.4642	2.154	.1	.9	0.4985	0.8669	0.5750	1.739	.1
25.0	0.4226	0.9063	0.4663	2.145	65.0	30.0	0.5000	0.8660	0.5774	1.732	60.0
	Cos θ	Sin θ	Cot θ	Tan θ	Degrees		Cos θ	Sin θ	Cot θ	Tan θ	Degrees

Table 4   A—51

Table 4. Continued

Degrees	Sin θ	Cos θ	Tan θ	Cot θ		Degrees	Sin θ	Cos θ	Tan θ	Cot θ	
30.0	0.5000	0.8660	0.5774	1.732	60.0	35.0	0.5736	0.8192	0.7002	1.428	55.0
.1	0.5015	0.8652	0.5797	1.725	.9	.1	0.5750	0.8181	0.7028	1.423	.9
.2	0.5030	0.8643	0.5820	1.718	.8	.2	0.5764	0.8171	0.7054	1.418	.8
.3	0.5045	0.8634	0.5844	1.711	.7	.3	0.5779	0.8161	0.7080	1.412	.7
.4	0.5060	0.8625	0.5867	1.704	.6	.4	0.5793	0.8151	0.7107	1.407	.6
.5	0.5075	0.8616	0.5890	1.698	.5	.5	0.5807	0.8141	0.7133	1.402	.5
.6	0.5090	0.8607	0.5914	1.691	.4	.6	0.5821	0.8131	0.7159	1.397	.4
.7	0.5105	0.8599	0.5938	1.684	.3	.7	0.5835	0.8121	0.7186	1.392	.3
.8	0.5120	0.8590	0.5961	1.678	.2	.8	0.5850	0.8111	0.7212	1.387	.2
.9	0.5135	0.8581	0.5985	1.671	.1	.9	0.5864	0.8100	0.7239	1.381	.1
31.0	0.5150	0.8572	0.6009	1.664	59.0	36.0	0.5878	0.8090	0.7265	1.376	54.0
.1	0.5165	0.8563	0.6032	1.658	.9	.1	0.5892	0.8080	0.7292	1.371	.9
.2	0.5180	0.8554	0.6056	1.651	.8	.2	0.5906	0.8070	0.7319	1.366	.8
.3	0.5195	0.8545	0.6080	1.645	.7	.3	0.5920	0.8059	0.7346	1.361	.7
.4	0.5210	0.8536	0.6104	1.638	.6	.4	0.5934	0.8049	0.7373	1.356	.6
.5	0.5225	0.8526	0.6128	1.632	.5	.5	0.5948	0.8039	0.7400	1.351	.5
.6	0.5240	0.8517	0.6152	1.625	.4	.6	0.5962	0.8028	0.7427	1.347	.4
.7	0.5255	0.8508	0.6176	1.619	.3	.7	0.5976	0.8018	0.7454	1.342	.3
.8	0.5270	0.8499	0.6200	1.613	.2	.8	0.5990	0.8007	0.7481	1.337	.2
.9	0.5284	0.8490	0.6224	1.607	.1	.9	0.6004	0.7997	0.7508	1.332	.1
32.0	0.5299	0.8480	0.6249	1.600	58.0	37.0	0.6018	0.7986	0.7536	1.327	53.0
.1	0.5314	0.8471	0.6273	1.594	.9	.1	0.6032	0.7976	0.7563	1.322	.9
.2	0.5329	0.8462	0.6297	1.588	.8	.2	0.6046	0.7965	0.7590	1.317	.8
.3	0.5344	0.8453	0.6322	1.582	.7	.3	0.6060	0.7955	0.7618	1.313	.7
.4	0.5358	0.8443	0.6346	1.576	.6	.4	0.6074	0.7944	0.7646	1.308	.6
.5	0.5373	0.8434	0.6371	1.570	.5	.5	0.6088	0.7934	0.7673	1.303	.5
.6	0.5388	0.8425	0.6395	1.564	.4	.6	0.6101	0.7923	0.7701	1.299	.4
.7	0.5402	0.8415	0.6420	1.558	.3	.7	0.6115	0.7912	0.7729	1.294	.3
.8	0.5417	0.8406	0.6445	1.552	.2	.8	0.6129	0.7902	0.7757	1.289	.2
.9	0.5432	0.8396	0.6469	1.546	.1	.9	0.6143	0.7891	0.7785	1.285	.1
33.0	0.5446	0.8387	0.6494	1.540	57.0	38.0	0.6157	0.7880	0.7813	1.280	52.0
.1	0.5461	0.8377	0.6519	1.534	.9	.1	0.6170	0.7869	0.7841	1.275	.9
.2	0.5476	0.8368	0.6544	1.528	.8	.2	0.6184	0.7859	0.7869	1.271	.8
.3	0.5490	0.8358	0.6569	1.522	.7	.3	0.6198	0.7848	0.7898	1.266	.7
.4	0.5505	0.8348	0.6594	1.517	.6	.4	0.6211	0.7837	0.7926	1.262	.6
.5	0.5519	0.8339	0.6619	1.511	.5	.5	0.6225	0.7826	0.7954	1.257	.5
.6	0.5534	0.8329	0.6644	1.505	.4	.6	0.6239	0.7815	0.7983	1.253	.4
.7	0.5548	0.8320	0.6669	1.499	.3	.7	0.6252	0.7804	0.8012	1.248	.3
.8	0.5563	0.8310	0.6694	1.494	.2	.8	0.6266	0.7793	0.8040	1.244	.2
.9	0.5577	0.8300	0.6720	1.488	.1	.9	0.6280	0.7782	0.8069	1.239	.1
34.0	0.5592	0.8290	0.6745	1.483	56.0	39.0	0.6293	0.7771	0.8098	1.235	51.0
.1	0.5606	0.8281	0.6771	1.477	.9	.1	0.6307	0.7760	0.8127	1.230	.9
.2	0.5621	0.8271	0.6796	1.471	.8	.2	0.6320	0.7749	0.8156	1.226	.8
.3	0.5635	0.8261	0.6822	1.466	.7	.3	0.6334	0.7738	0.8185	1.222	.7
.4	0.5650	0.8251	0.6847	1.460	.6	.4	0.6347	0.7727	0.8214	1.217	.6
.5	0.5664	0.8241	0.6873	1.455	.5	.5	0.6361	0.7716	0.8243	1.213	.5
.6	0.5678	0.8231	0.6899	1.450	.4	.6	0.6374	0.7705	0.8273	1.209	.4
.7	0.5693	0.8221	0.6924	1.444	.3	.7	0.6388	0.7694	0.8302	1.205	.3
.8	0.5707	0.8211	0.6950	1.439	.2	.8	0.6401	0.7683	0.8332	1.200	.2
.9	0.5721	0.8202	0.6976	1.433	.1	.9	0.6414	0.7672	0.8361	1.196	.1
35.0	0.5736	0.8192	0.7002	1.428	55.0	40.0	0.6428	0.7660	0.8391	1.192	50.0
	Cos θ	Sin θ	Cot θ	Tan θ	Degrees		Cos θ	Sin θ	Cot θ	Tan θ	Degrees

Table 4. Continued

Degrees	Sin θ	Cos θ	Tan θ	Cot θ	
40.0	0.6428	0.7660	0.8391	1.192	50.0
.1	0.6441	0.7649	0.8421	1.188	.9
.2	0.6455	0.7638	0.8451	1.183	.8
.3	0.6468	0.7627	0.8481	1.179	.7
.4	0.6481	0.7615	0.8511	1.175	.6
.5	0.6494	0.7604	0.8541	1.171	.5
.6	0.6508	0.7593	0.8571	1.167	.4
.7	0.6521	0.7581	0.8601	1.163	.3
.8	0.6534	0.7570	0.8632	1.159	.2
.9	0.6547	0.7559	0.8662	1.154	.1
41.0	0.6561	0.7547	0.8693	1.150	49.0
.1	0.6574	0.7536	0.8724	1.146	.9
.2	0.6587	0.7524	0.8754	1.142	.8
.3	0.6600	0.7513	0.8785	1.138	.7
.4	0.6613	0.7501	0.8816	1.134	.6
.5	0.6626	0.7490	0.8847	1.130	.5
.6	0.6639	0.7478	0.8878	1.126	.4
.7	0.6652	0.7466	0.8910	1.122	.3
.8	0.6665	0.7455	0.8941	1.118	.2
.9	0.6678	0.7443	0.8972	1.115	.1
42.0	0.6691	0.7431	0.9004	1.111	48.0
.1	0.6704	0.7420	0.9036	1.107	.9
.2	0.6717	0.7408	0.9067	1.103	.8
.3	0.6730	0.7396	0.9099	1.099	.7
.4	0.6743	0.7385	0.9131	1.095	.6
.5	0.6756	0.7373	0.9163	1.091	.5
.6	0.6769	0.7361	0.9195	1.087	.4
.7	0.6782	0.7349	0.9228	1.084	.3
.8	0.6794	0.7337	0.9260	1.080	.2
.9	0.6807	0.7325	0.9293	1.076	.1
43.0	0.6820	0.7314	0.9325	1.072	47.0
.1	0.6833	0.7302	0.9358	1.069	.9
.2	0.6845	0.7290	0.9391	1.065	.8
.3	0.6858	0.7278	0.9424	1.061	.7
.4	0.6871	0.7266	0.9457	1.057	.6
.5	0.6884	0.7254	0.9490	1.054	.5
.6	0.6896	0.7242	0.9523	1.050	.4
.7	0.6909	0.7230	0.9556	1.046	.3
.8	0.6921	0.7218	0.9590	1.043	.2
.9	0.6934	0.7206	0.9623	1.039	.1
44.0	0.6947	0.7193	0.9657	1.036	46.0
.1	0.6959	0.7181	0.9691	1.032	.9
.2	0.6972	0.7169	0.9725	1.028	.8
.3	0.6984	0.7157	0.9759	1.025	.7
.4	0.6997	0.7145	0.9793	1.021	.6
.5	0.7009	0.7133	0.9827	1.018	.5
.6	0.7022	0.7120	0.9861	1.014	.4
.7	0.7034	0.7108	0.9896	1.011	.3
.8	0.7046	0.7096	0.9930	1.007	.2
.9	0.7059	0.7083	0.9965	1.003	.1
45.0	0.7071	0.7071	1.0000	1.000	45.0
	Cos θ	Sin θ	Cot θ	Tan θ	Degrees

Table 5   A—53

Table 5. Four-Place Logarithms of Trigonometric Functions
Angle θ in Degrees. Attach -10 to Logarithms Obtained from This Table

Angle θ	log sin θ	log cos θ	log tan θ	log cot θ		Angle θ	log sin θ	log cos θ	log tan θ	log cot θ	
0°00′	No value	10.0000	No value	No value	90°00′	8°00′	9.1436	9.9958	9.1478	10.8522	82°00′
10	7.4637	10.0000	7.4637	12.5363	50	10	9.1525	9.9956	9.1569	10.8431	50
20	7.7648	10.0000	7.7648	12.2352	40	20	9.1612	9.9954	9.1658	10.8342	40
30	7.9408	10.0000	7.9409	12.0591	30	30	9.1697	9.9952	9.1745	10.8255	30
40	8.0658	10.0000	8.0658	11.9342	20	40	9.1781	9.9950	9.1831	10.8169	20
50	8.1627	10.0000	8.1627	11.8373	10	50	9.1863	9.9948	9.1915	10.8085	10
1°00′	8.2419	9.9999	8.2419	11.7581	89°00′	9°00′	9.1943	9.9946	9.1997	10.8003	81°00′
10	8.3088	9.9999	8.3089	11.6911	50	10	9.2022	9.9944	9.2078	10.7922	50
20	8.3668	9.9999	8.3669	11.6331	40	20	9.2100	9.9942	9.2158	10.7842	40
30	8.4179	9.9999	8.4181	11.5819	30	30	9.2176	9.9940	9.2236	10.7764	30
40	8.4637	9.9998	8.4638	11.5362	20	40	9.2251	9.9938	9.2313	10.7687	20
50	8.5050	9.9998	8.5053	11.4947	10	50	9.2324	9.9936	9.2389	10.7611	10
2°00′	8.5428	9.9997	8.5431	11.4569	88°00′	10°00′	9.2397	9.9934	9.2463	10.7537	80°00′
10	8.5776	9.9997	8.5779	11.4221	50	10	9.2468	9.9931	9.2536	10.7464	50
20	8.6097	9.9996	8.6101	11.3899	40	20	9.2538	9.9929	9.2609	10.7391	40
30	8.6397	9.9996	8.6401	11.3599	30	30	9.2606	9.9927	9.2680	10.7320	30
40	8.6677	9.9995	8.6682	11.3318	20	40	9.2674	9.9924	9.2750	10.7250	20
50	8.6940	9.9995	8.6945	11.3055	10	50	9.2740	9.9922	9.2819	10.7181	10
3°00′	8.7188	9.9994	8.7194	11.2806	87°00′	11°00′	9.2806	9.9919	9.2887	10.7113	79°00′
10	8.7423	9.9993	8.7429	11.2571	50	10	9.2870	9.9917	9.2953	10.7047	50
20	8.7645	9.9993	8.7652	11.2348	40	20	9.2934	9.9914	9.3020	10.6980	40
30	8.7857	9.9992	8.7865	11.2135	30	30	9.2997	9.9912	9.3085	10.6915	30
40	8.8059	9.9991	8.8067	11.1933	20	40	9.3058	9.9909	9.3149	10.6851	20
50	8.8251	9.9990	8.8261	11.1739	10	50	9.3119	9.9907	9.3212	10.6788	10
4°00′	8.8436	9.9989	8.8446	11.1554	86°00′	12°00′	9.3179	9.9904	9.3275	10.6725	78°00′
10	8.8613	9.9989	8.8624	11.1376	50	10	9.3238	9.9901	9.3336	10.6664	50
20	8.8783	9.9988	8.8795	11.1205	40	20	9.3296	9.9899	9.3397	10.6603	40
30	8.8946	9.9987	8.8960	11.1040	30	30	9.3353	9.9896	9.3458	10.6542	30
40	8.9104	9.9986	8.9118	11.0882	20	40	9.3410	9.9893	9.3517	10.6483	20
50	8.9256	9.9985	8.9272	11.0728	10	50	9.3466	9.9890	9.3576	10.6424	10
5°00′	8.9403	9.9983	8.9420	11.0580	85°00′	13°00′	9.3521	9.9887	9.3634	10.6366	77°00′
10	8.9545	9.9982	8.9563	11.0437	50	10	9.3575	9.9884	9.3691	10.6309	50
20	8.9682	9.9981	8.9701	11.0299	40	20	9.3629	9.9881	9.3748	10.6252	40
30	8.9816	9.9980	8.9836	11.0164	30	30	9.3682	9.9878	9.3804	10.6196	30
40	8.9945	9.9979	8.9966	11.0034	20	40	9.3734	9.9875	9.3859	10.6141	20
50	9.0070	9.9977	9.0093	10.9907	10	50	9.3786	9.9872	9.3914	10.6086	10
6°00′	9.0192	9.9976	9.0216	10.9784	84°00′	14°00′	9.3837	9.9869	9.3968	10.6032	76°00′
10	9.0311	9.9975	9.0336	10.9664	50	10	9.3887	9.9866	9.4021	10.5979	50
20	9.0426	9.9973	9.0453	10.9547	40	20	9.3937	9.9863	9.4074	10.5926	40
30	9.0539	9.9972	9.0567	10.9433	30	30	9.3986	9.9859	9.4127	10.5873	30
40	9.0648	9.9971	9.0678	10.9322	20	40	9.4035	9.9856	9.4178	10.5822	20
50	9.0755	9.9969	9.0786	10.9214	10	50	9.4083	9.9853	9.4230	10.5770	10
7°00′	9.0859	9.9968	9.0891	10.9109	83°00′	15°00′	9.4130	9.9849	9.4281	10.5719	75°00′
10	9.0961	9.9966	9.0995	10.9005	50	10	9.4177	9.9846	9.4331	10.5669	50
20	9.1060	9.9964	9.1096	10.8904	40	20	9.4223	9.9843	9.4381	10.5619	40
30	9.1157	9.9963	9.1194	10.8806	30	30	9.4269	9.9839	9.4430	10.5570	30
40	9.1252	9.9961	9.1291	10.8709	20	40	9.4314	9.9836	9.4479	10.5521	20
50	9.1345	9.9959	9.1385	10.8615	10	50	9.4359	9.9832	9.4527	10.5473	10
8°00′	9.1436	9.9958	9.1478	10.8522	82°00′	16°00′	9.4403	9.9828	9.4575	10.5425	74°00′
	log cos θ	log sin θ	log cot θ	log tan θ	Angle θ		log cos θ	log sin θ	log cot θ	log tan θ	Angle θ

Table 5. Continued

Angle θ	log sin θ	log cos θ	log tan θ	log cot θ		Angle θ	log sin θ	log cos θ	log tan θ	log cot θ	
16°00′	9.4403	9.9828	9.4575	10.5425	74°00′	24°00′	9.6093	9.9607	9.6486	10.3514	66°00′
10	9.4447	9.9825	9.4622	10.5378	50	10	9.6121	9.9602	9.6520	10.3480	50
20	9.4491	9.9821	9.4669	10.5331	40	20	9.6149	9.9596	9.6553	10.3447	40
30	9.4533	9.9817	9.4716	10.5284	30	30	9.6177	9.9590	9.6587	10.3413	30
40	9.4576	9.9814	9.4762	10.5238	20	40	9.6205	9.9584	9.6620	10.3380	20
50	9.4618	9.9810	9.4808	10.5192	10	50	9.6232	9.9579	9.6654	10.3346	10
17°00′	9.4659	9.9806	9.4853	10.5147	73°00′	25°00′	9.6259	9.9573	9.6687	10.3313	65°00′
10	9.4700	9.9802	9.4898	10.5102	50	10	9.6286	9.9567	9.6720	10.3280	50
20	9.4741	9.9798	9.4943	10.5057	40	20	9.6313	9.9561	9.6752	10.3248	40
30	9.4781	9.9794	9.4987	10.5013	30	30	9.6340	9.9555	9.6785	10.3215	30
40	9.4821	9.9790	9.5031	10.4969	20	40	9.6366	9.9549	9.6817	10.3183	20
50	9.4861	9.9786	9.5075	10.4925	10	50	9.6392	9.9543	9.6850	10.3150	10
18°00′	9.4900	9.9782	9.5118	10.4882	72°00′	26°00′	9.6418	9.9537	9.6882	10.3118	64°00′
10	9.4939	9.9778	9.5161	10.4839	50	10	9.6444	9.9530	9.6914	10.3086	50
20	9.4977	9.9774	9.5203	10.4797	40	20	9.6470	9.9524	9.6946	10.3054	40
30	9.5015	9.9770	9.5245	10.4755	30	30	9.6495	9.9518	9.6977	10.3023	30
40	9.5052	9.9765	9.5287	10.4713	20	40	9.6521	9.9512	9.7009	10.2991	20
50	9.5090	9.9761	9.5329	10.4671	10	50	9.6546	9.9505	9.7040	10.2960	10
19°00′	9.5126	9.9757	9.5370	10.4630	71°00′	27°00′	9.6570	9.9499	9.7072	10.2928	63°00′
10	9.5163	9.9752	9.5411	10.4589	50	10	9.6595	9.9492	9.7103	10.2897	50
20	9.5199	9.9748	9.5451	10.4549	40	20	9.6620	9.9486	9.7134	10.2866	40
30	9.5235	9.9743	9.5491	10.4509	30	30	9.6644	9.9479	9.7165	10.2835	30
40	9.5270	9.9739	9.5531	10.4469	20	40	9.6668	9.9473	9.7196	10.2804	20
50	9.5306	9.9734	9.5571	10.4429	10	50	9.6692	9.9466	9.7226	10.2774	10
20°00′	9.5341	9.9730	9.5611	10.4389	70°00′	28°00′	9.6716	9.9459	9.7257	10.2743	62°00′
10	9.5375	9.9725	9.5650	10.4350	50	10	9.6740	9.9453	9.7287	10.2713	50
20	9.5409	9.9721	9.5689	10.4311	40	20	9.6763	9.9446	9.7317	10.2683	40
30	9.5443	9.9716	9.5727	10.4273	30	30	9.6787	9.9439	9.7348	10.2652	30
40	9.5477	9.9711	9.5766	10.4234	20	40	9.6810	9.9432	9.7378	10.2622	20
50	9.5510	9.9706	9.5804	10.4196	10	50	9.6833	9.9425	9.7408	10.2592	10
21°00′	9.5543	9.9702	9.5842	10.4158	69°00′	29°00′	9.6856	9.9418	9.7438	10.2562	61°00′
10	9.5576	9.9697	9.5879	10.4121	50	10	9.6878	9.9411	9.7467	10.2533	50
20	9.5609	9.9692	9.5917	10.4083	40	20	9.6901	9.9404	9.7497	10.2503	40
30	9.5641	9.9687	9.5954	10.4046	30	30	9.6923	9.9397	9.7526	10.2474	30
40	9.5673	9.9682	9.5991	10.4009	20	40	9.6946	9.9390	9.7556	10.2444	20
50	9.5704	9.9677	9.6028	10.3972	10	50	9.6968	9.9383	9.7585	10.2415	10
22°00′	9.5736	9.9672	9.6064	10.3936	68°00′	30°00′	9.6990	9.9375	9.7614	10.2386	60°00′
10	9.5767	9.9667	9.6100	10.3900	50	10	9.7012	9.9368	9.7644	10.2356	50
20	9.5798	9.9661	9.6136	10.3864	40	20	9.7033	9.9361	9.7673	10.2327	40
30	9.5828	9.9656	9.6172	10.3828	30	30	9.7055	9.9353	9.7701	10.2299	30
40	9.5859	9.9651	9.6208	10.3792	20	40	9.7076	9.9346	9.7730	10.2270	20
50	9.5889	9.9646	9.6243	10.3757	10	50	9.7097	9.9338	9.7759	10.2241	10
23°00′	9.5919	9.9640	9.6279	10.3721	67°00′	31°00′	9.7118	9.9331	9.7788	10.2212	59°00′
10	9.5948	9.9635	9.6314	10.3686	50	10	9.7139	9.9323	9.7816	10.2184	50
20	9.5978	9.9629	9.6348	10.3652	40	20	9.7160	9.9315	9.7845	10.2155	40
30	9.6007	9.9624	9.6383	10.3617	30	30	9.7181	9.9308	9.7873	10.2127	30
40	9.6036	9.9618	9.6417	10.3583	20	40	9.7201	9.9300	9.7902	10.2098	20
50	9.6065	9.9613	9.6452	10.3548	10	50	9.7222	9.9292	9.7930	10.2070	10
24°00′	9.6093	9.9607	9.6486	10.3514	66°00′	32°00′	9.7242	9.9284	9.7958	10.2042	58°00′
	log cos θ	log sin θ	log cot θ	log tan θ	Angle θ		log cos θ	log sin θ	log cot θ	log tan θ	Angle θ

Table 5   A—55

Table 5. Continued

Angle θ	log sin θ	log cos θ	log tan θ	log cot θ		Angle θ	log sin θ	log cos θ	log tan θ	log cot θ	
32°00′	9.7242	9.9284	9.7958	10.2042	58°00′	39°00′	9.7989	9.8905	9.9084	10.0916	51°00′
10	9.7262	9.9276	9.7986	10.2014	50	10	9.8004	9.8895	9.9110	10.0890	50
20	9.7282	9.9268	9.8014	10.1986	40	20	9.8020	9.8884	9.9135	10.0865	40
30	9.7302	9.9260	9.8042	10.1958	30	30	9.8035	9.8874	9.9161	10.0839	30
40	9.7322	9.9252	9.8070	10.1930	20	40	9.8050	9.8864	9.9187	10.0813	20
50	9.7342	9.9244	9.8097	10.1903	10	50	9.8066	9.8853	9.9212	10.0788	10
33°00′	9.7361	9.9236	9.8125	10.1875	57°00′	40°00′	9.8081	9.8843	9.9238	10.0762	50°00′
10	9.7380	9.9228	9.8153	10.1847	50	10	9.8096	9.8832	9.9264	10.0736	50
20	9.7400	9.9219	9.8180	10.1820	40	20	9.8111	9.8821	9.9289	10.0711	40
30	9.7419	9.9211	9.8208	10.1792	30	30	9.8125	9.8810	9.9315	10.0685	30
40	9.7438	9.9203	9.8235	10.1765	20	40	9.8140	9.8800	9.9341	10.0659	20
50	9.7457	9.9194	9.8263	10.1737	10	50	9.8155	9.8789	9.9366	10.0634	10
34°00′	9.7476	9.9186	9.8290	10.1710	56°00′	41°00′	9.8169	9.8778	9.9392	10.0608	49°00′
10	9.7494	9.9177	9.8317	10.1683	50	10	9.8184	9.8767	9.9417	10.0583	50
20	9.7513	9.9169	9.8344	10.1656	40	20	9.8198	9.8756	9.9443	10.0557	40
30	9.7531	9.9160	9.8371	10.1629	30	30	9.8213	9.8745	9.9468	10.0532	30
40	9.7550	9.9151	9.8398	10.1602	20	40	9.8227	9.8733	9.9494	10.0506	20
50	9.7568	9.9142	9.8425	10.1575	10	50	9.8241	9.8722	9.9519	10.0481	10
35°00′	9.7586	9.9134	9.8452	10.1548	55°00′	42°00′	9.8255	9.8711	9.9544	10.0456	48°00′
10	9.7604	9.9125	9.8479	10.1521	50	10	9.8269	9.8699	9.9570	10.0430	50
20	9.7622	9.9116	9.8506	10.1494	40	20	9.8283	9.8688	9.9595	10.0405	40
30	9.7640	9.9107	9.8533	10.1467	30	30	9.8297	9.8676	9.9621	10.0379	30
40	9.7657	9.9098	9.8559	10.1441	20	40	9.8311	9.8665	9.9646	10.0354	20
50	9.7675	9.9089	9.8586	10.1414	10	50	9.8324	9.8653	9.9671	10.0329	10
36°00′	9.7692	9.9080	9.8613	10.1387	54°00′	43°00′	9.8338	9.8641	9.9697	10.0303	47°00′
10	9.7710	9.9070	9.8639	10.1361	50	10	9.8351	9.8629	9.9722	10.0278	50
20	9.7727	9.9061	9.8666	10.1334	40	20	9.8365	9.8618	9.9747	10.0253	40
30	9.7744	9.9052	9.8692	10.1308	30	30	9.8378	9.8606	9.9772	10.0228	30
40	9.7761	9.9042	9.8718	10.1282	20	40	9.8391	9.8594	9.9798	10.0202	20
50	9.7778	9.9033	9.8745	10.1255	10	50	9.8405	9.8582	9.9823	10.0177	10
37°00′	9.7795	9.9023	9.8771	10.1229	53°00′	44°00′	9.8418	9.8569	9.9848	10.0152	46°00′
10	9.7811	9.9014	9.8797	10.1203	50	10	9.8431	9.8557	9.9874	10.0126	50
20	9.7828	9.9004	9.8824	10.1176	40	20	9.8444	9.8545	9.9899	10.0101	40
30	9.7844	9.8995	9.8850	10.1150	30	30	9.8457	9.8532	9.9924	10.0076	30
40	9.7861	9.8985	9.8876	10.1124	20	40	9.8469	9.8520	9.9949	10.0051	20
50	9.7877	9.8975	9.8902	10.1098	10	50	9.8482	9.8507	9.9975	10.0025	10
38°00′	9.7893	9.8965	9.8928	10.1072	52°00′	45°00′	9.8495	9.8495	10.0000	10.0000	45°00′
10	9.7910	9.8955	9.8954	10.1046	50						
20	9.7926	9.8945	9.8980	10.1020	40						
30	9.7941	9.8935	9.9006	10.0994	30						
40	9.7957	9.8925	9.9032	10.0968	20						
50	9.7973	9.8915	9.9058	10.0942	10						
39°00′	9.7989	9.8905	9.9084	10.0916	51°00′						
	log cos θ	log sin θ	log cot θ	log tan θ	Angle θ		log cos θ	log sin θ	log cot θ	log tan θ	Angle θ

Table 6. Natural Logarithms of Numbers

n	$\ln n$	n	$\ln n$	n	$\ln n$
0.0	— *	4.5	1.5041	9.0	2.1972
0.1	7.6974	4.6	1.5261	9.1	2.2083
0.2	8.3906	4.7	1.5476	9.2	2.2192
0.3	8.7960	4.8	1.5686	9.3	2.2300
0.4	9.0837	4.9	1.5892	9.4	2.2407
0.5	9.3069	5.0	1.6094	9.5	2.2513
0.6	9.4892	5.1	1.6292	9.6	2.2618
0.7	9.6433	5.2	1.6487	9.7	2.2721
0.8	9.7769	5.3	1.6677	9.8	2.2824
0.9	9.8946	5.4	1.6864	9.9	2.2925
1.0	0.0000	5.5	1.7047	10	2.3026
1.1	0.0953	5.6	1.7228	11	2.3979
1.2	0.1823	5.7	1.7405	12	2.4849
1.3	0.2624	5.8	1.7579	13	2.5649
1.4	0.3365	5.9	1.7750	14	2.6391
1.5	0.4055	6.0	1.7918	15	2.7081
1.6	0.4700	6.1	1.8083	16	2.7726
1.7	0.5306	6.2	1.8245	17	2.8332
1.8	0.5878	6.3	1.8405	18	2.8904
1.9	0.6419	6.4	1.8563	19	2.9444
2.0	0.6931	6.5	1.8718	20	2.9957
2.1	0.7419	6.6	1.8871	25	3.2189
2.2	0.7885	6.7	1.9021	30	3.4012
2.3	0.8329	6.8	1.9169	35	3.5553
2.4	0.8755	6.9	1.9315	40	3.6889
2.5	0.9163	7.0	1.9459	45	3.8067
2.6	0.9555	7.1	1.9601	50	3.9120
2.7	0.9933	7.2	1.9741	55	4.0073
2.8	1.0296	7.3	1.9879	60	4.0943
2.9	1.0647	7.4	2.0015	65	4.1744
3.0	1.0986	7.5	2.0149	70	4.2485
3.1	1.1314	7.6	2.0281	75	4.3175
3.2	1.1632	7.7	2.0412	80	4.3820
3.3	1.1939	7.8	2.0541	85	4.4427
3.4	1.2238	7.9	2.0669	90	4.4998
3.5	1.2528	8.0	2.0794	95	4.5539
3.6	1.2809	8.1	2.0919	100	4.6052
3.7	1.3083	8.2	2.1041		
3.8	1.3350	8.3	2.1163		
3.9	1.3610	8.4	2.1282		
4.0	1.3863	8.5	2.1401	$\ln 10$	2.3026
4.1	1.4110	8.6	2.1518	$2 \ln 10$	4.6052
4.2	1.4351	8.7	2.1633	$3 \ln 10$	6.9078
4.3	1.4586	8.8	2.1748	$4 \ln 10$	9.2103
4.4	1.4816	8.9	2.1861	$5 \ln 10$	11.5129

*Attach -10 to these logarithms.

Table 7   A—57

Table 7. Exponential Functions

x	e^x	e^{-x}	x	e^x	e^{-x}
0.00	1.0000	1.0000	2.5	12.182	0.0821
0.05	1.0513	0.9512	2.6	13.464	0.0743
0.10	1.1052	0.9048	2.7	14.880	0.0672
0.15	1.1618	0.8607	2.8	16.445	0.0608
0.20	1.2214	0.8187	2.9	18.174	0.0550
0.25	1.2840	0.7788	3.0	20.086	0.0498
0.30	1.3499	0.7408	3.1	22.198	0.0450
0.35	1.4191	0.7047	3.2	24.533	0.0408
0.40	1.4918	0.6703	3.3	27.113	0.0369
0.45	1.5683	0.6376	3.4	29.964	0.0334
0.50	1.6487	0.6065	3.5	33.115	0.0302
0.55	1.7333	0.5769	3.6	36.598	0.0273
0.60	1.8221	0.5488	3.7	40.447	0.0247
0.65	1.9155	0.5220	3.8	44.701	0.0224
0.70	2.0138	0.4966	3.9	49.402	0.0202
0.75	2.1170	0.4724	4.0	54.598	0.0183
0.80	2.2255	0.4493	4.1	60.340	0.0166
0.85	2.3369	0.4274	4.2	66.686	0.0150
0.90	2.4596	0.4066	4.3	73.700	0.0136
0.95	2.5857	0.3867	4.4	81.451	0.0123
1.0	2.7183	0.3679	4.5	90.017	0.0111
1.1	3.0042	0.3329	4.6	99.484	0.0101
1.2	3.3201	0.3012	4.7	109.95	0.0091
1.3	3.6693	0.2725	4.8	121.51	0.0082
1.4	4.0552	0.2466	4.9	134.29	0.0074
1.5	4.4817	0.2231	5	148.41	0.0067
1.6	4.9530	0.2019	6	403.43	0.0025
1.7	5.4739	0.1827	7	1096.6	0.0009
1.8	6.0496	0.1653	8	2981.0	0.0003
1.9	6.6859	0.1496	9	8103.1	0.0001
2.0	7.3891	0.1353	10	22026	0.00005
2.1	8.1662	0.1225			
2.2	9.0250	0.1108			
2.3	9.9742	0.1003			
2.4	11.023	0.0907			

Answers to Odd-numbered Exercises

Exercises 1–1, p. 5

1. integer, rational, real; irrational, real   3. imaginary; irrational, real   5. $3, \dfrac{7}{2}$ 7. $\dfrac{6}{7}, \sqrt{3}$

9. $6 < 8$ 11. $\pi > 1$ 13. $-4 < -3$ 15. $-\dfrac{1}{3} > -\dfrac{1}{2}$ 17. $\dfrac{1}{3}, -\dfrac{1}{2}$ 19. $-\dfrac{\pi}{5}, \dfrac{1}{x}$

21.   23.

25. $-18, -|-3|, -1, \sqrt{5}, \pi, |-8|, 9$ 27. $\dfrac{22}{7} = 3.1429$ 29. (a) to right of origin, (b) to left of -4

31. P, V variables; c constant   33. Yes

Exercises 1–2, 1–3, p. 10

1. 11   3. -11 5. 9   7. -3 9. -24 11. 35   13. -3 15. 20   17. 40   19. -1
21. 9   23. undefined   25. 20   27. -5 29. -9 31. 24   33. -6 35. 3
37. commutative law of multiplication   39. distributive law   41. associative law of addition
43. associative law of multiplication   45. positive   47. No; $6 - 2 \neq 2 - 6$

Exercises 1–4, p. 14

1. x^7 3. $2b^6$ 5. m^2 7. $\dfrac{1}{n^4}$ 9. a^8 11. t^{20} 13. $8n^3$ 15. a^2x^8 17. $\dfrac{8}{b^3}$ 19. $\dfrac{x^8}{16}$

21. 1   23. 3   25. $\dfrac{1}{6}$ 27. s^2 29. $-t^{14}$ 31. $64x^{12}$ 33. 1   35. b^2 37. $\dfrac{a}{x^2}$ 39. $\dfrac{x^3}{64a^3}$

41. $64g^2s^6$ 43. $\dfrac{5a}{n}$ 45. -53 47. -10 49. $\dfrac{-wLx^3}{12EI}$

Exercises 1–5, p. 17

1. 45,000   3. 0.00201   5. 3.23   7. 18.6   9. 4×10^4 11. 8.7×10^{-3} 13. 6.89×10^0
15. 6.3×10^{-2} 17. 2.04×10^{14} 19. 4.85×10^9 21. 9.77×10^6 23. 3.66×10^5
25. 2.25×10^4 lb/in.^{2} 27. 0.0000000000016 W   29. 4500 Ω 31. 1.1×10^{-5} ft
33. 0.00000000000000000000000167 g   35. 8.64×10^5 mi   37. 2.59×10^{10} cm^2
39. $6.03 \times 10^{-3} \, \Omega = 6.03$ mΩ

Exercises 1–6, p. 20

1. 5   3. -11 5. 5   7. -6 9. $3\sqrt{2}$ 11. $2\sqrt{3}$ 13. $3j$ 15. $2\sqrt{3}j$ 17. 5   19. 31
21. $8\sqrt{3}$ 23. 7   25. 20 m   27. No; true for $a \geq 0$

Exercises 1–7, p. 23

1. $8x$ 3. $4x + y$ 5. $a + c - e$ 7. $-a^2b - a^2b^2$ 9. $-v + 5x - 4$ 11. $5a - 5$
13. $-5a + 2$ 15. $7r - 2s$ 17. $19c - 50$ 19. $3n - 9$ 21. $-2t^2 + 18$ 23. $6a$
25. $2a\sqrt{xy} + 1$ 27. $4c - 6$ 29. $8p - 5q$ 31. $-4x^2 + 22$ 33. $R + 1$ 35. $3x - 395$

Exercises 1–8, p. 25

1. a^3x 3. $-a^2c^3x^3$ 5. $-8a^3x^5$ 7. $2a^4x$ 9. $a^2x + a^2y$ 11. $-3s^3 + 15st$
13. $5m^3n + 15m^2n$ 15. $3x^2 - 3xy + 6x$ 17. $a^2b^2c^5 - ab^3c^5 - a^2b^3c^4$ 19. $acx^4 + acx^3y^3$
21. $x^2 + 2x - 15$ 23. $2x^2 + 9x - 5$ 25. $6a^2 - 7ab + 2b^2$ 27. $x^3 + 2x^2 - 8x$
29. $x^3 - 2x^2 - x + 2$ 31. $x^5 - x^4 - 6x^3 + 4x^2 + 8x$ 33. $2x^3 + 6x^2 - 8x$ 35. $4x^2 - 20x + 25$
37. $x^2 + 6ax + 9a^2$ 39. $x^2y^2z^2 - 4xyz + 4$ 41. $-x^3 + 2x^2 + 5x - 6$ 43. $6x^4 + 21x^3 + 12x^2 - 12x$
45. $8000 - 5x^2$ 47. $wl^4 - 2wl^2x^2 + wx^4$

Exercises 1–9, p. 27

1. $-4x^2y$ 3. $4t^4/r^2$ 5. $4x^2$ 7. $-6a$ 9. $a^2 + 4y$ 11. $t - 2rt^2$ 13. $q + 2p - 4q^3$

15. $\dfrac{2L}{R} - R$ 17. $\dfrac{1}{3a} - \dfrac{2b}{3a} + \dfrac{a}{b}$ 19. $x^2 + a$ 21. $x - 1$ 23. $4x^2 - x - 1, R = -3$

25. $x^2 + x - 6$ 27. $2x^2 + 4x + 2, R = 4x + 4$ 29. $x^2 - 2x + 4$ 31. $x - y$ 33. $V^2 - \dfrac{aV}{RT} + \dfrac{ab}{RT}$

35. $\dfrac{1}{R_1} + \dfrac{1}{R_2} + \dfrac{1}{R_3}$

Exercises 1–10, p. 31

1. 9 3. -1 5. 10 7. 5 9. -3 11. 1 13. $-\dfrac{7}{2}$ 15. 8 17. $\dfrac{10}{3}$ 19. $-\dfrac{13}{3}$

21. 2 23. 0 25. True for all values of x, identity   27. Left side 2 greater than right side for all values of x

Exercises 1–11, p. 35

1. $\dfrac{b}{a}$ 3. $\dfrac{m-1}{4}$ 5. $\dfrac{c+6}{a}$ 7. $2a + 8$ 9. $\dfrac{E}{I}$ 11. $\dfrac{M}{Afj}$ 13. $\dfrac{v_0 - v}{t}$ 15. $\dfrac{a + PV^2}{V}$

17. $\dfrac{l - a + d}{d}$ 19. $\dfrac{L - 2d - \pi r_2}{\pi}$ 21. $\dfrac{5F - 160}{9}$ 23. $\dfrac{wL}{R(w + L)}$ 25. \$5200, \$2600

27. 2 A, 4 A, 6 A   29. 6.5 ft   31. 36 in., 54 in.   33. 6 h after second car leaves   35. 6 L

Exercises for Chapter 1, p. 36

1. -10 3. -20 5. 2 7. -25 9. -4 11. 5 13. $4r^2t^4$ 15. $\dfrac{6m^2}{nt^2}$ 17. $\dfrac{z^6}{y^2}$ 19. $\dfrac{8t^3}{s^2}$

21. $3\sqrt{5}$ 23. $2\sqrt{5}j$ 25. $-a - 2ab$ 27. $5xy + 3$ 29. $2x^2 + 9x - 5$ 31. $hk - 3h^2k^4$
33. $7a - 6b$ 35. $13xy - 10z$ 37. $2x^3 - x^2 - 7x - 3$ 39. $-3x^2y + 24xy^2 - 48y^3$

41. $-9p^2 + 3pq + 18p^2q$ 43. $\dfrac{6q}{p} - 2 + \dfrac{3q^4}{p^3}$ 45. $x^2 - 2x + 3$ 47. $4x^3 - 2x^2 + 6x, R = -1$

49. $15r - 3s - 3t$ 51. $y^2 + 5y - 1, R = 4$ 53. 4 55. -5 57. $-\dfrac{7}{3}$ 59. 3

61. 2.5×10^4 mi/h   63. 176,000,000,000 C/kg   65. 2×10^{-7} in.   67. 0.000018 Pa·s   69. $\dfrac{5a - 2}{3}$

71. $\dfrac{4 - 2n}{3}$ 73. ϕ/B 75. $\dfrac{I - P}{Pr}$ 77. $\dfrac{nE - Ir}{In}$ 79. $\dfrac{D_p(N + 2)}{N}$ 81. $\dfrac{L - L_0}{L_0(t_2 - t_1)}$

83. $\dfrac{2S - n^2d + nd}{2n}$ 85. $12x - 2x^2$ 87. $252T_f - 6250$

89. 450 kg to carbon dioxide, 50 kg to carbon monoxide   91. \$15, \$5   93. after 7.5 h

Exercises 2–1, p. 44

1. $A = \pi r^2$ 3. $c = 2\pi r$ 5. $A = 5l$ 7. $A = s^2; s = \sqrt{A}$ 9. $w = 3000 - 10t$ 11. $I = 8t$

13. $3, -1$ 15. $11, -7$ 17. $-18, 70$ 19. $\dfrac{5}{2}, -\dfrac{1}{2}$ 21. $\dfrac{1}{4}a + \dfrac{1}{2}a^2, 0$

23. $3s^2 + s + 6, 12s^2 - 2s + 6$ 25. Square the value of the independent variable and add 2.
27. Cube the value of the independent variable and subtract this value from 6 times the value of the independent variable.

29. $y \neq 1$ 31. $y \geq 1$ 33. 54π cm^3 35. $\dfrac{39}{5}$ 37. $\dfrac{1}{16}p^2 + \dfrac{(60 - p)^2}{4\pi}$

39. $0.006T^2 + 2.8T + 0.012hT + 2.8h + 0.006h^2$

Exercises 2–2, p. 47

1. $(2, 1), (-1, 2), (-2, -3)$ 3.   5. Isosceles triangle   7. $(5,4)$

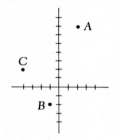

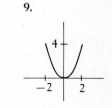

9. On a line parallel to the y-axis, one unit to the right
11. On a line bisecting the first and third quadrants
13. 0   15. To the right of the y-axis   17. Fourth quadrant   19. First, third

Exercises 2–3, p. 52

1.   3.   5.   7.   9.

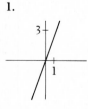   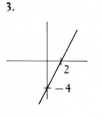   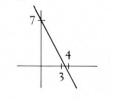   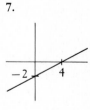   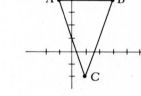

11.   13.   15.   17.   19.

    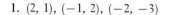   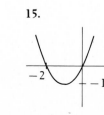   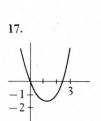

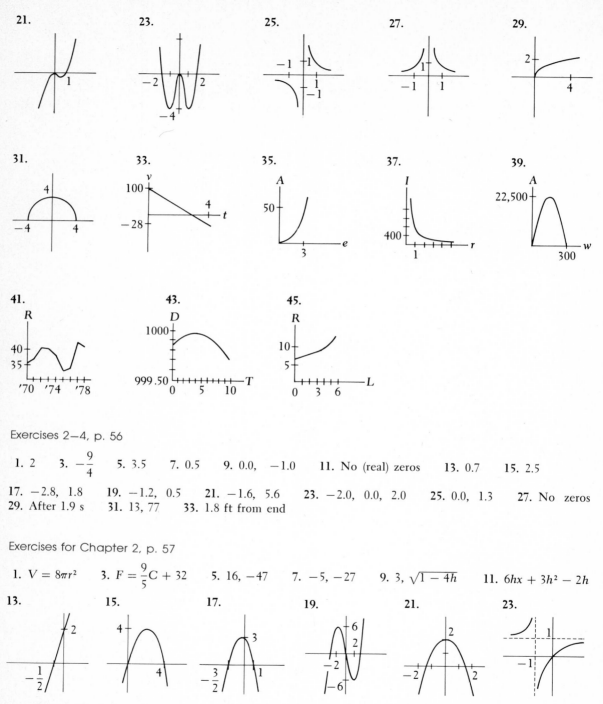

21.   **23.**   **25.**   **27.**   **29.**

31.   **33.**   **35.**   **37.**   **39.**

41.   **43.**   **45.**

Exercises 2—4, p. 56

1. 2   **3.** $-\dfrac{9}{4}$ **5.** 3.5   **7.** 0.5   **9.** 0.0, -1.0 **11.** No (real) zeros   **13.** 0.7   **15.** 2.5

17. -2.8, 1.8   **19.** -1.2, 0.5   **21.** -1.6, 5.6   **23.** -2.0, 0.0, 2.0   **25.** 0.0, 1.3   **27.** No zeros
29. After 1.9 s   **31.** 13, 77   **33.** 1.8 ft from end

Exercises for Chapter 2, p. 57

1. $V = 8\pi r^2$ **3.** $F = \dfrac{9}{5}C + 32$ **5.** 16, -47 **7.** -5, -27 **9.** 3, $\sqrt{1 - 4h}$ **11.** $6hx + 3h^2 - 2h$

13.   **15.**   **17.**   **19.**   **21.**   **23.**

25. -0.5 **27.** 0, 4   **29.** -1.5, 1.0   **31.** -2.4, 0.0, 2.4   **33.** -1.2, 1.2   **35.** 0   **37.** 0.4
39. 0.2, 5.8   **41.** 1.3   **43.** -0.7, 0.7   **45.** On a line in the first quadrant, one unit to the right of y-axis
47. 19

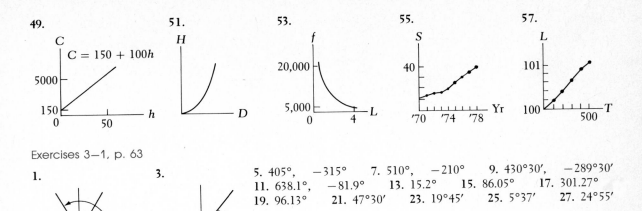

49. $C = 150 + 100h$ **51.** **53.** **55.** **57.**

Exercises 3—1, p. 63

1. **3.**

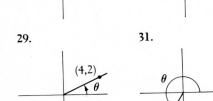

5. 405°, −315°   **7.** 510°, −210°   **9.** 430°30′, −289°30′
11. 638.1°, −81.9°   **13.** 15.2°   **15.** 86.05°   **17.** 301.27°
19. 96.13°   **21.** 47°30′   **23.** 19°45′   **25.** 5°37′   **27.** 24°55′

29. **31.**

Exercises 3—2, p. 65

1. $\sin \theta = \dfrac{3}{5}$, $\cos \theta = \dfrac{4}{5}$, $\tan \theta = \dfrac{3}{4}$, $\cot \theta = \dfrac{4}{3}$, $\sec \theta = \dfrac{5}{4}$, $\csc \theta = \dfrac{5}{3}$

3. $\sin \theta = \dfrac{8}{17}$, $\cos \theta = \dfrac{15}{17}$, $\tan \theta = \dfrac{8}{15}$, $\cot \theta = \dfrac{15}{8}$, $\sec \theta = \dfrac{17}{15}$, $\csc \theta = \dfrac{17}{8}$

5. $\sin \theta = \dfrac{\sqrt{15}}{4}$, $\cos \theta = \dfrac{1}{4}$, $\tan \theta = \sqrt{15}$, $\cot \theta = \dfrac{1}{\sqrt{15}}$, $\sec \theta = 4$, $\csc \theta = \dfrac{4}{\sqrt{15}}$

7. $\sin \theta = \dfrac{5}{\sqrt{29}}$, $\cos \theta = \dfrac{2}{\sqrt{29}}$, $\tan \theta = \dfrac{5}{2}$, $\cot \theta = \dfrac{2}{5}$, $\sec \theta = \dfrac{\sqrt{29}}{2}$, $\csc \theta = \dfrac{\sqrt{29}}{5}$

9. $\dfrac{1}{\sqrt{2}}$, $\sqrt{2}$ **11.** $\dfrac{\sqrt{5}}{2}$, $\dfrac{2}{\sqrt{5}}$ **13.** $\dfrac{\sqrt{51}}{7}$, $\dfrac{10}{7}$ **15.** $\dfrac{1}{\sqrt{17}}$, $\dfrac{\sqrt{17}}{4}$ **17.** $\sin \theta = \dfrac{4}{5}$, $\tan \theta = \dfrac{4}{3}$

19. $\tan \theta = \dfrac{1}{2}$, $\sec \theta = \dfrac{\sqrt{5}}{2}$ **21.** $\sec \theta$, $\tan \theta$

Exercises 3—3, p. 70

1. $\sin 40° = 0.64$, $\cos 40° = 0.77$, $\tan 40° = 0.84$, $\cot 40° = 1.19$, $\sec 40° = 1.30$, $\csc 40° = 1.56$
3. $\sin 15° = 0.26$, $\cos 15° = 0.97$, $\tan 15° = 0.27$, $\cot 15° = 3.73$, $\sec 15° = 1.04$, $\csc 15° = 3.86$
5. 0.3256   **7.** 2.356   **9.** 0.9250   **11.** 1.812   **13.** 0.8988   **15.** 0.9686   **17.** 0.1299   **19.** 0.8601
21. 40°10′   **23.** 61°50′   **25.** 45°10′   **27.** 66°30′   **29.** 13.8°   **31.** 78.4°   **33.** 47.2°   **35.** 49.9°
37. 0.5528   **39.** 0.8930   **41.** 7.991   **43.** 0.4097   **45.** 72°47′   **47.** 35°8′   **49.** 39°7′   **51.** 51°6′
53. 0.7582   **55.** 144.4°   **57.** 162 ft/s   **59.** 67.8 V

Exercises 3–4, p. 75

1.

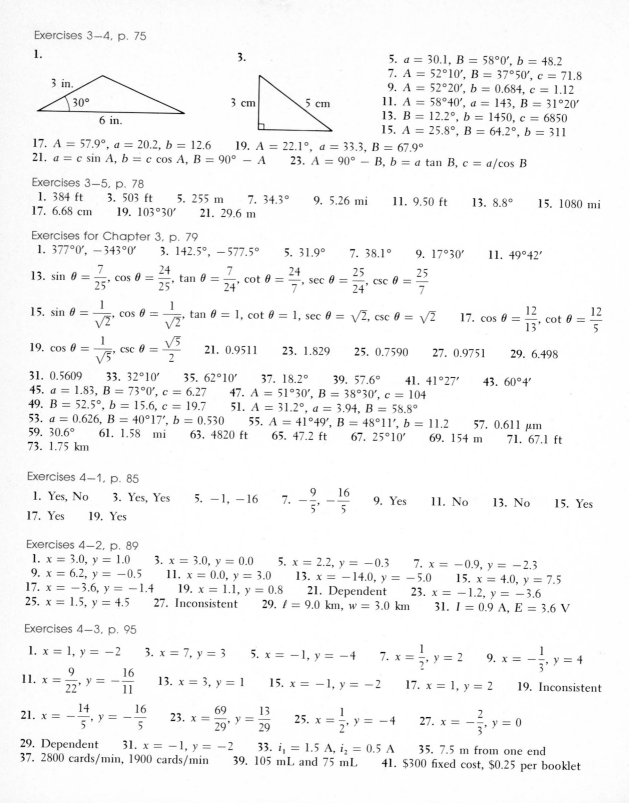

3.

5. $a = 30.1$, $B = 58°0'$, $b = 48.2$
7. $A = 52°10'$, $B = 37°50'$, $c = 71.8$
9. $A = 52°20'$, $b = 0.684$, $c = 1.12$
11. $A = 58°40'$, $a = 143$, $B = 31°20'$
13. $B = 12.2°$, $b = 1450$, $c = 6850$
15. $A = 25.8°$, $B = 64.2°$, $b = 311$

17. $A = 57.9°$, $a = 20.2$, $b = 12.6$ **19.** $A = 22.1°$, $a = 33.3$, $B = 67.9°$
21. $a = c \sin A$, $b = c \cos A$, $B = 90° - A$ **23.** $A = 90° - B$, $b = a \tan B$, $c = a/\cos B$

Exercises 3–5, p. 78

1. 384 ft   **3.** 503 ft   **5.** 255 m   **7.** 34.3°   **9.** 5.26 mi   **11.** 9.50 ft   **13.** 8.8°   **15.** 1080 mi
17. 6.68 cm   **19.** 103°30'   **21.** 29.6 m

Exercises for Chapter 3, p. 79

1. 377°0', −343°0'   **3.** 142.5°, −577.5°   **5.** 31.9°   **7.** 38.1°   **9.** 17°30'   **11.** 49°42'

13. $\sin\theta = \dfrac{7}{25}$, $\cos\theta = \dfrac{24}{25}$, $\tan\theta = \dfrac{7}{24}$, $\cot\theta = \dfrac{24}{7}$, $\sec\theta = \dfrac{25}{24}$, $\csc\theta = \dfrac{25}{7}$

15. $\sin\theta = \dfrac{1}{\sqrt{2}}$, $\cos\theta = \dfrac{1}{\sqrt{2}}$, $\tan\theta = 1$, $\cot\theta = 1$, $\sec\theta = \sqrt{2}$, $\csc\theta = \sqrt{2}$ **17.** $\cos\theta = \dfrac{12}{13}$, $\cot\theta = \dfrac{12}{5}$

19. $\cos\theta = \dfrac{1}{\sqrt{5}}$, $\csc\theta = \dfrac{\sqrt{5}}{2}$ **21.** 0.9511   **23.** 1.829   **25.** 0.7590   **27.** 0.9751   **29.** 6.498

31. 0.5609   **33.** 32°10'   **35.** 62°10'   **37.** 18.2°   **39.** 57.6°   **41.** 41°27'   **43.** 60°4'
45. $a = 1.83$, $B = 73°0'$, $c = 6.27$ **47.** $A = 51°30'$, $B = 38°30'$, $c = 104$
49. $B = 52.5°$, $b = 15.6$, $c = 19.7$ **51.** $A = 31.2°$, $a = 3.94$, $B = 58.8°$
53. $a = 0.626$, $B = 40°17'$, $b = 0.530$ **55.** $A = 41°49'$, $B = 48°11'$, $b = 11.2$ **57.** 0.611 μm
59. 30.6°   **61.** 1.58 mi   **63.** 4820 ft   **65.** 47.2 ft   **67.** 25°10'   **69.** 154 m   **71.** 67.1 ft
73. 1.75 km

Exercises 4–1, p. 85

1. Yes, No   **3.** Yes, Yes   **5.** −1, −16   **7.** $-\dfrac{9}{5}$, $-\dfrac{16}{5}$ **9.** Yes   **11.** No   **13.** No   **15.** Yes
17. Yes   **19.** Yes

Exercises 4–2, p. 89

1. $x = 3.0$, $y = 1.0$ **3.** $x = 3.0$, $y = 0.0$ **5.** $x = 2.2$, $y = -0.3$ **7.** $x = -0.9$, $y = -2.3$
9. $x = 6.2$, $y = -0.5$ **11.** $x = 0.0$, $y = 3.0$ **13.** $x = -14.0$, $y = -5.0$ **15.** $x = 4.0$, $y = 7.5$
17. $x = -3.6$, $y = -1.4$ **19.** $x = 1.1$, $y = 0.8$ **21.** Dependent   **23.** $x = -1.2$, $y = -3.6$
25. $x = 1.5$, $y = 4.5$ **27.** Inconsistent   **29.** $l = 9.0$ km, $w = 3.0$ km   **31.** $I = 0.9$ A, $E = 3.6$ V

Exercises 4–3, p. 95

1. $x = 1$, $y = -2$ **3.** $x = 7$, $y = 3$ **5.** $x = -1$, $y = -4$ **7.** $x = \dfrac{1}{2}$, $y = 2$ **9.** $x = -\dfrac{1}{3}$, $y = 4$

11. $x = \dfrac{9}{22}$, $y = -\dfrac{16}{11}$ **13.** $x = 3$, $y = 1$ **15.** $x = -1$, $y = -2$ **17.** $x = 1$, $y = 2$ **19.** Inconsistent

21. $x = -\dfrac{14}{5}$, $y = -\dfrac{16}{5}$ **23.** $x = \dfrac{69}{29}$, $y = \dfrac{13}{29}$ **25.** $x = \dfrac{1}{2}$, $y = -4$ **27.** $x = -\dfrac{2}{3}$, $y = 0$

29. Dependent   **31.** $x = -1$, $y = -2$ **33.** $i_1 = 1.5$ A, $i_2 = 0.5$ A   **35.** 7.5 m from one end
37. 2800 cards/min, 1900 cards/min   **39.** 105 mL and 75 mL   **41.** $300 fixed cost, $0.25 per booklet

Exercises 4—4, p. 101

1. -10 **3.** 29 **5.** 32 **7.** 93 **9.** 83 **11.** 96 **13.** $x = 3, y = 1$ **15.** $x = -1, y = -2$

17. $x = 1, y = 2$ **19.** Inconsistent   **21.** $x = -\dfrac{14}{5}, y = -\dfrac{16}{5}$ **23.** $x = \dfrac{69}{29}, y = \dfrac{13}{29}$

25. $x = \dfrac{1}{2}, y = -4$ **27.** $x = -\dfrac{2}{3}, y = 0$ **29.** Dependent   **31.** $x = -1, y = -2$

33. $s_0 = 15$ ft, $v = 10$ ft/s   **35.** $58, 31$ **37.** $\$600, \$7400$ **39.** $R = \dfrac{1}{600}T + \dfrac{11}{30}$

Exercises 4—5, p. 106

1. $x = 2, y = -1, z = 1$ **3.** $x = 4, y = -3, z = 3$ **5.** $x = \dfrac{1}{2}, y = \dfrac{2}{3}, z = \dfrac{1}{6}$

7. $x = \dfrac{2}{3}, y = -\dfrac{1}{3}, z = 1$ **9.** $x = \dfrac{4}{15}, y = -\dfrac{3}{5}, z = \dfrac{1}{3}$ **11.** $x = -2, y = \dfrac{2}{3}, z = \dfrac{1}{3}$

13. $x = \dfrac{3}{4}, y = 1, z = -\dfrac{1}{2}$ **15.** $r = 0, s = 0, t = 0, u = -1$

17. Eliminate x and the resulting system with y and z is dependent; choose a z value, then find y, then x; if $z = 0, y = -6, x = -10$; if $z = 1, y = -11, x = -17$

19. $-\dfrac{3}{22}$ A, $-\dfrac{39}{110}$ A, $\dfrac{27}{55}$ A   **21.** 16 parts/h, 20 parts/h, 28 parts/h   **23.** 50 cm³ alloy B, 50 cm³ alloy C

Exercises 4—6, p. 113

1. 122 **3.** 651 **5.** -439 **7.** 202 **9.** 128 **11.** 0.128 **13.** $x = -1, y = 2, z = 0$

15. $x = 2, y = -1, z = 1$ **17.** $x = 4, y = -3, z = 3$ **19.** $x = \dfrac{1}{2}, y = \dfrac{2}{3}, z = \dfrac{1}{6}$

21. $x = \dfrac{2}{3}, y = -\dfrac{1}{3}, z = 1$ **23.** $x = \dfrac{4}{15}, y = -\dfrac{3}{5}, z = \dfrac{1}{3}$ **25.** $x = -2, y = \dfrac{2}{3}, z = \dfrac{1}{3}$

27. $x = \dfrac{3}{4}, y = 1, z = -\dfrac{1}{2}$ **29.** $A = 125$ lb, $B = 60$ lb, $F = 75$ lb   **31.** $\$12,000, \$7000, \$1000$

Exercises for Chapter 4, p. 115

1. -17 **3.** -35 **5.** $x = 2.0, y = 0.0$ **7.** $x = 2.2, y = 2.7$ **9.** $x = 1.5, y = -1.9$

11. $x = 1.5, y = 0.3$ **13.** $x = 1, y = 2$ **15.** $x = \dfrac{1}{2}, y = -2$ **17.** $x = -\dfrac{1}{3}, y = \dfrac{7}{4}$

19. $x = \dfrac{11}{19}, y = -\dfrac{26}{19}$ **21.** $x = -\dfrac{6}{19}, y = \dfrac{36}{19}$ **23.** $x = \dfrac{43}{39}, y = \dfrac{7}{13}$ **25.** $x = 1, y = 2$

27. $x = \dfrac{1}{2}, y = -2$ **29.** $x = -\dfrac{1}{3}, y = \dfrac{7}{4}$ **31.** $x = \dfrac{11}{19}, y = -\dfrac{26}{19}$ **33.** $x = -\dfrac{6}{19}, y = \dfrac{36}{19}$

35. $x = \dfrac{43}{39}, y = \dfrac{7}{13}$ **37.** -115 **39.** 220 **41.** $x = 2, y = -1, z = 1$ **43.** $x = \dfrac{2}{3}, y = -\dfrac{1}{2}, z = 0$

45. $r = 3, s = -1, t = \dfrac{3}{2}$ **47.** $x = -\dfrac{1}{2}, y = \dfrac{1}{2}, z = 3$ **49.** $x = 2, y = -1, z = 1$

51. $x = \dfrac{2}{3}, y = -\dfrac{1}{2}, z = 0$ **53.** $r = 3, s = -1, t = \dfrac{3}{2}$ **55.** $x = -\dfrac{1}{2}, y = \dfrac{1}{2}, z = 3$ **57.** $x = \dfrac{8}{3}, y = -8$

59. $x = 1, y = 3$ **61.** -6 **63.** $-\dfrac{4}{3}$ **65.** $R_1 = 5\Omega, R_2 = 2\Omega$ **67.** $a = 10, b = 12, c = 15$

69. 450 mi/h, 50 mi/h   **71.** 11 ft   **73.** 79% nickel, 16% iron, 5% molybdenum

Exercises 5–1, p. 121

1. $40x - 40y$ 3. $2x^3 - 8x^2$ 5. $y^2 - 36$ 7. $9v^2 - 4$ 9. $25f^2 + 40f + 16$ 11. $4x^2 + 28x + 49$
13. $x^2 - 4xy + 4y^2$ 15. $36s^2 - 12st + t^2$ 17. $x^2 + 6x + 5$ 19. $c^2 + 9c + 18$ 21. $6x^2 + 13x - 5$
23. $20x^2 - 21x - 5$ 25. $20v^2 + 13v - 15$ 27. $6x^2 - 13xy - 63y^2$ 29. $2x^2 - 8$ 31. $8a^3 - 2a$
33. $6ax^2 + 24abx + 24ab^2$ 35. $16a^3 - 48a^2 + 36a$ 37. $x^2 + y^2 + 2xy + 2x + 2y + 1$
39. $x^2 + y^2 + 2xy - 6x - 6y + 9$ 41. $125 - 75t + 15t^2 - t^3$ 43. $8x^3 + 60x^2t + 150xt^2 + 125t^3$
45. $x^3 + 8$ 47. $64 - 27x^3$ 49. $Ri_1^2 + 2Ri_1i_2 + Ri_2^2$ 51. $192 - 16t - 16t^2$
53. $P + 3Pr + 3Pr^2 + Pr^3$

Exercises 5–2, p. 125

1. $6(x + y)$ 3. $5(a - 1)$ 5. $3x(x - 3)$ 7. $7b(by - 4)$ 9. $2(x + 2y - 4z)$
11. $3ab(b - 2 + 4b^2)$ 13. $4pq(3q - 2 - 7q^2)$ 15. $2(a^2 - b^2 + 2c^2 - 3d^2)$ 17. $(x + 2)(x - 2)$
19. $(10 + y)(10 - y)$ 21. $(9s + 5t)(9s - 5t)$ 23. $(12n + 13p^2)(12n - 13p^2)$ 25. $2(x + 2)(x - 2)$
27. $3(x + 3z)(x - 3z)$ 29. $(x^2 + 4)(x + 2)(x - 2)$ 31. $(x^4 + 1)(x^2 + 1)(x + 1)(x - 1)$
33. $(3 + b)(x - y)$ 35. $(a - b)(a + x)$ 37. $i(R_1 + R_2 + r)$ 39. $m(v_1 + v_2)(v_1 - v_2)$
41. $e(e + 2)(e - 2)$

Exercises 5–3, p. 128

1. $(x + 1)(x + 4)$ 3. $(s - 7)(s + 6)$ 5. $(x + 1)^2$ 7. $(x - 2)^2$ 9. $(3x + 1)(x - 2)$
11. $(3y + 1)(y - 3)$ 13. $(3t - 4u)(t - u)$ 15. $(9x - 2y)(x + y)$ 17. $(2m + 5)^2$ 19. $(2x - 3)^2$
21. $(3t - 4)(3t - 1)$ 23. $(8b - 1)(b + 4)$ 25. $(4p - q)(p - 6q)$ 27. $(12x - y)(x + 4y)$
29. $2(x - 1)(x - 6)$ 31. $2(2x - 1)(x + 4)$ 33. $(x + 1)^3$ 35. $(2x + 1)(4x^2 - 2x + 1)$
37. $16(t - 4)(t + 2)$ 39. $(x - 2L)(x - L)$

Exercises 5–4, p. 131

1. $\dfrac{14}{21}$ 3. $\dfrac{2ax^2}{2xy}$ 5. $\dfrac{2x - 4}{x^2 + x - 6}$ 7. $\dfrac{ax^2 - ay^2}{x^2 - xy - 2y^2}$ 9. $\dfrac{7}{11}$ 11. $\dfrac{2xy}{4y^2}$ 13. $\dfrac{2}{x + 1}$ 15. $\dfrac{x - 5}{2x - 1}$

17. $\dfrac{1}{4}$ 19. $\dfrac{3}{4}x$ 21. $\dfrac{1}{5a}$ 23. $\dfrac{3a - 2b}{2a - b}$ 25. $\dfrac{4x^2 + 1}{(2x + 1)(2x - 1)}$ (cannot be reduced)   27. $\dfrac{x - 4}{x + 4}$

29. $\dfrac{2x - 1}{x + 8}$ 31. $(x^2 + 4)(x - 2)$ 33. $\dfrac{x^2y^2(y + x)}{y - x}$ 35. $\dfrac{x + 3}{x - 3}$ 37. $-\dfrac{1}{2}$ 39. $\dfrac{(x + 5)(x - 3)}{(5 - x)(x + 3)}$

41. $\dfrac{x^2 + xy + y^2}{x + y}$ 43. $\dfrac{(x + 1)^2}{x^2 - x + 1}$ 45. (a)   47. (a)

Exercises 5–5, p. 135

1. $\dfrac{3}{28}$ 3. $6xy$ 5. $\dfrac{7}{18}$ 7. $\dfrac{xy^2}{bz^2}$ 9. $4t$ 11. $3(u + v)$ 13. $\dfrac{10}{3(a + 4)}$ 15. $\dfrac{x - 3}{x(x + 3)}$ 17. $\dfrac{3x}{5a}$

19. $\dfrac{(x + 1)(x - 1)(x - 4)}{4(x + 2)}$ 21. $\dfrac{x^2}{a + x}$ 23. $\dfrac{15}{4}$ 25. $\dfrac{7x^4}{3a^4}$ 27. $\dfrac{4t(2t - 1)(t + 5)}{(2t + 1)^2}$ 29. $\dfrac{1}{2}(x + y)$

31. $(x + y)(3p + 7q)$ 33. $\dfrac{(T + 100)(T - 400)}{2(T - 40)}$

Exercises 5–6, p. 140

1. $\dfrac{9}{5}$ 3. $\dfrac{8}{x}$ 5. $\dfrac{5}{4}$ 7. $\dfrac{3 + 7ax}{4x}$ 9. $\dfrac{ax - b}{x^2}$ 11. $\dfrac{30 + ax^2}{25x^3}$ 13. $\dfrac{14 - a^2}{10a}$

15. $\dfrac{-x^2 + 4x + xy + y - 2}{xy}$ 17. $\dfrac{7}{2(2x - 1)}$ 19. $\dfrac{5 - 3x}{2x(x + 1)}$ 21. $\dfrac{-3}{4(s - 3)}$ 23. $\dfrac{x + 6}{x^2 - 9}$

25. $\dfrac{2x - 5}{(x - 4)^2}$ 27. $\dfrac{x + 27}{(x - 5)(x + 5)(x - 6)}$ 29. $\dfrac{9x^2 + x - 2}{(3x - 1)(x - 4)}$ 31. $\dfrac{13t^2 + 27t}{(t - 3)(t + 2)(t + 3)^2}$

33. $\dfrac{x+1}{x-1}$ 35. $-\dfrac{(x+1)(x^3+x^2-3x-1)}{x^2(x+2)}$ 37. $\dfrac{h}{(x+1)(x+h+1)}$ 39. $\dfrac{-2hx-h^2}{x^2(x+h)^2}$

41. $\dfrac{y^2-rx+r^2}{r^2}$ 43. $\dfrac{2a-1}{a^2}$ 45. $\dfrac{3\pi l^3-12cl^2+\pi c^3}{3\pi l^3}$ 47. $\dfrac{b(y^2-x^2)}{(x^2+y^2)^2}$

Exercises 5—7, p. 145

1. 4   3. -3 5. $\dfrac{7}{2}$ 7. $\dfrac{16}{21}$ 9. -9 11. $-\dfrac{6}{5}$ 13. $\dfrac{5}{3}$ 15. -2 17. $\dfrac{3}{4}$ 19. 6   21. -5

23. $-\dfrac{7}{8}$ 25. No solution   27. $\dfrac{2}{3}$ 29. $\dfrac{3b}{1-2b}$ 31. $\dfrac{(2b-1)(b+6)}{2(b-1)}$

33. $\dfrac{2EI-2IV_0-p^2-ImV^2}{IV^2}$ 35. $\dfrac{rR-rR_2+RR_2}{R_2-R}$ 37. 3.6 min   39. 60 m, 36 m

Exercises for Chapter 5, p. 147

1. $12ax+15a^2$ 3. $4a^2-49b^2$ 5. $4a^2+4a+1$ 7. $b^2+3b-28$ 9. $2x^2-13x-45$
11. $16c^2+6cd-d^2$ 13. $3(s+3t)$ 15. $a^2(x^2+1)$ 17. $(x+12)(x-12)$
19. $(20r+t^2)(20r-t^2)$ 21. $(3t-1)^2$ 23. $(5t+1)^2$ 25. $(x+8)(x-7)$ 27. $(t-9)(t+4)$
29. $(2x-9)(x+4)$ 31. $(2x+5)(2x-7)$ 33. $(5b-1)(2b+5)$ 35. $4(x+4)(x-4)$

37. $(x+3)^3$ 39. $(2x+3)(4x^2-6x+9)$ 41. $(a-3)(b^2+1)$ 43. $(x+5)(n-x+5)$ 45. $\dfrac{16x^2}{3a^2}$

47. $\dfrac{3x+1}{2x-1}$ 49. $\dfrac{16}{5x(x-y)}$ 51. $\dfrac{6}{5-x}$ 53. $\dfrac{x+2}{2x(7x-1)}$ 55. $\dfrac{1}{x-1}$ 57. $\dfrac{16x-15}{36x^2}$

59. $\dfrac{5y+6}{2xy}$ 61. $\dfrac{-2(2a+3)}{a(a+2)}$ 63. $\dfrac{x^3+6x^2-2x+2}{x(x-1)(x+3)}$ 65. 2   67. $\dfrac{7}{2c+4}$ 69. $-\dfrac{(a-1)^2}{2a}$

71. 6   73. $\dfrac{1}{4}[(x+y)^2-(x-y)^2]=\dfrac{1}{4}(x^2+2xy+y^2-x^2+2xy-y^2)=\dfrac{1}{4}(4xy)=xy$

75. $(x-10)(x+7)$ 77. $4(3x^2+12x+16)$ 79. $\dfrac{1-t}{(t+1)^3}$ 81. $\dfrac{120T^4+20w^2x^2T^2-3w^4x^4}{120T^4}$

83. $\dfrac{\mu R}{r+R+\mu R}$ 85. $\dfrac{fp}{p-f}$ 87. $\dfrac{wL^3-24\theta EI}{4L}$ 89. $\dfrac{48}{7}$ days   91. 3.1 days

Exercises 6—1, p. 155

1. $a=1,\ b=-8,\ c=5$ 3. $a=1,\ b=-2,\ c=-4$ 5. Not quadratic   7. $a=1.\ b=-1,\ c=0$

9. 2, -2 11. $-1, 9$ 13. 3, 4   15. 0, -2 17. $\dfrac{3}{2},\ -\dfrac{3}{2}$ 19. $\dfrac{1}{3},\ 4$ 21. $-4,\ -4$ 23. $\dfrac{2}{3},\dfrac{3}{2}$

25. $\dfrac{1}{2},\ -\dfrac{3}{2}$ 27. 2, -1 29. $2b, -2b$ 31. $0, \dfrac{5}{2}$ 33. 0, -2 35. $b-a,\ -b-a$ 37. 10 s

39. $-3, -5$ 41. $4\Omega, 12\Omega$ 43. 12 mm, 8 mm

Exercises 6—2, p. 159

1. $-5, 5$ 3. $-\sqrt{7}, \sqrt{7}$ 5. $-3, 7$ 7. $-3 \pm \sqrt{7}$ 9. 2, -4 11. $-2, -1$ 13. $2 \pm \sqrt{2}$

15. $-5, 3$ 17. $-3, \dfrac{1}{2}$ 19. $\dfrac{1}{6}(3 \pm \sqrt{33})$ 21. $\dfrac{1}{4}(1 \pm \sqrt{17})$ 23. $-b \pm \sqrt{b^2-c}$

Exercises 6–3, p. 162

1. $2, -4$ 3. $-2, -1$ 5. $2 \pm \sqrt{2}$ 7. $-5, 3$ 9. $-3, \dfrac{1}{2}$ 11. $\dfrac{1}{6}(3 \pm \sqrt{33})$ 13. $\dfrac{1}{4}(1 \pm \sqrt{17})$

15. $\dfrac{1}{4}(7 \pm \sqrt{17})$ 17. $\dfrac{1}{2}(-5 \pm \sqrt{-5})$ 19. $\dfrac{1}{6}(1 \pm \sqrt{109})$ 21. $\dfrac{3}{2}, -\dfrac{3}{2}$ 23. $\dfrac{3}{4}, -\dfrac{5}{8}$

25. $-c \pm \sqrt{c^2 + 1}$ 27. $\dfrac{b + 1 \pm \sqrt{-3b^2 + 2b + 4b^2a + 1}}{2b^2}$ 29. 0.382 Pa   31. 0.915 in.

33. 3.06 mm   35. 8 in.

Exercises for Chapter 6, p. 163

1. $-4, 1$ 3. $2, 8$ 5. $\dfrac{1}{3}, -4$ 7. $\dfrac{1}{2}, \dfrac{5}{3}$ 9. $0, \dfrac{25}{6}$ 11. $-\dfrac{3}{2}, \dfrac{7}{2}$ 13. $-10, 11$ 15. $-1 \pm \sqrt{6}$

17. $-4, \dfrac{9}{2}$ 19. $\dfrac{1}{8}(3 \pm \sqrt{41})$ 21. $\dfrac{1}{2}(-1 \pm 3\sqrt{-1})$ 23. $\dfrac{1}{6}(-2 \pm \sqrt{58})$ 25. $-2 \pm 2\sqrt{2}$

27. $\dfrac{1}{3}(-4 \pm \sqrt{10})$ 29. $-1, \dfrac{5}{4}$ 31. $\dfrac{1}{4}(-3 \pm \sqrt{-47})$ 33. $\dfrac{-1 \pm \sqrt{-1}}{a}$ 35. $\dfrac{-3 \pm \sqrt{9 + 4a^3}}{2a}$

37. $-5, 6$ 39. $\dfrac{1}{4}(1 \pm \sqrt{33})$ 41. $3 \pm \sqrt{7}$ 43. 0 (3 is not a solution)   45. $-5 \pm 5\sqrt{-79}$

47. $\dfrac{E \pm \sqrt{E^2 - 4PR}}{2R}$ 49. 10 units   51. $\dfrac{2.5 \pm \sqrt{6.25 - 50.4n}}{25.2}$ 53. 8 V, 12 V   55. 0.106 in.

57. 25

Exercises 7–1, p. 168

1. $+, -, -$ 3. $+, +, -$ 5. $+, +, +$ 7. $+, -, +$

9. $\sin \theta = \dfrac{1}{\sqrt{5}}$, $\cos \theta = \dfrac{2}{\sqrt{5}}$, $\tan \theta = \dfrac{1}{2}$, $\cot \theta = 2$, $\sec \theta = \dfrac{1}{2}\sqrt{5}$, $\csc \theta = \sqrt{5}$

11. $\sin \theta = -\dfrac{3}{\sqrt{13}}$, $\cos \theta = -\dfrac{2}{\sqrt{13}}$, $\tan \theta = \dfrac{3}{2}$, $\cot \theta = \dfrac{2}{3}$, $\sec \theta = -\dfrac{1}{2}\sqrt{13}$, $\csc \theta = -\dfrac{1}{3}\sqrt{13}$

13. $\sin \theta = \dfrac{12}{13}$, $\cos \theta = -\dfrac{5}{13}$, $\tan \theta = -\dfrac{12}{5}$, $\cot \theta = -\dfrac{5}{12}$, $\sec \theta = -\dfrac{13}{5}$, $\csc \theta = \dfrac{13}{12}$

15. $\sin \theta = -\dfrac{2}{\sqrt{29}}$, $\cos \theta = \dfrac{5}{\sqrt{29}}$, $\tan \theta = -\dfrac{2}{5}$, $\cot \theta = -\dfrac{5}{2}$, $\sec \theta = \dfrac{1}{5}\sqrt{29}$, $\csc \theta = -\dfrac{1}{2}\sqrt{29}$

17. II   19. II   21. IV   23. III

Exercises 7–2, p. 173

1. $\sin 20°$; $-\cos 40°$ 3. $-\tan 75°$; $-\csc 58°$ 5. $-\sin 57°$; $-\cot 6°$ 7. $\cos 40°$; $-\tan 40°$
9. -0.2588 11. -0.2756 13. -1.036 15. -2.366 17. 0.2339 19. -0.8936 21. 0.9732
23. -1.767 25. -0.6036 27. -1.838 29. $28°, 208°$ 31. $201°20', 338°40'$ 33. $60°30', 119°30'$
35. $97°0', 263°0'$ 37. $238.0°, 302.0°$ 39. $66.4°, 293.6°$ 41. $62.2°, 242.2°$ 43. $15.8°, 195.8°$
45. $252°19', 287°41'$ 47. $125°33', 305°33'$ 49. -0.7002 51. -0.7771 53. $<$ 55. $=$
57. 72.7 lb   59. 416
61. $\cos(-\theta) = x/r$; $\tan(-\theta) = -y/x$; $\cot(-\theta) = x/-y$; $\sec(-\theta) = r/x$; $\csc(-\theta) = r/-y$
63. (a) 5.671 (b) -1.428

Exercises 7—3, p. 178

1. $\dfrac{\pi}{12}, \dfrac{5\pi}{6}$ 3. $\dfrac{5\pi}{12}, \dfrac{11\pi}{6}$ 5. $\dfrac{7\pi}{6}, \dfrac{3\pi}{2}$ 7. $\dfrac{8\pi}{9}, \dfrac{13\pi}{9}$ 9. 72°, 270°   11. 10°, 315°   13. 170°, 300°

15. 15°, 27°   17. 0.401   19. 4.40   21. 5.82   23. 3.11   25. 43.0°   27. 172°   29. 140.4°
31. 939.7°   33. 0.7071   35. 3.732   37. −1.732   39. −0.1219   41. 0.9057   43. 0.5132
45. −0.4797   47. −0.9890   49. 0.3142, 2.8278   51. 2.9326, 6.0736   53. 0.8308, 5.4522
55. 2.4432, 3.8408   57. $1.43\pi = 4.49$ (closest 3 sig. digit result)   59. 15.7 cm/s

Exercises 7—4, p. 182

1. 10.5 in.   3. 52.4 in.²   5. 12 rad   7. 2.88 in.²   9. 0.262 ft   11. 129 km   13. 5650 cm
15. 21.5 ft   17. 75.4 rad/s   19. 3700 mi/h   21. 5200 ft/min   23. 2.60×10^{-6} rad/s
25. 25,100 ft/min   27. 66.0 cm²   29. 4.847×10^{-6} 31. 7.13×10^7 mi

Exercises for Chapter 7, p. 183

1. $\sin\theta = \dfrac{4}{5}$, $\cos\theta = \dfrac{3}{5}$, $\tan\theta = \dfrac{4}{3}$, $\cot\theta = \dfrac{3}{4}$, $\sec\theta = \dfrac{5}{3}$, $\csc\theta = \dfrac{5}{4}$

3. $\sin\theta = -\dfrac{2}{\sqrt{53}}$, $\cos\theta = \dfrac{7}{\sqrt{53}}$, $\tan\theta = -\dfrac{2}{7}$, $\cot\theta = -\dfrac{7}{2}$, $\sec\theta = \dfrac{\sqrt{53}}{7}$, $\csc\theta = -\dfrac{\sqrt{53}}{2}$

5. $-\cos 48°$; $\tan 14°$ 7. $-\sin 71°$; $\sec 15°$ 9. $\dfrac{2\pi}{9}$; $\dfrac{17\pi}{20}$ 11. $\dfrac{4\pi}{15}$; $\dfrac{9\pi}{8}$ 13. 252°; 130°

15. 12°; 330°   17. 32.1°   19. 206.3°   21. 1.745   23. 0.358   25. 4.58   27. 2.38
29. −0.4226   31. −0.4663   33. −1.082   35. −0.4258   37. −1.638   39. 4.230   41. −0.5878
43. −0.8660   45. 0.5564   47. 1.195   49. 10.3°, 190.3°   51. 118.2°, 241.8°   53. 17°0′, 163°0′
55. 70°40′, 289°20′   57. 136°14′, 223°46′   59. 66°47′, 246°47′   61. 0.5760, 5.707   63. 4.186, 5.239
65. −120 V   67. 0.393 ft   69. 108 cm²   71. 188 in./s   73. 18.0 cm   75. 6.66 mm
77. 84,800 cm/min   79. 3.58×10^5 km

Exercises 8—1, p. 191

1.   3.   5.   7.   9.   11.   13.

15.   17.   19.   21.   23.

25. 3.22, 7.97   27. −62.9, 44.1   29. 2.11, −8.79   31. −2.53, 0.788

Exercises 8—2, p. 195

1. $R = 24.2$, $\theta = 52.6°$ with **A**   **3.** $R = 7.78$, $\theta = 66.7°$ with **A**   **5.** $R = 10.0$, $\theta = 58.8°$
7. $R = 2.74$, $\theta = 111.0°$ **9.** $R = 2130$, $\theta = 107.7°$ **11.** $R = 1.42$, $\theta = 299.2°$
13. $R = 29.2$, $\theta = 10.8°$ **15.** $R = 47.0$, $\theta = 101.0°$ **17.** $R = 27.2$, $\theta = 33.0°$
19. $R = 12.7$, $\theta = 25.2°$ **21.** $R = 50.1$, $\theta = 50.3°$ **23.** $R = 230$, $\theta = 125.1°$

Exercises 8—3, p. 199

1. 81.5 N, 56.5° from 45-N force   **3.** 850 N, 10.0° from 520-N force   **5.** 510 km, 28.1° S of W
7. 37.7 mi, 77.4° S of W   **9.** $v_H = 80.3$ ft/s, $v_V = 89.2$ ft/s   **11.** 31.6 lb, 71.6°
13. 206 m/s, 14.0° from direction of plane   **15.** Yes   **17.** 94.0 N   **19.** 128 m/s, 20.2° from horizontal
21. 6.96 rad/s²   **23.** 4.06 A/m, 11.6° with magnet

Exercises 8—4, p. 205

1. $b = 38.1$, $C = 66°0'$, $c = 46.1$ **3.** $a = 2790$, $B = 2590$, $C = 109.0°$
5. $B = 12.0°$, $C = 150.0°$, $c = 7.44$ **7.** $a = 111$, $A = 149.7°$, $C = 9.6°$
9. $A = 125°30'$, $a = 0.0777$, $c = 0.005\ 83$ **11.** $A = 99.4°$, $b = 55.1$, $c = 24.4$
13. $A = 68.1°$, $a = 552$, $c = 537$
15. $A_1 = 61.5°$, $C_1 = 70.4°$, $c_1 = 5.62$; $A_2 = 118.5°$, $C_2 = 13.4°$, $c_2 = 1.38$
17. $A_1 = 107.3°$, $a_1 = 5280$, $C_1 = 41.3°$; $A_2 = 9.9°$, $a_2 = 950$, $C_2 = 138.7°$ **19.** No solution
21. 7.83 ft, 10.6 ft   **23.** 25,200 ft   **25.** 23.0 mi   **27.** 27,300 km

Exercises 8—5, p. 209

1. $A = 50.3°$, $B = 75.7°$, $c = 6.31$ **3.** $A = 70.9°$, $B = 11.1°$, $c = 4750$
5. $A = 34.7°$, $B = 40.7°$, $C = 104.6°$ **7.** $A = 18.2°$, $B = 22.2°$, $C = 139.6°$
9. $A = 6.0°$, $B = 16.0°$, $c = 1150$ **11.** $A = 82.3°$, $b = 21.6$, $C = 11.4°$
13. $A = 38.8°$, $B = 36.6°$, $b = 97.9$ **15.** $A = 46.9°$, $B = 61.8°$, $C = 71.3°$
17. $A = 137.9°$, $B = 33.7°$, $C = 8.4°$ **19.** $b = 29.5$, $C = 14.4°$, $c = 14.9$ **21.** 1140 m   **23.** 96.9°
25. 8.88 km/h, 13.4° with bank   **27.** 42.4°

Exercises for Chapter 8, p. 209

1. $A_x = 57.4$, $A_y = 30.5$ **3.** $A_x = -0.754$, $A_y = -0.528$ **5.** $R = 602$, $\theta = 57.1°$ with **A**
7. $R = 5950$, $\theta = 33.6°$ with **A**   **9.** $R = 965$, $\theta = 8.6°$ **11.** $R = 26.1$, $\theta = 146°0'$
13. $R = 71.9$, $\theta = 336.4°$ **15.** $R = 99.2$, $\theta = 359.3°$ **17.** $b = 18.1$, $C = 64°0'$, $c = 17.5$
19. $A = 21.2°$, $b = 34.8$, $c = 51.5$ **21.** $A = 39.9°$, $a = 51.9$, $C = 30.1°$
23. $A_1 = 54.8°$, $a_1 = 12.7$, $B_1 = 68.6°$; $A_2 = 12.0°$, $a_2 = 3.24$, $B_2 = 111.4°$
25. $A = 32.3°$, $b = 267$, $C = 17.7°$ **27.** $A = 148.7°$, $B = 9.3°$, $c = 5.66$
29. $A = 36.9°$, $B = 25.0°$, $C = 118.1°$ **31.** $A = 20.6°$, $B = 35.6°$, $C = 123.8°$ **33.** 0.0291 h
35. 27.0 ft/s, 33.7° with horizontal   **37.** 268 mi/h, 465 mi/h   **39.** 770 ft   **41.** 174 m   **43.** 57.7°
45. 186 mi   **47.** 110 lb   **49.** 310 lb, 330.4°

Exercises 9–1, p. 215

1. 0, −0.7, −1, −0.7, 0, 0.7, 1, 0.7, 0, −0.7, −1, −0.7, 0, 0.7, 1, 0.7, 0

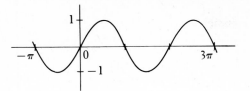

3. −3, −2.1, 0, 2.1, 3, 2.1, 0, −2.1, −3, −2.1, 0, 2.1, 3, 2.1, 0, −2.1, −3

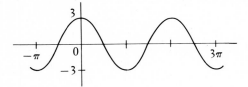

5.

7.

9.

11.

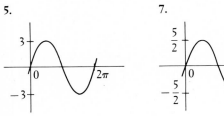
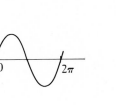
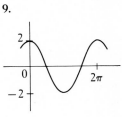
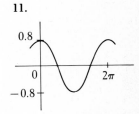

13.

15.

17.

19.

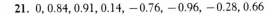

21. 0, 0.84, 0.91, 0.14, −0.76, −0.96, −0.28, 0.66

23. 1, 0.54, −0.42, −0.99, −0.65, 0.28, 0.96, 0.75

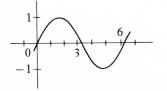
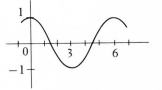

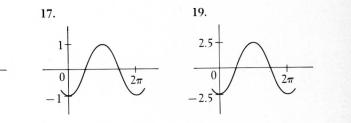

Exercises 9—2, p. 218

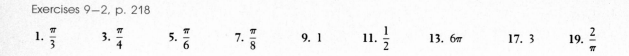

1. $\dfrac{\pi}{3}$ 3. $\dfrac{\pi}{4}$ 5. $\dfrac{\pi}{6}$ 7. $\dfrac{\pi}{8}$ 9. 1   11. $\dfrac{1}{2}$ 13. 6π 17. 3   19. $\dfrac{2}{\pi}$

21.

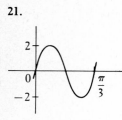

23.

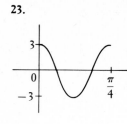

25.

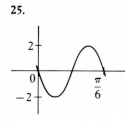

27.

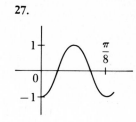

29.

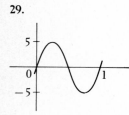

31.

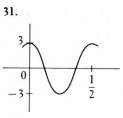

33.

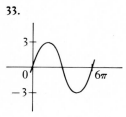

35.

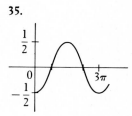

37.

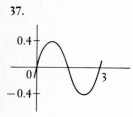

39.

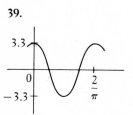

41.

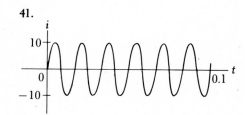

43.

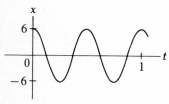

Exercises 9—3, p. 221

1. $1, 2\pi, \dfrac{\pi}{6}(R)$

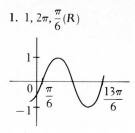

3. $1, 2\pi, \dfrac{\pi}{6}(L)$

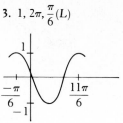

5. $2, \pi, \dfrac{\pi}{4}(L)$

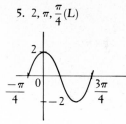

7. $1, \pi, \dfrac{\pi}{2}(R)$

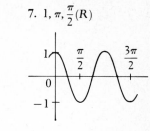

9. $\dfrac{1}{2}, 4\pi, \dfrac{\pi}{2}(R)$

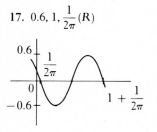

11. $3, 6\pi, \pi(L)$

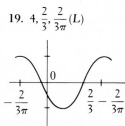

13. $1, 2, \dfrac{1}{8}(L)$

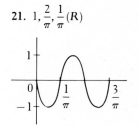

15. $\dfrac{3}{4}, \dfrac{1}{2}, \dfrac{1}{20}(R)$

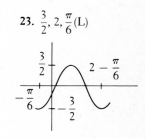

17. $0.6, 1, \dfrac{1}{2\pi}(R)$

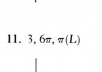

19. $4, \dfrac{2}{3}, \dfrac{2}{3\pi}(L)$

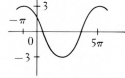

21. $1, \dfrac{2}{\pi}, \dfrac{1}{\pi}(R)$

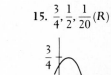

23. $\dfrac{3}{2}, 2, \dfrac{\pi}{6}(L)$

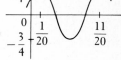

25.

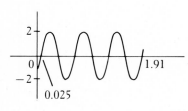

27.

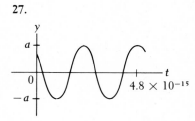

Exercises 9—4, p. 226

1. undef., -1.7, -1, -0.58, 0, 0.58, 1, 1.7, undef., -1.7 -1, -0.58, 0

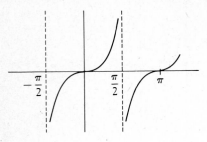

3. undef., 2, 1.4, 1.2, 1, 1.2, 1.4, 2, undef., -2, -1.4, -1.2, -1

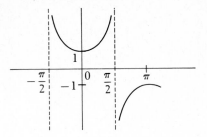

5.

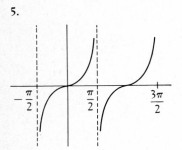

7.

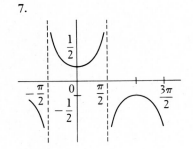

9.

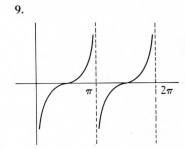

11.

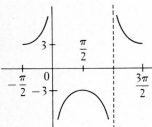

13.

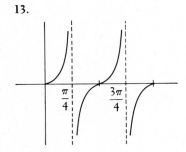

15.

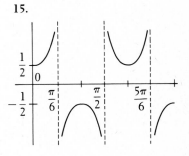

17.

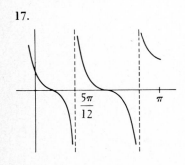

19.

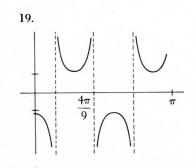

21.

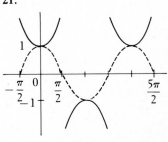

23.

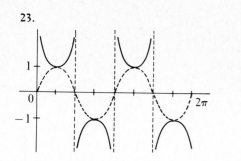

25.

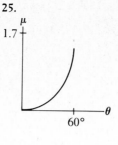

27.

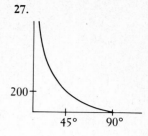

Exercises 9—5, p. 230

1.

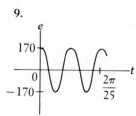

3.

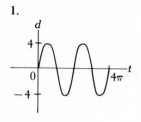

5.

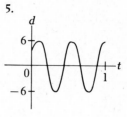

7.

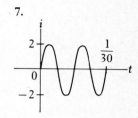

9.

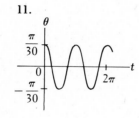

11.

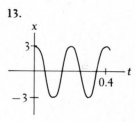

13.

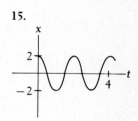

15.

Exercises 9—6, p. 235

1.

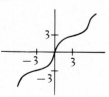

3.

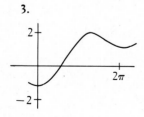

5.

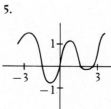

7.

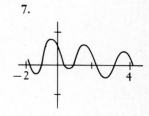

9.

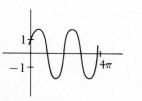

11.

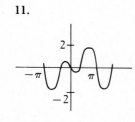

13.

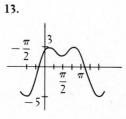

15.

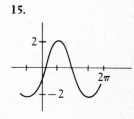

17.

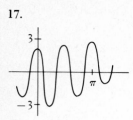

19.

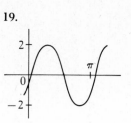

21.

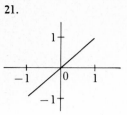

23.

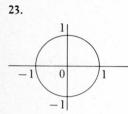

25.

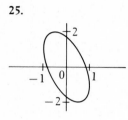

27.

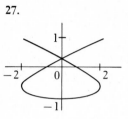

29.

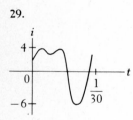

31.

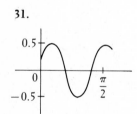

33.

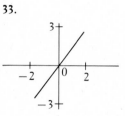

Exercises for Chapter 9, p. 236

1.

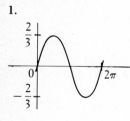

3.

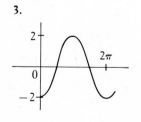

5.

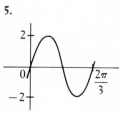

7.

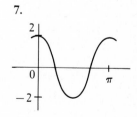

9.

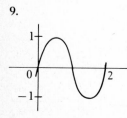

11.

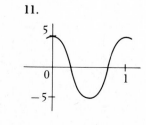

13.

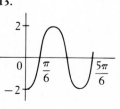

15.

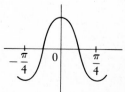

17.

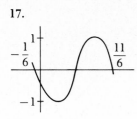

19.

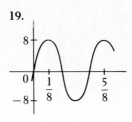

21.

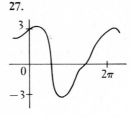

23.

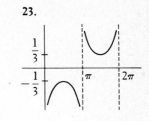

25.

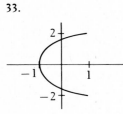

27.

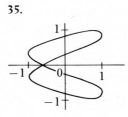

29.

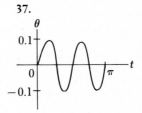

31.

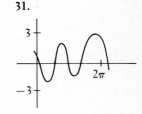

33.

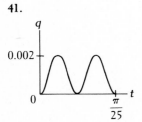

35.

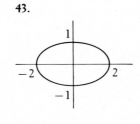

37.

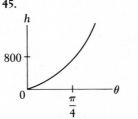

39.

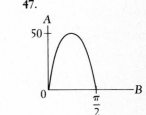

41.

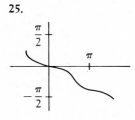

43.

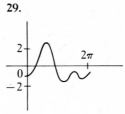

45.

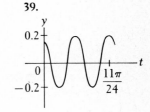

47.

Exercises 10–1, p. 242

1. x^3 **3.** $\dfrac{1}{a^4}$ **5.** $\dfrac{4a^2}{x^2}$ **7.** $\dfrac{n^2}{5a}$ **9.** 1   **11.** -7 **13.** $\dfrac{n^3}{2}$ **15.** $\dfrac{1}{a^3 b^6}$ **17.** $\dfrac{1}{a+b}$

19. $\dfrac{2x^2 + 3y^2}{x^2 y^2}$ **21.** $\dfrac{b^3}{432a}$ **23.** $\dfrac{4}{t^4 v^4}$ **25.** $\dfrac{x^8 - y^2}{x^4 y^2}$ **27.** $\dfrac{36a^2 + 1}{9a^4}$ **29.** $\dfrac{ab}{a+b}$ **31.** $\dfrac{4n^2 - 4n + 1}{n^4}$

33. $-\dfrac{x}{y}$ **35.** $\dfrac{a^2 - ax + x^2}{ax}$ **37.** $\dfrac{t^2 + t + 2}{t^2}$ **39.** $\dfrac{2x}{(x+1)(x-1)}$ **41.** $\dfrac{rR}{r+R}$ **43.** $\dfrac{r_1 r_2}{(\mu - 1)(r_2 - r_1)}$

Exercises 10–2, p. 246

1. 5   3. 3   5. 16   7. 10^{25} 9. $\dfrac{1}{2}$ 11. $\dfrac{1}{16}$ 13. 25   15. 4096   17. $\dfrac{1}{110}$ 19. $\dfrac{6}{7}$

21. $-\dfrac{1}{2}$ 23. 24   25. $\dfrac{39}{1000}$ 27. $\dfrac{9}{100}$ 29. $a^{7/6}$ 31. $\dfrac{1}{y^{9/10}}$ 33. $s^{23/12}$ 35. $\dfrac{1}{y^{13/12}}$ 37. $2ab^2$

39. $\dfrac{1}{8a^3 b^{9/4}}$ 41. $\dfrac{27}{64t^3}$ 43. $\dfrac{b^{11/10}}{2a^{1/12}}$ 45. $\dfrac{2}{3}x^{1/6}y^{11/12}$ 47. $\dfrac{x}{(x+2)^{1/2}}$ 49. $\dfrac{a^2+1}{a^4}$ 51. $\dfrac{a+1}{a^{1/2}}$

53. 4.72×10^{22} 55. 55.6%

Exercises 10–3, p. 250

1. $2\sqrt{6}$ 3. $3\sqrt{5}$ 5. $xy^2\sqrt{y}$ 7. $qr^3\sqrt{pr}$ 9. $x\sqrt{5}$ 11. $3ac^2\sqrt{2ab}$ 13. $2\sqrt[3]{2}$ 15. $2\sqrt[5]{3}$

17. $2\sqrt[3]{a^2}$ 19. $2st\sqrt[4]{4r^3 t}$ 21. 2   23. $ab\sqrt[3]{b^2}$ 25. $\dfrac{1}{2}\sqrt{6}$ 27. $\dfrac{\sqrt{ab}}{b}$ 29. $\dfrac{1}{2}\sqrt[3]{6}$ 31. $\dfrac{1}{3}\sqrt[5]{27}$

33. $2\sqrt{5}$ 35. 2   37. 200   39. 2000   41. $\sqrt{2a}$ 43. $\dfrac{1}{2}\sqrt{2}$ 45. $\sqrt[3]{2}$ 47. $\sqrt[8]{2}$ 49. $\dfrac{1}{6}\sqrt{6}$

51. $\dfrac{\sqrt{b(a^2+b)}}{ab}$ 53. $a+b$ 55. $\dfrac{1}{2}\sqrt{4x^2+1}$ 57. $\dfrac{\pi\sqrt{6}}{4} = 1.92s$ 59. $\dfrac{\sqrt[3]{4MN^2\rho^2}}{2N\rho}$

Exercises 10–4, p. 252

1. $5\sqrt{3}$ 3. $\sqrt{5}-\sqrt{7}$ 5. $3\sqrt{5}$ 7. $-4\sqrt{3}$ 9. $-2\sqrt{2}$ 11. $19\sqrt{7}$ 13. $-4\sqrt{5}$

15. $23\sqrt{3}-6\sqrt{2}$ 17. $\dfrac{7}{3}\sqrt{15}$ 19. 0   21. $13\sqrt[3]{3}$ 23. $\sqrt[4]{2}$ 25. $(a-2b^2)\sqrt{ab}$

27. $(3-2a)\sqrt{10}$ 29. $(2b-a)\sqrt[3]{3a^2 b}$ 31. $\dfrac{(a^2-c^3)\sqrt{ac}}{a^2 c^3}$ 33. $\dfrac{(a-2b)\sqrt[3]{ab^2}}{ab}$ 35. $\dfrac{2b\sqrt{a^2-b^2}}{b^2-a^2}$

37. $-\dfrac{b}{a}$

Exercises 10–5, p. 254

1. $\sqrt{30}$ 3. $2\sqrt{3}$ 5. 2   7. $2\sqrt[5]{2}$ 9. 50   11. 16   13. $\dfrac{1}{3}\sqrt{30}$ 15. $\dfrac{1}{33}\sqrt{165}$

17. $\sqrt{6}-\sqrt{15}$ 19. $8-12\sqrt{3}$ 21. -1 23. $39-12\sqrt{3}$ 25. $48+9\sqrt{15}$ 27. $36+13\sqrt{66}$
29. $a\sqrt{b}+\sqrt{ac}$ 31. $5n\sqrt{3}+10\sqrt{mn}$ 33. $2a-3b+2\sqrt{2ab}$ 35. $\sqrt{6}-\sqrt{10}-2$ 37. $\sqrt[6]{72}$

39. $\sqrt[12]{a^3 b^7 c^4}$ 41. 1   43. $2x\sqrt{x}+x\sqrt[6]{8y^4}-2\sqrt[6]{x^3 y^2}-y$ 45. $\dfrac{2-a-a^2}{2a}$

47. $4x^2+x-2y-4x\sqrt{x-2y}$ (valid for $x \geq 2y$)   49. $\dfrac{c}{a}$

Exercises 10–6, p. 256

1. $\sqrt{7}$ 3. $\dfrac{1}{2}\sqrt{14}$ 5. $\dfrac{1}{6}\sqrt[3]{9x^2}$ 7. $\dfrac{1}{2}\sqrt[6]{4a^3}$ 9. $\dfrac{a\sqrt{2}-b\sqrt{a}}{a}$ 11. $\dfrac{3\sqrt{a}-\sqrt{3b}}{3}$

13. $\dfrac{1}{4}(\sqrt{7}-\sqrt{3})$ 15. $\dfrac{1}{3}(\sqrt{35}+\sqrt{14})$ 17. $-\dfrac{3}{8}(\sqrt{5}+3)$ 19. $\dfrac{1}{13}(9+\sqrt{3})$

21. $\dfrac{1}{11}(\sqrt{7}+3\sqrt{2}-6-\sqrt{14})$ 23. $\dfrac{1}{13}(4-\sqrt{3})$ 25. $\dfrac{1}{17}(-56+9\sqrt{15})$ 27. $\dfrac{1}{14}(4-\sqrt{2})$

29. $\dfrac{8(3\sqrt{a}+2\sqrt{b})}{9a-4b}$ 31. $-\dfrac{\sqrt{x^2-y^2}+\sqrt{x^2+xy}}{y}$ 33. $km\sqrt{m(E-E_1)}$

Exercises for Chapter 10, p. 257

1. $\dfrac{2}{a^2}$ 3. $\dfrac{2d^3}{c}$ 5. 375 7. $\dfrac{1}{8000}$ 9. $\dfrac{t^4}{9}$ 11. -28 13. $64a^2b^5$ 15. $-8m^9n^6$

17. $\dfrac{2y-x^2}{x^2y}$ 19. $\dfrac{2y}{x+y}$ 21. $\dfrac{b}{ab-3}$ 23. $\dfrac{(x^3y^3-1)^{1/3}}{y}$ 25. $4a(a^2+4)^{1/2}$ 27. $\dfrac{-2(x+1)}{(x-1)^3}$

29. $2\sqrt{17}$ 31. $b^2c\sqrt{ab}$ 33. $3ab^2\sqrt{a}$ 35. $2tu\sqrt{21st}$ 37. $\dfrac{5\sqrt{2s}}{2s}$ 39. $\dfrac{1}{9}\sqrt{33}$ 41. $mn^2\sqrt[4]{8m^2n}$

43. $\sqrt{2}$ 45. $14\sqrt{2}$ 47. $-7\sqrt{7}$ 49. $3ax\sqrt{2x}$ 51. $(2a+b)\sqrt[3]{a}$ 53. $10-\sqrt{55}$

55. $4\sqrt{3}-4\sqrt{5}$ 57. $-45-7\sqrt{17}$ 59. $33-7\sqrt{21}$ 61. $-\dfrac{8+\sqrt{6}}{29}$ 63. $\dfrac{13-2\sqrt{35}}{29}$

65. $\dfrac{\sqrt{a^2b^2+a}}{a}$ 67. $\dfrac{15-2\sqrt{15}}{4}$ 69. $\dfrac{e^{i\alpha t}}{e^{i\omega t}}$ 71. 0.011 73. $\dfrac{\sqrt{3RMT}}{M}$; 483 m/s

75. $\dfrac{\sqrt{LC_1C_2(C_1+C_2)}}{2\pi LC_1C_2}$

Exercises 11–1, p. 263

1. $9j$ 3. $-2j$ 5. $2\sqrt{2}j$ 7. $\dfrac{1}{2}\sqrt{7}j$ 9. $-7;\,7$ 11. $4;\,-4$ 13. $-j$ 15. 1 17. 0

19. $-2j$ 21. $2+3j$ 23. $-2+3j$ 25. $3\sqrt{2}-2\sqrt{2}j$ 27. -1 29. $6+7j$ 31. $-2j$
33. $x=2,\,y=-2$ 35. $x=10,\,y=-6$ 37. $x=0,\,y=-1$ 39. $x=-2,\,y=3$
41. It is a real number.

Exercises 11–2, p. 266
1. $5-8j$ 3. $-9+6j$ 5. $7-5j$ 7. $-5j$ 9. -1 11. $-8+21j$ 13. $7+49j$
15. $-8-20j$ 17. $22+3j$ 19. $-42-6j$ 21. $-18\sqrt{2}j$ 23. $25\sqrt{5}j$ 25. $3\sqrt{3}j$
27. $-4\sqrt{3}+6\sqrt{7}j$ 29. $-28j$ 31. $3\sqrt{7}+3j$ 33. $-40-42j$ 35. $-2-2j$

37. $\dfrac{1}{29}(-30+12j)$ 39. $\dfrac{2}{37}(6+j)$ 41. $-j$ 43. $\dfrac{1}{11}(-13+8\sqrt{2}j)$ 45. $\dfrac{1}{3}(2+5\sqrt{2}j)$

47. $\dfrac{1}{5}(-1+3j)$ 49. $(a+bj)+(a-bj)=2a$ 51. $(a+bj)-(a-bj)=2bj$

Exercises 11–3, p. 268

1.   3.   5. $8+j$ 7. $-3j$

9. $-1 + 4j$

11. $-2 + 3j$

13. $7 + j$

15. $4 - 11j$

17. $-2j$

19. $-13 + j$

21.

23.

Exercises 11—4, p. 271

1. $10(\cos 36.9° + j \sin 36.9°)$

3. $5(\cos 306.9° + j \sin 306.9°)$

5. $3.61(\cos 123.7° + j \sin 123.7°)$

7. $6.00(\cos 203.6° + j \sin 203.6°)$

9. $2(\cos 60° + j \sin 60°)$

11. $8.01(\cos 295.9° + j \sin 295.9°)$

13. $3(\cos 180° + j \sin 180°)$ **15.** $9(\cos 90° + j \sin 90°)$ **17.** $2.94 + 4.05j$ **19.** $-1.39 + 0.80j$

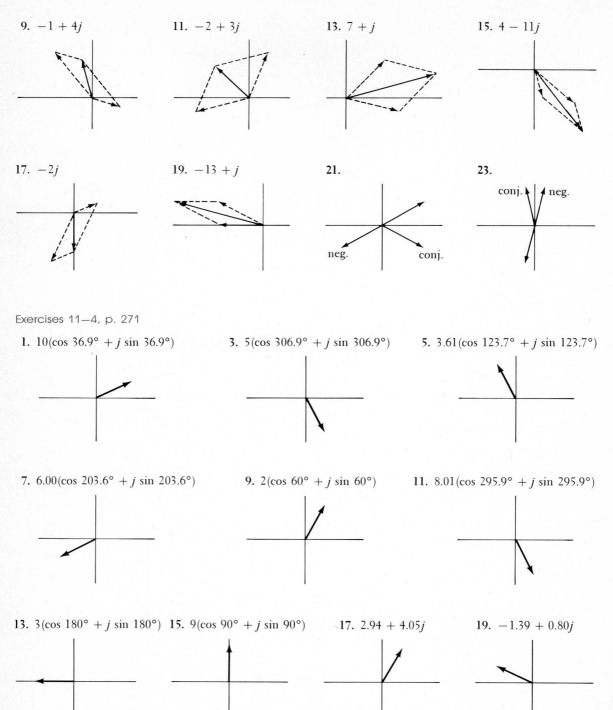

21. $9.68 - 2.50j$ **23.** -6 **25.** 8 **27.** $-4.71 - 0.595j$

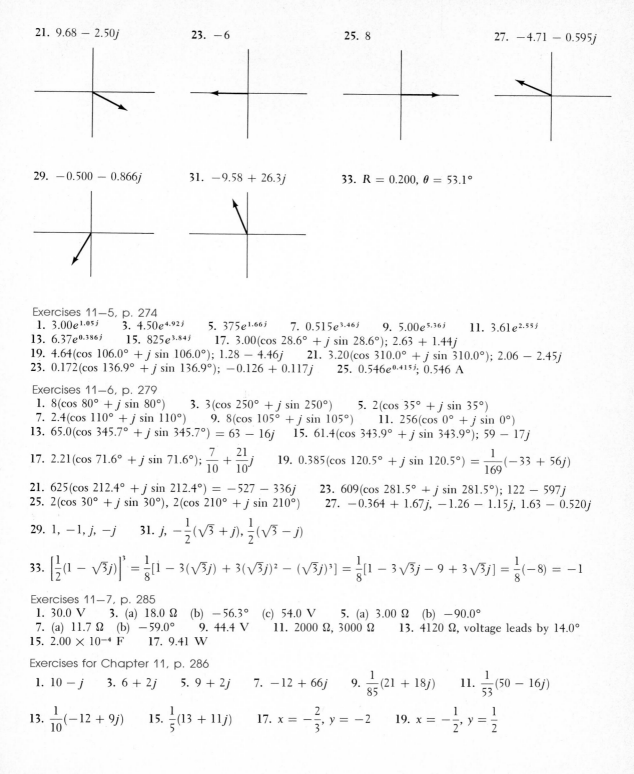

29. $-0.500 - 0.866j$ **31.** $-9.58 + 26.3j$ **33.** $R = 0.200, \theta = 53.1°$

Exercises 11–5, p. 274

1. $3.00e^{1.05j}$ **3.** $4.50e^{4.92j}$ **5.** $375e^{1.66j}$ **7.** $0.515e^{3.46j}$ **9.** $5.00e^{5.36j}$ **11.** $3.61e^{2.55j}$
13. $6.37e^{0.386j}$ **15.** $825e^{3.84j}$ **17.** $3.00(\cos 28.6° + j \sin 28.6°)$; $2.63 + 1.44j$
19. $4.64(\cos 106.0° + j \sin 106.0°)$; $1.28 - 4.46j$ **21.** $3.20(\cos 310.0° + j \sin 310.0°)$; $2.06 - 2.45j$
23. $0.172(\cos 136.9° + j \sin 136.9°)$; $-0.126 + 0.117j$ **25.** $0.546e^{0.415j}$; 0.546 A

Exercises 11–6, p. 279

1. $8(\cos 80° + j \sin 80°)$ **3.** $3(\cos 250° + j \sin 250°)$ **5.** $2(\cos 35° + j \sin 35°)$
7. $2.4(\cos 110° + j \sin 110°)$ **9.** $8(\cos 105° + j \sin 105°)$ **11.** $256(\cos 0° + j \sin 0°)$
13. $65.0(\cos 345.7° + j \sin 345.7°) = 63 - 16j$ **15.** $61.4(\cos 343.9° + j \sin 343.9°)$; $59 - 17j$

17. $2.21(\cos 71.6° + j \sin 71.6°)$; $\dfrac{7}{10} + \dfrac{21}{10}j$ **19.** $0.385(\cos 120.5° + j \sin 120.5°) = \dfrac{1}{169}(-33 + 56j)$

21. $625(\cos 212.4° + j \sin 212.4°) = -527 - 336j$ **23.** $609(\cos 281.5° + j \sin 281.5°)$; $122 - 597j$
25. $2(\cos 30° + j \sin 30°), 2(\cos 210° + j \sin 210°)$ **27.** $-0.364 + 1.67j, -1.26 - 1.15j, 1.63 - 0.520j$

29. $1, -1, j, -j$ **31.** $j, -\dfrac{1}{2}(\sqrt{3} + j), \dfrac{1}{2}(\sqrt{3} - j)$

33. $\left[\dfrac{1}{2}(1 - \sqrt{3}j)\right]^3 = \dfrac{1}{8}[1 - 3(\sqrt{3}j) + 3(\sqrt{3}j)^2 - (\sqrt{3}j)^3] = \dfrac{1}{8}[1 - 3\sqrt{3}j - 9 + 3\sqrt{3}j] = \dfrac{1}{8}(-8) = -1$

Exercises 11–7, p. 285

1. 30.0 V   **3.** (a) 18.0 Ω (b) $-56.3°$ (c) 54.0 V   **5.** (a) 3.00 Ω (b) $-90.0°$
7. (a) 11.7 Ω (b) $-59.0°$ **9.** 44.4 V   **11.** 2000 Ω, 3000 Ω   **13.** 4120 Ω, voltage leads by $14.0°$
15. 2.00×10^{-4} F   **17.** 9.41 W

Exercises for Chapter 11, p. 286

1. $10 - j$ **3.** $6 + 2j$ **5.** $9 + 2j$ **7.** $-12 + 66j$ **9.** $\dfrac{1}{85}(21 + 18j)$ **11.** $\dfrac{1}{53}(50 - 16j)$

13. $\dfrac{1}{10}(-12 + 9j)$ **15.** $\dfrac{1}{5}(13 + 11j)$ **17.** $x = -\dfrac{2}{3}, y = -2$ **19.** $x = -\dfrac{1}{2}, y = \dfrac{1}{2}$

21. $3 + 11j$

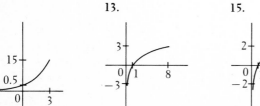

23. $4 + 8j$

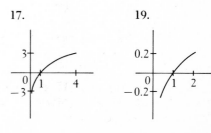

25. $1.41(\cos 315° + j \sin 315°) = 1.41e^{5.50j}$
27. $7.28(\cos 254.1° + j \sin 254.1°) = 7.28e^{4.43j}$
29. $4.67(\cos 76.7° + j \sin 76.7°)$; $4.67e^{1.34j}$
31. $10(\cos 0° + j \sin 0°)$; $10e^{0j}$ **33.** $-1.41 - 1.41j$
35. $-2.72 + 4.19j$ **37.** $1.94 + 0.495j$
39. $-1.74 + 5.08j$

41. $15.0(\cos 84.0° + j \sin 84.0°)$ **43.** $8.00(\cos 59.0° + j \sin 59.0°)$
45. $1020(\cos 160.0° + j \sin 160.0°)$ **47.** $27.0(\cos 331.5° + j \sin 331.5°)$

49. $32(\cos 270° + j \sin 270°) = -32j$ **51.** $\dfrac{625}{2}(\cos 270° + j \sin 270°) = -\dfrac{625}{2}j$

53. $1.00 + 1.73j$, -2, $1.00 - 1.73j$
55. $\cos 67.5° + j \sin 67.5°$, $\cos 157.5° + j \sin 157.5°$, $\cos 247.5° + j \sin 247.5°$, $\cos 337.5° + j \sin 337.5°$
57. $12.5\ \Omega$, $-53.1°$ **59.** $10.2\ \Omega$, current leads by $8.7°$ **61.** 36.1 V   **63.** 814 lb, $317.5°$

6.5 $\dfrac{u - j\omega n}{u^2 - \omega^2 n^2}$ **67.** $e^{j\pi} = \cos \pi + j \sin \pi = -1$

Exercises 12—1, p. 290

1. $\log_3 27 = 3$ **3.** $\log_4 256 = 4$ **5.** $\log_4\left(\dfrac{1}{16}\right) = -2$ **7.** $\log_2\left(\dfrac{1}{64}\right) = -6$ **9.** $\log_8 2 = \dfrac{1}{3}$

11. $\log_{1/4}\left(\dfrac{1}{16}\right) = 2$ **13.** $81 = 3^4$ **15.** $9 = 9^1$ **17.** $5 = 25^{1/2}$ **19.** $3 = 243^{1/5}$ **21.** $0.1 = 10^{-1}$

23. $16 = (0.5)^{-4}$ **25.** 2 **27.** -2 **29.** 343 **31.** $\dfrac{1}{4}$ **33.** 9 **35.** $\dfrac{1}{64}$ **37.** 0.2 **39.** -3

41. $t = \log_2\left(\dfrac{N}{1000}\right)$ **43.** $N = N_0 e^{-kt}$

Exercises 12—2, p. 293

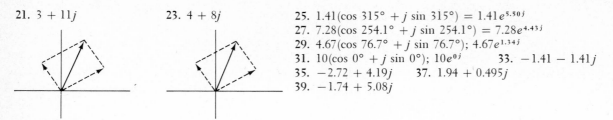

1.   **3.**   **5.**   **7.**   **9.**

11.   **13.**   **15.**   **17.**   **19.**

21.   23.   25.   27.

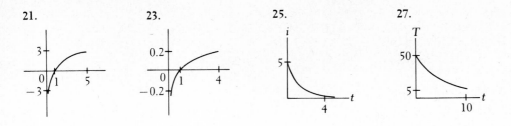

Exercises 12–3, p. 297

1. $\log_5 x + \log_5 y$ 3. $\log_7 5 - \log_7 a$ 5. $3 \log_2 a$ 7. $\log_6 a + \log_6 b + \log_6 c$ 9. $\frac{1}{4}\log_5 y$

11. $\frac{1}{2}\log_2 x - 2 \log_2 a$ 13. $\log_b ac$ 15. $\log_5 3$ 17. $\log_b x^{3/2}$ 19. $\log_e 4n^3$ 21. -5 23. 2.5

25. $\frac{1}{2}$ 27. $\frac{3}{4}$ 29. $2 + \log_3 2$ 31. $-1 - \log_2 3$ 33. $\frac{1}{2}(1 + \log_3 2)$ 35. $4 + 3 \log_2 3$

37. $3 + \log_{10} 3$ 39. $-2 + 3 \log_{10} 3$ 41. $y = 2x$ 43. $y = \frac{x}{5}$ 45. $y = \frac{49}{x^3}$ 47. $y = 2(2ax)^{1/5}$

49. 0.602 51. -0.301 53.   55. $S = \log_e\!\left(\dfrac{T^C}{P^{nR}}\right)$

Exercises 12–4, p. 301
1. 2.7536 3. $8.8062 - 10$ 5. 6.9657 7. $6.0682 - 10$ 9. 0.0224 11. $9.3773 - 10$
13. 8.8652 15. $8.6512 - 10$ 17. 27400 19. 0.0496 21. 2000 23. 0.724 25. 89.02
27. 4.065×10^{-4} 29. 1.427 31. 0.005788 33. 9.0607 35. $8.8751 - 10$ 37. 5.1761
39. $1.0000 - 100$

Exercises 12–5, p. 304
1. 85.50 3. 0.03742 5. 98.50 7. 1.757 9. $94,580$ 11. 3.844 13. 1.500 15. 25.33
17. 3.740 19. 0.003190 21. 1011 23. 1.46×10^9 25. $80,200 \text{ m}^2$ 27. 752.6 mg
29. 332.4 m/s 31. 0.2319 ft

Exercises 12–6, p. 308
1. $9.5767 - 10$ 3. 0.1072 5. $9.7916 - 10$ 7. 0.1834 9. $9.8982 - 10$ 11. $9.2766 - 10$
13. $28°10'$ 15. $50°16'$ 17. $48°56'$ 19. $1°40'$ or $1°50'$ 21. $a = 85.35, b = 11.87, B = 7°55'$
23. $b = 9506, C = 42°10', c = 6703$ 25. $a = 12.22, C = 68°8', c = 12.31$
27. $A = 37°58', B = 52°2', c = 485.3$ 29. 30.50 ft 31. $21.85 \text{ lb}, 52.24 \text{ lb}$ 33. 19.97 lb
35. $-32°3'$

Exercises 12–7, p. 312
1. 3.258 3. 0.4447 5. -0.6912 7. -4.917 9. 1.921 11. 3.418 13. 1.933 15. 1.795
17. 3.940 19. 0.3293 21. -0.00904 23. -4.351 25. 0.4314 27. 1.940 29. $12,000$
31. 8.7 33. $y = 3x$ 35. 8.155% 37. 0.384 s 39. 257 yr

Exercises 12–8, p. 316

1. 4   3. 0.861   5. 0.285   7. 0.203   9. 4.11   11. 14.2   13. 4   15. 4   17. −0.162

19. 2   21. 4   23. 1.42   25. 0.00203 s   27. 10^{11} 29. $10^{8.25} = 1.78 \times 10^8$ 31. 3.922×10^{-4}

33. 3.35   35. 3.50

Exercises 12–9, p. 320

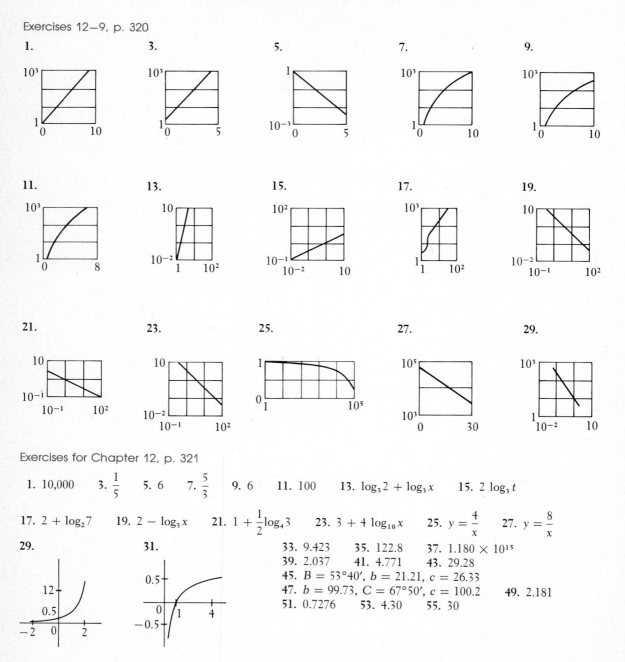

1.   3.   5.   7.   9.

11.   13.   15.   17.   19.

21.   23.   25.   27.   29.

Exercises for Chapter 12, p. 321

1. 10,000   3. $\frac{1}{5}$ 5. 6   7. $\frac{5}{3}$ 9. 6   11. 100   13. $\log_3 2 + \log_3 x$ 15. $2 \log_3 t$

17. $2 + \log_2 7$ 19. $2 - \log_3 x$ 21. $1 + \frac{1}{2}\log_4 3$ 23. $3 + 4 \log_{10} x$ 25. $y = \frac{4}{x}$ 27. $y = \frac{8}{x}$

29.   31.   33. 9.423   35. 122.8   37. 1.180×10^{15}

39. 2.037   41. 4.771   43. 29.28

45. $B = 53°40'$, $b = 21.21$, $c = 26.33$

47. $b = 99.73$, $C = 67°50'$, $c = 100.2$ 49. 2.181

51. 0.7276   53. 4.30   55. 30

57.   **59.**

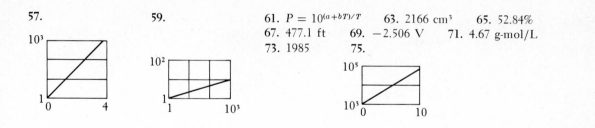

61. $P = 10^{(a+bT)/T}$ **63.** 2166 cm³   **65.** 52.84%
67. 477.1 ft   **69.** -2.506 V   **71.** 4.67 g-mol/L
73. 1985   **75.**

Exercises 13–1, p. 328

1. $x = 1.8, y = 3.6; x = -1.8, y = -3.6$ **3.** $x = 0.0, y = -2.0; x = 2.7, y = -0.7$
5. $x = 1.5, y = 0.2$ **7.** $x = 1.6, y = 2.5$
9. $x = 1.1, y = 2.8; x = -1.1, y = 2.8; x = 2.4, y = -1.8; x = -2.4, y = -1.8$ **11.** No solution
13. $x = -2.8, y = -1.0; x = 2.8, y = 1.0; x = 2.8, y = -1.0; x = -2.8, y = -1.0$
15. $x = 0.7, y = 0.7; x = -0.7, y = -0.7$ **17.** $x = 0.0, y = 0.0; x = 0.9, y = 0.8$ **19.** $x = 1.0, y = 0.0$
21. 360 m, 210 m   **23.** 1.3 A, 1.7 A; 2.3 A, 0.7 A

Exercises 13–2, p. 331

1. $x = 0, y = 1; x = 1, y = 2$ **3.** $x = -\dfrac{19}{5}, y = \dfrac{17}{5}; x = 5, y = -1$

5. $x = \dfrac{2}{7}(3 + \sqrt{2}), y = \dfrac{2}{7}(-1 + 2\sqrt{2}); x = \dfrac{2}{7}(3 - \sqrt{2}), y = \dfrac{2}{7}(-1 - 2\sqrt{2})$

7. $x = \dfrac{2}{3}, y = \dfrac{9}{2}; x = -3, y = -1$ **9.** $x = -2, y = 4; x = 2, y = 4$

11. $x = 1, y = 2; x = -1, y = 2$ **13.** $x = 1, y = 0; x = -1, y = 0; x = \dfrac{1}{2}\sqrt{6}, y = \dfrac{1}{2}; x = -\dfrac{1}{2}\sqrt{6}, y = \dfrac{1}{2}$

15. $x = \sqrt{19}, y = \sqrt{6}; x = \sqrt{19}, y = -\sqrt{6}; x = -\sqrt{19}, y = \sqrt{6}; x = -\sqrt{19}, y = -\sqrt{6}$

17. $x = \dfrac{1}{11}\sqrt{22}, y = \dfrac{1}{11}\sqrt{770}; x = \dfrac{1}{11}\sqrt{22}, y = -\dfrac{1}{11}\sqrt{770}; x = -\dfrac{1}{11}\sqrt{22}, y = \dfrac{1}{11}\sqrt{770}; x = -\dfrac{1}{11}\sqrt{22},$

$y = -\dfrac{1}{11}\sqrt{770}$ **19.** $x = -5, y = -2; x = -5, y = 2; x = 5, y = -2; x = 5, y = 2$

21. 0 ft, 0 s; 50 ft, 1.25 s   **23.** 8, 13   **25.** 4.47 km, 8.94 km   **27.** 8 in., 12 in.

Exercises 13–3, p. 335

1. $-3, -2, 2, 3$ **3.** $1, -2$ **5.** $-\dfrac{1}{2}, \dfrac{1}{4}$ **7.** $-\dfrac{1}{2}, \dfrac{1}{2}$ **9.** 1, 9   **11.** $\dfrac{64}{729}, 1$

13. $-27, 125$ **15.** 5   **17.** $-2, -1, 3, 4$ **19.** 18   **21.** 2000   **23.** 24 ft by 32 ft

Exercises 13–4, p. 338

1. 12   **3.** 2   **5.** 2, 3   **7.** 32   **9.** 16   **11.** 9   **13.** 12   **15.** 7, -1 **17.** 0   **19.** 5   **21.** 6

23. 258   **25.** $\dfrac{v_0^2 - v^2}{2g}$ **27.** $\dfrac{k^2}{2n(1 - k)}$ **29.** 9 in. by 12 in.   **31.** 5.20 mi

Exercises for Chapter 13, p. 339

1. $x = -0.9$, $y = 3.5$; $x = 0.8$, $y = 2.6$ 3. $x = 2.0$, $y = 0.0$; $x = 1.6$, $y = 0.6$
5. $x = 0.8$, $y = 1.6$; $x = -0.8$, $y = 1.6$ 7. $x = -1.2$, $y = 2.7$; $x = 1.2$, $y = 2.7$
9. $x = 0$, $y = 0$; $x = 2$, $y = 16$

11. $x = \dfrac{1}{12}(1 + \sqrt{97})$, $y = \dfrac{1}{18}(5 - \sqrt{97})$; $x = \dfrac{1}{12}(1 - \sqrt{97})$, $y = \dfrac{1}{18}(5 + \sqrt{97})$

13. $x = 7$, $y = 5$; $x = 7$, $y = -5$; $x = -7$, $y = 5$; $x = -7$, $y = -5$

15. $x = -2$, $y = 2$; $x = \dfrac{2}{3}$, $y = \dfrac{10}{9}$ 17. $-4, -2, 2, 4$ 19. $1, 16$ 21. $\dfrac{1}{3}, -\dfrac{1}{7}$ 23. $\dfrac{25}{4}$ 25. 11

27. 8 29. $\dfrac{9}{16}$ 31. 7 33. $r = \sqrt{\dfrac{\sqrt{\pi^2 h^4 + 4S^2} - \pi h^2}{2\pi}}$ 35. 0.75 s, 1.5 s   37. $x = 16$, $y = 15$

39. 493 ft

Exercises 14–1, p. 343

1. 0 3. 0 5. -40 7. 46 9. 8 11. 183 13. -28 15. 14 17. Yes   19. Yes
21. No   23. No   25. Yes   27. Yes   29. $(4x^3 + 8x^2 - x - 2) \div (2x - 1) = 2x^2 + 5x + 2$; No

Exercises 14–2, p. 347

1. $x^2 + 3x + 2$, $R = 0$ 3. $x^2 - x + 3$, $R = 0$ 5. $2x^4 - 4x^3 + 8x^2 - 17x + 42$, $R = -40$
7. $2x^3 + 3x^2 + 5x + 17$, $R = 46$ 9. $x^2 + x - 4$, $R = 8$ 11. $x^3 - 3x^2 + 10x - 45$, $R = 183$
13. $2x^3 - x^2 - 4x - 12$, $R = -28$ 15. $x^4 + 2x^3 + x^2 + 7x + 4$, $R = 14$
17. $x^5 + 2x^4 + 4x^3 + 8x^2 + 18x + 36$, $R = 66$ 19. $x^6 + 2x^5 + 4x^4 + 8x^3 + 16x^2 + 32x + 64$, $R = 0$
21. Yes   23. No   25. Yes   27. No   29. Yes   31. No

Exercises 14–3, p. 351
(Note: Unknown roots listed)

1. $-2, -1$ 3. $-2, 3$ 5. $-2, -2$ 7. $-j, -\dfrac{2}{3}$ 9. $2j, -2j$ 11. $3, -1$ 13. $-2, 1$

15. $\dfrac{1}{4}(1 + \sqrt{17})$, $\dfrac{1}{4}(1 - \sqrt{17})$ 17. $2, -3$ 19. $-2j, 3, -3$

Exercises 14–4, p. 356

1. $1, -1, -2$ 3. $2, -1, -3$ 5. $\dfrac{1}{2}, 5, -3$ 7. $\dfrac{1}{3}, -3, -1$ 9. $-2, -2, 2 \pm \sqrt{3}$

11. $2, 4, -1, -3$ 13. $1, -\dfrac{1}{2}, 1 \pm \sqrt{3}$ 15. $\dfrac{1}{2}, -\dfrac{2}{3}, -3, -\dfrac{1}{2}$ 17. $2, 2, -1, -1, -3$

19. $\dfrac{1}{2}, 1, 1, j, -j$ 21. $\dfrac{15}{2}$ 23. a 25. 2 in., or 1.17 in.

Exercises 14–5, p. 359

1. 0.59 3. 0.38 5. 1.71 7. -0.77 9. 2.56 11. 3.24 13. 0.68 15. $2.30, -1.30$
17. 7.01 ft   19. 0.0763 m

Exercises for Chapter 14, p. 359

1. 1 3. -107 5. Yes   7. No   9. $x^2 + 4x + 10$, $R = 11$ 11. $2x^2 - 7x + 10$, $R = -17$
13. $x^3 - 3x^2 - 4$, $R = -4$ 15. $2x^4 + 10x^3 + 4x^2 + 21x + 105$, $R = 516$ 17. No   19. Yes
21. (Unlisted roots) $\dfrac{1}{2}(-5 \pm \sqrt{17})$ 23. (Unlisted roots) $\dfrac{1}{3}(-1 \pm \sqrt{14}j)$ 25. (Unlisted roots), $4, -3$

27. (Unlisted roots) $2, -2$ 29. $1, 2, -4$ 31. $-1, -1, \dfrac{5}{2}$ 33. $\dfrac{5}{3}, -\dfrac{1}{2}, -1$

35. $\frac{1}{2}, -1, \sqrt{2}j, -\sqrt{2}j$ **37.** 0.75   **39.** 1.91   **41.** 5   **43.** 1, 0.4, 1.5, -0.6 (last three are irrational)

45. 7 ft, 7 ft, 11 ft   **47.** 1.64

Exercises 15—1, p. 368

1. 39   **3.** 30   **5.** 50   **7.** -40 **9.** -6 **11.** -86 **13.** 118   **15.** -2

17. $x = 2, y = -1, z = 3$ **19.** $x = -1, y = \frac{1}{3}, z = -\frac{1}{2}$ **21.** $x = -1, y = 0, z = 2, t = 1$

23. $x = 1, y = 2, z = -1, t = 3$ **25.** $\frac{2}{7}$ A, $\frac{18}{7}$ A, $-\frac{8}{7}$ A, $-\frac{12}{7}$ A   **27.** 100 mL, 300 mL, 200 mL

Exercises 15—2, p. 375

1. -60 **3.** -56 **5.** 0   **7.** 0   **9.** 57   **11.** -124 **13.** -13 **15.** -118 **17.** -72

19. 0   **21.** $x = 0, y = -1, z = 4$ **23.** $x = \frac{1}{3}, y = -\frac{1}{2}, z = 1$ **25.** $x = 2, y = -1, z = -1, t = 3$

27. $x = 1, y = 2, z = -1, t = -2$ **29.** $\frac{33}{16}$ A, $\frac{11}{8}$ A, $-\frac{5}{8}$ A, $-\frac{15}{8}$ A, $-\frac{15}{16}$ A

31. PPM of SO_2, NO, NO_2, CO: 0.5, 0.3, 0.2, 5.0

Exercises 15—3, p. 380

1. $a = 1, b = -3, c = 4, d = 7$ **3.** $x = 2, y = 3$ **5.** $\begin{pmatrix} 1 & 10 \\ 0 & 2 \end{pmatrix}$ **7.** $\begin{pmatrix} 0 & 0 \\ 1 & 6 \\ 1 & 0 \end{pmatrix}$

9. $\begin{pmatrix} 0 & 9 & -13 & 3 \\ 6 & -7 & 7 & 0 \end{pmatrix}$ **11.** Cannot be added   **13.** $\begin{pmatrix} -1 & 13 & -20 & 3 \\ 8 & -13 & 6 & 2 \end{pmatrix}$

15. $\begin{pmatrix} -3 & -6 & 5 & -6 \\ -6 & -4 & -17 & 6 \end{pmatrix}$ **17.** $A + B = B + A = \begin{pmatrix} 3 & 1 & 0 & 7 \\ 5 & -3 & -2 & 5 \\ 10 & 10 & 8 & 0 \end{pmatrix}$

19. $-(A - B) = B - A = \begin{pmatrix} 5 & -3 & -6 & -7 \\ 5 & 3 & 0 & -3 \\ -8 & 12 & 8 & 4 \end{pmatrix}$ **21.** $\begin{pmatrix} 24 & 18 & 0 & 0 \\ 15 & 12 & 9 & 0 \\ 0 & 9 & 15 & 18 \end{pmatrix}$

Exercises 15—4, p. 386

1. $(-8 \quad -12)$ **3.** $\begin{pmatrix} -15 & 15 & -26 \\ 8 & 5 & -13 \end{pmatrix}$ **5.** $\begin{pmatrix} 29 \\ -29 \end{pmatrix}$ **7.** $\begin{pmatrix} -7 & -5 \\ 8 & 0 \\ 14 & 10 \end{pmatrix}$

9. $\begin{pmatrix} 33 & -22 & 7 \\ 31 & -12 & 5 \\ 15 & 13 & -1 \\ 50 & -41 & 12 \end{pmatrix}$ **11.** $\begin{pmatrix} -62 & 68 \\ 73 & -27 \end{pmatrix}$ **13.** $AB = (40), BA = \begin{pmatrix} -1 & 3 & -8 \\ 5 & -15 & 40 \\ 7 & -21 & 56 \end{pmatrix}$

15. $AB = \begin{pmatrix} -5 \\ 10 \end{pmatrix}$, BA not defined   17. $AI = IA = A$ 19. $AI = IA = A$ 21. $B = A^{-1}$

23. $B = A^{-1}$ 25. Yes   27. No

29. 800 ft of brass pipe, 1000 ft of steel pipe; 1620 ft of brass pipe, 2240 ft of steel pipe

Exercises 15–5, p. 393

1. $\begin{pmatrix} -2 & -\frac{5}{2} \\ -1 & -1 \end{pmatrix}$ 3. $\begin{pmatrix} -\frac{1}{3} & \frac{1}{6} \\ \frac{2}{15} & \frac{1}{30} \end{pmatrix}$ 5. $\begin{pmatrix} \frac{3}{4} & \frac{1}{2} \\ -\frac{1}{4} & 0 \end{pmatrix}$ 7. $\begin{pmatrix} -\frac{1}{4} & -\frac{1}{8} \\ \frac{1}{16} & \frac{5}{32} \end{pmatrix}$ 9. $\begin{pmatrix} -3 & 2 \\ 2 & -1 \end{pmatrix}$

11. $\begin{pmatrix} -\frac{1}{2} & -2 \\ \frac{1}{2} & 1 \end{pmatrix}$ 13. $\begin{pmatrix} \frac{2}{9} & -\frac{5}{9} \\ \frac{1}{9} & \frac{2}{9} \end{pmatrix}$ 15. $\begin{pmatrix} \frac{3}{8} & \frac{1}{16} \\ -\frac{1}{4} & \frac{1}{8} \end{pmatrix}$ 17. $\begin{pmatrix} -18 & -7 & 5 \\ -3 & -1 & 1 \\ -5 & -2 & 1 \end{pmatrix}$ 19. $\begin{pmatrix} 3 & -4 & -1 \\ -4 & 5 & 2 \\ 2 & -3 & -1 \end{pmatrix}$

21. $\begin{pmatrix} 2 & 4 & \frac{7}{2} \\ -1 & -2 & -\frac{3}{2} \\ 1 & 1 & \frac{1}{2} \end{pmatrix}$ 23. $\begin{pmatrix} \frac{5}{2} & -2 & -2 \\ -1 & 1 & 1 \\ \frac{7}{4} & -\frac{3}{2} & -1 \end{pmatrix}$ 25. $\begin{pmatrix} 2 & 4 & \frac{7}{2} \\ -1 & -2 & -\frac{3}{2} \\ 1 & 1 & \frac{1}{2} \end{pmatrix}$ 27. $\begin{pmatrix} \frac{5}{2} & -2 & -2 \\ -1 & 1 & 1 \\ \frac{7}{4} & -\frac{3}{2} & -1 \end{pmatrix}$

Exercises 15–6, p. 398

1. $x = \frac{1}{2}, y = 3$ 3. $x = \frac{1}{2}, y = -\frac{5}{2}$ 5. $x = -4, y = 2, z = -1$ 7. $x = -1, y = 0, z = 3$

9. $x = 1, y = 2$ 11. $x = -\frac{3}{2}, y = -2$ 13. $x = -3, y = -\frac{1}{2}$ 15. $x = \frac{4}{5}, y = -\frac{22}{5}$

17. $x = 2, y = -4, x = 1$ 19. $x = 2, y = -\frac{1}{2}, x = 3$ 21. 10 lb, 8 lb, 12 lb

23. 8 of type A, 10 of type B

Exercises for Chapter 15, p. 399

1. 6   3. 186   5. -438 7. 44   9. 6   11. 186   13. -438 15. 44   17. -9

19. -44 21. $\begin{pmatrix} 1 & -3 \\ 8 & -5 \\ -8 & -2 \\ 3 & -10 \end{pmatrix}$ 23. $\begin{pmatrix} 3 & 0 \\ -12 & 18 \\ 9 & 6 \\ -3 & 21 \end{pmatrix}$ 25. Cannot be subtracted   27. $\begin{pmatrix} 7 & -6 \\ -4 & 20 \\ -1 & 6 \\ 1 & 15 \end{pmatrix}$

29. $\begin{pmatrix} 13 \\ -13 \end{pmatrix}$ 31. $\begin{pmatrix} 34 & 11 & -5 \\ 2 & -8 & 10 \\ -1 & -17 & 20 \end{pmatrix}$ 33. $\begin{pmatrix} -2 & \frac{5}{2} \\ -1 & 1 \end{pmatrix}$ 35. $\begin{pmatrix} \frac{2}{15} & \frac{1}{60} \\ -\frac{1}{15} & \frac{7}{60} \end{pmatrix}$ 37. $\begin{pmatrix} 11 & 10 & 3 \\ -4 & -4 & -1 \\ 3 & 3 & 1 \end{pmatrix}$

39. $\begin{pmatrix} \dfrac{1}{2} & -\dfrac{1}{2} & -1 \\ -3 & 2 & 1 \\ -4 & 3 & 2 \end{pmatrix}$ 41. $x = -3, y = 1$ 43. $x = -2, y = 7$ 45. $x = -1, y = -3, z = 0$

47. $x = 1, y = \dfrac{1}{2}, x = -\dfrac{1}{3}$ 49. $x = 3, y = 1, z = -1$ 51. $x = 1, y = 2, z = -3, t = 1$

53. $F_1 = 12$ lb, $F_2 = 9$ lb   55. $p_1 = \$60, p_2 = \$50, p_3 = \$90$ 57. 30 g, 50 g, 20 g

59. $70°, 80°, 100°, 110°$ 61. $\begin{pmatrix} 15{,}000 & 10{,}000 \\ 20{,}000 & 18{,}000 \\ 8{,}000 & 30{,}000 \end{pmatrix} + \begin{pmatrix} 18{,}000 & 12{,}000 \\ 30{,}000 & 22{,}000 \\ 12{,}000 & 40{,}000 \end{pmatrix} = \begin{pmatrix} 33{,}000 & 22{,}000 \\ 50{,}000 & 40{,}000 \\ 20{,}000 & 70{,}000 \end{pmatrix}$

Exercises 16–1, p. 407

1. $7 < 12$ 3. $20 < 45$ 5. $-4 > -9$ 7. $16 < 81$ 9. $x > -2$ 11. $x \le 4$ 13. $1 < x < 7$
15. $x < -9, x \ge -4$ 17. $x > 0$ 19. $x \le 0$ 21. $x < -1, x > 1$ 23. $2 \le x < 6$
25. $x > 0, y > 0$ 27. $y > x$ 29. Multiply both members by x.
31. Multiply by y and take square roots.   33. $3.5 < t < 15.3$ s, $h > 200$ m

35. $V = \dfrac{k}{a}$ if $r < a$, $V = \dfrac{k}{r}$ if $r > a$

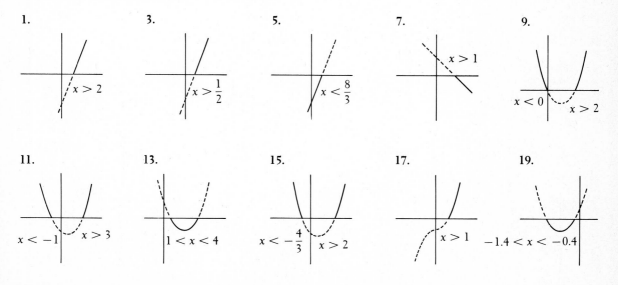

Exercises 16–2, p. 411
[*Note:* Solid portion of curves gives desired values of x.]

21. **23.** **25.** **27.**

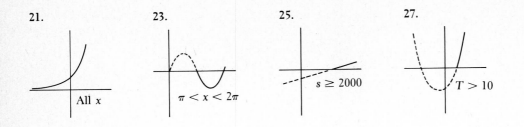

All x $\pi < x < 2\pi$ $s \geq 2000$ $T > 10$

Exercises 16—3, p. 415

1. $x > -3$ 3. $x < \dfrac{12}{7}$ 5. $x \leq 4$ 7. $x > \dfrac{9}{2}$ 9. $-1 < x < 1$ 11. $x \leq -2, x \geq \dfrac{1}{3}$

13. $\dfrac{1}{3} < x < \dfrac{1}{2}$ 15. All x   17. $-2 < x < 0, x > 1$ 19. $-2 < x < -1, x > 1$ 21. $x < 3, x > 8$

23. $-6 < x \leq \dfrac{3}{2}$ 25. $-1 < x < 2$ 27. $-5 < x < -1, x > 7$ 29. $-1 < x < \dfrac{3}{4}, x > 6$

31. $2 < x < 4, 5 < x < 9$ 33. $x \leq -2, x \geq 1$ 35. $-1 \leq x \leq 0$ 37. $t < \dfrac{15}{4}$ s

39. $-20°C < T < -16.2°C, 6.2°C < T < 10°C$

Exercises 16—4, p. 418

1. $3 < x < 5$ 3. $x < 1 \ \ x > \dfrac{7}{2}$ 5. $\dfrac{1}{6} \leq x \leq \dfrac{3}{2}$ 7. $x < -\dfrac{3}{2}, x > 0$ 9. $-10 < x < 2$

11. $x \leq -1, x \geq \dfrac{7}{3}$ 13. $-4 < x < -2, -1 < x < 1$ 15. $x < -4, -2 < x < -1, x > 1$

17. $y < \dfrac{1}{4}$ ft if $|x - 6| < 2$ ft   19. 5 in., 11 in.

Exercises 16—5, p. 424

1. **3.** **5.** **7.** **9.**

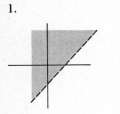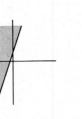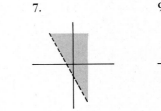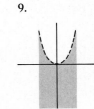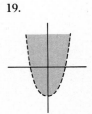

11. **13.** **15.** **17.** **19.**

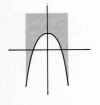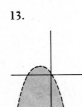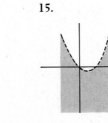

21.   **23.**   **25.**   **27.**

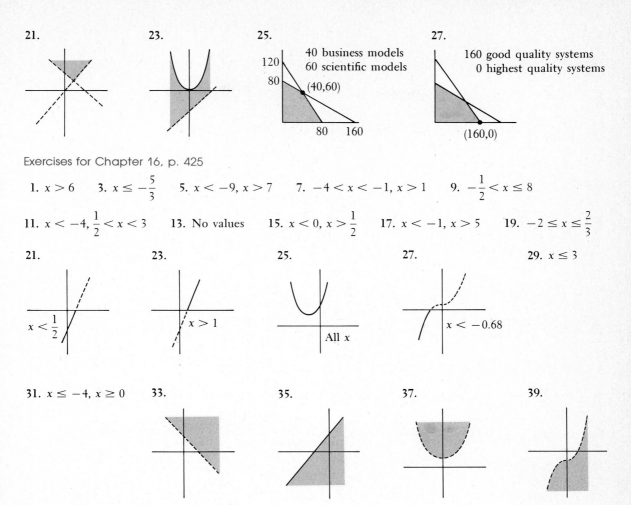

40 business models
60 scientific models

120
80
(40,60)

80   160

160 good quality systems
0 highest quality systems

(160,0)

Exercises for Chapter 16, p. 425

1. $x > 6$ **3.** $x \le -\dfrac{5}{3}$ **5.** $x < -9, x > 7$ **7.** $-4 < x < -1, x > 1$ **9.** $-\dfrac{1}{2} < x \le 8$

11. $x < -4, \dfrac{1}{2} < x < 3$ **13.** No values   **15.** $x < 0, x > \dfrac{1}{2}$ **17.** $x < -1, x > 5$ **19.** $-2 \le x \le \dfrac{2}{3}$

21.   **23.**   **25.**   **27.**   **29.** $x \le 3$

$x < \dfrac{1}{2}$ $x > 1$ All x $x < -0.68$

31. $x \le -4, x \ge 0$ **33.**   **35.**   **37.**   **39.**

41. $\dfrac{1}{x} > 0, \dfrac{1}{y} < 0, \dfrac{1}{x} > \dfrac{1}{y}$ **43.** Divide both members by y; then use $x - 1 > y$.   **45.** $x \le 80$ ft

47. $x > 16$ in.   **49.** $0 < R_1 < 0.73 \ \Omega, 7.27 \ \Omega < R_2 < 8 \ \Omega$ **51.**

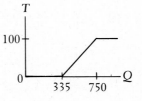

T

100

0

335   750 Q

Exercises 17—1, p. 429

1. 6   **3.** $\dfrac{4}{3}$ **5.** $\dfrac{1}{5}$ **7.** 40   **9.** 40,000 to 1   **11.** 19.2   **13.** 900 lb/in.²   **15.** 24 calculations/min

17. 1.44 Ω **19.** 32.5 r/min   **21.** 9080 g   **23.** 12.5 m/s   **25.** 27.0 in.   **27.** 72,000 ft-lb
29. 100 mg, 120 mg   **31.** 4.0 ft, 6.0 ft

Exercises 17–2, p. 434

1. $y = kz$ 3. $w = kxy^3$ 5. $r = \dfrac{16}{y}$ 7. $p = \dfrac{16q}{r^3}$ 9. 25   11. 50   13. 180   15. 2.56×10^5

17. 2.40 in.   19. $p = 30000t$ 21. 7680 BTU/h   23. $I = \dfrac{10^6}{r^2}$ 25. $R = \dfrac{5.00 \times 10^{-5}\, l}{A}$

27. $f = k\sqrt{T}$, 738 Hz   29. 135 ft   31. 23.3 cm/s   33. $P = \dfrac{k}{V^{3/2}}$, 2400 kPa   35. 0 ft/s²

Exercises for Chapter 17, p. 436

1. 10^6 3. $\dfrac{50}{7}$ 5. 3.25 in.   7. 1.72 L   9. 675,000   11. 492 g   13. $y = 3x^2$ 15. $v = \dfrac{128x}{y^3}$

17. 71.9 ft   19. 11.7 in.   21. 22.5 hp   23. $R = \dfrac{5}{18} A$ 25. $64.0\,\pi$ unit²   27. 551 ft/s

29. $\dfrac{1.28 \times 10^5 r^4}{l^2}$ 31. 50.0 Hz   33. 67.3×10^6 mi   35. $E = 0.139 (\tan\theta + \cot\theta)$

Exercises 18–1, p. 444

1. 4, 6, 8, 10, 12   3. 13, 9, 5, 1, -3 5. 22   7. -62 9. 37   11. $49b$ 13. 440   15. $-\dfrac{85}{2}$

17. $n = 6$, $s = 150$ 19. $d = -\dfrac{2}{19}$, $l = -\dfrac{1}{3}$ 21. $a = 19$, $l = 106$ 23. $n = 62$, $s = -4867$

25. $n = 23$, $l = 6$ 27. $n = 8$, $d = \dfrac{1}{14}(b + 2c)$ 29. $a = 36$, $d = 4$, $s = 540$

31. $a = 3$, $d = -\dfrac{1}{3}$, $s = 15$ 33. 5050   35. 100, 500   37. 19th   39. 6400 ft

Exercises 18–2, p. 447

1. 45, 15, 5, $\dfrac{5}{3}$, $\dfrac{5}{9}$ 3. 2, 6, 18, 54, 162   5. 16   7. $\dfrac{1}{125}$ 9. $\dfrac{1}{9}$ 11. 2×10^6 13. 248   15. 255

17. $a = 1$, $r = 3$ 19. $n = 5$, $s = \dfrac{2343}{25}$ 21. 32   23. \$219.11   25. \$597.53   27. 3.80 years

29. 22.0 ft   31. 0.0319 in.   33. 64.6%   35. $s = \dfrac{a - rl}{1 - r}$

Exercises 18–3, p. 451

1. 8   3. $\dfrac{25}{4}$ 5. $\dfrac{400}{21}$ 7. 8   9. $\dfrac{10000}{9999}$ 11. $\dfrac{1}{2}(5 + 3\sqrt{3})$ 13. $\dfrac{1}{3}$ 15. $\dfrac{40}{99}$ 17. $\dfrac{2}{11}$

19. $\dfrac{91}{333}$ 21. $\dfrac{11}{30}$ 23. $\dfrac{100741}{999000}$ 25. 24.0 ft

Exercises 18–4, p. 455

1. $t^3 + 3t^2 + 3t + 1$ 3. $16x^4 - 32x^3 + 24x^2 - 8x + 1$ 5. $x^5 + 10x^4 + 40x^3 + 80x^2 + 80x + 32$
7. $64a^6 - 192a^5b^2 + 240a^4b^4 - 160a^3b^6 + 60a^2b^8 - 12ab^{10} + b^{12}$
9. $625x^4 - 1500x^3 + 1350x^2 - 540x + 81$ 11. $64a^6 + 192a^5 + 240a^4 + 160a^3 + 60a^2 + 12a + 1$
13. $x^{10} + 20x^9 + 180x^8 + 960x^7 + \cdots$ 15. $1 + 2x + 3x^2 + 4x^3 + \cdots$ 17. 1.049   19. 9.980
21. 3.009   23. 0.924   25. $56a^3b^5$ 27. $10264320x^8b^4$ 29. $T^4 + 4T^3h + 6T^2h^2 + 4Th^3 + h^4$

31. $1 - \dfrac{x}{a} + \dfrac{x^3}{2a^3} - \cdots$

Exercises for Chapter 18, p. 456

1. 81   **3.** 1.28×10^{-6} **5.** $-\dfrac{119}{2}$ **7.** $\dfrac{16}{243}$ **9.** $\dfrac{195}{2}$ **11.** $\dfrac{1023}{96}$ **13.** 81   **15.** $\dfrac{9}{16}$ **17.** 186

19. $\dfrac{455}{2}$ (AP), 127 (GP) or 43 (GP)   **21.** $\dfrac{7}{9}$ **23.** $\dfrac{75}{99}$ **25.** $\dfrac{41}{333}$ **27.** $\dfrac{1}{6}$

29. $x^4 - 8x^3 + 24x^2 - 32x + 16$ **31.** $x^{10} + 5x^8 + 10x^6 + 10x^4 + 5x^2 + 1$

33. $1 - \dfrac{1}{2}a^2 - \dfrac{1}{8}a^4 - \dfrac{1}{16}a^6 - \cdots$ **35.** $1 + 6x + 24x^2 + 80x^3 + \cdots$ **37.** 30.133   **39.** 0.124

41. 1,001,000   **43.** 195   **45.** \$6633.24   **47.** \$8590   **49.** 20.0 s   **51.** 10^{-20} atm

Exercises 19—1, p. 465

[*Note:* "Answers" to trigonometric identities are intermediate steps of suggested reductions of the left member.]

1. $1.483 = \dfrac{1}{0.6745}$ **3.** $\left(\dfrac{1}{2}\sqrt{3}\right)^2 + \left(-\dfrac{1}{2}\right)^2 = \dfrac{3}{4} + \dfrac{1}{4} = 1$ **5.** $\dfrac{\cos\theta}{\sin\theta} \cdot \dfrac{1}{\cos\theta} = \dfrac{1}{\sin\theta}$

7. $\dfrac{\sin x}{\dfrac{\sin x}{\cos x}} = \dfrac{\sin x}{1} \cdot \dfrac{\cos x}{\sin x}$ **9.** $\sin y\left(\dfrac{\cos y}{\sin y}\right)$ **11.** $\sin x\left(\dfrac{1}{\cos x}\right)$ **13.** $\csc^2 x(\sin^2 x)$

15. $\sin x(\csc^2 x) = (\sin x)(\csc x)(\csc x) = \sin x\left(\dfrac{1}{\sin x}\right)\csc x$ **17.** $\sin x \csc x - \sin^2 x = 1 - \sin^2 x$

19. $\tan y \cot y + \tan^2 y = 1 + \tan^2 y$ **21.** $\sin x\left(\dfrac{\sin x}{\cos x}\right) + \cos x = \dfrac{\sin^2 x + \cos^2 x}{\cos x} = \dfrac{1}{\cos x}$

23. $\cos\theta\left(\dfrac{\cos\theta}{\sin\theta}\right) + \sin\theta = \dfrac{\cos^2\theta + \sin^2\theta}{\sin\theta} = \dfrac{1}{\sin\theta}$

25. $\sec\theta\left(\dfrac{\sin\theta}{\cos\theta}\right)\csc\theta = \sec\theta\left(\dfrac{1}{\cos\theta}\right)(\sin\theta\csc\theta) = \sec\theta(\sec\theta)(1)$

27. $\cot\theta(\sec^2\theta - 1) = \cot\theta\tan^2\theta = (\cot\theta\tan\theta)\tan\theta$ **29.** $\dfrac{\sin x}{\cos x} + \dfrac{\cos x}{\sin x} = \dfrac{\sin^2 x + \cos^2 x}{\cos x \sin x} = \dfrac{1}{\cos x \sin x}$

31. $(1 - \sin^2 x) - \sin^2 x$ **33.** $\dfrac{\sin x(1 + \cos x)}{1 - \cos^2 x} = \dfrac{1 + \cos x}{\sin x}$

35. $\dfrac{(1/\cos x) + (1/\sin x)}{1 + (\sin x/\cos x)} = \dfrac{(\sin x + \cos x)/\cos x \sin x}{(\cos x + \sin x)/\cos x} = \dfrac{\cos x}{\cos x \sin x}$

37. $\dfrac{\sin^2 x}{\cos^2 x}\cos^2 x + \dfrac{\cos^2 x}{\sin^2 x}\sin^2 x = \sin^2 x + \cos^2 x$ **39.** $4\sin x + \dfrac{\sin x}{\cos x} = \sin x\left(4 + \dfrac{1}{\cos x}\right)$

41. $\dfrac{1}{\cos x} + \dfrac{\sin x}{\cos x} + \dfrac{\cos x}{\sin x} = \dfrac{\sin x + \cos^2 x + \sin^2 x}{\sin x \cos x}$ **43.** $(2\sin^2 x - 1)(\sin^2 x - 1)$

45. $\dfrac{\cot 2y(\sec 2y + \tan 2y) - \cos 2y(\sec 2y - \tan 2y)}{\sec^2 2y - \tan^2 2y} = \dfrac{\cot 2y \sec 2y + 1 - 1 + \cos 2y \tan 2y}{1}$

47. Infinite GP: $\dfrac{1}{1 - \sin^2 x} = \dfrac{1}{\cos^2 x}$ **49.** $\mu = \dfrac{w\sin\theta}{w\cos\theta} = \dfrac{\sin\theta}{\cos\theta} = \tan\theta$ **51.** $\sin\theta(\sin^2\theta) = \sin\theta(1 - \cos^2\theta)$

Exercises 19–2, p. 470

1. $\sin 105° = \sin 60° \cos 45° + \cos 60° \sin 45° = \dfrac{\sqrt{3}}{2} \cdot \dfrac{\sqrt{2}}{2} + \dfrac{1}{2} \cdot \dfrac{\sqrt{2}}{2} = 0.9659$

3. $\cos 15° = \cos(60° - 45°) = \cos 60° \cos 45° + \sin 60° \sin 45°$

$$= \left(\dfrac{1}{2}\right)\left(\dfrac{1}{2}\sqrt{2}\right) + \left(\dfrac{1}{2}\sqrt{3}\right)\left(\dfrac{1}{2}\sqrt{2}\right) = \dfrac{1}{4}\sqrt{2} + \dfrac{1}{4}\sqrt{6} = \dfrac{1}{4}(\sqrt{2} + \sqrt{6}) = 0.9659$$

5. $-\dfrac{33}{65}$ 7. $-\dfrac{56}{65}$ 9. $\sin 3x$ 11. $\cos x$

13. $\sin(270° - x) = \sin 270° \cos x - \cos 270° \sin x = (-1)\cos x - 0(\sin x)$

15. $\cos\left(\dfrac{1}{2}\pi - x\right) = \cos \dfrac{1}{2}\pi \cos x + \sin \dfrac{1}{2}\pi \sin x = 0(\cos x) + 1(\sin x)$

17. $\cos(30° + x) = \cos 30° \cos x - \sin 30° \sin x = \dfrac{1}{2}\sqrt{3} \cos x - \dfrac{1}{2}\sin x = \dfrac{1}{2}(\sqrt{3} \cos x - \sin x)$

19. $\sin\left(\dfrac{\pi}{4} + x\right) = \sin \dfrac{\pi}{4} \cos x + \cos \dfrac{\pi}{4} \sin x = \dfrac{1}{2}\sqrt{2} \cos x + \dfrac{1}{2}\sqrt{2} \sin x$

21. $(\sin x \cos y + \cos x \sin y)(\sin x \cos y - \cos x \sin y) = \sin^2 x \cos^2 y - \cos^2 x \sin^2 y$
$$= \sin^2 x(1 - \sin^2 y) - (1 - \sin^2 x)\sin^2 y$$

23. $(\cos \alpha \cos \beta - \sin \alpha \sin \beta) + (\cos \alpha \cos \beta + \sin \alpha \sin \beta)$ 25. 27. 29. 31. Use indicated method.

33. $\sin(\omega t + \phi - \alpha)$ 35. $2A \sin \dfrac{2\pi t}{T} \cos \dfrac{2\pi x}{\lambda}$

Exercises 19–3, p. 474

1. $\sin 60° = \sin 2(30°) = 2 \sin 30° \cos 30° = 2\left(\dfrac{1}{2}\right)\left(\dfrac{1}{2}\sqrt{3}\right) = \dfrac{1}{2}\sqrt{3}$

3. $\cos 120° = \cos 2(60°) = \cos^2 60° - \sin^2 60° = \left(\dfrac{1}{2}\right)^2 - \left(\dfrac{1}{2}\sqrt{3}\right)^2 = -\dfrac{1}{2}$

5. $\dfrac{24}{25}$ 7. $\dfrac{3}{5}$ 9. $2 \sin 8x$ 11. $\cos 8x$ 13. $\cos^2 \alpha - (1 - \cos^2 \alpha)$

15. $(\cos^2 x - \sin^2 x)(\cos^2 x + \sin^2 x) = (\cos^2 x - \sin^2 x)(1)$ 17. $\dfrac{2 \tan x}{\sin 2x} = \dfrac{2(\sin x/\cos x)}{2 \sin x \cos x} = \dfrac{1}{\cos^2 x}$

19. $\dfrac{\sin 3x \cos x - \cos 3x \sin x}{\sin x \cos x} = \dfrac{\sin 2x}{\dfrac{1}{2}\sin 2x}$

21. $\sin(2x + x) = \sin 2x \cos x + \cos 2x \sin x = (2 \sin x \cos x)(\cos x) + (\cos^2 x - \sin^2 x)\sin x$
23. Use indicated method.

25. $\cos \alpha = \dfrac{A}{C}$, $\sin \alpha = \dfrac{B}{C}$:

$A \sin 2t + B \cos 2t = C\left(\dfrac{A}{C}\sin 2t + \dfrac{B}{C}\cos 2t\right)$

$= C(\cos \alpha \sin 2t + \sin \alpha \cos 2t)$

Exercises 19–4, p. 476

1. $\cos 15° = \cos \dfrac{1}{2}(30°) = \sqrt{\dfrac{1 + \cos 30°}{2}} = \sqrt{\dfrac{1.8660}{2}} = 0.9659$

3. $\sin 75° = \sin \dfrac{1}{2}(150°) = \sqrt{\dfrac{1 - \cos 150°}{2}} = \sqrt{\dfrac{1.8660}{2}} = 0.9659$

5. $\sin 3\alpha$ **7.** $4 \cos 2x$ **9.** $\dfrac{1}{26}\sqrt{26}$ **11.** $\dfrac{1}{10}\sqrt{2}$ **13.** $\pm \sqrt{\dfrac{2}{1 - \cos \alpha}}$

15. $\tan\dfrac{1}{2}\alpha = \dfrac{1 - \cos \alpha}{\sin \alpha} = \dfrac{\sin \alpha}{1 + \cos \alpha}$ **17.** $\dfrac{1 - \cos \alpha}{2 \sin \dfrac{1}{2}\alpha} = \dfrac{1 - \cos \alpha}{2\sqrt{\dfrac{1}{2}(1 - \cos \alpha)}} = \sqrt{\dfrac{1 - \cos \alpha}{2}}$

19. $2\left(\dfrac{1 - \cos \alpha}{2}\right) - \left(\dfrac{1 + \cos \alpha}{2}\right)$ **21.** $\sqrt{1 - 2 \cos \alpha + \cos^2\alpha + \sin^2\alpha\,(\cos^2\beta + \sin^2\beta)} = \sqrt{2 - 2 \cos \alpha}$

Exercises 19—5, p. 480

1. $\dfrac{\pi}{2}$ **3.** $\dfrac{3\pi}{4}, \dfrac{7\pi}{4}$ **5.** $\dfrac{\pi}{3}, \dfrac{2\pi}{3}, \dfrac{4\pi}{3}, \dfrac{5\pi}{3}$ **7.** $\dfrac{\pi}{3}, \dfrac{2\pi}{3}, \dfrac{4\pi}{3}, \dfrac{5\pi}{3}$ **9.** $0, \dfrac{\pi}{6}, \dfrac{5\pi}{6}, \pi$

11. $\dfrac{\pi}{12}, \dfrac{\pi}{4}, \dfrac{5\pi}{12}, \dfrac{3\pi}{4}, \dfrac{13\pi}{12}, \dfrac{5\pi}{4}, \dfrac{17\pi}{12}, \dfrac{7\pi}{4}$ **13.** $\dfrac{\pi}{2}, \dfrac{3\pi}{2}$ **15.** $0, \dfrac{\pi}{3}, \pi, \dfrac{5\pi}{3}$ **17.** $\dfrac{\pi}{4}, \dfrac{3\pi}{4}, \dfrac{5\pi}{4}, \dfrac{7\pi}{4}$ **19.** $3.57, 5.85$

21. $0.26, 1.31, 3.40, 4.45$ **23.** $0, \pi$ **25.** $\dfrac{3\pi}{8}, \dfrac{7\pi}{8}, \dfrac{11\pi}{8}, \dfrac{15\pi}{8}$ **27.** $0.79, 1.25, 3.93, 4.39$ **29.** 0.955

31. 1.41 units of time   **33.** $-0.95, 0.00, 0.95$ **35.** $0, 4.49$

Exercises 19—6, p. 483

1. y is the angle whose tangent is x.   **3.** y is the angle whose cotangent is $3x$.

5. y is twice the angle whose sine is x.   **7.** y is 5 times the angle whose cosine is $2x$.

9. $\dfrac{\pi}{3}$ **11.** $\dfrac{3\pi}{4}$ **13.** $\dfrac{3\pi}{4}$ **15.** $\dfrac{\pi}{3}$ **17.** $\dfrac{5\pi}{6}$ **19.** $\dfrac{\pi}{4}$ **21.** $x = \dfrac{1}{3}\arcsin y$ **23.** $x = 4 \tan y$

25. $x = \dfrac{1}{3}\text{arcsec}\,(y - 1)$ **27.** $x = 1 - \cos(1 - y)$ **29.** I, II   **31.** II, III   **33.** $k = \dfrac{m\left(\arccos\dfrac{x}{A}\right)^2}{t^2}$

35. $\theta = \dfrac{1}{2}\arcsin\dfrac{2E}{E_0}$

Exercises 19—7, p. 487

1. $\dfrac{\pi}{3}$ **3.** 0 **5.** $-\dfrac{\pi}{3}$ **7.** $\dfrac{\pi}{3}$ **9.** $\dfrac{\pi}{6}$ **11.** $-\dfrac{\pi}{4}$ **13.** $\dfrac{\pi}{4}$ **15.** -1.309 **17.** $\dfrac{1}{2}\sqrt{3}$ **19.** $\dfrac{1}{2}\sqrt{2}$

21. -1.150 **23.** -1 **25.** $\dfrac{x}{\sqrt{1 - x^2}}$ **27.** $\dfrac{1}{x}$ **29.** $\dfrac{3x}{\sqrt{9x^2 - 1}}$ **31.** $2x\sqrt{1 - x^2}$

33. $\sin\left[\text{Arcsin}\dfrac{3}{5} + \text{Arcsin}\dfrac{5}{13}\right] = \dfrac{3}{5} \cdot \dfrac{12}{13} + \dfrac{4}{5} \cdot \dfrac{5}{13} = \dfrac{56}{65}$

35. let $b = $ side opp. β; $\tan \beta = \dfrac{b}{1} = b$; $\tan \alpha = a + b = a + \tan \beta$; $\alpha = \text{Arctan}(a + \tan \beta)$

Exercises for Chapter 19, p. 488

1. $\sin(90° + 30°) = \sin 90° \cos 30° + \cos 90° \sin 30° = (1)\left(\dfrac{1}{2}\sqrt{3}\right) + (0)\left(\dfrac{1}{2}\right) = \dfrac{1}{2}\sqrt{3}$

3. $\sin(180° - 45°) = \sin 180° \cos 45° - \cos 180° \sin 45° = 0\left(\dfrac{1}{2}\sqrt{2}\right) - (-1)\left(\dfrac{1}{2}\sqrt{2}\right) = \dfrac{1}{2}\sqrt{2}$

5. $\cos 2(90°) = \cos^2 90° - \sin^2 90° = 0 - 1 = -1$

7. $\sin \frac{1}{2}(90°) = \sqrt{\frac{1}{2}(1 - \cos 90°)} = \sqrt{\frac{1}{2}(1 - 0)} = \frac{1}{2}\sqrt{2}$ **9.** $\sin 5x$ **11.** $4 \sin 12x$ **13.** $2 \cos 12x$

15. $2 \cos x$ **17.** $-\frac{\pi}{2}$ **19.** 0.2618 **21.** $-\frac{1}{3}\sqrt{3}$ **23.** 0 **25.** $\dfrac{\dfrac{1}{\cos y}}{\dfrac{1}{\sin y}} = \dfrac{1}{\cos y} \cdot \dfrac{\sin y}{1}$

27. $\sin x \csc x - \sin^2 x = 1 - \sin^2 x$ **29.** $\dfrac{1 - \sin^2 \theta}{\sin \theta} = \dfrac{\cos^2 \theta}{\sin \theta}$ **31.** $\cos \theta \left(\dfrac{\cos \theta}{\sin \theta}\right) + \sin \theta = \dfrac{\cos^2 \theta + \sin^2 \theta}{\sin \theta}$

33. $\dfrac{(\sec^2 x - 1)(\sec^2 x + 1)}{\tan^2 x} = \sec^2 x + 1$ **35.** $2\left(\dfrac{1}{\sin 2x}\right)\left(\dfrac{\cos x}{\sin x}\right) = 2\left(\dfrac{1}{2 \sin x \cos x}\right)\left(\dfrac{\cos x}{\sin x}\right) = \dfrac{1}{\sin^2 x}$

37. $\dfrac{1}{2}\left(2 \sin \dfrac{\theta}{2} \cos \dfrac{\theta}{2}\right)$ **39.** $\dfrac{1}{\cos x} + \dfrac{\sin x}{\cos x} = \dfrac{(1 + \sin x)(1 - \sin x)}{\cos x(1 - \sin x)} = \dfrac{1 - \sin^2 x}{\cos x(1 - \sin x)}$

41. $\cos[(x - y) + y]$ **43.** $\sin 4x(\cos 4x)$ **45.** $\dfrac{\sin x}{\dfrac{1}{\sin x} - \dfrac{\cos x}{\sin x}} = \dfrac{\sin^2 x}{1 - \cos x} = \dfrac{1 - \cos^2 x}{1 - \cos x}$

47. $\dfrac{\sin x \cos y + \cos x \sin y + \sin x \cos y - \cos x \sin y}{\cos x \cos y - \sin x \sin y + \cos x \cos y + \sin x \sin y} = \dfrac{2 \sin x \cos y}{2 \cos x \cos y}$ **49.** $x = \dfrac{1}{2}\arccos \dfrac{1}{2}y$

51. $x = \dfrac{1}{5}\sin \dfrac{1}{3}\left(\dfrac{1}{4}\pi - y\right)$ **53.** $0, \dfrac{\pi}{2}, \pi, \dfrac{3\pi}{2}$ **55.** $\dfrac{\pi}{6}, \dfrac{5\pi}{6}, \dfrac{7\pi}{6}, \dfrac{11\pi}{6}$ **57.** $0, \pi$ **59.** 0 **61.** $\dfrac{1}{x}$

63. $2x\sqrt{1 - x^2}$ **65.** $\cos x(\cos^2 x) = \cos x(1 - \sin^2 x)$ **67.** $2 \sin^2 x = 1 - \cos 2x; \sin^2 x = \dfrac{1}{2}(1 - \cos 2x)$

69. $t = 3 \arcsin \dfrac{y}{20}$ **71.** $\cos^2 \alpha - 3 \sin^2 \alpha$

73. $1 - 2r^2 + r^4 + 2r^2 - 2r^2\cos \beta = (1 - r^2)^2 + 4r^2\left(\dfrac{1 - \cos \beta}{2}\right)$ **75.** $54.7°$

Exercises 20–1, p. 496

1. $2\sqrt{29}$ **3.** 3 **5.** $\sqrt{85}$ **7.** 7 **9.** $\dfrac{5}{2}$ **11.** undefined   **13.** $-\dfrac{7}{6}$ **15.** 0 **17.** $\dfrac{1}{3}\sqrt{3}$

19. $-\dfrac{1}{3}\sqrt{3}$ **21.** $20.0°$ **23.** $98.5°$ **25.** parallel   **27.** perpendicular   **29.** $8, -2$ **31.** -3

33. two sides equal $2\sqrt{10}$ **35.** $m_1 = \dfrac{1}{4}, m_2 = \dfrac{5}{4}$ **37.** 10

Exercises 20–2, p. 501

1. $4x - y + 20 = 0$ **3.** $7x - 6y - 16 = 0$ **5.** $x - y + 2 = 0$ **7.** $y = -3$ **9.** $x = -3$
11. $3x - 2y - 12 = 0$ **13.** $x + 3y + 5 = 0$ **15.** $x + 7y - 18 = 0$

17.

19.

21. $y = \dfrac{3}{2}x - \dfrac{1}{2}; m = \dfrac{3}{2}, b = -\dfrac{1}{2}$ **23.** $y = \dfrac{5}{2}x + \dfrac{5}{2}; m = \dfrac{5}{2}, b = \dfrac{5}{2}$

25. -2 **27.** 1 **29.** $m_1 = m_2 = \dfrac{3}{2}$ **31.** $m_1 = 2, m_2 = -\dfrac{1}{2}$

33. $x + 2y - 4 = 0$ **35.** $3x + y - 18 = 0$ **37.** $s = 50t + 10$

39. $L = \dfrac{2}{3}F + 15$ **41.** 3.35 kJ   **43.** $n = \dfrac{7}{6}t + 10$; at 6:30, $n = 10$; at 8:30, $n = 150$

45.

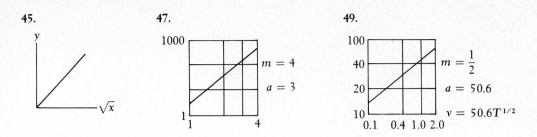

47.

49.

Exercises 20—3, p. 506

1. $(2, 1)$, $r = 5$ 3. $(-1, 0)$, $r = 2$ 5. $x^2 + y^2 = 9$ 7. $x^2 + y^2 - 4x - 4y - 8 = 0$
9. $x^2 + y^2 + 4x - 10y + 24 = 0$ 11. $x^2 + y^2 - 4x - 2y - 3 = 0$ 13. $x^2 + y^2 + 6x - 10y + 9 = 0$
15. $x^2 + y^2 - 4x - 10y + 4 = 0$; $x^2 + y^2 + 4x + 10y + 4 = 0$

17. $(0,0)$
$r = 5$

19. $(1,0)$
$r = 3$

21. $(-4,5)$
$r = 7$

23. $(1,2)$
$r = \frac{1}{2}\sqrt{22}$

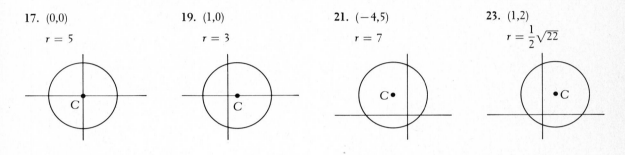

25. Symmetrical to both axes and origin   27. Symmetrical to y-axis   29. $(7, 0)$, $(-1, 0)$
31. $3x^2 + 3y^2 + 4x + 8y - 20 = 0$, circle
33. $x^2 + y^2 = 2.79$ (assume center of circle at center of coordinate system)
35. $x^2 + y^2 = 576$, $x^2 + y^2 + 36y + 315 = 0$ (in inches)

Exercises 20—4, p. 511

1. $F(1,0)$, $x = -1$
3. $F(-1,0)$, $x = 1$
5. $F(0,2)$, $y = -2$
7. $F(0,-1)$, $y = 1$

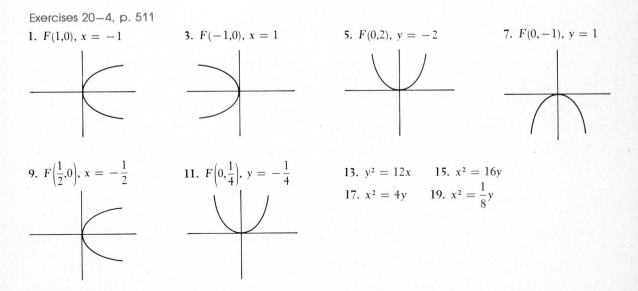

9. $F\left(\frac{1}{2},0\right)$, $x = -\frac{1}{2}$
11. $F\left(0,\frac{1}{4}\right)$, $y = -\frac{1}{4}$

13. $y^2 = 12x$ 15. $x^2 = 16y$

17. $x^2 = 4y$ 19. $x^2 = \frac{1}{8}y$

21. $y^2 - 2y - 12x + 37 = 0$ **23.** $x^2 - 2x + 8y - 23 = 0$ **25.** $x = 2$, $y = 4$ **29.**

27. $x^2 = 100y$

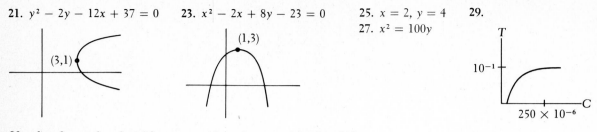

31. $y^2 = 8x$ or $x^2 = 8y$ with vertex midway between island and shore

Exercises 20–5, p. 517

1. $V(2,0)$, $V(-2,0)$
  $F(\sqrt{3},0)$, $F(-\sqrt{3},0)$

3. $V(0,6)$, $V(0,-6)$
  $F(0,\sqrt{11})$, $F(0,-\sqrt{11})$

5. $V(3,0)$, $V(-3,0)$
  $F(\sqrt{5},0)$, $F(-\sqrt{5},0)$

7. $V(0,7)$, $V(0,-7)$
  $F(0)$, $\sqrt{45})$, $F(0, -\sqrt{45})$

9. $V(0,4)$, $V(0,-4)$
  $F(0,\sqrt{14})$,
  $F(0,-\sqrt{14})$

11. $V\left(\dfrac{5}{2},0\right)$, $V\left(-\dfrac{5}{2},0\right)$
  $F(\sqrt{21}/2,0)$, $F(-\sqrt{21}/2,0)$

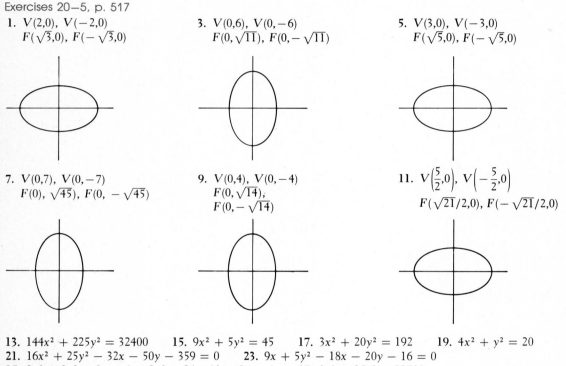

13. $144x^2 + 225y^2 = 32400$ **15.** $9x^2 + 5y^2 = 45$ **17.** $3x^2 + 20y^2 = 192$ **19.** $4x^2 + y^2 = 20$
21. $16x^2 + 25y^2 - 32x - 50y - 359 = 0$ **23.** $9x + 5y^2 - 18x - 20y - 16 = 0$
25. $2x^2 + 3y^2 - 8x - 4 = 2x^2 + 3(-y)^2 - 8x - 4$ **27.** $9x^2 + 25y^2 = 22500$
29. $2.70x^2 + 2.76y^2 = 7.45 \times 10^7$ **31.** major axis = 8.5 in., minor axis = 6.0 in.

Exercises 20–6, p. 523

1. $V(5,0)$, $V(-5,0)$
  $F(13,0)$, $F(-13,0)$

3. $V(0,3)$, $V(0,-3)$
  $F(0,\sqrt{10})$, $F(0,-\sqrt{10})$

5. $V(\sqrt{2},0)$, $V(-\sqrt{2},0)$
  $F(\sqrt{6},0)$, $F(-\sqrt{6},0)$

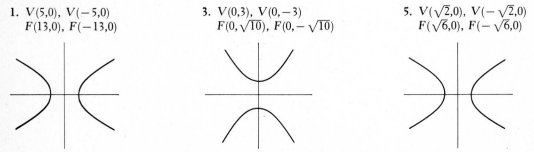

7. $V(0,\sqrt{5})$, $V(0,-\sqrt{5})$
   $F(0,\sqrt{7})$, $F(0,-\sqrt{7})$

9. $V(0,2)$, $V(0,-2)$
   $F(0,\sqrt{5})$, $F(0,-\sqrt{5})$

11. $V(2,0)$, $V(-2,0)$
   $F\left(\frac{2}{3}\sqrt{13},0\right)$, $F\left(-\frac{2}{3}\sqrt{13},0\right)$

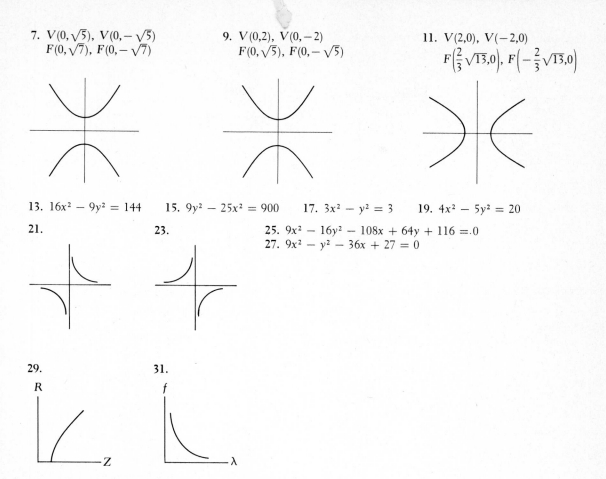

13. $16x^2 - 9y^2 = 144$ 15. $9y^2 - 25x^2 = 900$ 17. $3x^2 - y^2 = 3$ 19. $4x^2 - 5y^2 = 20$

21.   23.   25. $9x^2 - 16y^2 - 108x + 64y + 116 = 0$
              27. $9x^2 - y^2 - 36x + 27 = 0$

29.
R

31.
f

Z   λ

33. dist(rifle to P) $-$ dist(target to P) $=$ constant
    (related to distance from rifle to target)

Exercises 20—7, p. 528

1. Parabola, $(-1,2)$ 3. Hyperbola, $(1,2)$ 5. Ellipse, $(-1,0)$ 7. Parabola, $(-3,1)$

9. $y^2 - 6y - 16x - 7 = 0$ 11. $x^2 + 6x - 4y + 17 = 0$ 13. $16x^2 + 25y^2 + 64x - 100y - 236 = 0$
15. $16x^2 - 9y^2 + 32x + 18y - 137 = 0$

17. Parabola, $(-1,-1)$ **19.** Ellipse, $(-3,0)$ **21.** Hyperbola, $(0,4)$ **23.** Parabola, $(1,0)$

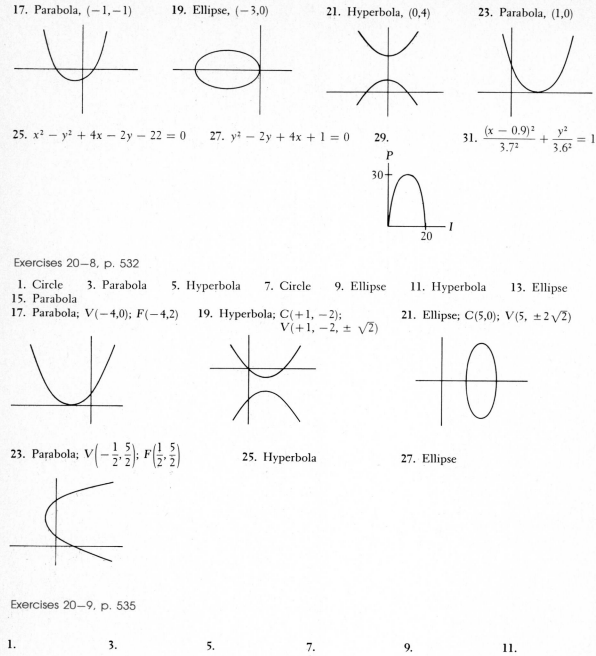

25. $x^2 - y^2 + 4x - 2y - 22 = 0$ **27.** $y^2 - 2y + 4x + 1 = 0$ **29.**   **31.** $\dfrac{(x - 0.9)^2}{3.7^2} + \dfrac{y^2}{3.6^2} = 1$

Exercises 20—8, p. 532

1. Circle   **3.** Parabola   **5.** Hyperbola   **7.** Circle   **9.** Ellipse   **11.** Hyperbola   **13.** Ellipse
15. Parabola
17. Parabola; $V(-4,0)$; $F(-4,2)$ **19.** Hyperbola; $C(+1, -2)$;   **21.** Ellipse; $C(5,0)$; $V(5, \pm 2\sqrt{2})$
$\qquad\qquad\qquad\qquad\qquad\qquad V(+1, -2, \pm \sqrt{2})$

23. Parabola; $V\left(-\dfrac{1}{2}, \dfrac{5}{2}\right)$; $F\left(\dfrac{1}{2}, \dfrac{5}{2}\right)$ **25.** Hyperbola   **27.** Ellipse

Exercises 20—9, p. 535

1.   **3.**   **5.**   **7.**   **9.**   **11.**

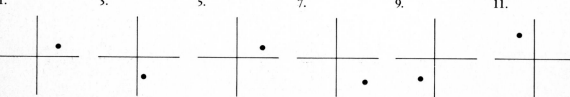

13. $\left(2, \dfrac{\pi}{6}\right)$ **15.** $\left(1, \dfrac{7\pi}{6}\right)$ **17.** $(-4, -4\sqrt{3})$ **19.** $(2.77, -1.15)$ **21.** $r = 3 \sec \theta$ **23.** $r = a$

25. $r = 4 \cot \theta \csc \theta$ **27.** $r^2 = \dfrac{4}{1 + 3 \sin^2\theta}$ **29.** $x^2 + y^2 - y = 0$ **31.** $x = 4$

33. $x^4 + y^4 - 4x^3 + 2x^2y^2 - 4xy^2 - 4y^2 = 0$ **35.** $(x^2 + y^2)^2 = 2xy$

37. $s = \sqrt{x^2 + y^2} \arctan\left(\dfrac{y}{x}\right)$, $A = \dfrac{1}{2}(x^2 + y^2) \arctan\left(\dfrac{y}{x}\right)$ **39.** $r = 100 \tan \theta \sec \theta$

Exercises 20–10, p. 538

1.

3.

5.
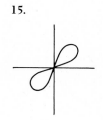

7.
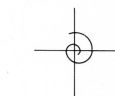

9.

11.
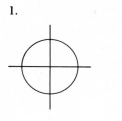

13.
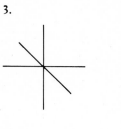

15.
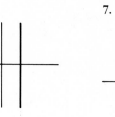

17.
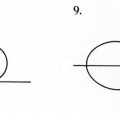

19.

21.
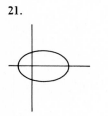

23.
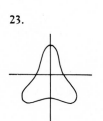

25.
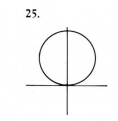

27.
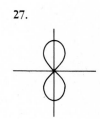

Exercises for Chapter 20, p. 539

1. $4x - y - 11 = 0$

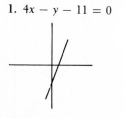

3. $2x + 3y + 3 = 0$

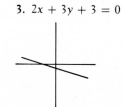

5. $x^2 + y^2 - 2x + 4y - 5 = 0$

7. $y^2 = 12x$

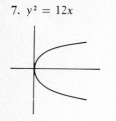

9. $9x^2 + 25y^2 = 900$

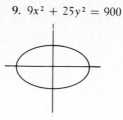

11. $144y^2 - 169x^2 = 24336$

13. $(-3,0)$, $r = 4$

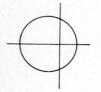

15. $(0,-5)$, $y = 5$

17. $V(0,4)$, $V(0,-4)$
$F(0,\sqrt{15})$, $F(0,-\sqrt{15})$

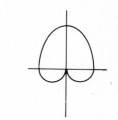

19. $V(2,0)$, $V(-2,0)$
$F\left(\frac{2}{5}\sqrt{35},0\right)$, $F\left(-\frac{2}{5}\sqrt{35},0\right)$

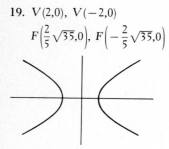

21. $V(4,-8)$, $F(4,-7)$

23. $(2,-1)$

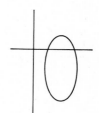

25.

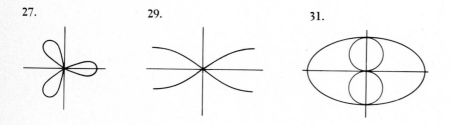

27.   **29.**   **31.**

33. $\theta = \text{Arctan } 2 = 1.11$ **35.** $r^2\cos 2\theta = 16$ **37.** $(x^2 + y^2)^3 = 16x^2y^2$

39. $3x^2 + 4y^2 - 8x - 16 = 0$ **41.** $(1.90, 1.55)$, $(1.90, -1.55)$, $(-1.90, 1.55)$, $(-1.90, -1.55)$

43. $m_1 = -\dfrac{12}{5}$, $m_2 = \dfrac{5}{12}$; $d_1^2 = 169$, $d_2^2 = 169$, $d_3^2 = 338$ **45.** $x^2 - 6x - 8y + 1 = 0$

47.

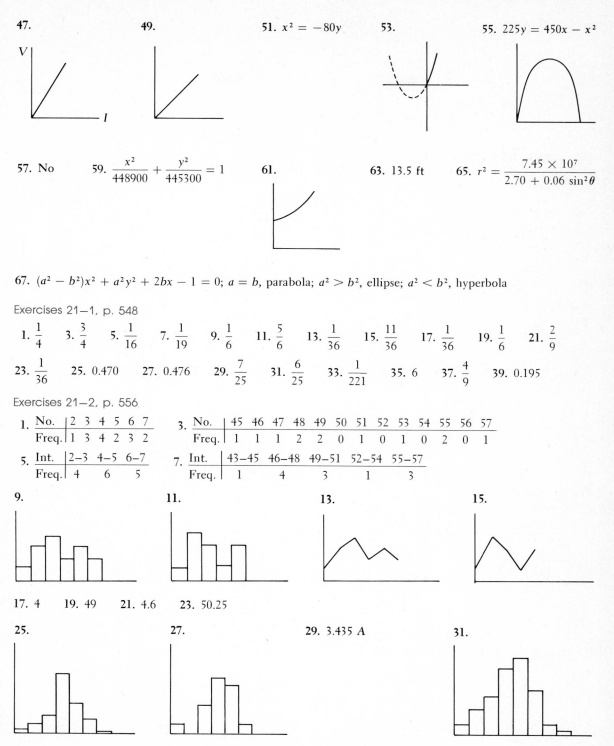

49.

51. $x^2 = -80y$

53.

55. $225y = 450x - x^2$

57. No

59. $\dfrac{x^2}{448900} + \dfrac{y^2}{445300} = 1$

61.

63. 13.5 ft

65. $r^2 = \dfrac{7.45 \times 10^7}{2.70 + 0.06 \sin^2\theta}$

67. $(a^2 - b^2)x^2 + a^2y^2 + 2bx - 1 = 0$; $a = b$, parabola; $a^2 > b^2$, ellipse; $a^2 < b^2$, hyperbola

Exercises 21–1, p. 548

1. $\dfrac{1}{4}$ **3.** $\dfrac{3}{4}$ **5.** $\dfrac{1}{16}$ **7.** $\dfrac{1}{19}$ **9.** $\dfrac{1}{6}$ **11.** $\dfrac{5}{6}$ **13.** $\dfrac{1}{36}$ **15.** $\dfrac{11}{36}$ **17.** $\dfrac{1}{36}$ **19.** $\dfrac{1}{6}$ **21.** $\dfrac{2}{9}$

23. $\dfrac{1}{36}$ **25.** 0.470 **27.** 0.476 **29.** $\dfrac{7}{25}$ **31.** $\dfrac{6}{25}$ **33.** $\dfrac{1}{221}$ **35.** 6 **37.** $\dfrac{4}{9}$ **39.** 0.195

Exercises 21–2, p. 556

1.

No.	2	3	4	5	6	7
Freq.	1	3	4	2	3	2

3.

No.	45	46	47	48	49	50	51	52	53	54	55	56	57
Freq.	1	1	1	2	2	0	1	0	1	0	2	0	1

5.

Int.	2–3	4–5	6–7
Freq.	4	6	5

7.

Int.	43–45	46–48	49–51	52–54	55–57
Freq.	1	4	3	1	3

9.

11.

13.

15.

17. 4   **19.** 49   **21.** 4.6   **23.** 50.25

25.

27.

29. 3.435 A

31.

33. 20.9   **35.**

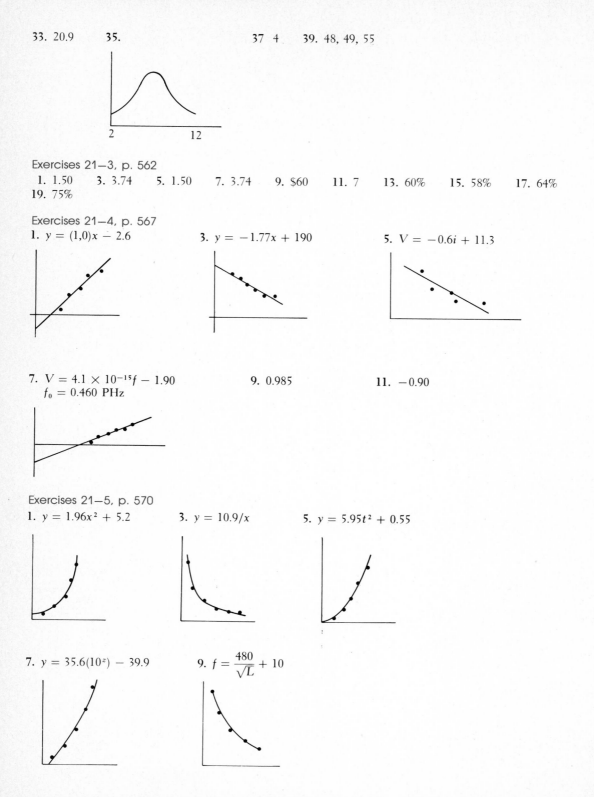

37 4   **39.** 48, 49, 55

Exercises 21—3, p. 562

1. 1.50   **3.** 3.74   **5.** 1.50   **7.** 3.74   **9.** $60   **11.** 7   **13.** 60%   **15.** 58%   **17.** 64%
19. 75%

Exercises 21—4, p. 567

1. $y = (1,0)x - 2.6$

3. $y = -1.77x + 190$

5. $V = -0.6i + 11.3$

7. $V = 4.1 \times 10^{-15}f - 1.90$
  $f_0 = 0.460$ PHz

9. 0.985

11. -0.90

Exercises 21—5, p. 570

1. $y = 1.96x^2 + 5.2$

3. $y = 10.9/x$

5. $y = 5.95t^2 + 0.55$

7. $y = 35.6(10^z) - 39.9$

9. $f = \dfrac{480}{\sqrt{L}} + 10$

Exercises for Chapter 21, p. 572

1. $\dfrac{5}{6}$ **3.** $\dfrac{1}{108}$ **5.** $\dfrac{5}{92}$ **7.** $\dfrac{10}{69}$ **9.** 3.6   **11.** 0.8   **13.** 0.264 Pa·s   **15.** 0.014 Pa·s

17. 0.927 in.   **19.** 0.012 in.   **21.** 4

23.   **25.** $\dfrac{4}{9}$ **27.** 3×10^{-5} **29.** $R = 0.0985T + 25.0$ **31.** $y = 1.04 \tan x - 0.02$

33. $y = 1.10\sqrt{x} + 0.01$

Exercises B—1, p. A—11

1. MHz, 1 MHz $= 10^6$ Hz   **3.** mm, 1 mm $= 10^{-3}$ m   **5.** kilovolt, 1 kV $= 10^3$ V
7. milliampere, 1 mA $= 10^{-3}$ A   **9.** 10^5 cm   **11.** 63,360 in.   **13.** 13.3 cm   **15.** 14.9 L
17. 144 in.^{2} **19.** 2.50×10^{-4} m^2 **21.** 2040 g   **23.** 13.6 L   **25.** 7600 kg·cm/s   **27.** 0.101 hp
29. 130 tons   **31.** 37 mi/h   **33.** 770 mi/h   **35.** 345 lb/ft^3 **37.** 101,000 Pa

Exercises B—2, p. A—14

1. 24 is exact.   **3.** 3 is exact, 74.6 is approx.   **5.** 1063 is approx.
7. 100 and 200 are approx., 3200 is exact.   **9.** 3, 4   **11.** 3, 4   **13.** 3, 3   **15.** 1, 6
17. (a) 3.764, (b) 3.764   **19.** (a) 0.01 (b) 30.8   **21.** (a) same (b) 78.0   **23.** (a) 0.004 (b) same
25. (a) 4.93 (b) 4.9   **27.** (a) 57900 (b) 58000   **29.** (a) 861 (b) 860   **31.** (a) 0.305 (b) 0.31

Exercises B—3, p. A—17

1. 51.2   **3.** 1.70   **5.** 431.4   **7.** 30.9   **9.** 62.1   **11.** 270   **13.** 160   **15.** 27,000   **17.** 5.7
19. 4.39   **21.** 10.2   **23.** 22   **25.** 17.62   **27.** 18.85   **29.** 21.0 lb   **31.** First plane, 70 mi/h
33. 62.1 lb/ft^3 **35.** 850,000 lb   **37.** 115 ft/s

Exercises C—4, p. A—30

1. 56.02   **3.** 4162.1   **5.** 18.65   **7.** 0.3954   **9.** 14.14   **11.** 0.5251   **13.** 13.35   **15.** 944.6
17. 0.7349   **19.** -0.7594 **21.** -1.337 **23.** 1.015   **25.** 41.35°   **27.** -1.182 **29.** 0.5862
31. 6.695   **33.** 3.508   **35.** 0.005685   **37.** 2.053   **39.** 5.765   **41.** 4.501×10^{10} **43.** 497.2
45. 6.648   **47.** 401.2   **49.** 8.841   **51.** 2.523   **53.** 10.08   **55.** 22.36   **57.** 20.3°   **59.** 4729
61. 3.301×10^4 **63.** 1.056   **65.** 55.5°   **67.** 3.277   **69.** 8.125   **71.** 1.000   **73.** 1.000
75. 12.90   **77.** 8.001   **79.** 8.053   **81.** 0.04259   **83.** 0.4219   **85.** 0.7822   **87.** 2.0736465
89. 124.3

Exercises D—3, p. A—35

1. 85°   **3.** 140°   **5.** 25°   **7.** 25°   **9.** 70°   **11.** 56°   **13.** 5   **15.** 17   **17.** 8   **19.** 4.90
21. 10.6   **23.** 28.3   **25.** 3.3 in., 4.0 in.   **27.** 16   **29.** 25 ft   **31.** 10 yd   **33.** 18.46 in.
35. 32.7 cm   **37.** 214.6 cm   **39.** 62.8 ft   **41.** 28 in.^{2} **43.** 13 yd^2 **45.** 24 m^2 **47.** 154 in.^{2}
49. 216 ft^3 **51.** 20 mm^3 **53.** 924 in.^{3} **55.** 153 in.^{3} **57.** 27.1 ft^3 **59.** 689 m^3 **61.** 208 in.^{2}
63. 537 m^2 **65.** 3220 ft^2 **67.** 343 cm^2

Index

譯自中國文

TRANSLATIONS FROM THE CHINESE

by Arthur Waley

ILLUSTRATED BY
CYRUS LE ROY BALDRIDGE

New York: Alfred A. Knopf: Mcmxli

895.1
W173t
1941

Preface by Arthur Waley

THERE ARE one or two questions which readers of ancient Chinese poetry, translated into another language, are bound to ask. Is it really at all like our poetry? Does it scan, does it rhyme? The answer to these questions is that (compared, for example, with Japanese poetry) Chinese traditional poetry is very similar to ours. Its lines have a fixed number of syllables and rhyme is obligatory; so that old Chinese poetry strongly resembles traditional English verse, and is not at all like the free verse of Europe and America today.

Modern Chinese poets have of course experimented in free verse; but the tendency is always to come back to rhyme and strict form. Most of the poems in this book are either in lines of five syllables or in lines of seven syllables all the way through. In the English, so far as possible, a stress represents each syllable; so that a Chinese reader will easily recognize the metre of the original. I have not used rhyme, because what is really, in the long run, of most interest to American readers is what the poems say; and if one uses rhyme, it is impossible not to sacrifice sense to sound. For the same reason, I have chosen poems which say something interesting. Those are the ones that translate best. It does not at all follow that they rank highest as poetry in the original; but with very few exceptions the poems in this book are by poets whom the Chinese themselves have always greatly admired. I have not attempted to set up any new gods.

And now a word about the subjects with which the poems deal. The most conspicuous feature of European poetry is its pre-occupation with love. This is apparent not only in actual "love-poems," but in all poetry where the personality of the writer is in any way obtruded. The poet tends to exhibit himself in a romantic light; in fact, to recommend himself as a lover.

The Chinese poet has a tendency different but analogous. He recommends himself not as a lover, but as a friend. He poses as a person of infinite leisure (which we should most like our friends to possess) and free from worldly ambitions (which constitute the greatest bars to friendship). He would have us think of him as a boon companion, a great drinker of wine, who will not disgrace a social gathering by quitting it sober.

To the European poet the relation between man and woman is a thing of supreme importance and mystery. To the average Chinese poet it is something commonplace, obvious—a need of the body, not a satisfaction of the *emotions*. These he reserves entirely for friendship. I have been criticized for saying something like this; but the vast mass of classical Chinese poetry amply confirms my view. Accordingly we find that while our poets tend to lay stress on physical courage and other qualities normally admired by women, Po Chü-i is not ashamed to write such a poem as "Alarm at entering the Gorges." Our classical poets imagine themselves very much as Art has portrayed them—bareheaded and wild-eyed, with shirts unbuttoned at the neck as though they feared that a seizure of emotion might at any minute suffocate them. The Chinese poet tends to introduce himself as a timid recluse, "Reading the Book of Changes at the Northern Window," playing chess with a Taoist priest, or practising calligraphy with an occasional visitor.

I do not mean to say that the gentle and reflective attitude traditional in Chinese poetry in any way gives us a key to the whole of Chinese life. Martial vigour, administrative ability, romantic love, all played their part; but in the whole bulk of classical poetry, say from the seventh to the fourteenth century, how minute a proportion for a moment touches any of these themes!

And now the translater must add a line or two of self-defence. The translations here printed were made over twenty years ago. Since then my own knowledge of Chinese and the general study of it in America and Europe have made enormous progress. In arranging the poems for this illustrated edition I have corrected a certain number of mistakes. But on the whole I have reprinted the poems as they stood in 1918 and 1919. There is a great deal that specialists might quarrel with; but not much, I hope, that will be definitely misleading to the general public. To understand unfailingly anything written a thousand years and more ago is not easy; but my Chinese friends have generally assured me that these translations come pretty close to the original; closer, they have sometimes been kind enough to say, than those of any other translater.

Contents

POEMS BY PO CHÜ-I

Translations from the Chinese

Battle

By Ch'ü Yüan (332–295 B.C.?)

*Author of the famous poem "Li Sao"
or "Falling into Trouble"*

*Finding that he could not influence
the conduct of his prince, he drowned
himself in the river Mi-lo. The modern Dragon Boat Festival is supposed
to be in his honour.*

"We grasp our battle-spears: we don our breast-plates of hide.
The axles of our chariots touch: our short swords meet.
Standards obscure the sun: the foe roll up like clouds.
Arrows fall thick: the warriors press forward.
They menace our ranks: they break our line.
The left-hand trace-horse is dead: the one on the right
    is smitten.
The fallen horses block our wheels: they impede the
    yoke-horses!"

3

They grasp their jade drum-sticks: they beat the
    sounding drums.
Heaven decrees their fall: the dread Powers are angry.

The warriors are all dead: they lie on the moor-field.
They issued but shall not enter: they went but shall
    not return.
The plains are flat and wide; the way home is long.
Their swords lie beside them: their black bows, in their hand.

Though their limbs were torn, their hearts could not
    be repressed.
They were more than brave: they were inspired with the
    spirit of "Wu".[1]
Steadfast to the end, they could not be daunted.
Their bodies were stricken, but their souls have taken
    Immortality—
Captains among the ghosts, heroes among the dead.

[1] *I.e.*, military genius.

4

The Man-Wind
and the Woman-Wind

*A "fu", or prose-poem, by Sung Yü (fourth century B. C.)
nephew of Ch'ü Yüan.*

HSIANG, king of Ch'u, was feasting in the Orchid-tower
Palace, with Sung Yü and Ching Ch'ai to wait upon him.
A gust of wind blew in and the king bared his breast to
meet it, saying: "How pleasant a thing is this wind which
I share with the common people." Sung Yü answered: "This
is the Great King's wind. The common people cannot share
it." The king said: "Wind is a spirit of Heaven and Earth. It
comes wide spread and does not choose between noble and
base or between high and low. How can you say 'This is the
king's wind'?" Sung answered: "I have heard it taught that in
the crooked lemon-tree birds make their nests and to empty
spaces winds fly. But the wind-spirit that comes to different
things is not the same." The king said: "Where is the wind
born?" and Sung answered: "The wind is born in the ground.
It rises in the extremities of the green p'ing-flower. It pours
into the river-valleys and rages at the mouth of the pass. It
follows the rolling flanks of Mount T'ai and dances beneath
the pine-trees and cypresses. In gusty bouts it whirls. It
rushes in fiery anger. It rumbles low with a noise like thunder,
tearing down rocks and trees, smiting forests and grasses.

"But at last abating, it spreads abroad, seeks empty places and crosses the threshold of rooms. And so growing gentler and clearer, it changes and is dispersed and dies.

"It is this cool clear Man-Wind that, freeing itself, falls and rises till it climbs the high walls of the Castle and enters the gardens of the Inner Palace. It bends the flowers and leaves with its breath. It wanders among the osmanthus and pepper-trees. It lingers over the fretted face of the pond, to steal the soul of the hibiscus. It touches the willow leaves and scatters the fragrant herbs. Then it pauses in the courtyard and turning to the North goes up to the Jade Hall, shakes the hanging curtains and lightly passes into the inner room.

"And so it becomes the Great King's wind.

"Now such a wind is fresh and sweet to breathe and its gentle murmuring cures the diseases of men, blows away the stupor of wine, sharpens sight and hearing and refreshes the body. This is what is called the Great King's wind."

The king said: "You have well described it. Now tell me of the common people's wind." Sung said: "The common people's wind rises from narrow lanes and streets, carrying clouds of dust. Rushing to empty spaces it attacks the gateway, scatters the dust-heap, sends the cinders flying, pokes among foul and rotting things, till at last it enters the tiled windows and reaches the rooms of the cottage. Now this wind is heavy and turgid, oppressing man's heart. It brings fever to his body, ulcers to his lips and dimness to his eyes. It shakes him with coughing; it kills him before his time.

"Such is the Woman-Wind of the common people."

6

The following is a sample of Sung Yü's prose:

Master Tēng-t'u

By Sung Yü (third century B. C.)

ONE DAY when the Chamberlain, master Tēng-t'u, was in attendance at the Palace he warned the King against Sung Yü, saying: "Yü is a man of handsome features and calm bearing and his tongue is prompt with subtle sentences. Moreover, his character is licentious. I would submit that your Majesty is ill-advised in allowing him to follow you into the Queen's apartments." The King repeated Tēng-t'u's words to Sung Yü. Yü replied: "My beauty of face and calmness of bearing were given me by Heaven. Subtlety of speech I learnt from my teachers. As for my character, I deny that it is licentious." The King said: "Can you substantiate your statement that you are not licentious? If you cannot, you must leave the Court." Sung Yü said: "Of all the women in the world, the most beautiful are the women of the land of Ch'u. And in all the land of Ch'u there are none like the women of my own village. And in my village there are none that can be compared with the girl next door.

"The girl next door would be too tall if an inch were added to her height, and too short if an inch were taken away. Another grain of powder would make her too pale; another touch of rouge would make her too red. Her eye-

7

brows are like the plumage of the kingfisher, her flesh is like snow. Her waist is like a roll of new silk, her teeth are like little shells. A single one of her smiles would perturb the whole city of Yang and derange the suburb of Hsia-ts'ai.[1] For three years this lady has been climbing the garden wall and peeping at me, yet I have never succumbed.

"How different is the behaviour of master Tēng-t'u! His wife has a woolly head and misshapen ears; projecting teeth irregularly set; a crook in her back and a halt in her gait. Moreover, she has running sores in front and behind.

"Yet Tēng-t'u fell in love with her and caused her to bear him five children.

"I would have your Majesty consider which of us is the debauchee."

Sung Yü was not dismissed from court.

[1] Fashionable quarters in the capital of Ch'u state.

The Great Summons

When Ch'ü Yüan (fourth century B.C.) had been exiled from the Court for nine years, he became so despondent that he feared his soul would part from his body and he would die. It was then that he made the poem called "The Great Summons", calling upon his soul not to leave him.

Green Spring receiveth
The vacant earth;
The white sun shineth;
Spring wind provoketh
To burst and burgeon
Each sprout and flower.
In those dark caves where Winter lurketh
Hide not, my Soul!
O Soul come back again! O, do not stray!

O Soul come back again and go not east or west,
or north or south!
For to the East a mighty water drowneth Earth's
other shore;
Tossed on its waves and heaving with its tides
The hornless Dragon of the Ocean rideth:
Clouds gather low and fogs enfold the sea
And gleaming ice drifts past.
O Soul go not to the East,
To the silent Valley of Sunrise!

O Soul go not to the South
Where mile on mile the earth is burnt away
And poisonous serpents slither through the flames;
Where on precipitous paths or in deep woods
Tigers and leopards prowl,
And water-scorpions wait;
Where the king-python rears his giant head.
O Soul, go not to the South
Where the three-footed tortoise spits disease!

O Soul go not to the West
Where level wastes of sand stretch on and on;
And demons rage, swine-headed, hairy-skinned,
With bulging eyes;
Who in wild laughter gnash projecting fangs.
O Soul go not to the West
Where many perils wait!

O Soul go not to the North,
To the Lame Dragon's frozen peaks;
Where trees and grasses dare not grow;
Where a river runs too wide to cross
And too deep to plumb,
And the sky is white with snow
And the cold cuts and kills.
O Soul seek not to fill
The treacherous voids of the North!

O Soul come back to idleness and peace.
In quietude enjoy
The lands of Ching and Ch'u.
There work your will and follow your desire
Till sorrow is forgot,
And carelessness shall bring you length of days.
O Soul come back to joys beyond all telling!

Where thirty cubits high at harvest-time
The corn is stacked;
Where pies are cooked of millet and bearded-maize.
Guests watch the steaming bowls
And sniff the pungency of peppered herbs.
The cunning cook adds slices of bird-flesh,
Pigeon and yellow-heron and black-crane.
They taste the badger-stew.
O Soul come back to feed on foods you love!

Next are brought
Fresh turtle, and sweet chicken cooked in cheese
Pressed by the men of Ch'u.
And pickled sucking-pig
And flesh of whelps floating in liver-sauce
With salad of minced radishes in brine;
All served with that hot spice of southernwood
The land of Wu supplies.
O Soul come back to choose the meats you love!

Roasted daw, steamed widgeon and grilled quail—
On every fowl they fare.
Boiled perch and sparrow broth,—in each preserved
The separate flavour that is most its own.
O Soul come back to where such dainties wait!

The four strong liquors are warming at the fire
So that they grate not on the drinker's throat.
How fragrant rise their fumes, how cool their taste!
Such drink is not for louts or serving-men!
And wise distillers from the land of Wu
Blend unfermented spirit with white yeast
And brew the *li* of Ch'u.
O Soul come back and let your yearnings cease!

Reed-organs from the lands of T'ai and Ch'in
And Wei and Chēng
Gladden the feasters, and old songs are sung:
The "Rider's Song" that once
Fu-hsi, the ancient monarch, made;
And the harp-songs of Ch'u.
Then after prelude from the flutes of Chao
The ballad-singer's voice rises alone.
O Soul come back to the hollow mulberry-tree![1]

Eight and eight the dancers sway,
Weaving their steps to the poet's voice

[1] The harp.

Who speaks his odes and rhapsodies;
They tap their bells and beat their chimes
Rigidly, lest harp and flute
Should mar the measure.
Then rival singers of the Four Domains
Compete in melody, till not a tune
Is left unsung that human voice could sing.
O Soul come back and listen to their songs!

Then women enter whose red lips and dazzling teeth
Seduce the eye;
But meek and virtuous, trained in every art;
Fit sharers of play-time,
So soft their flesh and delicate their bones.
O Soul come back and let them ease your woe!

Then enter other ladies with laughing lips
And sidelong glances under moth-eye brows;
Whose cheeks are fresh and red;
Ladies both great of heart and long of limb,
Whose beauty by sobriety is matched.
Well-padded cheeks and ears with curving rim,
High-arching eyebrows, as with compass drawn,
Great hearts and loving gestures—all are there;
Small waists and necks as slender as the clasp
Of courtiers' brooches.
O Soul come back to those whose tenderness
Drives angry thoughts away!

Last enter those
Whose every action is contrived to please;
Black-painted eyebrows and white-powdered cheeks.
They reek with scent; with their long sleeves they brush
The faces of the feasters whom they pass,
Or pluck the coats of those who will not stay.
O Soul come back to pleasures of the night!

A summer-house with spacious rooms
And a high hall with beams stained red;
A little closet in the southern wing
Reached by a private stair.
And round the house a covered way should run
Where horses might be trained.
And sometimes riding, sometimes going afoot
You shall explore, O Soul, the parks of spring;
Your jewelled axles gleaming in the sun
And yoke inlaid with gold;
Or amid orchises and sandal-trees
Shall walk in the dark woods.
O Soul come back and live for these delights!

Peacocks shall fill your gardens; you shall rear
The roc and phœnix, and red jungle-fowl,
Whose cry at dawn assembles river storks
To join the play of cranes and ibises;
Where the wild-swan all day

Pursues the glint of idle king-fishers.
O Soul come back to watch the birds in flight!

He who has found such manifold delights
Shall feel his cheeks aglow
And the blood-spirit dancing through his limbs.
Stay with me, Soul, and share
The span of days that happiness will bring;
See sons and grandsons serving at the Court
Ennobled and enriched.
O Soul come back and bring prosperity
To house and stock!

The roads that lead to Ch'u
Shall teem with travellers as thick as clouds,
A thousand miles away.
For the Five Orders of Nobility
Shall summon sages to assist the King
And with godlike discrimination choose
The wise in council; by their aid to probe
The hidden discontents of humble men
And help the lonely poor.
O Soul come back and end what we began!

Fields, villages and lanes
Shall throng with happy men;
Good rule protect the people and make known

The King's benevolence to all the land;
Stern discipline prepare
Their natures for the soft caress of Art.
O Soul come back to where the good are praised!

Like the sun shining over the four seas
Shall be the reputation of our King;
His deeds, matched only in Heaven, shall repair
The wrongs endured by every tribe of men,—
Northward to Yu and southward to Annam,
To the Sheep's Gut Mountain and the Eastern Seas.
O Soul come back to where the wise are sought!

Behold the glorious virtues of our King
Triumphant, terrible;
Behold with solemn faces in the Hall
The Three Grand Ministers walk up and down,—
None chosen for the post save landed-lords
Or, in default, Knights of the Nine Degrees.
At the first ray of dawn already is hung
The shooting-target, where with bow in hand
And arrows under arm,
Each archer does obeisance to each,
Willing to yield his rights of precedence.
O Soul come back to where men honour still
The name of the Three Kings.[1]

---

[1] Yü, T'ang and Wēn, the three just rulers of antiquity.

16

Cock-Crow Song

Anonymous (first century B. C.)

In the eastern quarter dawn breaks, the stars flicker pale.
The morning cock at Ju-nan mounts the wall and crows.
The songs are over, the clock[1] run down, but still the
    feast is set.
The moon grows dim and the stars are few; morning has
    come to the world.
At a thousand gates and ten thousand doors the fish-shaped
    keys turn;
Round the Palace and up by the Castle, the crows and
    magpies are flying.

[1] A water-clock.

Lament of Hsi-chün

About the year 110 B. C. a Chinese Princess named Hsi-chün was sent, for political reasons, to be the wife of a central Asian nomad king, K'un Mo, king of the Wu-sun. When she got there, she found her husband old and decrepit. He only saw her once or twice a year, when they drank a cup of wine together. They could not converse, as they had no language in common.

My people have married me
In a far corner of Earth:
Sent me away to a strange land,
To the king of the Wu-sun.
A tent is my house,
Of felt are my walls;
Raw flesh my food
With mare's milk to drink.
Always thinking of my own country,
My heart sad within.
Would I were a yellow stork
And could fly to my old home!

The Orphan

Anonymous (first century B.C.)

To be an orphan,
To be fated to be an orphan,
How bitter is this lot!
When my father and mother were alive
I used to ride in a carriage
With four fine horses.
But when they both died,
My brother and sister-in-law
Sent me out to be a merchant.
In the south I travelled to the "Nine Rivers"
And in the east as far as Ch'i and Lu.
At the end of the year when I came home
I dared not tell them what I had suffered—
Of the lice and vermin in my head,
Of the dust in my face and eyes.
My brother told me to get ready the dinner,
My sister-in-law told me to see after the horses.
I was always going up into the hall
And running down again to the parlour.
My tears fell like rain.

In the morning they sent me to draw water,
I didn't get back till night-fall.
My hands were all sore
And I had no shoes.
I walked the cold earth
Treading on thorns and brambles.
As I stopped to pull out the thorns,
How bitter my heart was!
My tears fell and fell
And I went on sobbing and sobbing.
In winter I have no great-coat;
Nor in summer, thin clothes.
It is no pleasure to be alive.
I had rather quickly leave the earth
And go beneath the Yellow Springs.[1]
The April winds blow
And the grass is growing green.
In the third month—silkworms and mulberries,
In the sixth month—the melon-harvest.
I went out with the melon-cart
And just as I was coming home
The melon-cart turned over.
The people who came to help me were few,
But the people who ate the melons were many,
All they left me was the stalks—
To take home as fast as I could.
My brother and sister-in-law were harsh,

[1] Hades.

20

They asked me all sorts of awful questions.
Why does everyone in the village hate me?
I want to write a letter and send it
To my mother and father under the earth,
And tell them I can't go on any longer
Living with my brother and sister-in-law.

The Sick Wife

She had been ill for years and years;
She sent for me to say something.
She couldn't say what she wanted
Because of the tears that kept coming of themselves.
"I have burdened you with orphan children,
With orphan children two or three.
Don't let our children go hungry or cold;
If they do wrong, don't slap or beat them.
When you take out the baby, rock it in your arms.
Don't forget to do that."
Last she said,
"When I carried them in my arms they had no clothes
And now their jackets have no linings."   [*She dies.*

I shut the doors and barred the windows
And left the motherless children.
When I got to the market and met my friends, I wept.
I sat down and could not go with them.
I asked them to buy some cakes for my children.
In the presence of my friends I sobbed and cried.
I tried not to grieve, but sorrow would not cease.
I felt in my pocket and gave my friends some money.
When I got home I found my children

Calling to be taken into their mother's arms.
I walked up and down in the empty room
This way and that a long while.
Then I went away from it and said to myself,
"I will forget and never speak of her again."

Meeting in the Road

In a narrow road where there was not room to pass
My carriage met the carriage of a young man.
And while his axle was touching my axle
In the narrow road I asked him where he lived.
"The place where I live is easy enough to find,
Easy to find and difficult to forget.
The gates of my house are built of yellow gold,
The hall of my house is paved with white jade,
On the hall table flagons of wine are set,
I had summoned to serve me dancers of Han-tan.[1]
In the midst of a courtyard grows a cassia-tree,—
And candles on its branches flaring away in the night."

[1] Capital of the kingdom of Chao, where the people were famous for their beauty.

24

"Old Poem"

At fifteen I went with the army,
At fourscore I came home.
On the way I met a man from the village,
I asked him who there was at home.
"That over there is your house,
All covered over with trees and bushes."
Rabbits had run in at the dog-hole,
Pheasants flew down from the beams of the roof.
In the courtyard was growing some wild grain;
And by the well, some wild mallows.
I'll boil the grain and make porridge,
I'll pluck the mallows and make soup.
Soup and porridge are both cooked,
But there is no one to eat them with.
I went out and looked towards the east,
While tears fell and wetted my clothes.

The Golden Palace

Anonymous (first century B. C.)

We go to the Golden Palace:
We set out the jade cups.
We summon the honoured guests
To enter at the Golden Gate.
They enter at the Golden Gate
And go to the Golden Hall.
In the Eastern Kitchen the meat is sliced and ready—
Roast beef and boiled pork and mutton.
The Master of the Feast hands round the wine.
The harp-players sound their clear chords.

The cups are pushed aside and we face each other at chess:
The rival pawns are marshalled rank against rank.
The fire glows and the smoke puffs and curls;
From the incense-burner rises a delicate fragrance.
The clear wine has made our cheeks red;
Round the table joy and peace prevail.
May those who shared in this day's delight
Through countless autumns enjoy like felicity.

Fighting South of the Castle

Anonymous (circa 124 B. C.)

They fought south of the Castle,
They died north of the wall.
They died in the moors and were not buried.
Their flesh was the food of crows.
"Tell the crows we are not afraid;
We have died in the moors and cannot be buried.
Crows, how can our bodies escape you?"
The waters flowed deep
And the rushes in the pool were dark.
The riders fought and were slain:
Their horses wander neighing.
By the bridge there was a house.[1]
Was it south, was it north?
The harvest was never gathered.
How can we give you your offerings?
You served your Prince faithfully,
Though all in vain.
I think of you, faithful soldiers;
Your service shall not be forgotten.
For in the morning you went out to battle
And at night you did not return.

[1] There is no trace of it left. This passage describes the havoc of war. The harvest has not been gathered: therefore corn-offerings cannot be made to the spirits of the dead.

27

The Eastern Gate

Anonymous (first century B. C.)

A poor man determines to go out into the world and make his fortune. His wife tries to detain him.

I went out at the eastern gate:
I never thought to return.
But I came back to the gate with my heart full of sorrow.

There was not a peck of rice in the bin:
There was not a coat hanging on the pegs.
So I took my sword and went towards the gate.
My wife and child clutched at my coat and wept:
"Some people want to be rich and grand:
I only want to share my porridge with you.
Above, we have the blue waves of the sky:
Below, the yellow face of this little child."
                    "Dear wife, I cannot stay.
                    Soon it will be too late.
                    When one is growing old
                    One cannot put things off."

Old and New

Anonymous (first century B. C.)

She went up the mountain to pluck wild herbs;
She came down the mountain and met her former husband.
She knelt down and asked her former husband
"What do you find your new wife like?"
"My new wife, although her talk is clever,
Cannot charm me as my old wife could.
In beauty of face there is not much to choose,
But in usefulness they are not at all alike.
My new wife comes in from the road to meet me;
My old wife always came down from her tower.
My new wife is clever at embroidering silk;
My old wife was good at plain sewing.
Of silk embroidery one can do an inch a day;
Of plain sewing, more than five feet.
Putting her silks by the side of your sewing,
I see that the new will not compare with the old."

South of the Great Sea

My love is living
To the south of the Great Sea.
What shall I send to greet him?
Two pearls and a comb of tortoise-shell:
I'll send them to him packed in a box of jade.
They tell me he is not true:
They tell me he dashed my box to the ground,
Dashed it to the ground and burnt it
And scattered its ashes to the wind.
From this day to the ends of time
I must never think of him,
Never again think of him.
The cocks are crowing,
And the dogs are barking—
My brother and his wife will soon know.[1]
The autumn wind is blowing;
The morning wind is sighing.
In a moment the sun will rise in the east
And then *it* too will know.

[1] *I.e.*, about her engagement being broken off.

30

The Other Side of the Valley

I am a prisoner in the hands of the enemy,
Enduring the shame of captivity.
My bones stick out and my strength is gone
Through not getting enough to eat.
My brother is a Mandarin
And his horses are fed on maize.
Why can't he spare a little money
To send and ransom me?

Oaths of Friendship

In the country of Yüeh when a man made friends with another
they set up an altar of earth and sacrificed upon it a dog and a cock,
reciting this oath as they did so:

If you were riding in a coach
And I were wearing a "li",[1]
And one day we met in the road,
You would get down and bow.
If you were carrying a "tēng",[2]
And I were riding on a horse,
And one day we met in the road
I would get down for you.

Shang Ya!
I want to be your friend
For ever and ever without break or decay.
When the hills are all flat
And the rivers are all dry,
When it lightens and thunders in winter,
When it rains and snows in summer,
When Heaven and Earth mingle—
Not till then will I part from you.

[1] A peasant's coat made of straw.
[2] An umbrella under which a cheap-jack sells his wares.

Burial Songs

[1]

"The Dew on the Garlic-leaf"
Sung at the burial of kings and princes.

How swiftly it dries,
The dew on the garlic-leaf.
The dew that dries so fast
To-morrow will fall again.
But he whom we carry to the grave
Will never more return.

[2]

"The Graveyard"
Sung at the burial of common men.

What man's land is the graveyard?
It is the crowded home of ghosts,—
Wise and foolish shoulder to shoulder.
The King of the Dead claims them all;
Man's fate knows no tarrying.

Five "Tzŭ-yeh" Songs

[1]

At the time when blossoms
Fall from the cherry-tree:
On a day when yellow birds
Hovered in the branches—
You said you must stop,
Because your horse was tired:
I said I must go,
Because my silkworms were hungry.

[2]

All night I could not sleep
Because of the moonlight on my bed.
I kept on hearing a voice calling:
Out of Nowhere, Nothing answered "yes".

[3]

I will carry my coat and not put on my belt;
With unpainted eyebrows I will stand at the
    front window.
My tiresome petticoat keeps on flapping about;
If it opens a little, I shall blame the spring wind.

[4]

I heard my love was going to Yang-chou
And went with him as far as Ch'u-shan.
For a moment when you held me fast in your
    outstretched arms
I thought the river stood still and did not flow.

[5]

I have brought my pillow and am lying at the
    northern window,
So come to me and play with me awhile.
With so much quarrelling and so few kisses
How long do you think our love can last?

The Autumn Wind

By Wu-ti (157-87 B. C.), sixth emperor of the Han dynasty. He came to the throne when he was only sixteen. In this poem he regrets that he is obliged to go on an official journey, leaving his mistress behind in the capital. He is seated in his state barge surrounded by his ministers.

Autumn wind rises: white clouds fly.
Grass and trees wither: geese go south.
Orchids all in bloom: chrysanthemums smell sweet.
I think of my lovely lady: I never can forget.
Floating-pagoda boat crosses Fēn River.
Across the mid-stream white waves rise;
Flute and drum keep time to sound of the rowers' song;
Amidst revel and feasting, sad thoughts come;
Youth's years how few! Age how sure!

Seventeen Old Poems

The following seventeen poems are from a series known as the Nineteen Pieces of Old Poetry. Some have been attributed to Mei Shēng (first century B. C.), and one to Fu I (first century A. D.). They are manifestly not all by the same hand nor of the same date. Internal evidence shows that No. 3 at least was written after the date of Mei Shēng's death. These poems had an enormous influence on all subsequent poetry, and many of the habitual clichés of Chinese verse are taken from them. I have omitted two because of their marked inferiority.

[1]

On and on, always on and on
Away from you, parted by a life-parting.[1]
Going from one another ten thousand "li",
Each in a different corner of the World.
The way between is difficult and long,
Face to face how shall we meet again?
The Tartar horse prefers the North wind,
The bird from Yüeh nests on the Southern branch.
Since we parted the time is already long,
Daily my clothes hang looser round my waist.
Floating clouds obscure the white sun,
The wandering one has quite forgotten home.

[1] The opposite of a parting by death.

Thinking of you has made me suddenly old,
The months and years swiftly draw to their close.
I'll put you out of my mind and forget for ever
And try with all my might to eat and thrive.[1]

[2]

Green, green,
The grass by the river-bank.
Thick, thick,
The willow trees in the garden.
Sad, sad,
The lady in the tower.
White, white,
Sitting at the casement window.
Fair, fair,
Her red-powdered face.
Small, small,
She puts out her pale hand.
Once she was a dancing-house girl,
Now she is a wandering man's wife.
The wandering man went, but did not return.
It is hard alone to keep an empty bed.

[1] The popular, but erroneous, interpretation of these two lines is:

"That I'm cast away and rejected I will not repine,
But only hope with all my heart you're well."

[3]

Green, green,
The cypress on the mound.
Firm, firm,
The boulder in the stream.
Man's life lived within this world,
Is like the sojourning of a hurried traveller.
A cup of wine together will make us glad,
And a little friendship is no little matter.

Yoking my chariot I urge my stubborn horses.
I wander about in the streets of Wan and Lo.
In Lo Town how fine everything is!
The "Caps and Belts" [1] go seeking each other out.
The great boulevards are intersected by lanes,
Wherein are the town-houses of Royal Dukes
The two palaces stare at each other from afar,
The twin gates rise a hundred feet.
By prolonging the feast let us keep our hearts gay,
And leave no room for sadness to creep in.

[1] High officers.

39

[4]

Of this day's glorious feast and revel
The pleasure and delight are difficult to describe.
Plucking the lute they sent forth lingering sounds,
The new melodies in beauty reached the divine.
Skilful singers intoned the high words,
Those who knew the tune heard the trueness of their singing.
We sat there each with the same desire
And like thoughts by each unexpressed:
"Man in the world lodging for a single life-time
Passes suddenly like dust borne on the wind.
Then let us hurry out with high steps
And be the first to reach the highways and fords:
Rather than stay at home wretched and poor
For long years plunged in sordid grief."

[5]

In the north-west there is a high house,
Its top level with the floating clouds.
Embroidered curtains thinly screen its windows,
Its storied tower is built on three steps.
From above there comes a noise of playing and singing,
The tune sounding, oh! how sad!
Who can it be, playing so sad a tune?
Surely it must be Ch'i Liang's[1] wife.

[1] Who had no father, no husband, and no children.

40

The tranquil "D" follows the wind's rising,
The middle lay lingers indecisive.
To each note, two or three sobs,
Her high will conquered by overwhelming grief.
She does not regret that she is left so sad,
But minds that so few can understand her song.
She wants to become those two wild geese
That with beating wings rise high aloft.

[6]

Crossing the river I pluck hibiscus-flowers:
In the orchid-swamps are many fragrant herbs.
I gather them, but who shall I send them to?
My love is living in lands far away.
I turn and look towards my own country:
The long road stretches on for ever.
The same heart, yet a different dwelling:
Always fretting, till we are grown old!

[7]

A bright moon illumines the night-prospect:
The house-cricket chirrups on the eastern wall.
The Handle of the Pole-star points to the Beginning
    of Winter.
The host of stars is scattered over the sky.
The white dew wets the moor-grasses,—

With sudden swiftness the times and seasons change.
The autumn cicada sings among the trees,
The swallows, alas, whither are they gone?

Once I had a same-house friend,
He took flight and rose high away.
He did not remember how once we went hand in hand,
But left me like footsteps behind one in the dust.

In the South is the Winnowing-fan and the Pole-star
    in the North,
And a Herd-boy[1] whose ox has never borne the yoke.
A friend who is not firm as a great rock
Is of no profit and idly bears the name.

[8]

In the courtyard there grows a strange tree,
Its green leaves ooze with a fragrant moisture.
Holding the branch I cut a flower from the tree,
Meaning to send it away to the person I love.
Its sweet smell fills my sleeves and lap.
The road is long, how shall I get it there?
Such a thing is not fine enough to send:
But it may remind him of the time that has past since he left.[2]

[1] Name of a star. The Herd-boy, who is only figuratively speaking a herd-boy, is like the friend who is no real friend.
[2] I.e. (supposing he went away in the autumn), remind him that spring has come.

[9]

Far away twinkles the Herd-boy star;
Brightly shines the Lady of the Han River.
Slender, slender she plies her white fingers.
Click, click go the wheels of her spinning-loom.
At the end of the day she has not finished her task;
Her bitter tears fall like streaming rain.
The Han River runs shallow and clear;
Set between them, how short a space!
But the river water will not let them pass,
Gazing at each other but never able to speak.

[10]

Turning my chariot I yoke my horses and go.
On and on down the long roads
The autumn winds shake the hundred grasses.
On every side, how desolate and bare!
The things I meet are all new things,
Their strangeness hastens the coming of old age.
Prosperity and decay each have their season.
Success is bitter when it is slow in coming.
Man's life is not metal or stone,
He cannot far prolong the days of his fate.
Suddenly he follows in the way of things that change.
Fame is the only treasure that endures.

The Eastern Castle stands tall and high;
Far and wide stretch the towers that guard it.
The whirling wind uprises and shakes the earth;
The autumn grasses grow thick and green.
The four seasons alternate without pause,
The year's end hurries swiftly on.
The Bird of the Morning Wind is stricken with sorrow,
The frail cicada suffers and is hard pressed.
Free and clear, let us loosen the bonds of our hearts.
Why should we go on always restraining and binding?
In Yen and Chao are many fair ladies,
Beautiful people with faces like jade.
Their clothes are made all of silk gauze,
They stand at the door practising tranquil lays.
The echo of their singing, how sad it sounds!
By the pitch of the song one knows the stops have
        been tightened.
To ease their minds they arrange their shawls and belts;
Lowering their song, a little while they pause.
"I should like to be those two flying swallows
Who are carrying clay to nest in the eaves of your house."

I drive my chariot up to the Eastern Gate;
From afar I see the graveyard north of the Wall.
The white aspens how they murmur, murmur;
Pines and cypresses flank the broad paths.
Beneath lie men who died long ago;
Black, black is the long night that holds them.
Deep down beneath the Yellow Springs,
Thousands of years they lie without waking.

In infinite succession light and darkness shift,
And years vanish like the morning dew.
Man's life is like a sojourning,
His longevity lacks the firmness of stone and metal.
For ever it has been that mourners in their turn
        were mourned,
Saint and Sage,—all alike are trapped.
Seeking by food to obtain Immortality
Many have been the dupe of strange drugs.
Better far to drink good wine
And clothe our bodies in robes of satin and silk.

[13]

The dead are gone and with them we cannot converse.
The living are here and ought to have our love.
Leaving the city-gate I look ahead
And see before me only mounds and tombs.
The old graves are ploughed up into fields,
The pines and cypresses are hewn for timber.
In the white aspens sad winds sing;
Their long murmuring kills my heart with grief.
I want to go home, to ride to my village-gate.
I want to go back, but there's no road back.

[14]

The years of a lifetime do not reach a hundred,
Yet they contain a thousand years' sorrow.
When days are short and the dull nights long,
Why not take a lamp and wander forth?
If you want to be happy you must do it now,
There is no waiting till an after-time.
The fool who's loath to spend the wealth he's got
Becomes the laughing-stock of after ages.
It is true that Master Wang became immortal,
But how can *we* hope to share his lot?

Cold, cold the year draws to its end,
The crickets and grasshoppers make a doleful chirping.
The chill wind increases its violence.
My wandering love has no coat to cover him.
He gave his embroidered furs to the Lady of Lo,
But from me his bedfellow he is quite estranged.
Sleeping alone in the depth of the long night
In a dream I thought I saw the light of his face.
My dear one thought of our old joys together,
He came in his chariot and gave me the front reins.
I wanted so to prolong our play and laughter,
To hold his hand and go back with him in his coach.
But, when he had come he would not stay long
Nor stop to go with me to the Inner Chamber.
Truly without the falcon's wings to carry me
How can I rival the flying wind's swiftness?
I go and lean at the gate and think of my grief,
My falling tears wet the double gates.

At the beginning of winter a cold spirit comes,
The North Wind blows—chill, chill.
My sorrows being many, I know the length of the nights,
Raising my head I look at the stars in their places.

On the fifteenth day the bright moon is full,
On the twentieth day the "toad and hare" wane.[1]
A stranger came to me from a distant land
And brought me a single scroll with writing on it;
At the top of the scroll was written "Do not forget",
At the bottom was written "Goodbye for Ever".
I put the letter away in the folds of my dress,
For three years the writing did not fade.
How with an undivided heart I loved you
I fear that you will never know or guess.

[17]

The bright moon, oh, how white it shines,
Shines down on the gauze curtains of my bed.
Racked by sorrow I toss and cannot sleep.
Picking up my clothes, I wander up and down.
My absent love says that he is happy,
But I would rather he said he was coming back.
Out in the courtyard I stand hesitating, alone.
To whom can I tell the sad thoughts I think?
Staring before me I enter my room again;
Falling tears wet my mantle and robe.

---

[1] The "toad and hare" correspond to our "man in the moon". The waning
of the moon symbolizes the waning of the lover's affection.

Li Fu-jēn

By Wu-ti

The sound of her silk skirt has stopped.
On the marble pavement dust grows.
Her empty room is cold and still.
Fallen leaves are piled against the doors.
     Longing for that lovely lady
How can I bring my aching heart to rest?

The above poem was written by Wu-ti when his mistress, Li Fu-jēn, died. Unable to bear his grief, he sent for wizards from all parts of China, hoping that they would be able to put him into communication with her spirit. At last one of them managed to project her shape on to a curtain. The emperor cried:

> *Is it or isn't it?*
> *I stand and look.*
> *The swish, swish of a silk skirt.*
> *How slow she comes!*

Song of Snow-White Heads

By Cho Wēn-chün

Ssŭ-ma Hsiang-ju (died 118 B. C.) was a young poet who had lost his position at court owing to ill-health. One day Cho Wēn-chün, a rich man's daughter, heard him singing at a feast given by her father. She eloped with him that night, and they set up a wine-shop together. After a time Hsiang-ju became famous as a poet, but his character was marred by love of money. He sold love-poems, which the ladies of the palace sent to the emperor in order to win his favour. Finally, he gave presents to the "ladies of Mo-ling", hoping to secure a concubine. It was this step that induced his mistress, Cho Wēn-chün, to write the following poem.

Our love was pure
As the snow on the mountains:
White as a moon
Between the clouds—
They're telling me
Your thoughts are double;
That's why I've come
To break it off.
To-day we'll drink
A cup of wine.
To-morrow we'll part
Beside the Canal:

Walking about,
Beside the Canal,
Where its branches divide
East and west.
Alas and alas,
And again alas.
So must a girl
Cry when she's married,
If she find not a man
Of single heart,
Who will not leave her
Till her hair is white.

To His Wife

By General Su Wu? (circa 100 B. C.)

Since our hair was plaited and we became man and wife
The love between us was never broken by doubt.
So let us be merry this night together,
Feasting and playing while the good time lasts.

I suddenly remember the distance that I must travel;
I spring from bed and look out to see the time.
The stars and planets are all grown dim in the sky;
Long, long is the road; I cannot stay.
I am going on service, away to the battle-ground,
And I do not know when I shall come back.
I hold your hand with only a deep sigh;
Afterwards, tears—in the days when we are parted.
With all your might enjoy the spring flowers,
But do not forget the time of our love and pride.
Know that if I live, I will come back again,
And if I die, we will go on thinking of each other.

Li Ling

[Parting from Su Wu]

(Authorship Uncertain)

The good time will never come back again:
In a moment,—our parting will be over.
Anxiously—we halt at the road-side,
Hesitating—we embrace where the fields begin.
The clouds above are floating across the sky:
Swiftly, swiftly passing: or blending together.
The waves in the wind lose their fixed place
And are rolled away each to a corner of Heaven.
From now onwards—long must be our parting,
So let us stop again for a little while.
I wish I could ride on the wings of the morning wind
And go with you right to your journey's end.

*Li Ling and Su Wu were both prisoners in the land of the Huns.
After nineteen years Su Wu was released. Li Ling would not go back
with him. When invited to do so, he got up and danced, singing:*

I came ten thousand leagues
Across sandy deserts

In the service of my Prince,
To break the Hun tribes.
My way was blocked and barred,
My arrows and sword broken.
My armies had faded away,
My reputation had gone.

My old mother is long dead.
Although I want to requite my Prince
How can I return?

Ch'in Chia

Ch'in Chia (first century A. D.) was summoned to take up an appointment at the capital at a time when his wife was ill and staying with her parents. He was therefore unable to say goodbye to her, and sent her three poems instead. This is the last of the three.

Solemn, solemn the coachman gets ready to go:
"Chiang, chiang" the harness bells ring.
At break of dawn I must start on my long journey:
At cock-crow I must gird on my belt.
I turn back and look at the empty room:
For a moment I almost think I see you there.
One parting, but ten thousand regrets:
As I take my seat, my heart is unquiet.
What shall I do to tell you all my thoughts?
How can I let you know of all my love?
Precious hairpins make the head to shine
And bright mirrors can reflect beauty.
Fragrant herbs banish evil smells
And the scholar's harp has a clear note.
The man in the Book of Odes[1] who was given a quince
Wanted to pay it back with diamonds and rubies.
When I think of all the things you have done for me,
How ashamed I am to have done so little for you!
Although I know that it is a poor return,
All I can give you is this description of my feelings.

[1] Odes, v, 10.

55

Ch'in Chia's Wife's Reply

My poor body is alas unworthy:
I was ill when first you brought me home.
Limp and weary in the house—
Time passed and I got no better.
We could hardly ever see each other:
I could not serve you as I ought.
Then you received the Imperial Mandate:
You were ordered to go far away to the City.
Long, long must be our parting:
I was not destined to tell you my thoughts.
I stood on tiptoe gazing into the distance,
Interminably gazing at the road that had taken you.
With thoughts of you my mind is obsessed:
In my dreams I see the light of your face.
Now you are started on your long journey
Each day brings you further from me.
Oh that I had a bird's wings
And high flying could follow you.
Long I sob and long I cry:
The tears fall down and wet my skirt.

Song

By Sung Tzŭ-hou (second century A.D.)

On the Eastern Way at the city of Lo-yang
At the edge of the road peach-trees and plum-trees grow;
On the two sides,—flower matched by flower;
Across the road,—leaf touching leaf.

A spring wind rises from the north-east;
Flowers and leaves gently nod and sway.
Up the road somebody's daughter comes
Carrying a basket, to gather silkworms' food.

> [She sees the fruit trees in blossom and, forgetting about
> her silkworms, begins to pluck the branches.]

With her slender hand she breaks a branch from the tree;
The flowers fall, tossed and scattered in the wind.

> The tree says:

"Lovely lady, I never did you harm;
Why should you hate me and do me injury?"

The lady answers:

"At high autumn in the eighth and ninth moons
When the white dew changes to hoar-frost,
At the year's end the wind would have lashed your boughs,
Your sweet fragrance could not have lasted long.
Though in the autumn your leaves patter to the ground,
When spring comes, your gay bloom returns.
But in men's lives when their bright youth is spent
Joy and love never come back again."

Satire on Paying Calls in August

By Ch'ēng Hsiao (circa A.D. 250)

When I was young, throughout the hot season
There were no carriages driving about the roads,
People shut their doors and lay down in the cool:
Or if they went out, it was not to pay calls.
Nowadays—ill-bred, ignorant fellows,
When they feel the heat, make for a friend's house.
The unfortunate host, when he hears someone coming
Scowls and frowns, but can think of no escape.
"There's nothing for it but to rise and go to the door,"
And in his comfortable seat he groans and sighs.

The conversation does not end quickly:
Prattling and babbling, what a lot he says!
Only when one is almost dead with fatigue
He asks at last if one isn't finding him tiring.
[One's arm is almost in half with continual fanning:
The sweat is pouring down one's neck in streams.]
Do not say that this is a small matter:
I consider the practice a blot on our social life.
I therefore caution all wise men
That August visitors should not be admitted.

On the Death of His Father

By Wei Wēn-ti, son of Ts'ao Ts'ao, who founded the dynasty of Wei, and died in A. D. 220. (The poem has been wrongly attributed to Han Wēn-ti, died 157 B. C.)

I look up and see / his curtains and bed:
I look down and examine / his table and mat.
The things are there / just as before.
But the man they belonged to / is not there.
His spirit suddenly / has taken flight
And left me behind / far away.
To whom shall I look, / on whom rely?
My tears flow / in an endless stream.
"Yu, yu" / cry the wandering deer
As they carry fodder / to their young in the wood.
Flap, flap / fly the birds
As they carry their little ones / back to the nest.
I alone / am desolate
Dreading the days / of our long parting:
My grieving heart's / settled pain
No one else / can understand.
There is a saying / among people
"Sorrow makes us / grow old".

60

Alas, alas / for my white hairs!
All too early / they have come!
Long wailing, / long sighing
My thoughts are fixed on my sage parent.
They say the good / live long:
Then why was *he* / not spared?

The Campaign Against Wu

Two Poems by Wei Wên-ti (A. D. 188–227)

[1]

My charioteer hastens to yoke my carriage,
For I must go on a journey far away.
"Where are you going on your journey far away?"
To the land of Wu where my enemies are.
But I must ride many thousand miles,
Beyond the Eastern Road that leads to Wu.
Between the rivers bitter winds blow,
Swiftly flow the waters of Huai and Ssŭ.
I want to take a skiff and cross these rivers,
But alas for me, where shall I find a boat?
To sit idle is not my desire:
Gladly enough would I go to my country's aid.

[2]

(He abandons the campaign)

In the North-west there is a floating cloud
Stretched on high, like a chariot's canvas-awning.
Alas that I was born in these times,
To be blown along like a cloud puffed by the wind!
It has blown me away far to the South-east,
On and on till I came to Wu-hui.
Wu-hui is not my country:
Why should I go on staying and staying here?
I will give it up and never speak of it again,—
This being abroad and always living in dread.

The Ruins of Lo-yang

By Ts'ao Chih (A. D. 192–232), third son of Ts'ao Ts'ao.
He was a great favourite with his father till he made a mistake in a
campaign. In this poem he returns to look at the ruins of Lo-yang,
where he used to live. It had been sacked by Tung Cho.

I climb to the ridge of Pei Mang Mountain
And look down on the city of Lo-yang.
In Lo-yang how still it is!
Palaces and houses all burnt to ashes.
Walls and fences all broken and gaping,
Thorns and brambles shooting up to the sky.
I do not see the old old-men:
I only see the new young men.
I turn aside, for the straight road is lost:
The fields are overgrown and will never be
    ploughed again.
I have been away such a long time
That I do not know which street is which.
How sad and ugly the empty moors are!
A thousand miles without the smoke of a chimney.
I think of the house I lived in all those years:
    I am heart-tied and cannot speak.

64

The preceding poem vaguely recalls a famous Anglo-Saxon fragment which I will make intelligible by semi-translation:

"Wondrous was the wall-stone,
 Weirdly[1] broken;
 Burgh-steads bursten,
 Giants' work tumbleth,
 Roofs are wrenched,
 Towers totter,
 Bereft of rune-gates.
 Smoke is on the plaster,
 Scarred the shower-burghs,
 Shorn and shattered,
 By eld under-eaten.
 Earth's grip haveth
 Wealders[2] and workmen."

[1] By Fate.
[2] Rulers.

The Cock-Fight

By Ts'ao Chih

Our wandering eyes are sated with the dancer's skill,
Our ears are weary with the sound of "kung"
    and "shang".[1]
Our host is silent and sits doing nothing:
All the guests go on to places of amusement.

On long benches the sportsmen sit ranged
Round a cleared room, watching the fighting-cocks.
The gallant birds are all in battle-trim:
They raise their tails and flap defiantly.
Their beating wings stir the calm air:
Their angry eyes gleam with a red light.
Where their beaks have struck, the fine feathers are
    scattered:
With their strong talons they wound again and again.
Their long cries enter the blue clouds;
Their flapping wings tirelessly beat and throb.
"Pray God the lamp-oil lasts a little longer,
Then I shall not leave without winning the match!"

[1] Notes of the scale.

66

A Vision

By Ts'ao Chih

In the Nine Provinces there is not room enough:
I want to soar high among the clouds,
And, far beyond the Eight Limits of the compass,
Cast my gaze across the unmeasured void.
I will wear as my gown the red mists of sunrise,
And as my skirt the white fringes of the clouds:
My canopy—the dim lustre of Space:
My chariot—six dragons mounting heavenward:
And before the light of Time has shifted a pace
Suddenly stand upon the World's blue rim.
     The doors of Heaven swing open,
The double gates shine with a red light.
I roam and linger in the palace of Wēn-ch'ang,[1]
I climb up to the hall of T'ai-wei.[1]
The Lord God lies at his western lattice:
And the lesser Spirits are together in the eastern gallery.
They wash me in a bath of rainbow-spray
And gird me with a belt of jasper and rubies.
I wander at my ease gathering divine herbs:
I bend down and touch the scented flowers.
Wang-tzŭ[2] gives me drugs of long-life
And Hsien-mēn[2] hands me strange potions.
By the partaking of food I evade the rites of Death:
My span is extended to the enjoyment of life everlasting.

[1] Stars.   [2] Immortals.

Regret

By Yüan Chi (A.D. 210-263)

When I was young I learnt fencing
And was better at it than Crooked Castle.[1]
My spirit was high as the rolling clouds
And my fame resounded beyond the World.
I took my sword to the desert sands,
I watered my horse at the Nine Moors.
My flags and banners flapped in the wind,
And nothing was heard but the song of my drums.

War and its travels have made me sad,
And a fierce anger burns within me:
It's thinking of how I've wasted my time
That makes this fury tear my heart.

[1] A famous general.

The Curtain of the Wedding Bed

By Liu Hsün's wife (third century A. D.)

After she had been married to him for a long while, General Liu Hsün sent his wife back to her home, because he had fallen in love with a girl of the Ssu-ma family.

Flap, flap, you curtain in front of our bed!
I hung you there to screen us from the light of day.
I brought you with me when I left my father's house;
Now I am taking you back with me again.
I will fold you up and lay you flat in your box.
Curtain—shall I ever take you out again?

Taoist Song

By Chi K'ang (A. D. 223-262)

I will cast out Wisdom and reject Learning.
My thoughts shall wander in the Great Void (*bis*)
Always repenting of wrongs done
Will never bring my heart to rest.
I cast my hook in a single stream;
But my joy is as though I possessed a Kingdom.
I loose my hair and go singing;
To the four frontiers men join in my refrain.
This is the purport of my song:
"My thoughts shall wander in the Great Void."

A Gentle Wind

By Fu Hsüan (died A. D. 278)

A gentle wind fans the calm night:
A bright moon shines on the high tower.
A voice whispers, but no one answers when I call:
A shadow stirs, but no one comes when I beckon,
The kitchen-man brings in a dish of lentils:
Wine is there, but I do not fill my cup.
Contentment with poverty is Fortune's best gift:
Riches and Honour are the handmaids of Disaster.
Though gold and gems by the world are sought and prized,
To me they seem no more than weeds, or chaff.

Woman

By Fu Hsüan

How sad it is to be a woman!
Nothing on earth is held so cheap.
Boys stand leaning at the door
Like Gods fallen out of Heaven.
Their hearts brave the Four Oceans,
The wind and dust of a thousand miles.
No one is glad when a girl is born:
By *her* the family sets no store.
When she grows up, she hides in her room
Afraid to look a man in the face.
No one cries when she leaves her home—
Sudden as clouds when the rain stops.
She bows her head and composes her face,
Her teeth are pressed on her red lips:
She bows and kneels countless times.
She must humble herself even to the servants.
His love is distant as the stars in Heaven,
Yet the sunflower bends toward the sun.
Their hearts more sundered than water and fire—
A hundred evils are heaped upon her.

Her face will follow the years' changes:
Her lord will find new pleasures.
They that were once like substance and shadow
Are now as far as Hu from Ch'in.[1]
Yet Hu and Ch'in shall sooner meet
Than they whose parting is like Ts'an and Ch'ēn.[2]

[1] Two lands.
[2] Two stars.

Day Dreams

By Tso Ssŭ (*third century A.D.*)

When I was young I played with a soft brush
And was passionately devoted to reading all sorts of books.
In prose I made Chia I my standard:
In verse I imitated Ssŭ-ma Hsiang-ju.
But then the arrows began singing at the frontier.
And a winged summons came flying to the City.
Although arms were not my profession,
I had once read Jang-chü's war-book.
I shouted aloud and my cries rent the air:
I felt as though Tung Wu were already annihilated.
The scholar's knife cuts best at its first use
And my dreams hurried on to the completion of my plan.
I wanted at a stroke to clear the Yang-tze and Hsiang,
At a glance to quell the Tibetans and Hu.
When my task was done, I should not accept a barony,
But refusing with a bow, retire to a cottage in the country.

74

The Scholar in the Narrow Street

By Tso Ssŭ

Flap, flap, the captive bird in the cage
Beating its wings against the four corners.
Depressed, depressed the scholar in the narrow street:
Clasping a shadow, he dwells in an empty house.
When he goes out, there is nowhere for him to go:
Bunches and brambles block up his path.
He composes a memorial, but it is rejected and unread,
He is left stranded, like a fish in a dry pond.
Without—he has not a single farthing of salary:
Within—there is not a peck of grain in his larder.
His relations upbraid him for his lack of success:
His friends and callers daily decrease in number.
Su Ch'in used to go preaching in the North
And Li Ssŭ sent a memorandum to the West.
I once hoped to pluck the fruits of life:
But now alas, they are all withered and dry.
Though one drinks at a river, one cannot drink more
 than a bellyful;
Enough is good, but there is no use in satiety.
The bird in a forest can perch but on one bough,
And this should be the wise man's pattern.

The Desecration of the Han Tombs

By Chang Tsai (third century A.D.)

At Pei-mang how they rise to Heaven,
Those high mounds, four or five in the fields!
What men lie buried under these tombs?
All of them were Lords of the Han world.
"Kung" and "Wēn"[1] gaze across at each other:
The Yüan mound is all grown over with weeds.
When the dynasty was falling, tumult and disorder arose,
Thieves and robbers roamed like wild beasts.
Of earth[2] they have carried away more than one handful,
They have gone into vaults and opened the secret doors.
Jewellèd scabbards lie twisted and defaced:
The stones that were set in them, thieves have carried away,
The ancestral temples are hummocks in the ground:
The walls that went round them are all levelled flat.
Over everything the tangled thorns are growing:
A herd-boy pushes through them up the path.
Down in the thorns rabbits have made their burrows:
The weeds and thistles will never be cleared away.

[1] Names of two tombs.
[2] In the early days of the dynasty a man stole a handful of earth from the imperial tombs, and was executed by the police. The emperor was furious at the lightness of the punishment.

76

Over the tombs the ploughshare will be driven
And peasants will have their fields and orchards there.
They that were once lords of a thousand hosts
Are now become the dust of the hills and ridges.
I think of what Yün-mēn[1] said
And am sorely grieved at the thought of "then" and "now".

[1] Yün-mēn said to Mēng Ch'ang-chün [died 279 B. C.], "Does it not grieve you to think that after a hundred years this terrace will be cast down and this pond cleared away?" Mēng Ch'ang-chün wept.

Bearer's Song

By Miu Hsi (died A. D. 245)

When I was alive, I wandered in the streets of the Capital:
Now that I am dead, I am left to lie in the fields.
In the morning I drove out from the High Hall:
In the evening I lodged beneath the Yellow Springs.[1]
When the white sun had sunk in the Western Chasm
I hung up my chariot and rested my four horses.
Now, even the mighty Maker of All
Could not bring the life back to my limbs.
Shape and substance day by day will vanish:
Hair and teeth will gradually fall away.
Forever from of old men have been so:
And none born can escape this thing.

Cf. the "Han Burial Songs", p. 33.

[1] Hades.

78

The Valley Wind

By Lu Yün (A. D. 262–303)

Living in retirement beyond the World,
Silently enjoying isolation,
I pull the rope of my door tighter
And stuff my window with roots and ferns.
My spirit is tuned to the Spring-season:
At the fall of the year there is autumn in my heart.
Thus imitating cosmic changes
My cottage becomes a Universe.

Inviting Guests

By Ch'ēng-kung Sui (died A. D. 273)

I sent out invitations
To summon guests.
I collected together
All my friends.
Loud talk
And simple feasting:
Discussion of philosophy,
Investigation of subtleties.
Tongues loosened
And minds at one.
Hearts refreshed
By discharge of emotion!

Twelve Poems

By T'ao Ch'ien (A.D. 372–427)

[1]

Shady, shady the wood in front of the Hall:
At midsummer full of calm shadows.
The south wind follows summer's train:
With its eddying puffs it blows open my coat.
I am free from ties and can live a life of retirement.
When I rise from sleep, I play with books and harp.
The lettuce in the garden still grows moist:
Of last year's grain there is always plenty left.
Self-support should maintain strict limits:
More than enough is not what I want.
I grind millet and make good wine:
When the wine is heated, I pour it out for myself.
My little children are playing at my side,
Learning to talk, they babble unformed sounds.
These things have made me happy again
And I forget my lost cap of office.
Distant, distant I gaze at the white clouds:
With a deep yearning I think of the Sages of Antiquity.

[2]

In the quiet of the morning I heard a knock at my door:
I threw on my clothes and opened it myself.
I asked who it was who had come so early to see me:
He said he was a peasant, coming with good intent.
He brought a present of wine and rice-soup,
Believing that I had fallen on evil days.
"You live in rags under a thatched roof
And seem to have no desire for a better lot.
The rest of mankind have all the same ambitions:
You, too, must learn to wallow in their mire."
"Old man, I am impressed by what you say,
But my soul is not fashioned like other men's.
To drive in their rut I might perhaps learn:
To be untrue to myself could only lead to muddle.
Let us drink and enjoy together the wine you have brought:
For my course is set and cannot now be altered."

[3]

Chill and harsh the year draws to its close:
In my cotton dress I seek sunlight on the porch.
In the southern orchard all the leaves are gone:
In the north garden rotting boughs lie heaped.
I empty my cup and drink it down to the dregs:
I look towards the kitchen, but no smoke rises.
Poems and books lie piled beside my chair:
But the light is going and I shall not have time to read them.
My life here is not like the Agony in Ch'ēn,[1]
But often I have to bear bitter reproaches.
Let me then remember, to calm my heart's distress,
That the Sages of old were often in like case.

[4]

I built my hut in a zone of human habitation,
Yet near me there sounds no noise of horse or coach.
    Would you know how that is possible?
A heart that is distant creates a wilderness round it.
I pluck chrysanthemums under the eastern hedge,
Then gaze long at the distant summer hills.
The mountain air is fresh at the dusk of day:
The flying birds two by two return.
In these things there lies a deep meaning;
Yet when we would express it, words suddenly fail us.

[1] Confucius was maltreated in Ch'ēn.

Blaming Sons

[An Apology for His Own Drunkenness]

White hair covers my temples,
I am wrinkled and seared beyond repair,
And though I have got five sons,
They all hate paper and brush.
A-shu is eighteen:
For laziness there is none like him.
A-hsüan does his best,
But really loathes the Fine Arts.
Yung-tuan is thirteen,
But does not know "six" from "seven".[1]
T'ung-tzŭ in his ninth year
Is only concerned with things to eat.
If Heaven treats me like this,
What can I do but fill my cup?

[1] Written in Chinese with two characters very easy to distinguish.

A long time ago
I went on a journey,
Right to the corner
Of the Eastern Ocean.
The road there
Was long and winding,
And stormy waves
Barred my path.
What made me
Go this way?
Hunger drove me
Into the World.
I tried hard
To fill my belly:
And even a little
Seemed a lot.
But this was clearly
A bad bargain,
So I went home
And lived in idleness.

Substance, Shadow, and Spirit

High and low, wise and simple, all busily hoard up the
    moments of life. How greatly they err!
Therefore I have to the uttermost exposed the bitterness
    both of Substance and Shadow, and have made
    Spirit show how, by following Nature, we may dis-
    solve this bitterness.

Substance speaks to Shadow:

Heaven and Earth exist for ever:
Mountains and rivers never change.
But herbs and trees in perpetual rotation
Are renovated and withered by the dews and frosts:
And Man the wise, Man the divine—
Shall he alone escape this law?
Fortuitously appearing for a moment in the World
He suddenly departs, never to return.
How can he know that the friends he has left
Are missing him and thinking of him?
Only the things that he used remain;
They look upon them and their tears flow.
Me no magical arts can save,
Though you may hope for a wizard's aid.
I beg you listen to this advice—
When you can get wine, be sure to drink it.

86

Shadow replies:

There is no way to preserve life.
Drugs of Immortality are instruments of folly.
I would gladly wander in Paradise,
But it is far away and there is no road.
Since the day that I was joined to you
We have shared all our joys and pains.
While you rested in the shade, I left you a while:
But till the end we shall be together.
Our joint existence is impermanent:
Sadly together we shall slip away.
That when the body decays Fame should also go
Is a thought unendurable, burning the heart.
Let us strive and labour while yet we may
To do some deed that men will praise.
Wine may in truth dispel our sorrow,
But how compare it with lasting Fame?

Spirit expounds:

God can only set in motion:
He cannot control the things he has made.
Man, the second of the Three Orders,
Owes his precedence to Me.
Though I am different from you,
We were born involved in one another:
Nor by any means can we escape
The intimate sharing of good and ill.

87

The Three Emperors were saintly men,
Yet to-day—where are they?
P'ēng[1] lived to a great age,
Yet he went at last, when he longed to stay.
And late or soon, all go:
Wise and simple have no reprieve.
Wine may bring forgetfulness,
But does it not hasten old-age?
If you set your hearts on noble deeds,
How do you know that any will praise you?
By all this thinking you do Me injury:
You had better go where Fate leads—
Drift on the Stream of Infinite Flux,
Without joy, without fear:
When you must go—then go,
And make as little fuss as you can.

[8]

Moving House

My old desire to live in the Southern Village
Was not because I had taken a fancy to the house.
But I heard it was a place of simple-minded men
With whom it were a joy to spend the mornings
    and evenings.
Many years I had longed to settle here:

[1] The Chinese Methuselah.

Now at last I have managed to move house.
I do not mind if my cottage is rather small
So long as there's room enough for bed and mat.
Often and often the neighbours come to see me
And with brave words discuss the things of old.
Rare writings we read together and praise:
Doubtful meanings we examine together and settle.

[9]

New Corn

Swiftly the years, beyond recall.
Solemn the stillness of this fair morning.
I will clothe myself in spring-clothing
And visit the slopes of the Eastern Hill.
By the mountain-stream a mist hovers,
Hovers a moment, then scatters.
There comes a wind blowing from the south
That brushes the fields of new corn.

[10]

Returning to the Fields

When I was young, I was out of tune with the herd:
My only love was for the hills and mountains.
Unwitting I fell into the Web of the World's dust

And was not free until my thirtieth year.
The migrant bird longs for the old wood:
The fish in the tank thinks of its native pool.
I had rescued from wildness a patch of the Southern Moor
And, still rustic, I returned to field and garden.
My ground covers no more than ten acres:
My thatched cottage has eight or nine rooms.
Elms and willows cluster by the eaves:
Peach trees and plum trees grow before the hall.
Hazy, hazy the distant hamlets of men.
Steady the smoke of the half-deserted village,
A dog barks somewhere in the deep lanes,
A cock crows at the top of the mulberry tree.
At gate and courtyard—no murmur of the World's dust:
In the empty rooms—leisure and deep stillness.
Long I lived checked by the bars of a cage:
Now I have turned again to Nature and Freedom.

[11]

Reading the Book of Hills and Seas

In the month of June the grass grows high
And round my cottage thick-leaved branches sway.
There is not a bird but delights in the place where it rests:
And I too—love my thatched cottage.

I have done my ploughing:
I have sown my seed.
Again I have time to sit and read my books.
In the narrow lane there are no deep ruts:
Often my friends' carriages turn back.
In high spirits I pour out my spring wine
And pluck the lettuce growing in my garden.
A gentle rain comes stealing up from the east
And a sweet wind bears it company.
My thoughts float idly over the story of King Chou.
My eyes wander over the pictures of Hills and Seas.
At a single glance I survey the whole Universe.
He will never be happy, whom such pleasures fail to please!

[12]

Flood

The lingering clouds, rolling, rolling,
And the settled rain, dripping, dripping,
In the Eight Directions—the same dusk.
The level lands—one great river.
Wine I have, wine I have:
Idly I drink at the eastern window.
Longingly—I think of my friends,
But neither boat nor carriage comes.

Climbing A Mountain

By Tao-yün (circa A. D. 400), wife of General Wang Ning-chih.
The general was so stupid that she finally deserted him.

High rises the Eastern Peak
Soaring up to the blue sky.
Among the rocks—an empty hollow,
Secret, still, mysterious!
Uncarved and unhewn,
Screened by nature with a roof of clouds.
Times and Seasons, what things are you
Bringing to my life ceaseless change?
I will lodge for ever in this hollow
Where Springs and Autumns
unheeded pass.

Sailing Homeward

By Chan Fang-shēng (fourth century A. D.)

Cliffs that rise a thousand feet
Without a break,
Lake that stretches a hundred miles
Without a wave,
Sands that are white through all the year,
Without a stain,
Pine-tree woods, winter and summer
Ever-green,
Streams that for ever flow and flow
Without a pause,
Trees that for twenty thousand years
Your vows have kept,
You have suddenly healed the pain of a traveller's heart,
And moved his brush to write a new song.

Plucking the Rushes

[*A boy and girl are sent to gather rushes for thatching*]

Anonymous (fourth century A. D.)

Green rushes with red shoots,
Long leaves bending to the wind—
You and I in the same boat
Plucking rushes at the Five Lakes.
We started at dawn from the orchid-island:
We rested under the elms till noon.
You and I plucking rushes
Had not plucked a handful when night came!

Ballad of the Western Island
in the North Country

"Seeing the plum-tree I thought of the Western Island
And I plucked a branch to send to the North Country.
I put on my dress of apricot-yellow silk
And bound up my hair black as the crow's wing.
But which is the road that leads to the Western Island?
I'll ask the man at the ferry by the Bridge of Boats.
But the sun is sinking and the orioles flying home:
And the wind is blowing and sighing in the walnut-tree.
I'll stand under the tree just beside the gate:
I'll stand by the door and show off my enameled hair-pins."
She's opened the gate, but her lover has not come:
She's gone out at the gate to pluck red lotus.
As she plucks the lotus on the southern dyke in autumn,
The lotus flower stands higher than a man's head.
She bends down and plays with the lotus seeds,
The lotus seeds are green like the lake-water.
She gathers the flowers and puts them into her gown—
The lotus-bud that is red all through.
She thinks of her lover, her lover that does not come:
She looks up and sees the wild geese flying—
The Western Island is full of wild geese.
To look for her lover she climbs the Blue Tower.
The tower is high: she looks, but cannot see:

All day she leans on the balcony rails.
The rail is twisted into a twelve-fold pattern.
She lets fall her hand white like the colour of jade.
She rolls up the awning, she sees the wide sky,
And the sea-water waving its vacant blue.
"The sea shall carry my dreams far away,
So that you shall be sorry at last for my sorrow.
If the South wind only knew my thoughts
It would blow my dreams till they got to the Western Island."

The Scholar Recruit

By Pao Chao (died A. D. 466)

Now late
I follow Time's Necessity:[1]
Mounting a barricade I pacify remote tribes.
Discarding my sash I don a coat of hide.
Rolling up my skirts I shoulder a black bow.
Even at the very start my strength fails:
What will become of me before it's all over?

[1] *I.e.*, "enlist".

The Red Hills

By Pao Chao

Red hills lie athwart us as a menace in the west,
And fiery mountains glare terrible in the south.
The body burns, the head aches and throbs:
If a bird light here, its soul forthwith departs.
Warm springs pour from cloudy pools
And hot smoke issues between the rocks.
The sun and moon are perpetually obscured:
The rain and dew never stay dry.
There are red serpents a hundred feet long,
And black snakes ten girths round.
The sand-spitters shoot their poison at the sunbeams:
The flying insects are ill with the shifting glare.
The hungry monkeys dare not come down to eat:
The morning birds dare not set out to fly.
At the Ching river many die of poison:
Crossing the Lu one is lucky if one is only ill.
Our living feet walk on dead ground:
Our high wills surmount the snares of Fate.
The Spear-boat General[1] got but little honour:
The Wave-subduer[2] met with scant reward.
If our Prince still grudges the things that are easy to give,[3]
Can he hope that his soldiers will give what is hardest to give?[4]

[1] Hou Yen (first cent. B. C.). [2] Ma Yüan (first cent. A. D.).
[3] Rewards and titles. [4] Life.

98

Song of the Men of Chin-ling

[Marching Back into the Capital]

By Hsieh T'iao (fifth century A. D.)

Chiang-nan is a glorious and beautiful land,
And Chin-ling an exalted and kingly province!
The green canals of the city stretch on and on
And its high towers stretch up and up.
Flying gables lean over the bridle-road:
Drooping willows cover the Royal Aqueduct.
Shrill flutes sing by the coach's awning,
And reiterated drums bang near its painted wheels.
The names of the deserving shall be carved on the
    Cloud Terrace.[1]
And for those who have done valiantly rich
    reward awaits.

[1] The Record Office.

Song

By Tsang Chih (sixth century A. D.)

I was brought up under the Stone Castle:
My window opened on to the castle tower.
In the castle were beautiful young men
Who waved to me as they went in and out.

Dreaming of a Dead Lady

"I heard at night your long sighs
And knew that you were thinking of me."
As she spoke, the doors of Heaven opened
And our souls conversed and I saw her face.
She set me a pillow to rest on
And she brought me meat and drink.

I stood beside her where she lay,
But suddenly woke and she was not there:
And none knew how my soul was torn,
How the tears fell surging over my breast.

The Liberator

[A Political Allegory]

By Wu-ti, Emperor of the Liang dynasty (A. D. 464–549)

In the high trees—many doleful winds:
The ocean waters—lashed into waves.
If the sharp sword be not in your hand,
How can you hope your friends will remain many?
Do you not see that sparrow on the fence?
Seeing the hawk it casts itself into the snare.
The fowler to catch the sparrow is delighted:
The Young Man to see the sparrow is grieved.
He takes his sword and cuts through the netting:
The yellow sparrow flies away, away.
Away, away, up to the blue sky
And down again to thank the Young Man.

Lo-yang

By the Emperor Ch'ien Wên-ti (*sixth century A. D.*)

A beautiful place is the town of Lo-yang:
The big streets are full of spring light.
The lads go driving out with harps in their hands:
The mulberry girls go out to the fields with their baskets.
Golden whips glint at the horses' flanks,
Gauze sleeves brush the green boughs.
Racing dawn, the carriages come home,—
And the girls with their high baskets full of fruit.

People Hide Their Love

By Wu-ti

Who says
That it's by my desire,
This separation, this living so far from you?
My dress still smells of the lavender you gave:
My hand still holds the letter that you sent.
Round my waist I wear a double sash:
I dream that it binds us both with a same-heart knot.
Did not you know that people hide their love,
Like the flower that seems too precious to be picked?

The Rejected Wife

By Yüan-ti (A. D. 508–554)

Entering the Hall, she meets the new wife:
Leaving the gate, she runs into her former husband.
Words stick: she does not manage to say anything:
She presses her hands together and hesitates.
Agitates moon-like fan—sheds pearl-like tears—
Realizes she loves him just as much as ever:
That her present pain will never come to an end.

The Ferry

By the Emperor Ch'ien Wên-ti, of the Liang dynasty,
who reigned during the year A. D. 500.

Of marsh-mallows my boat is made,
The ropes are lily-roots.
The pole-star is athwart the sky:
The moon sinks low.
It's at the ferry I'm plucking lilies,
But it might be the Yellow River—
So afraid you seem of the wind and waves,
So long you tarry at the crossing.[1]

[1] A lady is waiting for her lover at the ferry which crosses a small stream. When he does not come, she bitterly suggests that he is as afraid of the little stream as though it were the Yellow River, the largest river in China.

The Waters of Lung-t'ou

[The North-west Frontier]

By Hsü Ling (A. D. 507–583)

The road that I came by mounts eight thousand feet:
The river that I crossed hangs a hundred fathoms.
The brambles so thick that in summer one cannot pass!
The snow so high that in winter one cannot climb!
With branches that interlace Lung Valley is dark:
Against cliffs that tower one's voice beats and echoes.
I turn my head, and it seems only a dream
That I ever lived in the streets of Hsien-yang.

Flowers and Moonlight
on the Spring River

By Yang-ti (A. D. 605–617), Emperor of the Sui dynasty

The evening river is level and motionless—
The spring colours just open to their full.
Suddenly a wave carries the moon[1] away
And the tidal water comes with its freight of stars.[1]

[1] I.e., the reflection in the water.

Winter Night

My bed is so empty that I keep on waking up:
As the cold increases, the night-wind begins to blow.
It rustles the curtains, making a noise like the sea:
Oh that those were waves which could carry me back to you!

Tchirek Song

Altun (A. D. 486-566) was a Tartar employed by the Chinese in drilling their troops "after the manner of the Huns". He could not read or write. The "Yo Fu Kuang T'i" says: Kao Huan attacked Pi, king of Chou, but lost nearly half his men. Kao Huan fell ill of sadness and Pi, to taunt him, sent out a proclamation, which said:

> Kao Huan, that son of a mouse
> Dared to attack King Pi.
> But at the first stroke of sword and bow,
> The aggressor's plot recoiled on himself.

When this reached Kao Huan's ears, he sat up in bed and tried to comfort his officers. All the nobles were summoned to his room, and Altun was asked to sing them a song about Tchirek, his native land.

He sang:

> Tchirek River
> Lies under the Dark Mountains:
> Where the sky is like the sides of a tent
> Stretched down over the Great Steppe.
> The sky is gray, gray:
> And the steppe wide, wide:
> Over grass that the wind has battered low
> Sheep and oxen roam.

"Altun" means "gold" in Tartar. No one could teach him to write the Chinese character for gold, till at last some one said: "Draw the roof of your house and then put a few strokes underneath." He thus learnt, in a rough fashion, to write his own name.

Business Men

By Ch'ēn Tzŭ-ang (A. D. 656–698)

Business men boast of their skill and cunning
But in philosophy they are like little children.
Bragging to each other of successful depredations
They neglect to consider the ultimate fate of the body.
What should they know of the Master of Dark Truth
Who saw the wide world in a jade cup,
By illumined conception got clear of Heaven and Earth:
On the chariot of Mutation entered the Gate of Immutability?

On Going to a Tavern

By Wang Chi

These days, continually fuddled with drink,
I fail to satisfy the appetites of the soul.
But seeing men all behaving like drunkards,[1]
How can I alone remain sober?

[1] Written during the war which preceded the T'ang dynasty.

Tell Me Now

By Wang Chi (A. D. 584-644)

"Tell me now, what should a man want
But to sit alone, sipping his cup of wine?"
I should like to have visitors come and discuss philosophy
And not to have the tax-collector coming to collect taxes:
My three sons married into good families
And my five daughters wedded to steady husbands.
Then I could jog through a happy five-score years
And, at the end, need no Paradise.

Stone Fish Lake

By Yüan Chieh (flourished circa A.D. 723-772)

Yüan Chieh, a contemporary of Li Po, has not hitherto been mentioned in any European book. "His subjects were always original, but his poems are seldom worth quoting," is a Chinese opinion of him.

I loved you dearly, Stone Fish Lake,
With your rock-island shaped like a swimming fish!
On the fish's back is the Wine-cup Hollow
And round the fish,—the flowing waters of the Lake.
The boys on the shore sent little wooden ships,
Each made to carry a single cup of wine.
The island-drinkers emptied the liquor-boats
And set their sails and sent them back for more.
On the shores of the Lake were jutting slabs of rock
And under the rocks there flowed an icy stream.
Heated with wine to rinse our mouths and hands
In those cold waters was a joy beyond compare!

Of gold and jewels I have not any need;
For Caps and Coaches I do not care at all.
But I wish I could sit on the rocky banks of the Lake
For ever and ever staring at the Stone Fish.

Prose Letter

By Wang Wei (A. D. 699–759)

To the Bachelor-of-Arts P'ei Ti

OF LATE during the sacrificial month, the weather has been calm and clear, and I might easily have crossed the mountain. But I knew that you were conning the classics and did not dare disturb you. So I roamed about the mountain-side, rested at the Kan-p'ei Temple, dined with the mountain priests, and, after dinner, came home again. Going northwards, I crossed the Yüan-pa, over whose waters the unclouded moon shone with dazzling rim. When night was far advanced, I mounted Hua-tzŭ's Hill and saw the moonlight tossed up and thrown down by the jostling waves of Wang River. On the wintry mountain distant lights twinkled and vanished; in some deep lane beyond the forest a dog barked at the cold, with a cry as fierce as a wolf's. The sound of villagers grinding their corn at night filled the gaps between the slow chiming of a distant bell.

Now I am sitting alone. I listen, but cannot hear my grooms and servants move or speak. I think much of old days: how hand in hand, composing poems as we went, we walked down twisting paths to the banks of clear streams.

We must wait for Spring to come: till the grasses sprout and the trees bloom. Then wandering together in the spring hills we shall see the trout leap lightly from the stream, the white gulls stretch their wings, the dew fall on the green moss. And in the morning we shall hear the cry of curlews in the barley-fields.

It is not long to wait. Shall you be with me then? Did I not know the natural subtlety of your intelligence, I would not dare address to you so remote an invitation. You will understand that a deep feeling dictates this course.

Written without disrespect by Wang Wei, a dweller in the mountains.

Drinking Alone by Moonlight

Three Poems by Li Po (A. D. 701–762)

[1]

A cup of wine, under the flowering trees;
I drink alone, for no friend is near.
Raising my cup I beckon the bright moon,
For he, with my shadow, will make three men.
The moon, alas, is no drinker of wine;
Listless, my shadow creeps about at my side.
Yet with the moon as friend and the shadow as slave
I must make merry before the Spring is spent.
To the songs I sing the moon flickers her beams;
In the dance I weave my shadow tangles and breaks.
While we were sober, three shared the fun;
Now we are drunk, each goes his way.
May we long share our odd, inanimate feast,
And meet at last on the Cloudy River of the sky.[1]

---

[1] The Milky Way.

[2]

In the third month the town of Hsien-yang
Is thick-spread with a carpet of fallen flowers.
Who in Spring can bear to grieve alone?
Who, sober, look on sights like these?
Riches and Poverty, long or short life,
By the Maker of Things are portioned and disposed;
But a cup of wine levels life and death
And a thousand things obstinately hard to prove.
When I am drunk, I lose Heaven and Earth.
Motionless—I cleave to my lonely bed.
At last I forget that I exist at all,
And at *that* moment my joy is great indeed.

[3]

If High Heaven had no love for wine,
There would not be a Wine Star in the sky.
If Earth herself had no love for wine,
There would not be a city called Wine Springs.[1]
Since Heaven and Earth both love wine,
I can love wine, without shame before God.
Clear wine was once called "a Saint";[2]
Thick wine was once called "a Sage".[2]

Of Saint and Sage I have long quaffed deep,
What need for me to study spirits and *hsien*?[3]
At the third cup I penetrate the Great Way;
A full gallon—Nature and I are one . . .
But the things I feel when wine possesses my soul
I will never tell to those who are not drunk.

---

[1] Ch'iu-ch'üan, in Kansuh.
[2] "History of Wei Dynasty" (Life of Hsü Mo): "A drunken visitor said, 'Clear wine I account a Saint: thick wine only a Sage'."
[3] The lore of Rishi, Immortals.

In the Mountains on
A Summer Day

By Li Po

Gently I stir a white feather fan,
With open shirt sitting in a green wood.
I take off my cap and hang it on a jutting stone;
A wind from the pine-trees trickles on my bare head.

Self-Abandonment

By Li Po

I sat drinking and did not notice the dusk,
Till falling petals filled the folds of my dress.
Drunken I rose and walked to the moonlit stream;
The birds were gone, and men also few.

Waking from Drunkenness on a Spring Day

By Li Po

"Life in the World is but a big dream;
I will not spoil it by any labour or care."
So saying, I was drunk all the day,
Lying helpless at the porch in front of my door.
When I woke up, I blinked at the garden-lawn;
A lonely bird was singing amid the flowers.
I asked myself, had the day been wet or fine?
The Spring wind was telling the mango-bird.
Moved by its song I soon began to sigh,
And as wine was there I filled my own cup.
Wildly singing I waited for the moon to rise;
When my song was over, all my senses had gone.

To Tan Ch'iu

By Li Po

My friend is lodging high in the Eastern Range,
Dearly loving the beauty of valleys and hills.
At green Spring he lies in the empty woods,
And is still asleep when the sun shines on high.
A pine-tree wind dusts his sleeves and coat;
A pebbly stream cleans his heart and ears.
I envy you, who far from strife and talk
Are high-propped on a pillow of blue cloud.

Clearing at Dawn

By Li Po

The fields are chill; the sparse rain has stopped;
The colours of Spring teem on every side.
With leaping fish the blue pond is full;
With singing thrushes the green boughs droop.
The flowers of the field have dabbled their
    powdered cheeks;
The mountain grasses are bent level at the waist.
By the bamboo stream the last fragment of cloud
Blown by the wind slowly scatters away.

Poems by Po Chü-i

Life of Po Chü-i

772 Born on 20th of 1st month.

800 Passes his examinations.

806 Receives a minor post at Chou-chih, near the capital.

807 Made Scholar of the Han Lin Academy.

811 Retires to Wei River, being in mourning for his mother.

814 Returns to Court.

815 Banished to Hsün-yang.

818 Removed to Chung-chou.

820 Reprieved and returns to Court.

822 Governor of Hangchow.

825 Governor of Soochow.

826 Retires owing to illness.

827 Returns to Ch'ang-an.

829 Settles permanently at Lo-yang.

831 Governor of Honan, the province of which Lo-yang
         was capital.

833 Retires owing to illness.

839 Has paralytic stroke in tenth month.

846 Dies in the eighth month.

Introduction

PO CHÜ-I was born at T'ai-yüan in Shansi. Most of his childhood was spent at Jung-yang in Honan. His father was a second-class Assistant Department Magistrate. He tells us that his family was poor and often in difficulties.

He seems to have settled permanently at Ch'ang-an in 801. This town, lying near the north-west frontier, was the political capital of the Empire. In its situation it somewhat resembled Madrid. Lo-yang, the Eastern city, owing to its milder climate and more accessible position, became, like Seville in Spain, a kind of *social* capital.

Soon afterwards he met Yüan Chēn, then aged twenty-two, who was destined to play so important a part in his life. Five years later, during a temporary absence from the city, he addressed to Yüan the following poem:

> Since I left my home to seek official State
> Seven years I have lived in Ch'ang-an.
> What have I gained? Only you, Yüan;
> So hard it is to bind friendships fast.
> We have roamed on horseback under the flowering trees;
> We have walked in the snow and warmed our hearts with wine.
>   We have met and parted at the Western Gate
> And neither of us bothered to put on Cap or Belt.
> We did not go up together for Examination;
> We were not serving in the same Department of State.

127

The bond that joined us lay deeper than outward things;
The rivers of our souls spring from the same well!

Of Yüan's appearance at this time we may guess something from a picture which still survives in copy; it shows him, a youthful and elegant figure, visiting his cousin Ts'ui Ying-ying, who was a lady-in-waiting at Court.[1] At this period of his life Po made friends with difficulty, not being, as he tells us "a master of such accomplishments as calligraphy, painting, chess or gambling, which tend to bring men together in pleasurable intercourse". Two older men, T'ang Ch'ü and Tēng Fang, liked his poetry and showed him much kindness; another, the politician K'ung T'an, won his admiration on public grounds. But all three died soon after he got to know them. Later he made three friends with whom he maintained a lifelong intimacy: the poet Liu Yü-hsi (called Mēng-tē), and the two officials Li Chien and Ts'ui Hsuan-liang. In 805 Yüan Chēn was banished for provocative behaviour towards a high official. The T'ang History relates the episode as follows: "Yüan was staying the night at the Fu-shui Inn; just as he was preparing to go to sleep in the Main Hall, the court-official Li Shih-yüan also arrived. Yüan Chēn should have offered to withdraw from the Hall. He did not do so and a scuffle ensued. Yüan, locked out of the building, took off his shoes and stole round to the back, hoping to find another way in. Li followed with a whip and struck him across the face."

[1] Yüan told of this intrigue in the 'Story of Ts'ui Ying-ying'. See p. 299. Upon this fragment is founded the famous XIV cent. drama, 'The Western Pavilion'.

The separation was a heavy blow to Po Chü-i. In a poem called "Climbing Alone to the Lo-yu Gardens" he says:

> I look down on the Twelve City Streets:—
> Red dust flanked by green trees!
> Coaches and horsemen alone fill my eyes;
> I do not see whom my heart longs to see.
> K'ung T'an has died at Lo-yang;
> Yüan Chēn is banished to Ching-mēn. . . .

In 804 on the death of his father, and again in 811 on the death of his mother, he spent periods of retirement on the Wei River near Ch'ang-an. It was during the second of these periods that he wrote the long poem (260 lines) called "Visiting the Wuchēn Temple". Soon after his return to Ch'ang-an, which took place in the winter of 814, he fell into official disfavour. In two long memorials entitled "On Stopping the War", he had criticized the handling of a campaign against an unimportant tribe of Tartars, which he considered had been unduly prolonged. In a series of poems he had satirized the rapacity of minor officials and called attention to the intolerable sufferings of the masses.

His enemies soon found an opportunity of silencing him. In 814 the Prime Minister, Wu Yüan-hēng, was assassinated in broad daylight by an agent of the revolutionary leader Wu Yüan-chi. Po, in a memorial to the Throne, pointed out the urgency of remedying the prevailing discontent. He held at this time the post of assistant secretary to the Princes' tutor. He should not have criticized the Prime Minister (for being murdered!) until the official Censors had spoken, for he held a Palace appointment which did not carry with it the right of censorship.

His opponents also raked up another charge. His mother had met her death by falling into a well while looking at flowers. Chü-i had written two poems entitled "In Praise of Flowers" and "The New Well". It was claimed that by choosing such subjects he had infringed the laws of Filial Piety. He was banished to Kiukiang (then called Hsün-yang) with the rank of Sub-Prefect. After three years he was given the Governorship of Chung-chou, a remote place in Ssech'uan. On the way up the Yangtze he met Yüan Chēn after three years of separation. They spent a few days together at I-ch'ang, exploring the rock-caves of the neighbourhood.

Chung-chou is noted for its "many flowers and exotic trees", which were a constant delight to its new Governor. In the winter of 819 he was recalled to the capital and became a second-class Assistant Secretary. About this time Yüan Chēn also returned to the city.

In 821 the Emperor Mou Tsung came to the throne. His arbitrary mis-government soon caused a fresh rising in the north-west. Chü-i remonstrated in a series of memorials and was again removed from the capital—this time to be Governor of the important town of Hangchow. Yüan now held a judicial post at Ningpo and the two were occasionally able to meet.

In 824 his Governorship expired and he lived (with the nominal rank of Imperial Tutor) at the village of Li-tao-li, near Lo-yang. It was here that he took into his household two girls, Fan-su and Man-tzŭ, whose singing and dancing enlivened his retreat. He also brought with him from Hangchow a famous "Indian rock", and two cranes of the celebrated "Hua-t'ing" breed. Other amenities of his life at this time were a recipe for making sweet wine, the gift of Ch'ēn Hao-hsien; a harp-melody taught him by Ts'ui Hsuan-liang; and a song called "Autumn Thoughts", brought by the concubine of a visitor from Ssech'uan.

In 825 he became Governor of Soochow. Here at the age of fifty-three he enjoyed a kind of second youth, much more sociable than that of thirty years before; we find him endlessly picnicking and feasting. But after two years illness obliged him to retire.

He next held various posts at the capital, but again fell ill, and in 829 settled at Lo-yang as Governor of the Province of Honan. Here his first son, A-ts'ui, was born, but died in the following year.

In 831 Yüan Chēn also died.

Henceforth, though for thirteen years he continued to hold nominal posts, he lived a life of retirement. In 832 he repaired an unoccupied part of the Hsiang-shan monastery at Lung-mēn,[1] a few miles south of Lo-yang, and lived there, calling himself the Hermit of Hsiang-shan. Once he invited to dinner eight other elderly and retired officials; the occasion was recorded in a picture entitled "The Nine Old Men at Hsiang-shan". There is no evidence that his association with them was otherwise than transient, though legend (see "Mémoires Concernant les Chinois" and Giles, "Biographical Dictionary") has invested the incident with an undue importance. He amused himself at this time by writing a description of his daily life which would be more interesting if it were not so closely modelled on a famous memoir by T'ao Ch'ien. In the winter of 839 he was attacked by paralysis and lost the use of his left leg. After many months in bed he was again able to visit his garden, carried by Ju-man, a favourite monk.

[1] Famous for its rock-sculptures, carved in the sixth and seventh centuries.

In 842 Liu Yü-hsi, the last survivor of the four friends, and a constant visitor at the monastery, "went to wander with Yüan Chēn in Hades". The monk Ju-man also died.

The remaining years of Po's life were spent in collecting and arranging his Complete Works. Copies were presented to the principal monasteries (the "Public Libraries" of the period) in the towns with which he had been connected. He died in 846, leaving instructions that his funeral should be without pomp and that he should be buried not in the family tomb at Hsia-kuei, but by Ju-man's side in the Hsiang-shan Monastery. He desired that a posthumous title should not be awarded.

The most striking characteristic of Po Chü-i's poetry is its verbal simplicity. There is a story that he was in the habit of reading his poems to an old peasant woman and altering any expression which she could not understand. The poems of his contemporaries were mere elegant diversions which enabled the scholar to display his erudition, or the literary juggler his dexterity. Po expounded his theory of poetry in a letter to Yüan Chēn. Like Confucius, he regarded art solely as a method of conveying instruction. He is not the only great artist who has advanced this untenable theory. He accordingly valued his didactic poems far above his other work; but it is obvious that much of his best poetry conveys no moral whatever. He admits, indeed, that among his "miscellaneous stanzas" many were inspired by some momentary sensation or passing event. "A single laugh or a single sigh were rapidly translated into verse".

The didactic poems or "satires" belong to the period before his first banishment. "When the tyrants and favourites heard my Songs of Ch'in, they looked at one another and changed countenance", he boasts. Satire, in the European sense, implies *wit*; but Po's satires are as lacking in true wit as they are unquestionably full of true poetry. We must regard them simply as moral tales in verse.

In the conventional lyric poetry of his predecessors he finds little to admire. Among the earlier poems of the T'ang dynasty he selects for praise the series by Ch'ēn Tzŭ-ang, which includes "Business Men". In Li Po and Tu Fu he finds a deficiency of "fēng" and "ya". The two terms are borrowed from the Preface to the Odes. "Fēng" means "criticism of one's rules"; "ya", "moral guidance to the masses".

"The skill", he says in the same letter, "which Tu Fu shows in threading on to his *Lü-shih* ramification of allusions ancient and modern could not be surpassed; in this he is even superior to Li Po. But, if we take the 'Press-gang' and verses like that stanza:

At the palace doors the smell of meat and wine;
On the road the bones of one who was frozen to death.

what a small part of his whole work it represents!"

Content, in short, he valued far above form: and it was part of his theory, though certainly not of his practice, that this content ought to be definitely moral. He aimed at raising poetry from the triviality into which it had sunk and restoring it to its proper intellectual level. It is an irony that he should be chiefly known to posterity, in China, Japan, and the West, as the author of the "Everlasting Wrong".[1] He set little store by the poem himself, and, though a certain political moral might be read into it, its appeal is clearly romantic.

His other poem of sentiment, the "Lute Girl",[2] accords even less with his stated principles. With these he ranks his *Lü-shih*; and it should here be noted that all the satires and long poems are in the old style of versification, while his lighter poems are in the strict, modern form. With his satires he classes his "reflective" poems, such as "Singing in the Mountains", "On Being Removed from Hsün-yang", "Pruning Trees", etc. These are all in the old style.

No poet in the world can ever have enjoyed greater contemporary popularity than Po. His poems were "on the mouths of kings, princes, concubines, ladies, plough-boys, and grooms". They were inscribed "on the walls of village-schools, temples, and ships-cabins". "A certain Captain Kao Hsia-yü was courting a dancing-girl. 'You must not think I am an ordinary dancing-girl', she said to him, 'I can recite Master Po's "Everlasting Wrong"'. And she put up her price".

But this popularity was confined to the long, romantic poems and the *Lü-shih*. "The world", writes Po to Yüan Chēn, "values highest just those of my poems which I most despise. Of contemporaries you alone have understood my satires and reflective poems. A hundred, a thousand years hence perhaps some one will come who will understand them as you have done".

[1] Giles, "Chinese Literature", p. 169.   [2] *Ibid.*, p. 165.

135

The popularity of his lighter poems lasted till the Ming dynasty, when a wave of pedantry swept over China. At that period his poetry was considered vulgar, because it was not erudite; and prosaic, because it was not rhetorical. Although they valued form far above content, not even the Ming critics can accuse him of slovenly writing. His versification is admitted by them to be "correct".

Caring, indeed, more for matter than for manner, he used with facility and precision the technical instruments which were at his disposal. Many of the later anthologies omit his name altogether, but he has always had isolated admirers. Yüan Mei imitates him constantly, and Chao I (died 1814) writes: "Those who accuse him of being vulgar and prosaic know nothing of poetry."

Even during his lifetime his reputation had reached Japan, and great writers like Michizane were not ashamed to borrow from him. He is still held in high repute there, is the subject of a Nō Play and has even become a kind of Shintō deity. It is significant that the only copy of his works in the British Museum is a seventeenth-century Japanese edition.

It is usual to close a biographical notice with an attempt to describe the "character" of one's subject. But I hold myself absolved from such a task; for the poems which follow will enable the reader to perform it for himself.

Resignation

Keep off your thoughts from things that are past and done;
For thinking of the past wakes regret and pain.
Keep off your thoughts from thinking what will happen;
To think of the future fills one with dismay.
Better by day to sit like a sack in your chair;
Better by night to lie a stone in your bed.
When food comes, then open your mouth;
When sleep comes, then close your eyes.

After Passing the Examination

(A. D. 800)

For ten years I never left my books;
I went up . . . and won unmerited praise.
My high place I do not much prize;
The joy of my parents will first make me proud.
Fellow students, six or seven men,
See me off as I leave the City gate.
My covered couch is ready to drive away;
Flutes and strings blend their parting tune.
Hopes achieved dull the pains of parting;
Fumes of wine shorten the long road . . .
Shod with wings is the horse of him who rides
On a Spring day the road that leads to home.

Escorting Candidates to the Examination Hall

(A.D. 805)

At dawn I rode to escort the Doctors of Art;
In the eastern quarter the sky was still grey.
I said to myself, "You have started far too soon,"
But horses and coaches already thronged the road.
High and low the riders' torches bobbed;
Muffled or loud, the watchman's drum beat.
       Riders, when I see you prick
To your early levee, pity fills my heart.
When the sun rises and the hot dust flies
And the creatures of earth resume their great strife,
You, with your striving, what shall you each seek?
Profit and fame, for that is all your care.
But I, you courtiers, rise from my bed at noon
And live idly in the city of Ch'ang-an.
Spring is deep and my term of office spent;
Day by day my thoughts go back to the hills.

In Early Summer Lodging in
A Temple to Enjoy the Moonlight

(A. D. 805)

In early summer, with two or three more
That were seeking fame in the city of Ch'ang-an,
Whose low employ gave them less business
Than ever they had since first they left their homes,—
With these I wandered deep into the shrine of Tao,
For the joy we sought was promised in this place.
When we reached the gate, we sent our coaches back;
We entered the yard with only cap and stick.
Still and clear, the first weeks of May,
When trees are green and bushes soft and wet;
When the wind has stolen the shadows of new leaves
And birds linger on the last boughs that bloom.
Towards evening when the sky grew clearer yet
And the South-east was still clothed in red,
To the western cloister we carried our jar of wine;
While we waited for the moon, our cups moved slow.
Soon, how soon her golden ghost was born,
Swiftly, as though she had waited for us to come.

The beams of her light shone in every place,
On towers and halls dancing to and fro.
Till day broke we sat in her clear light
Laughing and singing, and yet never grew tired.
In Ch'ang-an, the place of profit and fame,
Such moods as this, how many men know?

Sick Leave

*(While Secretary to the Deputy-Assistant-Magistrate
of Chou-chih, near Ch'ang-an, in A. D. 806)*

Propped on pillows, not attending to business;
For two days I've lain behind locked doors.
I begin to think that those who hold office
Get no rest, except by falling ill!
For restful thoughts one does not need space;
The room where I lie is ten foot square.
By the western eaves, above the bamboo-twigs,
From my couch I see the White Mountain rise.
But the clouds that hover on its far-distant peak
Bring shame to a face that is buried in the World's dust.

Watching the Reapers

(A.D. 806)

Tillers of the soil have few idle months;
In the fifth month their toil is double-fold.
A south-wind visits the fields at night:
Suddenly the hill is covered with yellow corn.
Wives and daughters shoulder baskets of rice;
Youths and boys carry the flasks of wine.
Following after they bring a wage of meat
To the strong reapers toiling on the southern hill,
Whose feet are burned by the hot earth they tread,
Whose backs are scorched by flames of the shining sky.
Tired they toil, caring nothing for the heat,
Grudging the shortness of the long summer day.
A poor woman follows at the reapers' side
With an infant child carried close at her breast.
With her right hand she gleans the fallen grain;
On her left arm a broken basket hangs.
And I to-day . . . by virtue of what right
Have I never once tended field or tree?
My government-pay is three hundred tons;
At the year's end I have still grain in hand.
Thinking of this, secretly I grew ashamed;
And all day the thought lingered in my head.

142

Going Alone to Spend a Night
at the Hsien-yu Temple

(A.D. 806)

The crane from the shore standing at the top of the steps;
The moon on the pool seen at the open door;
Where these are, I made my lodging-place
And for two nights could not turn away.
I am glad I chanced on a place so lonely and still
With no companion to drag me early home.
Now that I have tasted the joy of being alone
I will never again come with a friend at my side.

Planting Bamboos

(A. D. 806)

Unrewarded, my will to serve the State;
At my closed door autumn grasses grow.
What could I do to ease a rustic heart?
I planted bamboos, more than a hundred shoots.
When I see their beauty, as they grow by the stream-side,
I feel again as though I lived in the hills,
And many a time on public holidays
Round their railing I walk till night comes.
Do not say that their roots are still weak,
Do not say that their shade is still small;
Already I feel that both in garden and house
Day by day a fresher air moves.
But most I love, lying near the window-side,
To hear in their branches the sound of the autumn-wind.

To Li Chien

(Part of a Poem, A.D. 807)

Worldly matters again draw my steps;
Worldly things again seduce my heart.
Whenever for long I part from Li Chien
Gradually my thoughts grow narrow and covetous.
I remember how once I used to visit you;
I stopped my horse and tapped at the garden-gate.
Often when I came you were still lying in bed;
Your little children were sent to let me in.
And you, laughing, ran to the front-door
With coat-tails flying and cap all awry.
On the swept terrace, green patterns of moss;
On the dusted bench, clean shadows of leaves.
To gaze at the hills we sat in the eastern lodge;
To wait for the moon we walked to the southern moor.
At your quiet gate only birds spoke;
In your distant street few drums were heard.
Opposite each other all day we talked,
And never once spoke of profit or fame.
Since we parted hands, how long has passed?
Thrice and again the full moon has shone.
For when we parted the last flowers were falling,
And to-day I hear new cicadas sing.
The scented year suddenly draws to its close,
Yet the sorrow of parting is still unsubdued.

An Early Levée

[*Addressed to Ch'ēn, the Hermit*]

At Ch'ang-an—a full foot of snow;
A levée at dawn—to bestow congratulations on the Emperor.
Just as I was nearing the Gate of the Silver Terrace,
After I had left the suburb of Hsin-ch'ang
On the high causeway my horse's foot slipped;
In the middle of the journey my lantern suddenly went out.
Ten leagues riding, always facing to the North;
The cold wind almost blew off my ears.
I waited for the bell outside the Five Gates;
I waited for the summons within the Triple Hall.
My hair and beard were frozen and covered with icicles;
My coat and robe—chilly like water.
Suddenly I thought of Hsien-yu Valley
And secretly envied Ch'ēn Chü-shih,
In warm bed-socks dozing beneath the rugs
And not getting up till the sun has mounted the sky.

146

Being on Duty all Night in the Palace and Dreaming of Hsien-yu Temple

At the western window I paused from writing rescripts;
The pines and bamboos were all buried in stillness.
The moon rose and a calm wind came;
Suddenly, it was like an evening in the hills.
And so, as I dozed, I dreamed of the South West
And thought I was staying at the Hsien-yu Temple.[1]
When I woke and heard the dripping of the Palace clock
I still thought it the murmur of a mountain stream.

[1] Where the poet used to spend his holidays.

The Letter

Preface: After I parted with Yüan Chēn, I suddenly dreamt one night that I saw him. When I awoke, I found that a letter from him had just arrived and, enclosed in it, a poem on the *paulovnia* flower.

We talked together in the Yung-shou Temple;
We parted to the north of the Hsin-ch'ang dyke.
Going home—I shed a few tears,
Grieving about things,—not sorry for you.
Long, long the road to Lan-t'ien;
You said yourself you would not be able to write.
Reckoning up your halts for eating and sleeping—
By this time you've crossed the Shang mountains.
Last night the clouds scattered away;
A thousand leagues, the same moonlight scene.
When dawn came, I dreamt I saw your face;
It must have been that you were thinking of me.
In my dream, I thought I held your hand
And asked you to tell me what your thoughts were.
And *you* said: "I miss you bitterly,
But there's no one here to send to you with a letter."
When I awoke, before I had time to speak,
A knocking on the door sounded "Doong, doong!"
They came and told me a messenger from Shang-chou
Had brought a letter,—a single scroll from you!

Up from my pillow I suddenly sprang out of bed,
And threw on my clothes, all topsy-turvy.
I undid the knot and saw the letter within;
A single sheet with thirteen lines of writing.
At the top it told the sorrows of an exile's heart;
At the bottom it described the pains of separation.
The sorrows and pains took up so much space
There was no room left to talk about the weather!
    But you said that when you wrote
You were staying for the night to the east of Shang-chou;
Sitting alone, lighted by a solitary candle
Lodging in the mountain hostel of Yang-Ch'ēng.
    Night was late when you finished writing,
The mountain moon was slanting towards the west.
What is it lies aslant across the moon?
A single tree of purple *paulovnia* flowers,
Paulovnia flowers just on the point of falling
Are a symbol to express "thinking of an absent friend".
Lovingly—you wrote on the back side,
To send in the letter, your "Poem of the Paulovnia Flower".
The "Poem of the Paulovnia Flower" has eight rhymes;
Yet these eight couplets have cast a spell on my heart.
They have taken hold of this morning's thoughts
And carried them to yours, the night you wrote your letter.
The whole poem I read three times;
Each verse ten times I recite.
So precious to me are the fourscore words
That each letter changes into a bar of gold!

Passing T'ien-mēn Street in Ch'ang-an and Seeing a Distant View of Chung-nan Mountain

The snow has gone from Chung-nan[1]; spring is almost come.
Lovely in the distance its blue colours, against the brown
    of the streets.
A thousand coaches, ten thousand horsemen pass down the
    Nine Roads;
Turns his head and looks at the mountains,—not one man!

[1] Part of the great Nan Shan range, fifteen miles south of Ch'ang-an.

Rejoicing at the Arrival of Ch'ēn Hsiung

(Circa A. D. 812)

When the yellow bird's note was almost stopped;
And half formed the green plum's fruit;
Sitting and grieving that spring things were over,
I rose and entered the Eastern Garden's gate.
I carried my cup and was dully drinking alone:
Suddenly I heard a knocking sound at the door.
Dwelling secluded, I was glad that someone had come;
How much the more, when I saw it was Ch'ēn Hsiung!
At ease and leisure,—all day we talked;
Crowding and jostling, the feelings of many years.
How great a thing is a single cup of wine!
For it makes us tell the story of our whole lives.

Golden Bells

When I was almost forty
I had a daughter whose name was Golden Bells.
Now it is just a year since she was born;
She is learning to sit and cannot yet talk.
Ashamed,—to find that I have not a sage's heart:
I cannot resist vulgar thoughts and feelings.
Henceforward I am tied to things outside myself:
My only reward,—the pleasure I am getting now.
If I am spared the grief of her dying young,
Then I shall have the trouble of getting her married.
My plan for retiring and going back to the hills
Must now be postponed for fifteen years!

Remembering Golden Bells

Ruined and ill,—a man of two score;
    Pretty and guileless,—a girl of three.
Not a boy,—but still better than nothing:
To soothe one's feeling,—from time to time a kiss!
There came a day,—they suddenly took her from me;
Her soul's shadow wandered I know not where.
And when I remember how just at the time she died
She lisped strange sounds, beginning to learn to talk,
Then I know that the ties of flesh and blood
Only bind us to a load of grief and sorrow.
At last, by thinking of the time before she was born,
By thought and reason I drove the pain away.
Since my heart forgot her, many days have passed
And three times winter has changed to spring.
This morning, for a little, the old grief came back,
Because, in the road, I met her foster-nurse.

Illness

Sad, sad—lean with long illness;
Monotonous, monotonous—days and nights pass.
The summer trees have clad themselves in shade;
The autumn "lan"[1] already houses the dew.
The eggs that lay in the nest when I took to bed
Have changed into little birds and flown away.
The worm that then lay hidden in its hole
Has hatched into a cricket sitting on the tree.
The Four Seasons go on for ever and ever:
In all Nature nothing stops to rest
Even for a moment. Only the sick man's heart
Deep down still aches as of old!

[1] The epidendrum.

At the End of Spring

To Yüan Chēn.[1] (A.D. 810)

The flower of the pear-tree gathers and turns to fruit;
The swallows' eggs have hatched into young birds.
When the Seasons' changes thus confront the mind
What comfort can the Doctrine of Tao give?
It will teach me to watch the days and months fly
Without grieving that Youth slips away;
If the Fleeting World is but a long dream,
It does not matter whether one is young or old.
But ever since the day that my friend left my side
And has lived an exile in the City of Chiang-ling,
There is one wish I cannot quite destroy:
That from time to time we may chance to meet again.

[1] Po Chü-i's great friend. See pages 259 and 270.

The Poem on the Wall

(A.D. 810)

[Yüan Chēn wrote that on his way to exile he had discovered
a poem inscribed by Po Chü-i, on the wall of the Lo-k'ou Inn.]

My clumsy poem on the inn-wall none cared to see.
With bird-droppings and moss's growth the letters were
    blotched away.
There came a guest with heart so full, that though a page
    to the Throne,
He did not grudge with his broidered coat to wipe off the
    dust, and read.

Chu-ch'ēn Village

(A.D. 811)

In Hsü-chou, in the District of Ku-fēng
There lies a village whose name is Chu-ch'ēn—
A hundred miles away from the county-town,
Amid fields of hemp and green of mulberry-trees.
Click, click goes the sound of the spinning-wheel;
Mules and oxen pack the village-streets.
The girls go drawing the water from the brook;
The men go gathering fire-wood on the hill.
So far from the town Government affairs are few;
So deep in the hills, man's ways are simple.
Though they have wealth, they do not traffic with it;
Though they reach the age, they do not enter the Army.
Each family keeps to its village trade;
Grey-headed, they have never left the gates.

Alive, they are the people of Ch'ēn Village;
Dead, they become the dust of Ch'ēn Village.
Out in the fields old men and young
Gaze gladly, each in the other's face.
In the whole village there are only two clans;
Age after age Chus have married Ch'ēns.
Near or distant, they have kinsmen in every house;
Young or old, they have friends wherever they go.

157

On white wine and roasted fowl they fare
At joyful meetings more than "once a week".
While they are alive, they have no distant partings;
To choose a wife they go to a neighbour's house.
When they are dead,—no distant burial;
Round the village graves lie thick.
They are not troubled either about life or death;
They have no anguish either of body or soul.
And so it happens that they live to a ripe age
And great-great-grandsons are often seen.

I was born in the Realms of Etiquette;
In early years, unprotected and poor.
Alone, I learnt to distinguish between Evil and Good;
Untutored, I toiled at bitter tasks.
The World's Law honours Learning and Fame;
Scholars prize marriages and Caps.
With these fetters I gyved my own hands;
Truly I became a much-deceived man.
At ten years old I learnt to read books;
At fifteen, I knew how to write prose.
At twenty I was made a Bachelor of Arts;
At thirty I became a Censor at the Court.
Above, the duty I owe to Prince and parents;
Below, the ties that bind me to wife and child.
The support of my family, the service of my country—
For these tasks my nature is not apt.
I reckon the time that I first left my home;

From then till now,—fifteen Springs!
My lonely boat has thrice sailed to Ch'u;
Four times through Ch'in my lean horse has passed.
I have walked in the morning with hunger in my face;
I have lain at night with a soul that could not rest.
East and West I have wandered without pause,
Hither and thither like a cloud astray in the sky.
In the civil-war my old home was destroyed;
Of my flesh and blood many are scattered and lost.
    North of the River, and South of the River—
In both lands are the friends of all my life;
Life-friends whom I never see at all,—
Whose deaths I hear of only after the lapse of years.
Sad at morning, I lie on my bed till dusk;
Weeping at night, I sit and wait for dawn.
The fire of sorrow has burnt my heart's core;
The frost of trouble has seized my hair's roots.
In such anguish has my whole life passed;
Long I have envied the people of Ch'ēn Village.

Fishing in the Wei River

(A. D. 811)

In waters still as a burnished mirror's face,
In the depths of Wei, carp and grayling swim.
Idly I come with my bamboo fishing-rod
And hang my hook by the banks of Wei stream.
A gentle wind blows on my fishing-gear
Softly shaking my ten feet of line.
Though my body sits waiting for fish to come,
My heart has wandered to the Land of Nothingness.[1]
Long ago a white-headed man[2]
Also fished at the same river's side;
A hooker of men, not a hooker of fish,
At seventy years, he caught Wēn Wang.[2]
But I, when I come to cast my hook in the stream,
Have no thought either of fish or men.
Lacking the skill to capture either prey,
I can only bask in the autumn water's light.
When I tire of this, my fishing also stops;
I go to my home and drink my cup of wine.

[1] See "Chuang Tzǔ", chap. i, end.
[2] The Sage T'ai-kung sat still till he was seventy, apparently fishing, but really waiting for a Prince who would employ him. At last Wēn Wang, Prince of Chou, happened to come that way and at once made him his counsellor.

Illness and Idleness

(Circa A. D. 812)

Illness and idleness give me much leisure.
What do I do with my leisure, when it comes?
I cannot bring myself to discard inkstone and brush;
Now and then I make a new poem.
When the poem is made, it is slight and flavourless,
A thing of derision to almost every one.
Superior people will be pained at the flatness or the metre;
Common people will hate the plainness of the words.
I sing it to myself, then stop and think about it . . .

The Prefects of Soochow and P'ēng-tsē[1]
Would perhaps have praised it, but they died long ago.
    Who else would care to hear it?
No one to-day except Yüan Chēn,
And *he* is banished to the City of Chiang-ling,
For three years an usher in the Penal Court.
Parted from me by three thousand leagues
He will never know even that the poem was made.

[1] Wei Ying-wu, eighth century A. D., and T'ao Ch'ien, A. D. 372-427.

The Chrysanthemums
in the Eastern Garden

(A.D. 812)

The days of my youth left me long ago;
And now in their turn dwindle my years of prime.
With what thoughts of sadness and loneliness
I walk again in this cold, deserted place!
In the midst of the garden long I stand alone;
The sunshine, faint; the wind and dew chill.

The autumn lettuce is tangled and turned to seed;
The fair trees are blighted and withered away.
All that is left are a few chrysanthemum-flowers
That have newly opened beneath the wattled fence.
I had brought wine and meant to fill my cup,
When the sight of these made me stay my hand.
                    I remember, when I was young,
How easily my mood changed from sad to gay.
If I saw wine, no matter at what season,
Before I drank it, my heart was already glad.
                    But now that age comes,
A moment of joy is harder and harder to get.
And always I fear that when I am quite old
The strongest liquor will leave me comfortless.
Therefore I ask you, late chrysanthemum-flower
At this sad season why do you bloom alone?
Though well I know that it was not for my sake,
Taught by you, for a while I will open my face.

Winter Night

(Written during his retirement in A. D. 812)

My house is poor; those that I love have left me;
My body is sick; I cannot join the feast.
There is not a living soul before my eyes
As I lie alone locked in my cottage room.
My broken lamp burns with a feeble flame;
My tattered curtains are crooked and do not meet.
"Tsek, tsek" on the door-step and window-sill
Again I hear the new snow fall.
As I grow older, gradually I sleep less;
I wake at midnight and sit up straight in bed.
If I had not learned the "art of sitting and forgetting",[1]
How could I bear this utter loneliness?
Stiff and stark my body cleaves to the earth;
Unimpeded my soul yields to Change.[2]
So has it been for four hateful years,
Through one thousand and three hundred nights!

[1] Yen Hui told Confucius that he had acquired the "art of sitting and forgetting". Asked what that meant, Yen Hui replied, "I have learnt to discard my body and obliterate my intelligence; to abandon matter and be impervious to sense-perception. By this method I become one with the All-Pervading".—*Chuang Tzŭ*, chap. vi.
[2] "Change", the principle of endless mutation which governs the Universe.

Poems in Depression, at Wei Village

(A. D. 812)

[1]

I hug my pillow and do not speak a word;
In my empty room no sound stirs.
Who knows that, all day a-bed,
I am not ill and am not even asleep?

[2]

Turned to jade are the boy's rosy cheeks;
To his sick temples the frost of winter clings. . . .
Do not wonder that my body sinks to decay;
Though my limbs are old, my heart is older yet.

The Dragon of the Black Pool

[*A Satire*]

Deep the waters of the Black Pool, coloured like ink;
They say a Holy Dragon lives there, whom men have
    never seen.
Beside the Pool they have built a shrine; the authorities
    have established a ritual;
A dragon by itself remains a dragon, but men can make
    it a god.
Prosperity and disaster, rain and drought, plagues and
    pestilences—
By the village people were all regarded as the Sacred
    Dragon's doing.
They all made offerings of sucking-pig and poured libations
    of wine;
The morning prayers and evening gifts depended on
    a "medium's" advice.

When the dragon comes, ah!
The wind stirs and sighs
Paper money thrown, ah!
Silk umbrellas waved.
When the dragon goes, ah!
The wind also—still.
Incense-fire dies, ah!
The cups and vessels are cold.[1]
Meats lie stacked on the rocks of the Pool's shore;
Wine flows on the grass in front of the shrine.
I do not know, of all those offerings, how much the
    Dragon eats;
But the mice of the woods and the foxes of the hills are
    continually drunk and sated.
Why are the foxes so lucky?
What have the sucking-pigs done,
That year by year *they* should be killed, merely to glut
    the foxes?
That the foxes are robbing the Sacred Dragon and eating
    His sucking-pig,
Beneath the nine-fold depths of His pool, does He know
    or not?

[1] Parody of a famous Han dynasty hymn.

The People of Tao-chou

In the land of Tao-chou
Many of the people are dwarfs;
The tallest of them never grow to more than three feet.
They were sold in the market as dwarf slaves and yearly
    sent to Court;
Described as "an offering of natural products from the land
    of Tao-chou".
A strange "offering of natural products"; I never heard of
    one yet
That parted men from those they loved, never to meet again!
Old men—weeping for their grandsons; mothers for their
    children!
One day—Yang Ch'ēng came to govern the land;
He refused to send up dwarf slaves in spite of incessant
    mandates.
He replied to the Emperor "Your servant finds in the Six
    Canonical Books
'In offering products, one must offer what is there, and not
    what isn't there'
On the waters and lands of Tao-chou, among all the things
    that live
I only find dwarfish *people*; no dwarfish *slaves*".

The Emperor's heart was deeply moved and he sealed and
     sent a scroll
"The yearly tribute of dwarfish slaves is henceforth
     annulled."
              The people of Tao-chou,
Old ones and young ones, how great their joy!
Father with son and brother with brother henceforward
     kept together;
From that day for ever more they lived as free men.
             The people of Tao-chou
             Still enjoy this gift.
And even now when they speak of the Governor
Tears start to their eyes.
And lest their children and their children's children should
     forget the Governor's name,
When boys are born the syllable "Yang" is often used in
     their forename.

The Grain-Tribute

Written circa A.D. 812, showing one of the poet's periods of retirement. When the officials come to receive his grain-tribute, he remembers that he is only giving back what he had taken during his years of office. Salaries were paid partly in kind.

There came an officer knocking by night at my door—
In a loud voice demanding grain-tribute.
My house-servants dared not wait till the morning,
But brought candles and set them on the barn-floor.
Passed through the sieve, clean-washed as pearls,
A whole cart-load, thirty bushels of grain.
But still they cry that it is not paid in full:
With whips and curses they goad my servants and boys.
Once, in error, I entered public life;
I am inwardly ashamed that my talents were not sufficient.
In succession I occupied four official posts;
For doing nothing,—ten years' salary!
Often have I heard that saying of ancient men
That "good and ill follow in an endless chain".
And to-day it ought to set my heart at rest
To return to others the corn in my great barn.

The Old Harp

Of cord and cassia-wood is the harp compounded:
Within it lie ancient melodies.
Ancient melodies—weak and savourless,
Not appealing to present men's taste.
Light and colour are faded from the jade stops:
Dust has covered the rose-red strings.
Decay and ruin came to it long ago,
But the sound that is left is still cold and clear.
I do not refuse to play it, if you want me to:
But even if I play, people will not listen.

How did it come to be neglected so?
Because of the Ch'iang flute and the Ch'in flageolet.[1]

[1] Barbarous modern instruments.

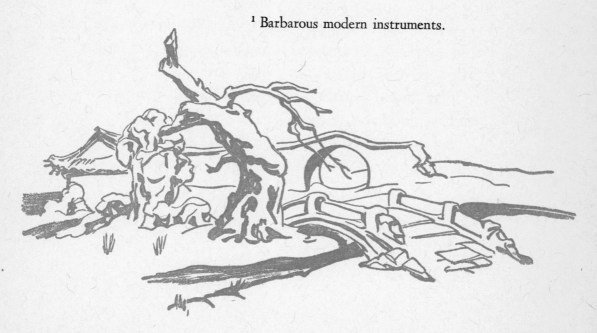

The Harper of Chao

The singers have hushed their notes of clear song:
The red sleeves of the dancers are motionless.
Hugging his lute, the old harper of Chao
Rocks and sways as he touches the five chords.
The loud notes swell and scatter abroad:
"Sa, sa," like wind blowing the rain.
The soft notes dying almost to nothing:
"Ch'ieh, ch'ieh", like the voice of ghosts talking.
Now as glad as the magpie's lucky song:
Again bitter as the gibbon's ominous cry.
His ten fingers have no fixed note:
Up and down—*kung, chih,* and *yü.*[1]
And those who sit and listen to the tune he plays
Of soul and body lose the mastery.
And those who pass that way as he plays the tune,
Suddenly stop and cannot raise their feet.

Alas, alas that the ears of common men
Should love the modern and not love the old.
Thus it is that the harp in the green window
Day by day is covered deeper with dust.

[1] Tonic, dominant and superdominant of the ancient five-note scale.

The Flower Market

In the Royal City spring is almost over:
Tinkle, tinkle—the coaches and horsemen pass.
We tell each other "This is the peony season":
And follow with the crowd that goes to the Flower Market.
"Cheap and dear—no uniform price:
The cost of the plant depends on the number of blossoms.
For the fine flower,—a hundred pieces of damask:
For the cheap flower,—five bits of silk.
Above is spread an awning to protect them:
Around is woven a wattle-fence to screen them.
If you sprinkle water and cover the roots with mud,
When they are transplanted, they will not lose their beauty."
Each household thoughtlessly follows the custom,
Man by man, no one realizing.
There happened to be an old farm labourer
      Who came by chance that way.
He bowed his head and sighed a deep sigh:
But this sigh nobody understood.
He was thinking, "A cluster of deep-red flowers
Would pay the taxes of ten poor houses".

The Prisoner

(*Written in A.D. 809*)

Tartars led in chains,
Tartars led in chains!
Their ears pierced, their faces bruised—they are driven into
the land of Ch'in.
The Son of Heaven took pity on them and would not have
them slain.
He sent them away to the south-east, to the lands of Wu
and Yüeh.
A petty officer in a yellow coat took down their names
and surnames.
They were led from the city of Ch'ang-an under escort of
an armed guard.
Their bodies were covered with the wounds of arrows,
their bones stood out from their cheeks.
They had grown so weak they could only march a single
stage a day.
In the morning they must satisfy hunger and thirst with
neither plate nor cup:
At night they must lie in their dirt and rags on beds that
stank with filth.
Suddenly they came to the Yangtze River and remembered
the waters of Chiao.[1]

[1] In Turkestan.

174

With lowered hands and levelled voices they sobbed a
      muffled song.
Then one Tartar lifted up his voice and spoke to the
      other Tartars,
"*Your* sorrows are none at all compared with *my* sorrows."
Those that were with him in the same band asked to hear
      his tale:
  As he tried to speak the words were choked by anger.
He told them "I was born and bred in the town of
      Liang-yüan.[1]
In the frontier wars of Ta-li[2] I fell into the Tartars' hands.
Since the days the Tartars took me alive forty years
      have passed:
They put me into a coat of skins tied with a belt of rope.
Only on the first of the first month might I wear my
      Chinese dress.
As I put on my coat and arranged my cap, how fast the
      tears flowed!
I made in my heart a secret vow I would find a way home:
I hid my plan from my Tartar wife and the children she had
      borne me in the land.
I thought to myself, 'It is well for me that my limbs are
      still strong',
And yet, being old, in my heart I feared I should never live
      to return.

[1] North of Ch'ang-an.
[2] The period Ta-li, A. D. 766-780.

The Tartar chieftains shoot so well that the birds are afraid
    to fly:
From the risk of their arrows I escaped alive and fled
    swiftly home.
Hiding all day and walking all night, I crossed the Great
    Desert.[1]
Where clouds are dark and the moon black and the sands
    eddy in the wind.
Frightened, I sheltered at the Green Grave,[2] where the
    frozen grasses are few:
Stealthily I crossed the Yellow River, at night, on the
    thin ice,
Suddenly I heard Han[3] drums and the sound of
    soldiers coming:
I went to meet them at the road-side, bowing to them as
    they came.
But the moving horsemen did not hear that I spoke the
    Han tongue:
Their Captain took me for a Tartar born and had me bound
    in chains.
They are sending me away to the south-east, to a low and
    swampy land:
No one now will take pity on me: resistance is all in vain.

[1] The Gobi Desert.
[2] The grave of Chao-chün, a Chinese girl who in 33 B. C. was "bestowed
upon the Khan of the Hsiung-nu as a mark of Imperial regard" [Giles].
Hers was the only grave in this desolate district on which grass would
grow.   [3] I.e., Chinese.

176

Thinking of this, my voice chokes and I ask of
     Heaven above,
Was I spared from death only to spend the rest of my years
     in sorrow?
My native village of Liang-yüan I shall not see again:
My wife and children in the Tartars' land I have
     fruitlessly deserted.
When I fell among Tartars and was taken prisoner, I pined
     for the land of Han:
Now that I am back in the land of Han, they have turned
     me into a Tartar.
Had I but known what my fate would be, I would not
     have started home!
For the two lands, so wide apart, are alike in the sorrow
     they bring.
        Tartar prisoners in chains!
Of all the sorrows of all the prisoners mine is the hardest
     to bear!
Never in the world has so great a wrong befallen the lot
     of man,—
A Han heart and a Han tongue set in the body of a Turk".

The Chancellor's Gravel-Drive

[A Satire on the Maltreatment of Subordinates]

A Government-bull yoked to a Government-cart!
Moored by the bank of Ch'an River, a barge loaded
    with gravel.
A single load of gravel,
How many pounds it weighs!
Carrying at dawn, carrying at dusk, what is it all for?
They are carrying it towards the Five Gates,
To the West of the Main Road.
Under the shadow of green laurels they are making a
    gravel-drive.
For yesterday arrove, newly appointed,
The Assistant Chancellor of the Realm,
And was terribly afraid that the wet and mud
Would dirty his horse's hoofs.
The Chancellor's horse's hoofs
Stepped on the gravel and remained perfectly clean;
But the bull employed in dragging the cart
Was almost sweating blood.
The Assistant Chancellor's business
Is to "save men, govern the country
And harmonize Yin and Yang."[1]
Whether the bull's neck is sore
Need not trouble him at all.

[1] The negative and positive principles in nature.

178

The Man Who Dreamed of Fairies

This poem is an attack on the Emperor Hsien-tsung, A. D. 806–820, who "was devoted to magic". A Taoist wizard told him that herbs of longevity grew near the city of T'ai-chou. The Emperor at once appointed him prefect of the place, "pour lui permettre d'herboriser plus à son aise" (Wieger, Textes III, p. 1723). When the censors protested, the Emperor replied: "The ruin of a single district would be a small price to pay, if it could procure longevity for the Lord of Men."

There was once a man who dreamt he went to Heaven:
His dream-body soared aloft through space.
He rode on the back of a white-plumed crane,
And was led on his flight by two crimson banners.
Whirring of wings and flapping of coat tails!
Jade bells suddenly all a-tinkle!
Half way to Heaven, he looked down beneath him,
Down on the dark turmoil of the World.
Gradually he lost the place of his native town;
Mountains and water—nothing else distinct.
The Eastern Ocean—a single strip of white:
The Hills of China,—five specks of green.
Gliding past him a host of fairies swept
In long procession to the Palace of the Jade City.

How should he guess that the children of Tzŭ-mēn[1]
Bow to the throne like courtiers of earthly kings?
They take him to the presence of the Mighty Jade Emperor:
He bows his head and proffers loyal homage.
The Emperor says: "We see you have fairy talents:
Be of good heart and do not slight yourself.
We shall send to fetch you in fifteen years
And give you a place in the Courtyard of Immortality."
Twice bowing, he acknowledged the gracious words:
Then woke from sleep, full of wonder and joy.
He hid his secret and dared not tell it abroad:
But vowed a vow he would live in a cave of rock.
From love and affection he severed kith and kin:
From his eating and drinking he omitted savoury and spice.
His morning meal was a dish of coral-dust:
At night he sipped an essence of dewy mists.
In the empty mountains he lived for thirty years
Daily watching for the Heavenly Coach to come.
The time of appointment was already long past,
But of wings and coach-bells—still no sound.
His teeth and hair daily withered and decayed:
His ears and eyes gradually lost their keenness.
One morning he suffered the Common Change
And his body was one with the dust and dirt of the hill.
Gods and fairies! If indeed such things there be,
Their ways are beyond the striving of mortal men.
If you have not on your skull the Golden Bump's protrusion,

[1] *I.e.*, the Immortals.

180

If your name is absent from the rolls of the Red Terrace,
In vain you learn the "Method of Avoiding Food":
For naught you study the "Book of Alchemic Lore".
Though you sweat and toil, what shall your trouble bring?
You will only shorten the five-score years of your span.
Sad, alas, the man who dreamt of Fairies!
For a single dream spoiled his whole life.

Magic

Boundless, the great sea.
Straight down,—no bottom: sideways,—no border.
Of cloudy waves and misty billows down in the uttermost
  depths
Men have fabled, in the midst there stand three sacred hills.
On the hills, thick growing,—herbs that banish Death.
Wings grow on those who eat them and they turn into
  heavenly "hsien".
The Lord of Ch'in[1] and Wu of Han[2] believed in these
  stories:
And magic-workers year by year were sent to gather the
  herbs.
The Blessed Islands, now and of old, what but an empty
  tale?
The misty waters spread before them and they knew not
  where to seek.
            Boundless, the great sea.
            Dauntless, the mighty wind.
Their eyes search but cannot see the shores of the
  Blessed Islands.

[1] The "First Emperor", 259-210 B. C.
[2] Wu Ti, 156-87 B. C.

182

They cannot find the Blessed Isles and yet they dare
    not return:
Youths and maidens that began the quest grew grey on
    board the boat.
They found that the writings of Hsü Fu[1] were all boasts
    and lies:
To the Lofty Principle and Great Unity in vain they raised
    their prayers.
              Do you not see
The graves on the top of Black Horse Hill[2] and the tombs
    at Mo-ling?[3]
What is left but the sighing wind blowing in the
    tangled grasses?
             Yes, and what is more,
The Dark and Primal Master of Sages in his five
    thousand words[4]
             Never spoke of herbs,
             Never spoke of "hsien",
Nor spoke of soaring in broad daylight up to the
    blue heaven.

[1] = Hsü Shih. Giles, 1276.
[2] The burial-places of these two Emperors.   [3] *Ibid.*
[4] Lao-tzü, in the Tao Tē Ching.

The Two Red Towers

[A Satire Against Clericalism]

The Two Red Towers
North and south rise facing each other.
I beg to ask, to whom do they belong?
To the two Princes of the period Chēng Yüan.[1]
The two Princes blew on their flutes and drew down fairies
    from the sky.
Who carried them off through the Five Clouds, soaring
    away to Heaven.
Their halls and houses, that they could take with them,
Were turned into Temples planted in the Dust of the World.
In the tiring-rooms and dancers' towers all is silent and still;
Only the willows like dancers' arms, and the pond
    like a mirror.
When the flowers are falling at yellow twilight, when things
    are sad and hushed,
One does not hear songs and flutes, but only chimes
    and bells.
The Imperial Patent on the Temple doors is written in letters
    of gold;
For nuns' quarters and monks' cells ample space is allowed.

[1] A. D. 785-805.

184

For green moss and bright moonlight—plenty of room
  provided;
In a hovel opposite is a sick man who has hardly room to
  lie down.
I remember once when at P'ing-yang they were building a
  great man's house
How it swallowed up the housing space of thousands of
  ordinary men.
The Immortals[1] are leaving us, two by two, and their houses
  are turned into Temples;
I begin to fear that the whole world will become
  a vast convent.

[1] Hsien Tsung's brothers?

The Charcoal-Seller

[A Satire Against "Kommandatur"]

An old charcoal-seller
Cutting wood and burning charcoal in the forest of the
    Southern Mountain.
His face, stained with dust and ashes, has turned to the colour
    of smoke.
The hair on his temples is streaked with gray: his ten fingers
    are black.
The money he gets by selling charcoal, how far does it go?
It is just enough to clothe his limbs and put food in his mouth.
Although, alas, the coat on his back is a coat without lining,
He hopes for the coming of cold weather, to send up the
    price of coal!
Last night, outside the city,—a whole foot of snow;
At dawn he drives the charcoal wagon along the frozen ruts.
Oxen,—weary; man,—hungry: the sun, already high;
Outside the Gate, to the south of the Market, at last they stop
    in the mud.
Suddenly, a pair of prancing horsemen. Who can it
    be coming?
A public official in a yellow coat and a boy in a white shirt.

In their hands they hold a written warrant: on their tongues
     —the words of an order;
They turn back the wagon and curse the oxen, leading them
     off to the north.
A whole wagon of charcoal,
More than a thousand pieces!
If officials choose to take it away, the woodman may
     not complain.
Half a piece of red silk and a single yard of damask,
The Courtiers have tied to the oxen's collar, as the price
     of a wagon of coal!

The Politician

I was going to the City to sell the herbs I had plucked;
On the way I rested by some trees at the Blue Gate.
Along the road there came a horseman riding;
Whose face was pale with a strange look of dread.
Friends and relations, waiting to say good-bye,
Pressed at his side, but he did not dare to pause.
I, in wonder, asked the people about me
Who he was and what had happened to him.
They told me this was a Privy Councillor
Whose grave duties were like the pivot of State.
His food allowance was ten thousand cash;
Three times a day the Emperor came to his house.
Yesterday he was called to a meeting of Heroes:
To-day he is banished to the country of Yai-chou.
So always, the Counsellors of Kings;
Favour and ruin changed between dawn and dusk!
Green, green,—the grass of the Eastern Suburb;
And amid the grass, a road that leads to the hills.
Resting in peace among the white clouds,
At last he has made a "coup" that cannot fail!

The Old Man with the Broken Arm

[A Satire on Militarism]

At Hsin-fēng an old man—four-score and eight;
The hair on his head and the hair of his eyebrows—white as
    the new snow.
Leaning on the shoulders of his great-grandchildren, he walks
    in front of the Inn;
With his left arm he leans on their shoulders; his right arm is
    broken.
I asked the old man how many years had passed since he
    broke his arm;
I also asked the cause of the injury, how and why it
    happened?
The old man said he was born and reared in the District
    of Hsin-fēng;
At the time of his birth—a wise reign; no wars or discords.
"Often I listened in the Pear-Tree Garden to the sound of
    flute and song;
Naught I knew of banner and lance; nothing of arrow
    or bow.
Then came the wars of T'ien-pao[1] and the great levy of men;
Of three men in each house,—one man was taken.

[1] A.D. 742-755

And those to whom the lot fell, where were they taken to?
Five months' journey, a thousand miles—away to Yün-nan.
We heard it said that in Yün-nan there flows the Lu River;
As the flowers fall from the pepper-trees, poisonous vapours
    rise.
When the great army waded across, the water seethed like
    a cauldron;
When barely ten had entered the water, two or three
    were dead.
To the north of my village, to the south of my village the
    sound of weeping and wailing,
Children parting from fathers and mothers; husbands parting
    from wives.
Everyone says that in expeditions against the Min tribes
Of a million men who are sent out, not one returns.
        I, that am old, was then twenty-four;
My name and fore-name were written down in the rolls
    of the Board of War.
In the depth of the night not daring to let any one know
I secretly took a huge stone and dashed it against my arm.
For drawing the bow and waving the banner now
    wholly unfit;
I knew henceforward I should not be sent to fight in Yün-nan.
Bones broken and sinews wounded could not fail to hurt;
I was ready enough to bear pain, if only I got back home.
My arm—broken ever since; it was sixty years ago.
One limb, although destroyed,—whole body safe!

But even now on winter nights when the wind and rain blow
From evening on till day's dawn I cannot sleep for pain.
       Not sleeping for pain
       Is a small thing to bear,
Compared with the joy of being alive when all the rest
   are dead.
For otherwise, years ago, at the ford of Lu River

My body would have died and my soul hovered by the bones
    that no one gathered.
A ghost, I'd have wandered in Yün-nan, always looking
    for home.
Over the graves of ten thousand soldiers, mournfully
    hovering."
          So the old man spoke,
        And I bid you listen to his words
        Have you not heard
That the Prime Minister of K'ai-yüan,[1] Sung K'ai-fu,
Did not reward frontier exploits, lest a spirit of aggression
    should prevail?
        And have you not heard
That the Prime Minister of T'ien-Pao, Yang Kuo-chung[2]
Desiring to win imperial favour, started a frontier war?
But long before he could win the war, people had lost
    their temper;
Ask the man with the broken arm in the village of Hsin-fēng!

---

[1] A. D. 713-742.
[2] Cousin of the notorious mistress of Ming-huang, Yang Kuei-fei.

192

Kept Waiting in the Boat at Chiu-k'ou Ten Days by an Adverse Wind

White billows and huge waves block the river crossing;
Wherever I go, danger and difficulty; whatever I do, failure.
Just as in my worldly career I wander and lose the road,
So when I come to the river crossing, I am stopped by
      contrary winds.
Of fishes and prawns sodden in the rain the smell fills my
      nostrils;
With the stings of insects that come with the fog, my whole
      body is sore.
I am growing old, time flies, and my short span runs out,
While I sit in a boat at Chiu-k'ou, wasting ten days!

Arriving at Hsün-yang

Two Poems

[1]

A bend of the river brings into view two triumphal arches;
That is the gate in the western wall of the suburbs of
    Hsün-yang.
I have still to travel in my solitary boat three or four
    leagues—
By misty waters and rainy sands, while the yellow
    dusk thickens.

We are almost come to Hsün-yang: how my thoughts
    are stirred
As we pass to the south of Yü Liang's[1] tower and the east
    of P'ên Port.
The forest trees are leafless and withered,—after the
    mountain rain;
The roofs of the houses are hidden low among the
    river mists.
The horses, fed on water grass, are too weak to carry
    their load;
The cottage walls of wattle and thatch let the wind blow
    on one's bed.
In the distance I see red-wheeled coaches driving from the
    town-gate;
They have taken the trouble, these civil people, to meet
    their new Prefect!

[1] Died A. D. 340. Giles, 2526.

On Board Ship:
Reading Yüan Chēn's Poems

I take your poems in my hand and read them beside
    the candle;
The poems are finished: the candle is low: dawn not
    yet come.
With sore eyes by the guttering candle still I sit in the dark,
Listening to waves that, driven by the wind, strike the prow
    of the ship.

Madly Singing in the Mountains

There is no one among men that has not a special failing:
And my failing consists in writing verses.
I have broken away from the thousand ties of life:
But this infirmity still remains behind.
Each time that I look at a fine landscape:
Each time that I meet a loved friend,
I raise my voice and recite a stanza of poetry
And am glad as though a God had crossed my path.
Ever since the day I was banished to Hsün-yang
Half my time I have lived among the hills.
And often, when I have finished a new poem,
Alone I climb the road to the Eastern Rock.
I lean my body on the banks of white stone:
I pull down with my hands a green cassia branch.
My mad singing startles the valleys and hills:
The apes and birds all come to peep.
Fearing to become a laughing-stock to the world,
I choose a place that is unfrequented by men.

Releasing a Migrant "Yen"
(Wild Goose)

At Nine Rivers,[1] in the tenth year,[2] in winter,—heavy snow;
The river-water covered with ice and the forests broken
    with their load.[3]
The birds of the air, hungry and cold, went flying
    east and west;
And with them flew a migrant "yen" loudly clamouring
    for food.
Among the snow it pecked for grass; and rested on the
    surface of the ice:
It tried with its wings to scale the sky; but its tired flight
    was slow.
The boys of the river spread a net and caught the bird
    as it flew;
They took it in their hands to the city-market and sold it
    there alive.
I that was once a man of the North am now an exile here:
Bird and man, in their different kind, are each strangers
    in the south.

[1] Kiukiang, the poet's place of exile.
[2] A. D. 815. His first winter at Kiukiang.
[3] By the weight of snow.

And because the sight of an exiled bird wounded an
    exile's heart,
I paid your ransom and set you free, and you flew away to
    the clouds.
Yen, Yen, flying to the clouds, tell me, whither shall you go?
Of all things I bid you, do not fly to the land of the
    north-west;
In Huai-hsi there are rebel bands[1] that have not been
    subdued;
And a thousand thousand armoured men have long been
    camped in war.
The official army and the rebel army have grown old in
    their opposite trenches;
The soldier's rations have grown so small, they'll be glad
    of even you.
The brave boys, in their hungry plight, will shoot you and
    eat your flesh;
They will pluck from your body those long feathers and
    make them into arrow-wings!

[1] The revolt of Wu Yüan-chi.

To His Brother Hsing-chien, who was Serving in Tung-ch'uan

(A.D. 815)

Sullen, sullen, my brows are ever knit;
Silent, silent, my lips will not move.
It is not indeed that I choose to sorrow thus;
If I lift my eyes, who would share my joy?
Last Spring *you* were called to the West
To carry arms in the lands of Pa and Shu;
And this Spring *I* was banished to the South
To nurse my sickness on the River's oozy banks.
You are parted from me by six thousand leagues;
In another world, under another sky.
Of ten letters, nine do not reach;
What can I do to open my sad face?
Thirsty men often dream of drink;
Hungry men often dream of food.
Since Spring came, where do my dreams lodge?
Ere my eyes are closed, I have travelled to Tung-ch'uan.

Starting Early from the Ch'u-ch'ēng Inn

(A. D. 815)

Washed by the rain, dust and grime are laid;
Skirting the river, the road's course is flat.
The moon has risen on the last remnants of night;
The travellers' speed profits by the early cold.
In the great silence I whisper a faint song;
In the black darkness are bred sombre thoughts.
On the lotus-banks hovers a dewy breeze;
Through the rice-furrows trickles a singing stream.
At the noise of our bells a sleeping dog stirs;
At the sight of our torches a roosting bird wakes.
Dawn glimmers through the shapes of misty trees . . .
For ten miles, till day at last breaks.

Rain

(A.D. 815)

Since I lived a stranger in the City of Hsün-yang
Hour by hour bitter rain has poured.
On few days has the dark sky cleared;
In listless sleep I have spent much time.
The lake has widened till it almost joins the sky;
The clouds sink till they touch the water's face.
Beyond my hedge I hear the boatmen's talk;
At the street-end I hear the fisher's song.
Misty birds are lost in yellow air;
Windy sails kick the white waves.
In front of my gate the horse and carriage-way
In a single night has turned into a river-bed.

The Beginning of Summer

(A. D. 815)

At the rise of summer a hundred beasts and trees
Join in gladness that the Season bids them thrive.
Stags and does frolic in the deep woods;
Snakes and insects are pleased by the rank grass.
Wingèd birds love the thick leaves;
Scaly fish enjoy the fresh weeds.
But to one place Summer forgot to come;
I alone am left like a withered straw . . .
        Banished to the world's end;
Flesh and bone all in distant ways.
From my native-place no tidings come;
Rebel troops flood the land with war.
Sullen grief, in the end, what will it bring?
I am only wearing my own heart away.
Better far to let both body and mind
Blindly yield to the fate that Heaven made.
Hsün-yang abounds in good wine;
I will fill my cup and never let it be dry.
On Pēn River fish are cheap as mud;
Early and late I will eat them, boiled and fried.
With morning rice at the temple under the hill,
And evening wine at the island in the lake . . .
Why should my thoughts turn to my native land?
For in this place one could well end one's age.

Visiting the Hsi-lin Temple

(Written during his exile)

I dismount from my horse at the Hsi-lin Temple;
I throw the porter my slender riding-whip.
In the morning I work at a Government office-desk;
In the evening I become a dweller in the Sacred Hills.
In the second month to the north of Kuang-lu
The ice breaks and the snow begins to melt.
On the southern plantation the tea-plant thrusts its sprouts;
Through the northern sluice the veins of the spring ooze.

This year there is war in An-hui,
In every place soldiers are rushing to arms.
Men of learning have been summoned to the Council Board;
Men of action are marching to the battle-line.
Only I, who have no talents at all,
Am left in the mountains to play with the pebbles of
    the stream.

Hearing the Early Oriole

(Written in exile)

When the sun rose I was still lying in bed;
An early oriole sang on the roof of my house.
For a moment I thought of the Royal Park at dawn
When the Birds of Spring greeted their Lord from his trees.
I remembered the days when I served before the Throne
Pencil in hand, on duty at the Ch'ēng-ming;[1]
At the height of spring, when I paused an instant from work,
Morning and evening, was *this* the voice I heard?
Now in my exile the oriole sings again
In the dreary stillness of Hsün-yang town . . .
The bird's note cannot really have changed;
All the difference lies in the listener's heart.
If he could but forget that he lives at the World's end,
The bird would sing as it sang in the Palace of old.

[1] Name of a palace at Ch'ang-an.

Dreaming that I went with Lu and Yu
to visit Yüan Chēn

(Written in exile)

At night I dreamt I was back in Ch'ang-an;
I saw again the faces of old friends.
And in my dreams, under an April sky,
They led me by the hand to wander in the spring winds.
Together we came to the village of Peace and Quiet;
We stopped our horses at the gate of Yüan Chēn.
Yüan Chēn was sitting all alone;
When he saw me coming, a smile came to his face.
He pointed back at the flowers in the western court;
Then opened wine in the northern summer-house.
He seemed to be saying that neither of us had changed;
He seemed to be regretting that joy will not stay;
That our souls had met only for a little while,
To part again with hardly time for greeting.
I woke up and thought him still at my side;
I put out my hand; there was nothing there at all.

206

To a Portrait Painter
who desired Him to Sit

You, so bravely splashing reds and blues!
Just when *I* am getting wrinkled and old.
Why should you waste the moments of inspiration
Tracing the withered limbs of a sick man?
Tall, tall is the Palace of Ch'i-lin;[1]
But my deeds have not been frescoed on its walls.
Minutely limned on a foot of painting silk—
What can I do with a portrait such as *that*?

[1] One of the "Record Offices" of the T'ang dynasty, where meritorious deeds were illustrated on the walls.

Separation

Yesterday I heard that such-a-one was gone;
This morning they tell me that so-and-so is dead.
Of friends and acquaintances more than two-thirds
Have suffered change and passed to the Land of Ghosts.
Those that are gone I shall not see again;
They, alas, are for ever finished and done.
Those that are left,—where are they now?
They are all scattered,—a thousand miles away.
Those I have known and loved through all my life,
On the fingers of my hand—how many do I count?
Only the prefects of T'ung, Kuo and Li
And Fēng Province—just those four.[1]
Longing for each other we are all grown gray;
Through the Fleeting World rolled like a wave in
    the stream.
Alas that the feasts and frolics of old days
Have withered and vanished, bringing us to this!
When shall we meet and drink a cup of wine
And laughing gaze into each other's eyes?

---

[1] Yüan Chēn [d. 831], Ts'ui Hsüan-liang [d. 833], Liu Yü-hsi [d. 842], and Li Chien [d. 821].

The Red Cockatoo

Sent as a present from Annam—
A red cockatoo.
Coloured like the peach-tree blossom,
Speaking with the speech of men.
And they did to it what is always done
To the learned and eloquent.
They took a cage with stout bars
And shut it up inside.

Eating Bamboo-Shoots

My new province is a land of bamboo-groves:
Their shoots in spring fill the valleys and hills.
The mountain woodman cuts an armful of them
And brings them down to sell at the early market.
Things are cheap in proportion as they are common;
For two farthings, I buy a whole bundle.
I put the shoots in a great earthen pot
And heat them up along with boiling rice.
The purple nodules broken,—like an old brocade;
The white skin opened,—like new pearls.
Now every day I eat them recklessly;
For a long time I have not touched meat.
All the time I was living at Lo-yang
They could not give me enough to suit my taste,
Now I can have as many shoots as I please;
For each breath of the south-wind makes a new bamboo!

Having Climbed to the Topmost Peak
of the Incense-Burner Mountain

Up and up, the Incense-Burner Peak!
In my heart is stored what my eyes and ears perceived.
All the year—detained by official business;
To-day at last I got a chance to go.
Grasping the creepers, I clung to dangerous rocks;
My hands and feet—weary with groping for hold.
There came with me three or four friends,
But two friends dared not go further.
At last we reached the topmost crest of the Peak;
My eyes were blinded, my soul rocked and reeled.
The chasm beneath me—ten thousand feet;
The ground I stood on, only a foot wide.
If you have not exhausted the scope of seeing and hearing,
How can you realize the wideness of the world?
The waters of the River looked narrow as a ribbon,
P'ēn Castle smaller than a man's fist.
How it clings, the dust of the world's halter!
It chokes my limbs: I cannot shake it away.
Thinking of retirement,[1] I heaved an envious sigh,
Then, with lowered head, came back to the Ants' Nest.

---

[1] *I.e.*, retirement from office.

Alarm at First Entering the Yang-Tze Gorges

(*Written in A.D. 818, when he was being towed
up the rapids to Chung-chou.*)

Above, a mountain ten thousand feet high:
Below, a river a thousand fathoms deep.
A strip of green, walled by cliffs of stone:
Wide enough for the passage of a single reed.[1]
At Chü-t'ang a straight cleft yawns:
At Yen-yü islands block the stream.
Long before night the walls are black with dusk;
Without wind white waves rise.
The big rocks are like a flat sword:
The little rocks resemble ivory tusks.

[1] See Odes, v. 7.

We are stuck fast and cannot move a step.
How much the less, three hundred miles?[1]
Frail and slender, the twisted-bamboo rope:
Weak, the dangerous hold of the towers' feet.
A single slip—the whole convoy lost:
And *my* life hangs on *this* thread!
I have heard a saying "He that has an upright heart
Shall walk scathless through the lands of Man and Mo".[2]
How can I believe that since the world began
In every shipwreck none have drowned but rogues?
And how can I, born in evil days[3]
And fresh from failure,[4] ask a kindness of Fate?
Often I fear that these un-talented limbs
Will be laid at last in an un-named grave!

[1] The distance to Chung-chou.   [2] Dangerous savages.
[3] Of civil war.   [4] Alluding to his renewed banishment.

After Lunch

After lunch—one short nap:
On waking up—two cups of tea.
Raising my head, I see the sun's light
Once again slanting to the south-west.
Those who are happy regret the shortness of the day;
Those who are sad tire of the year's sloth.
But those whose hearts are devoid of joy or sadness
Just go on living, regardless of "short" or "long".

On Being Removed from Hsün-yang
and Sent to Chung-chou

A remote place in the mountains of Pa (Ssech'uan)

Before this, when I was stationed at Hsün-yang,
Already I regretted the fewness of friends and guests.
Suddenly, suddenly,—bearing a stricken heart
I left the gates, with nothing to comfort me.
Henceforward,—relegated to deep seclusion
In a bottomless gorge, flanked by precipitous mountains,
Five months on end the passage of boats is stopped
By the piled billows that toss and leap like colts.
The inhabitants of Pa resemble wild apes;
Fierce and lusty, they fill the mountains and prairies.
Among such as these I cannot hope for friends
And am pleased with anyone who is even remotely human!

215

Planting Flowers on the Embankment

(Written when Governor of Chung-chou)

I took money and bought flowering trees
And planted them out on the bank to the east of the Keep.
I simply bought whatever had most blooms,
Not caring whether peach, apricot, or plum.
A hundred fruits, all mixed up together;
A thousand branches, flowering in due rotation.
Each has its season coming early or late;
But to all alike the fertile soil is kind.
The red flowers hang like a heavy mist;
The white flowers gleam like a fall of snow.
The wandering bees cannot bear to leave them;
The sweet birds also come there to roost.
In front there flows an ever-running stream;
Beneath there is built a little flat terrace.
Sometimes I sweep the flagstones of the terrace;
Sometimes, in the wind, I raise my cup and drink.
The flower-branches screen my head from the sun;
The flower-buds fall down into my lap.
Alone drinking, alone singing my songs
I do not notice that the moon is level with the steps.
The people of Pa do not care for flowers;
All the spring no one has come to look.
But their Governor General, alone with his cup of wine
Sits till evening and will not move from the place!

216

Prose Letter to Yüan Chēn

(*A. D. 818*)

NIGHT of the tenth day of the fourth month. Lo-t'ien[1] says:
O Wei-chih,[2] Wei-chih, it is three years since I saw your face
and almost two years since I had a letter from you. Is man's
life so long that he can afford such partings? Much less should
hearts joined by glue be set in bodies remote as Hu and
Yüeh.[3] In promotion we could not be together; and in failure
we cannot forget each other. Snatched and wrenched apart,
separately each of us grows grey. O Wei-chih, what is to be
done? But this is the work of Heaven and there is no use in
speaking of it.

When I first arrived at Hsün-yang, Hsiung Ju-tēng[4] came
with the letter which you had written the year before, when
you were so ill. First you told me of the progress of your illness, next of your feelings while you were ill and last you
spoke of all our meetings and partings, and of the occasion of
your own difficulties and dangers. You had no time to write
more, but sent a bundle of your writings with a note attached,
which said, "Later on I will send a message by Po Minchung.[5]
Ask him for news and that will do instead of a letter". Alas!

---

[1] Other name of Po Chü-i.   [2] Other name of Yüan Chēn.
[3] The extreme North and South of China.
[4] A poet, several of whose short poems are well-known.
[5] The son of Po Chü-i's uncle Po Chi'-k'ang.

Is it thus that Wei-chih treats me? But again, I read the poem you wrote when you heard I had been banished:

The lamp had almost spent its light: shadows filled the room,
The night I heard that Lo-t'ien was banished to Kiu-kiang.
And I that had lain sick to death sat up suddenly in bed;
A dark wind blowing rain entered at the cold window.

If even strangers' hearts are touched by these lines, much more must mine be; so that to this day I cannot recite them without pain. Of this matter I will say no more, but tell you briefly what has passed of late.

It is more than three years since I came to Kiu-kiang. All this time my body has been strong and my heart much at peace. There has been no sickness in my household, even among the servants. Last summer my elder brother arrived from Hsü-chou, leading by the hand six or seven little brothers and sisters, orphans of various households. So that I have under my eyes all those who at present demand my care. They share with me cold and heat, hunger and satiety. This is my first consolation.

The climate of the River Province is somewhat cool, so that fevers and epidemics are rare. And while snakes and mosquitoes are few, the fish in the Pēn are remarkably fat, the River wine is exceedingly good, and indeed for the most part the food is like that of the North Country. Although the mouths within my doors are many and the salary of a Sub-Prefect is small, by a thrifty application of my means, I am yet able to provide for my household without seeking any

218

man's assistance to clothe their backs or fill their bellies. This is my second consolation.

In the autumn of last year I visited Lu Shan[1] for the first time. Reaching a point between the Eastern Forest and Western Forest Temples, beneath the Incense-Burner Peak, I was enamoured by the unequalled prospect of cloud-girt waters and spray-clad rocks. Unable to leave this place, I built a cottage here. Before it stand ten tall pines and a thousand tapering bamboos. With green creepers I fenced my garden; with white stones I made bridge and path. Flowing waters encircle my home; flying spray falls between the eaves. Red pomegranate and white lotus cluster on the steps of the pond. All is after this pattern, though I cannot here name each delight. Whenever I come here alone, I am moved to prolong my stay to ten days; for of the things that have all my life most pleased me, not one is missing. So that not only do I forget to go back, but would gladly end my days here. This is my third consolation.

Remembering that not having had news of me for so long, you might be in some anxiety with regard to me, I have hastened to set your mind at rest by recording these three consolations. What else I have to tell shall be set out in due order, as follows. . . .[2]

Wei-chih, Wei-chih! The night I wrote this letter I was sitting at the mountain-window of my thatched hut. I let my brush run as my hand willed and wrote at hazard as my

[1] A famous mountain near Kiu-kiang.
[2] What followed is omitted in the printed text.

thoughts came. When I folded it and addressed it, I found that dawn had come. I raised my head and saw only a few mountain-priests, some sitting, some sleeping. I heard the mournful cries of mountain apes and the sad twitterings of valley birds. O friend of all my life, parted from me by a thousand leagues, at such times as this "dim thoughts of the World"[1] creep upon me for a while; so, following my ancient custom, I send you these three couplets:

I remember how once I wrote you a letter sitting in the Palace at night,
At the back of the Hall of Golden Bells, when dawn was coming
      in the sky.
This night I fold your letter—in what place?
Sitting in a cottage on Lu Shan, by the light of a late lamp.
The caged bird and fettered ape are neither of them dead yet;
In the world of men face to face will they ever meet again?

O Wei-chih, Wei-chih! This night, this heart—do you know them or not? Lo-t'ien bows his head.

[1] This expression is used by Yüan Chēn in a poem addressed to Po Chü-i. By "the World", he means their life together at Court.

220

The Fifteenth Volume

Having completed the fifteenth volume of his works, the poet sends it to his friends Yüan Chēn and Li Chien, with a jesting poem.

(Written in A. D. 818)

My long poem, the "Eternal Grief",[1] is a beautiful and
    moving work;
My ten "Songs of Shensi" are models of tunefulness.
I cannot prevent Old Yüan from stealing my best rhymes;
But I earnestly beg Little Li to respect my ballads and songs.
While I am alive riches and honour will never fall to my lot;
But well I know that after I am dead the fame of my books
    will live.
This random talk and foolish boasting forgive me, for to-day
I have added Volume Fifteen to the row that stands
    to my name.

[1] See Giles, "Chinese Literature," p. 169.

221

Invitation to Hsiao Chü-shih[1]

(Written when Governor of Chung-chou)

Within the Gorges there is no lack of men;
They are people one meets, not people one cares for.
At my front door guests also arrive;
They are people one sits with, not people one knows.
When I look up, there are only clouds and trees;
When I look down—only my wife and child.
I sleep, eat, get up or sit still;
Apart from that, nothing happens at all.
But beyond the city Hsiao the hermit dwells;
And with *him* at least I find myself at ease.
For *he* can drink a full flagon of wine
And is good at reciting long-line poems.
Some afternoon, when the clerks have all gone home,
At a season when the path by the river bank is dry,
I beg you, take up your staff of bamboo-wood
And find your way to the parlour of the Government House.

[1] This poem, and those appearing on pp. 223, 224, and 225, were written
when the poet was Governor of a remote part of Szechuan, in the extreme
west of China.

To Li Chien

(A. D. 818)

The province I govern is humble and remote;
Yet our festivals follow the Courtly Calendar.
At rise of day we sacrificed to the Wind God,
When darkly, darkly, dawn glimmered in the sky.
Officers followed, horsemen led the way;
They brought us out to the wastes beyond the town,
Where river mists fall heavier than rain,
And the fires on the hill leap higher than the stars.

Suddenly I remembered the early levées at Court
When you and I galloped to the Purple Yard.
As we walked our horses up Dragon Tail Street
We turned our heads and gazed at the Southern Hills.
Since we parted, both of us have been growing old;
And our minds have been vexed by many anxious cares.
Yet even now I fancy my ears are full
Of the sound of jade tinkling on your bridle-straps.

The Spring River

(A. D. 820)

Heat and cold, dusk and dawn have crowded one upon
    the other;
Suddenly I find it is two years since I came to Chung-chou.
Through my closed doors I hear nothing but the morning
    and evening drum;
From my upper windows all I see is the ships that come
    and go.[1]
In vain the orioles tempt me with their song to stray beneath
    the flowering trees;
In vain the grasses lure me by their colour to sit beside
    the pond.
There is one thing and one alone I never tire of watching—
The spring river as it trickles over the stones and babbles
    past the rocks.

[1] "The Emperor Saga of Japan [reigned A. D. 810-23] one day quoted to his Minister, Ono no Takamura, the couplet:
'Through my closed doors I hear nothing but the morning and evening drum;
From my upper windows in the distance I see ships that come and go.'

Takamura, thinking these were the Emperor's own verses, said: 'If I may venture to criticize an august composition, I would suggest that the phrase "in the distance" be altered.' The Emperor was delighted, for he had purposely changed 'all I see' to 'in the distance I see'. At that time there was only one copy of Po Chü-i's poems in Japan and the Emperor, to whom it belonged, had allowed no one to see it."—From the *Kōdanshō* [twelfth century].

After Collecting the Autumn Taxes

From my high castle I look at the town below
Where the natives of Pa cluster like a swarm of flies.
How can I govern these people and lead them aright?
I cannot even understand what they say.
But at least I am glad, now that the taxes are in,
To learn that in my province there is no discontent.
I fear its prosperity is not due to me
And was only caused by the year's abundant crops,
The papers that lie on my desk are simple and few;
My house by the moat is leisurely and still.
In the autumn rain the berries fall from the eaves;
At the evening bell the birds return to the wood.
A broken sunlight quavers over the southern porch
Where I lie on my couch abandoned to idleness.

Lodging with the Old Man
of the Stream

(A. D. 820)

Men's hearts love gold and jade;
Men's mouths covet wine and flesh.
Not so the old man of the stream;
He drinks from his gourd and asks nothing more.
South of the stream he cuts firewood and grass;
North of the stream he has built wall and roof.
Yearly he sows a single acre of land;
In spring he drives two yellow calves.
In these things he finds great repose;
Beyond these he has no wish or care.
By chance I met him walking by the water-side;
He took me home and lodged me in his thatched hut.
When I parted from him, to seek market and Court,
This old man asked my rank and pay.
Doubting my tale, he laughed loud and long:
"Privy Councillors do not sleep in barns".

To His Brother Hsing-chien

(A. D. 820)

Can the single cup of wine
We drank this morning have made my heart so glad?
This is a joy that comes only from within,
Which those who witness will never understand.
I have but two brothers
And bitterly grieved that both were far away;
This Spring, back through the Gorges of Pa,
I have come to them safely, ten thousand leagues.
Two sisters I had
Who had put up their hair, but not twined the sash;[1]
Yesterday both were married and taken away
By good husbands in whom I may well trust.
I am freed at last from the thoughts that made me grieve,
As though a sword had cut a rope from my neck.
And limbs grow light when the heart sheds its care:
Suddenly I seem to be flying up to the sky!

Hsing-chien, drink your cup of wine
Then set it down and listen to what I say.
Do not sigh that your home is far away;
Do not mind if your salary is small.
Only pray that as long as life lasts,
You and I may never be forced to part.

[1] I.e., got married.

The Pine-Trees in the Courtyard

(A.D. 820)

Below the hall
The pine-trees grow in front of the steps,
Irregularly scattered,—not in ordered lines.
Some are tall and some are low:
The tallest of them is six roods high;
The lowest but ten feet.
They are like wild things
And no one knows who planted them.
They touch the walls of my blue-tiled house;
Their roots are sunk in the terrace of white sand.
Morning and evening they are visited by the wind and moon;
Rain or fine,—they are free from dust and mud.
In the gales of autumn they whisper a vague tune;
From the suns of summer they yield a cool shade.
At the height of spring the fine evening rain
Fills their leaves with a load of hanging pearls.
At the year's end the time of great snow
Stamps their branches with a fret of glittering jade.
Of the Four Seasons each has its own mood;
Among all the trees none is like another.
Last year, when they heard I had bought this house,
Neighbours mocked and the World called me mad—
That a whole family of twice ten souls

228

Should move house for the sake of a few pines!
Now that I have come to them, what have they given me?
They have only loosened the buckles of my care.
Yet even so, they are "profitable friends",[1]
And fill my need of "converse with wise men".
Yet when I consider how, still a man of the world,
In belt and cap I scurry through dirt and dust,
From time to time my heart twinges with shame
That I am not fit to be master of my pines!

[1] See "Analects of Confucius" 4 and 5, where three kinds of "profitable friends" and three kinds of "profitable pleasures" are described; the third of the latter being "plenty of intelligent companions".

Sleeping on Horseback

(A. D. 822)

We had rode long and were still far from the inn;
My eyes grew dim; for a moment I fell asleep.
Under my right arm the whip still dangled;
In my left hand the reins for an instant slackened.
Suddenly I woke and turned to question my groom:
"We have gone a hundred paces since you fell asleep,"
Body and spirit for a while had exchanged place;
Swift and slow had turned to their contraries.
For these few steps that my horse had carried me
Had taken in my dream countless aeons of time!
True indeed is that saying of Wise Men
"A hundred years are but a moment of sleep".

Parting from the Winter Stove

(A. D. 822)

On the fifth day after the rise of Spring,
Everywhere the season's gracious altitudes!
The white sun gradually lengthening its course,
The blue-grey clouds hanging as though they would fall;
The last icicle breaking into splinters of jade;
The new stems marshalling red sprouts.
The things I meet are all full of gladness;
It is not only I who love the Spring.
To welcome the flowers I stand in the back garden;
To enjoy the sunlight I sit under the front eaves.
Yet still in my heart there lingers one regret;
Soon I shall part with the flame of my red stove!

Children

(*Written circa A.D. 820*)

My niece, who is six years old, is called "Miss Tortoise";
My daughter of three,—little "Summer Dress".
One is beginning to learn to joke and talk;
The other can already recite poems and songs.
At morning they play clinging about my feet;
At night they sleep pillowed against my dress.
Why, children, did you reach the world so late,
Coming to me just when my years are spent?
Young things draw our feelings to them;
Old people easily give their hearts.
The sweetest vintage at last turns sour;
The full moon in the end begins to wane.
And so with men the bonds of love and affection
Soon may change to a load of sorrow and care.
But all the world is bound by love's ties;
Why did I think that I alone should escape?

Pruning Trees

Trees growing,—right in front of my window;
The trees are high and the leaves grow thick.
Sad alas! the distant mountain view
Obscured by this, dimly shows between.
One morning I took knife and axe;
With my own hand I lopped the branches off.
Ten thousand leaves fall about my head;
A thousand hills come before my eyes.
Suddenly, as when clouds or mists break
And straight through, the blue sky appears;
Again, like the face of a friend one has loved
Seen at last after an age of parting.
First there came a gentle wind blowing;
One by one the birds flew back to the tree.
To ease my mind I gazed to the South East;
As my eyes wandered, my thoughts went far away.
Of men there is none that has not some preference;
Of things there is none but mixes good with ill.
It was not that I did not love the tender branches;
But better still,—to see the green hills!

Being Visited by a Friend During Illness

I have been ill so long that I do not count the days;
At the southern window, evening—and again evening.
Sadly chirping in the grasses under my eaves
The winter sparrows morning and evening sing.
By an effort I rise and lean heavily on my bed;
Tottering I step towards the door of the courtyard.
By chance I meet a friend who is coming to see me;
Just as if I had gone specially to meet him.
They took my couch and placed it in the setting sun;
They spread my rug and I leaned on the balcony-pillar.
Tranquil talk was better than any medicine;
Gradually the feelings came back to my numbed heart.

On the Way to Hang-chow: Anchored on the River at Night

Little sleeping and much grieving,—the traveller
Rises at midnight and looks back towards home.
The sands are bright with moonlight that joins the shores;
The sail is white with dew that has covered the boat.
Nearing the sea, the river grows broader and broader:
Approaching autumn, the nights longer and longer.
Thirty times we have slept amid mists and waves,
And still we have not reached Hang-chow!

Stopping the Night at Jung-yang

I grew up at Jung-yang;
I was still young when I left.
On and on,—forty years passed
Till again I stayed for the night at Jung-yang.
When I went away, I was only eleven or twelve;
This year I am turned fifty-six.
Yet thinking back to the times of my childish games,
Whole and undimmed, still they rise before me.
The old houses have all disappeared;
Down in the village none of my people are left.
It is not only that streets and buildings have changed;
But steep is level and level changed to steep!
Alone unchanged, the waters of Ch'iu and Yu
Passionless,—flow in their old course.

The Hat Given to the Poet
by Li Chien

Long ago a white-haired gentleman
You made the present of a black gauze hat.
The gauze hat still sits on my head;
But you already are gone to the Nether Springs.
The thing is old, but still fit to wear;
The man is gone and will never be seen again.
Out on the hill the moon is shining to-night
And the trees on your tomb are swayed by the
    autumn wind.

The Silver Spoon

*While on the road to his new province, Hang-chow, in A.D. 822,
he sends a silver spoon to his niece A-kuei, whom he had been obliged
to leave behind with her nurse, old Mrs. Ts'ao.*

To distant service my heart is well accustomed;
When I left home, it wasn't *that* which was difficult
But because I had to leave Miss Kuei at home—
For this it was that tears filled my eyes.
Little girls ought to be daintily fed:
Mrs. Ts'ao, please see to this!
That's why I've packed and sent a silver spoon;
You will think of me and eat up your food nicely!

The Big Rug

That so many of the poor should suffer from cold what can
      we do to prevent?
To bring warmth to a single body is not much use.
I wish I had a big rug ten thousand feet long,
Which at one time could cover up every inch of the City.

Good-bye to the People of Hang-chow

(A. D. 824)

Elders and officers line the returning road;
Wine and soup load the parting table.
I have not ruled you with the wisdom of Shao Kung;[1]
What is the reason your tears should fall so fast?
My taxes were heavy, though many of the people were poor;
The farmers were hungry, for often their fields were dry.
All I did was to dam the water of the Lake[2]
And help a little in a year when things were bad.

[1] A legendary ruler who dispensed justice sitting under a wild pear-tree.
[2] Po Chü-i built the dam on the Western Lake which is still known as "Po's dam".

Getting Up Early
on a Spring Morning

(Part of a poem written when Governor of Soochow in A.D. 825)

The early light of the rising sun shines on the beams
    of my house;
The first banging of opened doors echoes like the roll
    of a drum.
The dog lies curled on the stone step, for the earth is wet
    with dew;
The birds come near to the window and chatter, telling
    that the day is fine.
With the lingering fumes of yesterday's wine my head is
    still heavy;
With new doffing of winter clothes my body has
    grown light.

Written when Governor of Soochow

(A.D. 825)

A Government building, not my own home.
A Government garden, not my own trees.
But at Lo-yang I have a small house
And on Wei River I have built a thatched hut.
I am free from the ties of marrying and giving in marriage;
If I choose to retire, I have somewhere to end my days.
And though I have lingered long beyond my time,
To retire now would be better than not at all!

Losing A Slave-Girl

(Date uncertain)

Around my garden the little wall is low;
In the bailiff's lodge the lists are seldom checked.
I am ashamed to think we were not always kind;
I regret your labours, that will never be repaid.
The caged bird owes no allegiance;
The wind-tossed flower does not cling to the tree.

Where to-night she lies none can give us news;
Nor any knows, save the bright watching moon.

Lazy Man's Song

(A. D. 811)

I have got patronage, but am too lazy to use it;
I have got land, but am too lazy to farm it.
My house leaks; I am too lazy to mend it.
My clothes are torn; I am too lazy to darn them.
I have got wine, but am too lazy to drink;
So it's just the same as if my cellar were empty.
I have got a harp, but am too lazy to play;
So it's just the same as if it had no strings.
My wife tells me there is no more bread in the house;
I want to bake, but am too lazy to grind.
My friends and relatives write me long letters;
I should like to read them, but they're such a bother
    to open.
I have always been told that Chi Shu-yeh[1]
Passed his whole life in absolute idleness.
But he played the harp and sometimes transmuted metals,
So even *he* was not so lazy as I.

[1] Also known as Chi K'ang, a famous Quietist.

244

After Getting Drunk
Becoming Sober in the Night

Our party scattered at yellow dusk and I came home to bed;
I woke at midnight and went for a walk, leaning heavily
    on a friend.
As I lay on my pillow my vinous complexion, soothed by
    sleep, grew sober;
In front of the tower the ocean moon, accompanying the
    tide, had risen.
The swallows, about to return to the beams, went back to
    roost again;
The candle at my window, just going out, suddenly revived
    its light.
All the time till dawn came, still my thoughts were muddled;
And in my ears something sounded like the music of flutes
    and strings.

The Grand Houses at Lo-yang

(Circa A. D. 829)

By woods and water, whose houses are these
With high gates and wide-stretching lands?
From their blue gables gilded fishes hang;
By their red pillars carven coursers run.
Their spring arbours, warm with caged mist;
Their autumn yards with locked moonlight cold.
To the stem of the pine-tree amber beads cling;
The bamboo-branches ooze ruby-drops.
Of lake and terrace who may the masters be?
Staff-officers, Councillors-of-State.
All their lives they have never come to see,
But know their houses only from the bailiff's map!

The Cranes

(A. D. 830)

The western wind has blown but a few days;
Yet the first leaf already flies from the bough.
On the drying paths I walk in my thin shoes;
In the first cold I have donned my quilted coat.
Through shallow ditches the floods are clearing away;
Through sparse bamboos trickles a slanting light.
In the early dusk, down an alley of green moss,
The garden-boy is leading the cranes home.

On A Box
Containing His Own Works

I break up cypress and make a book-box;
The box well-made,—and the cypress-wood tough.
In it shall be kept what author's works?
The inscription says PO LO-T'IEN.
All my life has been spent in writing books,
From when I was young till now that I am old.
First and last,—seventy whole volumes;
Big and little,—three thousand themes. [1]
Well I know in the end they'll be scattered and lost;
But I cannot bear to see them thrown away,
With my own hand I open and shut the locks,
And put it carefully in front of the book-curtain.
I am like Tēng Pai-tao; [2]
But to-day there is not any Wang Ts'an. [3]
All I can do is to divide them among my daughters
To be left by them to give to my grandchildren.

---

[1] I.e., separate poems, essays, etc.
[2] Who was obliged to abandon his only child on the roadside.
[3] Who rescued a foundling.

On Being Sixty

Addressed to Liu Mēng-tē, who had asked for a poem.
He was the same age as Po Chü-i.

Between thirty and forty, one is distracted by the Five Lusts;
Between seventy and eighty, one is a prey to
    a hundred diseases.
But from fifty to sixty one is free from all ills;
Calm and still—the heart enjoys rest.
I have put behind me Love and Greed; I have done with
    Profit and Fame;
I am still short of illness and decay and far from
    decrepit age.
Strength of limb I still possess to seek the rivers and hills;
Still my heart has spirit enough to listen to flutes and strings.
At leisure I open new wine and taste several cups;
Drunken I recall old poems and sing a whole volume.
Mēng-tē has asked for a poem and herewith I exhort him
Not to complain of three-score, "the time of obedient ears".[1]

[1] Confucius said that it was not till *sixty* that "his ears obeyed him". This age was therefore called "the time of obedient ears".

On His Baldness

(A.D. 832)

At dawn I sighed to see my hairs fall;
At dusk I sighed to see my hairs fall.
For I dreaded the time when the last lock should go . . .
They are all gone and I do not mind at all!
I have done with that cumbrous washing and getting dry;
My tiresome comb for ever is laid aside.
Best of all, when the weather is hot and wet,
To have no top-knot weighing down on one's head!
I put aside my dusty conical cap;
      And loose my collar-fringe.
In a silver jar I have stored a cold stream;
On my bald pate I trickle a ladle-full.
Like one baptized with the Water of Buddha's Law,
I sit and receive this cool, cleansing joy.
Now I know why the priest who seeks Repose
Frees his heart by first shaving his head.

Thinking of the Past

(A. D. 833)

In an idle hour I thought of former days;
And former friends seemed to be standing in the room.
And then I wondered "Where are they now?"
Like fallen leaves they have tumbled to the Nether Springs.
Han Yü[1] swallowed his sulphur pills,
Yet a single illness carried him straight to the grave.
Yüan Chēn smelted autumn stone[2]
But before he was old, his strength crumbled away.
Master Tu possessed the "Secret of Health":
All day long he fasted from meat and spice.
The Lord Ts'ui, trusting a strong drug,
Through the whole winter wore his summer coat.
Yet some by illness and some by sudden death . . .
All vanished ere their middle years were passed.

Only I, who have never dieted myself
Have thus protracted a tedious span of age,
     I who in young days
Yielded lightly to every lust and greed;
Whose palate craved only for the richest meat
And knew nothing of bismuth or calomel.

[1] The famous poet, d. A. D. 824.
[2] Carbamide crystals.

When hunger came, I gulped steaming food;
When thirst came, I drank from the frozen stream.
With verse I served the spirits of my Five Guts;[1]
With wine I watered the three Vital Spots.
Day by day joining the broken clod
I have lived till now almost sound and whole.
There is no gap in my two rows of teeth;
Limbs and body still serve me well.
Already I have opened the seventh book of years;
Yet I eat my fill and sleep quietly;
I drink, while I may, the wine that lies in my cup,
And all else commit to Heaven's care.

[1] Heart, liver, stomach, lungs and kidney.

Old Age

Addressed to Liu Yü-hsi, who was born in the same year

(A.D. 835)

We are growing old together, you and I,
Let us ask ourselves, what is age like?
The dull eye is closed ere night comes;
The idle head, still uncombed at noon.
Propped on a staff, sometimes a walk abroad;
Or all day sitting with closed doors.
One dares not look in the mirror's polished face;
One cannot read small-letter books.
Deeper and deeper, one's love of old friends;
Fewer and fewer, one's dealings with young men.
One thing only, the pleasure of idle talk
Is great as ever, when you and I meet.

A Mad Poem Addressed to My Nephews and Nieces

(A. D. 835)

The World cheats those who cannot read;
I, happily, have mastered script and pen.
The World cheats those who hold no office;
I am blessed with high official rank.
      The old are often ill;
I, at this day have not an ache or pain.
      They are often burdened with ties;
But I have finished with marriage and giving in marriage.
No changes happen to disturb the quiet of my mind;
No business comes to impair the vigour of my limbs.
Hence it is that now for ten years
Body and soul have rested in hermit peace.
And all the more, in the last lingering years
What I shall need are very few things.
A single rug to warm me through the winter;
One meal to last me the whole day.
It does not matter that my house is rather small;
One cannot sleep in more than one room!
It does not matter that I have not many horses;
One cannot ride in two coaches at once!
As fortunate as me among the people of the world

254

Possibly one would find seven out of ten.
As contented as me among a hundred men
Look as you may, you will not find one.
In the affairs of others even fools are wise;
In their own business even sages err.
To no one else would I dare to speak my heart,
So my wild words are addressed to my nephews and nieces.

To a Talkative Guest

(A. D. 836)

The town visitor's easy talk flows in an endless stream;
The country host's quiet thoughts ramble timidly on.
"I beg you, Sir, do not tell me about things at Ch'ang-an;
For you entered just when my harp was tuned and lying
    balanced on my knees."

Climbing the Terrace of Kuan-yin and Looking at the City

Hundreds of houses, thousands of houses,—like a chessboard.
The twelve streets like a field planted with rows of cabbage.
In the distance perceptible, dim, dim—the fire of
    approaching dawn;

And a single row of stars lying to the west of the Five Gates.

Climbing the Ling Ying Terrace
and Looking North

Mounting on high I begin to realize the smallness of
    Man's Domain;
Gazing into distance I begin to know the vanity of the
    Carnal World.
I turn my head and hurry home—back to the Court
    and Market,
A single grain of rice falling—into the Great Barn.

Dreaming of Yüan Chēn

(This was written eight years after Yüan Chēn's death,
when Po Chü-i was sixty-eight)

At night you came and took my hand and we wandered
    together in my dream;
When I woke in the morning there was no one to stop the
    tears that fell on my handkerchief.
On the banks of the Ch'ang my aged body three times[1] has
    passed through sickness;
At Hsien-yang[2] to the grasses on your grave eight times has
    autumn come.
You lie buried beneath the springs and your bones are
    mingled with the clay.
I—lodging in the world of men; my hair white as snow.
A-wei and Han-lang[3] both followed in their turn;
Among the shadows of the Terrace of Night did you know
    them or not?

[1] Since you died.
[2] Near Ch'ang-an, modern Si-ngan-fu.
[3] Affectionate names of Li Chien and Ts'ui Hsüan-liang.

Going to the Mountains
with a little Dancing Girl, Aged Fifteen

(Written when the poet was about sixty-five)

Two top-knots not yet plaited into one.
Of thirty years—just beyond half.
You who are really a lady of silks and satins
Are now become my hill and stream companion!
At the spring fountains together we splash and play:
On the lovely trees together we climb and sport.
Her cheeks grow rosy, as she quickens her sleeve-dancing:
Her brows grow sad, as she slows her song's tune.
Don't go singing the song of the Willow Branches,[1]
When there's no one here with a heart for you to break!

[1] A plaintive love-song, to which Po Chü-i had himself written words.

My Servant Wakes Me

(A. D. 839)

My servant wakes me: "Master, it is broad day.
Rise from bed; I bring you bowl and comb.
Winter comes and the morning air is chill;
To-day your Honour must not venture abroad."
When I stay at home, no one comes to call;
What must I do with the long, idle hours?
Setting my chair where a faint sunshine falls
I have warmed wine and opened my poetry-books.

Since I Lay Ill

(A. D. 840)

Since I lay ill, how long has passed?
Almost a hundred heavy-hanging days.
The maids have learnt to gather my medicine-herbs;
The dog no longer barks when the doctor comes.
The jars in my cellar are plastered deep with mould;
My singer's carpets are half crumbled to dust.
How can I bear, when the Earth renews her light,
To watch from a pillow the beauty of Spring unfold?

Song of Past Feelings

(Circa A. D. 840)

WHEN LO-T'IEN[1] was old, he fell ill of a palsy. So he made a list of his possessions and examined his expenses, that he might reject whatever had become superfluous. He had in his employ a girl about twenty years old called Fan Su, whose postures delighted him when she sang or danced. But above all she excelled in singing the "Willow Branch," so that many called her by the name of this song, and she was well known by this name in the town of Lo-yang. But she was on the list of unnecessary expenses and was to be sent away.

He had too a white horse with black mane, sturdy and sure-footed, which he had ridden for many years. It stood on the list of things which could be dispensed with, and was to be sold. When the groom led the horse through the gate, it tossed its head and looked back, neighing once with a sound in its voice that seemed to say: "I know I am leaving you and long to stay." Su, when she heard the horse neigh, rose timidly, bowed before me and spoke sweetly, as shall hereafter be shown. When she had done speaking her tears fell.

[1] I.e., Po Chü-i himself.

263

When first I heard Su's words, I was too sad to speak and could not answer her. But in a little while I ordered the bridle to be turned and the sleeve reversed. Then I gave her wine and drank a cup myself, and in my happiness sang a few score notes. And these notes turned into a poem, a poem without fixed measure, for the measure followed my irregular tune. In all there were 255 words.

Alas! I am no Sage. I could neither forget past feelings nor show such sensibility as this beast reputed incapable of feeling! Things that happen lay hold of my heart, and when my heart is moved, I cannot control it. Therefore, smiling at myself, I called this song *"A Song of Past Feelings Unforgotten."*
The Song says:

> *I was selling my white horse*
> *And sending Willow Branch away.*
> *She covered her dark eyebrows;*
> *He trailed his golden halter.*
> *The horse, for want of speech,*
> *Neighed long and turned his head;*
> *And Willow Branch, twice bowing,*
> *Knelt long and spoke to me:*
> *"Master, you have ridden this horse five years,*
> *One thousand eight hundred days;*
> *Meekly he has borne the bit,*
> *Without shying, without bolting.*
> *And I have served you for ten years,*
> *Three thousand and six hundred days;*

Patient carrier of towel and comb,[1]
    Without complaint, without loss.
And now, though my shape is lowly,
    I am still fresh and strong.
And the colt is still in his prime,
    Without lameness or fault.
Why should you not use the colt's strength
    To replace your sick legs?
Why should you not use my song to gladden your
        casual cup?
Need you in one morning send both away,
    Send them away never to return?
This is what Su would say to you before she goes,
And this is what your horse meant also
    When he neighed at the gate.
Seeing my distress, who am a woman,
And hearing its cries, that is but a horse,
Shall our master alone remain pitiless?"

I looked up and sighed: I looked down and laughed.
Then I said:
    "Dear horse, stop your sad cries!
    Sweet Su, dry your bitter tears!
    For you shall go back to your stall;
    And you to the women's room.
    For though I am ill indeed,

[1] I.e., performing the functions of a wife.

And though my years are at their close,
The doom of Hsiang Chi[1] has not befallen me yet.
Must I in a single day
Lose the horse I rode and the lady I loved?
Su, O Su!
Sing once again the Song of the Willow Branch!
And I will pour you wine in that golden cup
And take you with me to the Land of Drunkenness."

[1] Who, surrounded at the battle of Kai-hsia (202 B. C.), gave his horse
to a boatman, lest it should fall into the hands of the enemy.

A Dream of Mountaineering

(Written when he was over seventy)

At night, in my dream, I stoutly climbed a mountain,
Going out alone with my staff of holly-wood.
A thousand crags, a hundred hundred valleys—
In my dream-journey none were unexplored
And all the while my feet never grew tired
And my step was as strong as in my young days.
Can it be that when the mind travels backward
The body also returns to its old state?
And can it be, as between body and soul,
That the body may languish, while the soul is still strong?
Soul and body—both are vanities:
Dreaming and waking—both alike unreal.
In the day my feet are palsied and tottering;
In the night my steps go striding over the hills.
As day and night are divided in equal parts—
Between the two, I *get* as much as I *lose*.

Ease

*Congratulating himself on the comforts of his life
after his retirement from office. (Written circa A.D. 844)*

Lined coat, warm cap and easy felt slippers,
In the little tower, at the low window, sitting over the
    sunken brazier.
Body at rest, heart at peace; no need to rise early.
I wonder if the courtiers at the Western Capital know of
    these things, or not?

The Philosophers

Lao-tzŭ

"Those who speak know nothing;
Those who know are silent."
These words, as I am told,
Were spoken by Lao-tzŭ.
If we are to believe that Lao-tzŭ
   Was himself *one who knew*,
How comes it that he wrote a book
   Of five thousand words?

Chuang-tzŭ, the Monist

Chuang-tzŭ levels all things
And reduces them to the same Monad.
But I say that even in their sameness
Difference may be found.
Although in following the promptings of
     their nature
They display the same tendency,
Yet it seems to me that in some ways
A phœnix is superior to a reptile!

On Hearing Someone Sing a Poem by Yüan Chēn

(Written long after Chēn's death)

No new poems his brush will trace:
    Even his fame is dead.
His old poems are deep in dust
    At the bottom of boxes and cupboards.
Once lately, when someone was singing,
    Suddenly I heard a verse—
Before I had time to catch the words
    A pain had stabbed my heart.

Illness

(*Written circa A.D. 842, when he was paralyzed*)

Dear friends, there is no cause for so much sympathy.
I shall certainly manage from time to time to take my
    walks abroad.
All that matters is an active mind, what is the use of feet?
By land one can ride in a carrying-chair; by water, be rowed
    in a boat.

Taoism and Buddhism

(Written shortly before his death)

A traveller came from across the seas
Telling of strange sights.
"In a deep fold of the sea-hills
I saw a terrace and tower.
In the midst there stood a Fairy Temple
With one niche empty.
They all told me this was waiting
For Lo-t'ien to come."

Traveller, I have studied the Empty Gate;[1]
I am no disciple of Fairies.
The story you have just told
Is nothing but an idle tale.
The hills of ocean shall never be
Lo-t'ien's home.
When I leave the earth it will be to go
To the Heaven of Bliss Fulfilled.[2]

[1] Buddhism. The poem is quite frivolous, as is shown by his claim to
Bodhisattva-hood.
[2] The "tushita" Heaven, where Bodhisattvas wait till it is time for them
to appear on earth as Buddhas.

Last Poem

They have put my bed beside the unpainted screen;
They have shifted my stove in front of the blue curtain.
I listen to my grandchildren, reading me a book;
I watch the servants, heating up my soup.
With rapid pencil I answer the poems of friends;
I feel in my pockets and pull out medicine-money.
When this superintendence of trifling affairs is done,
I lie back on my pillows and sleep with my face
     to the South.

[*Here End the Poems of Po Chü-i*]

The Little Lady of Ch'ing-hsi

[A Children's Song]

Her door opened on the white water
Close by the side of the timber bridge:
That's where the little lady lived
All alone without a lover.

The Story of Miss Li

By Po Hsing-chien (A. D. 799–831)
Brother of Po Chü-i

MISS LI, ennobled with the title "Lady of Ch'ien-kuo", was once a prostitute in Ch'ang-an. The devotion of her conduct was so remarkable that I have thought it worth while to record her story. In the T'ien-pao era[1] there was a certain nobleman, Governor of Ch'ang-chou and Lord of Jung-yang, whose name and surname I will omit. He was a man of great wealth and highly esteemed by all. He had passed his fiftieth year and had a son who was close on twenty, a boy who in literary talent outstripped all his companions. His father was proud of him and had great hopes of his future. "This", he would say, "is the 'thousand-league colt' of our family". When the time came for the lad to compete at the Provincial Examinations, his father gave him fine clothes and a handsome coach with richly caparisoned horses for the journey; and to provide for his expense at the Capital, he gave him a large sum of money, saying, "I am sure that your talent is such that you will succeed at the first attempt; but I am giving you two

[1] A. D. 742-56.

275

years' supply, that you may pursue your career free from all anxiety". The young man was also quite confident and saw himself getting the first place as clearly as he saw the palm of his own hand.

Starting from P'i-ling[1] he reached Ch'ang-an in a few weeks and took a house in the Pu-chēng quarter. One day he was coming back from a visit to the Eastern Market. He entered the City by the eastern gate of P'ing-k'ang and was going to visit a friend who lived in the south-western part of the town. When he reached the Ming-k'o Bend, he saw a house of which the gate and courtyard were rather narrow; but the house itself was stately and stood well back from the road. One of the double doors was open, and at it stood a lady, attended by her maid-servant. She was of exquisite, bewitching beauty, such as the world has seldom produced.

When he saw her, the young man unconsciously reined in his horse and hesitated. Unable to leave the spot, he purposely let his whip fall to the ground and waited for his servant to pick it up, all the time staring at the lady in the doorway. She too was staring and met his gaze with a look that seemed to be an answer to his admiration. But in the end he went away without daring to speak to her.

But he could not put the thought of her out of his mind and secretly begged those of his friends who were most expert in the pleasures of Ch'ang-an to tell him what they knew of the girl. He learnt from them that the house belonged to a low and unprincipled woman named Li. When he asked

[1] In Kiang-su, near Ch'ang-chou.

276

what chance he had of winning the daughter, they answered: "The woman Li is possessed of considerable property, for her previous dealings have been with wealthy and aristocratic families, from whom she has received enormous sums. Unless you are willing to spend many thousand pounds, the daughter will have nothing to do with you."

The young man answered: "All I care about is to win her. I do not mind if she costs a million pounds." The next day he set out in his best clothes, with many servants riding behind him, and knocked at the door of Mrs. Li's house. Immediately a page-boy drew the bolt. The young man asked, "Can you tell me whose house this is?" The boy did not answer, but ran back into the house and called out at the top of his voice, "Here is the gentleman who dropped his whip the other day!"

Miss Li was evidently very much pleased. He heard her saying, "Be sure not to let him go away. I am just going to do my hair and change my clothes; I will be back in a minute". The young man, in high spirits, followed the page-boy into the house. A white-haired old lady was going upstairs, whom he took to be the girl's mother. Bowing low, the young man addressed her as follows: "I am told that you have a vacant plot of land, which you would be willing to let as building-ground. Is that true?" The old lady answered, "I am afraid the site is too mean and confined; it would be quite unsuitable for a gentleman's house. I should not like to offer it to you". She then took him into the guest-room, which was a very handsome one, and asked him to be seated, saying, "I have a daughter who has little either of beauty or accomplishment, but she is fond of seeing strangers. I should like you to meet her".

So saying, she called for her daughter, who presently entered. Her eyes sparkled with such fire, her arms were so dazzling white and there was in her movements such an exquisite grace that the young man could only leap to his feet in confusion and did not dare raise his eyes. When their salutations were over, he began to make a few remarks about the weather; and realized as he did so that her beauty was of a kind he had never encountered before.

They sat down again. Tea was made and wine poured out. The vessels used were spotlessly clean. He lingered till the day was almost over; the curfew-drum sounded its four beats. The old lady asked if he lived far away. He answered

278

untruthfully, "Several leagues beyond the Yen-p'ing Gate", hoping that they would ask him to stay. The old lady said, "The drum has sounded. You will have to go back at once, unless you mean to break the law".

The young man answered, "I was being so agreeably entertained that I did not notice how rapidly the day had fled. My house is a long way off and in the city I have no friends or relations. What am I to do?" Miss Li then interposed, saying, "If you can forgive the meanness of our poor home, what harm would there be in your spending the night with us?" He looked doubtfully at the girl's mother, but met with no discouragement.

Calling his servants, he gave them money and told them to buy provisions for the night. But the girl laughingly stopped him, saying, "That is not the way guests are entertained. Our humble house will provide for your wants tonight, if you are willing to partake of our simple fare and defer your bounty to another occasion". He tried to refuse, but in the end she would not allow him to, and they all moved to the western hall. The curtains, screens, blinds and couches were of dazzling splendour; while the toilet-boxes, rugs, and pillows were of the utmost elegance. Candles were lighted and an excellent supper was served. After supper the old lady retired, leaving the lovers engaged in the liveliest conversation, laughing and chattering completely at their ease.

After a while the young man said: "I passed your house the other day and you happened to be standing at the door. And after that, I could think of nothing but you; whether I lay down to rest or sat down to eat, I could not stop thinking of you." She laughed and answered: "It was just the same with me." He said: "You must know that I did not come to-day simply to look for building-land. I came hoping that you would fulfil my lifelong desire; but I was not sure how you would welcome me. What—"

He had not finished speaking when the old woman came back and asked what they were saying. When they told her, she laughed and said, "Has not Mencius written that 'the re-lationship between men and women is the groundwork of society'? When lovers are agreed, not even the mandate of a parent will deter them. But my daughter is of humble birth. Are you sure that she is fit to 'present pillow and mat' to a great man?"

He came down from the daïs and, bowing low, begged that she would accept him as her slave. Henceforward the old lady regarded him as her son-in-law; they drank heavily to-gether and finally parted. Next morning he had all his boxes and bags brought round to Mrs. Li's house and settled there permanently. Henceforward he shut himself up with his mis-tress and none of his friends ever heard of him. He consorted only with actors and dancers and low people of that kind, passing the time in wild sports and wanton feasting. When his money was all spent, he sold his horses and men-servants. In about a year his money, property, servants and horses were all gone.

For some time the old lady's manner towards him had been growing gradually colder, but his mistress remained as devoted as ever. One day she said to him, "We have been together a year, but I am still not with child. They say that the spirit of the Bamboo Grove answers a woman's prayers as surely as an echo. Let us go to his temple and offer a libation".

The young man, not suspecting any plot, was delighted to take her to the temple, and having pawned his coat to buy sweet wine for the libation, he went with her and performed the ceremony of prayer. They stayed one night at the temple and came back next day. Whipping up their donkey, they soon arrived at the north gate of the P'ing-k'ang quarter. At this point his mistress turned to him and said, "My aunt's house is in a turning just near here. How would it be if we were to go there and rest for a little?"

He drove on as she directed him, and they had not gone more than a hundred paces, when he saw the entrance to a spacious carriage-drive. A servant who belonged to the place came out and stopped the cart, saying, "This is the entrance". The young man got down and was met by some one who came out and asked who they were. When told that it was Miss Li, he went back and announced her. Presently a married lady came out who seemed to be about forty. She greeted him, saying, "Has my niece arrived?" Miss Li then got out of the cart and her aunt said to her: "Why have you not been to see me for so long?" At which they looked at one another and laughed. Then Miss Li introduced him to her aunt and when that was over they all went into a side garden near the Western Halberd Gate. In the middle of the garden was a pagoda, and round it grew bamboos and trees

281

of every variety, while ponds and summer-houses added to its air of seclusion. He asked Miss Li if this were her aunt's estate; she laughed, and spoke of something else.

Tea of excellent quality was served; but when they had been drinking it for a little while, a messenger came galloping up on a huge Fergana horse, saying that Miss Li's mother had suddenly been taken very ill and had already lost consciousness, so that they had better come back as quickly as possible.

Miss Li said to her aunt: "I am very much upset. I think I had better take the horse and ride on ahead. Then I will send it back, and you and my husband can come along later." The young man was anxious to go with her, but the aunt and her servants engaged him in conversation, flourishing their hands in front of him and preventing him from leaving the garden. The aunt said to him: "No doubt my sister is dead by this time. You and I ought to discuss together what can be done to help with the expenses of the burial. What is the use of running off like that? Stay here and help me to make a plan for the funeral and mourning ceremonies."

It grew late; but the messenger had not returned. The aunt said: "I am surprised he has not come back with the horse. You had better go there on foot as quickly as possible and see what has happened. I will come on later."

The young man set out on foot for Mrs. Li's house. When he got there he found the gate firmly bolted, locked and sealed. Astounded, he questioned the neighbours, who told him that the house had only been let to Mrs. Li and that, the lease having expired, the landlord had now resumed possession. The old lady, they said, had gone to live elsewhere. They did not know her new address.

At first he thought of hurrying back to Hsüan-yang and questioning the aunt; but he found it was too late for him to get there. So he pawned some of his clothes, and, with the proceeds, bought himself supper and hired a bed. But he was too angry and distressed to sleep, and did not once close his eyes from dusk till dawn. Early in the morning he dragged himself away and went to the "aunt's house". He knocked on the door repeatedly, but it was breakfast-time and no one answered. At last, when he had shouted several times at the top of his voice, a footman walked majestically to the door. The young man nervously mentioned the aunt's name and asked whether she was at home. The footman replied: "No one of that name here." "But she lived here yesterday evening", the young man protested; "why are you trying to deceive me? If she does not live here, who *does* the house belong to?" The footman answered: "This is the residence of His Excellency Mr. Ts'ui. I believe that yesterday some persons hired a corner of the grounds. I understand that they wished to entertain a cousin who was coming from a distance. But they were gone before nightfall."

The young man, perplexed and puzzled to the point of madness, was absolutely at a loss what to do next. The best he could think of was to go to the quarters in Pu-chēng, where he had installed himself when he first arrived at Ch'-ang-an. The landlord was sympathetic and offered to feed him. But the young man was too much upset to eat, and having fasted for three days fell seriously ill. He rapidly grew worse, and the landlord, fearing he would not recover, had him moved straight to the undertaker's shop. In a short time the whole of the undertaker's staff was collected round him, offering sympathy and bringing him food. Gradually he got better and was able to walk with a stick.

The undertaker now hired him by the day to hold up the curtains of fine cloth, by which he earned just enough to support himself. In a few months he grew quite strong again, but whenever he heard the mourners' doleful songs, in which they regretted that they could not change places with the corpse, burst into violent fits of sobbing and shed streams of tears over which they lost all control, then he used to go home and imitate their performance.

Being a man of intelligence, he very soon mastered the art and finally became the most expert mourner in Ch'-ang-an. It happened that there were two undertakers at this time between whom there was a great rivalry. The undertaker of the east turned out magnificent hearses and biers, and in this respect his superiority could not be contested. But the mourners he provided were somewhat inferior. Hearing of our young man's skill, he offered him a large sum for his services. The eastern undertaker's supporters, who were familiar with the repertoire of his company, secretly taught the young man several fresh tunes and showed him how to fit the words to them. The lessons went on for several weeks, without any one being allowed to know of it. At the end of that time the two undertakers agreed to hold a competitive exhibition of their wares in T'ien-mēn Street. The loser was to forfeit 50,000 cash to cover the cost of the refreshments provided. Before the exhibition an agreement was drawn up and duly signed by witnesses.

A crowd of several thousand people collected to watch the competition. The mayor of the quarter got wind of the proceedings and told the chief of police. The chief of police told the governor of the city. Very soon all the gentlemen of Ch'ang-an were hurrying to the spot and every house in the town was empty. The exhibition lasted from dawn till midday. Coaches, hearses and all kinds of funeral trappings were successively displayed, but the undertaker of the west could establish no superiority. Filled with shame, he set up a platform in the south corner of the square. Presently a man with a long beard came forward, carrying a hand-bell and attended by several assistants. He wagged his beard, raised his eyebrows, folded his arms across his chest and bowed. Then, mounting the platform, he sang the "Dirge of the White Horse". When it was over, confident of an easy victory, he glared round him, as if to imply that his opponents had all vanished. He was applauded on every side and was himself convinced that his talents were a unique product of the age and could not possibly be called into question.

After a while the undertaker of the east put together some benches in the north corner of the square, and a young man in a black hat came forward, attended by five assistants and carrying a bunch of hearse-plumes in his hand. It was the young man of our story.

285

He adjusted his clothes, looked timidly up and down, and then cleared his throat and began his tune with an air of great diffidence.

He sang the dirge "Dew on the Garlic".[1] His voice rose so shrill and clear that "its echoes shook the forest trees". Before he had finished the first verse, all who heard were sobbing and hiding their tears.

When the performance was over, every one made fun of the western undertaker, and he was so much put out that he immediately removed his exhibits and retired from the contest. The audience was amazed by the collapse of the western undertaker and could not imagine where his rival had procured so remarkable a singer.

[1] See page 33.

It happened that the Emperor had recently issued an order commanding the governors of outside provinces to confer with him at the capital at least once a year.

At this time the young man's father, who was governor of Ch'ang-chou, had recently arrived at the capital to make his report. Hearing of the competition, he and some of his colleagues discarded their official robes and insignia, and slipped away to join the crowd. With them was an old servant, who was the husband of the young man's foster-nurse. Recognizing his foster-son's way of moving and speaking, he was on the point of accosting him, but not daring to do so, he stood weeping silently. The father asked him why he was crying, and the servant replied, "Sir, the young man who is singing reminds me of your lost son". The father answered: "My son became the prey of robbers, because I gave him too much money. This cannot be he." So saying, he also began to weep and, leaving the crowd, returned to his lodging.

But the old servant went about among the members of the troupe, asking who it was that had just sung with such skill. They all told him it was the son of such a one; and when he asked the young man's own name, that too was unfamiliar, for he was living under an *alias*. The old servant was so much puzzled that he determined to put the matter to the test for himself. But when the young man saw his old friend walking towards him, he winced, turned away his face, and tried to hide in the crowd. The old man followed him and catching his sleeve, said: "Surely it is you!" Then they embraced and wept. Presently they went back together to his

287

father's lodging. But his father abused him, saying: "Your conduct has disgraced the family. How dare you show your face again?" So saying, he took him out of the house and led him to the ground between the Ch'ü-chiang Pond and the Apricot Gardens. Here he stripped him naked and thrashed him with a horse-whip, till the young man succumbed to the pain and collapsed. The father then left him and went away.

But the young man's singing-master had told some of his friends to watch what happened to him. When they saw him stretched inanimate on the ground, they came back and told the other members of the troupe.

The news occasioned universal lamentation, and two men were despatched with a reed mat to cover up the body. When they got there they found his heart still warm, and when they had held him in an upright posture for some time, his breathing recommenced. So they carried him home between them and administered liquid food through a reed-pipe. Next morning, he recovered consciousness; but after several months he was still unable to move his hands and feet. Moreover, the sores left by his thrashing festered in so disgusting a manner that his friends found him too troublesome, and one night deposited him in the middle of the road. However, the passers-by, harrowed by his condition, never failed to throw him scraps of food.

So copious was his diet that in three months he recovered sufficiently to hobble with a stick. Clad in a linen coat,—which was knotted together in a hundred places, so that it looked as tattered as a quail's tail,—and carrying a broken saucer in his hand, he now went about the idle quarters of the town, earning his living as a professional beggar.

Autumn had now turned to winter. He spent his nights in public lavatories and his days haunting the markets and booths.

One day when it was snowing hard, hunger and cold had driven him into the streets. His beggar's cry was full of woe and all who heard it were heart-rent. But the snow was so heavy that hardly a house had its outer door open, and the streets were empty.

When he reached the eastern gate of An-i, about the seventh or eighth turning north of the Hsün-li Wall, there was a house with the double-doors half open.

It was the house where Miss Li was then living, but the young man did not know.

He stood before the door, wailing loud and long.

Hunger and cold had given such a piteous accent to his cry that none could have listened unmoved.

Miss Li heard it from her room and at once said to her servant, "That is so-and-so. I know his voice". She flew to the door and was horrified to see her old lover standing before her so emaciated by hunger and disfigured by sores that he seemed scarcely human. "Can it be you?" she said. But the young man was so overcome by bewilderment and excitement that he could not speak, but only moved his lips noiselessly.

She threw her arms round his neck, then wrapped him in her own embroidered jacket and led him to the parlour. Here, with quavering voice, she reproached herself, saying, "It is my doing that you have been brought to this pass". And with these words she swooned.

Her mother came running up in great excitement, asking who had arrived. Miss Li, recovering herself, said who it was. The old woman cried out in rage: "Send him away! What did you bring him in here for?"

But Miss Li looked up at her defiantly and said: "Not so! This is the son of a noble house. Once he rode in grand coaches and wore golden trappings on his coat. But when he came to our house, he soon lost all he had; and then we plotted together and left him destitute. Our conduct has indeed been inhuman! We have ruined his career and robbed

him even of his place in the category of human relationships. For the love of father and son is implanted by Heaven; yet we have hardened his father's heart, so that he beat him with a stick and left him on the ground.

"Every one in the land knows that it is I who have reduced him to his present plight. The Court is full of his kinsmen. Some day one of them will come into power. Then an inquiry will be set afoot, and disaster will overtake us. And since we have flouted Heaven and defied the laws of humanity, neither spirits nor divinities will be on our side. Let us not wantonly incur a further retribution!

"I have lived as your daughter for twenty years. Reckoning what I have cost you in that time, I find it must be close on a thousand pieces of gold. You are now aged sixty, so that by the price of twenty more years' food and clothing, I can buy my freedom. I intend to live separately with this young man. We will not go far away; I shall see to it that we are near enough to pay our respects to you both morning and evening."

The "mother" saw that she was not to be gainsaid and fell in with the arrangement. When she had paid her ransom, Miss Li had a hundred pieces of gold left over; and with them she hired a vacant room, five doors away. Here she gave the young man a bath, changed his clothes, fed him with hot soup to relax his stomach, and later on fattened him up with cheese and milk. In a few weeks she began to place before him all the choicest delicacies of land and sea; and she clothed him with cap, shoes and stockings of the finest quality. In a short time he began gradually to put on flesh, and by the end of the year, he had entirely recovered his former health.

One day Miss Li said to him: "Now your limbs are stout again and your will strong! Sometimes, when deeply pondering in silent sorrow, I wonder to myself how much you remember of your old literary studies?" He thought and answered: "Of ten parts I remember two or three."

Miss Li then ordered the carriage to be got ready and the young man followed her on horseback. When they reached the classical bookshop at the side-gate south of the Flag-tower, she made him choose all the books he wanted, till she had laid out a hundred pieces of gold. Then she packed them in the cart and drove home. She now made him dismiss all other thoughts from his mind and apply himself only to study. All the evening he toiled at his books, with Miss Li at his side, and they did not retire till midnight. If ever she found that he was too tired to work, she made him lay down his classics and write a poem or ode.

In two years he had thoroughly mastered his subjects and was admired by all the scholars of the realm. He said to Miss Li, "Now, surely, I am ready for the examiners!" but she would not let him compete and made him revise all he had learnt, to prepare for the "hundredth battle". At the end of the third year she said, "Now you may go". He went in for the examination and passed at the first attempt. His reputation spread rapidly through the examination rooms and even older men, when they saw his compositions, were filled with admiration and respect, and sought his friendship.

But Miss Li would not let him make friends with them, saying, "Wait a little longer! Nowadays when a bachelor of arts has passed his examination, he thinks himself fit to hold the most advantageous posts at Court and to win a universal reputation. But your unfortunate conduct and disreputable past put you at a disadvantage beside your fellow-scholars. You must 'grind, temper and sharpen' your attainments, that you may secure a second victory. Then you will be able to match yourself against famous scholars and contend with the illustrious".

The young man accordingly increased his efforts and enhanced his value. That year it happened that the Emperor had decreed a special examination for the selection of candidates of unusual merit from all parts of the Empire. The young man competed, and came out top in the "censorial essay". He was offered the post of Army Inspector at Ch'ēng-tu Fu. The officers who were to escort him were all previous friends.

When he was about to take up his post, Miss Li said to him, "Now that you are restored to your proper station in life, I will not be a burden to you. Let me go back and look after the old lady till she dies. You must ally yourself with some lady of noble lineage, who will be worthy to carry the sacrificial dishes in your Ancestral Hall. Do not injure your prospects by an unequal union. Good-bye, for now I must leave you".

The young man burst into tears and threatened to kill himself if she left him, but she obstinately refused to go with him. He begged her passionately not to desert him, and she at

293

last consented to go with him across the river as far as Chien-mēn.[1] "There", she said, "you must part with me". The young man consented and in a few weeks they reached Chien-mēn. Before he had started out again, a proclamation arrived announcing that the young man's father, who had been Governor of Ch'ang-chou, had been appointed Governor of Ch'ēng-tu and Intendant of the Chien-nan Circuit. Next morning the father arrived, and the young man sent in his card and waited upon him at the posting-station. His father did not recognize him, but the card bore the names of the young man's father and grandfather, with their ranks and titles. When he read these, he was astounded, and bidding his son mount the steps he caressed him and wept. After a while he said: "Now we two are father and son once more," and bade him tell his story. When he heard of the young man's adventures, he was amazed. Presently he asked: "And where is Miss Li?" He replied: "She came with me as far as here, but now she is going back again."

"I cannot allow it", the father said. Next day he ordered a carriage for his son and sent him on to report himself at Ch'ēng-tu; but he detained Miss Li at Chien-mēn, found her a suitable lodging and ordered a match-maker to perform the initial ceremonies for uniting the two families and to accomplish the six rites of welcome. The young man came back from Ch'ēng-tu and they were duly married. In the years that followed their marriage, Miss Li showed herself a devoted

[1] The "Sword-gate": commanding the pass which leads into Szechuan from the north.

wife and competent housekeeper, and was beloved by all her relations.

Some years later both the young man's parents died, and in his mourning observances he showed unusual piety. As a mark of divine favour, magic toadstools grew on the roof of his mourning-hut,[1] each stem bearing three plants. The report of his virtue reached even the Emperor's ears. Moreover, a number of white swallows nested in the beams of his roof, an omen which so impressed the Emperor that he raised his rank immediately.

When the three years of mourning were over, he was successively promoted to various distinguished posts and in the

[1] See "Book of Rites", xxxii, 3. On returning from his father's burial a son must not enter the house; he should live in an "out-house", mourning for his father's absence.

course of ten years was Governor of several provinces. Miss Li was given the fief of Chien-kuo, with the title "The Lady of Chien-kuo".

He had four sons who all held high rank. Even the least successful of them became Governor of T'ai-yüan, and his brothers all married into great families, so that his good fortune both in public and private life was without parallel.

How strange that we should find in the conduct of a prostitute a degree of constancy rarely equalled even by the heroines of history! Surely the story is one which cannot but provoke a sigh!

My great-uncle was Governor of Chin-chou; subsequently he joined the Ministry of Finance and became Inspector of Waterways, and finally Inspector of Roads. In all these three offices he had Miss Li's husband as his colleague, so that her story was well known to him in every particular. During the Chēng-yüan period[1] I was sitting one day with Li Kung-tso[2] of Lung-hai; we fell to talking of wives who had distinguished themselves by remarkable conduct. I told him the story of Miss Li. He listened with rapt attention, and when it was over, asked me to write it down for him. So I took up my brush, wetted the hairs and made this rough outline of the story.

[Dated] *Autumn, eighth month of the year Yi-hai* (A. D. 795)

[1] A. D. 785-805.   [2] A writer.

The Pitcher

By Yüan Chēn (A. D. 779-831)

I dreamt I climbed to a high, high plain;
And on the plain I found a deep well.
My throat was dry with climbing and I longed to drink;
And my eyes were eager to look into the cool shaft.
I walked round it; I looked right down;
I saw my image mirrored on the face of the pool.
An earthen pitcher was sinking into the black depths;
There was no rope to pull it to the well-head.
I was strangely troubled lest the pitcher should be lost,
And started wildly running to look for help.
From village to village I scoured that high plain;
The men were gone: the dogs leapt at my throat.
I came back and walked weeping round the well;
Faster and faster the blinding tears flowed—
Till my own sobbing suddenly woke me up;
My room was silent; no one in the house stirred;
The flame of my candle flickered with a green smoke;
The tears I had shed glittered in the candle-light.
A bell sounded; I knew it was the midnight-chime;
I sat up in bed and tried to arrange my thoughts:

297

The plain in my dream was the graveyard at Ch'ang-an,
Those hundred acres of untilled land.
The soil heavy and the mounds heaped high;
And the dead below them laid in deep troughs.
Deep are the troughs, yet sometimes dead men
Find their way to the world above the grave.
And to-night my love who died long ago
Came into my dream as the pitcher sunk in the well.
That was why the tears suddenly streamed from my eyes,
Streamed from my eyes and fell on the collar of my dress.

The Story of Ts'ui Ying-ying

By Yüan Chēn (A. D. 799-831)

DURING the Chēng-yüan[1] period of the T'ang dynasty there lived a man called Chang.[2] His nature was gentle and refined, and his person of great beauty. But his deeper feelings were resolutely held in restraint, and he would indulge in no license. Sometimes his friends took him to a party and he would try to join their frolics; but when the rest were shouting and scuffling their hardest, Chang only pretended to take his share. For he could never overcome his shyness. So it came about that though already twenty-three, he had not yet enjoyed a woman's beauty. To those who questioned him he answered, "It is not such as Master Tēng-t'u[3] who are true lovers of beauty; for they are merely profligates. I consider myself a lover of beauty, who happens never to have met with it. And I am of this opinion because I know that, in other things, whatever is beautiful casts its spell upon me; so that I cannot be devoid of feeling". His questioners only laughed.

[1] A. D. 785-805.   [2] I.e., Yüan Chēn himself.
[3] Type of the indiscriminate lover, fourth century B. C.

About this time Chang went to Puchow. Some two miles east of the town there is a temple called the P'-u-chiu-ssǔ, and here he took up his lodging. Now it happened that at this time the widow of a certain Ts'ui was returning to Ch'ang-an.[1] She passed through Puchow on her way and stayed at the same temple. This lady was born of the Chēng family and Chang's mother was also a Chēng. He unravelled their relationship and found that they were second-cousins.

This year General Hun-Chan[2] died at Puchow. There was a certain Colonel Ting Wēn-ya who ill-treated his troops. The soldiers accordingly made Hun-Chan's funeral the occasion of a mutiny, and began to plunder the town. The Ts'ui family had brought with them much valuable property and many slaves. Subjected to this sudden danger when far from home, they had no one from whom they could seek protection.

Now it happened that Chang had been friendly with the political party to which the commander at Puchow belonged. At his request a guard was sent to the temple and no disorder took place there. A few days afterwards the Civil Commissioner Tu Chio was ordered by the Emperor to take over the command of the troops. The mutineers then laid down their arms.

The widow Chēng was very sensible of the service which Chang had rendered. She therefore provided dainties and invited him to a banquet in the middle hall. At table she

[1] The capital of China at that time; now called Hsi-an-fu.
[2] Born A. D. 735; died 799. Famous for his campaigns against the Tibetans and Uighurs.

300

turned to him and said, "I, your cousin, a lonely and widowed relict, had young ones in my care. If we had fallen into the hands of the soldiery, I could not have helped them. Therefore the lives of my little boy and young daughter were saved by your protection, and they owe you eternal gratitude. I will

now cause them to kneel before you, their merciful cousin, that they may thank you for your favours". First she sent for her son, Huan-lang, who was about ten years old, a handsome and gentle child. Then she called to her daughter, Ying-ying: "Come and bow to your cousin. Your cousin saved your life."

301

For a long while she would not come, saying that she was not well. The widow grew angry and cried: "Your cousin saved your life. But for his help, you would now be a prisoner. How can you treat him so rudely?"

At last she came in, dressed in everyday clothes, with a look of deep unhappiness in her face. She had not put on any ornaments. Her hair hung down in coils, the black of her two eyebrows joined, her cheeks were not rouged. But her features were of exquisite beauty and shone with an almost dazzling lustre.

Chang bowed to her, amazed. She sat down by her mother's side and looked all the time towards her, turning from him with a fixed stare of aversion, as though she could not endure his presence.

He asked how old she was. The widow answered, "She was born in the year of the present Emperor's reign that was a year of the Rat, and now it is the year of the Dragon in the period Chēng-yüan.[1] So she must be seventeen years old".

Chang tried to engage her in conversation, but she would not answer, and soon the dinner was over. He was passionately in love with her and wanted to tell her so, but could find no way.

Ying-ying had a maid-servant called Hung-niang, whom Chang sometimes met and greeted. Once he stopped her and was beginning to tell her of his love for her mistress; but she was frightened and ran away. Then Chang was sorry he had not kept silence.

[1] I.e., A. D. 800.

Next day he met Hung-niang again, but was ashamed and did not say what was in his mind. But this time the maid herself broached the subject and said to Chang, "Master, I dare not tell her what you told me, or even hint at it. But since your mother was a kinswoman of the Ts'uis, why do you not seek my mistress's hand on that plea?"

Chang said, "Since I was a child in arms, my nature has been averse to intimacy. Sometimes I have idled with wearers of silk and gauze, but my fancy was never once detained. I little thought that in the end I should be entrapped.

"Lately at the banquet I could scarcely contain myself; and since then, when I walk, I forget where I am going and when I eat, I forget to finish my meal, and do not know how to endure the hours from dawn to dusk.

"If we were to get married through a matchmaker and perform the ceremonies of Sending Presents and Asking Names, it would take many months, and by that time you would have to look for me 'in the dried-fish shop'. What is the use of giving me such advice as that?"

The maid replied, "My mistress clings steadfastly to her chastity, and even an equal could not trip her with lewd talk. Much less may she be won through the stratagems of a maid-servant. But she is skilled in composition, and often when she has made a poem or essay, she is restless and dissatisfied for a long while after. You must try to provoke her by a love-poem. There is no other way".

Chang was delighted and at once composed two Spring Poems to send her. Hung-niang took them away and came back the same evening with a coloured tablet, which she gave to Chang, saying, "This is from my mistress". It bore the title "The Bright Moon of the Fifteenth Night". The words ran:

To wait for the moon I am sitting in the western parlour;
To greet the wind, I have left the door ajar.
When a flower's shadow stirred and brushed the wall,
For a moment I thought it the shadow of a lover coming.

Chang could not doubt her meaning. That night was the fourth after the first decade of the second month. Beside the eastern wall of Ts'ui's apartments there grew an apricot-tree; by climbing it one could cross the wall. On the next night (which was the night of the full moon) Chang used the tree as a ladder and crossed the wall. He went straight to the western parlour and found the door ajar. Hung-niang lay asleep on the bed. He woke her, and she cried in a voice of astonishment, "Master Chang, what are you doing here?" Chang answered, half-truly: "Ts'ui's letter invited me. Tell her I have come." Hung-niang soon returned, whispering, "She is coming, she is coming". Chang was both delighted and surprised, thinking that his salvation was indeed at hand.

At last Ts'ui entered.

Her dress was sober and correct, and her face was stern. She at once began to reprimand Chang, saying, "I am grateful for the service which you rendered to my family. You gave support to my dear mother when she was at a loss how to save her little boy and young daughter. How came you to send me a wicked message by the hand of a low maid-servant? In protecting me from the license of others, you acted nobly. But now that you wish to make me a partner to your own licentious desires, you are asking me to accept one wrong in exchange for another.

"How was I to repel this advance? I would gladly have hidden your letter, but it would have been immoral to harbour a record of illicit proposals. Had I shown it to my mother, I should ill have requited the debt we owe you. Were I to entrust a message of refusal to a servant or concubine, I feared it might not be truly delivered. I thought of writing a letter to tell you what I felt; but I was afraid I might not be able to make you understand. So I sent those trivial verses, that I might be sure of your coming. I have no cause to be ashamed of an irregularity which had no other object but the preservation of my chastity".

With these words she vanished. Chang remained for a

long while petrified with astonishment. At last he climbed back over the wall and went home in despair.

Several nights after this he was lying asleep near the verandah, when some one suddenly woke him. He rose with a startled sigh and found that Hung-niang was there, with bed-clothes under her arm and a pillow in her hand. She shook Chang, saying, "She is coming, she is coming. Why are you asleep?" Then she arranged the bed-clothes and pillow and went away.

Chang sat up and rubbed his eyes. For a long while he thought he must be dreaming, but he assumed a respectful attitude and waited.

Suddenly Hung-niang came back, bringing her mistress with her. Ts'ui, this time, was languid and flushed, yielding and wanton in her air, as though her strength could scarcely support her limbs. Her former severity had utterly disappeared.

That night was the eighth of the second decade. The crystal beams of the sinking moon twinkled secretly across their bed. Chang, in a strange exaltation, half-believed that a fairy had come to him, and not a child of mortal men.

At last the temple bell sounded, dawn glimmered in the sky and Hung-niang came back to fetch her mistress away. Ts'ui turned on her side with a pretty cry, and followed her maid to the door.

The whole night she had not spoken a word.

Chang rose when it was half-dark, still thinking that perhaps it had been a dream. But when it grew light, he saw her powder on his arm and smelt her perfume in his clothes. A tear she had shed still glittered on the mattress.

For more than ten days afterwards he did not see her again. During this time he began to make a poem called "Meeting a Fairy", in thirty couplets. It was not yet finished, when he chanced to meet Hung-niang in the road. He asked her to take the poem to Ts'ui.

After this Ts'ui let him come to her, and for a month or more he crept out at dawn and in at dusk, the two of them living together in that western parlour of which I spoke before.

Chang often asked her what her mother thought of him. Ts'ui said, "I know she would not oppose my will. So why should we not get married at once?"

Soon afterwards, Chang had to go to the capital. Before starting, he tenderly informed her of his departure. She did not reproach him, but her face showed pitiable distress. On the night before he started, he was not able to see her.

After spending a few months in the west, Chang returned to Puchow and again lodged for several months in the same building as the Ts'uis. He made many attempts to see Ying-ying alone, but she would not let him do so. Remembering that she was fond of calligraphy and verse, he frequently sent her his own compositions, but she scarcely glanced at them.

It was characteristic of her that when any situation was at its acutest point, she appeared quite unconscious of it. She talked glibly, but would seldom answer a question. She expected absolute devotion, but herself gave no encouragement.

307

Sometimes when she was in the depth of despair, she would affect all the while to be quite indifferent. It was rarely possible to know from her face whether she was pleased or sorry.

One night Chang came upon her unawares when she was playing on the harp, with a touch full of passion. But when she saw him coming, she stopped playing. This incident increased his infatuation.

Soon afterwards, it became time for him to compete in the Literary Examinations, and he was obliged once more to set out for the western capital.

The evening before his departure, he sat in deep despondency by Ts'ui's side, but did not try again to tell her of his love. Nor had he told her that he was going away, but she seemed to have guessed it, and with submissive face and gentle voice, she said to him softly: "Those whom a man leads astray, he will in the end abandon. It must be so, and I will not reproach you. You deigned to corrupt me and now you deign to leave me. That is all. And your vows of 'faithfulness till death'—they too are cancelled. There is no need for you to grieve at this parting, but since I see you so sad and can give you no other comfort—you once praised my harp-playing; but I was bashful and would not play to you. Now I am bolder, and if you choose, I will play you a tune."

She took her harp and began the prelude to "Rainbow Skirts and Feather Jackets".[1] But after a few bars the tune broke off into a wild and passionate dirge.

[1] A gay court tune of the eighth century.

308

All who were present caught their breath; but in a moment she stopped playing, threw down her harp and, weeping bitterly, ran to her mother's room.

She did not come back.

Next morning Chang left. The following year he failed in his examinations and could not leave the capital. So, to unburden his heart, he wrote a letter to Ts'ui. She answered him somewhat in this fashion: "I have read your letter and cherish it dearly. It has filled my heart half with sorrow, half with joy. You sent with it a box of garlands and five sticks of paste, that I may decorate my head and colour my lips.

"I thank you for your presents; but there is no one now to care how I look. Seeing these things only makes me think of you and grieve the more.

"You say that you are prospering in your career at the capital, and I am comforted by that news. But it makes me fear you will never come back again to one who is so distant and humble. But *that* is settled for ever, and it is no use talking of it.

"Since last autumn I have lived in a dazed stupor. Amid the clamour of the daytime, I have sometimes forced myself to laugh and talk; but alone at night I have done nothing but weep. Or, if I have fallen asleep my dreams have always been full of the sorrows of parting. Often I dreamt that you came to me as you used to do, but always before the moment of our joy your phantom vanished from my side. Yet, though we are still bedfellows in my dreams, when I wake and think of it, the time when we were together seems very far off. For since we parted, the old year has slipped away and a new year has begun. . . .

"Ch'ang-an is a city of pleasure, where there are many snares to catch a young man's heart. How can I hope that you will not forget one so sequestered and insignificant as I? And indeed, if you were to be faithful, so worthless a creature could never requite you. But our vows of unending love— those I at least can fulfil.

"Because you are my cousin, I met you at the feast. Lured by a maid-servant, I visited you in private. A girl's heart is not in her own keeping. You 'tempted me by your ballads'[1] and I could not bring myself to 'throw the shuttle'.[2]

"Then came the sharing of pillow and mat, the time of perfect loyalty and deepest tenderness. And I, being young and foolish, thought it would never end.

"Now, having 'seen my Prince',[3] I cannot love again; nor, branded by the shame of self-surrender, am I fit to perform 'the service of towel and comb';[4] and of the bitterness of the long celibacy which awaits me, what need is there to speak?

"The good man uses his heart; and if by chance his gaze has fallen on the humble and insignificant, till the day of his death, he continues the affections of his life. The cynic cares nothing for people's feelings. He will discard the small to follow the great, look upon a former mistress merely as an ac-

[1] As Ssŭ-ma tempted Cho Wēn-chün, second century B. C.
[2] As the neighbour's daughter did to Hsieh Kun (A. D. fourth century), in order to repel his advances.
[3] Odes I. 1., X. 2.　　[4] = become a bride.

310

complice in sin, and hold that the most solemn vows are made only to be broken. He will reverse all natural laws—as though Nature should suddenly let bone dissolve, while cinnabar resisted the fire. The dew that the wind has shaken from the tree still looks for kindness from the dust; and such, too, is the sum of *my* hopes and fears.

"As I write, I am shaken by sobs and cannot tell you all that is in my heart. My darling, I am sending you a jade ring that I used to play with when I was a child. I want you to wear it at your girdle, that you may become firm and flawless as this jade, and, in your affections, unbroken as the circuit of this ring.

"And with it I am sending a skein of thread and a tea-trough of flecked bamboo. There is no value in these few things. I send them only to remind you to keep your heart pure as jade and your affection unending as this round ring. The bamboo is mottled as if with tears, and the thread is tangled as the thoughts of those who are in sorrow. By these tokens I seek no more than that, knowing the truth, you may think kindly of me for ever.

"Our hearts are very near, but our bodies are far apart. There is no time fixed for our meeting; yet a secret longing can unite souls that are separated by a thousand miles.

"Protect yourself against the cold spring wind, eat well—look after yourself in all ways and do not worry too much about your worthless handmaid,

Ts'ui Ying-ying."

Chang showed this letter to his friends and so the story became known to many who lived at that time. All who heard it were deeply moved; but Chang, to their disappointment, declared that he meant to break with Ts'ui. Yüan Chên, of Honan, who knew Chang well, asked him why he had made this decision.

Chang answered:

"I have observed that in Nature whatever has perfect beauty is either itself liable to sudden transformations or else is the cause of them in others. If Ts'ui were to marry a rich gentleman and become his pet, she would for ever be changing, as the clouds change to rain, or as the scaly dragon turns into the horned dragon. I, for one, could never keep pace with her transformations.

"Of old, Hsin of the Yin dynasty and Yu of the Chou dynasty ruled over kingdoms of many thousand chariots, and their strength was very great. Yet a single woman brought them to ruin, dissipating their hosts and leading these monarchs to the assassin's knife. So that to this day they are a laughing-stock to all the world. I know that my constancy could not withstand such spells, and that is why I have curbed my passion."

At these words all who were present sighed deeply.

A few years afterwards Ts'ui married some one else and Chang also found a wife. Happening once to pass the house where Ts'ui was living, he called on her husband and asked to see her, saying he was her cousin. The husband sent for her, but she would not come. Chang's vexation showed itself in his face. Some one told Ts'ui of this and she secretly wrote the poem:

> Since I have grown so lean, my face has lost its beauty.
> I have tossed and turned so many times that I am too tired
> > to leave my bed.
> It is not that I mind the others seeing
> > How ugly I have grown;
> It is you who have caused me to lose my beauty,
> > Yet it is you I am ashamed should see me!

Chang went away without meeting her, and a few days afterwards, when he was leaving the town, wrote a poem of final farewell, which said:

> You cannot say that you are abandoned and deserted;
> > For you have found some one to love you.
> Why do you not convert your broodings over the past
> > Into kindness to your present husband?

After that they never heard of one another again. Many of Chang's contemporaries praised the skill with which he extricated himself from this entanglement.

Hearing that His Friend
Was Coming Back from the War

By Wang Chien (circa A. D. 830)

In old days those who went to fight
In three years had one year's leave.
But in *this* war the soldiers are never changed;
They must go on fighting till they die on the battle-field.
I thought of you, so weak and indolent,
Hopelessly trying to learn to march and drill.
That a young man should ever come home again
Seemed about as likely as that the sky should fall.
Since I got the news that you were coming back,
Twice I have mounted to the high hall of your home.
I found your brother mending your horse's stall;
I found your mother sewing your new clothes.
I am half afraid; perhaps it is not true;
Yet I never weary of watching for you on the road.
Each day I go out at the City Gate
With a flask of wine, lest you should come thirsty.
Oh that I could shrink the surface of the World,
So that suddenly I might find you standing at my side.

The South

By Wang Chien

In the southern land many birds sing;
Of towns and cities half are unwalled.
The country markets are thronged by wild tribes;
The mountain-villages bear river-names.
Poisonous mists rise from the damp sands;
Strange fires gleam through the night-rain.
And none passes but the lonely fisher of pearls
Year by year on his way to the South Sea.

A Protest in the Sixth Year of Ch'ien Fu [A.D. 879]

By Ts'ao Sung (flourished circa A. D. 870–920)

The hills and rivers of the lowland country
    You have made your battle-ground.
How do you suppose the people who live there
    Will procure "firewood and hay"?[1]
Do not let me hear you talking together
    About titles and promotions;
For a single-general's reputation
    Is made out of ten thousand corpses.

[1] The necessaries of life.

Autumn

By Ou-yang Hsiu (b. 1007; d. 1072)

MASTER OU-YANG was reading his books[1] at night when he heard a strange sound coming from the north-west. He paused and listened intently, saying to himself: "How strange, how strange!" First there was a pattering and rustling; but suddenly this broke into a great churning and crashing, like the noise of waves that wake the traveller at night, when wind and rain suddenly come; and where they lash the ship, there is a jangling and clanging as of metal against metal.

Or again, like the sound of soldiers going to battle, who march swiftly with their gags[2] between their teeth, when the captain's voice cannot be heard, but only the tramp of horses and men moving.

I called to my boy, bidding him go out and see what noise this could be. The boy said: "The moon and stars are shining; the Milky Way glitters in the sky. Nowhere is there any noise of men. The noise must be in the trees."

[1] The poem was written in A. D. 1052, when Ou-yang was finishing his "New History of the T'ang Dynasty".   [2] Pieces of wood put in their mouths to prevent their talking.

317

"I-hsi! alas!" I said, "this must be the sound of Autumn. Oh, why has Autumn come? For as to Autumn's form, her colours are mournful and pale. Mists scatter and clouds withdraw. Her aspect is clean and bright. The sky is high and the sunlight clear as crystal. Her breath is shivering and raw, pricking men's skin and bones; her thoughts are desolate, bringing emptiness and silence to the rivers and hills. And hence it is that her whisperings are sorrowful and cold, but her shouts are wild and angry. Pleasant grasses grew soft and green, vying in rankness. Fair trees knit their shade and gave delight. Autumn swept the grasses and their colour changed; she met the trees, and their boughs were stripped. And because Autumn's being is compounded of sternness, therefore it was that they withered and perished, fell and decayed. For Autumn is an executioner,[1] and her hour is darkness. She is a warrior, and her element is metal. Therefore she is called 'the doom-spirit of heaven and earth';[2] for her thoughts are bent on stern destruction.

"In Spring, growth; in Autumn, fruit: that is Heaven's plan. Therefore in music the note *shang* is the symbol of the West and *I-tsē* is the pitch-pipe of the seventh month. For *shang* means 'to strike'; when things grow old they are stricken by grief. And *I* means 'to slay'; things that have passed their prime must needs be slain. Plants and trees have no feelings; when their time comes they are blown down.

---

[1] Executions took place in autumn. See *Chou Li*, Book xxxiv (Biot's translation, tom. ii, p. 286).
[2] "Book of Rites", I. 656 (Couvreur's edition).

318

But man moves and lives and is of creatures most divine. A hundred griefs assail his heart, ten thousand tasks wear out his limbs, and each inward stirring shakes the atoms of his soul. And all the more, when he thinks of things that his strength cannot achieve or grieves at things his mind cannot understand, is it strange that cheeks that were steeped in red should grow withered as an old stick, and hair that was black as ebony should turn as spangled as a starry sky? How should ought else but what is fashioned of brass or stone strive to outlast the splendour of a tree? Who but man himself is the slayer of his youth? Why was I angered at Autumn's voice?"

The boy made no answer: he was sleeping with lowered head. I could hear nothing but the insects chirping shrilly on every side as though they sought to join in my lamentation.

The Pedlar of Spells

By Lu Yu (A.D. 1125–1210)

An old man selling charms in a cranny of the town wall.
He writes out spells to bless the silkworms and spells to
   protect the corn.
With the money he gets each day he only buys wine.
But he does not worry when his legs get wobbly,
For he has a boy to lean on.

The Herd-Boy

By Lu Yu

In the southern village the boy who minds the ox
With his naked feet stands on the ox's back.
Through the hole in his coat the river wind blows;
Through his broken hat the mountain rain pours.
On the long dyke he seemed to be far away;
In the narrow lane suddenly we were face to face.

The boy is home and the ox is back in its stall;
And a dark smoke oozes through the thatched roof.

Boating in Autumn

By Lu Yu

Away and away I sail in my light boat;
My heart leaps with a great gust of joy.
Through the leafless branches I see the temple in the wood;
Over the dwindling stream the stone bridge towers.
Down the grassy lanes sheep and oxen pass;
In the misty village cranes and magpies cry.

Back in my home I drink a cup of wine
And need not fear the greed[1] of the evening wind.

[1] Which "eats" men

How I Sailed on the Lake
Till I Came to the Eastern Stream

By Lu Yu

Of Spring water,—thirty or forty miles:
In the evening sunlight,—three or four houses.
Youths and boys minding geese and ducks:
Women and girls tending mulberries and hemp.
The place,—remote: their coats and scarves old:
The year,—fruitful: their talk and laughter gay.
The old wanderer moors his flat boat
And staggers up the bank to pluck wistaria flowers.

On the Birth of His Son

By *Su Tung-p'o* (*A. D.* 1036–1101)

Families, when a child is born
Want it to be intelligent.
I, through intelligence,
Having wrecked my whole life,
Only hope the baby will prove
Ignorant and stupid.
Then he will crown a tranquil life
By becoming a Cabinet Minister.

The Little Cart

A Seventeenth-Century Chinese Poem by Ch'ēn Tzŭ-lung

The following song describes the flight of a husband and wife from a town menaced by the advancing Manchus. They find the whole country-side deserted.

The little cart jolting and banging through the yellow haze
    of dusk.
  The man pushing behind: the woman pulling in front.
They have left the city and do not know where to go.
"Green, green, those elm-tree leaves: *they* will cure my hunger,
If only we could find some quiet place and sup on
      them together."
      The wind has flattened the yellow mother-wort:
      Above it in the distance they see the walls of a house.
"There surely must be people living who'll give you
      something to eat."
They tap at the door, but no one comes: they look in,
    but the kitchen is empty.
They stand hesitating in the lonely road and their tears
    fall like rain.

Ch'ēn Tzŭ-lung was born in 1607. He became a soldier, and in 1637 defeated the rebel, Hsü Tu. After the suicide of the last Ming emperor, he offered his services to the Ming princes who were still opposing the Manchus. In 1647 he headed a conspiracy to place the Ming prince Lu on the throne. His plans were discovered and he was arrested by Manchu troops. Escaping their vigilance for a moment, he leapt into a river and was drowned.

This volume, illustrated and decorated by Cyrus LeRoy Baldridge, was planned by Richard Ellis and produced under his direction. It was composed in a special Monotype cutting of Frederic W. Goudy's Deepdene type made for this edition, with swash letters and revised characters designed by Mr Ellis and with the approval of Mr Goudy. The paper, patterned after old papers of the orient, was manufactured by the P. H. Glatfelter Company, Spring Grove, Pennsylvania. The full-color illustrations were reproduced in Similetone by the Zeese-Wilkinson Company, Long Island City, New York. The cloth, in a natural finish, was made by Bancroft Mills, Wilmington, Delaware. The Composition, Electrotyping, Printing and Binding were by The Haddon Craftsmen, Camden, New Jersey.